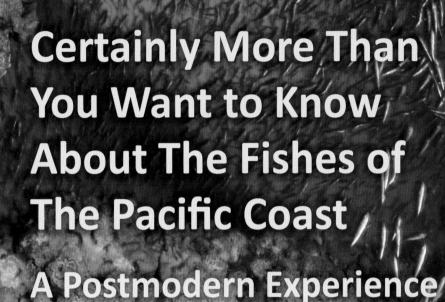

Certainly More Than You Want to Know About The Fishes of The Pacific Coast

A Postmodern Experience

Milton S. Love
University of California, Santa Barbara

Really Big Press
Santa Barbara, California

©2011
Really Big Press
P.O. Box 60123
Santa Barbara
California, 93160
reallybigpress.com

ISBN 978-0-9628725-6-3

The very nice cover image is an oil on canvas painting called *Chinese Fishmonger*, painted in 1881 by Theodore Wores (1859–1939). Born in San Francisco, Wores began art training at 12 years of age, and by the age of 16 he was studying at the Academy of Fine Arts in Munich. He returned to San Francisco six years later and started painting scenes in Chinatown including the very evocative one that appears on the cover. For the next 20 years, the painter traveled widely in Europe, Japan, and the South Pacific, displaying a talent both for portraiture and landscapes. Returning to the San Francisco area in 1903, Wores was active in the artistic community and served as the dean of the San Francisco Institute of Art from 1907–1913. He was also a member of the Society for Sanity in Art, a group opposed both to Modern Art and, one supposes, to the Society for Insanity in Art.

That lovely quillback rockfish on the first page, and on the page margins, is by Zach Ferdana.

You know that amazing photograph of juvenile bocaccio at Platform Gilda on the previous page? It's by Scott Gietler.

So, how many of the fishes in *Chinese Fishmonger* can you identify? Don't waste your time on the invertebrates; never forget, invertebrates are merely fish food. I checked with some of my colleagues (like Greg Cailliet, Bob Lea, and Peter Moyle) about identifications and now let's look at the painting below and make some guesses.

1–3 = These are too dark, so we have no idea, although Peter jested that they are "black cod", which was kind of clever. 4 and 6 = These are interesting because they kind of look like mixtures of several species and may have been Wores' attempt at artistic license. 5 = I think this is likely a brown rockfish, although the fins are a bit too red. 7 = Likely a starry flounder based on body shape. 8–10 = Definitely starry flounder based on the striped fins and the body shape. 11 = This is a seaperch. I like black perch because of the body color and that this species is abundant in the area. 12 = I thought this was shaped like an English sole, but Peter thought the tail was striped and thus another starry flounder. 13 = This one definitely looks like a black perch. The color is right, the shape is right, and I think I see a bit of orange on the lips. 14 = The blunt, roundy head and the closeness of the eyes say Dover sole. 15, 18 = Without a doubt these are lingcod. 16 = Peter, who knows far more about anadromous fishes than I, says Chinook salmon, 'cause it has a...yellow eye. And also both the body color and shape are right, the size is right, and this was a popular commercial species at that time and place. 19 = A surfperch, of the genus *Hyperprosopon*, most probably a walleye. 20 = This one is tough. It could be a sucker (*Catostomus* sp.) or maybe a Pacific herring. 17 = A yelloweye rockfish, based on the black gums.

TABLE OF CONTENTS

TODD WINNER

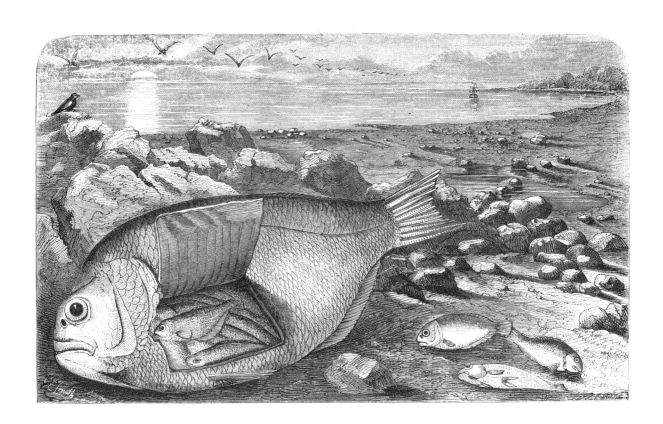

To JANE, SHOSHANNA, and ELAN.

And to the Old Stinking Ninth[1]

[1]During the Chinese Cultural Revolution: "There were the Nine Black Categories…Landlords, Rich Peasants, Counter-Revolutionaries, Bad Elements, Rightists, Traitors, Special Agents, Capitalist Roaders, and the Old Stinking Ninth, who were the intellectuals" P. Hessler, quoting Teacher Kong in *River Town* (HarperCollins, 2001).

And Thanks To....

Without putting too fine a point on it, this book would have been just very, very sad without the kind help of simply a ton of folks.

Roberta Bloom did yeoman, or perhaps yeowoman, duty, sprucing up (and sometimes repairing) the photographs, laying out text and images, and generally being responsible for the "look" of this book. Thank you, Bertie, for all your efforts. And while we are on the topic, Cheri Rae and both of her eagle eyes served as copy editor of the text, catching errors both egregious and kind of subtle.

I would like to thank Scott Gietler for not only providing a large number of images, but also for sharing his vast observations on fish behavior. Kitty Mecklenburg was a veritable font of information regarding Alaskan fishes and her encyclopedic knowledge of their distributions is quite remarkable. Kirk Lombard and Janna Nichols were always pleasant in the face of my many demands on their time and talents.

With remarkably little prodding, the following folks reviewed sections of the manuscript: Greg Goldsmith, Bernard Hanby, Robert Lauth, Kevin Lee, Kirk Lombard, and Susan McDermott. I thank them all for their services. Of course, any errors egregious or otherwise are mine, although now that I think about it, these people would also share at least a bit of the responsibility, wouldn't they?

Above and beyond the call of duty, Makato Okamoto went to a Tokyo fish market, bought a saury, and photographed it for me.

Roy Qi took fish photographs and searched out others on various angler websites.

The fine folks at the Natural History Museum of Los Angeles County, Rick Feeney, Jeff Siegel, and Christine Thacker, allowed me to paw through their collection.

Here are the people I pestered and who responded with facts, opinions, and stories, almost always with more or less good grace (I have undoubtedly forgotten to list some of you. This is churlish behavior at best and yet more evidence that I am at least moderately narcissistic): Alisa Abookire, Gerald Allen, Larry Allen, Jessie Alstatt, Marcos Alverez, Eric Anderson, David Andrew, Kevin Bailey, Jeff Barr, Bill Beebe, Giacomo Bernardi, Joe Bizzarro, Jennifer Bloeser, Roger Bly, Terri Bonnet, Jennifer Bright, Andrew Brooks, Abel Brumo, Matthew Bryan, John Butler, Kurt Byers, Greg Calliet, Lindsay Calkins, Mark Carr, Jay Carroll, Jenn Caselle, David Catania, Sam Chew Chin, Scott Clark, Jeffrey Cohen, Ronald Coleman, Jason Cope, Matt Craig, Debra Day, Ed DeMartini, E. J. Dick, Miriam Doyle, Willy Dunne, Dave Ebert, William Eschmeyer, Jeff Fargo, Marco Farrell, Rick Feeney, John Field, Jenn Finn, Sarah Gaichas, Scott Gietler, Ken Gobalet, Greg Goldsmith, Ramona de Graaf, Bob Hannah, Phil Hastings, Doug Hay, Selina Heppell, Jon Heifetz, Eric Hilton, Ted Hobson, Jerry Hoff, John Hyde, Tomio Iwamoto, Nancy Jacobsen-Stout, Scott Johnson, Richard Kacmar, Dan Kimura, Daiji Kitagawa, Cynthia Klepadlo, Donna Kline, Jane Knowles, Mick Kronman, Dave Kushner, Tom Laidig, Andy Lamb, Ami Latker, Robert Lauth, Robert Lea, Bruce Leaman, Kevin Lee, Chris Lowe, Mark Lowry, Matt Lum, Shayne MacLellan, Andrew Malavansky, Doug Markle, Karen Martin, Alec MacCall, Jeff Marliave, Marco Martinez Muñoz, Ann Matarese, Bruce McCarter, Mike McCorkle, John McCosker, Merit McCrea, Chris Miller, Eric Miller, Brad Mongeau, John Moore, Larry Moulton, Peter Moyle, Hans Mueter, Kris Munk, Joseph Nelson, Mary Nishimoto, Victoria O'Connell, Makoto Okamoto, Alexey Orlov, Jay Orr, Wayne Palsson, Michael Parsley, Don Pearson, Ted Pietsch, Dan Pondella, Steve Ralston, Dan Richards, Roy Qi, Ed Ries, Tyson Roberts, Ross Robertson, Chris Rooper, Jorge A. Rosales Casián, Richard Rosenblatt, Gorgonio Ruiz-Campos, Kate Rutherford, Rubi A. Ruz Cruz, Enric Sala, Donna Schroeder, Pat Shelton, Jeff Siegel, Linda Snook, John Snow, Oscar Sosa-Nishizaki, Rick Stanley, Jonn Stephens, Duane Stevenson, J. D. Stewart, Gary Takeuchi, David Thomas, Rebecca Thomas, Tim Thomas, Josie Thompson, Tierney Thys, Jonathan Toal, Pamela Tom, Ray Troll, Jack Turnock, John VanAmerongen, Waldo Wakefield, H.J. Walker, Bill Watson, Diane Watters, Tom Wilderbuer, Mark Wilkins, Jonathon Williams, Carrie Wilson, Tina Wyllie Echeverria, Jennifer Yakimishyn, Lynne Yamanaka, Mary Yoklavich, and Anne York.

Introduction

On 23 February 1850, British Foreign Secretary Henry John Temple Palmerston met with two traders, Joseph Braithwaite and George Martin, both late of West Africa. It was the beginning of the so-called "River Nunez Affair," a diplomatic imbroglio that...[1]

Oops, that's the introduction to my next book. The one you are currently manhandling, thus making it unsalable, is on the marine fishes of the Pacific Coast.

I wrote this book for two reasons:

First, and of course of most interest to you, I want you to be able to impress your friends with your knowledge of Pacific Coast fishes. I want you, a person whose personality is forever occluded by those of your associates, to finally emerge from the straitjacket of mediocrity that has been your lot in life.

And the other reason for writing this book? Oh, I want to make big, big bucks.

[1]With apologies to the very interesting *Palmerston and Africa—The Rio Nunez Affair* (Roderick Braithwaite, 1996, British Academic Press).

A Highly Selective History of Dead Pacific Coast Ichthyologists

We start off with Steller[1], who just paid a call,
He stopped off, collected, then left here, that's all.
He was European and thought this was the sticks,
Which makes certain sense; there was *no* Motel Six.

Pallas[2] also came here, and also collected,
'Bout froze off his tushie, but many species erected.
He was a great favorite of Catherine the Great,
Who from all that we've heard would have made a fine date.

Now Walbaum's[3] a person we hate to defame,
But he gave us each salmon's harsh tongue twisting name,
Saying *keta* and *kisutch* requires not a deft touch,
But *Oncorhynchus tshawytscha* is just, just too much.

Sir John Richardson[4], a British naval surgeon,
Described many fishes, without too much urgin',
In the Arctic one day, he shot a bold scout,
For eating some one and not spitting him out.

Dr. Ayres[5] was the first to dwell on our fair shores,
He lived in the City, 'mongst miners and whores.
A physician he was with no experts to guide him,
But he bought lots of fishes and then he described them.

Though Gill[6] didn't live here, he did lots of work,
He named many species, though he was a jerk.
In matters of taxa he thought Ayres a great fright,
But we know looking back that the Doc had it right.

Now Jackson[7], and Cary[8], and Gibbons[9] could boast,
And Agassiz, L.[10] out on the East Coast.
That they studied sea perches without much asperity,
So excited they were about viviparity.

Steindachner[11] came here and, Germanically efficient,
In describing fish species he wasn't deficient,
In Vienna one winter, when he was quite old,
His museum lacked heat and he died of the cold.

There was Lockington[12], too, a fine English fellow,
He studied flatfishes and appeared to be mellow.
But a man of his time and a man of his place,
He was pretty harsh on the subject of race.

Soon after came Jordan[13], that tower of a gent,
For West Coast fish science he was heaven-sent.
He was a true guru of piscinel knowledge,
Along with hygiene, and peace, and running a college.

Tarleton Bean[14] from Alaska, he early reported,
He found many new species, with Inuits consorted.
Now I'm not saying that Bean did something illicit,
But up there on the ice, perhaps everyone's complicit.

Now Gilbert's[15] a fabulous namer of fishes,
But woe to them that ignored his dark wishes.
When his son became a lawyer to Gilberts' great fears,
He didn't speak to the man for a number of years.

Evermann[16] was Jordan's main partner in crime,
Though he was second author, just every time.
I'm not saying D. Jordan was one to shirk,
But I've always suspected Dr. E. did the work.

The Eigenmann, C.[17], waxed physiological,
While Eigenmann, R.[18], was more biological.
They made quite a splash doing what they did best,
And then disappeared into the Midwest.

Now, Clemens[19] and Wilby[20] were Canadians, two,
'Twas boring up there, they didn't know what to do,
So they wrote a large tome on matters piscine,
And neatly described that cool northern scene.

And then there was Hart[21], up the very same way,
He was quite Canadian, what more need we say?
He wasn't amusing as some sure might wish,
But, oh what the hell, he sure knew his fish.

Of Hubbs, Carl[22] and Laura[23], they were a fine pair,
They worked down at Scripps, now who can compare?
They cranked out their papers on many a topic,
To have missed all their work, you must be myopic.

There were others of course, including Barnhart[24],
And Myers[25], and Snyder[26], and Girard[27] for a start.
Plus Phillips[28], Bolin[29], Goode[30], and DeLacy[31],
And for sure Spencer Baird[32], they all wrote nothing racy.

But of scientists living, Heaven forefend
We just won't write of them, lest we offend.

¹Georg Wilhelm Steller (1709–1746)

²Peter Simon Pallas (1741–1811)

³Johann Julius Walbaum (1724–1799)

⁴John Richardson (1787–1865)

⁵William O. Ayres (1805–1887)

⁶Theodore Nicholas Gill (1837–1914)

⁷A. C. Jackson

⁸Thomas G. Cary (1824–1888)

⁹William P. Gibbons (1812–1897)

¹⁰Louis Agassiz (1807–1873)

¹¹Franz Steindachner (1834–1919)

¹²William N. Lockington (ca. 1840–1902)

¹³David Starr Jordan (1851–1931)

¹⁴Tarleton Hoffman Bean (1846–1916)

¹⁵Charles Henry Gilbert (1859–1928)

¹⁶Barton Warren Evermann (1853–1932)

¹⁷Carl H. Eigenmann (1863–1927)

¹⁸Rosa Smith Eigenmann (1858–1947)

¹⁹Wilbert A. Clemens (1910–1963)

²⁰George Van Wilby (1896–1964)

²¹John L. Hart (1914–1973)

²²Carl Leavitt Hubbs (1894–1979)

²³Laura Hubbs (1893–1988)

²⁴Percy S. Barnhart (1881–1951)

²⁵George S. Myers (1905–1985)

²⁶John Otterbein Snyder (1867–1943)

²⁷Charles Girard (1822–1895)

²⁸Julius B. Phillips (1904–1995)

²⁹Rolf L. Bolin (1901–1973)

³⁰George Brown Goode (1830–1902)

³¹Allan C. Delacy (1912–1989)

³²Spencer Fullerton Baird (1823–1887)

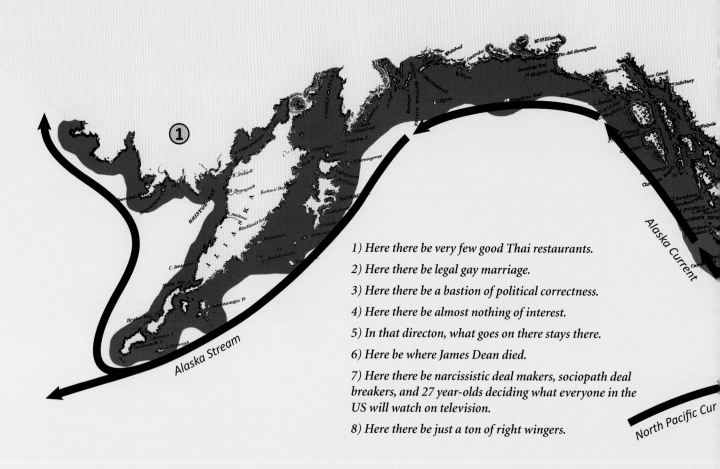

1) Here there be very few good Thai restaurants.

2) Here there be legal gay marriage.

3) Here there be a bastion of political correctness.

4) Here there be almost nothing of interest.

5) In that directon, what goes on there stays there.

6) Here be where James Dean died.

7) Here there be narcissistic deal makers, sociopath deal breakers, and 27 year-olds deciding what everyone in the US will watch on television.

8) Here there be just a ton of right wingers.

All Any Rational Person Needs to Know about the Zoogeography of Pacific Coast Fishes

– There are four fish provinces between the Bering Sea and southern Baja California. The boundaries of these provinces are kind of mushy.

– These provinces reflect both the survival of fish eggs and larvae and the movements of older fishes.

– In turn, fish survival and movements are based on the messy interactions of such oceanographic parameters as current pattern and strength, water temperature (often reflective of current pattern and strength), and upwelling[1]. Upwelling is important because it 1) helps determine plankton densities (and fishes both eat plankton and their eggs and larvae are eaten by plankton) and 2) may block larval transport.

– Generally, ocean waters get warmer the further south you go and the fish provinces reflect this. However, there are upwelling centers off northern Baja California that are real cold and harbor a number of colder-water species.

– The California Current is a major player in determining fish provinces. Its strength varies from season to season and year to year. The strength of the California Current is driven by, among other factors, the North Pacific High and the Aleutian Low (see Checkley and Barth 2009).

– Surface waters in the Pacific Ocean, north of about 20°N, vary between warmer and cooler phases, each phase lasting maybe 20–30 years. This is called the Pacific Decadal Oscillation.

– Physical barriers of many sorts, such as various promentories (e.g., Cape Mendocino, Point Conception, and Punta Colnett), Santa Monica Bay, and the Columbia River Plume, tend to restrict movements of eggs, larvae, and perhaps older fishes.

– El Niños and La Ninas, although much fun to observe and fear, mostly cause short-term fish movements and do not fundamentally alter the fish provinces of the Pacific Coast.

Interested in that fine down-home biological oceanography? Well, there's no accounting for taste. But, if you are, many inspiring hours can be yours when you cuddle up with Baumgartner et al. (1992), Mantua et al. (1997), Minobe (1997), Francis et al. (1998), Benson and Trites (2002), Miller et al. (2004), and Checkley and Barth (2009).

[1]Upwelling occurs when relatively deep, cold, and nutrient-rich waters are brought to the surface. Following upwelling, there are phytoplankton blooms that produce zooplankton population explosions.

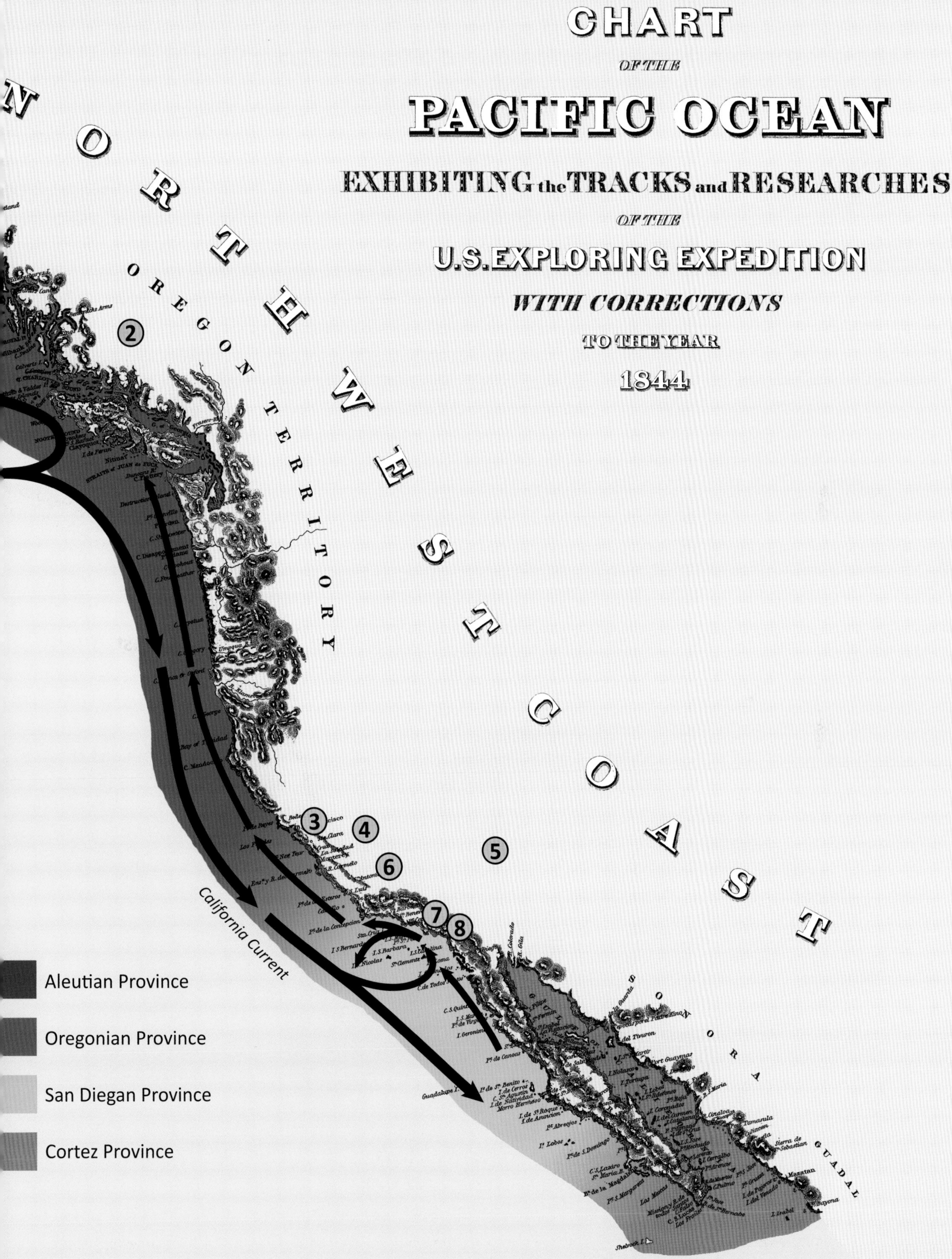
CHART
OF THE
PACIFIC OCEAN
EXHIBITING the TRACKS and RESEARCHES
OF THE
U.S. EXPLORING EXPEDITION
WITH CORRECTIONS
TO THE YEAR
1844
NORTH WEST COAST
OREGON TERRITORY
SONORA
California Current
2
3
4
5
6
7
8
Aleutian Province
Oregonian Province
San Diegan Province
Cortez Province

Zoogeographic provinces more or less after Briggs (1974)

Least Representational Rendering of a Pacific Coast Fish in a Publication Published after about, oh, 1920.

We don't understand why it is, but many of the drawings of fishes created before about 1920 are just useless. Yes, yes, we know about the lovely work produced by Pieter Bleeker and several others, but in many of these works the number of spines are correct and someone drew the right number of lateral line pores, but the totality of the image, the gestalt if you will, just sucks.

And why is that? And what is it with World War I? Because something happened after the War that made many of the renderings just a whole lot better. In some instances the difference is as striking as the change that occurred in Italian frescoes of the Medieval Period, the ones that look like a mildly depressed nine-year-old painted them, and the lovely images of the Renaissance. So what caused the post-WWI change? Did the Volstead Act force sobriety on biological illustrators? Or, conversely, was the level of imbibing actually higher in response to Prohibition, lending a sort of Runyanesque quality to the work? What about the Smoot-Hawley Tariff, just how did that factor in? And did the grittiness of the farmers plight in the late 1920s, and the calamitous Depression that followed, bring with it a burst of Realism that so characterizes fish drawings after that period. Really, many of the fishes drawn in the latter part of the 20th Century look like poster children for Socialist Realism. I saw a recently rendered illustration that might more properly be called "Heroic White Seaperch on the March."

Which brings us to the point that, whatever the cause, there is no excuse for a poorly executed fish drawing produced after the first twenty percent of the 20th Century. And, in that spirit, I think it is salutary to point out a relatively recent fish portrayal that perhaps does not adhere to these high standards. And, after searching through thousands of entries, I believe we have a winner.

The winning entry, ostensibly a rendering of a black rockfish (*Sebastes melanops*), is found in: W. A. Clemens and G. V. Wilby. 1949. *Fishes of the Pacific Coast of Canada* (Fisheries Research Board of Canada, Bulletin 68). I have taken the liberty of presenting two comments which might have been made by the selection panel: "Faintly reminiscent of the characterization of the bull in *Guernica*." "It puts me in the mind of the description of the tea Arthur Dent was served on Zaphod Beeblebrox's spaceship in Douglas Addam's *Hitchhiker's Guide to the Galaxy*: 'It was almost completely unlike tea.'"

How the Fish Got Its Scientific Name

What's with *Hydrolagus colliei*, *Semicossyphus pulcher*, *Hippoglossus stenolepis*, and all those other abstruse scientific names? If good old American names were just fine for such patriots as George Washington (Father of His Country), Kazimierz Pulaski (Father of American Cavalry), and Nikola Tesla (Father of, According to His Disciples, Just About Everything), why aren't they good enough for fishes? Well, they are, of course. It is only because of a vast, insidious, recondite and other scary words conspiracy, bent on undermining all that we hold dear, that fishes have scientific names.

No, no, just kidding.

I think.

See, the deal is that, back in the 18th century, scientists in various countries were calling the same organism (not just fishes, but any organism) by names in their native languages. Well, we can imagine the confusion that was engendered when the same species had French, English, and Swedish names. Not only that, but some of these names were five or more words long, and just unwieldy as all get out, particularly when you had to write them out with a sharpened bird feather. Thus it was that the 18th-century botanist, Karl von Linne, hit upon three very clever ideas:

First, he figured that all organisms should have Latin and Greek names. This was clever for two reasons: These were languages that were understood by all researchers at the time, and—without meaning to slight the entire Roman Empire (which after all had had a very good run indeed)—Latin was a dead language and hence did not change.

Second, Linne convinced the world that all organisms should have precisely two names, one for genus and one for species.

Third, Linne changed his name to Carolus Linnaeus. Researchers around the world, clearly under the spell of a dude *whose own name was in Latin*, fell into line.

From the time of Linnaeus, if you described a new species, you got to name it. Oh, there were rules of course. For instance, you couldn't name it after yourself. And, as mentioned previously, generally you had to make some pathetic attempt to fashion the name out of Latin- or Greek-derived words. Historically, most organisms were given names that were somehow descriptive of the organism. Take the Arctic flounder, *Pleuronectes glacialis*, for instance. *Pleuronectes* is Greek for "side" and "swimmer" (they do swim on their sides) and *glacialis* means "icy" in Latin (for their abundance in northern seas). But as also can be seen from our species accounts, with their dozens of *jordani*, *gilberti*, and *ritteri*, the process was often used to honor colleagues, friends, or those who were financially well-endowed (interestingly, being physically well-endowed is rarely a path to having a fish named after you). For instance, in the late 19th and early 20th centuries David Starr Jordan and his ichthyologist homies were fairly tripping over themselves naming fishes after Timothy Hopkins. *Xesiurus hopkinsi*, *Sebastes hopkinsi*, *Petrotyx hopkinsi*, *Mycteroperca hopkinsi*, *Hynnis hopkinsi*, and *Gnathypops hopkinsi*, all honored the rich guy who poured a skip loader full of lucre atop Dr. Jordan and his endeavors. And while this practice still exists today, there are elements in the taxonomic community that view it as just slightly dishabille: "Of course, my dear, it is, one supposes, perfectly fine to name the Chilean mung fish after Pablo Neruda, such a fine poet after all."

To all of this I say, who the hell cares? If someone wants to name a fish after their devoted postal carrier ("honoring Ms. Davis, who twice had her kneecap ripped off by rottweilers while delivering junk mail to those neighbors whose derelict Dodge Dart was the only bright spot in an otherwise scrofulous trailer park"), seventh- grade teacher ("honoring Mr. Garanfutti, who taught me more than I ever really had to know about hygiene"), or CPAs ("honoring Bristad, Narwhal, and Peachstem, without whom I would be writing this from a minimum security federal facility"), I say, fine. Hey, I once named a fish parasite after my girlfriend, and you know what, the world did not come to an end. Really, the world did not come to an end. Not yet, anyway.

Species Accounts

HOW I PICKED THE SPECIES DISCUSSED HEREIN

I don't know.

I do know that I have chosen some of the fishes that live in marine or estuarine waters, from the Beaufort Sea, way up there in Alaska, to Cabo San Lucas, at the tip of Baja California, and out about 200 miles. I couldn't include them all, of course, as there are more than 1,500 of these (I just this minute counted and got 1,512, but that is likely to change). The economically important ones (in both a recreational and commercial sense) were easy to choose, of course, as were the species that maybe no one catches, but are often seen. I tried to maintain some geographic balance so as not to be too California-centric, but that seems to have crept in anyway. In general, I just went with fishes that seemed to be meaningful in some vague way. In addition, if there is nothing known about a species, what is the use of including it, right? So, someone actually had to know at least something about the life of a species before I could acquire that information, prettily repackage it, and sell it to you. Does that make sense?

HOW I DECIDED ON THE ORDER OF THE SPECIES WITHIN THIS BOOK

We are held in thrall to systematists, those folks who decide how organisms are related to one another. Like Archimedes contemplating a bust of Homer, systematists spend the best years of their lives immersing themselves in such arcana as the number of caudal fin elements in mud minnows, the position of muscle attachment sites on the skulls of catfishes, and the shape of the suborbital bones in some god-forsaken sculpin. Recently, some members of this august fraternity have been using various forms of genetic techniques in this same single-minded pursuit. And after pondering long and hard, these bravos deduce which fishes are primitive and which advanced, which species are closely related, and how many angels can dance on the gill cover of a scorpionfish. And every decade or so they meet in solemn deliberation and, in a ceremony with roots buried deep in both gravitas and an Alpha Omega Gamma kegger, produce yet another volume of the American Fisheries Society's *Names of Fishes*, a publication for those who are truly One With The Fishes (not to be confused with those who ran afoul of various East Coast crime families). The species therein are listed starting from the most primitive to those that are most advanced with closely related fish snuggling next to one another. So, for those of us who are but nameless renal tubules in the kidney that is ichthyology, well, we just follow the order in the Good Book.

WHAT ABOUT FISH KEYS?

A fish key is a tool that, using physical characters for instance, helps the errant researcher figure out what species is clutched in hand.

Repeat after me: "This book has no fish keys."

Not that I did not consider it. Oh my, yes.

But a good key is just a whole lot of work, and really something not to be attempted by some lightweight like me. The key that I fashioned for *The Rockfishes of the Northeast Pacific* (University of California Press, 2002) almost killed me, and I stole most of *that* from *Guide to the Coastal Marine Fishes of California* (Miller and Lea, 1972). In *Fishes of Alaska* (American Fisheries Society, 2002), Kitty Mecklenburg created a very nice key to many species—perhaps if you caught your fish up there on the North Slope while freezing your nether regions, you might want to try that book.

HOW I CITED SOURCES

I could have cited sources for every fact in this book. But that screws up the narrative and is almost physically painful to read. So I have included citations only when I directly quote something or when I just damn well felt like it. And, if I know the person who wrote the paper, I use both their first and last names. And I do that to humanize the process. Always remember that scientific papers are, for the most part, written in a way that dehumanizes them. This is intentional; emotions get in the way of narrative and could be misconstrued as making the data suspect. There is a strain of thought that the ultimate scientific paper reads like it was written by a constipated robot or by one of those zombies in *Plan 9 from Outer Space*.

The Rules

INFORMATION ON FAMILIES

When I list information regarding the taxonomic status of a group, or how many genera or species there are worldwide, I mostly (although not exclusively) follow Joe Nelson's *Fishes of the World* (John Wiley and Sons, 2006) take on the matter. Joe's been thinking about these things for a long time and, hey, I have to take someone's advice, right?

ETYMOLOGY AND COLLOQUIAL NAMES

In general, I have used the American Fisheries Society's *Common and Scientific Names of Fishes* (American Fisheries Society, 2004) for both the scientific and "official" English name. However, since that list came out, there have been a number of scientific name changes that I thought were warranted. The walleye pollock, *Theragra chalcogramma*, for instance, was appropriately moved to the genus *Gadus*. In those instances where I have disagreements with the AFS official English name, I first let you know and then proceed to unfairly belittle the AFS name and those who codified it.

Scientific Names: Whenever possible I give the meaning of the genus and species name. In a few cases, the person(s) who described the species did not give the rationale for a name and I could not figure it out. If you figure it out, let me know.

Colloquial Names: I did not include every name that has ever been given to every species. That would not have made good theater, except, perhaps, for the theater of the absurd. I have included the occasional colloquial name when the name is 1) in wide use, 2) fun, or 3) of historical importance. I also often have included the names used in Japan or Mexico.

Unlike bird people, who would write Scarlet Tanager every chance they got, I have not capitalized the first letters of fish names (e.g., Kelp Bass) unless the name is a proper noun (like Chinook). The two exceptions are at the beginning of each species account (where it kind of looks right) and in the index (where it also looks correct). I understand the American Fisheries Society and American Society of Ichthyologists and Herpetologists Joint Names Committee has commanded us to fall into line, but having a fish's name in capital letters just looks...wrong. Really, when I see Kelp Bass or White Seabass, all those capital letters just give me the willies. It looks like those emails I get from fourth- graders: "Dear Mr. Milton, for my science project I have to write about a fish. I picked the Bolivian Bearded Rock Sucker. Please send me everything you know about the Bolivian Bearded Rock Sucker and please send me that today because the Bolivian Bearded Rock Sucker project is due tomorrow." Want to see dueling views on this issue? Do you really or are you just humoring me? Okay, check out Nelson et al. (2002) and Kendall (2002).

THE BASICS

Maximum length comes first and, when I figured I had a reasonable estimate, maximum weight. Geographic range comes next, starting with the overall range and then a more specific one for the eastern Pacific. This is frequently followed by what is nothing more than an educated guess regarding where the species is reasonably abundant and, mea culpa, may have little in common with reality. By the way, in this section I use the terms "abundant" and "common" kind of interchangeably, or at least with almost no regard to any discernible standard. That is followed by a depth range, again often with a range that might (who knows?) be typical. To save space, I often give both the geographic and depth ranges in telegraphic form, not in full sentences. Oh, and when I write something like "Within our range" that means from the Beaufort Sea to just around the Pacific corner of Cabo San Lucas. For lesser-known geographic locations, I give a bit more information in parentheses (e.g., Del Mar (Southern California)).

After that may come something about egg diameter, larval lengths at hatching, flexion, and transformation, and age-length and length-weight relationships, thus rounding out a very full and useful section. Note that for a number of economically important species there are a number of these growth and length-weight relationships, frequently from different parts of a species' range. When this occurs, I often just give data from a recent study that utilized a lot of fish and that used total length (I am very fond of total length). Really, if you are interested in comparing and contrasting you probably have the wherewithal to get that data on your own. Parenthetically, I must also add that the whole length-weight thing has turned into a gigantic can of worms and I kind of regret having even gotten into it. After I found these relationships in various papers, my associate Mary Nishimoto plotted them and a remarkable number were just wildly weird—obviously something had happened twixt the taking of the original data and the publishing of the formulae. In a substantial number of instances, I just went with the formula given on the Pacific States Marine Recreational Fisheries Monitoring website (http://www.recfin.org), figuring that if the information is wrong I can always blame that faceless entity. In general, then, you should take all of these with a substantial dollop of caveat emptor.

SALIENT CHARACTERS

I'm sorry to admit it, but giving descriptions of fishes is just about the most tedious thing imaginable and, life being so short, I just present the most Spartan accounts. These are likely just barely sufficient for you to be able to figure out what fish you saw when diving or fishing. But be of good cheer for there are any number of books that take great delight in helping you tell apart the "slimy kelp slurper" from the "spotted kelp slurper" (hint: look for the spots). These include Eschmeyer et al. (1983), Thomson et al. (2000), Mecklenburg et al. (2002), Ebert (2003), Humann and DeLoach (2004, 2008), and still my favorite, good ol' Miller and Lea (1972). The new kids on the fish identification guide block are Andy Lamb's and Phil Edgell's *Coastal Fishes of the Pacific Northwest* (Harbour Publishing, 2010) and Byersdorfer and Watson (*Field Guide to Common Marine Fishes and Invertebrates of Alaska*. Alaska Sea Grant, 2010). These folks clearly want to help you figure out what fish you have in your hand. Photographs illustrate many of the species accounts. Sadly, I chose many of these images for their aesthetic values rather than to help you with identifications. Sometimes I include more than one image if I got really excited about several images and could not decide between them.

Fish Fins and About Where to Find Them

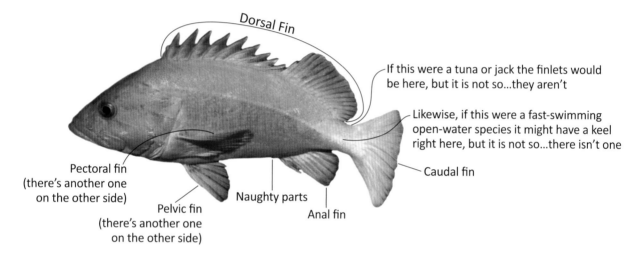

Dorsal Fin

If this were a tuna or jack the finlets would be here, but it is not so...they aren't

Likewise, if this were a fast-swimming open-water species it might have a keel right here, but it is not so...there isn't one

Caudal fin

Pectoral fin
(there's another one
on the other side)

Pelvic fin
(there's another one
on the other side)

Naughty parts

Anal fin

LIFE HISTORY

I start with the earliest part of a species' juvenile life, just when it settles out of the plankton. I rarely discuss anything about a species' larval life; larvae look like bits of glop to me and I can't relate to them. If you are interested in fish larvae, I wash my hands of you and you are on your own. (Okay, not completely on your own. Try Moser (1996) and the Ichthyoplankton Information System of the National Marine Fisheries Service). I then talk a bit about the habitat the species occupies and perhaps something about its spawning behavior and movements. This is followed by maximum age, sizes and ages at maturity, spawning seasons, food habits, and predators. Note that fishes are plastic in their life history traits. That is, such things as growth rates, size and age at maturity, reproductive season, and food habits can vary greatly between maturity stages, years, and locations. Please don't pester me with trivial differences between what you have observed and what I wrote. On the other hand, egregious errors on my part deserve condemnation.

Regarding fish lengths: Biologists measure fishes in all kinds of ways. To dreadfully oversimplify, taxonomists and systematists (who mostly work with preserved specimens) tend to use standard length, researchers who deal with dead fish often use fork length, and those of us (like me) who survey fishes underwater use total length. There are a number of exceptions to this rule. For instance, some billfish biologists use the length from the back of the eye socket to the fork of the tail fin (eye-fork-length, EFL). The figure resting nearby shows some of the more commonly used lengths. One length I do not exemplify is disk width (DW), the widest part in the flattened bodies of certain cartilaginous fishes.

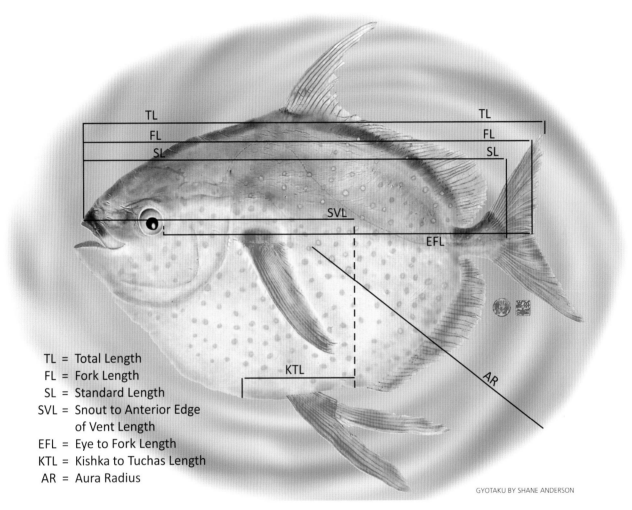

TL = Total Length
FL = Fork Length
SL = Standard Length
SVL = Snout to Anterior Edge
        of Vent Length
EFL = Eye to Fork Length
KTL = Kishka to Tuchas Length
AR = Aura Radius

GYOTAKU BY SHANE ANDERSON

Regarding conversions to English units: In general, I first present such measurements as depth, weight, length, and temperature in metric units or degrees Celsius. Then in parentheses I give the English and Fahrenheit equivalents. This was a huge pain in the ass and I kind of wish you people would metricate yourselves. You will notice that for very small measurements (less than 1 cm or just a few grams) I only give the metric units. That is because converting a tiny measurement like 1.5 mm to inches is just dumb.

FISHERY

I often start this section with a sentence or two about historic subsistence or artisanal fisheries as practiced by Native American, First Nation, Aleut, and Inupiat peoples. Frequently, however, I omit this because these people used just about every species they caught and they caught a very wide variety of species, particularly the nearshore ones. I do mention specific examples where for some reason there is a "gee whiz" factor or I just felt like it. Other than that, just assume that these extremely creative and very capable peoples caught and utilized just about every fish they could get their hands on. This is followed by discussion of any commercial or recreational fisheries. You will quickly note that I use the term "fishermen" rather than "fishers." I apologize to any and all who are offended; it is not meant to disquiet. Rather, I find that those who practice the commercial or recreational end of things usually refer to themselves as "fishermen" regardless of their gender.

ORIGINS AND RELATIONSHIPS

Herein there be the fossil record and current thinking about whom is related to whom. For estimates of when a taxa first evolved, I usually give the most recent date possible for that period (based on dates given in the GeoWhen Database). For instance, if the genus has been found as far back as the Miocene (5.3–23 million years ago), I will list the 5.3-million-year figure, unless the paper is more specific.

MISCELLANY

There are often just interesting things about a species that do not seem to fit in any other category. I stuck them here.

REMARKS

This is the place for some kind of big picture or overarching airy-fairy statement.

THE JAWLESS FISHES

In a less artful day, when smart young women could hope only to be the governess of children of rich widowers, the lampreys and hagfishes were classified in the class (or superclass or supraclass or whatever) Agnatha. Recently, I have noted that some ichthyologists are getting downright snippy and use the term "jawless fishes." Jawless fishes are all eel-like and do not have paired fins (pelvics and pectorals). Whether lampreys and hagfishes are closely related to each other is a source of some contention. In fact, some folks argue that hagfishes, because they lack vertebrae, are not vertebrates and hence are not even fishes. It is important to remember that despite their, well, *minimalist* appearance, hagfishes and lampreys are not some sort of geeky degenerates, hanging around the edges of the Evolutionary Prom. Rather, they are likely the proud survivors of several ancient lineages and if they had their own tartans they would be wearing kilts today. The earliest jawless fish thus far uncovered is the parasitic lamprey *Priscomyzon riniensis* from a 360-million-year-old Devonian formation.

ORDER MYXINIFORMES

FAMILY MYXINIDAE—Hagfishes

Hagfishes are eel-like animals that lack jaws, bones, paired fins (pelvics and pectorals), and (in the adults) lateral lines. Worldwide there are seven genera and at least 73 species. In our area, there are at least six species.

The hagfish figures prominently in the novel *Polar Star* by Martin Cruz Smith (Random House, 1989). Let's look in on out-of-favor Investigator Arkady Renko, now a crewman on the Russian trawler, *Polar Star*, in the Bering Sea. A crewwoman winds up dead, on the seafloor, and then is trawled up by the *Polar Star*. During an informal autopsy on the vessel, with Renko and a doctor present, a hagfish emerges from the body: "The eel's head, an eyeless stump with fleshy horns and a puckered mouth, whipped from side to side against Zina Patiashvili's stomach; then the entire eel, as long as an arm, slid seemingly forever out of her...the doctor stabbed, snapping the scalpel in two against the deck." Gooshy good, yes?

Eptatretus stoutii
(Lockington, 1878)
Pacific Hagfish

"And thus I clothe my naked villainy, with odd old ends stol'n out of holy writ, and seem a saint, when most I play the devil."
King Richard III, William Shakespeare

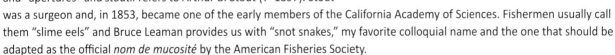

ETYMOLOGY AND SEVERAL LOVELY COLLOQUIAL NAMES: *Eptatretus* comes from the Greek and means "seven" and "apertures" and *stoutii* refers to Arthur B. Stout (?–1897). Stout was a surgeon and, in 1853, became one of the early members of the California Academy of Sciences. Fishermen usually call them "slime eels" and Bruce Leaman provides us with "snot snakes," my favorite colloquial name and the one that should be adapted as the official *nom de mucosité* by the American Fisheries Society.

THE BASICS: Maximum length: 82 cm (32 in) TL. The Ranges: Hecate Strait (British Columbia) to Punta San Pablo (central Baja California). 16–966 m (53–3,168 ft). Along the California coast, most Pacific hagfish live in perhaps 91–366 m (300–1,200 ft). Eggs: about 2.4 cm (0.9 in) in diameter. Length-weight parameters (TL, mm, gr): (females) $W = 0.00000794L^{2.77}$; (males) $W = 0.0000209L^{2.6}$ (Reid 1990).

SALIENT CHARACTERS: Let's face it, hagfish are the most proudly disgusting creatures on earth. They are blind and eel-shaped, with 10–14 round gill openings on each side of their body. They have no jaws; a rasp-like structure thrusts out of their permanently gaping mouths. They come in a variety of appealing colors, usually gray or brown, and occasionally white or mottled. Probably the best way to tell if your fish is a hagfish is to look at the hand holding the fish. If it's completely covered with thick, ropy slime, that's all the proof you need.

LIFE HISTORY: Hagfish are truly singular fish that live over a wide range of habitats. We see them in holes in mud, curled on mud or in sponges (very frequently from my observations), in rock crevices, and swimming as much as a meter into the water column. Young hagfish emerge from their eggs at about 6.3 cm (3 in) TL. My observations of young fish on deep-water mudflats off Central California imply that they are patchy in their distribution, with one strip of mud housing dozens of fish and an adjacent patch having none. Hagfish may be most active at night. One study demonstrated that this species migrates into somewhat deeper waters in the summer.

We are a little short on facts about this species. Off Oregon, a few males are mature at 26 cm (10 in) TL, 50% at 35 cm (14 in), and almost all are mature by 42 cm (17 in). For females, these values are 30 cm (12 in), 42 cm (17 in), and 51 cm (20 in), respectively. On the other hand, in Southern California, maturation may occur at slightly smaller sizes. Here, a few males are mature at 25.5 cm (10 in) TL, 50% at about 29.5 cm (12 in), and 100% at 40.5 cm (16 in). Values for females are 29.5 cm (12 in), about 33.5 cm (14 in), and 50.5 cm (20 in), respectively. Females reputedly mature at between 7 and 12 years old. Occasionally a hermaphrodite is found. Eggs (eerily resembling little cocktail hot dogs connected to each other by strands) occur in batches and these batches range from 5–82 eggs. It is likely that Pacific hagfish spawn throughout the year.

There is not much information out there regarding the food habits of our slimy little friends. It looks like they consume squids, octopuses, sergestid shrimps, fish parts, polychaetes, amphipods, eggs, and euphausiids. When feeding on carrion, hagfish spin their bodies around to rip off chunks. Jordan (1922), waxing unusually dramatic, wrote of the hagfish: "Fastening its sucker-like mouth with rasping teeth within the gill openings of a large fish, it gnaws into the body, devouring all the muscular system of its 'host' and reducing it to a mere hulk...When the victim finally dies, the parasite makes its escape; and sometimes when a poor wreck is hauled up in a net, the pirate may be observed thrusting its eyeless head from out of the hole, and then pumping incontinently into the water in search of a new boarding house." Well, all very dramatic to be sure. But how accurate is it? While hagfish clearly attack animals trapped in nets, it is unclear how often they attack healthy, free-swimming ones. This species can live for at least 9 months without feeding. Hagfish predators include copper rockfish, bluntnose sixgill sharks, sablefish, California sea lions, harbor seals, and northern elephant seals. Sablefish, elephant seals, and other Pacific hagfish eat their eggs.

FISHERY: As noted above by Jordan, for years hagfish were of interest to commercial fishermen only because they attacked and ate fishes snared in netting. Barraclough (1948) noted: "The hag-fish is one of the most repulsive predators found in the sea...Some of the flounders [caught in nets] had been reduced to a limp skeleton covered with skin." And so it might have continued except for the overfishing of hagfish in the Korean fishery. Yes, there was a hagfish fishery there; the fish were both eaten and, of more importance

ARTHUR B. STOUT

In the 19th century, it was almost a given that, should one stick around the California Academy of Sciences long enough, someone would name something after you. And while Arthur B. Stout was certainly a force in the Academy, he was also a flaming racist and in a reflection of the times, he was well respected in California for his anti-Chinese views. In *The Unwelcome Immigrant: The American Image of the Chinese, 1785–1882* (University of California Press, 1969), S.C. Miller notes that Stout "insisted, unabashed, that the introduction of Chinese and Negroes into America would be like 'a cancer' in 'the biological, social, religious, and political systems.' There was nothing to be gained by such an infusion and everything to be lost. Improvements on the 'Divine excellence' of the Anglo-Saxons seemed unlikely. 'Until Islamism and Paganism alike sink into oblivion, and Christianity enters, like sunlight into chaos, to illuminate and revivify this ancient world [China]…we cannot permit Asiatics to enter,' he concluded." And that is Dr. Stout.

Oh, wait a minute, I have one more *bon mot* from Dr. Stout, "By intermingling with Europeans, we are but reproducing our own Caucasian type; by commingling with the Eastern Asiatics, we are creating degenerate hybrids" (Gardner 1999).

Nope, changed my mind. For in the minutes of the California Academy of Sciences, 15 July 1878, we find this notation: "Dr. Stout, as corresponding secretary [of the CAS], reported the receipt from France of a pamphlet announcing the formation in Paris of an 'Indo-Chinese Society,' portions of which, after translation, he read. His remarks, especially in so far as they involved the Chinese question, then a matter of political controversy, elicited considerable discussion; but he insisted upon the importance of the subject" (Leviton and Aldrich 1997). The "considerable discussion" reference was Victorian-speak for "Cripes, Artie, can't you just give it a rest for once? We just want to smoke these lovely seegars, drink this excellent brandy, and talk about this new species of mugwort."

FRAT BOYS OF THE DEEP

What kind of fishes are hagfishes? Well, in one study conducted in the Monterey Bay Submarine Canyon, food odor was released from a container that also contained high levels of carbon dioxide, which effectively removed much of the oxygen from the water. A Pacific hagfish happened by, entered the beaker containing the CO_2 and "the animal quickly lost consciousness, sank to the bottom, and rolled over on its dorsal side. After approximately 20 seconds, the hagfish recovered and resumed tracking the odor plume back to the release rig. Twice more the same individual approached and entered the beaker, then lost consciousness" (Tamburri et al. 2000).

perhaps, their skins were turned into "eel skin" leather for wallets and the like. Sus Kato (1990) visited a Korean hagfish processing plant and reported that a good hagfish skinner (and don't we just love "The Hagfish Skinners" as a rock band name) could skin about 409 kg (900 lb) of hagfish in a working day.

And thus it was that in 1986 and 1987, South Korean businessmen obtained samples of Pacific hagfish from California and a fishery started there in 1988. Well, as one might expect, Gold Rush fever struck at a number of West Coast ports, as every boat that could float was out there trapping the little goopers. But, like that big strike at Mormon Bar, the Rush did not last long. It soon emerged that the quality of hagfish skin, actually the amount of tiny holes in the skin, varies from place to place and that many of the fish living off Southern California and Baja California had skins that were not usable. Buyers started lowering their prices, the guys on the water got grumpy, and within a few years the fishery

kind of petered out. However, I note that here in the early 21st century, there is, yet again, a pretty good-sized fishery off the northeastern Pacific, this time as live fish product. So, who knows?

Once in a while an angler catches one.

MISCELLANY: The operative term here is "slime," lots and lots of slime (and hence the quote from Shakespeare that begins this account). Hagfishes have a series of mucous pores on the sides of their bodies, each with a number of slime glands that produce copious amounts of the gooey stuff. You can take a 5-gallon bucket of fresh seawater, put a hagfish in it, and in a few minutes that bucket is filled with slime. And this is not just your run-of-the-mill slime. No, hagfish slime is extra special because it contains numerous tiny threads that kind of stiffen the product. You can reach around in that bucket and pick most

of it up in a kind of end-of-the-world-as-we-know-it clump. In fact, the glands contain two morphologically distinct types of cells. When broken, the contents of mucous cells interact with seawater to form...well, mucous. Similarly, gland thread cells release long fibrous threads that embed in the mucous.

And why all that slime? That is a good, and not totally an-swered, question. One use appears to be to protect a hagfish's carrion meals from some competitors, at least from snails, although amphipods seem to ignore the stuff. Davies et al. (2006) report on a second possibility. These three intrepid biologists, probably after drinking a few too many Molson's at Bamfield's only decent bar, de-cided to see what would happen if they anchored two 15 kg (33 lb) frozen pig legs off western Vancouver Island. And one of the things

that happened is that both Pacific hagfish and spotted ratfish came around to munch on the porker. What is of most inter-est, however, is their observation of two freshly deceased ratfish lying close to one of the legs. They report that they saw no obvious wounds to the fish but "there was extensive subsurface hemorrhaging around the mouth of one ratfish and strands of mucous on the second and we infer rapid respiratory failure from the hagfish mucous that was prevalent in the water column around the carrion." And why wouldn't hagfish clog up their own gills with snot? It has been proposed that these fish can also respire through their skins and thus avoid drowning in mucous.

Hagfish are also good at quickly tying and untying themselves in knots.

REMARKS: I believe there is some evidence that karma requires certain bank executives involved in creating toxic assets to return as hagfish a minimum of 17 times (and be very, very good when they do) in order to expiate their requisite guilt—and their slimy behavior in their first-go-round.

OTHER SPECIES

Eptatretus deani
(Evermann & Goldsborough, 1907)
Black Hagfish

Black hagfish grow to 63.5 cm (25 in) TL and live from southeastern Alaska to Isla Guadalupe (central Baja California), at depths of 107–2,743 m (353–9,052 ft). Off California, they are typically at depths of 600–1,200 m (1,968–3,936 ft). Black hagfish feed on crustaceans, polychaetes, fishes, brittle stars, and decaying whales. A few males are mature at 28 cm (11 in) TL, 50% at 34 cm (14 in), and all are mature at 44 cm (17 in). For females, these lengths are 33 cm (13 in), 38 cm (15 in), and 42 cm (17 in), respectively. Fecundity ranges from about 8–30 eggs. At least some individuals are hermaphroditic. Length-weight parameters (TL, cm, gr): (females) $W = 0.001831L^{2.99}$; (males) $W = 0.00356L^{2.81}$ (Barss 1993).

ON HAGFISH

Oh hagfish, thou gray Prince of Icky,
Your alimentary habits are sick-y
   But when your poor maw,
   Lacks large teeth or jaw,
I suppose that you can't be too picky.

ORDER PETROMYZONTIFORMES

FAMILY PETROMYZONTIDAE—Lampreys

Worldwide, there are eight genera and about 34 species of petromyzontids (all of the Northern Hemisphere species are in this family), with three species in our range. All lampreys spend their early youth buried in the sediments of rivers and streams, although some are later anadromous and others strictly freshwater. When they emerge, some species become parasitic on other fishes and some do not. Parasitic lampreys attach to their hosts using a disc-shaped oral sucker that rasps away the host's flesh and allows for ease of bloodletting. They produce an anticoagulant that prevents blood clotting and thus the too-precipitate end to the meal. There are various summaries of the life histories of Pacific Coast lampreys and Kostow (2002) is a nice, compact one.

Lampetra ayresii
(Günther, 1870)
River Lamprey

ETYMOLOGY: *Lampetra* comes from the Latin "to suck" and "stone" and *ayresii* honors William O. Ayres (1805–1887). Ayres was the first curator of ichthyology at the California Academy of Science and a very good ichthyologist. Having moved to San Francisco in 1854, he immediately began to describe new species of fishes based on whatever was brought into the bayside markets. In the process, he, like a number of others, was simply hammered by the evil Theodore Gill (see the longjaw mudsucker, *Gillichthys mirabilis*) who thought he owned all Pacific Coast fishes. Gill's relentless hectoring, quite without foundation, caused the rather retiring Ayres to quit ichthyology in 1864. In 1871, Ayres left San Francisco, bound first for Chicago, and then on to Connecticut, where he taught at Yale University and practiced medicine. He died in Brooklyn, New York.
THE BASICS: Maximum Length: 31.1 cm (12 in) TL. The Ranges: Tee Harbor (southeastern Alaska) to San Francisco Bay.
SALIENT CHARACTERS: River lampreys are eel-shaped fish, with a disc-shaped sucker-like mouth and seven round gill openings. They can have yellow, brown, silvery, or blue-black backs, along with yellow fins, and a dark gray blotch on the tail. See Mecklenburg et al. (2002) for a comparison with the Pacific lamprey.
LIFE HISTORY: In British Columbia, young fish begin to emerge from freshwater rocky nurseries in July and begin to metamorphose, although metamorphosis is not complete for almost a year. In the following spring and summer, the fish, moving both day and night, migrate downstream to the ocean, entering it from about May (and possibly April) to July. In the ocean, staying in nearshore waters, they feed on other fishes and remain in saltwater for a few months, returning to freshwater in

the fall and late winter. Fish appear to remain in shallow nearshore waters for the few months they are in the ocean. Spawning occurs in the spring, from April to June, and based on laboratory observations, most females die within hours of spawning and most males croak after about 3 weeks. Thus, 2 years pass from the time river lampreys metamorphose until they die after spawning. It appears that, on occasion, a few river lampreys may spend their entire lives in freshwater. One study estimated that there are a whopping 6.5 million young adults entering the Strait of Georgia. Beamish (1980) describes

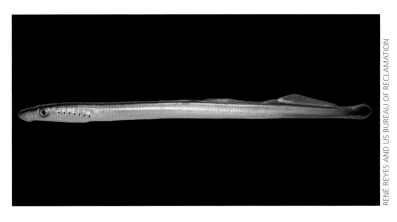

spawning behavior, as seen in aquaria, this way: "Prior to spawning, lamprey constructed nests approximately 15 cm [5.9 in] in diameter in the gravel by lifting rocks out of the nest area with the oral disc and by vigorous digging movements. Just prior to spawning a male would glide up and down the body of the female with his oral disc and eventually attach dorsally behind the head of the female, twisting his tail around the body of the female." Females produce 11,398–37,288 eggs.

Unlike the parasitic Pacific lamprey, river lampreys are predators; they feed by biting chunks off of fishes. This likely causes a relatively high mortality rate, although some prey survive. In one study, 11.5% of all Pacific herring captured had river lamprey wounds. Most attacks are on the dorsal and anterior parts of body. All five species of salmon, Pacific herring, and northern anchovy are commonly eaten. Predators include lingcod, striped bass, glaucous-winged gulls, pigeon guillemots, and harbor seals.

FISHERY: Apparently none to speak of.

RELATIONSHIPS: Genetic sequencing shows it is most closely related to the freshwater *Lampetra hubbsi* and also, and unfortunately, indistinguishable genetically from the freshwater *Lampetra richardsoni*. These genetically indistinguishable forms may have diverged less than 70,000 years ago.

WILLIAM O. AYRES, FRONTIER ICHTHYOLOGIST

So you think you have problems as a fish biologist? Think your life is stressful, what with dealing with grant proposals, supervisors who don't understand the worth of your research, disgruntled students, and significant others who merely look puzzled when you wax enthusiastic about the work you do?

Well, my friend, these are like mere pimples on the heinie of a wildebeest compared to the travails of my favorite ichthyologist, Dr. William O. Ayres, of San Francisco. Dr. Ayres, a physician, traveled from Connecticut to Gold Rush San Francisco. During his stay, Ayres described a large number of Pacific Coast fishes, presumably between prescribing either a good dose of leeches or an overdose of laudanum, to his many patients. And his taxonomic work was done under rather primitive conditions. For instance, in his years in The City, the town routinely burned to the ground; the lack of scientific journals meant that some of his fish descriptions had to be published in the *Daily Placer Times*, right next to ads (in the 15 March 1853 issue) for: 1) "Dr. J. Sanborn, Thomsonian, Botanic, and Hydropathic Practitioner," 2) "Rump Pork," and 3) "Powdered Opium."

More to the point, San Francisco of that time was—if not completely lawless—perilously close to it. Crime was rampant and the city government, from the legislators to the sheriff, was in the pocket of the criminals. In 1856, James King of William, the crusading editor of the *Evening Bulletin*, ran afoul of James P. Casey, lately released from Sing Sing prison and recently elected to the San Francisco Board of Supervisors. Casey, incensed over a blistering King editorial, gathered some friends, rode a coach to King's office, and shot him. Following the shooting, Casey ran to a coach occupied by three henchmen and prepared to make a run for the city jail where his friend the sheriff was expected to provide protection. Dr. Ayres was in a curiously intimate position to view what happened next. Years later, Ayres wrote: "A carriage was standing at the entrance to Dunbar alley [sic], the rear of the police office. It was undoubtedly about to start. I sprang on the step and as I did so, Dave Scannell's [Casey's henchman] pistol was thrust directly in my face.

I looked in, and saw Casey on the seat with Scannell with his pistol pointed out of the opposite window. The driver started his horses, and I was thrown to the ground, but was on my feet in an instant, and away with the crowd who were pursuing the carriage at full speed, yelling with every breath 'Hang him! Kill him!'

"The horses were, of course, too light-footed for us, but we all, however, knew their destination, the county jail. The building in Broadway near Kearney was at an elevation, then, of about eight feet above the level of the street, which had been graded down to that extent. On the bank above stood every one of the most noted gamblers and shoulder strikers in the city. Their faces were well known to me, Charley Duane, Dan Aldrich and a host of others. There they stood; a dangerous looking company quietly looking down on the angry crowd that filled the street and surged back and forth in its intense excitement. How came those men to be there?

"I have no doubt they were there in position when the shot was fired, and James King of William fell. I was waiting for the first pistol shot which I well knew would be the prelude to a fearful scene of bloodshed, when a man rushed past me, and began scrambling up one of the posts of a balcony directly at my back. I saw it was Thomas S. King, the brother of James King of William. He at once began a harangue of almost delirious frenzy and after a few words only, he shouted out, '…who will go with me and drag the murderer of my brother from the jail?' He could not utter another word. The fierce and savage yell, 'I,' 'I,' 'I,' from hundred of throats was perfectly deafening, and the revolvers came out like magic ready for sharp service.

"Thomas S. King leaped to the ground, and started with a rush, but he had not crossed half the breadth of Broadway, before he stopped, and at the same moment, the crowd began to grow quiet. Some one had touched them on the back and whispered, 'The Vigilance Committee has organized.'"

Ayres does not go on to complete the story. The killing, coming as it did after a stream of murders and general mayhem had left the respectable citizens of San Francisco roiling in anger, led to the formation of the Vigilance Committee of 1856. Soon after King's death, the Committee forced the sheriff to hand over Casey and, one supposes with Dr. Ayres in attendance, Casey was hung. Before it disbanded, the Committee strung up a few more individuals and banished many others.

Entosphenus tridentatus
(Richardson, 1836)
Pacific Lamprey

ETYMOLOGY AND COLLOQUIAL NAMES: *Entosphenus* comes from the Greek for "within" and "wedge" (the anterior tooth is wedge-shaped) and *tridentatus* is Latin for "three" and "toothed." So what does this latter refer to? Hold up a Pacific lamprey and look into its sucking disc. Now right there above the mouth you will see a bar (it's called a "supraoral lamina") that has three teeth on it and the middle one is shorter than the other two. That's the "three-toothed" origin of the species' name. Pacific lampreys are frequently called "eels" and California's Eel River is named for this fish. They are called "yufutsuyat-sume" in Japanese. Previously as *Lampetra tridentata*.

THE BASICS: Maximum Length: 85 cm (34 in) TL. Maximum Weight: At least 0.5 kg (1 lb). The Ranges: Honshu and Kamchatka to the eastern Chukchi Sea, and from the Bering Sea to Punta Canoas (northern Baja California) on the mainland and apparently as far southward as the region around Isla Clarión, Revillagigedo Archipelago, Mexico. They are reasonably abundant from at least Kamchatka to the eastern Bering Sea and to at least Rio Santo Domingo (30°43'N, 116°02'W) (northern Baja California). In the ocean, near surface waters to 1,508 m (4,949 ft), mostly in 500 m (1,640 ft) and shallower. Hatching length = about 4–5 mm TL. Length-weight parameters (TL, cm, kg): (sexes combined) $W = 0.0000462L^{2.1648}$ (Orlov et al. 2008).

SALIENT CHARACTERS: Pacific lampreys are eel-shaped fish, with a disc-shaped sucker-like mouth and seven round gill openings. They usually have brown to almost black backs and pale bellies. See Mecklenburg et al. (2002) for a comparison with river lampreys.

LIFE HISTORY: Pacific lamprey ammocoetes (the larval stage) start life under gravel in freshwater. After a short time (measured in weeks) they emerge (usually at night) and drift down current until they find a backwater filled with silt or mud. Ammocoetes live under the stream or river floor and suck organic stuff and algae from the substrata. After perhaps 3–7 years, and with the development of large eyes and that cool sucking mouth (among other changes), the fish metamorphose into the kitschy predator we all know and love. From this point on, there is a lot of variability between individuals and likely between geographic areas. The transformation season (they do not feed during this time) apparently varies with location and may start anytime during the year. However, much of that seems to occur from summer to fall and the newly revitalized fish then begin to migrate to the sea. At this point they are capable of feeding on other fishes. Most entry into marine waters occurs from December–June (although there is some

RENÉ REYES AND US BUREAU OF RECLAMATION

evidence for a later marine entry of Oregon fish). Kostow (2002) noted, in the Rogue and Umatilla rivers of Oregon, "massive peaks of out-migration" would in some years occur over just a few days. Once in the ocean, not much is known about where they go or what they do (other than that they suck stuff out of other fishes, of course). It appears that the ocean phase lasts from 1–3.5 years, and lampreys have been taken way offshore in the center of the Bering Sea and in the Pacific Ocean off Kamchatka. At sea, the fish do make vertical migrations and are in shallower waters at night. Genetic analyses imply either that all of the fish on the Pacific Coast form a single population (Goodman et al. 2008) or that there is genetic differentiation of fish in the Pacific Northwest (Lin et al. 2008). So, like what is a backcountry biologist supposed to think?

From winter to summer (again, depending on location), the fish (now between 13 and at least 72 cm, 5–28 in, TL) return and begin to ascend rivers and streams, migrating at night. In the Columbia River, lampreys tend to begin their upstream migrations earlier in years with low water discharge and high water temperatures. In one Oregon river, lampreys averaged 11.1 km (6.9 mi) per day, with a maximum rate of 20.9 km (13 mi) per day. While it is likely that some fish return to their natal streams, what percentages do is unknown. In small streams, lampreys migrate only a short distance before finding some place to spawn; while in major river systems they can travel hundreds of kilometers (as much as 1,500 km, 932 mi) before being satisfied. Many fish overwinter part of the way through this migration before spawning in the following spring. Over-wintering fish shelter under boulders in riffles. Most fish spend some time in freshwater (some as much as one year) before spawning. Spawning occurs as early as January (for instance in the Santa Clara River, Southern California) and all the way into summer. Peter Moyle (2002) notes that in some watersheds, like the Klamath River (Northern California), fish that enter the river in the spring may spawn soon thereafter, while fall-run fish may wait until the next year.

As noted above, spawning occurs in freshwater gravel beds, from January–July, likely starting earlier in the year in the more southerly watersheds. A nest is created when a female and male move rocks around and create a little divot. To move a stone, the lamprey attaches its mouth to the rock, and swims backwards. If a rock is particularly unwieldy, both parents latch on and pull. (I'm telling you, if it weren't for the fact that some of us feel repulsion for these fish, this kind of behavior would be considered sooo cute.) Eventually, the fish create a nice little depression. Prior to spawning, a female will attach herself to a rock and the male either attaches himself to her head or to the same rock (now they are parallel, see?) and they release the sperm and eggs. The fertilized eggs drift into the nest and attach to the rocky bottom. Some parents-to-be then loosen more rocks from above the nest and all kinds of debris then flow down and cover the eggs. Doug Markle and Abel Brumo tell me that they have also seen a parent "open its mouth and roll the substrate where they had just spawned; the eggs would rise and drift downstream" or vigorously dig about in the pocket of eggs, dispersing them into rocky nooks and crannies. All of this is repeated a number of times until the fish run out of, well, you know what. Not

ROMANCE FOR
JAW-CHALLENGED FISHES

What's the purpose at this season
That I love you without reason
Never felt this way before
As I sweep the river floor.

Though your company's such bliss
Locking lips we just can't kiss
For mating's driven by compulsion
Thus we shall triumph, through repulsion

only rocks are moved about; one observer saw a male lamprey glom onto a sculpin that was resting in the nest and escort it out. While most Pacific lampreys die soon after spawning, there is pretty good evidence that some individuals survive all the frivolity, re-migrate to the ocean, and return to spawn a second time. One study found that a female living in Oregon produces between 98,000–238,400 eggs.

Pacific lampreys are parasitic; they glom onto a fish, rasp away the skin, and suck out various and sundry liquids. Most fishes are attacked from the bottom and from behind. Flatfishes are generally attacked on their blind sides, often near the pectoral and pelvic fins and on the gill covers. In laboratory studies, these lampreys will hang on to a host for up to several days. Many hosts do not die after attacks, as various surveys show high incidences of fishes with lamprey scars. For instance, one study of sockeye and coho salmon off the Fraser River (British Columbia) found that 66% of the sockeyes and 20% of the cohos had Pacific lamprey wounds. Along with various salmon, Pacific lampreys parasitize numerous flatfishes, Pacific cod, Pacific hakes, rougheye and yellowmouth rockfishes, sablefish, steelhead,

walleye pollock, and whales. Pacific lampreys are eaten by a broad assortment of predators including fishes (e.g., rockfishes, various sharks, sablefish, and white sturgeons), birds (e.g., great blue herons, common murres, gulls, and terns), seals, sea lions, dolphins, sperm whales, and minks. There is speculation that large numbers of out-migrating lampreys may sometimes reduce predation on salmon smolts because predators have lampreys on their minds.

FISHERY: Historically, Pacific lampreys were an important part of the diets of some Native American and First Nation peoples. Even today, lampreys are caught in substantial numbers in artisanal subsistence fisheries. Most of the fish are caught as they migrate upstream, often at the base of waterfalls or rapids where the fish tend to congregate. The fish are caught by nets, by hand, or with hooks. While lampreys have always been used for food (they were often roasted or dried), they also served other purposes. For instance, the peoples living on the mid-Columbia Plateau used lamprey oil for food, as a hair conditioner, and as a cure for earaches. With the arrival of Europeans, Pacific lampreys were rarely commercially fished for food. Rather, they were used as rations for salmon, as fishmeal, for the vitamin A in their livers, and as a source of anticoagulants. Recently, relatively small amounts have been caught commercially for food, mainly for export.

RELATIONSHIPS: Pacific lampreys are most closely related to three freshwater forms, *Lampetra similis*, *L. macrosoma*, and *L. lethophaga*.

REMARKS: Construction of dams on the outlet to Elsie Lake in British Columbia, blocking both emigration of young fish and immigration of adults, led to the extinction of the population above the dam.

CHONDRICHTHYES –
SHARKS, SKATES, RAYS, and RATFISHES

The Chondrichthyans, not a Fabian Socialist group at 1920s Oxford, but rather the sharks, skates, rays, and ratfishes, are beyond doubt the most successful group of fishes in the world. Oh, they may be kind of light in the number of species department (somewhere around 1,150) and they don't really dominate any particular fish community, but for sheer endurance, through the tumult and hubbub of 400 million-plus years, this group has got the goods. All Chondrichthyes have 1) a cartilaginous skeleton (they lack true bones), 2) tooth-like, placoid scales (except for the chimaeras), 3) fins without bony rays, and 4) internal fertilization.

INFORMATION PLEASE
For more information on these fishes, you might consider perusing, or better yet purchasing, Dave Ebert's swell volume, *Sharks, Rays, and Chimaeras of California* (University of California Press, 2003) and Leonard Compagno's various volumes on the sharks of the world.

A Wee Primer on Chondrichthyan Reproduction

In the good old days, when you and I were young and lilacs last in the door-yard bloom'd, sharks, skates, rays, and chimaerids engaged in one of three forms of reproduction: they were oviparous, ovoviparous, or viviparous. We now know that these categories were charmingly naïve and merely the prattlings of innocents. So today we have replaced them with terms that sound like they came from the story line of a particularly obscure robot manga. Fortunately we have Marshall and White (2005) to help us out. Let's listen in:

Oviparity: "Once fertilized, the relatively large eggs of oviparous species...become encapsulated in tough, keratinized shells. Almost all of the embryonic development occurs inside the egg case after it has been deposited in the external environment."

Aplacental Viviparity (also referred to as *viviparous without a yolk sac placenta*): "Aplacental viviparous species can be separated into 3 main groups, namely those with: "(1) an aplacental yolk sac; or (2) placental analogues; and (3) those [embryos] which derive their nutrition from eating continually ovulated eggs (oophagous) and/or other embryos (adelphophagous)... The embryos of aplacental viviparous species rely solely on the yolk reserves located within the mother's body. The embryos are retained within the mother's body throughout their development without any maternal placental connection." Placental analogues are "structures which have a function similar to a mammalian placenta, but which have no physical connection to the mother." Examples are structures produced by the uterine wall that secrete nutritive liquid into the mouths of embryos. In oophagous species, the embryo "hatches from its egg capsule and commences feeding on the eggs which are continuously ovulated into the uterus. In adelphophagous species...the first hatched embryo consumes all other developing embryos in that uterus."

Placental Viviparity: "The embryos commence their development in the same way as aplacental species, with the eggs becoming encapsulated in an egg case inside the uterus and the embryo being nourished by yolk from the yolk sac...However, after a period, the yolk sac attaches to the wall of the uterus and forms a yolk sac placenta with the yolk stalk forming the umbilical cord."

ORDER CHIMAERIFORMES

FAMILY CHIMAERIDAE—Ratfishes or Shortnose Chimaeras

Ratfishes are circumglobal in marine waters throughout the world. There are two genera and perhaps 45 species (and probably a few more undescribed ones), and likely three species off the Pacific Coast. Ratfishes are oviparous. Ratfish-like animals in the order Chimaeriformes, where our species reside, lived at least as far back as the Early Carboniferous (as much as 360 million years ago) in what is now Indiana and Montana. The family Chimaeridae (genus *Belgorodon*) first appeared in the Cretaceous (71 million years ago or more) in Russia. Tooth plates of unidentified chimaeras are known from California from the Paleocene (55-plus million years ago) and the fin spine of the fossil ratfish *Edaphodon* sp. was found in a Miocene deposit (15 million years old or so) in Kern County (Southern California).

Dave Ebert tells me that in South Africa, Chile, and Asia, some folks eat chimaeras.

Hydrolagus colliei
(Lay & Bennett, 1839)
Spotted Ratfish

A species that looks like it would have traded puns with the March Hare in Alice in Wonderland.

Mating ratfish. The male is on our left, and grasping the female's pectoral fin with his tenaculum.

ETYMOLOGY AND COLLOQUIAL NAME: *Hydrolagus* aptly means "water" and "hare" in Greek and *colliei* honors the Scottish-born Dr. Alexander Collie (1793–1835), a surgeon/naturalist on the HMS *Blossom*, a survey ship that explored the Pacific Ocean from 1825–1828. At least as early as 1884, this species was called "ratfish" along the Pacific Coast. A while back, they were also called "whitespotted ratfish."

THE BASICS: Maximum Length: 100 cm (39 in) TL. Barnett et al. (2009) suggest that fish over about 63 cm (25 in) TL are rare. Maximum Weight: 1.8 kg (3.9 lb). The Ranges: Western Gulf of Alaska to near Punta Prieta (26°59'N, 114°02'W) (southern Baja California); two isolated populations in the Gulf of California: one at Isla Tiburon, the other in the Bahiá de La Paz–Cabo San Lucas region. Ratfish appear to be fairly common at least as far north as Cape Fairweather (southeast Alaska). Surface–971 m (3,185 ft), occasionally in intertidal waters. Most fish live in about 50–400 m (164–1,312 ft), and in Southern California between 115–160 m (377–525 ft). Ratfish are often found in shallower waters in the northern part of their range. As an example, in places like Puget Sound, they will move into just a few meters of water at night. Length-weight parameters (snout-to-vent length, SVL, mm, kg): (sexes combined) W = 0.0000002459L$^{2.755}$ (Barnett et al. 2009).

RATFISH RULE

Ray Troll, my associate, has a thing for ratfish, and *Hydrolagus trolli* was named for him. Among his many artistic endeavors is the following song, penned by Ray and Russell Wodehouse:

Let me tell you a little story 'bout a fishy friend of mine
Goatfish, Spookfish, chimaera et tu

Comin' from the water with his eyes blue green
Nasty little claspers say my boy is set and good to go
Down 20 fathoms, he got lovin' on his head
One fish, two fish, dead fish blue
One fish two fish dead fish blue
One fish, two fish dead fish blue

Can see you in your dreams, they can feel you in the dark
Cruising up above you, swimming down below

Coming up behind you, don't it fill you full of dread
From way below the ocean, it's your final wish

Gonna spin your head around, gonna sting you in the butt
Gangsta style is ratfish style, they're coming to your town

Dating back 300 million years in time
Strictly my opinion but the ratfish rule!
Hydrolagus colliei the water rabbit king
Shining like a Navajo, meck a leck a hiney ho

Rub him just the wrong way, yer gonna be dead
I wish you was a ratfish too
I wish you was a ratfish too
I wish you'all was a ratfish too
Puget Sound is gonna drown in prehistoric sharks

Way before the dinosaurs, it's their world you know
Pink and black are coming back, get this thru your head

A creature from your nightmares, a spotty little fish
No party in your mouth, gonna hit you in the gut

Be jammin' in your living room, wear your momma's gown

SALIENT CHARACTERS: This is an adorably bizarre fish. It has a large head that resembles a rat and a long tapering body, ending in a pointy little tail. Each fish has a long, venomous spine in front of its dorsal fin and scale-less skin. Spotted ratfish are usually brown, occasionally silvery, always with white spots. Their eyes are an exquisite green.

LIFE HISTORY: Ratfish are just one of the cutest and most bizarre species on the Pacific Coast. Both juveniles and adults live over a very wide range of habitats, all the way from boulder fields to mud bottoms. And here's a surprise; one was collected in the Columbia River estuary about 8 km (5 mi) upstream from the mouth. In the Northwest, ratfish eggs have been found in waters as shallow as the intertidal. I have seen very small (like 5 cm, 2 in, TL) fish over seafloors as deep as 160 m (529 ft) and slightly larger fish in 280 m (918 ft), so it appears that females can also release eggs in pretty deep water. The smallest free-living fish I have heard of was 4 cm (2 in) SL long. Ratfish have been collected from waters down to at least 5.8°C (42°F) and we have seen them in waters as warm as 11.2°C (52°F). During submersible work, we see them either singly or all the way up to medium-sized herds. There is some evidence that ratfish are most active at night. Didier (2004), thinking about

spotted ratfish reproduction, wrote: "Spawning generally occurs on flat, muddy or sandy substrates, but spawned egg capsules have also been observed on pebbly bottoms and in beds of seaweed. Females spawn two egg capsules simultaneously, one from each oviduct, which are deposited onto the ocean floor...Captive *H. colliei* have been observed to lay a pair of eggs every 7 to 10 days...It is likely that all females store sperm...it is likely that the spawning season lasts several months, perhaps up to 6 months." Copulation takes from 37–120 minutes.

So, what do males do with that little doodlywop (also called a *frontal tenaculum*) on their foreheads? For a long time, all we knew was what Lockington (1879a) wrote of a ratfish that was caught off Alaska: "I do not believe that anything is on record which tends to prove the use of the curious projection upon the nose. The action of the individual in question [the ratfish], which saluted the cabin-boy who hauled it up by taking a piece out of his finger with this appendage, tends to prove that it is a weapon of offence." Well, I guess that depends on how you feel about the war between the sexes, because male ratfish use the tenaculum during mating, grasping the pectoral fin of the female during copulation. On 15 September 2003, Takuji Oyama took some very nice pictures of this while diving in about 30 m (99 ft) of water off the Brooks Peninsula (northwestern Vancouver Island). He watched a pair mate for about 5 minutes before they swam off. I have one of these images on the previous page.

To date, no one has come up with a foolproof way to age ratfish, but at least some observers assume a maximum age of about 15 years. Females grow larger than males. Fish mature at different lengths in different parts of their range. For instance, females are larger at maturity north of Pt. Conception compared to those to the south and males are larger at first maturity north of Cape Mendocino. Thus far, the smallest mature female was 19 cm (8 in) SVL (tip of snout to anterior edge of vent) and the smallest mature male was 14 cm (6 in). In one study along much of the West Coast, 50% of females matured at 20.3 cm (8 in) SVL and 50% of males at 15.7 cm (6 in). Although it is less than crystal-clear, spotted ratfish may spawn throughout the year with perhaps a May–October peak. Females produce about 20–29 eggs per year. In aquaria, a number of observers have noted that females take a long time (say 18–72 hours) to extrude an egg and that eggs can remain attached to the female by a filament for 3–6 days. Young ratfish may stay in the eggs for from 5–10 months before hatching. Spotted ratfish are opportunistic, and likely nocturnal, feeders, with diets that run the gamut of benthic and epibenthic animals. Commonly eaten prey include fishes, brachyuran and hermit crabs, shrimps, gastropods, sea urchins, polychaetes, bivalves, clam siphons, and isopods. One study found that fish smaller than about 20 cm (8 in) TL ate primarily polychaetes. Predators include fishes (e.g., bluntnose sixgill sharks, sablefish, soupfin sharks, spiny dogfish, and spotted ratfish), birds (e.g., buffleheads, common murres, and pigeon guillemots), sea lions, and Humboldt squids. Northern elephant seals eat the eggs.

RICH ZADE

FISHERY: Historically (well, mostly in the 19th century) ratfish were caught in commercial fisheries in the Northwest and their livers were rendered for oil, which was useful as a lubricant and, in those bygone days, as a medicine. In carrying out that tradition, I should note that my friend Lynne Yamanaka's dad would often put some ratfish in a pail, let them rot, and then skim off the oil to lubricate his guns. Later, ratfish taken in trawl fisheries were ground up and sold as mink food. In a remarkable flush of optimism, Bensussen's (1976) master thesis focused on trying to prepare ratfish meat in such a way as to make it palatable. He failed, but it was a glorious defeat, a veritable Pickett's Charge of culinary exploits. For after much labor the best he could get out of a taste panel was "Not awful."

Recreational anglers commonly take ratfish.

MISCELLANY: Like their namesakes, these animals are difficult to cuddle up to. First, they have that long, sharp dorsal spine. That spine has a shallow groove that contains a venom gland (it's that kind of gray tissue). Bruce Halstead (reported in Halstead and Bunker 1952) scratched himself with the spine from a live one and reported: "In about five minutes there was a mild, dull ache in the area about the scratch which lasted for about ten minutes. The eruption disappeared completely in about 30 minutes." Other reports have it that the dull ache lasts for days. Ratfish can also bite you with their fused teeth. Oh, and the viscera has been reported to be toxic to laboratory animals. In particular, the reproductive organs are probably not safe to eat.

MORE MISCELLANIES: As do sharks, skates, and rays, spotted ratfish use the pores on their heads to detect the electric fields of potential prey items. And they have very large livers that help them achieve something like neutral buoyancy allowing them to stay up in the water column with relatively little energy expenditure.

MORE MORE MISCELLANY: An albino fish was caught in Puget Sound.

ORIGINS: Although tooth plates of fossil chimaeras have been collected in California from as far back as the Paleocene (56 million years ago or older), no fossil specimen of *Hydrolagus* is known. However, *Hydrolagus* appears to be closely related to fishes of the genus *Chimaera* and fossil chimaeras have been identified as far back as the Eocene (34 million years ago or more).

REMARKS: As of this writing, there are just a lot of ratfish in Puget Sound. Yes, an estimated 200 million ratfish, forming a very substantial proportion of all fishes in the area, prance about these waters.

ALEXANDER COLLIE

Dr. Collie collected and kept notes on many of the animals and plants collected on the *Blossum* expedition, including a spotted ratfish collected in Monterey Bay. This was later described by another *Blossum* naturalist, George Tradescant Lay who, along with Edward Turner Bennett, named it after Dr. Collie. In 1829, Collie emigrated to the then-frontier Swan River area in southwestern Australia. Over the rest of his short life (he died of tuberculosis when quite young), Collie was both physician and colonial administrator in this region. Collie's letters home are often quite melancholy, likely because the settlements on the southwestern coast did not immediately fulfill their early promises. His missives are laced with such statements as "The arrival of a vessel once, twice or perhaps three times a year, no new books unless I should make one… just the same dullness day and day, no books to read, no fresh faces," "We are all out of patience at the delayed arrival of his Excellency, of the thousands of young ladies he was to bring out." On the other hand, having a little power did bring out as much exuberance as an Aberdeen upbringing would allow: "But why so mopish? Am I not Chief Magistrate here? Only this morning did I exercise a little sweet authority by fining two fellows for misconduct, and lecturing a third. Do I not say to a black fellow – 'Go—to the bush'? and he goeth." Proving yet again that a little power is good for what ails you. On the other hand, the "thousands of young ladies" that apparently were promised but not provided would have helped too.

Both the Collie River and the town of Collie, located about 200 km south of Perth, are also named for him. When in Collie, at least during wet winters, don't forget to view the water overflowing the Wellington Dam and, most any time, visit the Replica Underground Coal Mine. Both are treats for all ages.

THE SHARKS

Sharks (and barely pubescent boy bands) have a stranglehold on the American imagination. Why else would some cable television networks simply dote on these animals, with their "Shark Week," or "Shark Month," or "Shark Interdecadal Period," if not that viewers just can't seem to get enough of them? One could scarcely imagine "Anteater Week," or "Flying Squirrel Day," or even "Tufted Titmouse Hour" on the Discovery Channel. In fact, if it were not for sharks and Hitler ("Welcome to the History Channel, All Nazis All the Time"), any number of cable channels would be reduced to penury.

And while we have at least some idea of what draws us to Hitler and his minions, what is there about sharks that we find so compelling? It can't just be their toothsome visages, else we would have the Barracuda or Moray Network. And it can't just be their (false) reputation as relentless predators of humans. If that were the case, we would also expect to see Subprime Mortgage Week on the Financial Channel. Actually, I think it is simpler than that. Sharks don't have lips. Really, I think that is it. A grouper has lips and who is afraid of a grouper?

How many shark species are there? More than 480.

ORDER HEXANCHIFORMES

FAMILY HEXANCHIDAE—Cow Sharks

Worldwide, there are three genera and six species of this colder-water marine group. Two species are found within our range. All species reproduce through aplacental viviparity (eggs develop within the mother but there is no maternal nutrient contribution). Members of this family lived in the Early Cretaceous (as much as 145 million years ago) of Japan. The oldest record of a hexanchid from the Pacific Coast is *Heptranchias howellii* from the Eocene (at least 33.9 million years ago) of British Columbia, Washington, and Oregon.

Hexanchus griseus
(Bonnaterre, 1788)
Bluntnose Sixgill Shark

ETYMOLOGY AND COLLOQUIAL NAMES: *Hexanchus* comes from two Greek words meaning "six" and "bend" (referring to the gills) and *griseus* is Latin for "gray." "Mud shark" and "sixgill shark" were also used. A current name in Japan is "kagurazame."

THE BASICS: Maximum Length: Females to about 4.8 m (16 ft) TL and males to 3.5 m (11 ft). Maximum Weight: Perhaps 600 kg (1,320 lb). The Ranges: Circumglobal in temperate and tropical waters. In the eastern North Pacific, south of the Aleutian Islands to Chile. Surface to at least 2,500 m (8,200 ft) or 3,000 m (9,840 ft). Adult fish usually live below 91 m (298 ft).

SALIENT CHARACTERS: No treatise needed here. If it has six gill slits on each side of its head, you are in business. Most sixgills are brown or blackish-gray on their backs and lighter underneath and they only have one dorsal fin (most other Pacific Coast sharks have two dorsal fins, don't cha know), sawtooth-like lower teeth, and a mouth on the underside of the head.

LIFE HISTORY: Juveniles tend to live in shallow waters, while adults may be found in a wide range of depths and habitats. I have seen them over boulder fields and steep rock walls in as much as 290 m (951 ft). Most of these were slowly cruising along a meter or so off the bottom, while one was lying on it. At least some adult

MILTON LOVE

sixgills migrate into shallow waters in the late spring and leave in the fall, and there seem to be certain places along our coast that these fish return to—or permanently live in—year after year. These include the Strait of Georgia (i.e., Hornby Island), Puget Sound, San Francisco Bay, and in Southern California off Carpinteria, Palos Verdes, and La Jolla. Permanent residents of some waters move about a bit, but movements are localized. Sixgills appear to be more active at night and some move into surface waters at this time.

Sixgills live to at least 11 years old and females grow larger than males. Off Hawai'i, males as small as 3.1 m (10 ft) TL were mature, while a 2.89 m (10 ft) male from Bermuda was also mature. In California waters, a 4.2 m (14 ft) female was mature. Females carry 47–108 embryos that are born at 61–74 cm (24–29 in) TL. Females may give birth every 1–2 years. Smaller bluntnose sixgill sharks tend to feed on cephalopods and fishes. As they get older, sixgills add seals, sea lions, and whales to their diets.

FISHERY: Historically, a small amount has been landed in the California commercial catch. Worldwide, they are landed for food, fishmeal, and oil. Sport anglers catch them occasionally.

MISCELLANY: 1) An albino sixgill was captured. 2) There are reports of sixgill liver eaters (not liver eaters with six gills, mind) getting poisoned, so watch out. 3) Sixgills are one of the only sharks we see when conducting manned submersible surveys—not only don't they avoid the sub, they will come over and kind of nuzzle it.

ORIGINS AND RELATIONSHIPS: An extinct *Hexanchus* lived in the Early Jurassic (about 190 million years ago). The University of California, Berkeley, Paleontological Museum lists fossils of two extinct *Hexanchus*, *H. primigenius* and *H. andersoni*, from Miocene deposits (at least 5.3 million years old) of Southern California. Fossils that may be bluntnose sixgill sharks have been taken from Pliocene deposits (at least 1.8 million years old) in Southern California and Baja California.

Notorynchus cepedianus
(Péron, 1807)
Broadnose Sevengill Shark

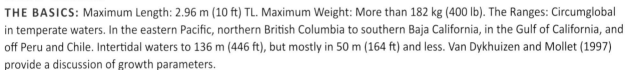

ETYMOLOGY AND COLLOQUIAL NAMES: *Notorynchus* comes from two Greek words meaning "back" and "snout" and *cepedianus* is Latin for "spotted." In my day, we were perfectly content to call them just "sevengill sharks." Their Japanese name is "ebisuzame."

THE BASICS: Maximum Length: 2.96 m (10 ft) TL. Maximum Weight: More than 182 kg (400 lb). The Ranges: Circumglobal in temperate waters. In the eastern Pacific, northern British Columbia to southern Baja California, in the Gulf of California, and off Peru and Chile. Intertidal waters to 136 m (446 ft), but mostly in 50 m (164 ft) and less. Van Dykhuizen and Mollet (1997) provide a discussion of growth parameters.

Length-weight parameters (TL, cm, kg):
(sexes combined) $W = 0.0000008741L^{3.333}$
(Van Dykhuizen and Mollet 1997).

SALIENT CHARACTERS: This is the only shark on our coast with seven gill slits. Makes it easy doesn't it? They have one dorsal fin and sawtooth-like lower teeth. Sevengills seem to vary in color. In Humboldt Bay, they are reported to be pale silvery-gray to reddish-brown, while in San Francisco Bay they come in olive-brown to muddy gray. Black spots on backs are also part of their look.

LIFE HISTORY: Young ones are born in shallow waters; in California, this translates to places like San Francisco and Humboldt bays. This is a relatively shallow water species; you can find them in bays and backwaters, along kelp beds, and over nearshore sandy bottoms

SCOTT MCGEE

on the open coast. They swim most anywhere in the water column, even on occasion sticking their heads above the surface, a behavior called "spy-hopping." In the spring and summer, these fish concentrate in places like Humboldt and San Francisco bays, but you can also find them in selected coastal spots, like in La Jolla Cove (Southern California). It is not completely clear what their seasonal movements are like, although some fish in South Africa may return to the same breeding grounds year after year. One female captured in Humboldt Bay was taken to the Monterey Bay Aquarium. Later released into Monterey Bay, the fish returned to Humboldt Bay in a few months. You often see females and males with scars on their backs, as well as pectoral and anal fins. At least some of these come from males biting the females during mating. This species may be most abundant in waters between 12–18°C (54–65°F).

The sevengill life span has not been established, although Smith et al. (1998) make a back-of-the-envelope guess of 32 years. Females grow larger than males. Looking at several studies, males mature at 140–160 cm (55–63 in) TL and perhaps 4–5 years old and females mature at 192–250 cm (76–98 in) and 11–21 years old. The birthing season is unknown, however mating appears to occur between April–September. Females carry between 67–104 eggs (although 82–95 embryos have been observed) and produce a brood of young every 2 years. For reasons that are obscure, the left ovary always carries more eggs than the right. In Humboldt and San Francisco bays, the young are born at 35–53 cm (14–21 in) TL.

Until they are quite large, broadnose sevengill sharks feed most extensively on fishes, particularly on bony fishes, and secondarily on crustaceans, bivalves, and cephalopods. As they grow older, they begin to feed more heavily on marine mammals (e.g., dolphins and harbor seals) and cartilaginous fishes (e.g., bat rays, brown smoothhounds, spiny dogfish, leopard sharks, skates, and each other). Here is what Dave Ebert, who likely knows as much as about this species as anyone, wrote in 1991: "A leopard shark was swimming near a mudbank in water approximately 30–40 cm deep...The force of the attack [from a sevengill] caused the predator to beach itself on the shallow mudflats with the prey dangling out of its mouth...Sevengill sharks seem to be most active nocturnally and on days when the sky is overcast. On clear, sunny and warm days, they apparently remain in the deeper water of bays and lagoons...In Humboldt Bay, sevengills have been observed foraging on the shallow-water mudflats during spring tides in the early morning, before sunrise."

FISHERY: Native Americans occasionally caught sevengills. Jordan (1887), calling it the "shovel-nosed shark," reported that from 1858–1868 sevengills were commercially important in Humboldt Bay. The fishery was conducted from April, when they entered the bay, to August, when they left. The sharks were taken with hook-and-line (the bait was a big wad of salted seal meat) in the deep channels between the mudflats, or were harpooned in the shallows. As with a number of early shark fisheries, this one was based on the large amounts of oil that could be rendered from the livers. You could score 3–8 gallons from one shark if you could stand the stench. It was noted that during the height of the fishery, one man made 700 gallons of oil in a season and that translated to $875 at $1.25 per gallon. Don't think that was much? Well, along that coast in 1860, you could buy a dozen ducks for $1.50 (*Up and Down California in 1860–1864*. W. H. Brewer. 1930. Yale University Press). And that was kind of it for the commercial fishery, although they were included in the shark liver fishery of the 1930s and 1940s, and a few are landed at California ports today. Artisanal fishermen along the Baja California coast catch a few. Today, sevengills are caught, indeed sometimes sought after, by a select group of shore, pier, and vessel fishermen. Most of these folks fish in San Francisco and nearby Tomales bays.

ORIGINS: The earliest *Notorynchus* known is *N. aptiensis* from the Early Cretaceous (as much as 145 million years ago) of France. The University of California, Berkeley, Paleontological Museum lists a *Notorynchus* sp. from the Miocene (at least 5.3 million years ago) of Southern California. One fossil, apparently of a broadnose sevengill shark, has been reported from a 100,000-year-old deposit in Southern California.

MISCELLANY: What appears to be an albino was caught in the 1952 shark derby in San Francisco Bay and a piebald (with a white background profusely spotted with dark spots) has also been taken close to The City. Halstead (1995) reported that the flesh and/or liver might in some circumstances be toxic.

ORDER SQUALIFORMES

FAMILY SQUALIDAE—Dogfish Sharks

The dogfishes are almost ubiquitous small marine sharks, found throughout tropical to subarctic waters. There are two genera and (if the 11 species described in Last et al. 2007 are kosher) about two dozen species, with one species within our range. *Squalogaleus*, a poorly known fish from the Late Jurassic (at least 200 million years ago), may have been a member of this family. *Protosqualus*, from the Early Cretaceous (perhaps as much as 125 million years ago), was in this family. For those of you wishing to immerse yourselves in all things dogfishy, get thee to Gallucci et al., *Biology and Management of Dogfish Sharks* (American Fisheries Society, 2009).

Squalus suckleyi
(Girard, 1854)

Spiny Dogfish

Like the splendidly deformed Richard III ("Now is the winter of our discontent made glorious summer by this son of York"*) the spiny dogfish is the fish everyone loves to hate.*

ETYMOLOGY AND COLLOQUIAL NAMES: *Squalus* comes from a Greek word related to "shark." *Suckleyi* honors George Suckley (1830–1869), naturalist and Civil War surgeon. The steelhead and Chinook salmon sections have a few things he penned. "Grayfish" was very commonly used on the Pacific Coast and "spinolies" was a popular name with Italian-American fishermen, at least in Southern California. They are called "abura-tsunozame" in Japan, "tiburón de espin" in Baja California, and "x'átgu" among the Tlingit.

THE BASICS: Maximum Length: About 130 cm (51 in) TL. Maximum Weight: 9.4 kg (20.7 lb). The Ranges: The Koreas northward to Russia and to the Bering Sea and southeastern Chukchi Sea, and Alaska to the Gulf of California. In the western

Pacific, they are abundant as far north as the Sea of Japan; along North America, they are common at least from the Kodiak Island area to Bahia San Quintin (northern Baja California). Some studies imply doggies are most abundant off British Columbia and Washington, where they are very, very common indeed. Intertidal to 1,236 m (4,054 ft), and perhaps to 1,244 m (4,105 ft); mostly from very shallow waters to perhaps 250 m (820 ft). Mature eggs: 3–4 cm (1–2 in). Tribuzio et al. (2010) seemingly spent the best years of their lives looking at dogfish growth rates from our coast and there is an embarrassment of riches (if you define that as just one damn

growth rate measure after another) in their paper. Here are their von Bertalanffy parameters for Gulf of Alaska fish (TL, cm): (females) L_∞ = 102.5, k = 0.06; (males) L_∞ = 87.2, k = 0.1. Length-weight parameters (TL, mm, kg): (sexes combined) W = 0.00000000189L$^{3.09}$ (RecFin 2009).

SALIENT CHARACTERS: Dogfish are relatively small sharks, gray or light brown on backs, and usually (but not always) with white spots on backs and sides. There are spines in front of each dorsal fin (these are occasionally broken off in larger individuals). These spines separate doggies from other sharks in the North Pacific, except for the horn shark, which has black spots and a squared-off head.

LIFE HISTORY: Spiny dogfish are relatively small sharks that can form humongous, nomadic schools that occur all the way from surface waters (particularly the smaller individuals) to the seafloor. The young, most often 24–30 cm (10–12 in) TL at birth, appear to be released in midwater in 10–140 m (33–459 ft) of water over deeper waters (at least off British Columbia). Saunders and McFarlane (1993), who made the previous observations on birth location, also note that the "tips of the needle-sharp spines are enclosed in skin" at birth. In the Strait of Georgia and Puget Sound, this pelagic juvenile phase can last 15–20 years (to about 60 cm, 19 in, TL), after which fish tend to move to the bottom and mature. On our coast, they tend to occur deeper in the southern part of their range. They have been found in waters of at least 3.5–15°C (38–59°F). Dogfish often form all-male or all-female schools, but they have to get together some time, right? In Puget Sound, doggies move into shallower waters at night and, at least in Southern California, they often move toward the surface when the sun sets. These fish are highly mobile, appearing for a few days in a location, then disappearing for who knows where. They can tolerate freshwater for at least short periods. Historically, dogfish were just incredibly abundant. How abundant? Here is Ketchen (1986) quoting a Canadian fisherman: "Clearing from Hardy Bay, and while on the approximate 30-mile course to Shushartie Bay, on the northern end of Vancouver Island, we ran through a dogfish school which extended for that distance, and as far as the eye could see to seaward." Heh, that is a powerful lot of dogfish.

Regarding movements, McFarlane and King (2003), discussing their tagging study of British Columbia fish, note: "Generally spiny dogfish were recaptured close to their release site; however, extensive migrations (up to 7000 km) did occur." In their study, most of the tens of thousands of fish tagged in the Strait of Georgia stayed there. Only a handful strayed. Similarly, fish in Puget Sound rarely enter outer coastal waters. On the other hand, a few dogfish make kind of impressive movements. Ketchen (1986), for instance, records two trans-Pacific recaptures; a fish released near Willapa Bay (Washington) in 1944 was recaptured 7 years later at the northern tip of Honshu and another tagged in northern Hecate Strait (British Columbia) was recaptured 2 years later at the northeastern tip of Hokkaido. Solitary individuals have been captured all across the North Pacific, all in pelagic waters. Several fish tagged off the west coast of Vancouver Island were recaptured off Mexico. Dogfish movements off California are not well understood. As you might expect, genetic analysis demonstrated that there were no population differences among fish living between the Gulf of Alaska and California.

Spiny dogfish live longer and mature later than any other shark species that has been studied. Doggies live to at least 80 years old and perhaps to 100. Females grow larger than males. There have been any number of studies looking at size and age at maturity and Saunders and McFarlane (1993), working with fish from British Columbia, is a nice example (although you might also peruse Ketchen 1972, 1975, Jones and Geen 1977, and Vega et al. 2009). Saunders and McFarlane found that a few females were mature at 80 cm (32 in) TL and 24 years; 50% were mature at 94 cm (37 in) and 35 years; and a few females were still immature at 110 cm (43 in) and 62 years old. S. and M. did not look at males, so for them we turn to Jones and Geen (1977) who found a few mature at 72 cm (28 in) TL, 50% at 78 cm (31 in), and 100% at maybe 94 cm (37 in). The bottom line is that spiny dogfish take just a god-awful long time to mature. Vega (2006) found that, in the eastern Pacific, fish in the north grow more slowly than those to the south, but northern ones reach a larger maximum size. Even within Puget Sound, fish in the north and south have different growth rates. And get this, Taylor and Gallucci (2009) found that from the 1940s to the 2000s, the size and age of maturity of fish in Puget Sound declined significantly, as did the average number of embryos produced per female. Fish in the northeast Pacific live longer and mature later than do those in the Atlantic.

Dogfish embryos derive all of their nutrition from their yolks (aplacental viviparity), the mothers don't supply anything additional (except, one assumes, their best wishes). Hamlett et al. (2005) reports that for the first 4–6 months, embryos are "incubated in a transparent, diaphanous and relatively fragile egg capsule, and embryo and capsule are called a *candle*." Who the hell thought of that name? And get this; females may gestate their eggs for up to *22 months*, meaning that females

DOGFISH

A dogfish from up near the Cape,
Had a clasper that looked like a grape,
Females with mere glances,
Disdained his advances,
Saying, "It's not just the size, but the shape."

reproduce every other year. As far as is known, that gestation period is the longest for any vertebrate, so let's give a big cheer for female spiny dogfish. Females release their young at least from September–January, likely peaking around November, and mating occurs around the same time. Females may mate with more than one male during a mating season. Eigenmann (1892) noted ripe females off Southern California in July and August, so maybe the season is earlier down there. Males mate every year and smaller males mate earlier in the year. Fecundity ranges from 2–116 young.

Let's put this bluntly: spiny dogfish are opportunistic feeders. They prey on midwater and benthic organisms, and their diets seem to vary in response to what is yummy and abundant in their environment. End of story. All right, here are more details. Juveniles, up there in the water column, feed primarily on plankton, including medusae. Larger dogs eat a lot of fishes. During summer months in the Pacific Northwest, for instance, dogfish come into shallow waters to just gorge on young Pacific herring, salmon, sticklebacks, and Pacific sand lances. They also gather around capelin and Pacific herring spawning areas. And they are big eaters of hakes wherever they find them. Important invertebrate prey includes euphausiids, squids, and squid eggs, and octopuses. More things they eat? All right, ctenophores, by-the-wind-sailors, medusae, polychaetes, shrimps, sea anemones, sponges, brittle stars, hermit crabs, flatworms, nudibranchs, clams, snails, and echiuroids. Larger individuals tend to eat more fishes than do smaller ones. Doggies are eaten by bluntnose sixgill, blue, salmon, and white sharks, lingcod, sablefish, Steller sea lions, seals, sperm whales, and minks. Two bald eagles were seen each with 7-pound dogfish clutched in their talons, and there is one case of a dogfish pup in the gut of an adult spiny dogfish.

FISHERY: Dogfish were very commonly caught by both Native Americans and First Nation peoples. Early on, it is likely that the fish were both eaten (at least on occasion) and their skins used as a type of sand paper. One of the lineages (one of the crests) of the Haida is a dogfish.

"Dogfish" by Johnny Kit Elswa.
Yale Collection of Western Americana. Beinecke Rare Book and Manuscript Library.

At least in historical times, dogfish were also widely captured by these indigenous peoples as a source of oil and most of it appears to have been sold to white settlers and miners for lighting and lubrication. And for information on this, we turn to James Swan, that very astute observer of Northwest natives of the 19th century: "The method of extracting as practiced by the Makahs [in Washington] is to collect the livers, which are put into a tub and kept until a considerable quantity has accumulated. They are then put into iron pots, and set to simmer near the fire; or else hot stones are placed among them and they are cooked by the heat until all the oil is extracted which is then carefully skimmed off and stored in receptacles, made of the paunches and intestines of whales, fish, and seals…When the livers are taken out, the head and back bone are also removed, and the rest of the body, being first slightly dried in the smoke, is steamed on hot stones till it is thoroughly cooked. It is then put into little baskets, made for the purpose, of soft cedar bark, and rolled and squeezed till all the liquid is extracted… It is boiled and allowed to cool and settle, and the oil is then skimmed off. After the oil is extracted, the flesh is washed in freshwater and again squeezed in the baskets, and in this state it is eaten by the Indians when other food is scarce. But dogfish is seldom tasted by the Makahs, and never until the oil has been thoroughly removed. The oil has a nauseous taste, and is not relished by these Indians, who are epicures in their way, and prefer the oil of whales and seals" (Swan 1868).

European settlers soon figured out that there was a market for dogfish oil and in the 19th and early 20th centuries, all around Puget Sound and the Strait of Georgia, dogfish oil rendering was the thing to do. For instance, in 1883, the Skidegate Oil Company at Skidegate Inlet (Queen Charlotte Islands) processed 400,000 fish, for 40,000 gallons of oil. It was about that time that a tax was imposed in the U.S. on imported dogfish oil and, as one might expect, there developed a lively dogfish oil smuggling ring. I suppose one can fall further than to become a dogfish oil smuggler, perhaps by dwelling in the dreary netherworld of the arbitrageur, but one can't fall *too* much further. Unfortunately, by the beginning of the 20th century, dogfish had lost its luster and the fishery sort of folded its tent and slunk off.

In the past 100 years, oh, my goodness, the world has been full of optimists about the commercial potential of spiny dogfish on the Pacific Coast. Even one so fatally upbeat as former Deputy Secretary of Defense Paul Wolfowitz, who testified on a number of occasions that the American takeover of Iraq would be a cakewalk, is but a pale reflection of a long line of dogfish marketers. Indeed, since the first processor moved to the Pacific Coast, there is nary a one who has not at one time or another lain awake at night and, in veritable spasms of enthusiasm, hallucinated about finding something to do with dogfish. Here, for instance, is J. L. McDonald in 1871 pumping for doggies. "Dogfish are abundant in the waters of Puget Sound. This fish is large and solid, and yield plump, healthy livers, rich in oil."

However, when processors set their sights beyond dogfish for oil, it was like trying to buy a piece of downtown Brigadoon, the dream kept slipping through their speculative fingers. Prince (1906) for example, noted that "the canning of dogfish has been successfully tried in eastern Canada and the fish when properly packed is by no means to be despised." And then, 12 years later, there is this from *Pacific Fishermen* (1918, 16(6):21–22): "The value of the fish for food has only recently been recognized. It is capable of being used in a variety of ways and it's an excellent food. It is canned in much the same manner as salmon, though a somewhat different method of preliminary treatment is required. It is packed on both the Atlantic and Pacific coasts and in 1-pound salmon cans." Unfortunately, at about the same time, John Cobb, a man who had never met a fish he did not want to put in a can, sighed the following (*The Canning of Fishery Products*, Miller Freeman, 1919): "The writer hesitated long over including sharks and greyfish [dogfish] in his fishes suitable for canning [*But why, John, why?*]…While the writer does not question that the flesh of these fishes fresh, smoked or salted is nutritious, and no doubt, pleasing to many palates [*Yes, yes?*], it is still a question whether the flesh can be canned in such a way as to be

WELL, SURE, THAT COULD BE A PROBLEM

From *Canning of Fishery Products* (J. N. Cobb, 1919): "One decided disadvantage, in a business way, to the canning of greyfish [spiny dogfish] is that the patent desire of the fishery authorities and the fishermen generally is to exterminate the species altogether."

Also, I didn't know that you could patent desires in the U.S. of 1919. If you managed to patent the desire to patent a desire, would that mean that people would have to pay you a royalty to desire that desire?

OH, THOSE CRAZY KIDS

In his diary detailing his days as a parish priest on the west coast of Vancouver Island beginning in 1875, the Reverend A. J. Brabar wrote this about dogfish and the local First Nation peoples: "Up to a couple of years ago they lived almost exclusively on fish and potatoes. They availed themselves of the presence of large schools of dog-fish to make dog-fish oil, which they sold to coasting schooners, receiving in exchange flour, molasses, tobacco, print-calico, and articles of dress. The old people who did most of the work objected to the buying of clothing, but the young people, especially the women, did not listen to the pleadings of their elders, and invested most of their earnings in the purchase of decent wearing apparel" (Moser 1926).

Proving, I suppose that the more things change the more they remain the same.

I should note that the next lines in his diary were: "I now made it a rule that no men should come to my house unless they wore pants!!" The double exclamation points are disquieting and one can only wonder at the extremis that led to this new rule.

palatable. [*Dang it.*] Several Pacific Coast salmon canners took up the business on a fairly large scale and with most disastrous financial results. Their failure was due exclusively to the fact that the flesh of these fishes contains a large percentage of urea. [*Well, yuck. But surely, a nation that drove the Boche out of the Belleau Woods can do something about this?*] The U. S. Bureau of Chemistry and private parties are now carrying on experiments looking to the elimination of the urea and the results so far obtained have been fairly satisfactory [*That's good isn't it? But still you look dubious.*] but, unfortunately, the flesh of the grayfish lack the solidity found in the flesh of other fishes, and thus is unsuitable for canning whole [*But, but, isn't there anything we can do?*], although it might be found suitable for canning in the shape of fish paste, loaf, or sausage." [*Ah, the old switcheroo. Excellent. Technology + Marketing = Dogfish dogs flying off the shelves.*]

And so, we now entered the Dogfish Doldrums, that time from the early 20th century to the 1930s when demand was limited to the few processors willing, albeit with poor grace, to reduce dogfish to oil and meal. It was the great vitamin A shark-liver market, which began in the U.S. in the mid-1930s and quickly spread to Canada, that put spiny dogfish back on the map, at least for one shining moment. High in vitamin A, dogfish livers quickly became a favorite target of Pacific Coast fishermen, to the point that in 1944 spiny dogfish was the most valuable fish species in British Columbia. Because you can only hit an elasmobranch population so hard, dogfish were quickly overfished and were saved only because, with the synthesis of vitamin A, the market for livers crashed in 1949 and 1950.

Soon after, the spiny dogfish, no longer the darling of the commercial fishing industry, started to rebound and, just as quickly, fishermen started to bitch about how many of them there were. This led to a number of innovative ways to just randomly kill or otherwise discourage them, including (Jensen 1966): "1) Attach streamers, bells, chains etc. to hundreds of dogfish and release them to frighten off the school...2) inoculate some of the dogfish with a fatal disease organism, such as had been done with rabbits in Australia, 3) dynamite the dogfish schools when they appear." Starting in the 1970s various small markets, mostly in the export trade, began to develop. As noted by Morrison (2004): "Three products are currently processed from dogfish: backs, belly flaps, and fins and tails...In Western Europe the backs are primarily used in institutional markets such as schools and prisons. A niche market for dogfish backs exists exclusively in the London metro area where they are used in fish and chips. The belly flaps are primarily exported to Germany where they are smoked and sold as a delicacy at upward of $20 per pound. The fins and tails are exported to Asia for shark fin soup." In an attempt to make spiny dogfish more palatable to American tastes, the FDA approved a new marketing name for the dogfish which is, *ta-da*, "cape shark." And soon thereafter, in the spirit of the moment, the winner of the National Fisheries Institute's New Tastes for a New Reality Cook-off Competition, was Cape Shark in Essence of Fennel. Yummy.

How long these markets will last or how long the dogfish stock will last, we shall see. Right now, on the Pacific Coast, dogfish are again notorious as a species that takes hooks away from more valuable species and wrecks havoc on fishing gear. However, its life history makes this species a poster child for one that should not be heavily fished. It takes 20-plus years for the females to mature (plenty of time to get caught before reproducing) and when they finally get around to reproducing, only a handful of young pop out. Another problem is that because females grow to be so much larger than males, they tend to be the target of any fishery and it's kind of difficult to sustain a fishery if you insist on taking the females, and often the ones that are not yet mature, out of the population.

Spiny dogfish are very commonly caught by sport fishermen, usually while folks are fishing for rockfishes and other bottom dwellers. Pier fishermen and shore anglers catch considerable numbers when the fish move inshore.

ORIGINS: A fossil *Squalus* is known from about 94 million years ago in the Cretaceous. The University of California, Berkeley, Paleontological Museum lists a *Squalus* from the Miocene (at least 5.3 million years ago) of Southern California.

MISCELLANY: Let's see what we have here. 1) Halstead (1995) noted that their dorsal spines are venomous: "Dorsal sting, which is located adjacent to the anterior margin...The venom gland appears as a glistening, whitish substance situated in a shallow groove on the back of the upper portion of each spine." On the other hand, I've been stuck pretty good and didn't feel anything unusual. 2) Dogfish are reported to engage in "spy-hopping," where they stick their heads above the water line. 3) Male doggies tend to have more vitamin A per gram of liver tissue than do similar-sized females. 4) One of the more popular dogfish products in Europe is smoked dogfish bellies, called "Schillerlocken," so named, one has heard, for its supposed resemblance to the hair sported by Johann Christoph Friedrich von Schiller (1759–1805). Not just Goethe's pal, Schiller was a remarkable poet, playwright, and historian, whose recurrent meditations on the freedom of the human soul inspired, among others, Beethoven, Brahms, and Hegel. Yep, what greater honor could those crazy Teutons bestow then naming smoked dogfish bellies after the author of "Ode to Joy"?

DO YOU WANT HASH BROWNS WITH THOSE?

In *The Canning of Fishery Products*, J. N. Cobb, pulling out all gastronomic stops, noted that dogfish eggs "Are used for making puddings, pancakes etc., and otherwise as a substitute for fowls' eggs." My friend Jim Allen tells me that some time in the 1970s he caught a dogfish in Santa Monica Bay. He opened it up and, along with a number of fetal sharks, he also saw three unfertilized eggs. Dogfish eggs are big and yellow and Jim, not averse to trying a new cuisine, albeit from no known culture, took them home, then scrambled, fried, and ate them. "They were pretty good," he reports, "although with kind of an astringent taste." For no particular reason, this reminds me that Samuel Taylor Coleridge's favorite Sunday breakfast was comprised of 6 fried eggs, seltzer water, and 1 glass of laudanum. Jeez, a glass of tincture of opium at breakfast may explain why Coleridge apparently was the inventor of the term "suspension of disbelief."

REMARKS: Until recently, *Squalus suckleyi* was considered to be part of a world-wide species, *Squalus acanthias*. This was before such luminaries as Hauser (2009), Verissimo et al. (2010), and Ebert et al. (2010) found a fairly substantial genetic difference between dogfish living in the North Pacific and those living in the Atlantic/South Pacific. Other researchers have found differences in life history between the two groups (e.g., North Pacific fish mature when older, live longer, and grow larger than those in other areas).

FAMILY SOMNIOSIDAE—Sleeper Sharks

Sleeper sharks are found just about everywhere you want to be (assuming you want to be in the ocean, all the way from the Arctic to the sub-Antarctic). Although there are perhaps seven genera and perhaps 17 species, only one species graces our range. A member of this family, in the genus *Cretascymnus*, has been found in the Late Cretaceous deposits (at least 71 million years ago) of Lebanon.

Somniosus pacificus
Bigelow & Schroeder, 1944
Pacific Sleeper Shark

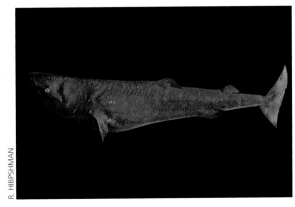

ETYMOLOGY AND COLLOQUIAL NAMES: *Somniosus* is derived from the Latin for "sleepy" and *pacificus* refers to where the species lives. Sleepers have been called "mud shark" and "ground shark" and they are "ondenzame" in Japanese.

THE BASICS: Maximum Length: 7.6 m (25 ft) TL, but largest adequately documented individual is 4.4 m (14 ft). Maximum Weight: Assuming a fish caught off Taiwan was this species, the largest one on record is 1,280 kg (4,198 lb). The Ranges: Japan to Bering Sea to off southern Baja California. Perhaps Peru and Chile, but reports of this species from South America may be of *Somniosus antarcticus*. It is likely that Pacific sleepers are relatively abundant at least in the western and eastern Bering Sea and along the Aleutian Islands. Surface or intertidal to about 2,205 m (7,232 ft). Length-weight parameters (TL, cm, kg): (sexes combined) $W = 0.000004257L^{3.135}$ (Yano et al. 2007).

SALIENT CHARACTERS: Sleepers are stubby, flaccid, thick, and other adjectives like that. They have two small dorsal fins, no anal fin, a caudal fin with a somewhat enlarged upper lobe, and a relatively small mouth. They are blackish, brown, green, or gray. It has been reported that the black pigment on the skins of Taiwanese specimens was a mucous layer that could be easily scrubbed off and that the underlying skin color was beige to light gray.

LIFE HISTORY: There is not a lot known about this species. Using acoustic tags in the northern Gulf of Alaska, Hulbert et al. (2006) found that: "The most striking behavioural feature was their extensive, nearly continuous vertical movements... The Pacific sleeper sharks traveled below the photic zone during the day and approached the surface at night...[the] smallest daily depth range was 36 m [118 ft] and the greatest was 724 m [2,375 ft]" and that at least one fish came to the surface. In this study, most individuals did not move much, although one migrated 457 km (284 mi). Pacific sleepers have been recorded in waters ranging from -0.2–11.8°C (32–54°F). On one of my submersible dives off Monterey, I was in maybe 300 m (984 ft) of water and saw a sleeper slowly cruising down a rocky slope. It looked like the Goodyear Blimp.

The maximum age and growth rates of this species are unknown. Females grow larger than males and are heavier than males at a given length. Pacific sleeper sharks practice aplacental viviparity; the embryos depend on their yolks for nutrition. Females are mature at about 370 cm (146 in) TL and a mature 397 cm (156 in) male has been captured. Females produce at least as many as 372 eggs, although how many of these turn into embryos is unknown. The young are born at about 40 cm (16 in) TL. Pacific sleeper sharks are apex predators, sucking up whatever is unfortunate enough to get in their way. Squids are very important, particularly in smaller individuals, and fishes often dominate the diets. Octopuses are another big favorite. Fishes seem to include any species in the neighborhood. Inexplicably, two albacore (one would have thought they were too fast) were found in a shark. Sleeper sharks also go for marine mammals, such as harbor seals and dolphins, and eat chunks of whales scavenged from whale falls. Less important prey include crabs, snails (such as hairy tritons [Oregon's official shell, by the by]), sponges, amphipods, hermit crabs, shrimps, and fishery offal.

FISHERY: Jordan (1887) noted that this species (he called it a "ground shark") was taken commercially around Victoria (British Columbia). And that is pretty much it. These fish are caught as bycatch in Alaska fisheries and they are popular in Taiwan, where their soft and tasteless flesh reminds diners of whale shark. Hey, what's not to like? I note that commercial fishermen in Oregon occasionally land sleepers.

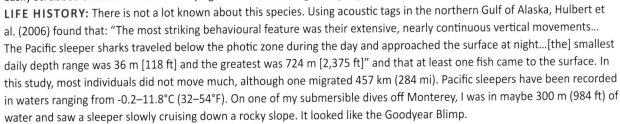

Jordan visited Wrangell Island (southeastern Alaska) and commented that at the north end of the island "stands a cannery from which tons of salmon heads and entrails are thrown into the sea. This offal attracts large numbers of the great sleeper shark—*Somniosus microcephalus*—a twenty-foot long, sluggish, greedy fish which gorges itself to repletion and then retreats at high water to rest in the adjacent bay. Ebb tide leaves it helpless in the mud; and during the course of a summer great numbers of sleepers and other sharks are thus destroyed. In the end, of course, the flesh decays, but teeth and occasionally fin spines are preserved as fossils, so that when—centuries hence—the bay fills up and dries out, it should form a very interesting ground for collectors" (Jordan 1922). Dang, can we check it out now?

ORIGINS: In Japan, a *Somniosus* sp. has been found in a Miocene (at least 5.3 million-year-old) deposit.

REMARKS: Barrett-Lennard et. al. (2011) tracked the fate of dead gray whales killed by orcas near Unimek Island (Alaska). They found that these carcasses were heavily preyed upon by sleeper sharks. They speculated that sleepers may seasonally aggregate to take advantage of the leftovers from the orcas' meals.

FAMILY DALATIIDAE—Kitefin Sharks

The dalatiids are an interesting assemblage of rather diminutive sharks that are circumglobal in temperate and tropical marine waters. The family is composed of seven genera and about 10 species and thus far only one has been found within our range. A second species, the pygmy shark (*Euprotomicrus bispinatus* Quoy & Gaimard, 1824), has been taken about 805 km (500 mi) off the coast of Southern California and I am rooting for it to get just a little closer. A shark that may be a member of this family, called *Somniosus crenulatus,* but apparently not of that genus, was found in Late Paleocene (at least 65.5 million years ago) strata in Morocco.

Isistius brasiliensis
(Quoy & Gaimard, 1824)

Cookiecutter Shark

A melon baller with fins.

ETYMOLOGY: *Isistius* is derived from two Greek words for "equal" and "sail" and *brasiliensis* refers to Brazil, off which the fish used in the original description was captured.

THE BASICS: Maximum Length: 56 cm (22 in) TL. The Ranges: Circumglobal in tropical and subtropical waters. In the eastern Pacific, at least from Isla Guadalupe (central Baja California) to Peru (13°46'S). Because elephant seals with fresh wounds have been observed off Central California, it is probable that these sharks live there. Surface waters to 3,500 m (11,480 ft).

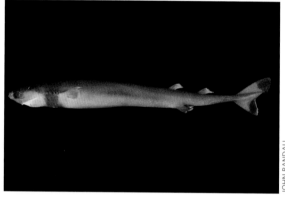

JOHN RANDALL

SALIENT CHARACTERS: Cookiecutters are elongated, tubular sharks with large eyes, two small and closely set dorsal fins, a caudal fin that is just barely asymmetrical, and a mouth full of very effective teeth. Their dorsal area is brown that graduates to a lighter belly.

LIFE HISTORY: Goodness, what a fascinating little shark is the cookiecutter. These are pelagic fishes that appear to migrate to surface waters at night and may retreat to deeper waters during the day (at least that's when they have been taken by deeper midwater trawls). Dave Ebert (2003) states that they may make daily vertical migrations of over 1,000 m (3,280 ft). In the Pacific, they have been found in 18–26°C (64–79°F). There is speculation that this is a schooling species. Along with their singular food habits, cookiecutters are also bioluminescent. This was first recorded by Frederick Debell Bennett (1806–1859), a naturalist who traveled to the Pacific on a whaler. In *Narrative of a Whaling Voyage Round the Globe from the Year 1833 to 1836* (Volume 2. Richard Bentley, London, 1840), we read that "When the larger specimen, taken at night, was removed into a dark apartment, it afforded a very extraordinary spectacle. The entire inferior [ventral] surface of the body and head emitted a vivid and greenish phosphorescent gleam, imparting to the creature, by its own light, a truly ghastly and terrible appearance."

With not much known about them, cookiecutters are Fish of Mystery. Females grow larger than males (these are rarely larger than 40 cm, 17 in, TL). Females are variously reported to mature at 38–44 cm (15–17 in) TL (Kiraly et al. 2003) or at

JOSHUA LAMBUS

"larger than 48 cm" (Nakano and Tabuchi 1990) and males perhaps at 31–37 cm (12–15 in) (Kiraly et al. 2003). Females produce at least 6–12 eggs and there appears to be no maternal nutrition supplied to the young (they practice aplacental viviparity). The young are probably 14–15 cm (6 in) TL at birth. But, with their powerful jaws and really large teeth, it is the feeding habits of cookiecutters that are so interesting. Cookiecutters likely feed on a wide variety of fishes, squids, elephant seals, and various whales and porpoises. Cookiecutters living near Hawai'i seem to be particularly fond of gnawing on swordfish as these billfish often have more than five bites taken out of their sides. While a cookiecutter may sometimes approach prey from the rear, it is believed that the shark often attacks from the front. The theory is that, as the prey passes by and the shark bites it (say on the side), the water's drag spins the shark around (like the hand of a clock), helping to slice open the flesh like a melon baller (assuming that melon ballers attack cantaloupes from the front). Jones (1971) helped demonstrate this using, as one would expect, a nectarine. Finding himself on a research vessel with a freshly caught cookiecutter, but no dead fish, he "pushed the teeth of a fresh, dead *Isistius* into the fruit and then rotated the body around that point. The result was...a neat, round, crater 'wound'." Some researchers have speculated that this shark might use its bioluminescence to attract and then attack prey. Thus far, only Spanish mackerels (*Scomberomorus* spp.) are known to eat cookiecutters.

ORIGINS: Fossil *Isistius* are known from the Late Paleocene (at least 55.8 million years ago) of Europe and South America.

MISCELLANY: Cookiecutters are willing to try eating just about everything, including the rubber sonar domes on nuclear submarines. This shark sheds all of its teeth as a unit and replaces them immediately. The number of photophores (light emitting structures) a cookiecutter has varies among individuals.

ABOUT 18 INCHES UP AND 5 INCHES OVER
AND YOU COULD HAVE CHANGED THE NAME TO BOBBITT-SHARK

(With thanks to Mary Nishimoto for pointing out the potential name change.)

"Despite the loss of a piece of his left calf from a shark bite Monday, Kula resident Mike Spalding still wants to become the third person known to swim the nearly 30-mile Alenuihaha Channel from the Big Island to Maui. The incident occurred in pitch-black darkness shortly after 8 p.m. Monday as Spalding, a 61-year-old Realtor and well-known open-ocean swimmer, was about four hours and 11 miles into his swim from the Big Island to Maui. He didn't see the animal that inflicted a superficial wound on his chest a few seconds before biting him in the calf, leaving a circular wound 3 inches in diameter and about 1 inch deep...[Shark expert John] Naughton said the only other incident he's aware of in which there was evidence that a person was bitten by a cookie-cutter shark was in July 1992. He said he was called into the Honolulu Medical Examiner's Office to examine the wounds on the back of a fisherman who had drowned. He had tied himself to an ice chest and was found floating about 15 miles off the coast of Waianae. The man had the distinctive, circular wounds left by cookie-cutter sharks, but the medical examiner thought the wounds were inflicted after death, he said" (Perry 2009).

ORDER SQUATINIFORMES

FAMILY SQUATINIDAE—Angel Sharks

Angel sharks are marine fish that live in the Pacific, southwestern Indian, and Atlantic oceans. There is but a single genus, about 15 species, and one occupies our range.

Squatina californica
Ayres, 1859
Pacific Angel Shark

ETYMOLOGY AND COLLOQUIAL NAMES: *Squatina* is an old name for this fish (Jordan and Evermann 1896 state that it is "akin to the English words "skate" and "squat") and *californica* refers to its first capture and subsequent description from San Francisco. "Angelito" is a name used in Mexico. "Angel shark" is an old name and of unknown derivation. "Angel" comes from the pectoral fins that give it a wing-like appearance. In Great Britain, another species is known as "monkfish," for the cowl-like appearance of the head.

THE BASICS: Maximum Length: 152 cm (60 in) TL. The Ranges: Puget Sound to Bahia Magdalena (southern Baja California) and Gulf of California to southern Chile. One old, and unverifiable, record from southeastern Alaska and the South American fish may be a different species. Angel sharks are fairly common to at least as far north as Tomales Bay (Northern California), but more abundant from Southern California southward. Surf zone to 205 m (672 ft), but mostly from perhaps 15–40 m (49–131 ft). Von Bertalanffy parameters (TL, cm): (sexes combined) L_∞ = 146, k = 0.235 (Cailliet et al. 1992).

SALIENT CHARACTERS: Angels are flattened with large pectoral fins that are not connected to the heads (they are connected, for instance, in guitarfish). The head is blunt, the eyes are on the top of the head, there are nasal barbels, and the mouth is up front (not underneath, as in the guitarfishes, rays, and skates). They are brown or gray on top (with darker mottlings) and white underneath. Some folks have speculated that individual pigment patterns may remain constant for long periods of time. On the other hand, some divers report that angels can very quickly go from lightly patterned to heavily mottled.

LIFE HISTORY: Angel sharks are benthic and often nearshore fish that prefer living on sand, but it's sand that is near (often 2 m, 7 ft, or less) rocks, eelgrass, or other structures. At times, such as during the summer, the fish really aggregate and you can find them lying on top of one another. One survey found up to 90 fish along a 100 m x 5 m (30 x 1.5 ft) strip. Angels appear to be very sensitive to light levels and tend to be active at night and somnolent (in fact buried) during the day. Even a full moon may be too bright for these fish. One exception to this rule is during the time when blacksmiths contract and die from the bacteria *Photobacterium damsellae* (see the blacksmith section). At this time, a few of these sharks may stir themselves during the day to feed on the carcasses. Not every fish moves about every night and each individual seems to have its own favorite time of the night in which to hunt. There is evidence, at least from Santa Catalina Island, that angels may be more active during the summer, moving into somewhat shallower waters as waters warm up and retreating a bit with fall cooling. While they clearly move about, many fish stay in a relatively restricted area (maybe 150 ha, 371 acres) for an extended period. Having noted that, some sharks may move as much as 7.3 km (4.5 mi) in a night and repeatedly come back to the same resting place each morning. Most of their time is spent on or just above the bottom, but one tagged fish swam as much as 91 m (298 ft) above the seafloor, so

IS THAT AN ANGEL SHARK HANGING FROM YOUR PANTS OR ARE YOU JUST HAPPY TO SEE ME?

Bobby Reid, just an excellent commercial fisherman out of Santa Barbara, tells this story about an angel shark's ability, when captured, to bend backward and bite (from Mick Kronman, unpublished). The story concerns a not-too-popular crewman: "This guy was a whiner. So one day we were pulling angel shark nets and even though I'd told him to be careful, he made a fatal mistake. He was holding a live shark by the tail in front of him when it bent backward and bit him right in the crotch, just missing his vitals."

KELLY BRACKEN

you never know. During at least some periods, angels will aggregate by sex. There appears to be only limited gene flow between angels living in the Gulf of California and those residing on the outer coast.

Lisa Natanson spent many a weary hour trying to age these animals. Of course, she was a graduate student at the time, and had no life, so there was no great loss there. On the other hand, it appears that figuring out the age of these fish is problematic, so a nice, pat, maximum age is just not in the current cards. Greg Cailliet and friends (1992), using tag return data and a subsequent von Bertalanffy growth function, figured that angels might live as long as 35 years. Females grow larger than males. Off California, 50% of females are mature at 107 cm (42 in) TL and all are mature at 112 cm (44 in). All males over 103 cm (41 in) are mature. In the Gulf of California, mature females as small as 85 cm (33 in) and mature males at 69 cm (27 in) have been captured. The species has aplacental viviparity; the embryos depend on their yolks for nutrition. Females carry anywhere from one to perhaps 13 young (and interestingly, usually only the left ovary is functional) and gestation lasts about 10 months. The young are released from March–June and mating likely occurs soon after the female gives birth. The young are about 21–26 cm (8–10 in) TL at birth. Angels eat a wide variety of fishes, as well as such invertebrates as squids (particularly in winter) and sea cucumbers. Angels are ambush predators and a partially buried, resting fish tends to lie near a reef, either parallel to or facing it, and usually pointing uphill. These fish can elevate their heads as much as 90 degrees and when they lunge at a prey, it is really fast, with strike speeds ranging from 30–100 msec in duration. Predators include white sharks, broadnose sevengill sharks, northern elephant seals, and sperm whales.

FISHERY: Native Americans commonly caught angel sharks. They were of almost no value in the commercial fishery until the late 1970s when as Mick Kronman (unpublished) reveals: "The shark's meteoric rise in popularity began with one fishermen, Tony Genovese. Tony… knew about Italy's angel shark fishery, and knew the product was of high quality, if properly handled. Genovese convinced Santa Barbara processor Mike Wagner, owner of Seafood Specialties, to try it in his retail market. [Parenthetically, may I say that Mike was one of the most innovative fish processors on the West Coast.] Plus, he offered to provide several fish free each week to test consumer acceptance. Wagner, in turn, challenged his fish cutters to develop a method for filleting the angel sharks, so they would appear in the retail case like rockfish fillets, laying flat with no skin or cartilage attached." Well, demand just took off. Mike promoted it for fish and chips and as a substitute for the then very popular thresher sharks, which were seasonally unavailable. During the height of the fishery, angels were taken mostly by gill net and some with trawls. The passage of Proposition 132 in California (in 1990), banning gill netting in nearshore waters, pretty much put the kibosh on the fishery, although a small number are landed each year. Angels are also important in the commercial and artisanal catches along the Baja California coast and in the Gulf of California. Anglers, particularly those folks working the edges of reefs or kelp beds, catch angel sharks fairly regularly.

ORIGINS AND RELATIONSHIPS: My goodness, angel sharks do go back a long way. So far the most ancient species is *Squatina alifera* which lived as early as the Middle Jurassic (maybe 170 million years ago) in what is now central and southern England and across to Bavaria. *Squatina lerichei* was a species that lived on the West Coast during the Miocene (at least 5.3 million years ago) and Pacific angel sharks are known from 100,000-year-old deposits in California. Despite their appearance, angel sharks appear to be more closely related to the more traditional "sharks," such as dogfish, rather than to skates and rays. Pacific angel sharks are most closely related to *Squatina dumeril*, a western North Atlantic species.

THE THINGS WE DO FOR SCIENCE

So, one of the ways you can tell the age of many shark species is by looking at the rings in their vertebrae. And one of the things that you can do to validate that the rings are laid down yearly is to inject a live fish with tetracycline. The fish incorporate the antibiotic in their bones, and that nice mark is then visible under UV light. One time I was involved in that validation process. I would go out on commercial gill netters and as the angels were brought up (nice and alive), I would point to one, give the fisherman a 5-dollar bill, take the fish, measure it, inject it with tetracycline, put a tag in it, and release it, hoping that someone would catch it again so that we could look at one of its vertebra and find the antibiotic mark. Naturally, if I wanted to inject lots of fish I would have to bring with me lots of 5-dollar bills. And that is the reason that, on several occasions, I found myself walking through a darkened harbor (the boats would leave at 2 a.m.), with a satchel containing 1) syringes (for the tetracycline), 2) vials of a liquid (the tetracycline), and 3) maybe $300 in small bills. I used to kind of worry how this might appear to an agent of the law, but then figured that I could always share that I was a biologist, giving me carte blanche to do almost any sketchy thing imaginable.

ORDER HETERODONTIFORMES

FAMILY HETERODONTIDAE—Bullhead Sharks or Horn Sharks

The family Heterodontidae, comprising approximately nine species, all in the genus *Heterodontus*, are found in the shallow marine waters of the Indo-Pacific. There are two species, *H. francisci* and *H. mexicanus*, on the Pacific Coast (*H. mexicanus* makes it as far north as Bahia Magdalena). All of these sharks have a spine at the front of each dorsal fin, an anal fin, and all are oviparous and produce spiral-shaped eggs.

Heterodontus francisci
(Girard, 1855)
Horn Shark

KALANI PATTERSON

On our coast, spiral eggs are unique to horn sharks.

ETYMOLOGY AND COLLOQUIAL NAME: *Heterodontus* comes from two Greek words meaning "different" and "teeth" and *francisci* is derived from "San Francisco." They are called "perro" in Mexico.

THE BASICS: Maximum Length: At least 96 cm (38 in) TL, reported to 122 cm (48 in). Maximum Weight: 10 kg (22 lb). The Ranges: San Francisco to Gulf of California and unconfirmed reports from Ecuador and Peru. They are common as far north as Southern California. Intertidal to depths of 200 m (656 ft). While convention-al wisdom holds that they are most common in nearshore waters, what are we to make of this statement in Barnhart (1932): "Large numbers being taken at a depth of over five hundred feet by rock-cod fishermen." Length-weight parameters (TL, mm, gr): (sexes combined) $W = 0.000009L^{2.995}$ (Miller et al. 2008a).

SALIENT CHARACTERS: This is one of the two shark species north of the U.S.-Mexico border with spines in front of each dorsal fin (the other is the spiny dogfish). Combine this with a brown or gray back, black spots (some fish may only have a few of these), and ridges along each eye and you can't miss.

LIFE HISTORY: Newly hatched horn sharks are often found in just a few meters of water (like maybe 5–10 ft). Juveniles live in sand patches, often near algae, rocks, or sand dollars, and sometimes in eelgrass, and tend to live in shallower water than

adults. Adults live mostly in rocky crevices and caves and among algae. On the Pacific coast of Mexico, they are occasional visitors to coastal lagoons. You often find adults holed up with spiny lobsters and California morays. These are generally solitary, and nonterritorial, fish that are strongly nocturnal. In general (albeit with a few idiosyncratic exceptions), individuals are virtually inert during the day, although it has been reported that horn sharks living in algae would move about a bit to keep their eyes in shadow. Juveniles may be a little more active during the day. On an average night, horn sharks start to perk up from 20–155 minutes after the sun sets. At this point they start making the rounds, often moving inshore, occasionally traveling all the way into the intertidal. Some time before dawn these fish return to their daytime lairs. Adults that live in rocks have spines that are more worn than those that live in algae. There have been reports that horn sharks migrate into considerably deeper waters in the winter—personally I kind of wonder if that is true. Mating occurs during the winter. A mating male bites a female's pectoral fin and copulation lasts 30–40 minutes. In captivity, a female was seen to lay 1–2 eggs per day at 11–14 day intervals for 4 months. Horn shark females lay their eggs (often as pairs) in shallow waters (sometimes into the lower intertidal) amid rocks. Females will lug these eggs in their mouths and wedge them into rock crevices.

There is one, perhaps sketchy, report of a horn shark living to be 25 years old, but no one seems to know if this is kosher. In general, growth rate and age and size at maturity are poorly known. Males and females mature at maybe 56–61 cm (22–24 in) TL. Females lay tough, spiral-shaped eggs. The eggs are laid between January–April. The young hatch out in 8–10 weeks (Barnhart 1932) or 7–9 months (Compagno 2001) depending on whom you choose to believe. Young sharks greet the day at as small as 12.1 cm (5 in) long. These fish eat crustaceans (e.g., shrimps, crabs, and isopods), small fishes, and mollusks (e.g., rock scallops, limpets, abalones, squids, and octopuses) and will occasionally enter tide pools to feed on green sea anemones. Seen one that has purple stains on its chin and teeth? It's likely from eating sea urchins. Northern elephant seals reportedly eat both horn sharks and their eggs.

GREATER LOVE HATH NO MALE

Dempster and Herald (1961) on observing horn sharks mating in an aquarium noted that the male inserted one clasper into the female, leaving one (as it were) dangling. They went on to note: "A garibaldi (*Hypsypops rubicunda*) in the same tank was attracted by this unused clasper and from time to time nipped at it. The hornshark [sic] paid no attention to the garibaldi's harassing activity."

FISHERY: Native Americans occasionally ate horn sharks. There has never been much of a commercial fishery for this fairly diminutive fish in the U.S., although in many years a few pounds are landed at California ports. They are an occasional catch in Baja California and Gulf of California artisanal fisheries. Recreational anglers take them from vessels, piers, and shore.

ORIGINS: The genus *Heterodontus*, in the form of *H. sarstedensis*, goes back at least to the Early Jurassic (perhaps as much as 200 million years ago) of Germany. The University of California, Berkeley, Paleontological Museum has a specimen identified as *Heterodontus* sp. from the Miocene (at least 5.3 million years ago) of Southern California. Remains of the modern horn shark were found in a 100,000-year-old deposit in Southern California.

FAMILY RHINCODONTIDAE—Whale Sharks

There is one species of whale shark. This is the largest fish in the world. A "Rhinocodontid," *Palaorhincodon dartevelli*, apparently in this family or at least closely related, is known from the Paleocene (at least 56 million years ago) of Europe and North Africa.

Rhincodon typus

Smith, 1828

Whale Shark

It's both the biggest fish in the world and covered with large spots. What's not to like?

ETYMOLOGY AND COLLOQUIAL NAMES: *Rhincodon* is formed from two Greek words for "file" and "tooth" and *typus* means "shape" in Greek. In the Gulf of California, they are called "ballena" and the Japanese word is "jinbeizame."

THE BASICS: Maximum Length: At least 18 m (59 ft) TL, possibly 21.4 m (70 ft). Maximum Weight: Who knows? Maybe 4,339 kg (9,545 lb)? The Ranges: Worldwide in tropical and subtropical waters. In the eastern Pacific, Patrick's Point, Humboldt County (Northern California) to northern Chile, but only occasionally off California. Surface to 1,400 m (4,592 ft) or more, but typically in perhaps 100 m (328 ft) or less.

SALIENT CHARACTERS: These are very distinctive animals with broad and flat heads, a large mouth near the tip of the head, tiny teeth, and long gill slits. They are dark gray, blue, brown, or greenish with lots of white or yellow dots and bars. The pattern of spots and stripes are unique to each individual.

LIFE HISTORY: Whale sharks are pelagic fish found both in nearshore waters and well out to sea. They tend to seasonally aggregate in discrete places, attracted to rich concentrations of such food items as the spawn of fishes and corals (from mass spawnings), as well as copepod and euphausiid swarms. Examples of these aggregations occur within the Gulf of California, where particularly hot spots include Bahía San Luis Gonzaga, Bahía de Los Angeles, Bahía de La Paz, El Baja, and Banco Gordo. In Bahía de Los Angeles, for instance, the sharks appear in about June and then leave no later than November, peaking from August–October. There seems to be some interesting stuff going on in the GOC as mostly small fish (less than 4 m, 13.1 ft) live in the northern part and larger females (mostly carrying young) live in the south. In addition, in one study (Eckert and Stewart 2001), some fish tagged in the Gulf remained there, but others left and headed westward, as far away as Micronesia. Eckert and Stewart speculate that some of the fish that leave the GOC do not return. In their study, whale sharks, although they averaged swimming speeds of 24 km (15 mi) per day, occasionally motivated as fast as 96 km (60 mi) per day. Studies in the Gulf of California demonstrate that these fish spend much of their time in waters from 20–32°C (68–90°F) [But note that other work found that on a single dive a whale shark can experience a range between 4.2–28.7°C (40–84°F) and over time may range from 3.4–29.9°C (38–86°F]. Worldwide, whale shark aggregations can be fairly large; for instance, more than 100 individuals were observed in a small area in the Gulf of Aden. Off Belize, aggregations of as many as 25 fish, all feeding on snapper spawn, were found in an area 50 m (164 ft) in diameter. In at least some locations and times, whale sharks make a series of dives to relatively deep waters (in one instance to 50–80 m, 164–262 ft) and this may be a way for the fish to find their plankton prey, as the sharks may be searching for a chemical cue. This species often forms single-sex aggregations. Genetic analyses imply that the whale sharks of the Pacific and Indian oceans form a single population that is genetically distinct (at a population level) from those in the Atlantic.

OCTAVIO ABURTO-OROPEZA

OCTAVIO ABURTO-OROPEZA

No one knows how long whale sharks live. A 7.7 m (25 ft) TL long male was 31 years old and a 7.5 m (25 ft) female was 27 years old. It is speculated that this species may live for 60 or more years. Size and age at maturation is not well understood. Underwater observations off Australia imply that males are mature at about 8 m (26 ft) and that almost all females are mature by 9 m (30 ft). Others have proposed that these fish mature at about 6 m (20 ft) and 10–30 years old. Eggs develop within the females but the mothers provide no nutrition to the embryos (aplacental viviparity). Females may give birth only every 2 years. The parturition season is also not well known. Off Taiwan, females appear to release young at least during the summer, but in the tropics small juveniles have been spotted throughout the year. A 10.8 m (35 ft) female contained over 300 embryos. New-borns are reported to be about 55–60 cm (2 ft) long and 1 kg (2.2 lb) at birth and grow to a whopping 1.4 m (5 ft) long and 20 kg (44 lb) by 4 months All in all, is it my imagination or is this section kind of unsatisfying? Whale sharks feed on a wide range of prey, including euphausiids, copepods, crab larvae, small fishes, squids, and the spawn of various invertebrates and fishes. They feed both by passively swimming through the water with their mouths open and by suction feeding. In suction feeding, a fish (often at or near the surface with its head up and tail down) will suck in great quantities of water and filter out prey. One study found that whale sharks can estimate how much food is in the water and will not feed until the densities of prey (in that instance zooplankton) reaches 10,000 individuals per m^3. Whale sharks have been seen to "cough," releasing material caught on gill rakers. Predators include blue marlins, blue sharks, orcas, and perhaps tiger and white sharks.

FISHERY: While not on the "A" list of commercial species, whale sharks do command a small, but loyal, following, particularly in Asia. They are very popular as a fresh fish in Taiwan, where their soft, bland flesh leads them to be called "tofu" sharks. Yummy, indeed. Elsewhere, there is some demand for the livers (as a source of oil) and the fins (for the omnipresent soups). Ship collisions may be a significant source of mortality.

ORIGINS: A fossil *Rhinocodon* lived in the Middle Miocene (10 million years ago or more) of southern France. *Rhincodon* sp. teeth from Pliocene deposits (at least 1.8 million years old) appear to be identical to *R. typus*.

MISCELLANY: Whale sharks reportedly have the thickest skin (at up to 14 cm, 6 in) of any animal.

WELCOME ALMOST TO CALIFORNIA

John Fitch (1951) reported on the, at the time, northernmost sighting of a whale shark, at South Island, Islas Los Coronados. Noting a jumping school of sardine, Mr. Offie Collins, skipper and owner of the sportfishing partyboat *Collever*, went over to investigate. Seeing a very large shark near the surface "Collins stayed near the shark for about 15 minutes and 'bumped it with the side of the boat several times for the benefit of the passengers.'"

Aha, and they wonder why whale sharks don't come around very often.

ORDER LAMNIFORMES

FAMILY ALOPIIDAE—Thresher Sharks

Threshers are pelagic and marine sharks found throughout the world from the cold temperate zone to the tropics. There are three thresher shark species, all in the genus *Alopias*, and all are found within our range. Threshers reproduce through a truly fabulous form of aplacental viviparity, termed *oophagy*, in which embryos eat some of the other eggs produced by the female. Every species comes equipped with that elongated upper lobe to the caudal fin, a lobe that is used to bash at prey species. These are warm-bodied animals, able to keep their core temperature well above that of the surrounding seawater. The family Alopiidae has been reported as having evolved either in the Late Cretaceous (at least 71 million years ago) or the Early Eocene (as much as 56 million years ago). You pays your money and you takes your choice. The earliest *Alopias*, *A. crochardi*, was found in Early Eocene formations (perhaps 56 million years old) of Europe. A fossil *Alopias* is listed as having been found in Miocene strata (at least 5.3 million years old) at Rosarito Beach (northern Baja California).

Alopias vulpinus
(Bonnaterre, 1788)

Thresher Shark

Thresher sharks are mostly coastal and pelagic fish with embarrassingly long upper caudal fin lobes.

ETYMOLOGY AND COLLOQUIAL NAMES: *Alopias* comes from the Greek for "fox-like" and *vulpinus* is Latin for, unbelievable as it may seem, "fox." Maybe Bonnaterre, back in 1788, was hitting the calvados pretty hard the day he described this species and just couldn't be bothered to come up with something more creative. "Coludo pinto," "Tiburon zorro común," and "ratón" are names from Mexico and commercial fishermen in Southern California often say "thrasher," 'cause it sounds more manly. The Japanese call them "ma-onaga."

THE BASICS: Maximum Length: 6.4 m (21 ft) TL and, who knows, maybe to 7.6 m (25 ft). Maximum Weight: 348 kg (767 lb). The Ranges: Circumglobal in temperate and occasionally tropical waters. In the eastern Pacific, west of Yakobi Island (southeastern Alaska) to Chile (including Gulf of California), but along the Pacific Coast of North America apparently rare south of about Punta Eugenia (central Baja California). Adults are seasonally abundant northward to off Vancouver Island. Surface waters to 572 m (1,876 ft). Von Bertalanffy parameters (TL, cm): (sexes combined) L_∞ = 465, k = 0.129, t_0 = -2.88 (Smith et al. 2008). Length-weight parameters (FL, cm, kg): (sexes combined) W = $0.0001882L^{2.519}$ (Kohler et al. 1995).

SALIENT CHARACTERS: Threshers are immediately identifiable by the remarkably long upper lobes of their caudal fin. They come in a variety of colors, including backs of purple, gray, brown, bluish, or almost black. Unlike the bigeye and pelagic threshers, common threshers have labial folds around the mouth, and the

ANN GREENING

origin of the second dorsal fin is aligned posterior to the free rear tip of the pelvic fin. The bigeye has a relatively large eye and a horizontal groove running from eye to midbody.

LIFE HISTORY: Young ones (maybe 0–3 years old) live in the nearshore waters of California and Baja California, mostly from the Santa Barbara Channel to Punta Eugenia (central Baja California) and primarily over the continental shelf. Small fish, in particular, often leap out of the water. A couple of my friends had one leap out of the water right in front of their boat; when it came back down it landed in the bow, a yummy surprise for chronically underpaid graduate students. Both juveniles and adults often hang out in the green waters along oceanographic fronts (areas of high productivity where there are substantial amounts of prey). Off California, juveniles are most often found from surface waters to depths of 46 m (150 ft) (and mostly in 20 m, 66 ft, and less). Older fish tend to live further offshore (they are relatively abundant out to more than 161 km, 100 mi). By day, they can be found from near-surface waters to depths of 200 m (656 ft) or more, often making vertical excursions. At night, these fish tend to stay shallow, mostly in 5–15 m (16–49 ft). Adult fish may move north-

ward into Southern California waters in the spring, where they release their young, and at least some then continue north-ward to off Vancouver Island. Come the fall, adults move southward and perhaps end up off Baja California. Subadults may move as far north as off the Columbia River and juveniles extend their range into Central California during warm-water years. Fish tagged off Southern California have traveled as far south as 869 km (540 mi) southwest of La Paz (Mexico). In general, fish aggregate by sex and size. Off the U.S. West Coast, fish have been found from 6–25°C (43–77°F) and mostly at 15–22°C (59–72°F). Genetic studies imply that fish living along the west coast of North America belong to a single population.

Maximum age and size and age at maturity are poorly understood. Maximum age has been estimated at between 20 and 50 years, with a recent estimate at 25 years for West Coast fish. Females may live longer than males. Off the West Coast, fe-males and males mature at around 300 cm (10 ft) TL and about 4 or 5 years old. Off California, females apparently give birth in the spring and mating occurs in summer, for a gestation time of about 9 months. Females typically harbor 2–4 (but sometimes at least as many as 7) embryos. The young are born at 100–160 cm (39-63 in) TL. Threshers primarily eat fishes, squids, and pelagic red crabs. Before feeding, these sharks smartly slap their fish prey with that singular upper caudal fin lobe. And lastly, reporting from Ireland in 1866, the inimitable H. Blake-Knox reported spotting a thresher shark catching a loon, so be on the lookout for that behavior. Harbor porpoise were seen chasing small thresher sharks, likely this species, in Monterey Bay.

FISHERY: As far back as 1887, David Starr Jordan observed that this species was commonly taken by Monterey Bay fisher-men, although at that time the fish were mostly rendered for their oil. The fishery remained small until a drift gill net fishery developed off Southern California in the late 1970s. An outgrowth of the bonito and barracuda fisheries, fishermen were soon setting nets 915 m (3,000 ft) or longer for a fish that was extremely popular in fresh fish markets. The nets were set at night, with one side attached to a buoy and the other to the vessel. During the height of the fishery, as noted by a fisherman (Kronman, unpublished): "Once we got the gear dialed in, the catches were unbelievable. We had nights when the entire net sank —buoys and all—because we had so much fish in it. Sometimes, it took hours, even a day, to get it back, working inch by inch with a hydraulic reel, boom winch and manpower—anything we could use to muscle the huge load aboard." As preor-dained as the sun rising in the east, overfishing put the hurt to this fishery, and it has never been as large as in those glory days. Threshers remain a commercially important species off California (although often a by-catch of the swordfish fishery) and along the Baja California coast; indeed, wherever they are found. Off California, they are mostly taken by gill nets.

Threshers, with their acrobatic abilities, are very popular with sport anglers. Off Southern California, there is a loyal fraternity that seeks them out (catching them mostly from May–August). Many threshers are tail-hooked, after slamming their tails into trolled lures. Pulling these fish in backwards apparently causes unexpectedly high mortality rates when they are later released. Small ones are occasionally taken from piers.

MISCELLANY: Both the red and white muscle of this species can be warmer than surrounding seawater.

OTHER SPECIES

Alopias pelagicus
Nakamura, 1935
Pelagic Thresher

FRANCO BANFI

Pelagic threshers grow to 3.83 m (13 ft) TL. They are circumtropical and are found from Southern California to Panama. El Niños bring them into Southern California and commercial catches there are overwhelmingly composed of mature females. An oceanic species, they are found from the surface to 700 m (2,296 ft) or more, in water temperatures from 14–28°C (58–82°F). They have a tendency to be slightly closer to the surface at night. Maximum life span is likely 21 years or longer. Females grow larger than males. Females tend to mature at 282–292 cm (9–10 ft) TL (8–9 years) (but at least as small as 264 cm, 9 ft) and males at 267–276 cm (9 ft) (7–8 years) (and as small as 259 cm, 9 ft). Off Taiwan, there does not seem to be a distinct birthing season. Females typically have 2 embryos (one per uterus) and fish are as small as 137 cm (54 in) TL at birth. Females may, on occasion, give birth in Southern California waters. In the eastern tropical Pacific, pelagic threshers feed on a variety of mesopelagic fishes. Handfuls are landed at California ports by commercial fishermen (although their flesh is considered inferior to that of *A. vulpinus*) and they are quite important along the Baja California coast and to a certain extent in the Gulf of California. Von Bertalanffy parameters (PCL, cm): (females) L_∞ = 197, k = 0.085, t_0 = -7.67; (males) L_∞ = 182, k = 0.118, t_0 = -5.48 (Liu et al. 1999).

Alopias superciliosus
(Lowe, 1841)
Bigeye Thresher

Bigeyes grow to 4.8 m (16 ft) TL and to at least 363.8 kg (802 lb). They are circumglobal and are found from Cape Mendocino (Northern California) to the Gulf of California, and possibly off Peru and northern Chile. Adults are reasonably common off Southern California, but are more abundant there during warm-water periods. Off Southern California, bigeyes usually stay a bit further offshore and deeper than *A. vulpinus*. They range from surface waters to depths of 723 m (2,371 ft), perhaps mostly in the upper 65 m (213 ft). This species can make extensive vertical movements between day and night (enduring water temperatures between 6–26°C, 43–79°F), with fish in deeper water during the day. Bigeyes often aggregate by size and sex. They live to at least 26 years and females grow larger than males. Males mature at 9–10 years old (as small as 276 cm, 9 ft, TL) and females at about 12–13 years old (341 cm, 11 ft). Females (with a gestation period of about 12 months) commonly carry 2 (but as many as 4) embryos and these can be as small as 100 cm (39 in) (or perhaps even 60 cm, 24 in) at birth. It is unclear whether this species has a discrete spawning season. Off California, bigeye threshers are opportunistic feeders, preying on epipelagic and mesopelagic fishes and squids. They are a moderately important commercial species in the Gulf of California and in some years fairly substantial numbers are taken in the California driftnet fishery. Von Bertalanffy parameters (PCL, cm): (females) L_∞ = 225, k = 0.092, t_0 = -4.21; (males) L_∞ = 219, k = 0.088, t_0 = -4.24 (Liu et al. 1998). Length-weight parameters (FL, cm, kg): (sexes combined) W = $0.00000L^{3.08}$ (Kohler et al. 1995).

FAMILY CETORHINIDAE—Basking Sharks

The basking shark is the only member of this family. This fish grows to become the second-largest fish in the world, second only to the redoubtable whale shark.

Cetorhinus maximus

(Gunnerus, 1765)

Basking Shark

ETYMOLOGY AND COLLOQUIAL NAMES: *Cetorhinus* is Greek for "whale" and "shark" (referring to a file or the rough skin of the shark) and *maximus* is Latin for "largest." They were called "capidolli" or "oil fish" by San Francisco fishermen in the early 20th century and the Japanese name is "ubazame."

THE BASICS: Maximum Length: At least 9.8 m (32 ft) TL and perhaps to 15.2 m (50 ft). Maximum Weight: Perhaps around 4,000 kg (8,800 lb). The Ranges: Circumglobal in colder waters. Seas of Japan and Okhotsk and western North Pacific Ocean, to the eastern North Pacific south of the Aleutian Islands, and the Gulf of Alaska to at least Punta Abreojos (26°42'N, 113°35'W) (central Baja California) (records from further south along the Baja California Peninsula and in the Gulf of California are poorly documented); Chile. Historically, apparently predictably found from perhaps Clayoquot Sound (Vancouver Island) southwards, although, today, basking shark sightings off British Columbia appear to be unusual. Surface to 1,264 m (4,146 ft).

SALIENT CHARACTERS: If the shark is bigger than your boat, it's probably a basking shark. These are immense animals, routinely 6–7.6 m (20–25 ft) long, usually colored brown, gray, or black, often with lighter patches. The caudal fin is crescent shaped and there is a distinct notch near the tip. Baskers have huge, white mouths and extremely long gill slits.

SHANE ANDERSON

ON THE AESTHETICS OF BASKING SHARK OIL

Mick Kronman (unpublished), quoting commercial fisherman Sam Ferris: "The oil was absolutely beautiful. A penny tossed in a 15-foot-deep, 15,000-gallon tank of oil took five minutes to hit the bottom, and you could see it all the way down."

LIFE HISTORY: Basking sharks are hefty pelagic animals, usually found over the continental shelf, that often swim right at the surface. These are quite mobile animals (i.e., in the Atlantic some migrate from Great Britain to Newfoundland, a distance of 6,589 km, 4,094 mi, and from southern New England to Brazil). However, in the eastern Pacific just what these movements are is a bit unclear, although some fish do migrate northward, as far as Alaska, as waters warm. For many years, there was an hypothesis that basking sharks, having run out in winter of the great quantities of zooplankton that keep them going and growing, migrated into deeper waters and kind of hunkered down, waiting for the new crop to arrive in spring. As with our belief that outsourcing all of our industries overseas would be an unalloyed blessing, this charming folk tale has been laid to rest. For instance, based on aerial monitoring from 1962–1985 in Central and Southern California, Squire (1990) found that at least a few fish are present throughout the year. In that study, peak densities occurred in October, with a lesser peak in the spring. Even more to the point, Sims et al. (2003) tagged a number of them off Great Britain and found that throughout the winter the fish kept moving (both vertically and horizontally). These vertical dives may be a way for these sharks to locate zooplankton, perhaps keying in on some chemical cue. They also found that the fish spent more time during the day in deeper waters and generally came up shallow at night. This is likely because the sharks were feeding on zooplankton that made similar day-night vertical migrations. While you might often see them singly or in small groups, herds of 100 or more individuals have been reported. And if one believes Gavin

Maxwell (see below), at least in the old days, they aggregated in simply enormous numbers. These aggregations will, at times, contain only one sex. Worldwide, there is no evidence of genetically isolated populations.

Sims et al. (2000) perhaps saw courtship behavior off southwestern England in May and June and noted that others have seen physical evidence (in the form of mating-related wounds) of reproductive activity. They reported that what appeared to be mature fish hung about the surface along oceanographic fronts and engaged in nose-to-tail following behavior, seemingly with a female in the front and males in back and on sides. Unfortunately, mating was not observed, so Sims and company get only a B+ for their efforts. Perhaps mating occurs somewhere below the surface. They also quote other research that determined that during summer months off western Scotland: "Females bore recent or unhealed cloacal wounds inflicted by the claw on the clasper of the male during copulation." Yow, I say, yow. Maxwell (1984, see next page) gives this stirring account of his first meeting with basking shark sperm: "This was a male fish, and during the tremendous struggle at the surface just after we had got the tail-sling into position, he emitted a great quantity of what we afterward found to be sperm. It was not a fluid, but hundreds of semi-opaque milky globules like golf-balls, varying in size, and looking as though made of Lalique glass. These, Dr. Harrison Matthews later discovered, were the spermatophores, each having a hard casing enclosing a central core of sperm."

No one knows how long baskers live, because Lisa Natanson and a small army of associates (like 15 co-authors 2008) found that the bands in basking shark vertebrae (counting them is the usual way to age a shark) are not laid down annually, so we are just plain out of luck. *My goodness, 15 co-authors. Just pointing out: it took one author to write the Bill of Rights.* Dave Ebert (2003) reports that males mature at 4–5 m (13–16 ft) TL and females at 8–9 m (26–30 ft). He also notes they are oophagous (aplacental viviparous), there are anecdotal reports of broods of up to six young, and the young are born at an estimated 1.5–2 m (5–7 ft) long. Basking sharks are filter-feeding plankton consumers that often appear to specialize in large copepods. As Sims and Quayle (1998) (working off southwest England) observed, basking sharks are "selective filter-feeders that choose the richest, most profitable plankton patches. They forage along thermal fronts and actively select areas that contain high densities of large zooplankton above a threshold density." These researchers speculate that the sharks may locate these dense patches of larger zooplankton by "electroreception of copepod muscle activity and olfaction of dimethyl sulphide, which is produced by phytoplankton when grazed by zooplankton." Interesting, yes? They also observed that individual sharks seemingly

"actively avoid each other when foraging in patches." I haven't noticed that off Southern California, where you can often see two or three sharks, mouths open, slowly moving together along the surface. Predators may include white sharks, sperm whales, and orcas.

FISHERY: At least during historical times, Native Americans on the Northwest Coast occasionally caught basking sharks and rendered them for their oil. Basking shark fisheries have existed in various parts of the world for many years and oil, meat (including fins), and skin are all valuable. Along the Pacific Coast, and more particularly off California, there have been repeated attempts to create a commercial fishery. Much to the relief of the baskers, these always seem to have foundered because of 1) low prices to the fishermen and 2) unpredictable availability of the product. For instance, the 1930s saw a small fishery for them in Monterey Bay. Those sharks were sent to the Monterey Fish By-Products Company [likely corporate motto: "You Really Didn't Want to Live in This Neighborhood Anyway"], where they were reduced to fertilizer, chicken and pet feed, and oil from their livers. At that time, an analysis noted that the largest basking shark sold to that company was a few inches under 30 feet long and weighed 8,600 pounds, had a liver (which comprises 17–25% of its body weight) that weighed 1,800 pounds, 60 percent of which was oil. Unfortunately, unlike some shark livers (such as those of soupfins), oil from basking sharks is not high in vitamin A; thus selling it was a little tricky. Max Schaefer, who ran the reduction business, soon found that he could peddle the liver oil for, as noted in his advertising brochure: "A tonic to build up the digestive system, enabling it to get out all nutrients contained in regular food…[Gives] relief in cases of neuritis, stomach ulcers, anemia, loss of appetite and weight, lack of energy, and asthmatic attacks…It promotes health and growth in children, builds up resistance to attacks of the usual ailments of youth, and furnishes energy for strenuous exertions…In older people it [defers] troubles common with age [and] enables them to keep on enjoying their full bodily vigor and energy." Clearly, Mr. Schaefer was as unbothered by Federal regulations governing truth in advertising as dietary supplement industries are today. The basking shark fishery pretty much died out in the early 1940s, as fishermen switched to the far more lucrative soupfin shark fishery. Other, later, attempts to create a commercial fishery, some using spotter planes and war-surplus landing craft, were also short-lived. Generally, low prices for the products and the unpredictable occurrence of the quarry made the fishery unprofitable.

And recreational angling? Here is a tale told by Tim Thomas. It appears that in the 1920s there was a recreational "fishery" for basking sharks in Monterey Bay. At that time, for 25 or 50 cents, tourists were ferried offshore where they harpooned these fish. An additional wrinkle was soon added where, after a fish was killed, it was brought to the boat, blown up with air, and local harpoon maker Henry Leppert would jump on the carcass and do a little dance. And thus are made those indelible memories for our visitors from Kankakee.

A LYRICAL AND POETIC TALE OF KILLING AND RENDERING BASKING SHARKS?

Sure, it's Gavin Maxwell's *Harpoon at a Venture* (Penguin Books, 1984). In about 1944, Maxwell, while in the British Army, saw, loved, and bought the small island of Soay off northwestern Scotland. Searching for an industry to improve the island's economy, Maxwell was struck by the large number of basking sharks that seasonally invaded the area. Based on only the sketchiest information, he determined to develop a fishery and rendering plant for these fish. In the event, within a few years his venture went belly up, partially because not enough sharks did the same. But his memoir of that time is a lovely paean to a time and place now long-gone:

"Down there in the clear water they were packed as tight as sardines, each barely allowing swimming room to the next, layer upon layer of them, huge grey shapes like a herd of submerged elephants, the furthest down dim and indistinct in the sea's dusk. A memory came back to me from childhood–Mowgli and the elephants' dance, and the drawing of the great heaving mass of backs in the jungle clearing."

"We hove to and held a consultation. It was difficult to concentrate; we were in the middle of a big shoal, and they were all round us. Some, close inshore under the cliffs, were 'breaching'—shooting clear out of the water, turning half over on their sides and falling back on to the surface with a tremendous smash. It was like the report of a gun, and left the surface dotted with seething white patches. I wondered what speed the shark must reach below water to carry several tons clear of the sea."

And while we are on the subject of Gavin Maxwell (he of *Ring of Bright Water* fame), why do all of the sprightly-wild-animal-that-came-into-my-life-and-shared-my-house books end with the animal dying? Why can't we have a book that ends with "And even today, when Archie the reticulated python has dined on a neighborhood cat, why he still climbs into bed with the missus and me"?

ORIGINS: *Cetorhinus parvus* is known from the Early Oligocene (perhaps 20 million years ago) of Europe. A *Cetorhinus* sp. lived in Southern California during the Miocene (at least 5.3 million years ago) and basking shark remains occur in Pliocene deposits (at least 1.8 million years ago) in San Diego.

MISCELLANY: 1) It has been reported that while baskers are generally seen swimming upright, dorsal fin up, at times they will lie on their sides or even swim belly up. 2) At least for a short time in the 1950s, a basking shark eradication program was created in British Columbia to get rid of those pesky fish because they were screwing up salmon gill nets. This worked too well, and today baskers are rarely observed off BC. 3) And just how yummilicious is basking shark oil? A report from 1931, commenting on basking shark catches in Monterey Bay, notes: "A very particular person was unwittingly given [basking] shark-liver oil on a salad and was unable to notice a difference from various other table oils" (Anon 1931). This implies that either A) basking shark oil taste okay, or B) the other "table" oils available in 1931 were perfectly awful. 4) Basking sharks will, at times, leap into the air. Filled to the brim with girlish glee, perhaps? Well, that is one idea. As breaching seems to occur more often during mating season, perhaps females are announcing their receptivity. Another possibility is that this may be an example of male-male competition for mates.

FAMILY LAMNIDAE—Mackerel Sharks

The mackerel sharks are pelagic marine fishes that are found throughout the world in subarctic to tropical waters. There are only three genera and five species, with four species within our range. But what the family lacks in diversity it makes up for in chutzpah. All of the lamnids within our range have an oophagous (aplacental viviparous) mode of reproduction; while in the uterus, embryos eat ovulating eggs. Lamnids have a cute countercurrent circulatory heat exchange system that allows them to have body temperatures well above surrounding sea temps (see Carey and Teal 1969 and Carey et al. 1971 for lots of details). Lamnids first appear in the fossil record in the Paleocene (way back there 56 million years ago or more).

Carcharodon carcharias
(Linnaeus, 1758)
White Shark

A Jungian archetype with serrated teeth.

ETYMOLOGY AND COLLOQUIAL NAMES: *Carcharodon* is Greek for "rough" and "tooth" and *carcharias* is the Ancient Greek word for this species. Commercial abalone divers in California used to call them "Mr. White." "Blanco" is the name in Mexico and "hohojirozame" is the Japanese word.

THE BASICS: Maximum Length: About 6 m (20 ft) TL, possibly to 6.4 m (21 ft). Maximum Weight: at least 1,554 kg (3,419 lb). The Ranges: Circumglobal, mostly in temperate waters. Northwest Bering Sea (59°56'N, 178°56'W) and Gulf of Alaska (60°17'N, 145°35'W) to Gulf of California and from Panama to Chile. Worldwide, their major centers of abundance are in the coastal waters of California and Baja California, Australia and New Zealand, South Africa and, before they were nailed hard, the Mediterranean Sea. They appear to be fairly abundant as far north as southeastern Alaska and British Columbia. Surf zone to 1,280 m (4,198 ft). Bruce (2008) presents 3 sets of von Bertalanffy parameters from 3 studies in various parts of the world and here is the one from the Pacific Coast (TL, m): (sexes combined) L_∞ = 7.7, k = 0.058, t_0 = -3.53. Length-weight parameters (TL, cm): (sexes combined) W = $0.00000303L^{3.188}$ (Compagno 2001).

SALIENT CHARACTERS: This is a stout shark with a distinctive triangular-shaped dorsal fin and a strong keel on the caudal fin. As you might expect, white sharks are not white. You will find them in brown, gray, or maybe gray-blue. Smaller fish have mostly long teeth without serrations, while those over about 2.7 m (9 ft) TL have very characteristic triangular, serrated teeth. There is often a small black spot at the pectoral fin base and/or on the underside of the pectoral fin tip. Shortfin mako sharks are the species you may confuse this one with. Makos are deep blue in color and have pointier snouts.

LIFE HISTORY: Damn, I hate writing this section. There has been so much written about charismatic megafauna that I have lost whatever vague interest I have in them. Suffice it to say that there are whole books and many scientific articles written about white sharks, great hulking volumes simply leaking blood and information from every pore. Why don't you look at these

when you are finished here? Worthy tomes include Klimley and Ainley (1996), Compagno (2001), Ebert (2003), and Boustany et al. (2008). But, because of my sworn obligations, here is some sort of quarter-assed overview of the species.

Juveniles appear to be born in specific nursery zones. The nearshore of Southern California and northern Baja California are such places and, in fact, juveniles are fairly common in the artisanal fisheries as far south as Bahia de Sebastian Vizcaino (central Baja California). However, there is no definitive proof that females give birth in these inshore waters, it is possible that birthing occurs somewhat offshore and the young swim toward shallow waters. Young fish may move pretty freely north and south within this zone. At the extreme, one young-of-the-year tagged in Southern California wound up in Bahia de Sebastian Vizcaino. One study found that juveniles tended to move toward the surface at night and that older juveniles dove deeper than younger ones. On the other hand, during the summer of 2010, there were a number of juvenile white sharks (including neonates) swimming during the day in the surface waters of Santa Monica Bay. Limbaugh (1963) observed: "Numerous imma-ture specimens observed near La Jolla were swimming along the bottom and just under the water, occasionally breaking the surface with the upper two-thirds of the dorsal fin. Less frequently, the tip of the caudal fin would project an inch or so as the shark dived. They entered the surf zone where the water depth was only 4 or 5 feet."

Okay, now for the adults, and mainly we will be discussing the adults that live off the West Coast of the U.S. As with juveniles, adults will also come into very shallow waters, as any surfer with only half a buttocks will attest. Dave Ebert (1991) notes that white sharks will occasionally engage in "spy-hopping," where they lift their heads above the water and kind of look around. While adult white sharks are, on occasion, found along much of the west coast of North America, large concen-trations exist in Central California (e.g., around the Farallon Islands, Ano Nuevo Island, and Point Reyes) and Isla Guadalupe (well offshore of central Baja California). As in other parts of the world, white sharks usually concentrate in areas with lots of seals and sea lions and such is the case at all of these sites. Adults hang out off Central California mostly from August to February with many or most males returning every year and females probably every other year. While at the islands, these fish spend most of their time in shallow waters, maybe in 50 m (164 ft) or less. Now here is the good part. In the winter, these animals begin to move offshore to the southwest (with males, on average, appearing to leave earlier than females), migrat-

SO MUCH TO COMMENT ON,
SO LITTLE SPACE

And this just in from Norman and Fraser's *Field Book of Giant Fishes* (G. P. Putnam and Sons, 1949): "Further testimony as to the voracious habits and catholic diet of this shark is provided by the late Sir Frederick McCoy, who wrote as follows concerning a specimen from Port Phillip, Australia: 'A specimen between 15 or 16 feet long had been observed for several days swimming around the ladies' baths, looking through the picket fence in such a disagreeable manner that the stationmaster had a strong hook and iron chain made so as to keep the rope out of reach of his teeth, and this, being baited with a large piece of pork made to look as much like a piece of lady as possible, was swallowed greedily, and then, with the aid of a crowd of helpers, the monster was got on shore.'"

This comparatively short discourse allows for a whole host of questions. For instance, the reference to a "catholic" diet puzzles me. Why would a white shark prefer to eat Catholics over other denominations? And then, what manner of shark would actually peek through the picket fence surrounding a ladies' bath? Is this just an echo of the unfortunate criminal past of so many of Australia's early European inhabitants? On the other hand, is "looking through the picket fence in a disagreeable manner" sufficient grounds to kill the poor animal? And without being too graphic, precisely what "piece of lady" was the pork made to look like? Who made the decision as to what anatomical landscape would be imaged and who was hired to fashion the meat into the correct visage? Surely, then, the artist involved would have a profound impact on the effectiveness of the bait. For instance, a ladies' elbow fashioned out of pork butt by John William Waterhouse (an artist whose renderings of young women are simply exquisite) might go over well with a white shark of a rather sensitive persuasion, but like a lead balloon for one that never really was attuned to the Pre-Raphaelites. Lastly, I note that Sir Frederick McCoy wrote "amongst" as well as "while" (as opposed to "whilst"). I have always suspected that the "st" used by those in the British Empire was but an affectation and that, when ex-colonials were not present, they dropped the pretense altogether.

ing 2,000–5,000 km (1,243–3,107 mi). While fish may travel as far as the Hawaiian Islands (some individuals do that year after year), most seem to head for an area about 2,500 km (1,553 mi) west of the Baja California Peninsula, an area that, at first glance, appears to be in the middle of nowhere. This quite broad expanse has been designated the "Café" or the Shared Offshore Foraging Area (SOFA) by various researchers with lots of time on their hands. At the Café, males tend to stay within an area of about 250 km (155 mi); females enter this area but are also more likely to roam over a broader expanse. What are the fish doing out there? Tough to tell, feeding and/or mating one supposes. White sharks may spend up to 8 months out there while performing a series of deep dives and shallow returns for hours at a time. Adults living around Isla Guadalupe seem to follow a similar pattern, arriving at the island as early as July and starting to leave for Café/SOFA in the winter and spring. It is likely that white sharks in the northeast Pacific migrated from a New Zealand-Australia population, but have been isolated from those fish for hundreds of thousands of years. Jorgensen et al. (2009) has more stuff about this.

Clearly, these are very motile animals and Bonfil et al. (2005) report on my favorite migration. After they tagged a female off South Africa, it made a beeline to Australia (averaging 4.7 km per hour, the fastest known sustained speed for a shark) and then came roaring back soon after. During its migration, the female swam into waters as cold as 3.4°C (38°F) and as deep as 980 m (3,214 ft). And while it spent most of its time at or near the surface, it also occupied almost 20% of its hours in waters 500–750 m (1,640–2,460 ft) deep. White sharks appear to be able to swim along bottom features that they cannot see, as evidenced by directional swimming in near-surface waters way up above La Jolla Submarine Canyon (Southern California). This species has a very broad temperature tolerance, at least from 3.4–27°C (38–81°F).

White sharks probably live to 40–50 years and possibly to 60 years. Females grow larger than males. Females mature at 4.5–5 m (15–16 ft) TL (12–17 years) and males at 3.6–3.8 m (12–13 ft) (7–9 years). In a study off South Africa, the smallest mature male was 2.9 m (10 ft) and the largest immature one was 3.1 m (10 ft). In utero, white shark embryos feed on unfertilized eggs (aplacental viviparity with oophagy). Gestation takes about 18 months and females give birth every 3 years, producing 2–17 pups. The pups are 120–150 cm (47–59 in) TL at birth and are born in the spring and summer. Young white sharks eat mostly fishes, while larger ones tend to concentrate on marine mammals. The younger ones have nice, slim teeth, the better to grab hold of slippery prey, and the larger fish grow thick, triangular and serrated ones, useful in ripping chunks out of things.

A feeding individual may slap its tail on the surface or even breach, perhaps as a way of warding off competitors. Marine mammal prey includes various pinnipeds (e.g., harbor and elephant seals, fur seals, California and Steller sea lions), porpoises and dolphins, sea otters (although they may not actually swallow them), sea birds, and whales (scavenging dead ones, it is often assumed). Off South Africa, both white and tiger sharks were observed feeding off the same whale. By folks who do this kind of thing, it has been estimated that one mouthful of whale fat can satisfy the basal metabolism of a white shark for 1.5 months. In other climes, they also eat turtles. One paper (Fergusson et al. 2000) characterized the white shark as a "habitual grab-releaser" of marine animals, willing to bite a wide variety of things, perhaps just to see if they are edible.

As far as predators go, Pyle et al. (1999) note that a 3–4 m (10–13 ft) long one was eaten by an orca off the Farallon Islands. After grabbing it near the surface: "The whale then came to the surface holding the shark by its back... For the following 15 minutes, the killer whale transported the shark along the surface" before starting to eat it. The researchers also noted that for the several months that the orcas frequented the area, white sharks did not appear to be around. Hey, kids, always remember what Ben Folds wrote: There's Always Someone Cooler Than You. Larger white sharks will also eat smaller ones.

THE NIGHT MEGALODON CAME TO CALL

RAY TROLL

FISHERY: Native Americans apparently captured white sharks on occasion. Historically, there has been no commercial or sport fishery for them off the West Coast of North America, although they are caught by accident in gill nets and longlines, and a handful of pounds are landed every so often in California. While they are only an occasional catch along the Baja California coast and in the Gulf of California, when commercial fishermen catch one it finds a ready market. Once, while bottom longlining for dogfish, I caught a small one off Long Beach (Southern California). It was truly tasty.

ORIGINS AND RELATIONSHIPS: Where do white sharks come from? Oh, well from mama white sharks, certainly. But from what fish did they evolve? Currently, there are two hypotheses, each one defended by bluff and hearty paleontologists. One holds that white sharks (at least the genus *Carcharodon*) originated from a group of extinct mako sharks (such as *Isurus hastalis*) and go back 43 million or more years. The other contends that these fish originated from the same lineage as the really big toothy sharks of horror movie fame, such as *Carcharocles megalodon*. Right now the mako shark proponents seem to have the edge, but don't count the megalodon folks out just yet. The University of California, Berkeley, Paleontological Museum has teeth reportedly from modern white sharks from the Miocene (at least 5.3 million years ago) of San Diego.

MISCELLANY: 1) Several studies demonstrate that the temperatures of the muscles, the eye and brain, and the viscera can be elevated as much as 14.3°C above that of the surrounding seawater. 2) A white shark poking around Seal Rocks off Victoria (Australia) was mobbed by about five large male seals. They kept making passes by its head until, after about two minutes, it

DINING ON DR. DOOLITTLE

Have you noticed that there are no children's stories about white sharks? Oh, there are lots of tales about prancing deer, fluffy bunnies, and bushy-tailed squirrels, but look as I might, there is nary one thin volume about white sharks. And it's not just that white sharks aren't cute, winsome, furry little warm bloods. No, because right next to such justly popular works as *Fawny—The Deer Who Wouldn't Chew*, *Cottonball—The Bunny Who Wouldn't Hop*, and *Nutcase—The Squirrel with Bubonic Plague*, are a host of stories about cute, winsome spiders, worms, and snakes. So, with these classic tales of various vermin, where, oh where, is that sensitive, magical story called *Gnashy—The White Shark Who was Strictly Kosher*? Actually, my friend and editor Cheri Rae notes that there is a children's book entitled *The Great White Man-Eating Shark: a Cautionary Tale*, by Margaret Maky (Puffin, 1996), so I kind of stand corrected.

took off. 3) There are reports of people being poisoned from eating white shark livers, so keep your white shark liver dining to a minimum. 4) South Africa was the first nation to afford protection to this species.

REMARKS: And regarding white shark attacks on folks along the Pacific Coast, I can't do better than John McCosker and Bob Lea (2006): "The majority of attacks occurred at or near the surface, nearshore, and often in the vicinity of pinniped colonies and/or river mouths and harbors. Attacks have now occurred during all months, and on surfers, breathhold and scuba divers, swimmers, hookah divers, kayakers, and, for the first time, on bodyboarders, a windsurfer, and a scuba diver using an electric propulsion device. Typical attack scenarios suggest that an adult *C. carcharias* mistakes its victim for a pinniped, its normal prey."

Isurus oxyrinchus

Rafinesque, 1810

Shortfin Mako

ETYMOLOGY AND COLLOQUIAL NAMES: *Isurus* is Greek for "equal" and "tail" (referring to the equal lengths of the caudal fin lobes) and *oxyrinchus* is Greek for "sharp" and "snout." Even today they are often called "bonito sharks." "Tintorera azul" is used in parts of Mexico and "ao zame" is the Japanese word.

THE BASICS: Maximum Length: 4 m (13 ft) TL, largest fish off the West Coast of the U.S. was 351 cm (12 ft). Maximum Weight: 555 kg (1,221 lb). The Ranges: Circumglobal, generally in warm waters. British Columbia to Chile. They are reasonably abundant from Oregon southward. Surface waters to 740 m (2,427 ft). Von Bertalanffy parameters (TL, cm): (sexes combined) $L_{\infty} = 411$, $k = 0.05$, $t_0 = -4.7$ (Ribot-Carballal et al. 2005). Length-weight parameters (FL, cm, kg): (sexes combined) $W = 0.0000052L^{3.14}$ (Kohler et al. 1995).

SALIENT CHARACTERS: Shortfin makos are sleek, torpedo-shaped fish, readily identified by their long, pointed snout and teeth, a large keel on their caudal peduncle, and deep-blue back. The only shark you are likely to confuse with this species is the blue shark, and it has a blunter snout, serrated teeth, a much longer upper caudal fin lobe, and a small keel on the caudal peduncle.

TRACY CLARK

LIFE HISTORY: The region between Point Conception (California) and Punta Colnett (northern Baja California), and particularly the Southern California Bight, is a pupping and nursery ground. Joe Bizzarro (2005) also found a few juveniles in the Bahia Magdalena complex (southern Baja California). Pups move into Central California waters during warm-water years. Based on both commercial and recreational catches, most of the makos swimming about in California waters are juveniles, although adult males are also frequently caught. Adult females are rare in those waters. Makos are most abundant in these waters from May–October. Several studies of short-term juvenile movements off Southern California demonstrate that 1) these fish tend to stay in relatively near-surface waters, mostly above the thermocline, particularly at night, 2) they conduct more vertical movements during the day (descending to as much as 324 m, 1,062 ft), and 3) they may stay in a specific area for at least a week or may travel away quickly, covering as much as 49 km (30 mi) in a day. Sepulveda et al. (2004) noted that the juveniles made two types of oscillatory depth behavior: "One in which the swimming pattern included repeated shallow oscillations as if the sharks were searching a small section of the water column and the second in which the oscillations seemed to be directed descents into deeper waters followed by rapid ascents, or 'bounce dives'. These 'bounce dives' were frequently associated with successful feeding events." During these deeper dives, makos encountered water temperatures as cold as 8.9°C (48°F). Off California, most catches are made in 15–25°C (59–77°F). Researchers working in La Jolla Submarine Canyon (Southern California) found that makos can detect bottom features (like canyons) even when they can't see them. They figured this out because a tagged mako, swimming at or near the surface, followed the contour of the canyon even though it was way below the fish. Fish tagged off Southern California have been recaptured near Hawai'i, Northern California, and off Acapulco (Mexico). Genetic analysis implies that there are no distinct populations worldwide, although the North Atlantic population does seem to be somewhat isolated.

Makos have proven to be a little tricky to age. They may live to 42 years old, but there seems to be some debate about that and it may be somewhat less. Females and males grow at the same rates. The average female size at maturity is about 2.7 m (9 ft) TL in the Southern Hemisphere and 3 m (10 ft) in the North Atlantic. It is suggested that, in the western and central North Pacific, females mature at about 16 years old and males at 6 years old. Off southern Baja California, males mature at 1.8 m (6 ft) and about 7 years old. Females gestate their young for maybe 12–18 months; hence they likely release young every 2–3 years. Birthing season may be from late winter to midspring and females reportedly produce between 1 and at least 25 young (and perhaps as many as 30) at a time. Mollett et al. (2000) question reports of very low brood estimates and feel that, on average, a female produces about 12–13 pups a year. The young are about 70 cm (28 in) TL at birth. Makos feed on fishes, sea turtles, squids, and small cetaceans. A 409 kg (900 lb) fish taken off Santa Barbara contained two whole makos and parts of a hammerhead. During those periods when the squirters are available, makos eat a lot of Humboldt squids. You can often find these sharks covered with those characteristic scars gained while attacking this prey. Feeding seems to occur during both day and night. Predators include white sharks and orcas.

FISHERY: While there is no directed fishery for mako sharks off California and Baja California, they are caught in pretty good numbers in the drift gill net and longline fisheries with some captured in set gill nets. Most of the fish taken off California are juveniles. In the U.S., makos are sold fresh. Throughout the world, this is a major commercial species that is marketed fresh, frozen, smoked, and salted. The liver is often processed for oil, the fins used for soup, the hides for leather, and the jaws and teeth for ornaments.

This is an important sport fish that is targeted by a select group of anglers. Charles Holder (1913), reminiscing about

IT'S AN OWY

On several occasions shortfin makos have been found with billfish spears imbedded in their bodies. A fish off South Africa had a bill of a sailfish in its eye and one off Baja California had a piece of blue marlin bill in its vertebral column.

FLIPPING OFF FLIPPER

Matt Goldsworthy observed a mako shark attacking dolphins off Noyo Harbor (Northern California): "The mako grabbed the side of a dolphin in midair… there were 50 or more dolphin jumping around, obviously for their lives, and it was hard to tell just what was going on in all the madness. The mako got airborne five times…[a dolphin] hit the water with its tail completely sheared off; it quickly bled to death" (*Sport Fishing* Magazine, October 2007).

fishing for makos off Santa Catalina Island, wrote: "I have played these fish of from four to ten feet, and a more determined fighter it would be difficult to find. When the game is about four feet long and goes into the air repeatedly and drops, to rush away, make the reel sing and scream, one is convinced that there is some balm in the shark Gilead." *Okay, Chuck, I give up. Just what the hell are you talking about?*

MISCELLANY: 1) The temperatures of muscles, eye/brain, and viscera are elevated. 2) A mako shark was responsible for a near-fatal attack on a person in the Red Sea. Clearly, this is the reason my ancestors parted it and walked across. 3) Shortfins are believed to be the fastest swimming of the sharks (on a short course). How fast? I don't know. 4) Two individuals of the circumglobal species, *Isurus paucus*, the longfin mako, have been taken off Southern California.

ORIGINS: An *Isurus sp.* is apparently known from the later Paleocene (at least 56 million years ago). An early mako shark from the West Coast is *Isurus hastalis* from Miocene deposits (at least 5.3 million years old) of Southern California. Remains of a shortfin mako are known from the Pliocene (at least 1.8 million years ago) of San Diego.

Lamna ditropis
Hubbs & Follett, 1947
Salmon Shark

A pelagic species with a romantic migration pattern.

ETYMOLOGY AND COLLOQUIAL NAMES: *Lamna* comes from the Greek and refers to a human-eating mythical monster and *ditropis* is also Greek and means "two" and "keel." They are called "nezumizame" in Japanese and are referred to as "mackerel sharks" and "herring sharks" in some Russian literature.

THE BASICS: Maximum Length: 3.1 m (10 ft) TL. Maximum Weight: At least 220 kg (484 lb). The Ranges: Korea and Japan to the Okhotsk and Bering seas (northward to Bering Strait) and the Gulf of Alaska to central Baja California. They are common from the Sea of Japan to the south Kuril Islands and from at least the Bering Sea to (during pupping season) somewhere off northern Baja California. Surface to 792 m (2,598 ft). Von Bertalanffy parameters (PCL, cm): (females) $L_\infty = 207$, $k = 0.17$, $t_0 = -2.3$; (males) $L_\infty = 183$, $k = 0.23$, $t_0 = -1.9$ (Goldman and Musick 2006). Length-weight parameters (PCL, cm, kg): (females) $W = 0.000082L^{2.759}$; (males) $W = 0.0000032L^{3.383}$ (Goldman and Musick 2006).

EVERGREEN FILMS INC.

SALIENT CHARACTERS: This is a pretty stubby shark, short and sort of stout. Their color ranges from dark bluish gray to black on backs and white bellies with dark blotches. Other characters include a large first dorsal fin, small second dorsal and anal fins, the first dorsal fin base almost directly above the pectoral fin base, and a homocercal (lobe of equal size) caudal fin. There is a strong keel along the caudal peduncle, and secondary keels are present along the lower caudal fin base.

LIFE HISTORY: Salmon sharks make very interesting migrations that, for the species as a whole, span a large chunk of the North Pacific. For starters, fish in the western North Pacific tend to be mature males and those in the eastern North Pacific mature females. In the summer or fall, males and females get together in the Gulf of Alaska to mate. Presumably, the males then return west where they spend the next year bragging to any dogfish that will listen. Meanwhile the females forage in such places as Prince William Sound, Shelikov Strait, and the Gulf of Alaska until some time between July–March (but mostly in the winter) when many, but apparently not all, migrate southward, way southward, as far southward as central Baja California and Hawai'i. Along the way, and this may be from southeast Alaska to Baja California, females give birth during late spring and early summer. After a number of months, these females move northward back to a summer in the subarctic. Because juveniles are not found well to the north, it looks like they slowly make their way northward, as only mature fish have been captured in the Gulf of Alaska, Prince William Sound, and the Bering Sea. Salmon shark pups are pelagic and are found both in nearshore waters and well offshore. Apparently during much of their lives, salmon sharks segregate by size and sex. This species has a temperature tolerance, for at least brief periods, of 2–24°C (36–75°F).

Salmon sharks live between 20 and 30 years. Females grow larger than males. In the eastern Pacific, males mature at 159–182 cm (5–6 ft) TL (3–5 years) and females at 199–222 (7 ft) (6–9 years). Females gestate 4–5 young for 9 months, and give birth in late spring and early summer. Salmon sharks are opportunistic predators, feeding on whatever is abundant and available. Commonly consumed prey include various salmon, northern anchovy, Pacific sauries, sablefish, capelins, spiny dogfish, arrowtooth flounder, rockfishes, and squids.

FISHERY: In Alaska, salmon sharks are caught as bycatch in other fisheries, so you only occasionally see them on the menu. I had "local salmon shark Moroccan style" in a restaurant in Halibut Cove (Alaska) and it was pretty good. What a Moroccan would have made of it is unclear. Japanese longliners catch them in good numbers and many are consumed in northern Japan. I have read that salmon shark heart is prepared as sashimi in some restaurants in Japan.

ORIGINS: The oldest fossil *Lamna* appears to be from the Early Paleocene (at least 62 million years ago). A number of *Lamna* species are known from the later Oligocene (at least 23 million years ago), and fossils from *L. ditropis* have been taken from 100,000-year-old deposits in Southern California.

MISCELLANY: The muscle, viscera, and eye/brain areas are warmer (to 21.2°C higher) than the surrounding seawater.

ORDER CARCHARHINIFORMES

FAMILY SCYLIORHINIDAE—Cat Sharks

Cat sharks are a fairly species-rich group of temperate to tropical marine fishes that are found throughout the world. There are 16 genera and around 115 species. Within our range swim five described and at least one deep-water undescribed species. Cat shark fossils (in the form of *Palaeoscyllium formosum*) are found as far back as the Middle Jurassic (perhaps 170 million years ago) of the United Kingdom. Most cat sharks lay eggs, although a few species produce live young. During deep-water submersible dives in Central California, we often see thousands of cat shark eggs covering lost fishing lines.

Cephaloscyllium ventriosum

(Garman, 1880)

Swell Shark

ETYMOLOGY AND COLLOQUIAL NAMES: *Cephaloscyllium* is derived from the Greek word for "head" and *Scyllium* (a now discarded name given to a genus of sharks) and *ventriosum* is Latin for "swell" (in the enlarging sense, not the slang term perhaps used by John Wayne to describe his best girl in *The Fighting Seabees*). California fishermen often call them "puffers" and folks further southwards off Baja California say "gata."

JOHN DUDDY

THE BASICS: Maximum Length: 110 cm (43 in) TL. The Ranges: Monterey Bay to Acapulco (Mexico), including Gulf of California; Chile. Swell sharks are fairly common as far north as about Morro Bay (Central California). 5–457 m (15–1,500 ft), mostly shallower than maybe 23 m (75 ft).

SALIENT CHARACTERS: Fat and squat, with flattened heads, swell sharks are brown above with dark saddles and round blackish dots. The underside is yellowish or whitish.

LIFE HISTORY: Swell sharks are small, slow-moving, benthic animals that live among nearshore reefs and algae. You usually see them by themselves, but occasionally they hang together in small groups. These are nocturnal animals. During the day they are simply inert in caves and rock crevices, while at night they bestir themselves and swim about, sometimes a few meters above the reefs.

Ain't nobody knows how old they get. Males mature at 82–85 cm (32–34 in) TL. Females are oviparous, produce purse-shaped eggs (with curling tendrils extending from corners), and these are laid among rocks and seaweeds. Females produce as many as 4 eggs at a time and the young hatch in 7.5–10 months depending on temperature. Females store sperm, apparently for a very, very long time. Shane Anderson, here at UCSB, had a female isolated in an aquarium and, after 5 years, she was still producing fertilized eggs. When do they lay the eggs? Dunno. Eigenmann (1892) reported that the eggs were extruded from December–February. Females in aquaria may lay them throughout the year. The young hatch at 12.5–15 cm (5–6 in) TL. Swell

CHRIS GROSSMAN

sharks feed at night on fishes, crustaceans, and gastropods. Tricas (1982) reports on this species' "Gulp Behavior" (where the "Shark rapidly raises its head, depresses its lower jaw, and sucks the fish into its oral cavity.") and the "Yawn Behavior" ("The closer a black-smith comes to the head of the shark, the wider the shark opens its mouth. If the prey moves away from the snout, the mouth begins to close. In the 'yawn' behavior, blacksmiths are captured when they inadvertently swim, or fortuitously drift in the shallow surge, into the fully expanded oral cavity of the shark, which is then snapped shut.") California sea lions eat swell sharks and northern elephant seals eat both the fish and their eggs. Neat little holes drilled into many swell shark eggs make it likely that certain snails eat the egg contents.

FISHERY: The remains of swell sharks are very occasionally found in Native American middens. Swell sharks are reputedly not good to eat, but I can't seem to find any scientific evidence for this. There is almost no commercial fishery for them, although in some years a few pounds are landed. Small amounts are also landed in Baja California and Gulf of California commercial fisheries, although they do not appear to be salable. They are taken in crab and lobster traps with some regularity and, historically, thrifty lobster fishermen would then use them as bait. Pier and boat fishermen occasionally take them.

ORGINS: A *Cephaloscyllium* sp. has been reported from a Miocene deposit (at least 5.3 million years old) in Southern California.

MISCELLANY: 1) True to their name, swell sharks are capable of inhaling water or air into their stomachs, thus causing them to swell up like placoid scale-covered balloons. 2) Shane Anderson, referred to above, has also seen swell sharks stranded on the mudflats of Morro Bay during receding tides. 3) The results of one study demonstrated that the tendrils of eggs laid by Santa Catalina Island and Isla Guadalupe fish are shorter than those from the Southern California mainland.

OTHER SPECIES

Apristurus brunneus
Gilbert, 1892)

Brown Cat Shark

Brown cat sharks grow to 71 cm (28 in) TL and live from Icy Point (58°N) (southeastern Alaska) to northern Baja California and from Panama to Chile. They are common in Southern California. These fish are found both on the bottom and in the water column (these latter are mostly juveniles and subadults) in 33–1,306 m (108–4,285 ft). Flammang et al. (2008), looking at animals from southern

PHIL EDGELL

California to Washington, found that a few females mature at 48.5 cm (19 in) TL, 50% at 50.1 cm (20 in), and all were mature at 58.1 cm (23 in). Southern California females mature at 42.5–47.5 cm (17–19 in) (Cross 1988). Flammang et al. also found that a few males were mature at 48.8 cm (19 in), 50% at 51.4 cm (20 in), and all at 54.7 cm (22 in). Females matured at a smaller size in lower latitudes (i.e., off Southern California) than off high latitudes (i.e., off Oregon) and the smallest mature males are found to the south. Females likely release young throughout the year and carry between 1–16 mature eggs. After they are laid, eggs may take as many as 27 months to hatch and the young are 7–9 cm (3–4 in) TL at birth. Brown cat sharks feed on large numbers of crustaceans (primarily shrimps and pelagic red crabs), fishes, and squids, along with isopods, mysid shrimps, and euphausiids. Length-weight parameters (TL, cm, gr): (females) W = 0.0000003.7L$^{3.341}$; (males) W = 0.0000024L$^{3.027}$ (Flammang et al. 2008).

Parmaturus xaniurus
(Gilbert, 1892)
Filetail Cat Shark

Filetails grow to at least 61 cm (24 in) TL; they have also been reported to 71 cm (28 in). Filetails are found from Cape Foulweather (44°07'N) (Oregon) to Baja California and in the Gulf of California, at depths of 88–1,250 m (290–4,100 ft). They are common in Southern California. Juveniles and subadults are found in the midwater and on the bottom, adults tend to be found on the bottom. A few females mature at as small as 36.9 cm (15 in) TL, 50% are mature at 50.1 cm (20 in), and all are mature at 54.3 cm (21 in). Lengths for males are 40.9 cm (16 in), 44.4 cm (18 in), and 47.8 cm (19 in), respectively. Females carry between 1–11 mature eggs and these are released from about July–September. Various crustaceans (e.g., pelagic red crabs, sergestid, and pasiphaed shrimps), fishes, squids, and mollusks are important in their diets. Length-weight parameters (TL, cm, gr): (males) $W = 0.000045L^{2.6}$; (females) $W = 0.000011L^{2.845}$ (Flammang et al. 2008).

FAMILY TRIAKIDAE—Hound Sharks

Found throughout the world, triakids are mostly smallish, mostly marine, and mostly shallow-water. Nine genera and at least 38 species make up the family; five species are found within our range. Triakids, such as *Paratriakis bettrechiensis*, go back to the Late Cretaceous (71 million years or more). For almost all of your eastern Pacific hound shark identification needs, try the keys and illustrations in Fischer et al. (1995).

Galeorhinus galeus
(Linnaeus, 1758)
Soupfin Shark or (if you have to) Tope

An underappreciated species that is found throughout the water column in a number of habitats.

ETYMOLOGY AND COLLOQUIAL NAMES: The derivation of *Galeorhinus* seems a bit obscure to me. Jordan and Evermann (1896) wrote that the word comes from two Greek words meaning "a kind of shark, like a weasel" and "shark." *Galeus* also comes from the Greek word for "weasel," so the combined name sort of means "weasel weasel," showing either a profound lack of imagination or a perfectly sublime amount of same. The American Fisheries Society official name for this species is "tope," a name that doubtless has a long and rich history in the British Isles, but which, frankly, I don't like. Here in the New World, specifically the West Coast of the New World, we have always called it the "soupfin shark," and by golly, that's our Gaia-given right. On a more cheerful note, in Great Britain other names include "penny-dog" and, in Wales, "ciglas" (meaning "blue dog"). "Oil shark" is an old name from 19th-century California and the folks along the Baja California coast say "tiburón sulfin."

THE BASICS: Maximum Length: About 2 m (6.5 ft) TL. Maximum Weight: In the eastern Pacific, about 45.5 kg (100 lb) for females and about 28.2 kg (62 lb) for males. The Ranges: Just about circumglobal in temperate waters. Northern British Columbia to the Gulf of California and from Ecuador to Chile in the eastern Pacific. Surf zone (you can sometimes see them with their dorsal fins out of the water) to 471 m (1,545 ft). Von Bertalanffy parameters (TL, mm): (sexes combined) $L_\infty = 1,829$, $k = 0.124$, $t_0 = -1.29$ (Moulton et al. 1992). Length-weight parameters (TL, cm, lb): (females) $W = 0.00000003236L^{4.1561}$; (males) $W = 0.000003879L^{3.1856}$ (Ripley 1946).

SALIENT CHARACTERS: Soupies are kind of elongated, kind of thick fish, with long, pointed snouts, and (listen up now) a wide lobe-let that occupies the top one-half of the upper lobe of

WALTER HEIM

BE THE FIRST ON YOUR BLOCK TO GET IN ON THE BOOMING SHAGREEN INDUSTRY

"During the war in Europe an inquiry was received at the Fisheries Experimental Station in Vancouver regarding the possibility of using shark skins as non-slip facing material for gloves and boots in the navy. Owing to their characteristic rough 'grain', the skins of certain sharks are well known in commercial use as abrasives ('shagreen') and this property suggested the above applications for contending with greasy or icy surfaces. The skinning of the fresh carcasses presented some difficulty, however. When using a knife to separate the skin from the connective tissue between the skin and the flesh, it was hard to avoid either cutting the skin, or including too much of the firmly adhering underlying tissue. An accidental observation was made some time later by Mr. E. P. Sidaway of the Research Engineering staff of the Station, when he had occasion to examine some soupfin shark carcasses that had been stored in the station's refrigerator rooms. No attempt had been made to prevent drying out of these carcasses and it was noticed that due to the desiccation that had taken place, the skin could now be quite readily stripped from the still frozen carcass" (Anon 1945).

the caudal fin. They are bluish or gray on backs and sides and white below. Young fish have a white edge to the pectoral fins, as well as black-tipped dorsal and caudal fins.

LIFE HISTORY: In Australia (and, one expects, other areas), juveniles aggregate in shallow-water nurseries and move into deeper coastal waters during winter, after which they return to the nursery grounds. Off the West Coast, adults are schooling fish that come into shallow waters in the warmer months. Jordan and Gilbert (1880), for instance, noted that huge schools appeared off Southern California in the spring. At that time, they believed that this species was more common in Southern California than all other species of sharks combined. When in shallow waters, soupies are found throughout the water column, over sand, low rocks, and along kelp beds. They can be quite abundant in such protected waters as San Francisco and San Diego bays and also along the open coast. Back in 1951, Herald and Ripley wrote that the "soupfin population in Northern California is composed mostly of males, in southern California mostly of females and in Central California of an approximate 50/50 ratio." As you might expect, this is a highly mobile species. Herald and Ripley reported one shark had moved "about 95 miles [153 km] southward in the short time of four days." Another fish moved about 1,770 km (1,100 mi) in 3.5 months, from Point Mugu (Southern California) to Hecate Strait (British Columbia). Females come in to shallow waters to give birth. Soupfins can form single-sex schools. Off Australia, soupies rise up into the midwaters at night (except around the full moon) and live near the bottom during the day. My commercial fishermen associates have seen the same thing off Southern California. Commercial gillnetters catch soupies 32 km (20 mi) and more off the Oregon-Washington Coast in near-surface waters and the same phenomenon occurs in the early summer in Bahia Sebastian de Vizcaino (central Baja California). Genetic studies imply that there are 6 distinct populations, located off western North America, eastern South America, southern Africa, southern Australia, New Zealand, and in the eastern Atlantic Ocean.

Soupfins live to at least 40 years old and perhaps to as much as 60 years. Females grow larger than males and males mature when smaller than females. A few males are mature at 140 cm (56 in) TL, most at 155 cm (62 in), and all at 170 cm (68 in). For females, these lengths are 155 cm (62 in), 160 cm (64 in), and 190 cm (76 in), respectively. Males mature at 8–9 years and females at perhaps around 12 years. Females are aplacental viviparous (embryos live off their yolks). In the eastern Pacific, females produce between 6–52 young per season and release their young (at 30–36 cm, 12–14 in, TL) from about March–July. Ovulation occurs in early summer and the gestation period is about one year. Soupfin sharks mostly feed on fishes, as well as squids, octopuses, and such planktonic forms as by-the-wind-sailors. White sharks and California sea lions eat them.

FISHERY: The remains of soupfins are commonly found in Native American middens. When David Starr Jordan surveyed the fisheries of the Long Beach (Southern California) area in 1880 (Jordan 1887), he found, of course, no Long Beach there. Instead, he saw a nearly endless strand of coastal wetlands, sand bars, and lagoons. And he noted that what little fishing there was focused on the "oil shark" [soupfin] that entered lagoons to reproduce. Even at the time, soupfins were recognized as a rich source of both oil and, by the Chinese, as a basis for soups. Until 1937, soupfins remained a minor species, caught mostly along the California coast and sold mostly to Asians for soups. It was about at that time that the F. E. Booth Company discovered high levels of vitamin A in the livers of soupfins and the fishery really took off. The soupfin fishery, which started in California, expanded into Oregon and Washington in 1940 and 1941, with the largest catches in 1942 and 1943.

Mick Kronman (unpublished) quotes one Santa Barbara fisherman as saying: "'Profits were amazing. In a very short time we went from harvesting sharks for their meat at $40 per ton to just cutting out their livers for $10–$14 per pound.' During a good trip in 1942, he notes, he filled 50 five-gallon cans of liver; each can weighed 40 pounds. That's 2,000 pounds at $10 per pound, more than enough to buy a house at the time."

This fisherman also commented on how the local boom fishery started, with one fish buyer who was ahead of the curve. "When he got wind that there was a lot of vitamin A in shark liver…he went to every little town on the coast and said he'd buy all the soupfin shark you could catch. 'I'll give you $40 per ton,' he said. In those days, that was very good money, and soupfin was considered sort of a pesky fish—there was a lot of it around. So my family went to work fishing soupfin. We bought a little truck that could carry five tons of shark and we'd catch it and deliver it to Monterey. We did that for almost a year, and then a light went on in someone's head. We asked, 'What's this guy doing with all this soupfin?' So a fisherman we knew drove a load of soupfin to Monterey and unloaded it at a cannery right there on the water. As soon as he unloaded his catch, he drove down the street, parked the truck, went back and peeked in the window. And there they were, slitting the sharks open, taking the livers, putting them in a can and throwing the shark through a trap-door back into the ocean. Well, the cat was out of the bag. Myers was a very congenial guy. After we found out, he said, 'I kept it to myself for a long time and made a ton of money. Now you guys can make a ton of money.' We took advantage of it and made a ton of money." After World War II, with the synthesis of vitamin A (combined with overfishing) catches plummeted and during the 1950s few were landed. Today, there is a small commercial fishery for them for the fresh fish trade and artisanal fishermen catch them in considerable numbers at least as far south as Bahia de Sebastian Vizcaino.

Soupies are caught from boats and piers by recreational anglers.

ORIGINS AND RELATIONSHIPS: Sharks of the genus *Galeorhinus* go back at least as far as the Late Cretaceous (at least 71 million years ago) from Europe and North America. Remains of soupfins have been found in late Pliocene deposits (at least 1.8 million years old) in California. Genetic analyses imply that they are perhaps most closely related to the Indo-West Pacific blacktip tope, *Hypogaleus hyugaensis*.

MISCELLANY: Brad Mongeau reports that he saw a group of juvenile jack mackerel rubbing themselves on a soupfin swimming in the nearshore waters of San Clemente Island.

REMARKS: Perhaps due to a ban on inshore gill nets in the early 21st century, soupies' numbers in Southern California seemed to have rebounded.

Mustelus

Smoothhounds are placental viviparous (the mother providing some nutrition to the embryos). The genus *Mustelus* (as *M. biddlei*) goes back to the Middle Paleocene (more than 55 million years ago) of Belgium. A *Mustelus* sp. has been found from Miocene deposits (5.3-plus million years ago) in Southern California.

Mustelus californicus

Gill, 1864

Gray Smoothhound

ETYMOLOGY AND COLLOQUIAL NAME: *Mustelus* comes from the Latin word meaning a "weasel" or "martin" and *californicus* for California, the site of its first capture by someone who wanted to describe it in a stultifying way. "Cristalino" and "cazón o tripa" are names from Mexico.

THE BASICS: Maximum Length: 1.3 m (49 in) TL, reported to 1.6 m (64 in). The Ranges: Cape Mendocino (Northern California) to Mazatlán (Mexico), including Gulf of California. They are fairly common at least as far north as Elkhorn Slough (Central California). Surf zone to 95 m (312 ft), but apparently mostly in maybe 12 m (40 ft) or less. Von Bertalanffy parameters (TL, mm): (sexes combined) $L_\infty = 1,544$, $k = 0.168$, $t_0 = -1.271$ (Yudin and Cailliet 1990). Length parameters (TL mm, kg): (sexes combined) $W = 0.000000021L^{2.88}$ (RecFin 2009).

SALIENT CHARACTERS: Like other smoothhounds, grays are elongated and relatively slim, with a first dorsal fin slightly behind the pectoral fin and a smooth margin to the posterior edge of that fin (it is frayed in brown smoothies). They are usually gray, but can be brown on back and side, and lighter below.

LIFE HISTORY: Gray smoothhounds are schooling and mostly nearshore fishes. They live

Exhibiting all of the sang froid of a cavalryman of the 4th Irish Dragoon Guards during the Charge of the Light Brigade, a gray smoothhound studiously ignores an encroaching crab.

in coastal bays and lagoons and on the open coast, over sand, mud, and in eelgrass (and you can sometimes see them schooling with leopard sharks). Several researchers have reported them to be more abundant in such backwaters as Anaheim Bay and Bolsa Chica (Southern California) in spring and summer. In these protected waters, fish seem to prefer temperatures of about 18°C (64°F) and higher and females will seek out the warmest temperatures available. Ebert (2003) reported that they were primarily a winter visitor to Central California. Grays appear to be most active at night.

Females live to at least 9 years old and males to at least 6 years old. Females grow larger than males. Along the California coast, males mature at 57–65 cm (22–26 in) TL (1–2 years old) and females at about 70 cm (28 in) and 2–3 years. In the Gulf of California, 50% of males are mature at 72.8 cm (29 in) TL and 50% of females at 86.2 cm (34 in). Females give birth from at least January–May, although Eigenmann (1891) believed the parturition season extended from September–February. Females produce anywhere from 3–16 young per season and the young are 20–30 cm (8–12 in) TL at birth. The gestation time is 10 months to one year. Gray smoothhounds are primarily bottom feeders, targeting invertebrates (mostly decapods, such as shrimps and crabs, as well as clams), as well as polychaetes, snails, octopuses, fat innkeepers, and fishes. Larger fish may eat more clams, while crab eating may decrease at the same time. Harbor porpoises eat them.

FISHERY: Native Americans appear to have captured this species with some regularity. The U.S. commercial catch has always been pretty small, although it is an important artisanal and commercial species along the Baja California coast and in the Gulf of California. Gray smoothhounds are commonly taken by surf and pier fishermen.

RELATIONSHIPS: Based on genetic analyses, this species is most closely related to a number of *Mustelus* species, including the brown smoothhound.

MISCELLANY: At least one albino fish has been captured.

Mustelus henlei
(Gill, 1863)
Brown Smoothhound

ETYMOLOGY AND COLLOQUIAL NAME: *Mustelus* comes from the Latin word meaning a "weasel" or "martin" and *henlei* refers to the brilliant German scientist Friedrich Gustav Jakob Henle (1809–1885). "Cazón o tripa" is used in Mexico.

THE BASICS: Maximum Length: 100 cm (39 in) TL. The Ranges: Northern Washington to the Gulf of California and along Ecuador and Peru. They are reasonably abundant at least as far north as Humboldt Bay (Northern California). Surf zone to 281 m (922 ft).

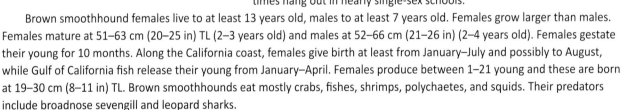

Von Bertalanffy parameters (TL, mm): (sexes combined) L_∞ = 977 mm, k = 0.224, t_0 = -1.296 (Yudin and Cailliet 1990). Length-weight parameters (TL, cm, kg): (sexes combined) W = $0.00000002089L^{2.88}$ (RecFin 2009).

SALIENT CHARACTERS: They have that basic sleek smoothhound look, have a frayed margin to the posterior edge of the first dorsal fin, and are brown on back and side.

LIFE HISTORY: Brown smoothhounds are schooling fish found both in bays and on the open coast. The young are released in shallow waters. Adults move inshore during the spring, often into very shallow waters, and then go deeper in the fall. As an example, researchers working in Tomales Bay (Northern California) found that these fish migrated in during the spring, when water temperatures were about 10°C (50°F), and left in the fall, when temperatures fell below 10°C. Similar movements (by adults) into and out of San Francisco Bay have been observed. When in inshore waters, these fish have a tendency to move into the shallows as the tide moves in and then retreat as the tide falls. Their along-shore movements appear to be limited, although one fish motivated 29 km (96 mi) from where it was tagged. Brownies live not only near the bottom, but also well up in the water column, sometimes over deep water. My associate, Mary Nishimoto, captured three fish (30–63 cm, 12–25 in, TL) about 30 m (98 ft) down, over hundreds of meters of water. Brownies are tolerant of fairly cold waters (down to at least 10°C, 50°F, and perhaps lower) and brackish waters (about 20 ppt). Like a number of other shark species, browns sometimes hang out in nearly single-sex schools.

Brown smoothhound females live to at least 13 years old, males to at least 7 years old. Females grow larger than males. Females mature at 51–63 cm (20–25 in) TL (2–3 years old) and males at 52–66 cm (21–26 in) (2–4 years old). Females gestate their young for 10 months. Along the California coast, females give birth at least from January–July and possibly to August, while Gulf of California fish release their young from January–April. Females produce between 1–21 young and these are born at 19–30 cm (8–11 in) TL. Brown smoothhounds eat mostly crabs, fishes, shrimps, polychaetes, and squids. Their predators include broadnose sevengill and leopard sharks.

FISHERY: Commercial fishermen in California, Baja California, and Gulf of California waters take browns in considerable numbers. Recreational anglers commonly take them from shore, piers, and in nearshore vessels.

RELATIONSHIPS: Based on genetic analyses, this species is most closely related to a range of *Mustelus* species, including the gray smoothhound.

MISCELLANY: A rudimentary hermaphroditic individual has been reported.

Triakis semifasciata

Girard, 1855

Leopard Shark

ETYMOLOGY AND COLLOQUIAL NAMES: *Triakis* comes from the Greek words meaning "three" and "point" (apparently referring to the 3-pointed teeth) and *semifasciata* is Latin for "halfbanded," referring to the distinctive saddles. They are called "tintorera pinta" and "leopardo" in some areas of Mexico.

THE BASICS: Maximum Length: 2.1 m (7 ft) TL. Maximum Weight: Officially, the heaviest fish weighed 18.5 kg (40.6 lb), although years ago a California Fish and Game biologist estimated

PETER BRYANT

that one measuring 202.1 cm (7 ft) weighed about 31.7 kg (70 lb). These large fish were almost certainly females. The largest male on record weighed 11.8 kg (26 lb) and was 134 cm (53 in) TL. The Ranges: Samish Bay (Washington) to Mazatlán

(Mexico), including the Gulf of California. Leopards are common to at least as far north as Humboldt Bay (Northern California). Surf zone to 156 m (515 ft). Von Bertalanffy parameters (TL, mm): (sexes combined) L_∞ = 1,536, k = 0.082, t_0 = -2.31 (Kusher et al. 1992). Length-weight parameters (TL, cm, kg): (sexes combined) W = $0.00000002089L^{2.88}$ (RecFin 2009).

SALIENT CHARACTERS: An elongated species with an abbreviated snout. These fish have a series of saddles on the back and large spots on the side; bigger ones develop a secondary series of large spots and blotches between these saddles. An occasional, anomalous, fish has numerous small spots and marks along the side.

LIFE HISTORY: Leopard sharks are mostly nearshore fish that occupy a wide range of habitats. Young are often birthed over mudflats or other shallow waters (from spring–fall) and aggregations of young fish are found in shallow, calm waters, often over sand, mud, or around eelgrass. Larger fish live over sand, mud, mixed sand and rocks, or in kelp beds. Here they may form large schools that can include gray smoothhounds, other benthic sharks, and bat rays. At various times, but particularly at night, leopard sharks will venture well into the water column, sometimes right to the surface, and sometimes into the kelp canopy. And speaking of matters nocturnal, it appears that leopard sharks are more active at night and will often range away from their circumscribed day-time haunts (as much as 10 km, 6 mi), only to return with the dawn.

These fish have a range of seasonal movements. Many leopard sharks enter semi-enclosed waters (e.g., Tomales Bay and Elkhorn Slough) in the spring and leave in the fall. Here they feed in the intertidal on high tides and retreat to somewhat deeper waters as tides fall. Water temperatures rising to 10–12°C (50–54°F) trigger their entrance into these waters and temperature dropping to these levels herald their departure. At least some of these fish return the following year and some individuals remain in these embayments throughout the year. Leopards leaving Elkhorn Slough tend to remain in nearby Monterey Bay. On the other hand, there are several locations along the shallow and more open coast, such as off La Jolla (Southern California), where aggregations remain throughout the year. Still another behavior is that of females occupying selected, very warm, very shallow, waters in the summer. This occurs, for instance, in a small cove at the Isthmus at Santa Catalina Island, where females (apparently not feeding) remain for months in a small, and mostly enclosed, area. It has been noted that the skins of these females become darker in the late afternoon. Although the more extended movements of leopard sharks are unclear, there are some tantalizing bits of evidence. For instance, several fish tagged at Santa Catalina Island moved to the Southern California mainland. One swam a total of 105 km (65 mi), stayed for 3 days, and then returned to Catalina. Leopard sharks often form single-sex schools. They are able to withstand water temperatures at least as cold as 7°C (45°F) and salinities as low as 15 ppt. Genetic studies found some evidence that there is limited gene dispersal in California waters and that some fish, for instance those in Humboldt Bay, may form isolated populations.

Ah, the advantages of a good ocean view. In August 2003, while standing on the second-floor walkway of the cliff-side National Marine Fisheries Service laboratory in La Jolla, Sue Smith (2005) was able to watch leopard sharks mate; her report was the first to document this behavior. She observed a group of nine adult fish milling about, in a more or less circular fashion, just off the beach in waters 1–3 m (3–10 ft) deep. The mating process seemed to have three stages. Initially, some fish would periodically turn over on their sides and flash their white bellies. At some point, two fish in the center of the group began to swim in parallel and then one fish (the male) "quickly moved forward and parallel...and wrapped its body around" the second fish (the female). "The two sharks then rolled together entwined, a slight forward momentum still carrying them slowly in the direction they had originally been swimming, then both appeared to rest on the bottom." The entwining lasted for not more than 15 seconds. In general, mating occurs shortly after females release their young.

Leopard sharks live to at least 26 years old (and probably more) and the sexes appear to grow at the same rates. Females grow larger than males. At least a few females are mature at about 104 cm (41 in) TL and 10 years old. A few males are mature at 100 cm (39 in) and 7 years old or perhaps even as small as 70 cm (28 in). Females are aplacental viviparous with the embryos providing their own nutrition from the yolks. Females

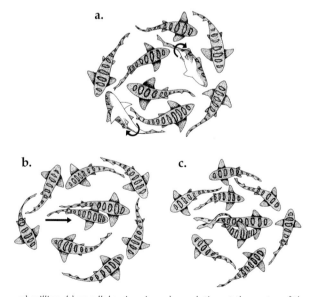

a) milling; b) parallel swimming; c) copulation at the center of the group (Smith 2005).

produce between at least 1–37 young per year and release these pups (at about 20 cm, 7 in, TL) from April–September. One study found that about 6% of the females examined had one barren ovisac (egg-containing capsule). Leopard sharks feed near the bottom. Smaller ones feed heavily on crabs and larger sharks eat mostly fishes, fish eggs (i.e., jacksmelt), fat innkeepers, cancer and other crabs, ghost shrimps, clams (mostly siphons), polychaetes, squids, octopuses, eelgrass, and algae. Predators include broadnose sevengill sharks. Hight and Lowe (2007) note that a male California sea lion killed 12 adult leopard sharks by chasing them up onto a beach at Santa Catalina Island.

FISHERY: Native Americans commonly ate leopard sharks. Commercial fishermen in California land substantial numbers and this is also an important commercial species in the Gulf of California. Recreational anglers like to catch them. And while it is particularly sought after in such spots as San Francisco and Humboldt bays, it has a small, but exuberant, following along much of the California coast.

ORIGINS AND RELATIONSHIPS: The genus *Triakis* goes back at least as far as the Paleocene (at least 55.8 million years ago) of Trinidad. *Triakis beali* is known from the Miocene (at least 5.3 million years ago) of Southern California. Remains of *T. semifasciata* have been found in Late Pliocene deposits (at least 1.8 million years old) in California. A genetic study found that leopard sharks may be most closely related to *Triakis scyllium* of the western Pacific.

MISCELLANY: 1) An albino one was taken in San Pablo Bay. 2) "On February 10, 1955, while exploring the bottom of Trinidad Bay in Humboldt Bay, California, a professional diver, John Adams, was repeatedly attacked by a fish identified as a 3-foot leopard shark. Adams was equipped with an Aqua-Lung and was moving slowly along the bottom when he was struck squarely on the left side of the head by the fish. Just after the first strike Adams noticed that his nose had been bleeding. Some of the blood was draining into his mouth from whence it was being exhaled through the exhaust tube of the "lung." These blood-tainted bubbles from the exhaust were apparently detected by the shark, since it was next observed making a pass at the rising stream of bubbles, snapping at them as it turned belly up. A few seconds later a strike, made directly at Adams' face, was warded off and the fish disappeared" (DeWitt 1955).

REMARKS: Dan Pondella and Larry Allen (2008) discerned an increase in numbers of leopard sharks in Southern California and attributed at least part of this to a ban on inshore gill nets.

OTHER SPECIES

Mustelus lunulatus
Jordan & Gilbert, 1882
Sicklefin Smoothhound

Sicklefins grow to 175 cm (69 in) TL. This is mostly a tropical species, found from San Diego to Talara (Peru) including the Gulf of California, and it lives over sandy seafloors from inshore to 94 m (308 ft). In the Gulf of California, a few females are mature at 100 cm (39 in) TL, 50% are mature at 103 cm (41 in), and all are mature at about 108 cm (43 in). Values for males are 89 cm (35 in), 91.5 cm (36 in), and about 95 cm (37 in), respectively. Sicklefins reproduce

annually, with a gestation time of about 11 months, and a brood size of 6–19 young per year. Females give birth from February–May and the young are 28–34 cm (11–13 in) TL at birth. Sicklefins eat mostly benthic crustaceans (like crabs and various shrimps), small fishes, snails, and the occasional squid, and are eaten by California sea lions. They are an important commercial species in the Gulf of California. Von Bertalanffy parameters (FL, mm): (females) L_∞ = 470, k = 0.235, t_0 = 1.23; (males) L_∞ = 455, k = 0.253, t_0 = 1.28 (Navia et al. 2006). Length-weight parameters (TL, cm, gr): (sexes combined) W = $0.005L^{2.92}$ (Navia et al. 2006).

FAMILY CARCHARHINIDAE—Requiem Sharks

The carcharhinids are an interesting group of mostly larger sharks, typical of tropical or warmer temperate waters. While many species are strictly marine, a number of them, notably the bull shark (*Carcharhinus leucas*), spend much of their time frolicking in freshwater. There are 12 genera, more than 50 species, and 16 live within our range (with at least six species entering Southern California waters). Fossils of "Carcharhinids" characterized as *Abdounia africania*, have been found from Paleocene deposits (at least 56 million years ago) of North Africa. Worldwide, the genus *Carcharhinus* lived at least as far back as the Middle Eocene (45 million years ago) and in what is now California several species occurred during the Miocene (at least 5.3 million years ago and probably earlier). To figure out your requiem shark, Ebert (2003) covers a lot of species and Fischer et al. (1995) has keys and illustrations to all of the eastern Pacific species.

Mating sharks. Just no family values.

Galeocerdo cuvier

(Péron & Lesueur, 1822)

Tiger Shark

A dentigerous fish with a penchant for dumpster diving and human flesh.

©MASA USHIODA-COOLWATERPHOTO

ETYMOLOGY AND COLLOQUAL NAMES: *Galeocerdo* comes from Greek words meaning "a kind of shark" and "fox" or "weasel" and *cuvier* refers to Baron Cuvier (1769–1832), a brilliant paleontologist, zoologist, government official, and one smooth operator, perhaps the smoothest in 18th- and early 19th- century France. "Tontorera chata" and similar names are used in Mexico and the Japanese name is "itachizame."

THE BASICS: Maximum Length: 5.5 m (18 ft) TL and possibly to 7.4 m (24 ft) TL. Maximum Weight: 810 kg (1,785 lb). The Ranges: Worldwide in tropical waters. In the eastern Pacific, Southern California to Peru, including the Gulf of California. There is an unverified sighting in Prince William Sound (northern Gulf of Alaska). During warm-water years, tigers occasionally enter Southern California waters. Surface and intertidal to at least 350 m (1,148 ft), and perhaps to 800 m (2,625 ft). Kneebone et al. (2008) present a table summarizing growth rate parameters from a number of studies. They found that, for western North Atlantic fish, a two-parameter von Bertalanffy growth function worked best and here it is (FL, cm): females: L_∞ = 347, k = 0.124; males: L_∞ = 330, k = 0.131, both with L_0 set at 62 cm. De Crosta et al. (1984) provide von Berts compiled from a couple dozen fish from Hawai'i. Length-weight parameters (FL, cm, kg): (sexes combined) W = $0.000002528L^{3.2603}$ (Kohler et al. 1995).

SALIENT CHARACTERS: Tigers are massive, thick-bodied fish. Dave Ebert (2003) notes the "broad head...very short, blunt snout...large broad mouth, long upper labial furrows, and spiracles." The name "tiger" comes from a series of black bars that are very visible in young individuals and then tend to fade or even disappear with age.

LIFE HISTORY: Tiger sharks are mostly tropical and mostly continental shelf and slope fish. Although you can often find them in very shallow nearshore waters, tigers also range well out to sea. A study in Australian waters found that tigers were more likely to occupy the edges of a seagrass bed than haunt its interior and that females frequented that habitat more than males. Acoustic tagging studies in Hawai'i have yielded equivocal data on movements. One showed that there was a tendency to move into very shallow waters at night and retreat somewhat during the day, while another showed the opposite. Another study in the same waters demonstrated that many individuals were very wide-ranging (particularly the juveniles). These individuals unpredictably swam between islands, stayed at each site for just a few minutes, and there might be years before a return to any given site. Some individuals are capable of substantial movements, as fish tagged off the East Coast of the U.S. were recaptured off Africa. At least some individuals make repetitive vertical movements ("yo-yo" diving). In one study, a fish entered waters as cold as 14.6°C (58°F). Three young juveniles (estimated to be 3–4 months old) were taken off Manhattan Beach (Southern California) demonstrating that females, at least on occasion, might give birth in Southern California waters.

Males live to at least 20 years and females to at least 22, although it would surprise no one if they reached about 30 years old. Females grow a bit slower and larger. Size at maturity probably varies with location. Off Hawai'i, males mature at about 292 cm (10 ft) TL and females at 330–345 cm (11–12 ft). Size at maturity in other studies range between 226–310 cm (8–10 ft) for males and 250–330 cm (8–11 ft) for females. Age at maturity appears to be

ALIMENTARY, MY DEAR WATSON

"The word dramatic naturally brings to mind the famous murder case in Sydney, Australia, in 1939, in which the tattooed arm of the victim, regurgitated by a tiger shark that had recently been placed in the Coogee Aquarium, provided the evidence that the man was murdered. Dr. V. M. Coppleson, an expert on shark attacks, examined the arm and was certain that it had been severed from the body of the victim by a sharp knife" (Randall 1992).

about 7–10 years old for both sexes. Females give birth every 3 years. Off Hawai'i, tigers mate in January and February, the sperm is stored until ovulation in June and July, and then the young are born in September and October of the following year (a gestation time of about 16 months). Females are not impregnated until about the following June and about 16 months after that they give birth again. Long believed to be strictly aplacental viviparous, with embryos living only off their yolks, Hamlett et al. (2005) speculate that mother tiger sharks may produce nutrients for embryos. Females give birth to between 3–82 pups, but the lower figure is believed to be artificially low, the result of females spontaneously releasing young upon capture. Pups are between 51–90 cm (20–35 in) TL at birth.

Goodness, but tiger sharks do eat essentially everything in the sea. No really, I am only slightly embroidering the truth here; it is almost impossible to overstate what these fish eat. Calling them opportunistic feeders is like defining Elvis as a "popular music singer from Mississippi with a penchant for grilled peanut butter and banana sandwiches." Bony fishes, sharks, rays, squids, seals, lobsters, crabs, medusae, dugongs, whale carcasses, and all points between are consumed. Tiger sharks are among the few organisms (along with fish hawks) that prey on sea snakes. The larger ones may also have a real penchant for eating sea turtles, sometimes shell and all. Witzell (1987) noted: "Japanese tuna longline fishermen in the Solomon Islands reportedly take the time to open incidentally captured [tiger] sharks to look for valuable hawksbill turtle shells." A study in Hawaiian waters found that smaller tiger sharks might feed primarily near the bottom at night, while large ones feed at the bottom at night and at the surface during the day. Lastly here is a quotable quote from Chris Lowe and Company's 1996 paper on tiger shark feeding habits off Hawai'i. Referring to human-derived stomach contents, they reported: "Small sharks had only kitchen scraps (chicken, ham bones, bologna sandwich, steak, Spam, and lemon and grapefruit rinds) in the stomachs (11%), whereas, medium (20%) and large size sharks (21%) contained kitchen scraps, along with other food related refuse such as tin foil, tin cans, plastic bags, cellophane, and cardboard in their stomachs."

ONE SMOOTH OPERATOR

Born in what is now eastern France, Cuvier was christened Jean-Leopold-Nicholas-Frédéric. As if this impediment to normal discourse was not enough, his parents, in a transparent attempt to curry favor, added the name Dagobert, after his godfather who was a local petty noble. Ironically, despite this abundance of christened names to choose from, Cuvier's family called him Georges, his dead brother's name. I don't think we have to hover about that twisted turn of events. Over a remarkably public professional life, which spanned the French Republic, Napoleon, and the return of the monarchy, Cuvier was able to navigate treacherous political waters without losing either face or, more importantly, his head. He did this through an incomparable combination of truly great talent, the almost unfailing ability to garner patrons of the left and the right, and a staggeringly strong and focused temperament. As one biographer wrote: "He was a man too passionate, too energetic, too productive and too conflict-ridden ever to have existed near the mean of life" (Outram 1984).

FISHERY: Tiger sharks are taken in the commercial and artisanal fisheries in the Gulf of California and in various other parts of the world. The flesh is sold fresh, frozen, salted, smoked, and dried and the fins are used (as in just about every shark species) for soup.

ORIGINS: The genus *Galeocerdo* apparently evolved during the Early Eocene, perhaps 53 million years ago. At least one species lived in the Miocene (at least 5.3 million years ago) in what is now Southern California. Modern tiger sharks perhaps lived as far back as the Pliocene (at least 1.8 million years ago).

MISCELLANY: An occasional albino tiger shark turns up.

REMARKS: Tiger sharks occasionally eat a person. There are, in fact, more confirmed attacks on people by this species than by any other, except for the great white.

Prionace glauca
(Linnaeus, 1758)
Blue Shark

WALTER HEIM

ETYMOLOGY AND COLLOQUIAL NAMES: *Prionace* comes from two Greek words, meaning "saw" and "point" and *glauca* means "bluish-green" or "grayish-blue" in Greek. They are called "blue whalers" in Russia, "azul" or "tiburón azul" in the Gulf of California, and "yoshikiri zame" off Japan.

THE BASICS: Maximum Length: 383 cm (13 ft) TL, and possibly to 4.8–6.5 m (16–21 ft). Maximum Weight: At least 240 kg (528 lb). The Ranges: Circumglobal in temperate and tropical waters. In the western Pacific, as far north as the southern Kuril Islands and thence from Kodiak Island to Chile, including the Gulf of California. Also found south of the Aleutian Islands as far north as 50°N. During some years, they are abundant as far north as the southern Kuril Islands and southeastern Alaska. In the North Pacific, they are present in greatest abundance between 20°N and 50°N, with strong fluctuations in seasonal abundance related to population shifts northward in summer and southward in winter. Surface to about 812 m (2,663 ft) and abundant from the surface to depths of more than 200 m (656 ft). Von Bertalanffy parameters (TL, mm): (females) L_∞ = 2,419, k = 0.251, t_0 = -0.795; (males) L_∞ = 2,953, k = 0.0175, t_0 = -1.113 (Cailliet and Bedford 1983, California). Nakano and Stevens (2008) present a number of other growth equations for fish from around the world. Length-weight parameters (TL, mm, kg): (sexes combined) W = $0.000000000826L^{2.88}$ (RecFin 2009).

SALIENT CHARACTERS: This is a distinctive shark with a slender body, long snout, and long pectoral fins. It is indigo-blue on back, metallic-blue on sides, and white beneath.

LIFE HISTORY: When you see a shark fin at the ocean surface along the west coast of North America, much of the time it is attached to a blue shark. In Southern California, for instance, you can often find these fish from the outer edge of kelp beds out to more than 322 km (200 mi) off the coast. Way back in 1892, Eigenmann reported that three 9-footers were taken in San Diego Bay, so at least in the past fairly large ones entered backwaters. Females release young as far north as Southern California and juveniles may make seasonal migrations to off the Columbia River and out more than 322 km (200 mi). In some years, juveniles can be locally extremely abundant. As an example, back in the early 1970s, while returning to Santa Barbara from Point Conception, I saw a small one every 200 m (656 ft) for perhaps 32 km (20 mi) just outside the kelp line.

 All life stages of this highly migratory fish are found off the west coast of North America, particularly off Southern California and Baja California. Mature females are believed to enter Southern California waters first, often in the early spring, followed by older juveniles, and then mature males (these last tend to hang offshore). As waters warm, these fish continue to move northward and often reach Alaska before heading south with the fall. Reportedly, more females travel into the far north than do males. Fish tagged in Soutvhern California have been recaptured as far southward as 1,287 km (800 mi) west of Nicaragua and westward to off Midway Island (central Pacific). Blues in other parts of the Pacific have moved up to 9,200 km (5,716 mi). Blue sharks have been found in waters between at least 4.4–29.8°C (40–86°F) and seem to favor waters somewhere between 10–20°C (50–68°F). Like a number of other pelagic sharks, this species tends to segregate by size and sex. Sciarrotta and Nelson (1977) acoustically tagged fish at Santa Catalina Island and got a sense of the species' daily movements: "From March to early June, the sharks made an evening-twilight migration from their epipelagic daytime habitat to the shallower waters bordering the island. From June to October, the sharks remained offshore throughout the day and night...The telemetry data indicated that the blue shark is basically nocturnal, showing highest activity in the early evening and lowest activity in the early daylight morning." Throughout the 24 hours, the sharks stayed mostly between 18–42 m (59–138 ft), they rarely descended to 100 m (328 ft). One study suggested that, in the North Pacific, blues mate in the early summer at 20–30°N and that females eventually move northwards and give birth at 35–45°N.

Blue sharks live to be at least 20 years old. In the North Pacific, both sexes tend to mature at around 200 cm (7 ft) TL (4–6 years for males, 5–7 years for females), although pregnant females as small as 183 cm (6 ft) have been captured. In a study in the Gulf of California, all males larger than 158 cm (62 in) TL were mature. These fish are placental viviparous; the embryos are connected to the female in utero. Mothers gestate the young for 9–12 months and give birth mostly in the late spring and summer, but that season may extend at some level to throughout the year. It is unclear if females breed every year. In the North Atlantic, 4-year-old females mate but nothing happens, while 5-year-olds mate, store the sperm, and when 6 years old they fertilize their eggs. Females may mate with more than one male (a brood may have more than one father) and broods can run between 1–135 young (with an average of about 35). The pups are 34–53 cm (13–21 in) TL at birth. Off our coast, blue sharks eat mostly fishes and squids, and also euphausiids, pelagic red crabs, shrimps, and pelagic octopuses. These fish appear to feed most heavily at night. Predators include white sharks, California sea lions, northern elephant seals, sperm whales, and orcas.

FISHERY: Blue shark remains are occasionally found in Native American middens but the species does not appear to have been widely consumed. Repeated attempts at finding markets for this species in California have been more-or-less failures, as there is the sense that blue sharks taste pretty bad, with meat that is often redolent of ammonia. Unfortunately, these fish are often taken as bycatch in swordfish and other pelagic California fisheries and almost always released, in numerous cases when in poor shape. Off Baja California, blue sharks are retained and sold fresh both locally and in other Mexican states. Most fish taken in the very large worldwide commercial fishery (with an estimated 6.2-6.5 million blues caught annually) are captured by pelagic longlines and gill nets, again often as bycatch in other fisheries. Nevertheless, this shark is a major component of the international shark fin trade. Norman and Fraser (1949) sum up a rather checkered past: "The flesh of these Sharks is white and firm, but is very tough and is said to have an unpleasant smell. It is canned for food in some countries, however, and is also employed as fertilizer. The natives of the Philippines and other parts of Asia eat it fresh, and at one time it was an article of diet among the poorer classes in Italy. The liver is rich in oil, and the skin provides a valuable economic product. With the dermal denticles untouched, the skin makes a good shagreen, from which are manufactured sword scabbards and coverings for sword grips, expensive Morocco bindings, coverings for jewel cases, and other articles; the crude skin is also converted into rasps for the use of cabinet-makers and metal polishers. With the denticles removed, and suitably tanned, the skin is converted into a durable leather, which is in some demand for shoes, bags, etc. In Ceylon, the Philippines and elsewhere there is a flourishing trade in the fins of these and other sharks and rays, which are exported in a dried state for making shark-fin soup. The delicate fin-rays are the essential parts for this purpose, as they dissolve into gelatine of pleasant flavor. The backbones of Blue Sharks are sometimes made up into walking-sticks by sailors."

Blue sharks are taken with some frequency by recreational anglers, particularly in Southern California, where many folks actually go out and target them.

ORIGINS: The genus *Prionace* seems to have evolved relatively recently. Modern blue sharks may have lived as far back as the Middle Pliocene (maybe 3 million years ago).

MISCELLANY: 1) Blue shark mating behavior is kind of sketchy. Males often bite the females during mating and, through selection, the skin on a female's back is noticeably thicker than that of males. Nevertheless, you can often see females with big bites taken out of them. And if that is not enough, Pratt and Carrier (2005) comment that: "The vagina of *Prionace glauca* is thick-walled to receive the sharp terminal edges of the clasper during mating...Abrasions, lesions and dark bruises from claspers are common on vaginal walls during and after mating season and are a good index of female sexual activity in *P. glauca* and other species." 2) If you spend enough time in offshore California waters you will eventually see a group of yellowtail or Pacific mackerel slamming into a blue shark. While this behavior remains something of a mystery, it is most likely that the fish are rubbing themselves along the shark's rough flanks, perhaps to remove parasites. 3) There is a report of a shark, likely a blue, leaping over a floating box about 97 km (60 mi) offshore of the Columbia River. The shark was scraping itself against the box in mid-leap. 4) Four two-headed blue sharks have been reported from the waters around Japan.

Carcharhinus leucas
(Müller & Henle, 1839)

Bull Shark

Bull sharks grow to 3.5 m (12 ft) TL long and at least 316.5 kg (698 lb). They are circumglobal in coastal warm waters and possibly reach as far north as Southern California. Along the eastern Pacific, this shark ranges from Isla Guadalupe (central Baja California) and southern Baja California to Paita (Peru), including the Gulf of California, in waters from one meter (3 ft) to 152 m (499 ft) deep. Bull sharks simply love freshwater and they are found in many subtropical and tropical rivers and lakes and, in the waters of the Caloosahatchee River (Florida) (and doesn't that name simply say "Buy an acre of land that is underwater") at least at 14.4–34.1°C (58–93°C). Females live to at least 28 years, males 23 years, and females grow larger than males. Estimates of size and age at maturity vary. Here is one (Cruz-Martinez et al. 2004) from the Gulf of Mexico: females mature at 204 cm (7 ft) TL and 10 years old and males at 190–200 cm (6–7 ft) and 9–10 years old.

ANDY MURCH

Females are placental viviparous, gestate the young for 10–12 months, and give birth to 1–22 pups. The young are 50–81 cm (20–32 in) TL at birth. In Lake Nicaragua, females may give birth throughout the year, in the Gulf of Mexico the season is April–August. For obscure reasons, only the right ovary is functional. They feed on all kinds of fishes, cephalopods, birds, turtles, and marine mammals. This is an fairly important commercial species in the Gulf of California and of considerable importance in other parts of the world. Worldwide, bull sharks are one of the most dangerous shark species, chomping-on-humans-wise.

Sharks of the genus *Carcharhinus* lived at least as far back as the Middle or Early Eocene (maybe 37 million years ago or more). Von Bertalanffy parameters (TL, cm): (males) L_∞ = 248.4, k = 0.1692, t_0 = -1.03; (females) L_∞ = 262.1, k = 0.1235, t_0 = -2.44 (Cruz-Martinez et al. 2004).

In 1937, a 38.2 kg (84 lb) bull shark was caught 2,800 km (1,739 mi) up the Mississippi River near Alton, Illinois. According to Thomerson et al. (1977), the lucky fisherman was "Dudge" Collins, who captured the unlucky fish back of the "trailer dike." Heh, heh. The temptation to do a whole *Deliverance* riff here is nigh on to overwhelming.

ON SHARK FIN SOUP

You remember the Battle of Verdun? Between 21 February and 18 December 1916, the German and French armies fought over a strategically worthless 10 square kilometers of land. Between the two sides there was a minimum of 700,000 casualties and after a while the fighting continued because, well, just because. Most of the fisheries for the cartilaginous fishes of the world are like Verdun; they are utterly doomed to failure. Today, they are perpetuated by people who know better, who know that the life histories of these fishes do not allow any but the most minimal take, but who continue in their suicidal ways because, well, just because.

So, people are catching too damn many sharks and much (although by no means all) of the world's bloated shark catch goes to feed the large demand in China for shark fin soup. As a part of Chinese medicine, sharks go back to at least the Tang Dynasty (618–907 CE) and shark fins as an expensive delicacy for the aristocracy harkens to the Ming Dynasty (1368–1644 CE). The part of the fin that is made into soup is the ceratotrichia. These are proteinaceous filaments that support the fins. Many soup eaters believe that the most preferred (long and thick) filaments come from large and powerful sharks. However, as part of a well-orchestrated cosmic and gastronomic jape, this is often not the case. In fact, it is often various rays and smaller sharks that have the right stuff.

JOE BIZZARRO'S BIG ADVENTURE

So, my friend Joe Bizzarro was conducting research on the food habits of fishes in Bahia Almejas, located on the Pacific side of southern Baja California. And, along with acquiring fishes from the local commercial fishermen, he was also scuba diving in the murky waters of the bay and taking bottom samples of the invertebrates that lived there. And each day, as he went out alone in his inflatable boat, his Mexican fishermen friends would wave goodbye to him from the shore. What a friendly thing to do, he thought. Near the end of the study, Joe was informed that his dive site was a major calving ground for large bull and hammerhead sharks. A bit shaken, he went to his fishermen friends and asked them if the story was true. Absolutely, they replied, why just 2 weeks ago we saw a bull shark attack and eat a coyote that was trying to swim across the lagoon. A person would have to be a fool to dive in these waters, they added, and that's the reason we were waving goodbye to you.

FAMILY SPHYRNIDAE— Hammerhead Sharks

The well-named hammerheads are a small group of mostly marine (but occasionally brackish water) fishes found throughout the world in warm temperate to tropical waters. There are two genera and eight species. Four species are known within our range and three occasionally occur off California, seemingly most often during warm-water intrusions. Females practice placental viviparity (there is a placental connection between embryo and mother) and do it well, thank you very much. Hammerheads are closely related to sharks in the family Carcharhinidae (perhaps most closely to *Rhizoprionodon*) and perhaps should be included in this family. It is believed that the split between the Sphyrnidae and Carcharhinidae occurred in the Early to Middle Eocene (perhaps around 40 million years ago). Fischer et al. (1995) has keys and illustrations of all of the eastern Pacific species. Not unlike certain mortgage brokers, larger hammerheads can be relatively dangerous animals.

Want to impress your friends? Sure you do; it's one of the few joys you have in a life otherwise devoid of meaning. Well, the next time the gang meets at Elaine's, just gavel for order and declaim: "Sphyrnids are unique in having bladelike lateral extensions of the prebranchial head at the level of the horizontal head rim" (quoted from Compagno, 1988). But what if Biff, Buffy, or (God forbid) Stinky are still sober enough to want to know *why* they have those bladelike extensions? Well, these might serve several functions. One possibility is that they help give lift to the head region, reducing the amount of energy needed to stay in the water column (and who can find fault with that?). Another theory is that the unique shape helps the shark as it twists, elevates, or depresses the head.

Sphyrna lewini
(Griffith & Smith, 1834)

Scalloped Hammerhead

Looking like a Senior Fellow at the Institute of Applied Anachronisms.

ETYMOLOGY AND COLLOQUIAL NAMES: *Sphyrna* is derived from the Greek word for "hammer" and *lewini* honors John William Lewin (1770–1819), an early illustrator and naturalist in Australia. In Mexico, among other names, they are called "cornuda barrosa" or "conuda común." Off Japan, their name is "aka-shumokuzame."

THE BASICS: Maximum Length: About 4.3 m (14 ft) TL. Maximum Weight: At least 160.1 kg (353 lb). The Ranges: Circumglobal, usually in tropical waters. In the eastern Pacific, Santa Barbara to Puerto Pizarro (Peru). Surface waters to at least 980 m (3,214 ft). One juvenile was caught in Southern California. Von Bertalanffy parameters (TL, cm): (females) L_∞ = 353.3, k = 0.156, t_0 = -0.633; (males) L_∞ = 336.4, k = 0.131, t_0 = -1.09 (Anislado-Tolentino and Robinson-Mendoza 2001). Length-weight

SEAPICS

parameters (TL, cm, kg): (females) $W = 0.00002L^{2.8}$; (males) $W = 0.0000105L^{2.87}$ (Anislado-Tolentino and Robinson-Mendoza 2001).

SALIENT CHARACTERS: Do we really have to go into any detail here? Okay, their heads look like hammers. Scalloped hammerheads are gray-brown and have three notches on the front of the head, rather than the two found in smooth hammerheads. Bonnetheads have rounded heads, with no large extensions.

LIFE HISTORY: Scalloped hammerheads are schooling, often coastal, mostly pelagic fish, commonly found in bays, estuaries, lagoons, and along the open coast. We see them in Southern California waters when waters warm, most often during El Niños. Young are birthed in quiet, shallow waters; the Bahia Magdalena complex (southern Baja California) is a good example. In Hawai'i, these young aggregate in turbid, shallow waters during the day and disperse at night to feed. This shark can form sexually segregated schools. In a series of papers, Klimley and other researchers (e.g., 1981, 1987, 1993) found that an aggregation living over a seamount offshore of La Paz (Gulf of California) exhibited several interesting behaviors. The fish grouped by day at the seamount, left at night (during which a fish also repeatedly migrated vertically), and returned the next day. The ability to home back to the original site seemed to depend on a shark's ability to detect maximum and minimum geomagnetic lines. And get this: a female tracked for 74 days in the Gulf of California made a series of rather intense vertical movements (from surface waters to at least 980 m, 3,214 ft), encompassing waters ranging from 4.8–27.8°C (41–82°F). This plunged her, for perhaps 30 minutes at a time, into waters containing essentially no oxygen. And who among us would be comfortable doing the same? Genetic studies demonstrate that there are some population differences between Indo-Pacific and Atlantic fish and, a moderate surprise here, there is likely a previously unrecognized and undescribed "cryptic" species in the Atlantic.

Scalloped hammerheads live to at least 35 years old. Off the Pacific coast of Mexico, females mature at 223 cm (7 ft) TL and 6 years old and males at 170 cm (6 ft) and 4 years old. Studies in other parts of the world yield about the same results, with males tending to mature at a smaller size than females. In the Bahia Magdalena complex, Joe Bizzarro (2005) found that females give birth from at least June–August; the season is somewhat longer in other parts of the world and may extend throughout the year in Hawai'i. Females gestate their young for 10 months, produce 13–31 young per season, and these are 35–45 cm (14–18 in) TL at birth. Scalloped hammerheads eat a very wide range of fishes, along with squids, octopuses, lobsters, shrimps, and crabs. Blacktip sharks (*Carcharhinus limbatus*) and orcas are known to be predators. Clarke (1971) found that adult males preyed on juveniles in a shallow Oahu bay.

FISHERY: Back in the 1940s, the livers of scalloped hammerheads caught in the Gulf of California were sent to the U.S. to be rendered for their vitamin A. The species remains important in the GOC where it is eaten fresh and salted and the fins are exported. Along with adult and juvenile fish, in the Gulf later-term embryos are also filleted and sold.

ORIGINS AND RELATIONSHIPS: This species is known from a Middle Pliocene deposit (perhaps 3 million years old) of Baja California. Based on a genetic analysis, Duncan et al. (2006) noted that the species had: "An origin in the Indo-West Pacific with Late Pleistocene radiations into the central Pacific (Hawai'i) and eastern Pacific (Central America) as well as recent interchange between oceans via southern Africa... oceanic dispersal by females is rare."

MISCELLANY: Phil Colla took a picture of one being cleaned by king angelfish, *Holacanthus passer*.

JOHN WILLIAM LEWIN

Born in England, Lewin arrived in Sydney, Australia, in 1800, apparently determined to make his mark as a teacher of art and a miniature and portrait painter. Given that the colony at the time was inhabited primarily by kidnappers, arsonists, and similar folk (likely forming a less-than-substantial market for miniaturists), it is not surprising that Lewin turned to other trades. Over the years, he developed into an excellent illustrator and pretty good naturalist, producing a number of books about the animals of the region. In 1810, he was appointed coroner of the colony, and one wonders if his talent for portraiture was utilized in this capacity.

OTHER SPECIES

Sphyrna tiburo
(Linnaeus, 1758)

Bonnethead

Bonnetheads reach about 1.5 m (46 in) TL and possibly 1.8 m (6 ft), and weights to at least 11.8 kg (26 lb). They range from San Diego to Paita (Peru), including the Gulf of California, and also live in the western Atlantic. This is a coastal, schooling, benthopelagic fish that will wander into the intertidal and has been taken to depths of 80 m (262 ft). Bonnetheads may school by sex and size. Males

ROSS ROBERTSON

live to about 6 years and females possibly to 12 years. Males mature at 68–80 cm (27–32 in) TL and about 2 years old and females at 80–90 cm (32–36 in) and also about 2 years old. Females can store sperm for up to 5 months and larger females will mate with more than one male. Females produce from 3–21 young and these are 24–30 cm (9–12 in) TL at birth. They are commonly taken off Mexico in commercial catches. Fossils of this species are known from Middle Pliocene deposits (perhaps 3 million years old) in Baja California. Bonnetheads are most closely related to the scoophead (*Sphyrna media*), smalleye hammerhead (*S. tudes*), and scalloped bonnethead (*S. corona*).

(MANY SHARK SPECIES AGGREGATE IN SINGLE-SEX SCHOOLS)

Two-Chambered Heart

Oh, we are out to sea,
Just me and the other guys,
But I remember the feel of your placoid scales,
When I'm cracking wise.

Two-chambered heart,
Two–chambered heart,
Both chambers miss you,
When we're far apart.

I long for your lipless jaws,
But you're across the ocean,
I'd bite in half an elephant seal,
To show you my devotion.

Two-chambered heart,
Two–chambered heart,
Both chambers miss you,
When we're far apart.

Mammals, they say,
Have heart chambers – four,
But they couldn't pine for you,
Any times more.

Two-chambered heart,
Two–chambered heart,
Both chambers miss you,
When we're far apart.

Sphyrna zygaena
(Linnaeus, 1758)
Smooth Hammerhead

Smooth hammerheads grow to 5 m (16 ft) TL and perhaps 400 kg (880 lb). They are found worldwide in warm waters and in the eastern Pacific from Central California to the Gulf of California and to Bahía de San Antonio (33°35'S) (Chile). Smoothies are pelagic and live both nearshore and well offshore. They inhabit surface waters and down to depths of 200 m (656 ft) and possibly deeper. Juveniles live in coastal lagoons. In the late 19th century, a number of smooth hammerheads were taken off Southern California, from as far out as Cortes Bank to inside San Diego Bay. All were caught in August and September. During the El Niño of 1957–58, at least 17 were taken in Southern California (to north of Santa Barbara). Smooth hammerheads mature at about 275–335 cm (9–11 ft) TL; females gestate young for 10–11 months, and produce 29–37 embryos. These are 50–60 cm (20–24 in) TL at birth. Smooth hammerheads off La Paz (Gulf of California) feed mostly on fishes and squids. This is an important commercial species along some of the Baja California coast (at least as far northward as Bahia de Sebastian Vizcaino) and in the Gulf of California, but watch out, there are reports of folks being poisoned from eating the livers. This species has been found in Miocene deposits (at least 5.3 million years old) in a number of places worldwide. Smooth hammerheads are most closely related to the great hammerhead, *Sphyrna mokarran*.

ORDER TORPEDINIFORMES

FAMILY TORPEDINIDAE—Torpedo Electric Rays

Electric rays are circumglobal, mostly benthic, marine fishes found in temperate and tropical waters, from very shallow waters down to depths of more than 1,000 m (3,280 ft). They come in two genera and about 22 species, only one of which lives within our range. The young provide all of their own nutrition from yolks. All electric rays are capable of delivering shocks through electric organs described as "kidney-shaped...located on each side of the flattened 'disk', which is formed by the greatly enlarged pectoral fins fused to the head" (Bray and Hixon 1978).

Folks have known about the electric rays' abilities for a long time, probably back to the first goober that tried to pick one up. In fact, the word "torpedo" comes from the Latin for "stiff" or "numb." Various Roman authors, including Oppian and Scribonius Largus, noted the numbness that the fish causes and Largus adds that headaches could be relieved by laying a fish on the noggin. And back in the Middle Ages, Lawrens Andrewe, in his *The Noble Lyfe & Nature of Man, Of Bestes, Serpentys, Fowles & Fisshes y be Moste Knowen,* wrote: "Torpido is a fisshe, but who-so handeleth hym shalbe lame & defe of lymmes that he shall fele no thyng."

Torpedo californica
Ayres, 1855
Pacific Electric Ray

The Starship Enterprise *with an attitude problem.*

ETYMOLOGY AND COLLOQUIAL NAMES: *Torpedo* comes from the Latin word for "stiff" or "numb" and *californica* refers to the site of its first capture in the San Francisco area. These fish are often referred to as "torpedo rays" or "Pacific torpedo rays."

THE BASICS: Maximum Length: More than 137 cm (5 ft) TL. Maximum Weight: 40.9 kg (90 lb). The Ranges: Japan; Wiah Point, Graham Island (northern British Columbia) to Bahia de Sebastian Vizcaino (central Baja California) and one record from the Gulf of California, typically from at least San Francisco Bay southward. Surf to 906 m (2,972 ft), but mostly in 60–200 m (197–656 ft). Von Bertalanffy parameters (TL, mm): (females) $L_\infty = 1,373$, $k = 0.0733$, $t_0 = -1.934$; (males) $L_\infty = 921$, $k = 0.1372$, $t_0 = -1.483$ (Neer and Cailliet 2001). Length-weight parameters (TL, mm, kg): (females) $W = 0.00002L^{3.0213}$; (males) $W = 0.00004L^{2.8753}$ (Neer and Cailliet 2001).

SALIENT CHARACTERS: These are unmistakable fish. First, they are flat and gray or bluish-gray, with black spots. Second, they are remarkably flabby. Third, if you touch the disk part of their bodies you are likely to get yourself nailed pretty good.

LIFE HISTORY: Pacific electric rays are kind of plastic-behaviored fish, which means that just when you think you can make some nice generalizations, it turns out you are incorrect. But, let's see what we can do. First, electric rays live mostly in sandy, muddy, and low-hard relief areas, except when they don't. For instance, I have seen a number of them over boulder fields and rock ridges in deep waters and my scuba-diving associates also see them over high relief, particularly at night. Second, electric rays tend to spend the daylight hours buried or semi-buried in the sand or mud, but not always. This is a pretty good generalization for shallow waters,

JIM LYLE

but in, say, 150 m (492 ft) we often see them roaming around during the day. However, I think it is fairly safe to say that this species tends to be more active at night. Third, electric rays more often than not stay within maybe 10 m (33 ft) of the bottom. This is kind of accurate, although my associate, Mary Nishimoto, caught a number of them in the water column at depths of 30–70 m (99–230 ft) over bottom depths of 300 m (984 ft). And get this, on one of our research cruises, Linda Snook observed one in midwaters 314 m (1,030 ft) below the surface over a bottom depth of 457 m (1,500 ft). Dave Ebert (2003) mentions an electric ray: "videotaped 17 km west of Point Pinos, Monterey County, swimming at a depth of 10 m over water 3,000 m deep." It is safe to say that these are usually solitary animals. However, lest we become too complacent about anything in this paragraph, Claudette Dorsey tells me that she once observed at least 27 fish, during daylight hours, in a relatively small area at Anacapa Island (Southern California). They were scattered throughout the water column and while some were purposely moving east, others were treading water.

Electric rays live to at least 16 years and probably longer. Females grow larger and slightly more slowly. They are aplacental viviparous (the embryos develop within the mother, but with no maternal nutrient contribution). A few males are mature at 61 cm (24 in) TL, median length at maturity is 64.5 cm (25 in, 6 years), and all are mature at about 85 cm (34 in). Values for females are 72.1 cm (28 in), 73.1 cm (29 in, 9 years), and about 76+ cm (30 in), respectively. Females may give birth throughout the year and a 100 cm (39 in) fish contained 17 young. Young ones, at as small as 13.9 cm (6 in) TL, have been caught. While there have been few food habit studies, they seem to prey only on fishes and primarily at night. Many electrics enter reefs at night, stun fishes, and then engulf them while doing a forward somersault. Well-grounded orcas eat them.

FISHERY: Historically, there was a small electric ray commercial fishery; these fish went to researchers of various sorts. Sport anglers occasionally take them, but no one is happy about it.

ORIGINS: Fish in the genus *Torpedo* have been around since at least the very Late Paleocene or very Early Eocene (about 55 million years ago) in what is now Belgium.

MISCELLANY: The Cooper's nutmeg, a small blood-sucking snail, makes a small cut through this ray's skin, inserts its proboscis, and sucks away. As many as seven snails have been seen on a single fish.

REMARKS: Able to deliver a stunning jolt of 45 volts or more, electric rays are rare among Pacific Coast fishes in being quite aggressive. Really, they will swim right at you and try to nail you a good one. And does it hurt? Yes. Enough to kill you? Probably not, but maybe enough to momentarily knock you out and have that regulator pop out of your mouth. Dick Bray, my associate who conducted a number of early experiments on these animals, described having a little one, the size of a dinner plate, land on his head.: "I knew something was about to happen, when I felt all of the fillings in my teeth begin to quiver."

ORDER RAJIFORMES

FAMILY RHINOBATIDAE— Guitarfish

Guitarfishes are mostly marine (a few species enter brackish or freshwater) and temperate to tropical fishes that mostly inhabit continental shelf depths. While there are four genera and more than 40 species, only four species live within our range, and only two of these swim as far north as Southern California. Guitarfishes are aplacental viviparous; the embryos develop within the mother, but there is no maternal nutrient contribution. Rhinobatid-like fishes (in the genera *Asterodermus*, *Belemnobatis*, and *Spathobatis*) are found in the Early and Middle Jurassic formations (maybe as old as 200 million years ago) of Europe.

Rhinobatos productus

Ayres, 1854

Shovelnose Guitarfish

Those benthic fish with eyes très triste.

ETYMOLOGY AND COLLOQUIAL NAMES: *Rhinobatos* comes from the Greek words for "shark" and "skate" and *productus* is Latin for "produced," from the meaning of extending something and referring to its pointy snout. These fish are sometimes called "banjos" or "banjo rays" and in Mexico they're called "guitarra" or "guitarra blanca."

SCOTT GIETLER

THE BASICS: Maximum Length: 1.6 m (62 in) TL. Maximum Weight: 9.8 kg (21.5 lb). The Ranges: San Francisco to southern Mexico, including the Gulf of California, typically at least to the Monterey Bay area. 1–91 m (3–298 ft), mostly down to about 12 m (40 ft) of water. Von Bertalanffy parameters (TL, cm): (females) L_∞ = 594, k = 0.016, t_0 = -3.8; (males) L_∞ = 142, k = 0.095, t_0 = -3.942 (Timmons and Bray 1997). Length-weight parameters (TL, mm, kg): (sexes combined) W = $0.000000005109L^{2.9678}$ (RecFin 2009).

SALIENT CHARACTERS: These fish are uniformly light brown or gray-brown above, white below, have a spade-shaped, flattened head, one row of spines down the back, and long, thin tail. Oh, and they also have the most soulful, woebegone eyes you have ever seen.

LIFE HISTORY: Shovelnoses are benthic fish that are usually found on soft seafloors (although you can find them near kelp beds) and often in quite shallow waters. Large aggregations can form on the open coast (down to depths of maybe 9.1 m, 30 ft), particularly during the summer. However, many fish enter embayments during summer months to give birth and mate. The best studied of these is in the Bahia Magdalena-Bahia Almejas complex (southern Baja California). Here females enter the bay in April and May, give birth in July and August, then mate with males who have entered the bay in June and July, and then (with the males) leave by September. Similar large aggregations in spring–fall have been noted in Mugu Lagoon (Southern California), although it is not clear if females give birth there. Apparently, guitarfishes are common in Anaheim Bay (Southern California) throughout year, although less so in the winter. Particularly during the day, guitarfishes often are buried in the sand, and they tend to be more active at night.

Shovelnoses live to at least 11 years old. Females grow larger than males. Off California, males mature at 90–100 cm (35–39 in) TL and females at as small as 99 cm (39 in). In southern Baja California, these fish may mature when somewhat smaller (i.e., males at around 80 cm, 32 in). Females appear to give birth between June–August, when they produce between 1–28 young. Juveniles are at least as small as 20–24 cm (8–9 in) TL at birth, although the Scripps Institution fish museum has a specimen that is 11.7 cm (5 in) TL long, so who knows? Shovelnoses feed heavily on shrimps, crabs, clams, and fishes, as well as gammarid amphipods, polychaetes, squids, fat innkeepers, and sand crabs. Large individuals tend to feed more on fishes. Guitarfish often feed in extremely shallow waters (as little as a few inches) and occasionally strand themselves on beaches. I have seen this on several occasions when fish chase spawning grunions. Predators include leopard sharks.

FISHERY: Shovelnoses were an important part of the seafood diet of Native Americans. They have never been a particularly important commercial fish in California waters (although small numbers are caught and sold each year). There is a considerable artisanal fishery for them along parts of the Pacific Coast of Baja California and in the Gulf of California. They are also a major bycatch in the trawl shrimp fishery of the GOC.

Shore, pier, and boat fishermen commonly take shovelnoses. In the past, people were not enthusiastic about catching them. However, while today only a few people actively seek them out, many dedicated pier and shore fishermen find them a welcome catch. And, although they sometimes act like a barrel of fuel oil when hooked, I have seen surf fishermen using light surfperch rigs occupied for a long time after a 10-pounder grabbed the hook.

ORIGINS AND RELATIONSHIPS: Guitarfishes have been around for a long time. Fossils of *Rhinobatos* are known from at least as far back as the Late Cretaceous (at least 71 million years ago) of (among other places) Europe and North America. A fossil *Rhinobatos* may have been found in Miocene deposits (at least 5.3 million years old) in Southern California. One study found that shovelnose guitarfish might be most closely related to the sawfishes, genus *Pristis*. It has been hypothesized that there are two species of "*Rhinobatos productus*," one living in the Gulf of California and one on the Pacific Coast, as there are differences in maximum size and size at first maturity among fishes living on the two sides of the peninsula.

MISCELLANY: Regarding an attack by a guitarfish on a diver off La Jolla (Southern California): "Mr. Fleming was collecting sand dollars, swimming to the bottom and returning to the surface for air. About 10 to 12 feet away from him were two guitarfish, a female followed by a male passing close to the bottom. The female made a deliberate turn and rose 10 to 16 feet, passed close to me, then dropped down to Mr. Fleming and went on. The same route was followed, close behind the female, by the male. Mr. Fleming was then working on the bottom with his feet 4 to 5 feet above, and the male deliberately bit him on the calf of the leg with its flat pavement teeth" (Limbaugh 1963). *Clasper envy, perhaps?*

Zapteryx exasperata
(Jordan & Gilbert, 1880)
Banded Guitarfish

A snazzy little guitarfish with racing stripes.

KEVIN LEE

ETYMOLOGY AND COLLOQUIAL NAMES: *Zapteryx* comes from the Greek for "intensive fins," alluding to the vertical fins that are larger than those of skates, and *exasperata* is Latin for "rough," from the prickly scales on this species' back. They are "guitarra rayada" or "guitarra prieta" in Mexico.

THE BASICS: Maximum Length: 125 cm (49 in) TL. Maximum Weight: A 94 cm (37 in) TL fish weighed 5.5 kg (13.8 lb). The Ranges: Jalama Beach (Central California) to the Gulf of California (commonly to about the San Diego area); reported as far south as Caleta La Cruz (Peru). However, Dave Ebert (2003) questions captures south of Mazatlán (Mexico). He notes a possible confusion with the more southerly *Zapteryx xystera*. Shallow waters, sometimes in tide pools, down to 200 m (656 ft), although most fish live in waters shallower than perhaps 9 m (30 ft).

SALIENT CHARACTERS: Shorter and heavier than shovelnose guitarfish, banded guitarfish are dark brown and banded with irregular dark bars. The underside is white or cream and spackled with black.

LIFE HISTORY: Pups are born in shallow waters at as small as 13 cm (5 in) TL. Adults live both in rocky areas and over soft seafloors. You often see them with their heads in crevices. As with shovelnose guitarfish, banded guitarfish enter the lagoons of Baja California to reproduce. In these waters, females and males enter in the spring, hang out until the females release their young, mate, and then everybody (well the adults, anyway) leaves. David Andrew reports that bandeds are nocturnal and in sandy areas tend to be well buried when inactive.

Females may grow larger than males. Males mature at between 55.5–69 cm (22–28 in) TL and females mature at about 77 cm (31 in). In Bahia Almejas (southern Baja California), females produce between 4–11 young (at 15–18 cm, 6–7 in, TL) from at least June–September. Banded guitarfish feed on such benthic invertebrates as mollusks and crustaceans.

FISHERY: There is no commercial fishery for this species in the U.S. Mexican artisanal commercial fishermen working the outer coast of Baja California (for instance in Bahia de Sebastian Vizcaino) land substantial numbers. Sport fishermen very occasionally take them in Southern California.

FAMILY PLATYRHYNIDAE—Thornbacks

The thornbacks, with only two genera and three species, are a small group of skate-like fishes found in the marine waters of the Pacific Ocean north of the Equator. One species is known from our range. A thornback, *Tethybatis selachoides*, lived in the Late Cretaceous (at least 71 million years ago) in what is now southern Italy.

Platyrhinoidis triseriata
(Jordan & Gilbert, 1880)
Thornback

ETYMOLOGY AND COLLOQUIAL NAME: *Platyrhinoidis* comes from the Greek words for "broad" and "snout" and *triseriata* is Latin for "three" and "row," referring to the three rows of spines on the back. I note that pier fishermen in California often call them "skates." *They are not skates, so stop it.*

THE BASICS: Maximum Length: 91 cm (36 in) TL. Maximum Weight: A 73.8 cm (29 in) TL fish weighed 2.6 kg (5.8 lb). The Ranges: Tomales Bay (Northern California) to the Gulf of California (likely an isolated population); they have also been reported from Ecuador. They appear to be less abundant north of Monterey Bay, but are occasionally taken as far north as San Francisco Bay. Surf to 137 m (449 ft), commonly down to at least 28 m (70 ft). Length-weight parameters (TL, mm, gr): (sexes combined) $W = 0.000007L^{2.9774}$ (Miller et al. 2008a).

SALIENT CHARACTERS: Thornbacks are flattened fish, composed of a round, flat head and a long tail. They tend to be gray-brown on top and white underneath. The best character (naturally) is the three rows of hooked spines on the back and tail.

LIFE HISTORY: Thornback young are birthed (at as small as 8.3 cm, 3 in) TL over shallow sandy seafloors, often in backwaters and other relatively calm waters. All sizes are found buried in sand and mud, in eelgrass beds, and in kind of sparse algal beds. John Stephens (1983), reporting on his surveys in King Harbor (Southern California), noted that the species: "Must emigrate

as it is only seasonally present and when present is found in large numbers." Scott Gietler saw large numbers of adults (as many as maybe 50) swimming about and kind of draped on each other, in a very small area of Marina del Rey. On the other hand, David Andrew finds that they are much more abundant in the La Jolla area during the winter than in the summer. This species seems to be quite active at night, although you will also see them swimming during the day.

Females mature at about 48 cm (19 in) and males at 37 cm (15 in) TL. Thornbacks are aplacental viviparous with embryos developing within the mother (the females give birth to live young), but there is no maternal nutrient contribution to the embryos. Females give birth from at least June–August and produce 1–15

KAWIKA CHETRON

embryos per season. Thornbacks eat lots of mysid shrimps, gammarid amphipods and other crustaceans, along with fishes, polychaetes, sea pens, and squids. Northern elephant seals eat them.

FISHERY: Native Americans commonly ate thornbacks. There does not seem to be any commercial or artisanal fisheries for them along the U.S.-Baja California coast. Surf and pier recreational anglers routinely catch them.

MISCELLANY: I have noticed that some anglers consider the spines to be venomous. They are not.

FAMILY RAJIDAE—Skates

Skates are benthic, mostly marine fishes (there is one estuarine species), that live from the intertidal down to depths of more than 3,000 m (9,840 ft). Of potential interest, Stick and Hreha (1989) report that gill-netters working near surface waters off Oregon and Washington caught a few skates more than 37 km (20 mi) off the coast. So, at times these fish may ascend well into the water column. Their bodies are flattened, more-or-less rounded, with a pitiful little tail harboring 0–2 dorsal fins. Most species have thorns and thorn patterns are species-specific. Males have patches of thorns on their disc edges that are used to hold on to the females during mating. With 26 genera, Ebert and Compagno (2007) stated that (at that time) there were about 246 species that have been described and that there were maybe 50–100 species still out there waiting to be discovered. So get out there, kids. Twenty-three species live within our range. Skates are oviparous; the large and leathery eggs develop external to the mother. In the northeast Pacific, the eggs of a number of species are preyed upon by such egg-drilling snails as the Oregon triton (*Fusitriton oregonensis*). At least some species lay their eggs in discrete and relatively small nursery grounds. In these nursery areas, egg densities may be quite high. For instance, Alaska skate eggs may reach 800,000 per km^2. Skates go back at least to the Late Cretaceous (about 97 million years ago). There is a *Raja* sp. fossil from the Miocene (at least 5.3 million years ago) of Southern California in the University of California, Berkeley, Paleontological Museum. Predators on skates include Atka mackerel, Pacific cod, Pacific halibut, sablefish, soupfin sharks, walleye pollock, Steller sea lions, harbor seals, sperm whales, and orcas. Skate eggs are eaten by a number of species of snails. They drill through the shells and eat out the insides.

Native American and First Nation peoples commonly consumed skates. And the skate is one of the crests, that is lineages, of the Haida. Swan (1868), writing of the people of the Cape Flattery (Washington) region noted that: "Skates are abundant, but as they usually make their appearance during the halibut season, they are seldom used, although the Indians like them very well; but they seem to prefer halibut." Particularly before World War II, skate pectoral fins (the "wings") were always in some demand and at least a few trawlers up and down the coast (but particularly in San Francisco) would supply them to fresh fish markets. Here they were purchased mostly by Italian, Japanese, French, and Chinese folks. Less than scrupulous fish processors (almost a truism, that) would also sell little round cut outs of the wings as "scallops." In fact, skates were most popular during depressions and recessions, when people could not afford more expensive fishes. After World War II, skates became less popular because, as noted by Bureau of Marine Fisheries (1949): "The decrease in landings following 1938 was a result of a shift to the shark fishery [for vitamin A in the livers] by nearly all fishermen [who no longer caught skates as bycatch], coupled with the entry of the United States into World War II. At the start of the war unfriendly aliens were barred from fishing the offshore waters. This action removed many of the Italian crew members from the drag boats [trawlers caught most of the skates]. The forced migration of people of Japanese descent from the coastal areas into relocation centers also contributed to the decrease in the demand. The Japanese market did not revive after the war, probably due to resettlement of these people in other areas and states." In the 21st century, skate fisheries are making something of a comeback, with substantial numbers being caught from Alaska to California. At least in California, skates are sold largely in Asian markets, as fresh, frozen, dried, or salted product. Skates are yummilicious, even if you are not French. Recreational anglers fishing from partyboats, small vessels, and on piers occasionally take various species.

Skate species are notoriously difficult to tell apart. Grown ichthyologists have said bad words, indeed many bad words, trying to figure them out. Fortunately, there are some nice guides to help you make a decision. Try Fischer et al. (1995), Mecklenburg et al. (2002), Ebert (2003), and Stevenson et al. (2007), and see how those work for you. The egg cases of many species are described in Stevenson et al. (2007) and Ebert and Davis (2007). And while we are on the subject, whatever that subject was, I note that some folks divide the family Rajidae into Arhynchobatidae (the softnose skates) and Rajidae (the hardnose skates). I have no idea if this is kosher and will stand the test of time, or if it is yet another example of such Human Follies as codpieces, the flexus art movement, and private health care insurance.

Bathyraja parmifera
(Bean 1881)
Alaska Skate

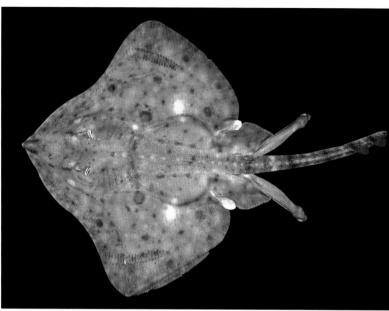

ETYMOLOGY AND COLLOQUIAL NAMES:
Raja comes from the Greek name for "skate" or "ray" and *parmifera* means "shield" and "I bear" in Latin. Some Russian researchers call them "threadnose skate" and the Japanese word is "kitatsunokasube."

THE BASICS: Maximum Length: 130 cm (51 in) TL. Maximum Weight: at least 18.8 kg (41.3 lb). The Ranges: Seas of Okhotsk and Japan to Chukchi Sea (one washed up on a beach near Point Hope), Aleutian Islands, and the eastern Gulf of Alaska to north of Vancouver Island (British Columbia). Common from the seas of Japan and Okhotsk to the central and eastern Bering Sea, to about Kodiak Island. They are the most abundant skate on the eastern Bering Sea shelf. 17–1,425 m (56–4,703 ft), typically at 50–200 m (164–656 ft). However, in the Sea of Japan these fish tend to be found in deeper waters, primarily in 300–500 m (984–1,640 ft). Gompertz parameters (TL, cm): (females) L_0 = 22.54, g = 0.19, G = 1.68, L_∞ = 120.51; (males) L_0 = 21.9, g = 0.23, G = 1.63, L_∞ = 111.26 (Matta and Gunderson 2007). Length-weight parameters (TL, cm, kg): (females) W = $0.000858L^{3.5}$; (males) W = $0.00194L^{3.28}$ (Orlov and Binohlan 2009).

SALIENT CHARACTERS: I tried, but I can't finesse this one. Apparently, there is no one character that neatly differentiates the Alaska skate from all other species. So, here in all its thorny glory is the dope: "The only Alaska species of *Bathyraja* with the following combination of characters: naked area surrounding the tail thorns; orbital thorns and scapular thorns present (orbital thorns may be reduced); dorsal surface dark brown or golden brown, often with lighter spots or blotches; total midline thorns typically 32 or less" (Stevenson et al. 2007).

LIFE HISTORY: Young Alaska skate hatch from eggs laid in specific nursery sites over soft seafloors in bottom depths of at least 145–316 m (476–1,036 ft). While the eggs are laid in relatively deep waters, young fishes move shallower to the inner and middle shelf, then migrate to the outer shelf and shallow slope as adults. During certain times of the year, the sexes may segregate by depth or geographic area. Alaska skate have been taken in waters as cold as 0.4°C (33°F) on up to at least 9.7°C (49°F).

Females live to at least 17 years, males to 15 years, and females grow larger than males. A few males mature at 85 cm (34 in) TL (about 8 years), 50% are mature at 92 cm (36 in), and all are mature at 100 cm (39 in) and 13 years. Values for females are 87 cm (34 in) (9 years), 93 cm (37 in) (10 years), and 102 cm (40 in) (14 years), respectively. In the eastern Bering Sea, Alaska skate spawn throughout the year with a peak in June and July. The embryos may spend as much as 3.5 years in the eggs before, with some relief, hatching out at as small as 20–21 cm (8 in) TL. Smaller Alaska skate feed mostly on polychaetes and crustaceans (e.g., gammarid amphipods, shrimps, and crabs). Larger individuals tend to target fishes, along with some squids and octopuses, and smaller amounts of polychaetes and brittle stars.

FISHERY: Currently, there appears to be relatively little in the way of a commercial fishery, although, knowing how these things work, as I write these words someone is trying to figure out how to create one.

RELATIONSHIPS: Alaska skates are kissing cousins of the newly-described leopard skate, *Bathyraja panthera*.

REMARKS: Turner (1886) notes that this skate is common along the Aleutian Islands. He says that they come toward shore in the evening, and are sometimes stranded as the tide goes out. "When a hard wind-storm is commencing these Rays may be seen sporting at the surface of the water like flashes of light or small white-caps just breaking; dozens at a time may be seen. There is no use made of their flesh. The Aleuts look with disgust upon these fish." He later states: "This [*B. parmifera*] and one of the large Sculpins...are the most disgusting inhabitants of that part of the sea...The mouth is capable of being projected 3 or more inches and is sufficient in power when projected to cause the hand to receive a smart blow." Turner goes on to state that Russian speakers of the time called them "morskoi chika" (sea gulls).

Raja binoculata

Girard, 1855

Big Skate

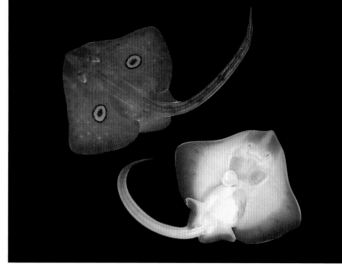

Newly hatched ones.   SHANE ANDERSON

ETYMOLOGY AND COLLOQUIAL NAME: *Raja* comes from the Greek name for "skate" or "ray" and *binoculata* is Latin for "two" and "eyed," referring to those lovely eyespots. Called "gangiei-rui" by the Japanese.

THE BASICS: Maximum Length: 244 cm (96 in) TL. Maximum Weight: to at least 91 kg (200 lb). The Ranges: Bering Sea and Aleutian Islands (at least as far west as Unalaska Island) to eastern Gulf of Alaska and Cabo Falsa (22°54'N, 110°02'W) (southern Baja California), and in the Gulf of California. They are common at least from the Gulf of Alaska southward. 2 m or less to 800 m (7–2,624 ft), typically in less than 100 m (328 ft). Von Bertalanffy parameters (TL, cm): (females) L_∞ = 248, k = 0.0796, t_0 = -1.075; (males) L_∞ = 153, k = 0.1524, t_0 = -0.632 (Gburski et al. 2007, Gulf of Alaska). McFarlane and King found that logistic growth curve parameters were most accurate (TL, mm): (females) L_a = 1,885, L_0 = 298, r = 0.2; (males) L_a = 1,630, L_0 = 336, r = 0.2 (McFarlane and King, 2006, British Columbia). Length-weight parameters (TL, mm, kg): (sexes combined) W = $0.00000002428L^{2.8549}$ (RecFin 2009).

SALIENT CHARACTERS: Bigs are pretty easy to identify. They have pointed snouts (although not as pointed as longnose skate), they have two prominent pectoral fin eyespots and, here is the clincher, they do not have a prominent notch on the rear edge of their pelvic fins (as do longnose skate). They come in a beguiling array of Bruegelian colors, including muddy brown, muddy gray, muddy olive, and the ever-popular muddy black, along with an assortment of little bright dots and dark mottlings.

LIFE HISTORY: Big skate usually associate with soft seafloors with or without nearby rocks. You can find them both in bays and off the coast. In San Francisco Bay, they can endure temperatures as warm as 19°C (66°F), and almost freshwater conditions (down to 2 ppt, although in the Bay they are rarely found in less than 20 ppt). Trawl surveys off Alaska find them in waters down to 2.5°C (37°F). Based on tagging studies off British Columbia most fish remain within 20 km (12 mi) of the tagging location. However, a few make very extensive migrations of up to at least 2,340 km (1,454 mi). For instance, one individual

went from Oregon to the eastern Bering Sea. In general, this species does not appear to make either extensive inshore-offshore or along-shore seasonal movements. It is likely that big skate spawn in discrete areas, probably over soft seafloors.

Big skate live to at least 30 years old. Females grow larger and faster than males. I find the studies on growth and maturity of this species (Zeiner and Wolf 1993; McFarlane and King 2006; Ebert et al. 2008) to be confusing, because they yield such different results. Apparently, fish mature at a larger size in the Gulf of Alaska and off Central California than off British Columbia. In the Gulf of Alaska, 50% of females are mature at 148.6 cm (59 in) TL and 50% of males 119.2 cm (47 in). By comparison, off British Columbia 50% of females were mature at 90 cm (35 in) and 50% of males at 72 cm

(28 in). Off Central California, males reportedly mature at 100–110 cm (39–43 in) and females at greater than 130 cm (51 in). Generally, a few fish are mature at as early as 4 years, 50% at perhaps 8–10 years, and all at about 12 years. Females produce as many as 7 embryos per egg case, but mostly 3–4. Big skate feed heavily on shrimps, crabs, and fishes. Other prey include clams, mysid shrimps, gammarid amphipods, cumaceans, isopods, and snails. Northern elephant seals are known to eat their egg cases, and broadnose sevengill sharks, brown rockfish, and Steller sea lions eat the fish.

FISHERY: There is a fairly large trawl and, sometimes, longline fishery for this species in various places along the coast, particularly off British Columbia and Alaska, but also off California. Recreational anglers catch them once in a while.

RELATIONSHIPS: Bigs are closely related to longnoses.

Raja rhina

Jordan & Gilbert, 1880

Longnose Skate

ETYMOLOGY AND COLLOQUIAL NAME: *Raja* comes from the Greek name for "skate" or "ray" and *rhina* is Greek for "snout" and "rasp." Called "gangiei-rui" in Japanese.

THE BASICS: Maximum Length: 189 cm (74 in) TL. The Ranges: Southeastern Bering Sea to about Punta San Juanico (25°59'N, 113°17'W) (southern Baja California), and Gulf of California. They are common from the Alaska Peninsula southward. 9–1,294 m (30–4,244 ft), and mostly in 50–200 m (164–656 ft). Von Bertalanffy

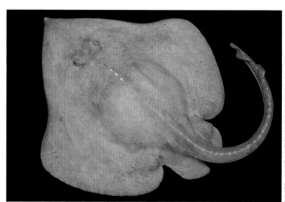

2009 CSUMB-MBNMS

parameters (TL, cm, females): L_∞ = 234, k = 0.0368, t_0 = -1.993; (males) L_∞ = 169, k = 0.0561, t_0 = -1.671 (Gburski et al. 2007, Gulf of Alaska). Von Bertalanffy parameters (TL, mm, females): L_∞ = 1,372, k = 0.06, t_0 = -1.8; (males) L_∞ = 1.315, k = 0.07, t_0 = -2.17 (McFarlane and King 2006, British Columbia). McFarlane and King found that logistic growth curve parameters were more accurate: (TL, mm, females) L_a = 1,094, L_o = 223, r = 0.21; (males) L_a = 1,075, L_o = 259, r = 0.2.

SALIENT CHARACTERS: Longnoses have, well, long, sharply pointed snouts and deeply notched pelvic fins. The dorsal surface is brown or gray and may have dark mottlings and blotches.

LIFE HISTORY: Longnose skate live over a wide range of habitats, but most characteristically inhabit mixed rock-soft sediment seafloors. I most often see them lying on sediment near rocks. Length at hatching is not known, but free-living fish as small as 12 cm (5 in) TL have been taken. They live in waters from at least 2 to perhaps 12.3°C (36–54°F). I observed a longnose skate nursery ground on a rock outcrop on the edge of Hueneme Submarine Canyon (Southern California) at a depth of about 130 m (426 ft). Here there were just lots of eggs strewn over large boulders.

Longnose skate live to at least 30 years old. Females grow larger than males. Similar to the situation with big skate, three studies (Zeiner and Wolf 1993; McFarlane and King 2006; Ebert et al. 2008) on size at maturation give quite different results. As with bigs, it appears that longnoses in the Gulf of Alaska mature when considerably larger than do those off British Columbia. However, maturation of BC fish seems to be at about the same length as for those off Central California. In the Gulf of Alaska, 50% of females are mature at 113 cm (45 in) TL and 50% of males at about 100 cm (39 in). Off British Columbia, 50% of females are mature at 83 cm (33 in) and 50% of males at 65 cm (26 in). In Central California, females appear to mature at around 70–100 cm (28–39 in) and males at about 62–74 cm (24–29 in). Summarizing across all studies, it appears a few fish are mature at as young as perhaps 5 years, many are mature by 14 years, and some do not mature until they are over 20 years old. Longnose skate eat a lot of fishes, crabs, shrimps and hermit crabs, along with some euphausiids, mantis shrimps, snails, squids, and octopuses. Smaller fish eat more crustaceans and larger ones consume more fishes and cephalopods. They are eaten by Steller sea lions, sperm whales, and, one assumes, other predators.

FISHERY: This is an important species in commercial fisheries in the Gulf of Alaska and off British Columbia and off lesser importance further south. Longnose are very occasionally taken by recreational anglers, mostly from boats, but also from piers.

RELATIONSHIPS: Longnoses are closely related to big skates.

OTHER SPECIES

Bathyraja abyssicola

(Gilbert, 1896)

Deepsea Skate

Deepsea skate reach 157 cm (62 in) TL. They are found off Japan, throughout much of the Bering Sea, along the Aleutian Islands south of Tanaga Island, and north of Unalaska Island (eastern Gulf of Alaska) to Islas Coronados (northern Baja California). A relatively deeper-dwelling form, they have been taken at 362–2,904 m (1,195–9,528 ft). Deepseas are closely related to Aleutian skates.

Bathyraja aleutica
(Gilbert, 1896)
Aleutian Skate

Aleutian skate reach 161 cm (64 in) TL, at least 23.1 kg (51 lb), and range from northern Japan to the Bering Sea, to Cape Mendocino (Northern California). They are abundant from at least the Kamchatka-Kuril Islands area to the Gulf of Alaska. Aleutians are found from 15–1,602 m (492–5,255 ft). Nursery grounds are soft seafloors at depths of at least 320–380 m (1,050–1,247 ft). After hatching, juveniles apparently first migrate into deeper waters (often to perhaps 800 m, 2,625 ft) and then move shallower (on to the shallow continental slope) as they mature. They have been taken in waters at least as cold as 1.6°C (35°F). Some Aleutians live at least 19 years. Smaller fish (less than 40 cm, 16 in, TL) eat fishes, cephalopods (both octopuses and squids), mysid shrimps, and isopods. As they grow, the importance of fishes increases. Minor prey includes anemones, amphipods, and crabs. The young hatch from eggs at about 25 cm (10 in) TL. Length-weight parameters (TL, mm, gr): (sexes combined) W = $0.0000004376L^{3.368}$ (Zenger 2004).

Bathyraja kincaidi

(Garman, 1908)

Sandpaper Skate

Sandpapers grow to a maximum length of 66 cm (26 in) TL and a weight of about 1.4 kg (3.1 lb). They are found from British Columbia to northern Baja California in 18–1,050 m (60–3,444 ft), most commonly from about 200–500 m (656–1,640 ft). They live to at least 18 years old. Males grow larger than females, but females appear to grow faster. A few females are mature at 45 cm (18 in, 4 years) TL, 50% at 46.7 cm (18 in, 7 years), and all at about 55 cm (22 in, 11 years). Values for males are about the same, 44.6 cm (18 in, 4 years), 49.2 cm (19 in, 7 years) and 56 cm (22 in, 11 years), respectively. Females spawn throughout the year, producing 2–22 eggs at a time, and young are about 11 cm (4 in) TL at birth. Sandpaper diets include crabs, euphausiids, fishes, hermit crabs, shrimps, octopuses, squids, polychaetes, and amphipods. Von Bertalanffy parameters (TL, mm): (sexes combined) L_∞ = 554.2, k = 0.213, t_0 = -2.112 (Perez 2005). Length-weight parameters (TL, mm, kg): (sexes combined) W = $0.000182L^{3.3896}$ (Perez 2005).

Bathyraja maculata

Ishiyama & Ishihara, 1977

Whiteblotched Skate

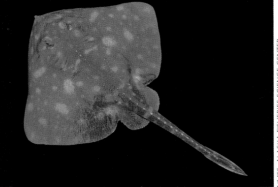

Whiteblotcheds grow to 147 cm (59 in) TL. They range from the seas of Okhotsk and Japan to the Bering Sea and Aleutian Islands and to Dixon Entrance, southeastern Alaska, at depths of 73–1,193 m (241–3,914 ft). They are common from the Sea of Okhotsk to the Aleutian Islands and Bering Sea, mostly in 100–800 m (328–2,624 ft). Whiteblotcheds live to at least 32 years old. Females likely grow larger than males. The median length at maturity for females is 95.5 cm (37 in) TL (23 years) and for males is 92.6 cm (37 in) (21 years).

Whiteblotcheds feed on a very wide variety of prey including many species of fishes, squids, crabs, gammarid amphipods, and shrimps. Of lesser importance are octopuses, hermit crabs, echiurioids, isopods, euphausiids, and larvaceans. Von Bertalanffy parameters (TL, cm): (sexes combined) L_∞ = 155.6, k = 0.036 (Ebert et al. 2009).

Bathyraja trachura
(Gilbert, 1892)
Roughtail Skate

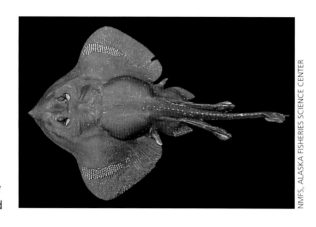

NMFS, ALASKA FISHERIES SCIENCE CENTER

Roughtails reach a maximum length of 106.4 cm (42 in) TL. They range from the Sea of Okhotsk to Cape Navarin (western Bering Sea) and the eastern Bering Sea and Gulf of Alaska to north of Isla Guadalupe (central Baja California). They are abundant from at least the Sea of Okhotsk to the deeper parts of the eastern Bering Sea and Gulf of Alaska. They live at 27–2,550 m (89–8,366 ft), typically in 600 m (1,968 ft) and more. Roughtails live to at least 20 years old and males and females grow at the same rates. Limited data imply that polychaetes are a very important part of their diets. They also eat fishes, squids, octopuses, pandalid shrimps, mysid shrimps, and isopods. Von Bertalanffy parameters (TL, cm): (sexes combined) L_∞ = 101.25, k = 0.09 (Davis et al. 2007).

Raja inornata
Jordan & Gilbert, 1881
California Skate

This species reaches a length of 75 cm (30 in) TL. It is found from the Strait of Juan de Fuca to southern Baja California and in the Gulf of California, at depths of 13–1,600 m (43–5,248 ft), mostly in 120 m (394 ft) or less. Major prey items include shrimps. fishes, and crabs. Length-weight parameters (TL, mm, kg): (sexes combined) W = $0.0000000243L^{2.85}$ (RecFin 2009).

TOTALLY UNRELATED RIFF #1—BECAUSE WE HAD SOME SPACE TO FILL

DID YOU KNOW?

That your cargo of fish is not necessarily lost if your vessel is commandeered by Welsh Separatists?

Yes, there you were heading down along the southeastern Alaska coast with 17 tons of nicely iced rockfishes in your hold. And wouldn't you know, just outside of Sitka, nine disaffected members of Plaid Cymru, frustrated with the slow pace of Welsh devolution, take over your vessel. And then, having thrown your fish out on deck, and iced down numerous 9-gallon casks of Plassey's Cwrw Tudno Ale, here they are drinking, chanting Llaeth i blentyn, cig i wr, cwrw i hen ("Milk for a child, meat for a man, beer for the old") and defying the Coast Guard, your lawyer, and a very junior representative from the British Embassy.

Okay, while all these attempts to end the standoff continue, just how long do you have before your rockfishes go bad? Well, if it is 9°C (48°F) out on deck, you have a total of 72 hours before you can kiss those fishes (assuming fish osculation is your bag) goodbye.

And a tip of the hat to O.M. Mel'nikov and E.F. Kleie, of the old Soviet Union Pacific Scientific Research Institute of Marine Fisheries and Oceanography, who way back in the early 1960s did that analysis for us (Kizevetter et al. 1965).

ORDER MYLIOBATIFORMES

And here come the stingrays.

All stingrays have spines located in the tail region. The stings are derived from placoid scales, are flat and pointed, and have edges that are lined with a series of backward-projecting barbs. Each sting is covered with skin and on its underside there are several grooves that contain venom-producing tissue. Altogether a thoroughly nasty business. When inserted into the hapless victim (or even into a victim with plenty of hap), the skin around the sting tends to break, releasing the tissue and its venom. Although ray stings are all located in the tail region, precise placement (ranging from near the base to well up the tail) varies with family. It's important to know that stingrays do not attack their victims; swimming over and sticking their spiny tushies at a feckless wader is not part of their repertoire. However, if you step on one, they lift up their tail region and slash, creating those characteristic wounds on the feet. Most stingray wounds are not fatal. Off California, round rays are responsible for virtually all wounds.

Here's a good example of what a stingray can do. In June 1608, Captain John Smith [yes, that Captain John Smith] was exploring Chesapeake Bay when, as reported by one of his men: "But our boate by reason of the ebbe, chansing to grownd upon a many shoules lying in the entrance, we spyed many fishes lurking in the reedes: our Captaine sporting himselfe by nayling them to the grownd with his sword, set us all a fishing in that manner; thus we took more in one houre then we could eate in a day.

But it chansed our Captaine taking a fish from his sword (not knowing her condition) being much in the fashion of a thornback, but along tayle like a ryding rodde, whereon the middest is a most poysoned sting, of 2 or 3 inches long, bearded like a saw on each side, which she strucke it on the wrist of his arme neare an inch and halfe; no blood nor wound was seene, but a little blew spot, but the torment was instantly so extreme, that in foure hours had so swollen his hand, arme and shoulder, we all with much sorrow concluded his funerall, and prepared his grave in an Island by, as himselfe directed." (Russell 1965). Well, so as not to keep you in suspense, I should tell you that Smith recovered soon after, ate the offending ray, and lived Happily Ever After (assuming that Ever After means dying in London in 1631).

FAMILY DASYATIDAE—Whiptail Stingrays

The Family Dasyatidae contains marine, estuarine, and freshwater fishes that are found throughout the world, from the tropics to cooler temperate zones. While most species are content to rest quietly on the seafloor, the pelagic stingray, included herein, is a water column dweller and spends its days looking askance at its lay-about cousins. The family includes six genera and maybe 68 species, only three of which enter our range. Females of this family practice (with some success I aver) aplacental viviparity (with embryos living off their yolks). Fischer et al. (1995) has a key to, and illustrations of, all of the eastern tropical Pacific species.

Dasyatis dipterura
(Jordan & Gilbert, 1880)

Diamond Stingray

ETYMOLOGY AND COLLOQUIAL NAMES: *Dasyatis* is Greek for "shaggy" or "rough" and "skate" and *dipterura* is formed of three Greek words "two," "wing," and "tail." Other names include "bullseye stingray," "shorttail stingray," or "whiptail stingray." I note that some folks think this species is a junior synonym of *Dasyatis brevis*. However, the name *Dasyatis dipterurus* was published in May 1880, five months before the name *D. brevis* hit the newsstands, and thus *dipterura* has priority. *So back off.*

THE BASICS: Maximum Length: 200 cm (79 in) TL and at least 88 cm (35 in) disc width (DW), possibly to 122 cm (48 in) DW. Maximum Weight: a 176 cm (69 in) TL, 97.5 cm (38 in) DW, female weighed 51.6 kg (113.5 lb). The Ranges: Central California to northern Chile, including the Gulf of California. Way back in the 1880s, these fish were relatively common in San Diego Bay. Today, they are occasional in Southern California and become more abundant as you go south. There are lots of them in the Bahia Magdalena complex (southern Baja California). Surf zone to 70 m (230 ft), but often in 17 m (55 ft) or less. Length-weight parameters (DW, cm, kg): (females) W = $0.00002DW^{3.1598}$; (males) W = $0.00001DW^{3.1953}$ (Smith 2005). Regarding growth rate estimates, Smith (2005) found that both the von Bertalanffy and Gompertz models were useful descriptors of growth, although for different purposes. Why don't you check out that thesis?

SALIENT CHARACTERS: These have very characteristic diamond-shaped bodies, with discs that are a bit wider than long and a long slender tail (with one or more spines about one-third the way up the tail). They are blackish, brown, or gray on backs.

LIFE HISTORY: Diamond stingrays live on sand and, when not on important business, usually bury themselves. They are more common in bays and lagoons, but are not uncommon on the open coast, even in the vicinity of kelp beds. The young are born in quiet waters. Diamonds tend to be found in shallower waters (often in as shallow as 2.1 m, 7 ft) in the summer. In the Bahia Magdalena-Bahia Almejas complex (southern Baja California), these fish tend to migrate into the bay in spring and leave in the fall. Here females give birth from June–September, typically in August and September. Mating occurs in the bay after the young are released.

A relatively long-lived elasmobranch, females live to at least 28 years and males to 19 years. Females grow more slowly, mature a bit later, and grow larger than males. Males mature at 5–8 years (47–50 cm, 19–20 in, DW) and females at 8–11 years (57–58 cm, 22–23 in). Females produce 1–4 young per season (at as small as 17 cm, 7 in, DW). Diamond stingrays excavate depressions in sand flats and feed mostly on such benthic invertebrates as crabs, clams, and polychaetes, and, very occasionally, on fishes.

FISHERY: Diamond stingray remains are only rarely found in Native American middens. They are an important part of the artisanal commercial catch in some parts of the Gulf of California, in the Bahia Magdalena (southern Baja California) complex, and are occasionally taken in Bahia de Sebastian Vizcaino. Sport fishermen only rarely hook one.

ORIGINS: The earliest *Dasyatis* is *Dasyatis speetoensis*, from the Early Cretaceous (perhaps as much as 146 million years ago) of the United Kingdom. On the Pacific Coast, a *Dasyatis* sp. is known from the Miocene deposits (at least 5.3 million years old) of Southern California and the diamond stingray has been found in 100,000-year-old deposits in Southern California.

Pteroplatytrygon violacea
(Bonaparte, 1832)
Pelagic Stingray

ETYMOLOGY AND COLLOQUIAL NAMES: The genus name is Greek and means "fin," "broad," and "*Trygon*," (an older genus name for a group of rays) and the species name comes from the Latin for "purple." Along Baja California they are called "gavilán" and the Japanese name is "karasu-ei." Some folks put this species in the genus *Dasyatis*.

THE BASICS: Maximum Length: 163 cm (64 in) TL, 80 cm (32 in) disc width (DW), and possibly to 96 cm (38 in) DW. The Ranges: Circumglobal in temperate and tropical waters; in the western Pacific as far north as the southern Kuril Islands; British Columbia to Baja California, and to central Chile. They are fairly common as far northward as Southern California. Surface to at least 330 m and perhaps to 381 (1,082–1,250 ft) over deep water, but mostly in 100 m (328 ft) and less.

OCTAVIO ABURTO-OROPEZA

SALIENT CHARACTERS: These are round-headed and extremely wide rays, often dark purplish, brown, or gray on back and purple or gray underneath.

LIFE HISTORY: Pelagic stingrays are epipelagic and oceanic fish that usually flap about over deep waters. They appear to be seasonal off Southern California, coming our way likely from the south as waters warm. Fish off Baja California and points north are at least 2 years old. They live in waters of about 10–31°C (50–89°F).

Pelagic stingrays live to at least 10 years old. Females grow larger than males, grow faster, and may be larger at age. Off our coast, males mature at less than 41.1 cm (16 in) DW (perhaps 2 years old) and females at 38.5 cm (15 in) (maybe 3 years old). Females are viviparous without a yolk sac placenta and only the left ovary and uterus are functional. In the northwestern Atlantic, rays copulate in March–June, but birthing season is not well understood. Mollett (2002) comments that females appear to give birth in winter off Central America. The gestation period is a fairly quick 2–3 months and females produce 4–13 young that are 14–24 cm (6–9 in) DW. Females ovulate perhaps twice a year. They eat various fishes, medusae, squids, salps, and crustaceans. Richard Hermann's friend Randy Morse saw one eaten by a northern elephant seal off Southern California.

FISHERY: These are a common bycatch in U.S. pelagic longline and gill net fisheries, although they do not appear to be salable. On the other hand, along the Baja California coast and in the Gulf of California, pelagics are occasionally landed and sold. Anglers very rarely take them.

MISCELLANY: John Snow found a barnacle, *Conchoderma virgatum*, attached to the spine of one.

RELATIONSHIPS: Pelagic stingrays are perhaps most closely related to *Dasyatis kuhlii* and *Pastinachus sephen*, two Indo-Pacific species.

FAMILY UROLOPHIDAE—Round Stingrays

(but I notice that some folks use Urotrygonidae)

The urolophids are a marine tropical and warm-temperate group of fishes that is limited to the western Pacific. There are a couple of genera and close to 25 species. Seven species live within our range, however only one makes it as far north as Southern California. Urolophids are aplacental viviparous. *Cyclobatis major*, which may be in this family, was described from the Cretaceous (at least 71 million years ago). Fischer et al. (1995) has a key to, and description of, the many urolophids that live in the tropical eastern Pacific.

Urobatis halleri
(Cooper, 1863)
Round Stingray

ETYMOLOGY AND COLLOQUIAL
NAMES: *Urobatis* comes from two Greek words for "tail" and "ray" and *halleri* refers to George Morris Haller (1852–1889). They are called "round rays" and "spotted stingrays" by some fishermen. "Raya redonda" is one name from Mexico. This and other species were called "stingaree" in the past. Stingaree (a corruption of "stingray") has a nice *fin de siècle* ring to it.

THE BASICS: Maximum Length: 56 cm (22 in) TL, 31 cm (12 in) disc width (DW). Maximum Weight: At least 1.4 kg (3 lb). The Ranges: Hum-

HERB GRUENHAGEN

boldt Bay (Northern California) to Ecuador, including the Gulf of California. They are common as far north as Santa Barbara and not uncommon as far north as inside Morro Bay (Central California). 0.9–21 m (3–70 ft), but reported to at least 91 m (298 ft), and mostly from really shallow waters to at least 28 m (70 ft) (based on David Andrew's observation off La Jolla, Southern California). Von Bertalanffy (DW, mm): (females) L_∞ = 250.5, k = 0. 0.11, t_0 = -5.4; (males) L_∞ = 347.8, k = 0.06, t_0 = -4.6 (Hale 2005). Length-weight parameters (DW, mm, gr): (sexes combined) W = $0.00003DW^{3.1312}$ (Miller et al. 2008a).

SALIENT CHARACTERS: These are sort of cute, small, and round rays. They have kind of thick and kind of small tails, with a spine about midway to the end. You might find them in brown, gray, or almost black, often with diffuse spots and dark cross-hatching on the back.

LIFE HISTORY: Young round rays are born at between 6.5–8 cm (3 in) DW in very shallow, quiet waters over sandy bottoms. Round rays at least periodically form really large and dense aggregations. In the gin-clear waters of Bahia de Los Angeles (Gulf of California), I have seen thousands of them cheeks by jowls (or maybe opercula by jowls and, now that I think about it, do round rays have jowls?) just off the nearshore fronting reefs. Round ray movements are poorly understood. For instance, although various observers have postulated that these rays move slightly offshore in the winter (with the average female tending to be a bit further out than the average male), this has not been well verified. In at least some areas, larger fish are found in somewhat deeper waters than the small ones. Large-scale, north-south migrations have not been proven. David Andrew has observed that this species is active at night. Larry Allen and his bunch (2002) estimated that there were about 280,000 round rays in San Diego Bay and that they were year-round residents. They can tolerate at least slightly brackish waters. Based on genetic studies, there are no great differences between Gulf of California and Southern California fish, although a little something may be different at Santa Catalina Island.

Nordell (1994) gives lots of description of mating behaviors. Read it if you want to know all about that stuff. Basically, males do a lot of chasing, circling, and, particularly, biting. There is also a lot of biting that does not lead to copulation—so go figure. "In bites that precede copulation, males bite the anterior portion of the females' disc and females do not struggle to free themselves...Mature males have sexually dimorphic dentition [some teeth are shaped differently than those of females] that may aid in holding females…The relative increase in female disc thickness in areas where they are bitten may function to minimize the amount of damage due to non-copulatory biting…most male biting does not result in copulation" (Nordell 1994).

Round stingrays live to at least 14 years old. Females produce between 2–12 young at a time and appear to give birth in the summer and fall. This species is aplacental viviparous with embryos living off their own yolks and the left uterus tends to have more embryos in it than the right. Sometime before birth, each embryo turns its tail in such a way that the spine is shielded to prevent uterine wall perforation during birth. Round stingrays uncover their benthic prey by rhythmically flapping their rostrums (snout area) and pectoral fins, thus propelling sediment away from underneath the animal. While diets vary with area, the following are perennial favorites: polychaetes, clams (often just the siphon tips), crustaceans (e.g., shrimps, gammarid and caprellid amphipods, crabs, and sand crabs), fishes, burrowing anemones, and sea cucumbers. Despite their bit of armament, giant sea bass, northern elephant seals, and California sea lions eat round stingrays.

FISHERY: Interestingly, round rays are only rarely found in most Native American middens, with the exception of numerous remains in the middens around San Diego Bay. Throughout their range, they are of little economic importance and are rarely eaten. They are commonly caught from piers and quiet surf areas in southern California, particularly from Long Beach Harbor southward.

ORIGINS: *Urolophus* (now *Urobatis*) sp. fossils lie quietly in at least 34 million-years-old Eocene strata. Remains of round stingrays have been found in Late Pliocene deposits (at least 1.8 million years old) in California.

MISCELLANY: If a stingray in Southern California waters nails you, chances are a round ray did it and that you are in good company. Chris Lowe reports that in the Seal Beach area alone, an average of about 350 wounds per year are reported, and in a good year 560 people get stuck. If you shuffle your feet when walking in the surf it won't happen.

Each summer a round ray starts to grow a new spine that is posterior to the current one. The old spine is usually shed in the fall (although apparently not always) at about the time the new spine is the length of the old one. Thus, for a time during the summer round rays have two spines and very occasionally a ray may have as many as four. Experiments show that a ray that has had its spine surgically removed can grow a new one relatively quickly, implying that rays that lose spines through accident or attack by a predator are not defenseless for long. However, broken spines are not replaced until the new spine-growing season.

GEORGE MORRIS HALLER

In Cooper's (1863) original description of this species, he writes: "While I was at San Diego the little son of Major G. O. Haller, U.S.A. was wounded in the foot, probably by one of these fish, while wading along a muddy shore of the bay. The wound was very painful for some hours, though small." The little boy was G. M. Haller. During 1861, his soldier father Granville Haller and family were stationed in San Diego, where the accident occurred. George Morris Haller had a short, but kind of exciting, life. At age 13, for instance, his father took him to the Battle of Gettysburg. In later years, Haller became a successful lawyer and real estate developer in both Port Townsend and Seattle (Washington). In 1889, while duck hunting on Puget Sound, he and two other hunters apparently capsized their canoes and all were drowned. In his obituary, a newspaper noted "During the Chinese agitation [actually a massive, and illegal, deportation of Chinese immigrants from the city] in Seattle several years ago, Mr. Haller was an active member of the Home Guards." *Whoopee.*

FAMILY GYMNURIDAE—Butterfly Rays

Butterfly rays form a small family of two genera and at least 11 species. These are mainly tropical and occasionally warm-temperate marine fishes that are found throughout the world and most of them live in relatively shallow waters. One species lives within our range.

Gymnura marmorata
(Cooper, 1864)
California Butterfly Ray

TRACY CLARK

ETYMOLOGY AND COLLOQUIAL NAME: *Gymnura* is Greek for "naked" and "tail" and *marmorata* is Latin for "marbled." They are "raya mariposa" in Mexico.

THE BASICS: Maximum Length: 122 cm (48 in) disc width (DW), possibly to 150 cm (59 in) DW. The Ranges: Point Conception (California) to Paita (Peru), including the Gulf of California. They are reasonably abundant at least as far north as about the Bolsa Chica wetlands (Southern California). Surf to 94 m (308 ft), usually in less than 10 m (33 ft). Length-weight parameters (DW, cm, kg): (females) W = $0.000004667L^{3.184}$; (males) W = $0.000004422L^{2.207}$ (Bizzaro, 2005).

SALIENT CHARACTERS: Another very broad ray, even broader than the pelagic stingray. They have pitiful little tails and likely suffer from tail envy, harboring really twisted emotions regarding bat rays. They run to grays, browns, or olive-browns on the back and may have light or dark spots, blotches, and mottlings.

LIFE HISTORY: This is a benthic animal of calm and shallow backwaters. Males mature at around 45 cm (18 in) DW and females at about 74 cm (29 in). In the Bahia Magdalena-Bahia Almejas complex (southern Baja California), most females give birth from March–October, although some of that may take place throughout the year. The young ones are born at 21–26.5 cm (8–11 in) DW. Males and females mate after the females give birth. Females practice aplacental viviparity (with the embryos ingesting nutrients produced by the mother's uterus). Butterfly rays root about seafloors digging out crabs and shrimps, clams, polychaetes, snails, and fishes.

FISHERY: In the 19th century, butterfly rays were occasionally sold in Los Angeles markets, but that's about it for California waters. This species forms major fisheries in various Mexican waters, such as the Bahia de Sebastian Vizcaino and Bahia Magdalena areas of Baja California, and in the Todos Santos region in the Gulf of California. Butterfly rays are occasionally caught by recreational anglers in Southern California. Ken Jones (2004) ate one and liked it.

ORIGINS: A species of the genus *Gymnura*, *G. grootaerti*, lived in the Late Cretaceous (about 94 million years ago). *Pteroplatea lapislutosa* was described from a Miocene deposit (at least 5.3 million years old) of southern California. *Pteroplatea* is now *Gymnura*, thus this is the oldest record of the genus from the West Coast.

FAMILY MYLIOBATIDAE—Eagle Rays

The eagle rays are marine fishes that are found in nearshore tropical to temperate waters worldwide. There are five genera and 27 species, four of which live within our range, and one reaches California.

Myliobatis californica

Gill, 1865

Bat Ray

ETYMOLOGY AND COLLOQUIAL NAMES: *Myliobatis* is Greek for (quite aptly) "grinder" and "ray" and *californica* refers to the original capture in Tomales Bay (Northern California). Recreational anglers sometimes call them "mud marlins." They are called "tecolota" along the Baja California coast.

THE BASICS: Maximum Length: 1.8 m (6 ft) disc width (DW). Maximum Weight: What was probably a female weighed in at 109 kg (240 lb), the largest male in the scientific literature weighed 16.8 kg (37 lb). The Ranges: Yaquina Bay (Oregon) to the Gulf of California, abundant between at least Arcata Bay (Northern California) and Bahia Magdalena (southern Baja California). Intertidal and surface waters to 108 m (354 ft). Surveys in Southern California imply that these fish are most abundant in 20 m (66 ft) and less. Martin and Cailliet (1988) gives you a smorgasbord of Von Bertalanffy values, see that paper for more details, but here are a few: (DW, mm): (females) 1) $L_\infty = 1,587$, $k = 0.0955$, $t_0 = -2.059$, 2) $L_\infty = 1,566$, $k = 0.099$, $t_0 = -1.935$, and 3) $L_\infty = 1,567$, $k = 0.096$, $t_0 = -2.040$; (males) 1) $L_\infty = 1,991$, $k = 0.059$, $t_0 = -2.860$, 2) $L_\infty = 1,004$, $k = 0.229$, $t_0 = -1,580$, and 3) $L_\infty = 1,517$, $k = 0.0834$, $t_0 = -2.55$. Length-weight parameters (TL, mm, kg): (sexes combined) $W = 0.00000001054L^{3.0928}$ (RecFin 2009).

SALIENT CHARACTERS: Bat rays are very distinctive, with flat bodies, blunt and elevated heads, and thick snouts. They are usually black or brown on top (except lighter near wing tips) and white underneath. The stinging spine (sometimes there are 2 or 3) is located at the base of the tail.

LIFE HISTORY: The young ones (22–31 cm, 9–12 in, DW) are birthed in shallow backwaters. This is a remarkably plastic animal; the juveniles and adults are found over sand and mud, among rocks, kelp beds, and eelgrass, along open coasts, in backwaters, and estuaries; on the bottom, in midwaters, and at the surface; in the nearshore and sometimes well out to sea. And you can't ask more from a fish than that. While you usually see bat rays kind of semi-buried in sand or lying on flat rocks, if you hang around the nearshore of Southern California long enough, you will eventually witness the movement of swarms of bat rays, often right at the surface, and all going the same way. There is something kind of unworldly about sitting on a boat, sober, watching hundreds of rays gently pulsing through the water and all going...somewhere. John Moore writes that during large squid runs in the La Jolla area: "There were at a minimum hundreds of bat rays. During several days of dives with good visibility, I recall looking up and seeing silhouettes of nearly endless fleets of bat rays going past. Yes, they were eating squid." Roger Bly saw a concentration of many dozens of young fish lying amid, and feeding on, sand dollars, in shallow waters off La Jolla.

In many areas, bat rays make seasonal inshore and offshore movements. As an example, in Northern California, fish enter Tomales Bay in the spring, when water temperatures rise above 10°C (50°F), and leave in the fall, as temperatures fall below

SAVING THE WORLD FOR OYSTER SHOOTERS

And this just in from *The California Oyster Industry*, E. M. Barrett, 1963, California Department of Fish and Game, Fish Bull. 123.

"The bat stingray is potentially very destructive and has had an important effect on oyster culture. By locating their beds on the tidal flats where they could be fenced, oyster growers have largely eliminated bat stingray depredations…At present oyster growers, with the permission of the Fish and Game Commission, are attempting to destroy the rays. At Morro Bay, the growers fish for them. At Humboldt Bay they drag the bottom with trawl nets and have also set traps…A company at Humboldt Bay caught and sent to a local fertilizer plant some 45,000 rays between 1955 and 1960. They have also tagged some, hoping to learn details of their migratory habits. If the same colonies of rays are shown to return to the same bays each year, it may be possible to eradicate this menace."

This is best read with The Imperial March from "Star Wars" in the background. Dum Dum Dum, Dum de Dum, Dum de Dum.

that mark. Some individuals return at least in subsequent years and may come back year after year. While in the bay, bat rays come into the shallowest and warmest mud flats during the day, and then move into deeper waters at night. During this season, the fish dig out pits in the mudflats, doing this most intensely from midday to early evening. Similar movements take place into the Bahia Magdalena-Bahia Almejas complex in southern Baja California. Here, females enter in the spring, followed some time after by the males. Bat rays are typically found in waters between 10–26°C (50–79°F), but the rays do not seem to prefer the higher end of that temperature range. In San Francisco Bay, you can find them in waters down to a pretty brackish 14 ppt, but mostly from around 25 ppt and up.

Here is Limbaugh (1955) on mating behavior: "At Punta Rocosa, Baja California, in August, at a depth of approximately 20 feet along a sandy bottom inside a rocky reef, bat rays were numerous, resting on the bottom and swimming freely a few feet above the bottom. A medium-sized female was being followed closely by two smaller males. The head of one male was under the female, pushing her in the region of the genitalia."

Bat rays live to at least 23 years. It is likely that females live much longer than males; the oldest male known was 6 years old. Females grow larger than males and have a slower growth rate. Males mature at as small as 45 cm (18 in) DW and all males are mature by 62.2 cm (25 in), about 2–3 years old. A few females are mature at 45.4 cm (18 in) (about 2 yrs), 50% at 88.1 cm (35 in), about 5 years, and all at 100.3 cm (40 in), around 9 years. Bat rays mate soon after the females give birth and the embryos gestate for 9–12 months. Bat ray embryos ingest nutrients produced by the mother's uterus (aplacental viviparity). Females give birth to 2–12 young from May–December, likely mostly in summer and fall. In searching for food, the rays fly over sand and mud flapping their fins to create depressions that may be 1 m (2–3 ft) wide, 51 cm (20 in) deep, and 5 m (15 ft) long. The fish then eat whatever is exposed in the sediment. In 1955, Limbaugh noted that bat rays also feed among rocks, where they preyed upon abalone. Major prey include clams and clam siphons, crabs, sand crabs, shrimps, polychaetes, scallops, snails, gammarid amphipods, fat innkeepers, sea cucumbers, squids, brittle stars, and fishes. Predators include broadnose sevengill, leopard, and white sharks.

FISHERY: Native Americans commonly caught bat rays and U.S. commercial fishermen land a few. They are landed in large numbers by commercial fishermen in the Gulf of California. Once reviled by sport fishermen, recreational anglers have now embraced them, albeit with care.

ORIGINS: Bat rays, at least members of the genus *Myliobatis*, go back a long way. The oldest fossil remains are of *M. dixoni* from the Middle Paleocene (more than 55 million years ago) from Belgium. What is probably a *Myliobatis* sp. fossil was found in Middle Eocene (at least 37 million years old) strata in southern California. Remains of our species of bat ray have been found in Late Pliocene deposits (at least 1.8 million years old) in California.

MISCELLANY: Relatively few stingray wounds off California are due to bat rays, most come from round rays. Bat rays may have as many as three stings. An albino bat ray was caught off Baja California.

REMARKS: I once ate a bat ray and it was really good. Unfortunately, they are such endearing creatures that I have felt guilty about it ever since. In past years, unscrupulous fish merchants have cut round pieces of bat ray wings (and other skates and rays) and sold them as "scallops." Interestingly, to my knowledge, no one has glued a bunch of scallop tissue together and called it "bat ray."

AND FROM THE LAND OF UNINTENDED CONSEQUENCES

VanBlaricom (1978) looked at the effects on seafloor organisms, particularly those that live in the sand and mud, of all the digging around and kerfuffle caused by bat rays and round stingrays when they excavate for prey. The first thing he noted was that a large number of small animals (e.g., amphipods, ostracods, and the like) were tossed into the water column and that speckled sanddabs were usually on hand to pick off these displaced citizens. But VanBlaricom also followed what happened to the animals in the pits excavated by the rays. He noted that organic material quickly settled into the holes and just as quickly relatively high densities of various small crustaceans (e.g., gammarid amphipods and ostracods) followed in to dine. After about three days, a new wave of animals displaced the first group and a third phase of organisms soon supplanted them.

ORDER ACIPENSERIFORMES

FAMILY ACIPENSERIDAE—Sturgeons

So hip, they make Lord Buckley seem like Dwight Eisenhower.

The sturgeons are an old and honored group of anadromous and freshwater fishes. Comprised of four genera and 25 species, they are found throughout much of the Northern Hemisphere. Sturgeons are oviparous. At least some species, such as the shovelnose sturgeon (*Scaphirhynchus platorynchus*), make kind of squeaking sounds. Eric Hilton (Virginia Institute of Marine Science) writes to me: "The oldest actual fossils of sturgeons that I know of are from the Late Cretaceous Santonian-Campanian Mill River Formation of Alberta (about 80–85 million years), which are little more than fragments of ornamented bone." He also notes that sturgeons may go back to the Early Cretaceous (perhaps 130 million years ago) as their sister group, the paddlefishes, are known from that period. A really beautifully preserved fossil sturgeon (*Priscosturion longipinnis*) from the Late Cretaceous was found in the gut of a fossil hadrosaur. The oldest fossil sturgeon from California is from Middle Miocene strata (maybe 12 million years ago).

Acipenser medirostris

Ayres, 1854

Green Sturgeon

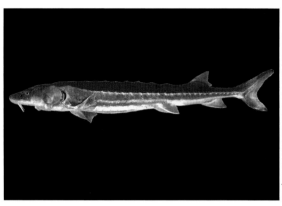

ETYMOLOGY AND COLLOQUIAL NAME: *Acipenser* comes from the Latin for "sturgeon" and *mediostris* is Latin for "moderate" and "snout," based on its snout length compared to the white sturgeon. One could reasonably argue that all snouts should be moderate if they know what's good for them. The Middle Way for snouts. The Japanese name is "chozame."

THE BASICS: Maximum Length: 270 cm (9 ft) TL. Maximum Weight: 175 kg (385 lb). The Ranges: Sea of Japan and Honshu, to the eastern Bering Sea (at Kuskokwim Bay), and the Gulf of Alaska to just south of Bahia de San Quintin (northern Baja California). They appear to be common from British Columbia to San Francisco Bay. Apparently they are not found in all rivers within their geographic range, being absent, for instance, from the Alsea and Siuslaw rivers of Oregon. At sea, they have been found in waters as deep as 110 m (361 ft), but most commonly in 70 m (230 ft) or less. Von Bertalanffy parameters (TL, cm): (sexes combined) L_∞ = 238, k = 0.053, t_0 = 0.053 (Beamesderfer et al. 2007). Length-weight parameters (TL, mm, kg): (sexes combined) W = 0.0000000005309$L^{3.348}$ (RecFin, 2009). Beamesderfer et al. (2007) has lots of other l-w parameters.

SALIENT CHARACTERS: Singular animals are the sturgeons. Elongated they be, with under-slung mouths and five rows of scutes (thick bony plates) arranged as follows: one on the back, one on the middle of each side, and one on each side of the belly. Greens tend to be olive-colored, although some are gray, and some have belly and side stripes. If unsure if you've got a green or white sturgeon, count the scutes on the midside row. Greenies have 23–30, whites have 38–48.

LIFE HISTORY: In the spring and summer, about 10–15 days after hatching in rivers, 2.3 cm (1 in) TL or larger green sturgeon larvae begin to migrate at night downstream to nursery areas. The larvae metamorphose into juveniles (now 6–8 cm, 2–3 in, TL) within maybe 45 days and these juveniles spend 1–4 years in estuaries and in the lower parts of rivers, after which they enter the ocean. Juveniles then either stay at sea until they mature or at least regularly return to it before they mature. Unusual among the sturgeons, greenies really spend most of the rest of their lives in the ocean or in estuaries. Unusual, too, is the restless nature of this species, as they make very extensive movements (up to nearly 1,000 km, 621 mi) along the coast. California fish tend to move northward into Oregon or Washington waters. Fish from throughout the species' range that are not going to spawn in a given year often spend summer and early fall months in such northwest estuaries as Willapa Bay, Grays Harbor, and the lower Columbia River and this might be to feed or for thermal regulation. Interestingly, green sturgeons are also known to congregate to the northwest of, or just north of, Vancouver Island. What these fish are doing is unknown.

Fish that are going to get lucky enter rivers from at least February–June and spawn from about April–June. Fish then either migrate back to sea soon after or hang out in deep pools (occasionally in fast-moving waters) for up to 6 months (until the first good rains) before leaving the scene of the slime. Spawning occurs in the Sacramento, Klamath, and Rogue rivers, and possibly in the Umpqua and Eel rivers, and spawning fish may move at least 105 km (65 mi) upstream. On the other hand, perfectly respectable rivers like the Skeena, Fraser, and Columbia get no love because even though there are seasonal concentrations of fish, no spawning occurs. Spawning takes place over cobble, gravel, and boulders in large and fast-flowing rivers with optimal spawning temperatures at 8–18°C (46–64°F) and maximum temperatures less than 20–22°C (68–73°F). Males may spawn with more than one female per season. The fertilized eggs settle into the spaces between rocks. Genetic analysis implies that there are at least two populations, one that includes fish in the Rogue, Klamath-Trinity, and Eel Rivers, and a southern population in the Sacramento River.

Green sturgeons live to at least 53 years old and females may grow larger and live longer than males. Beamesderfer et al. (2007) provide lots and lots and lots of information on all kinds of life history parameters. Read it, you'll like it. Size and age at first maturity have been estimated at between 8–18 years (120–185 cm, 47–73 in, TL) for males and 13–27 years for females (144–202 cm, 56–80 in). Females spawn every 2–5 years and produce from 59,000–242,000 eggs that hatch in 6–8 days after fertilization. Green sturgeons feed on the bottom on such prey as mysid shrimps and gammarid amphipods, as well as juvenile crabs, fishes, the occasional shrimp, and perhaps mollusks.

FISHERY: Native Americans caught green sturgeons in some numbers and today the Yuroks on the Klamath River (Northern California) target them. Greens were never a particularly important commercial species and, in fact, up until the late 19th century many white folks thought they were poisonous. Heh, heh, and this from the same people who put quids of tobacco on their gum lines. Even after that scare passed, the species was always considered to be inferior to white sturgeon. Today, most commercial catches occur as bycatch in salmon and white sturgeon fisheries in the Columbia River estuary, Willapa Bay, and Grays Harbor. Sport fishermen take them fairly commonly from San Francisco Bay northwards.

Acipenser transmontanus

Richardson, 1836

White Sturgeon

RENÉ REYES AND US BUREAU OF RECLAMATION

ETYMOLOGY: *Acipenser* comes from the Latin for "sturgeon" and *transmontanus* is Latin for "across mountains" referring to its occurring west of the Rocky Mountains.

THE BASICS: Maximum Length: Perhaps to 6 m (20 ft) FL. Noted ichthyocynic Peter Moyle (2002) avers that the largest length records for this species were made before 1900 and "were subject to inaccurate measurements and exaggerated reporting." Peter notes the largest recent record, from Oregon, was 3.2 m (11 ft) long. Maximum Weight: At least 630 kg (1,387 lb), and possibly to 817 kg (1,800 lb). The Ranges: Northern Gulf of Alaska to Ensenada (northern Baja California). They are abundant from the Fraser River area (British Columbia) to San Francisco Bay. While their usual southern freshwater limit is the Sacramento River, one was taken in the lower part of the Pajaro River in Santa Cruz (Central California). Nearshore to 122 m (400 ft) at sea. Von Bertalanffy parameters (TL, cm): (sexes combined) L_∞ = 261.2, k = 0.04027, t_0 = -3.638 (Kohlhurst et al. 1980). Length-weight parameters (TL, cm, kg): (sexes combined) W = $0.000001183L^{3.348}$ (Kohlhurst et al. 1980).

SALIENT CHARACTERS: A white sturgeon is easily separated from just about any other fish you are likely to stumble over. It is grayish-white, with five rows of scutes (bony plates) on its body: one on back, one on each flank, and one on each side of the belly. Very large fish have barely visible scutes. The mouth is underneath the head, with four barbels in the front. Green sturgeons are usually olive-green, occasionally gray, with 23–30 scutes along flanks (38–48 in whites), and one or two scutes after the dorsal fin (these are absent in white sturgeon). Chapman et al. (1996) report that the sex of white sturgeons cannot be determined externally. So why even try?

LIFE HISTORY: Larvae hatch at about 10 cm (4 in) TL and, with their nose sticking upwards, migrate down river, often to estuaries. Small white sturgeons cannot tolerate salt water but they get better at it as they grow. Older juveniles and adults often make their way to the sea. While it is not clear what percentage of fish migrate along the coast, a fish tagged in the Klamath River (Northern California) moved 1,060 km (659 mi) north to the Fraser River (British Columbia). Four other fish tagged in the Columbia River also wound up in the Fraser. However, although some white sturgeons spend time in salt water, this is by no means universal. As an example, many sturgeons in the Fraser River do not appear to ever enter the sea, although most live in the river's estuary as juveniles. Michael Parsley reports that white sturgeons will form tightly packed schools in the winter in at least some rivers. As an example, many hundreds ball up just below the Bonneville Dam on the Columbia River. Adults spawn in rivers (primarily in fast-flowing areas) over substrate variously referred to as "sandy," "muddy," "cobble," and "boulder," leading me to wonder if any one really knows what is going on. Females spawn several batches a season. After spawning, sturgeons tend to move down river. In the San Francisco Bay area, for instance, fish spawn in the upper Sacramento River and then return to the delta and lower bay. At least in the Columbia River, fish are more active at night when they tend to move into shallow waters. On ocassion, dozens will strand themselves in the intertidal of bays. There they wait for the tide to come in and effect a rescue.

A 3.2 m (11 ft) long fish was 82 years old, so some of those whale-like fish reported from 100 years back were probably older. I note that various sources mention "100-year-old" fish, but no one seems to have actually aged one that old. Males and females may grow at the same rate. Growth rates and size and age at maturity appear to vary all over the map (literally), with different groups of fish doing different things, perhaps reflecting varied food availability and water conditions. To give you an idea of this, Semakula and Larkin (1968) found that one Fraser River sturgeon that was 10 years old was larger than one that was 23 years old. Age at first maturity has been variously estimated for females at between at least 11–34 years and perhaps 11–22 years for males. And size at maturity? Chapman et al. (1996), reporting from San Francisco Bay, noted that females most likely mature at 95–135 cm (37–53 in) FL and males at 75–105 cm (30–41 in). This compares to Columbia River females that matured at 160–193 cm (63–76 in) FL. Depending on location, spawning occurs from February–July, at between 8.6–19°C (48–66°F), perhaps peaking at around 14°C (57°F). It is thought that females spawn every 2–9 years and males may also perhaps not reproduce annually. Fecundity has been variously reported at as little as 63,840 for a hatchery fish to an estimated 3–4 million eggs. The mature, adhesive, gray or brown, and spherical eggs are 2.6–4 mm in diameter and fish in the Sacramento River tend to have larger eggs than those from the Columbia River. Eggs hatch in about 4 days at 16°C (61°F) and 8–12 days at 12°C (54°F).

AN URGIN' FOR A STURGEON

With dinos I've traded some jokes
The mammoths were really nice blokes
  But fishing and pollution
  Leaves little solution
I might not survive all you folks.

Small fish, to perhaps 60–80 cm (24–32 in) TL, tend to feed on such bottom invertebrates as gammarid amphipods, mysid shrimps, polychaetes, insect larvae, clams, mussels, crabs, and fish eggs. Larger individuals often focus on fishes. Sturgeons feeding on herring eggs in San Francisco Bay often are seen jumping out of the water. Semakula and Larkin (1968) report that in the Fraser River, it was so common for sturgeon to be stuffed with eulachon in the spring (when the smelt spawn) that "the buyers of sturgeon deduct 2 lb from the weight of ungutted fish as a 'eulachon advance.'" White sturgeons are eaten by Steller sea lions and river otters, and one was eaten by another white sturgeon in the Fraser River.

FISHERY: White sturgeons were important to various North American indigenous peoples. In 1849, James Gilchrist Swan (1818–1900) deserted a wife and two children, a flourishing ship-fitting business, and the social constraints of Boston and headed for California and the Gold Rush. In 1852, he settled in a cedar cabin on the banks of Shoalwater (Willapa) Bay (Washington Territory), just north of the Columbia River. Within a few years, this literate observer and raconteur, this ultimately failed land speculator and alcoholic, this man with an almost modern sympathy for the northwest Native Americans, produced a marvelous book about life in this almost pristine environment. In the following passage, Swan (1857) reports on sturgeon fishing by the Native Americans of Shoalwater Bay in the 1850s: "Their method is to fasten a salmon-hook to a long line similar to a large-sized cod-line. The hook is then placed on the end of a pole, and the Indian goes along slowly in his canoe over the shoals, with the pole down, feeling for the fish. When the Indian feels the sturgeon, he sticks the hook into it, and, quickly hauling in the pole, slacks out some of the line, and prepares for a race. As soon as the sturgeon feels the hook, away he starts like an arrow, and the canoe goes shizzing and spinning along at a fearful rate, and requires a good deal of dexterous management to prevent being turned over. As the fish slackens speed, the Indian hauls in the line, and by perseverance at last tires the fish so that it is hauled to the surface of the water, and stunned by a blow on the head or nose with a heavy club carried for that purpose.

The fish, after being carried home, is opened, care being taken to save all the blood, which is put into a kettle with some choice cuts, and then boiled. The head, like that of the salmon, is esteemed the best part, and is either boiled, or cut in strips and broiled or roasted before the fire. The pith of the back bone is considered a great luxury, and is eaten raw; and, although not having more flavor than the white of an egg, is not unpalatable."

Meanwhile, hard on the Fraser River of British Columbia, Arthur Birch, 26-year-old Colonial Secretary at Government House in New Westminster wrote to his brother in 1864. After noting that the fleas were exceptionally plentiful and that all of the women at the previous week's Ball were married and pregnant, he went on to write: "I have got a very nice little Wooden Office & my room is charming now though I fear very cold in the winter. It is close onto the Fraser & the balcony & veranda over hang the water. All the Indians now fishing and it is great fun to watch them spearing Sturgeon which here run to the enormous size of 500 & 600 lb. The Indians drift down with the stream perhaps 30 canoes abreast with their long poles with spear attached kept within about a foot of the bottom of the River. When they feel a fish lying they raise the spear and thrust it at the fish seldom missing. The barb of the spear immediately disconnects from the pole but remains attached to a rope & you see sometimes 2 or 3 canoes being carried off at the same time down river at any pace by these huge fish" (Birch 1976). Lord (1866) also opines: "The long ligamentous cord, traversing the entire length of the spine, constitutes another delicacy, called *vesigna*, much relished by the Russians."

As far back as the Gold Rush, San Francisco was a major market for locally caught sturgeons. Most of these fish were smoked or caught only for their eggs and these were made into caviar. However, William N. Lockington (Lockington 1879a), an *habitué* of the San Francisco social scene in the 1870s, noted that sturgeon was often passed off on the unwary diner "Under the name of 'sea-basse,' and that curious dish called 'tenderloin of sole' is sturgeon again." I particularly like that word "basse," it has that kind of Long John Silver look to it.

The Columbia and Fraser rivers saw major fisheries for sturgeons beginning in the late 19th century. Pruter (1966) noted: "When white men arrived on the Columbia, sturgeon were abundant. At some places on the river, they were so numerous that they caused considerable damage to the gill nets used by salmon fishermen. For years, the smaller sturgeon (generally those under 50 pounds) caught by salmon fishermen were deliberately killed; and in a few places on the river, special efforts were made to eradicate them...About 1880, a commercial fishery commenced. In 1888, a rail shipment of frozen sturgeon to the east marked the beginning of an important fishery. Quick acceptance of smoked Columbia River sturgeon and of caviar made from sturgeon eggs stimulated rapid development of the fishery."

White sturgeons have a kind of checkered past and present. The great populations that held forth throughout such waterways as the Fraser, Columbia, and Sacramento rivers have been just hammered, both by commercial fishing and such activity as dam creation. In general, now-landlocked populations that exist above these dams are in very bad shape. Stocks below dams present a variable picture and there is still a rather bustling commercial and sport fishery on the Columbia River and a substantial sport fishery in such locations as around San Francisco Bay and some spots in British Columbia.

MISCELLANY: Several abnormalities have been reported. For instance, a small number of fish with seven rows of scutes live in both the Columbia and Sacramento-San Joaquin Delta. In addition, a few fish with misshapen fins (mostly curled pectoral fins) and abnormal barbels have been captured. Also white sturgeon with two types of snouts, rounded and pointed, apparently live in the Columbia River. And, last but not least, a hermaphrodite sturgeon has been found in San Francisco Bay.

REMARKS: Many of the sturgeon caught for the late 19th-century San Francisco markets were taken by Chinese fishermen using long gangs of hooks. Collins (1892) displaying the endemic anti-Chinese sentiment of the times wrote about the "Chinese sturgeon trawl" thusly: "This is a very cruel as well as a destructive way of catching fish [*implying, I suppose, that Anglo fishermen caught fish with kindness?*]. Each trawl has an average of eighty barbless hooks, which are as sharp as needles. They are fastened to the gangings in clusters of eight and ten, and when in the water are swung about by the action of the tide like the tentacles of an octopus reaching out for prey. A fish which approaches within a length of itself is pretty sure of being hooked by one or more of these treacherous devices."

During Gold Rush days, sturgeon eggs were commonly salted for caviar and in 1919, John Cobb noted that "Miss Ida Tuholski, of San Francisco" had been making sturgeon caviar for some years. Today, there is a fairly robust California caviar industry, based on eggs from farmed white sturgeon, and a likely equally robust illegal cottage industry producing the same product from wild fish.

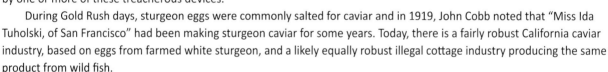

TOTALLY UNRELATED RIFF #2—BECAUSE WE HAD SOME SPACE TO FILL

BEST PUTDOWN OF ONE ICHTHYOLOGIST BY ANOTHER

And the envelope please...

And the winner is...David Starr Jordan!!

Yes, it was David Starr Jordan, egomaniacal ichthyologist, President of Stanford University etc., etc., etc. Here is what Jordan wrote (in History of Zoological Explorations of the Pacific Coast, California Fish and Game, volume 17, pages 156–158) regarding Dr. Charles Girard, a 19th-century fish taxonomist: "The Pacific Railroad survey was finished early in the [eighteen] fifties, and the fishes were described by Dr. Charles Girard, a pupil of Agassiz. Despite his unusually good facilities in the way of specimens and books, he did no really good work. He described a vast majority of the fishes of the coast, but in a very wooden way which proved a great set-back to the study of ichthyology. Girard indeed did all a man could do to make it difficult to determine the trout."

Accepting the award for Dr. Jordan is H.L. Mencken.

FAMILY ALBULIDAE—Bonefishes

Bonefishes are tropical (although a few species wander into temperate waters) fishes, found in marine, estuarine, and occasionally freshwater throughout the world. It was long thought that there were only a handful of species in two genera. Now, based on molecular studies, taxonomists are riven with disquietude and all is confusion, as what was once thought to be the worldwide *Albula vulpes* is now understood to be a number of similar-appearing species. Bonefishes are oviparous and have these retro, funky, and large leptocephali larvae that are secretly envied by more modern fishes.

Albula sp.
Bonefish

MILTON LOVE

ETYMOLOGY AND COLLOQUIAL NAME: *Albula* is Latin for "fox." It was called "ladyfish" until 1949, when the official name was changed. Curiously, there is no "gentlemanfish." Although previously referred to as *Albula vulpes*, works by Pfeiler (1996, 2008) and Pfeiler et al. (2002, 2008a,b) suggest there are a number of bonefish species in the eastern Pacific. An unnamed species, referred to as "*Albula* sp. A" by Pfeiler and coworkers, is found along the Pacific Coast of North America and in the Gulf of California.

THE BASICS: Maximum Length: About 33 cm (13 in) SL. The Ranges: San Francisco southward into the Gulf of California; its southern range limit is unknown. Our bonefish is quite common to at least as far north as San Diego Bay, and is occasional as far north as Marina del Rey (Southern California). Holder (1913) reported taking them at Santa Catalina Island. Nearshore waters. Larvae: hatching length = <3.2 mm, flexion length = about 1.5 cm (0.6 in), transformation length = about 7.1 cm (3 in). Von Bertalanffy parameters (SL, mm): (sexes combined) L_∞ = 278, k = 0.486, t_0 = -1.448 (Pfeiler et al. 2000). Length-weight parameters (SL, mm, gr): (sexes combined) W = $0.00001489L^{2.987}$ (Pfeiler et al. 2000).

SALIENT CHARACTERS: An elongated fish with a peculiar conical and protruding snout, small mouth, and under-slung jaw. The single dorsal fin is placed well back and over the pelvic fins. The back is silvery, with a faint blue or green blush, and some faint stripes or bars.

LIFE HISTORY: In the Gulf of California, bonefish leptocephali larvae develop in offshore waters for 6–7 months and then transform into benthic individuals during winter and spring in shallow (sometimes intertidal) sandy embayments. Recruiting fish apparently enter esteros only during the early parts of incoming tides and only at night. Leptocephali are as large as 7.1 cm (3 in) SL when they settle out and within 8–12 days they shrink to juveniles that are about 2.5 cm (1 in) SL. Juveniles continue to live in lagoons and other quiet waters, often near mangroves. Adults also inhabit the shallows, occasionally entering fresh or brackish waters, over soft seafloors and amid eelgrass and other vegetation.

We don't know much about the growth and reproduction of this species, although it does live to be at least 20 years old. Females at least as small as 20.5 cm (8 in) SL and 32 months old are mature. A reared male matured at 20.8 cm (8 in) and 32 months old. Based on an absence of larvae in the region, bonefish do not spawn in California or northern Baja California waters. In the Gulf of California, they spawn in spring–fall. Bonefish feed on such bottom creatures as polychaetes, shrimps, crabs, and various mollusks.

FISHERY: At least as far back as the late 19th century, commercial fishermen in San Diego Bay took a few bonefish, but they were not a particularly important species. There is no commercial fishery in the U.S. right now, although you can occasionally find them in the Mercado Negro fish market in Ensenada (northern Baja California). Recreational anglers catch them fairly often in various Southern California backwaters, particularly in San Diego Bay. Some folks even target them. Bonefish are a major bycatch in Gulf of California shrimp fisheries.

ORIGINS: Bonefishes go a long way back. Otoliths of *Albula campaniana* have been found in Cretaceous strata from at least 71 million years ago. In 1956, David reported that she had found a scale of a fish apparently related to *Albula* from Southern California Miocene deposits she believed to be at least 16 million years old.

FAMILY MURAENIDAE—Morays

Kind of a sprawling group of fishes, the muraenids are tropical and warm-temperate marine fishes, some of which routinely enter freshwater. There are perhaps 15 genera and around 185 species, seven of which appear within our range and two reach Southern California. Morays are oviparous and have planktonic leptocephalus larvae. A leptocephalus larva is thin, fairly large, and leaf-shaped, and can take a number of months to metamorphose into a juvenile. Interested in the various eastern Pacific species? See Fischer et al. (1995).

For centuries, rumors have persisted that the Romans fed slaves to farmed morays. This has always seemed improbable, as a popular Roman motto was "A Slave Saved is a Slave Earned," there not being too much upside to feeding expensive slaves to a bunch of frigging fish. Also, it is not true that the word "moray" comes from the Earl of Moray despite a throwaway line to that effect in *Quicksilver* by Neal Stephenson. "Moray" appears to be derived from the Greek word for "lamprey."

Gymnothorax mordax

Ayres, 1859

California Moray

One of the more mordant species on the Pacific Coast.

ETYMOLOGY AND COLLOQUIAL NAMES: *Gymnothorax* combines the Greek words for "naked" and "thorax" and *mordax* means "prone to bite" in Latin. They were called "California conger eels" in the 19th Century. "Moray eel" is still often used.
THE BASICS: Maximum Length: 152 cm (5 ft) TL. Maximum Weight: a 117.5 cm (46 in) fish weighed 6.7 kg (14.8 lb), so they grow even heavier than that. The Ranges: Point Conception (California) to Bahia Magdalena (southern Baja California). Morays are common northward to around Santa Catalina Island. Researchers have tentatively identified larvae captured off Colombia as this species. Occasionally found in tide pools and down to 40 m (131 ft), mostly in barely subtidal waters to 20 m (65 ft). Length-weight parameters (SL, mm, gr): (sexes combined) W = $0.0000001122L^{3.4274}$ (Quast 1968a).
SALIENT CHARACTERS: Morays are the only eels in our area without pectoral fins. They are light to dark brown or green, often with dark mottling. Other conspicuous characters include lots of sharp teeth and a small, round gill opening.

LIFE HISTORY: Little is known about this very interesting fish. As these things go, morays settle from the plankton to rocky reefs when pretty large, at around 10–15 cm (4–6 in) TL. This is a reef dweller and if there is not a crevice or cave in the vicinity, there will not be any morays. Very few, if any, larval morays have been captured in U.S. waters, and thus it is likely that morays off Southern California do not reproduce, perhaps due to relatively low water temperatures. If this is correct, the fish we see in Southern California drifted up as larvae from Baja California. Brad Morganeau reports on a Southern California moray he named Longfellow: "I visited this eel regularly over the course of about 5 years. His bottom jaw had a distinctive hook to the right. I have a hundred pictures of him. He is always in the same grotto. The first time I would

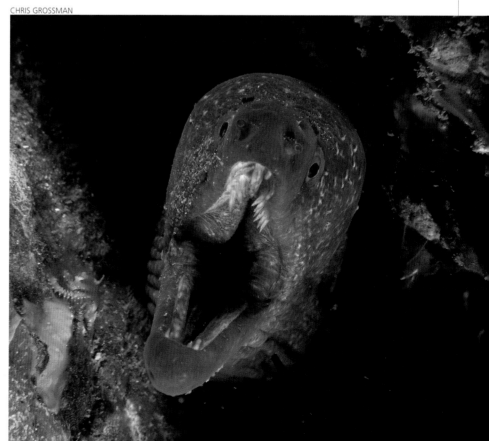

CHRIS GROSSMAN

swim down to his grotto, I would never see him, but I would yell out a funny sound…9 times out of 10 he would be there on the next dive. He would stick his head out and look at me as if to say, 'That you Brad?'"

The Birch Aquarium has one that lived for at least 35 years. California morays feed on crustaceans (e.g., spiny lobsters, shrimps, and crabs), fishes, and octopuses.

FISHERY: Bones of morays, quite possibly *G. mordax*, are found in the middens of the indigenous folks who once lived on Isla Cedros (central Baja California). Morays were a moderately important commercial species in the late 19th century in Southern California, where they were called "conger eel" or "congeree." There was a substantial market for them in the San Pedro fresh fish markets of the time and they were also salted and dried by the Chinese. However, at this juncture and in all fairness, one must observe that the Chinese fishermen of the 19th century appeared to follow the dictum, "If it swims, crawls, floats, or sits under a rock looking sullen—salt and dry it." Today, morays are sometimes caught in lobster traps, but they are rarely retained. While people rarely get up in the morning and say, "Today, I'm gonna go catch me a mess o'morays," they are occasionally taken by recreational anglers fishing from jetties, piers, and rocky shorelines.

MISCELLANY: 1) Divers are occasionally bitten by this fish. Most of those bitten have either A) stuck their hands in or near a crevice containing a moray (something your mother has told you repeatedly not to do) or B) speared one. 2) At least some moray species (perhaps this one, but no one has checked) have a truly nasty second set of jaws, I mean truly nasty. After grabbing a prey with its jaws and partially getting it down its throat, as Mehta and Wainwright (2007) explain in hushed tones, a moray will launch "raptorial pharyngeal jaws out of its throat and into its oral cavity, where the jaws grasp the struggling prey animal and transport it back to the throat and into the oesophagus." Okay, that's enough, thank you very much. 3) They are often seen with red rock shrimp crawling about on them, the shrimps likely cleaning the eels.

FAMILY OPHICHTHIDAE—Snake Eels or Worm Eels

Snake eels are mostly marine fishes with a few members that live in freshwater, apparently on a whim. With a whopping 52 genera and about 310 species, they are found throughout the world in tropical and warm-temperate waters. Eight species live within our range and three species enter Southern California. Snake eels are oviparous and have planktonic leptocephali larvae. Fischer et al. (1995) contain keys to, and descriptions of, the eastern Pacific species.

Ophichthus zophochir
(Jordan & Gilbert, 1882)
Yellow Snake Eel

SCOTT GIETLER

This likely is a yellow snake eel, but, who knows?

ETYMOLOGY: *Ophicthus* comes from two Greek words for "serpent" and "fish" and *zophochir* is Greek for "darkness" and "hand," referring to the dark pectoral fins.

THE BASICS: Maximum Length: 98 cm (39 in) TL. The Ranges: Humboldt Bay (Northern California) to Huacho (Peru), including the Gulf of California. They are pretty common to about as far north as the Long Beach (Southern California) area. Intertidal and surface waters to 110 m (361 ft). Larvae: hatching length = <7.5 mm, transformation length = greater than or equal to 14.7 cm (6 in).

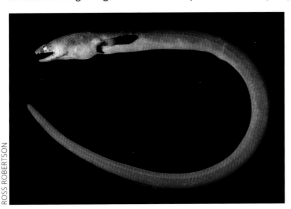

ROSS ROBERTSON

SALIENT CHARACTERS: Yellow snake eels are actually purplish or brown, with a kind of yellowy belly. The front nostril is tubular, there is a barbel between the front and rear nostrils, and usually two barbels behind the rear nostril.

LIFE HISTORY: Not much is known about these reclusive fish. They live in nearshore waters, often in coastal lagoons and estuaries that have a strong ocean influence. You find them in holes in the sand and mud, usually with just their heads sticking out. In southern Mexico, they spawn in the spring and their prey consists of fishes and crustaceans. They are only rarely eaten. Southern California recreational fishermen (often pier anglers) catch fair numbers of them.

TOTALLY UNRELATED RIFF #3—BECAUSE WE HAD SOME SPACE TO FILL

WHEN GOOD MARINE BIOLOGISTS GO BAD

Dr. Luca Turin started his professional life as a marine biologist, only to be seduced by perfumes, and ultimately, the quest for how our sense of smell works. In the process, he managed to run afoul of the dreaded Smell Research establishment and was subjected to the usual round of ridicule that attends anyone whose hypotheses run counter to the norm. Read all about this is Chandler, Burr. 2002. *The Emperor of Scent: A Story of Obsession*. Random House, New York.

FAMILY NEMICHTHYIDAE—Threadtail Snipe Eels

Snake eels are relatively deep-water marine and pelagic fishes, found throughout the world from the tropics to cold-temperate waters. There are three genera and about nine species, four of which occur within our range. Snipe eels are oviparous and have leptocephalus larvae.

Nemichthys scolopaceus
Richardson, 1848
Slender Snipe Eel

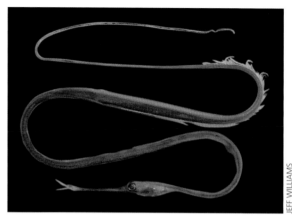

ETYMOLOGY AND COLLOQUIAL NAME: *Nemichthys* is Greek for "thread" and "fish" and *scolopaceus* is Latin for "snipe." They are "shigiunagi" in Japanese.

THE BASICS: Maximum Length: 145 cm (57 in) TL. The Ranges: Circumglobal in temperate and tropical waters; Japan; Gulf of Alaska to southern Chile (52°S), including the Gulf of California. Primarily mesopelagic and bathypelagic, sometimes over continental shelf, surface to 4,337 m (14,225 ft).

SALIENT CHARACTERS: These very distinctive fish are extremely long and thin, with singular-appearing curved jaws that do not close. At maturity, both males and females lose their teeth and the jaws of males shorten. The ones I have seen off Southern California, both those dead and those underwater, were blackish or dark brown.

LIFE HISTORY: Just about the big zippo is known about this species. The few that we have seen from manned submersibles have been swimming very close to the seafloor, over soft substrates. Fish in the Atlantic feed on midwater crustaceans.

FAMILY NETTASTOMATIDAE—Duckbill Eels

The duckbill eels are tropical and warm temperate fishes found in the Pacific, Atlantic, and Indian oceans. There are six genera and about 38 species, two species live within our geographic range.

Facciolella equatorialis
(Gilbert, 1891)
Dogface Witch Eel

ETYMOLOGY: In 1938, G. P. Whitley coined the genus *Facciolella* and does not appear to have given the derivation of the word. *Equatorialis* refers to the Equator, site of the species capture.

THE BASICS: Maximum Length: 90 cm (35.4 in). The Ranges: Point Conception (California) to at least Panama, including Islas Galápagos. At 64–1,000 m (210–3,280 ft). Eggs: 0.8–0.9 mm.

SALIENT CHARACTERS: This species is elongate and eel-like, with no pectoral fins and a pointed snout with a large fleshy tip.

LIFE HISTORY: This is a rarely caught and rarely observed species, and thus little is known of their behavior. I see them occasionally during deepwater surveys, always close to the bottom. John Butler, who took the very nice image that graces this account, writes: "One night we dove [with an ROV] in Scripps Canyon and saw lots of them. They were swimming heads down and diving into the mud. Whether that is their normal behavior or they were taking advantage of the ROV lights is not clear to me."

Dogfaces live to at least 6 years old. They may mature at three to four years old and fish may reproduce during the fall or winter. It is likely that this species feeds on small crustaceans.

ORDER CLUPEIFORMES

FAMILY ENGRAULIDAE—Anchovies

Anchovies are like the peanuts of the sea, everyone seems to eat them and no fish can seem to stop at just one. Easy to recognize, anchovies have prominent snouts and under-slung lower jaws, giving them kind of a reverse Hapsburg look. Engraulids are marine, estuarine, and freshwater fishes found throughout the world in tropical and temperate waters. There are 16 genera and maybe 139 species of which 14 species have been taken within our range. Four species reach as far north as Southern California. All anchovies are oviparous and have planktonic eggs and larvae. Can't get enough of these smarmy fishes? Check out the descriptions and keys of eastern tropical Pacific species in Fischer et al. (1995).

In the 1930s, American tuna fishermen, using anchovies for bait off Mexico and Central America, called them "bloodless."

Engraulis mordax
Girard, 1854

Northern Anchovy

A small schooling fish sporting the confused look of someone who has just read Wittgenstein.

ETYMOLOGY: *Engraulis* comes from the Greek word for a European anchovy and *mordax* means "biting" in Latin.

THE BASICS: 24.8 cm (10 in) TL. The Ranges: Yakutat (eastern Gulf of Alaska) to Cabo San Lucas (southern Baja California), and in the Gulf of California. Typically from at least southern British Columbia to Bahia Magdalena (southern Baja California), and in the Gulf of California. Surface and surf to 310 m (1,017 ft). Eggs: 1.2–1.6 mm x 0.7–0.8 mm. Larvae: hatching length = 2.5–3 mm, flexion length = 6.5–10 mm through 10.5–13.5 mm (0.2–0.6 in), transformation length = about 3.5–4 cm (1–2 in). Von Bertalanffy parameters (SL, mm): (sexes combined) L_∞ = 165.5, k = 0.299, t_0 = -1.71 (Spratt 1975). Length-weight parameters (TL, mm, kg): (sexes combined) W = $0.000000005601L^{2.984}$ (RecFin 2009).

SALIENT CHARACTERS: This is a long, reasonably round-in-cross-section fish, blue or green on back, and silvery on belly. Its anal fin begins below the rear of its dorsal fin. Northerns have large, underslung mouths. Slough anchovy are more compressed, the anal fin starts under the middle of the dorsal fin, and they look a bit more relaxed.

LIFE HISTORY: Northern anchovy are pelagic schooling fish that are an extremely important prey item for many marine animals. Larvae begin to school at about 1.1–1.2 cm (0.4–0.5 in) SL. Juveniles and adults are found anywhere from the surf zone (where they occasionally get thrown up on to beaches) to more than 482 km (300 mi) off the coast and schools are generally most abundant in the top 50 m (164 ft) of the water column. And while you can find them in offshore waters, they often live in such nearshore habitats as kelp beds, bays, coastal lagoons, and, in warmer waters, the occasional mangrove forest. Schooling is often more intense during the day with fish dispersing a bit at night and the fish may also be a bit shallower and/or inshore during the day. While a few enter (rarely) freshwater, they are most common in brackish and marine waters of perhaps 20 ppt and greater and they have been taken in waters between at least 8.5–25°C (47–77°F). This species may school with Pacific sardine, eulachon, and juvenile herring. This is a highly migratory species with schools charging up and down Central and Southern California and northern Baja California. One study conducted in Southern California found that the fish tended to hang inshore during the fall and move offshore in late winter. Several studies have implied that there is some genetic separation within the species, particularly between fish living in southern Baja California and those further to the north. One study identified a northern subpopulation located from Eureka (Northern California) to the Queen Charlotte Islands (British Columbia).

THE FOODS THAT DEFEATED HITLER—No. 27

"British Columbia anchovies have a fine, delicate flavour, comparable to that of the best Norwegian bristling sardines. During the war when packs of the latter were unavailable, British Columbia canned anchovies captured some of the markets for Norwegian canned sardines" (Roach and Harrison 1948).

This is a relatively short-lived species; it lives to about 7 years old and growth rates vary with geographic location. In one study, fish in Central California and offshore of Southern California tended to grow faster than those in nearshore Southern California and off Baja California. Size and age at maturity appears also to vary perhaps both with year and location. In general, a few fish are mature at as small as 8.1 cm (3 in) SL and maybe one year old. By 2 or 3 years old, most northern anchovy are mature, and all are mature by 15 cm (6 in) and 4 years old. During the 1982–1983 El Niño, northern anchovy tended to grow more slowly (perhaps due to reduced food availability), but on the other hand, their eggs matured faster and the fish spawned further north. Off California and Baja California, northerns spawn throughout the year, with a majority of the spawning occurring from about January–May. Off Oregon and Washington, most spawning appears to take place a bit later, maybe June–August. Spawning apparently only takes place at night and mostly between 10 p.m. and 4 a.m. On average, a newly mature female spawns about 5 times in her first reproductive season and 24 times by her fourth season. Larger females also produce more eggs per gram of body weight. Batch fecundity for a typical 1-yr-old is 5,896 and it is 12,895 for a 4-year-old. At least one study implies that this species spawns most heavily in upwelled waters. Spawning reportedly takes place in waters between at least 9.9–23.3°C (50–74°F) and mostly in 13–17.5°C (55–64°F). The eggs hatch in 2–4 days. Northern anchovy are almost entirely phyto- and zooplankton eaters. Diatoms, dinoflagellates, radiolarians, foraminifera, silicoflagellates and tintinnids are important, as are harpacticoid and calanoid copepods, crustacean larvae, euphausiids, mysid shrimps, polychaetes, cladocerans, fish eggs, and pelagic snails. Algae are also occasionally consumed. Northern anchovy are one of the most important prey species along the Pacific Coast. Without listing them all, suffice it to say that at least 90 species of fishes, birds, marine mammals, and invertebrates eat this species, and that number is undoubtedly an underestimate.

FISHERY: Northern anchovy were a very common catch of Native Americans in various places in Central and Southern California and were apparently caught in large quantities by First Nation peoples in the Victoria (British Columbia) area. Collins (1892) observed that they were dried by Chinese fishermen in San Diego and sold fresh in the markets of San Francisco. He went on to opine: "Attempts to pickle it in spices for the trade were made as early as 1879, but it is only in recent years that any considerable quantities have been packed this way…During 1888 the experiment of packing them in oil, as 'sardines,' was tried. Only a small amount was treated in this way, but it is said to have met with favor, and it is believed the experiment may lead to important results." *It didn't*.

Since the great "spiced anchovy" caper (heh, heh, pun intended) of the late 19th century, the commercial anchovy fisheries of the Pacific Coast have kind of staggered along, likely with the same gait that Carl "Bobo" Olson (The Hawaiian Swede) affected after being knocked out by Sugar Ray Robinson in 1955. Throughout the next century, the fish were caught, mostly by purse seine, for oil and meal, used as fish food, and occasionally canned, but mostly with landings that were and are modest compared to both Pacific sardine and Pacific mackerel. On the West Coast, most landings are in California, with occasional catches off Oregon and Washington. Today, most of the commercial catch is exported to places like Australia, where the fish are fed to farm-raised bluefin tuna.

However, it is as a baitfish that northern anchovy have shone. The use of this species as live bait goes back at least to 1910, when Southern California Japanese albacore fishermen caught and held them in bait tanks. Later, San Diego tuna clippers would catch northerns along the Baja California coast in such waters as Bahia Tortugas, Bahia Santa Maria, and Bahia Magdalena, on their way south to the tuna grounds. In addition, by the late 1920s and early 1930s, northern anchovy (along with Pacific sardine) were the overwhelmingly popular live bait in the burgeoning partyboat fisheries that sprang up throughout Southern California. In time, many piers also had live bait wells for their anglers. This species is still a mainstay of the partyboat livebait industry.

In my youth, working for a lovely gentleman named Ed Kennedy, I was a deckhand on a vessel that provided live bait for partyboats. We caught northern anchovy using a lampara net, a large net that encircled fish schools and drew them to the boat where they were placed in tanks with circulating water. At the time, Ed had been fishing anchovy for at least 30 years and I must say that, in retrospect, the fish were winning. Because I only got paid when we caught fish and because there were often nights where we did not catch fish, working for Ed was kind of like doing volunteer work at a halfway house. On the other hand, there were occasional moments at sea when, despite the meager pay, it was all worth it. I remember one time we had made a set on an anchovy school just south of the wharf at Santa Barbara. It was maybe 2 a.m. and just pitch-black. There was a lot of bioluminescence in the water and as we drew the net back toward us the fluttering shoal of anchovy inside the net caused its contents to simply pulsate with blue-green fire. I was struck dumb and Ed was sufficiently moved that he immediately had his third beer of the night, the can he had been saving for the ride back to the harbor.

DOMOIC, YOU KNOW I'M STOIC, 'BOUT YOU

It's one of the baddest boys of the food-derived toxins. Domoic acid (DA), an amino acid produced by diatoms of the genus *Pseudo-nitzschia*, accumulates in the digestive tracts of such planktivores as northern anchovy, Pacific mackerel, and Pacific sardine, and is magnified to lethal concentrations in such fish eaters as California sea lions and brown pelicans. Although it is likely that outbreaks of DA poisoning have occurred for a very long time along the Pacific Coast, well-documented events include the deaths of hundreds of pelicans in 1991 and equal numbers of California sea lions in the Monterey Bay area.

Pier fishermen often catch northern anchovy for bait, although I have seen thousands caught on such piers as San Francisco's Pier 7 and taken home to be eaten by lucky anglers. They are also taken on occasion by beach and bank fishermen plying relatively calm, inshore waters.

ORIGINS AND RELATIONSHIPS: *Engraulis* sp. fossils go back to the Late Miocene (at least 5.3 million years ago). While no one has looked at the relationship between northern and slough anchovies, Burridge (2002) poking around in anchovy DNA, estimated that northerns separated from *Engraulis ringens* (which lives off Peru) about 6–10 million years ago. A northern anchovy otolith was discovered in a Late Pliocene (at least 1.8- million-year-old) deposit in Southern California.

MISCELLANY: Various kinds of abnormal vertebral development have been noted, including both lordosis (dorso-ventral curvature) and scoliosis (lateral spinal curvature). Larry Allen et al. (2002) estimated that there were 42 million northern anchovy in San Diego Bay.

REMARKS: Northern anchovy have been in the California Current for at least 5 million years. But genetic evidence points to a huge crash in the population about 290,000 years ago when the entire population may have been comprised of less than 25,000 individuals. Lecomte et al. (2004) hypothesize that around that time, during a glacial maximum, there may have been virtually no upwelling (and thus little zooplankton) all along the Pacific Coast and this species may have starved. At some point, prevailing northwesterlies returned, followed by the northern anchovy. Like Pacific sardine, their pelagic compadres, northern anchovy populations go through boom and bust cycles and often good times for anchovies are bad times for sardine and vice versa. Off Southern California, over the last 2,000 years or so, anchovy numbers have undergone a series of up and downs, with each cycle spanning about 60 years.

Anchoa compressa
(Girard, 1858)
Deepbody Anchovy

Deepbodies grow to a rugged 16.5 cm (7 in) TL. They have been found from Morro Bay (Central California) to Bahia Magdalena (southern Baja California), commonly from about Long Beach (Southern California) southward. While they occur from the surf zone down to depths of perhaps 18.5 m (61 ft), they rarely seem to range deeper than about 12.1 m (60 ft). Young-of-the-year settle in shallow, calm waters in the summer. Deepbodies live mostly in such shallow and quiet coastal waters as Anaheim and San Diego bays, although large schools occasionally appear on the open coast. They live to at last 6 years old (but most die at 5 years or less), females grow larger than males, and fish mature when around 8 cm (3 in) SL long and one year old. Females produce between about 1,800–32,000 eggs. In Southern California, spawning occurs from March–August, apparently peaking around May. Spawning occurs at night.

Deepbody anchovy eat mostly small crustaceans (e.g., ostracods, copepods, cumaceans, amphipods, mysid shrimps, and crustacean larvae), as well as polychaetes, snails, insects, and arrow goby. Predators include California halibut, gray smoothhounds, and elegant and least terns. Although

Kind of neat, yes? This deepbody anchovy was preserved, then its flesh cleared, and bones stained.

never a particularly important commercial species, Collins (1892) noted that Chinese fishermen in San Diego Bay caught and dried them. Today, recreational anglers catch them from piers for use as live bait. The genus *Anchoa* goes back to the Late Miocene (at least 5.3 million years ago). Eggs: 0.6–0.9 mm. Larvae: hatching length = 1.5–2.5 mm, flexion length = 5.5–6.5 mm through 10–10.5 mm (0.2–0.4 in), transformation length = between 2–2.8 cm (1 in). Von Bertalanffy parameters (SL, mm): (females) L_∞ = 118, k = 0.5, t_0 = -0.61; (males) L_∞ = 110, k = 0.65, t_0 = 0.43 (Heath 1980). Length-weight parameters (SL, mm, gr): (sexes combined) W = $0.0000018L^{3.422}$ (Heath 1980).

Anchoa delicatissima
(Girard, 1854)
Slough Anchovy

Slough anchovy grow to 12.9 cm (5.1 in) SL and 21 gr, and are found from Marina del Rey (Southern California) to Bahia Magdalena (southern Baja California), mostly from Alamitos Bay (Southern California) southward. They are a nearshore species, living occasionally on the open coast, but more often in embayments (sometimes in estuaries) from the intertidal to a depth of at least 15.5 m (51 ft). Larry Allen et al. (2002) estimated that there were 18 million of them in San Diego Bay. Females grow larger than males and fish typically live to 2 years old (with a few females making it to 3). Fish mature at as small as 4.8 cm (2 in) SL and 1 year old. In California, spawning occurs at night from at least April–October, but mostly May–August. Females produce between 2,200–10,000 eggs. Slough anchovy are planktivores and feed on copepods and such other small crustaceans as cumaceans and cladocerans. Eggs: 0.8–1.1 x 0.5–0.6 mm. Larvae: hatching length = 2–2.5 mm, flexion length = 6–7 mm through 9.5–11 mm. Von Bertalanffy parameters (SL, mm): (females) L_∞ = 81, k = 1.03, t_0 = 0.06; (males) L_∞ = 76, k = 1.27, t_0 = 0.01 (Heath 1980). Length-weight parameters (SL, mm, gr): (sexes combined) W = $0.00000143L^{3.489}$ (Heath 1980).

FAMILY CLUPEIDAE—Herrings

The clupeids, close relatives of the anchovies, are a large group of marine, estuarine, freshwater, and anadromous fishes that live throughout the world. There are about 57 genera and 190 species, with 10 species within our range, eight of which reach into Southern California and points north. Clupeids are oviparous with planktonic eggs and larvae. Fossils of fish described as "clupeomorpha" have been found in Late Jurassic formations (at least 161 million years ago) and the oldest Clupeidae (i.e., *Knightia* spp.) are known at least from the Paleocene (a minimum of 55.8 million years ago). A poorly known clupeid, currently called *Bamlettia* cf. *chicoensis*, and described only from a couple of incomplete scales, was found in Late Cretaceous strata (at least 71 million years ago) in California. By the Miocene (5.3 million years ago and more), there were a number of herring-like fishes living along the Pacific Coast.

Alosa sapidissima
(Wilson, 1811)
American Shad

ETYMOLOGY: *Alosa* apparently comes from a Saxon word for the European shad and *sapidissima* is Latin for "most delicious."
THE BASICS: Maximum Length: 76 cm (30 in) TL. Maximum Weight: 5.5 kg (12.1 lb). The Ranges: Shad are native to the Atlantic and were introduced into the Sacramento River in 1873 (see below) and later into the Columbia, Snake, and Willamette rivers. Currently from Kamchatka (Russia) to the southeastern Bering Sea and Gulf of Alaska and to Bahia de Todos Santos (northern Baja California), most commonly from Washington State to San Francisco Bay. Surface waters to depths of 250 m (820 ft), and possibly to 375 m (1,230 ft). Eggs: unfertilized = 1.8 mm, fertilized = 2.5–3.8 mm. Larvae: hatching length = 5.7–10 mm. Length-weight parameters (FL, mm, kg): (sexes combined) $W = 0.00000006248L^{2.6254}$ (RecFin 2009).
SALIENT CHARACTERS: These are deep-bodied, rather compressed fish, with a blue back and silvery sides. They have a very noticeable row of keeled scales on the belly. A single row of dark spots on the back distinguishes them from everything other than Pacific sardine, and sardine are rounder in cross-section and do not have as sharp a series of belly scales.
LIFE HISTORY: After moving down stream from freshwater nursery grounds, juvenile American shad live in estuaries for a few months to several years, after which they move out to sea. While at sea they…well, who knows what they do? I've caught them in bottom gill nets off Central California in 37 m (120 ft) of water, so perhaps they frequent deeper waters. We do know that the fish remain at sea for as little as one year, returning as juveniles for a few months, or as adults to spawn. Depending on river system, adult fish may return as early as May, but mostly in the fall. Shad are anadromous and many or most return to their natal waters to spawn, although fish in Millerton Lake (California) are landlocked. Spawning occurs in the water column (no nests for them), mostly at night, and females spawn nightly until they run out of eggs. Peter Moyle (2002) reports that fish tagged in the Sacramento River have been recovered at sea as far north as Eureka (Northern California) and as far south as Monterey Bay. By the way, Peter's tome has a lot more details about American shad, so if you are interested in this species, his book is the place to go.

On the Pacific Coast, American shad live to at least 7 years old (11 years on the Atlantic Coast). Most males mature at 3–4 years (perhaps at around 30.5–44.7 cm, 12–18 in, FL) and most females at 4–5 years (38.3–48.5 cm, 15–19 in). Spawning occurs over sandy and gravel areas of rivers from April–September. During spawning, a male nudges a female and they swim side-by-side, releasing sperm and eggs. Females produce between 58,534–659,000 eggs. These eggs have been called "semi-demersal," being slightly heavier than freshwater. Hatching occurs in 3–12 days and the larvae transform to juveniles in about 4 weeks. American shad feed primarily in the water column and primarily on invertebrates. Depending on what is available major foods include euphausiids, mysid shrimps, copepods, gammarid and hyperiid amphipods, cladocerans, insects and insect larvae, and fish larvae. One study found small amounts of clams in their diets. Adults reportedly rarely feed during their upstream migrations. Predators include lingcod, soupfin and white sharks, spiny dogfish, striped bass, white sturgeons, harbor and northern fur seals, and Dall's porpoises. And in other news, at least two harbor porpoises choked to death while trying to swallow American shad.

LIVINGSTON STONE, ACE FEDERAL FISH MAVEN

It wasn't easy getting thousands of baby shad from the East Coast to the Sacramento River, but in 1873 Livingston Stone and his associates did it. Several years later Stone wrote of his adventure (Stone 1876), beginning his narrative by noting: "We left the shad-hatching works at Castleton, on the Hudson, for the Castleton railroad-station at 6 o'clock on the afternoon of Wednesday, June 25, with forty thousand young shad packed in eight cans of water, each holding ten gallons." Stone goes on to describe the hurdles and difficulties of shepherding these fish through 100°F Chicago and freezing snow-covered Wyoming Territory.

For 5 tense days, in unheated railroad cars, often refilling the containers with water of dubious quality, the intrepid shadmen kept their charges alive. Stone wrote: "We thought we had reason to feel encouraged. Our spirits rose accordingly. The terrible strain of the past five days of anxiety began to slacken. We did not know what was coming that very night, or we should not have felt so well over it, for the next night was the most alarming and critical of the whole journey." What happened was that as the train left Ogden, Utah, the night air temperature began to drop precipitously, as did the water in which the shad resided. The water had to be kept warmer than 16.6°C (62°F) and during previous cold periods Stone and associates had heated water over various stoves or even open fires in the train cars. But now the railroad men informed them that there was no way to heat water. Thinking fast, one of the men "persuaded the engineer to heat some iron couplings in the furnace of the engine, and then to put them when red hot into our pails filled with water. This water was, or course, dirty and unfit for use in many other respects; so Mr. Green took the larger tin pail, and filled it with warm [unclean] water, and set into it a smaller one containing good, but cold, water. In this way, he heated a sufficient quantity for immediate use." Well, that was the beginning of a long night filled with frantic men begging puzzled railroad employees to heat water in all sorts of ways.

But it all worked and a few days later, at about 9:10 p.m. on 2 July 1873, about 35,000 young shad from the Hudson River, New York, were deposited safely into the Sacramento River, at Tehama, California, thereby helping to assure that the natural fish assemblage of the Sacramento would be screwed up royally for the rest of eternity.

FISHERY: Historically, most of what commercial fishery there was for shad occurred on the Columbia and Sacramento rivers. In the early 20th century, many fresh or frozen fish were shipped by rail to eastern cities; some were salted and shipped to Asia, and the roe was canned. During World War II, when fish were in huge demand, large quantities were kippered and canned. In recent years, there has been a small commercial gill net fishery on the Columbia River and most of those fish are caught for their roe. I do see whole fish fairly often in the fish markets of San Francisco's Chinatown. Native American fisheries (with dipnets, hoopnets, and traps) for this species also occur on the Columbia.

Shad are taken fairly commonly from piers, beaches, and boats. Places like the Pacifica Pier and various sites in San Francisco Bay and up the Sacramento River can be good spots. Sport fishermen catch shad in two ways, angling and "bumping." While I am reasonably sure you already are familiar with angling, bumping may be something of a mystery. In this technique, a dip net is held vertically in the water while the angler stands on a boat or on the shore. When the shad hits the net, the fisherman twists and scoops and the fish is trapped. At least in the past, most shad were either returned to the water (which is fine) or discarded dead (which is stupid). Shad are a bit bony, but they make just the best smoked product. There are simply huge numbers of these fish in the Columbia River (maybe 4–5 million) and a pretty robust sport fishery has developed there. There is some thought that some of these fishermen may be part of a renegade commercial fishery that sells to San Francisco fish markets. Hey, are *all* those guys really taking them home to eat?

ORIGINS: The genus *Alosa* goes back at least to the Eocene (about 34 million years ago). Fossils of a fish that might be the American shad are found in Pliocene deposits (at least 1.8 million years old) on the East Coast.

REMARKS: A while back on the Columbia River, male shad were called "bucks" and females were called "does," on reflection possibly by people who had seen *Bambi* far too many times. Jordan (1922) wrote that he had caught the first shad (at Astoria) that had been recorded from that far north.

SHADY DEALINGS BY THE FOURTH ESTATE

I would imagine that there are nights when, unable to sleep, you get out of bed, drape your robes-de-chambre around your shoulders, and stumble barefoot along the dimly lit hallway to the kitchen. You root around in the pantry, fill a bowl with semi-sweet chocolate chips, and sitting in the dark at the breakfast nook, you ask yourself, yet again: "Who first caught a mature shad in California waters?"

Baltimore Harry, that's who.

Yes, Baltimore Harry. It's all here in *Recollections of a Newspaperman; A Record of Life and Events in California*, by Frank A. Leach (S. Levinson, San Francisco, 1917): "The State Sportsmen's association offered a reward for the first mature shad caught in our waters, but it was not until the spring of 1874 that any one was able to lay claim to the prize…While taking an early morning walk before breakfast, I strayed down on the Main Street wharf to see the fishermen's catches. On this occasion one of the fishermen, 'Baltimore Harry,' announced that he had been waiting for me as he had a strange fish for my inspection. He then presented me with a fish weighing about a pound and a half or two pounds, the like of which I had never seen, but from what I had read and heard I immediately concluded it was the first shad caught on the Pacific Coast. The fisherman said…there appeared to be great quantities of them but they were so small that they escaped through the meshes of his salmon net. I told Harry I thought I could classify his catch but preferred not to just then, and further said that if he would say nothing about this fish, when he caught another I would tell him how he could get $50 for it. The fish he gave me I carefully wrapped and carried to Mrs. Powell to whom I presented it, knowing her acquaintance with the fish and her fondness for it. She immediately pronounced it to be a shad. She cooked the fish and we had it for dinner that night. We thought then, and I have never had occasion to change that opinion, that it was the first shad caught and eaten in California. About two weeks later 'Baltimore Harry' showed me another shad he had caught, about the same size of the one given me. I gave him a letter of introduction to Ramon Wilson, president of the State Sportsmen's Association, and instructed him to give the shad to Mr. Wilson, which he did and received the $50 prize."

So, if I understand this right, Mr. Important Newspaper Editor cons a fish that he is pretty sure is worth $50 from a naïve fisherman and takes it home to eat. And he tells the fisherman, in essence, "Hey, if you catch *another* one, I will tell you how to make $50. Of course, if someone else catches one first and turns it in, then you are just plumb out of luck."

Clupea pallasii
Valenciennes, 1847
Pacific Herring

This is one of those species that people are always nattering about and calling "linchpin."

When Harry's Met Sally's. Herring sperm blanketing a British Columbia cove.

NAOMI AKUNE

ETYMOLOGY AND COLLOQUIAL NAMES: *Clupea* comes from the Latin word for "herring" and *pallasii* refers to Peter Simon Pallas (1741–1811). Pallas was a very talented German naturalist and explorer and apparently one of the most remarkably boring writers of the 18th and early 19th centuries. Canadians usually called them "pilchards" and back in the 19th century they were called "California herring" in the San Diego area. "Yaaw" is Tlingit and "nishin" is the Japanese name.

THE BASICS: Maximum Length: 46 cm (18 in) TL. The Ranges: Korea and Japan to the Arctic Ocean off Alaska and to northern Baja California; also in the Canadian Arctic (as far north and east as Viscount Melville Sound and south and east to Bathurst Inlet) and westward to the White Sea. In the western Pacific, they are abundant from the Sea of Japan northward. In the eastern Pacific and points north, they are abundant from Central California to the Chukchi Sea, then apparently sporadic eastward along the Beaufort Sea until you reach maybe the Tuktoyaktuk Harbour area and then fairly abundant to about Cape Parry (Amundsen Gulf). Early observations, way back in the 1880s, found them to be abundant in San Diego Bay and you can still find little small pockets of them in various Southern California bays and estuaries. Surface to 250 m (820 ft), almost always captured above 150 m (492 ft). The greater depths occasionally reported probably represent fish entering trawls above the maximum tow depth. Eggs: 1.2–1.8 mm. Larvae: hatching length = 5.6–7.5 mm, flexion length = about 1.6–1.9 cm (0.6–0.7 in), transformation length = 2.5–2.7 through 3.5 cm (1 in). A number of age-length curves, from fish from both Asian and North American waters, are plotted in Hay et al. (2008). Length-weight parameters (TL, mm, kg): (sexes combined) $W = 0.00000002519L^{2.849}$ (RecFin 2009).

SALIENT CHARACTERS: A compressed fish, with one short dorsal fin near the middle of the back, abdominal pelvic fins, barely feelable scutes on the belly, and no black spots on the side. You find them with bluish to greenish backs and silvery sides and bellies.

LIFE HISTORY: Young-of-the-year are frequently found schooling in nearshore, sometimes intertidal, waters, often near kelp, eelgrass, and rocky reefs, but also over open seafloors. Herring are most abundant in marine and estuarine waters but will, on occasion, move into freshwater. Some herring populations are highly migratory, moving inshore during spawning season, moving away to feeding areas soon after, and thence to winter offshore grounds after that. In some locations, for instance in the eastern Bering Sea, herring commonly winter 1,200 km (745 mi) or more from shore. At least during their offshore sojourns, fish may stay near the bottom during the day and rise up into midwaters at night. If a Pacific herring knows what is good for it, it will stay in a school and individuals within a school may associate with each other for more than 200 days while traveling over 185 km (115 m). In the southeastern Bering Sea, herring have been taken in waters as cold as −2.1°C (28°F).

There are all kinds of genetic, behavioral, and morphological studies that demonstrate that herring form semi-discrete or perhaps more accurately, semi-semi-discrete populations. Some groups of fish move about considerably and others do not and thus each bunch may have its own growth rate, size at first maturity, and/or spawning season. For instance, fish spawning in San Francisco and nearby Tomales bays (really just a duck confit's toss apart) have different growth rates and harbor somewhat different parasite communities. Even within a relatively small area, like in the Strait of Georgia or in Puget Sound, there are both migratory and nonmigratory stocks.

Pacific herring spawn in sheltered areas from the intertidal down to depths of about 20 m (66 ft). Most occurs in ocean or estuarine waters, although folks living in Shishmaref Inlet in the southeastern Chukchi Sea report that herring used to spawn in local freshwater rivers, so you never know. Spawning often occurs year after year in the same location. In some (but not all) areas, like San Francisco and Tomales bays, adult herring move in a couple of months prior to spawning. As spawning commences, males appear to just plaster the water with sperm, perhaps in some instances even before females lay their eggs. Sherwood et al. (1991) found a pheromone associated with herring sperm that may act to trigger release of eggs. Pheromone-crazed females lay their eggs on hard surfaces and, although a lot of work has been done on this, it is still not

JANNA NICHOLS

clear if every herring female thinks the same way about what is optimal spawning substrate. Suffice it to say that algae and other aquatic vegetation and boulders are often used, but at one time or another eggs have been observed on just about any available hard stuff. When spawning is heavy, females will lay eggs on top of previously deposited ones (occasionally to the tune of 20 egg layers deep and maybe 5 cm, 2 in, thick) and in these instances hatching of the inner eggs is poor. In at least some areas, spawning is heaviest at night, although plenty of daytime spawning can occur.

Older and larger fish tend to spawn earliest and a female spawns all of her eggs in 1–2 days. At some locations, spawning occurs in several waves that are around 2 weeks apart. Fish in San Francisco Bay tend to spawn on the quarter moon (when the tidal range is relatively low and currents are relatively weak). Whether a fish returns to spawn where it hatched is unknown, but wouldn't it be cool if it did?

Pacific herring live to at least 19 years old (that was one from the Beaufort Sea), but in general 15 years or less seems like the maximum life span for fish in most stocks. Fish living in Asian waters are larger at age than those in the Bering Sea and the latter are larger at age than fish from the northeast Pacific. In general, Pacific herring living in warmer waters mature at a younger age and may not live as long. California fish tend to mature at around 2 years, most are mature at 3 years off British Columbia, 3–4 (or perhaps 5) years in the eastern Bering Sea, and fish in Tuktoyaktuk Harbor, way the hell and gone in the Canadian Arctic, don't spawn until around 6–8 years old. Growth rates vary so much, even within very circumscribed areas (like Puget Sound),

DR. ROSS DOG FOOD IS DOGGONE GOOD

From Marie De Santis's lovely book *Neptune's Apprentice* (Presidio Press, 1984): "In the 1950s [California commercial fisherman] Freckles and a few others were supplying Dr. Ross Petfood with herring. This market seemed to have potential, until it was found that the herring made the dogs constipated. Freckles pleaded with them to add just a little castor oil to each can. But, alas, Dr. Ross just quit buying."

Yet another good idea that came a cropper (or, more precisely, a crapper).

that I won't even try to generalize size at first maturity. Over the entire geographic range of the species, fish spawn throughout the year, although here, too, water temperatures play a role. As a rule of thumb, or more precisely, pectoral ray, herring in more southerly areas spawn earliest (e.g., maybe September–April in California) and latest in the far north (June through, occasionally, September, in the northern Bering, Chukchi, and Beaufort seas). Spawning dates are highly variable, however, even among the various spawning populations within a relatively small area like Puget Sound. At some locations, a spawning season can last as long as 6 months. Spawning seasons for the entire west coast of North America are figured and discussed in simply excruciating detail in Stout et al. (2001). Females produce between 9,511–77,800 eggs and larger females have larger eggs. In general, females in the southern part of the range have more eggs per body length than do those further north. Eggs are colorless when first emitted, becoming silver-gray near hatching. Larvae hatch in anywhere from 6–21 days at 5–12°C (41–54°F) with optimum temperatures at perhaps 5–9°C (41–48°F). Eggs and larvae can survive salinities between 6.1–34.3 ppt (but best if spawned in 12–16 ppt) and eggs are more likely to die if exposed to air. There is simply a tonnage of information on early life history in Garrison and Miller (1982).

WHEN HERRINGS PASS GAS

As just about everyone knows by now, both Pacific and Atlantic herrings pass gas. But, for the thankfully few of you who inhabit the state of Idaho, live in shacks guarded by minefields, and thus have little or no truck with the more civilized world, I will explain. Both herring species produce gas either in the gut or swim bladder and, in what appears to be a controlled way, release it out their anal openings. This pulse of gas, termed a Fast Repetitive Tick (FRT) [really] is produced mostly at night and the rate of FRT production increases as the density of herring within a school increases. Thus, it appears that in herrings, as in humans, flatulence has a communicative function. The difference being that most of that kind of communication in humans is between 13-year-old males.

In the world of performance arts,
The herrings may just play their parts,
They comment on society,
And deny its propriety,
By releasing just millions of farts.

Herring are planktivores. While euphausiids and copepods often dominate their diets, they also consume a wide range of small prey including larvaceans, cladocerans, fish and crustacean larvae, hyperiid and gammarid amphipods, oligochaetes, ostracods, arrow worms, water column snails (*Limacina helicina*), and polychaetes. In at least one study, juveniles fed only during the day. Eastern Bering Sea and northern Gulf of Alaska fish do not feed much during the winter. Predator-prey-wise, in some locations on the Pacific Coast herring are just about the biggest game in town. Hay et al. (1992), referring to British Columbia waters, noted: "Herring may be the single most important prey for many seabird species. Most predation would occur on the juvenile stages, because most of the older age classes migrate further out to sea and are found in deeper waters." And Gerke (2002) opined: "Pacific herring provide the major food base for many marine birds, mammals, and fish and are heavily preyed upon throughout all stages of their life cycle." Just a zillion animals eat Pacific herring and I am not even going to try to list them all. By my count, at least 52 fish species, 16 sea bird species (undoubtedly a substantial underestimate), along with all kinds of seals and sea lions, whales, porpoises, and dolphins are on the list and I suspect this does not nearly do justice to what eats this fish. And not to be outdone, Pacific herring eggs are eaten by at least eight species of fishes, 37 bird species, as well as gray whales, snails, sea stars, kelp crabs, sea anemones, sea cucumbers, red sea urchins, gumboot chitons, and nudibranchs. To give you an idea of the intensity of the egg-dining experience, at one spawning site in British Columbia an estimated 20,000 surf scoters and 25,000 gulls ate herring roe and around one island in Prince William Sound, five bird species ate an estimated 857.1 metric tons of eggs.

FISHERY: Pacific herring were an important part of the diets of many of the coastal tribes all along the Pacific Coast. Undoubtedly one of the keenest observers of the First Nation peoples of the Pacific Northwest was John Jewitt (1783–1821). An Englishman, in 1803 Jewitt sailed as a blacksmith aboard the American trading vessel *Boston*, bound for Nootka Sound, on the west coast of Vancouver Island. Once anchored in the sound, the *Boston*'s captain and the chief of the local tribe commenced on the preliminaries leading to full-scale trading. And, in a stunningly short period of time, in what appears to be a remarkable combination of hubris, racism, and raw stupidity, the captain managed to deeply offend the chief, who was already angry for the past transgressions of white traders. That gentleman's pride was sufficiently wounded that he returned the following day with a number of associates and promptly massacred every one except for Jewitt and one other sailor. Through some fast talking, Jewitt managed to convince his captor that his talents as a blacksmith would be valuable and that, oh by the way, he was willing to become the chief's slave for life. For the next 2 years, Jewitt lived with the tribe, apparently keeping a rather scrupulous diary of the people's daily lives. He was rescued in 1805 and, upon his return to New England several years later, wrote an account of his experiences, one that has been published under various titles for almost 200 years.

Well, all of that was a fairly long-winded way to introduce this passage from Jewitt's diary regarding the capture of herring during their winter inshore migrations (I quote below from the very nice edition *The Adventures and Suffering of John R. Jewitt: Captive of Maquinna*, University of Washington Press, 1987): "The following method they employ to take the herring. A stick

PETER SIMON PALLAS

Born in Berlin, and trained as a physician, Pallas wrote a number of works on the animals of Europe. In 1767, clearly not interested in medicine, Pallas made his way to Russia where, at the invitation of Catherine the Great, he joined the Academy of Sciences in St. Petersburg. Within 2 years, he and a group of scientists embarked on a journey of exploration, traveling eastward to beyond Lake Baikal, an extremely strenuous and dangerous journey indeed. Over 6 years, Pallas acquired lots of animals and minerals, collected plants like a Prussian gopher, and made copious observations on the various human cultures he encountered. Most of the rest of his life was spent describing what he found in this and a subsequent expedition, along with acting as a tutor for Catherine's two grandkids, Alexander and Constantine. The fact that the former was complex and manipulative and the latter was generally clueless and tyrannical should not, I think, be laid at Pallas's door.

Although he was undeniably a brilliant scientist, there appears to be general agreement that his writing style left much to be desired. His work has been described by one translator as "both lifeless and dull," and Baron Cuvier commented that something should have been done to relieve the "long and dry enumeration of mines and forges, and often repeated catalogues of common plants and birds he encountered, which do not supply agreeable reading." On the other hand, Cuvier, who was often very complementary of Pallas's science, also tried to explain this dullness by noting that much of the writing was done under very difficult conditions (as quoted by B. Mearns and R. Mearns. 1988. *Biographies for Birdwatchers*. Academic Press, London): "Amongst people who bear the stamp of all the miseries of the country, generally disgustingly dirty, often frightfully ugly, and always dreadfully stupid —all this could but damp the liveliest imagination." *Gee, I'll say*.

While Pallas's best known work is his three-volume *Zoographia Rosso-Asiatica*, my favorite title is, of course, *On the Best Ways for Liberation from Helminths*, his homage to the tapeworms.

of about seven feet long, two inches broad, and half an inch thick, is formed from some hard wood, one side of which is set with sharp teeth, made from whale bone, at about half an inch apart. Provided with this instrument, the fisherman seats himself in the prow of the canoe, which is paddled by another, and whenever he comes to a shoal of herring, which cover the water in great quantities, he strikes it with both hands upon them, and at the same moment turning it up, brings it over the side of the canoe, into which he lets those that are taken drop. It is astonishing to see how many are caught by those dexterous at this kind of fishing, as they seldom fail when shoals are numerous, of taking as many as ten or twelve at a stroke, and in a very short time will fill a canoe with them."

Tribal peoples also collected herring eggs in large amounts. One of the first abundant seafoods harvested in the new year, eggs were often considered a "high-status" food, worthy of serving to special guests and also valuable as a trade item. Among at least some of the coastal nations, it was also a fishery in which women were involved in every aspect of the process. And while egg-covered algae were often collected, a number of tribes strove to make the process more efficient. They would put branches of hemlock or cedar weighted down with rocks in the intertidal zone. At high tide, herring would deposit their eggs on these structures, and the branches would be collected when the water receded. Most of the eggs were then dried for later consumption. Herring roe is still collected for home use by a number of coastal peoples. Stewart (1977) writes of a modern-day observation in British Columbia: "In the village of Skidegate long lengths of seaweed, creamy amber with spawn, hung from nearly every porch and sun deck; racks and clothes lines in gardens and carports were festooned with it. Some of the kelp was draped over the lines, but much of it hung down full length, held at the top with clothespins, blowing freely in the breeze. The owner of the large hardware store in Charlotte City said he hadn't a clothes pin left in the place."

With the coming of the Europeans, Pacific herring took on considerable commercial importance. In early San Francisco, for instance, herring were often seen in the fresh fish markets. The first export herring fishery occurred in British Columbia in 1877, when the locals salted some and sent them to South America. And for the better part of the next century there was always some demand for the fish for human consumption, for bait in other fisheries, or to be made into oil, fertilizer, or poultry food. In 1947, an attempt was made to develop a canning industry, due to the decline in sardine. This failed because: "To date no method has been devised that will prevent the product from falling apart in the can. This defect greatly reduces the 'eye appeal.'" (Bureau of Marine Fisheries 1949). *Yep, opening a can and seeing random herring shards would do that.*

And then, starting in the 1960s and 1970s, the Japanese—the world's premier fish appreciators—entered this sleepy scene. The Japanese started purchasing Pacific herring exclusively for their eggs. "Kozunoko," salted herring roe, has been a popular food in Japan for a long time, often as a part of New Year's celebrations. Kozunoko means "many children" and eating herring roe has been associated with fertility (although who would want to give birth to small herring, other than herring, of course, is beyond me). In the go-go 1970s, there was a lot of money floating around to purchase this high-status, high-priced food. The American and Canadian fisheries just took off, with seemingly every spawning population a target for gill netters and purse seiners. Dozens of fishermen crowding into small coves with seasons only a few hours long, and the potential for just a ton of money, made for the usual Wild West show. Tales floated around about Japanese fish buyers armed with

WHAT ABOUT "HERRING PETE"?

Ah, Herring Pete, what a good question. And for a semi-edifying and mildly diverting discourse on Peter "Herring Pete" Sather (reading time 0.35 minutes) see **Of Foxes, Humpies, and, in a Rather Tangential Way, Herring** in the section on pink salmon.

suitcases full of greenbacks (or in Canada, one would assume, pinkbacks), who would board a commercial vessel at sea, open up a few of the herring to check the egg quality, then hand over buckets o'cash. How nuts was the roe fishery? This nuts: On 15 March 1987, British Columbia purse seine fisherman Don Dawson made a single haul in Barkley Sound, on the west coast of Vancouver Island. The catch was so large (970 tons) it took 54 hours to complete the haul and the catch had to be shared with 13 different boats. The catch was worth an estimated $2.5 million (Canadian), or about $1.9 million in U.S. currency. Well, all good bubbles, be they tulip, South Seas, subprime mortgage, or herring roe, must come to an end. First, the Japanese economy went south, then kazunoko began to wane as a holiday gift (it is now often viewed as a cheaper, everyday food), and then Chinese and Russian herring roe started competing for the Japanese markets. Today, the herring roe fishery is still important, but some of the Comstock Lode aspect has gone out of the fishery.

Parenthetically, Japanese consumers also like their herring eggs on algae (often called "kazunoko kombu" or "komochi konbu"). There are now two major ways that eggs on algae are harvested. In the first method (which we might call string-the-algae-and-hope), widely practiced as far south as San Francisco Bay, harvesters string kelp in areas thought to contain spawning herring and later retrieve their, hopefully, egg-bearing algae. This is exactly what coastal tribes did, likely for thousands of years. However, some of the coastal peoples of British Columbia have tried to improve the process by creating artificial impoundments for the fish to use. In this technique, enclosures made of floating logs draped with netting are placed in bays near known spawning grounds. Then, giant kelp is strung on ropes within the impoundment. Soon after, a purse seine wraps a likely school and that seiner, along with its net full of fish, is towed to the impoundment by a second boat. The fish are released into the impoundment and everyone kind of keeps their fingers crossed. If all goes well, the females lay eggs on the kelp-on-a-rope, the males fertilize them, and everyone of at least two species is happy. After the blessed event, the herring are released and are free to go about their piscine-like business. Irv Leask was involved in this "fishery" and says it was a 24 hour a day process that went on for a month. He lost 30 pounds in that time. Of course, whenever sex is involved in this part of the galaxy, there will be complications. First, the school selected has to be about ready to spawn. Second, cut kelp starts to deteriorate immediately after being severed and the fish have to do their part within 6–10 days. Lastly, even if the herring spawn within that time period, they don't always spawn on the kelp. Sometimes, particularly if there are free herring spawning outside the impoundment, the imprisoned fish lay their eggs on the netting instead of on the algae. And it turns out that your typical Japanese consumer is not too fond of spawn-on-netting.

Along with all this exciting stuff, there are still small subsistence fisheries for herring in various places, all the way to the Beaufort Sea. Along with the roe fishery, Pacific herring are still in demand for bait both in the U.S. and overseas. And, on the recreational front, Pacific herring are often caught by pier, beach, and bank fishermen.

ORIGINS AND RELATIONSHIPS: Based on fossils found in Italy, the genus *Clupea* likely evolved back in the Middle Eocene (perhaps 50 million years ago). The fossil species *Clupea tiejei* from Late Miocene deposits in southern California demonstrates that herring were in that area at least 5.3 million years ago. Based on several studies, it appears that the separation between Pacific herring and the Atlantic species, *C. harengus*, occurred about 3.1 million years ago, when fish came into the Pacific Ocean from the Atlantic, as Arctic waters warmed, allowing free passage.

MISCELLANY: 1) Herring blood contains antifreeze compounds. 2) Experiments show that herring avoid bubbles, such as the type made by humpback whales. Larger schools are more reticent than individuals or small groups to cross bubble walls. 3) Inquiring researchers who played sounds that simulated those made by toothed whales (like dolphins and orcas) found that Pacific herring would cease feeding, drop down in the water column and begin to school. See what million of years of natural selection will do?

REMARKS: Is it an animal or a fungi? Well, no matter, because the pathogen *Ichthyophonus hoferi* has emerged as one of the major players in the kill-the-herring reality show (it also has shown up in such species as Chinook salmon, Pacific tomcod, Puget Sound rockfish, speckled sanddab, and surf smelt). Hershberger et al. (2004), working with Puget Sound herring, state: "We contend that infectious disease should not be dismissed as a major constraint limiting age structure and survival of Pacific herring populations in the region." Deriso et al. (2008), pondering the collapse of herring populations in Prince William Sound, found that *Ichthyophonus* (along with predation by hatchery-raise pink salmon, poor nutrition, and other factors) may be playing a role in impeding herring recovery.

Sardinops sagax
(Jenyns, 1842)
Pacific Sardine

Pacific sardine are small, pelagic schooling fish with a doomed story arc.

KEVIN LEE

ETYMOLOGY AND COLLOQUIAL NAMES: *Sardinops* is Latin for "sardine" and "like" and *sagax* means "alert" in Latin. "Pacific sardine" goes back to the 19th century. On the other hand, Italian fishermen called them "sardina," and "pilchard" was often used, particularly by Canadians.

THE BASICS: Maximum Length: 41 cm (16 in) TL. Maximum Weight: At least 0.5 kg (1.1 lb). The Ranges: In the North Pacific, from south of Japan to southern Kamchatka, to Cross Sound (southeastern Alaska) to Guaymas (Mexico), including the Gulf of California. These fish also live in the western and eastern South Pacific and off southern Africa. A highly migratory species, sardine are periodically abundant as far north as British Columbia, with occasional forays into southeastern Alaska. Surface waters and the surf zone to 150 m (495 ft) or perhaps 246 m (807 ft), young individuals occasionally wander into tide pools. Eggs: 1.3–2.1 mm. Larvae: hatching length = 3.5–3.8 mm, flexion length = 9–10.5 mm through 13–14.7 mm (0.4–0.6 in), transformation length = 2.5–4 cm (1–2 in). Von Bertalanffy parameters (SL, mm): L_∞ = 205, k = 1.19, t_0 fixed at zero (Butler et al. 1996). Length-weight parameters (TL, mm, kg): (sexes combined) W = $0.0000000032L^{3.15}$ (RecFin 2009).

SALIENT CHARACTERS: Another of the cookie-cutter clupeids; semicompressed, gill cover with striations, and dark spots on the sides. Their bodies are blue or green on back and silvery on belly.

LIFE HISTORY: Juveniles often recruit to quiet nearshore waters, although they can also be found a bit away from the coast, sometimes around drifting kelp mats. Sardine are commonly found from the surf zone out to more than 563 km (350 mi) offshore. Although often associated with the open ocean, they can be quite abundant in and around kelp beds, in bays and mangrove forests, and occasionally in estuaries. When abundant, sardine can be found in massive schools, sometimes also containing jack and Pacific mackerel, and northern anchovy. Although there is a tendency for sardine to school during daylight hours and disperse at night, at least one study found that some fish in Monterey Bay school both day and night. Sardine are quite sensitive to water temperatures and the population tends to move northward during warm-water periods and then retreat when waters cool. During really bad times, they are rare even as far north as California, and the main populations resides in Bahia de Sebastian Vizcaino (central Baja California) and environs. Seasonally, larger fish tend to move further northward than do smaller ones. Which takes us into the realm of populations and here biologists have spent many decades looking at a wide range of parameters (e.g., all kinds of meristic, morphological, genetic, and behavioral stuff) and they keep getting kind of cheesy and equivocal results. If populations do exist, they are not completely isolated. The West Coast populations appear to overlap considerably, particularly in Southern California and northern Baja California. Félix-Uraga et al. (2005), for instance, postulate three stocks labeled "cold," "temperate," and "warm." Each stock moves southward in the winter and spring, then northward in the summer and fall. The winter position of the "cold" stock is from California northward and this one migrates as far south as northern Baja California. The winter position of the "temperate" stock occurs from northern Baja California to about Bahia Magdalena (southern Baja California) and this contracts down the Baja California coast and centers in southern Baja California. The "warm" stock is centered around Cabo San Lucas (southern Baja California) in the winter and migrates up into the southern Gulf of California in spring. In the early 2000s, spawning was centered off Central California, but extended to British Columbia and Alaska to the north and all along northern and central Baja California.

Pacific sardine live to at least 16 years old, although few fish survive beyond 8 years. Growth rates and size at maturity appear to be quite plastic, dependent, one assumes, on water temperature and food availability. In one study, fish off Central California and those from the Southern California Bight were larger at age than those from north-central Baja California. On the other hand, the Baja California and Southern California Bight fish tended to mature earlier than those off Monterey. Overall, most fish are mature by about 2 years old and all are mature by 3. Based on egg collections, there is at least some spawning throughout the year off California and Baja California. However, off Southern California, most seems to occur between about February–August with peak spawning periods varying annually. Further south, in the Punta

COURTESY OF TIM THOMAS

Eugenia (southern Baja California) region, spawning may be most intense in the summer and early fall. In the Gulf of California, sardine spawn from November–May, peaking in December and January. Off California, spawning occurs primarily in the transition zone between upwelled inshore waters and those of the offshore California Current. Females are batch spawners, producing about 9,000–101,800 eggs at a go. An average female spawns once every 7 days. Throughout their range, it looks like spawning takes place at temperatures between maybe 13–25°C (55–77°F) or slightly more and peak spawning off California at maybe 12–14°C (57°F). Off California and Baja California, most spawning occurs at night between 7–11 p.m. The eggs are found mainly from surface waters to about 50 m (15 ft) and the larvae, depending on area, hang out down to maybe 70 m (21 ft) or so, but mostly in 30 m (98 ft) or less. Pacific sardine are planktivores and their diets vary depending on what is abundant at the time. Both phytoplankton (e.g., diatoms and dinoflagellates) and zooplankton (particularly copepods and euphausiids, but also larvaceans, fish eggs, and crustacean larvae) are consumed. While perhaps not a lynchpin species, as is its cousin, the Pacific herring, the Pacific sardine is eaten by its share of predators. A random sample of species includes arrowtooth flounder, blue and yellowtail rockfishes, blue, shortfin mako, soupfin, and white sharks, California halibut, Chinook and coho salmon, giant sea bass, kelp bass, lingcod, Pacific barracuda, Pacific hakes, Pacific mackerel, sailfish, starry flounder, striped marlins, swordfish, thresher sharks, white seabass, yellowtail, brown boobies, elegant terns, Heermann's gulls, sea lions, seals, whales, harbor porpoises, and Pacific white-sided dolphins. A study in the Gulf of California estimated that Humboldt squids ate up to 60,000 metric tons during the squids' 9-month residence, perhaps contributing to a very poor fishing season.

FISHERY: Sardine were a significant part of Native American fisheries. However, I think it is fair to say that the commercial sardine industry got off to a slow start. Collins (1892) noted as much when he wrote: "An attempt has recently been made to establish at San Francisco a sardine-canning industry, but the business had not developed to important proportions in 1888-89." Jordan (1884b) concurred: "The question of the possibility of canning it in oil, like the Sardine [of Europe], has been considerably discussed. It would probably prove unprofitable, from the high price of labor and the uncertain supply of fish." This, and his belief that the good sense of the German government would prevent them from starting World War I, seems to be among the few mistakes Jordan made in a long and eventful life.

Early on, the problem was less an absence of sardine along the California coast but rather the difficulty in catching the large numbers needed for an economically viable industry. Thus it was that after a number of false starts the sardine canner F.E. Booth of Monterey, taking the advice of fisherman Pietro Ferrante, purchased a lampara net from Morocco. Lamparas are encircling nets that have the advantage of being relatively light and thus easy for a few fishermen, in a relatively small vessel, to wrap a fairly substantial number of fish. The fishery was a veritable instant success and, with the coming of World War I, the market for canned sardine skyrocketed. By 1917, there were substantial fisheries all up and down the coast, extending into British Columbia, where from the 1920s to the mid-1940s the sardine fishery was the largest fishery in that province. Early on, canners, needing to somehow dispose of sardine heads and guts, and rotten fish, started "reducing" this waste to oil and fish meal. Within a bare number of years, these folks quickly figured out that the real money was not in putting fish in cans, but in the oil that was mostly used for paint, soap, and linoleum and for fish meal that was fed to chickens.

Parenthetically, it was only a matter of time before the same visionaries who gave us the Eton Crop, cloche hat, and four-wheel Steeldraulics on the Hupmobile, should turn their attention to the sardine. Why, they thought, should this fish only be useful as food, meal, and oil, particularly when its highest purpose might be...Pearl Essence? And indeed, Russell (1927) noted this product from the Dallas Pearl Essence Company. "This new product of the great fishing industry is a liquid used in coating artificial pearls, the backs of combs, brushes and all kinds of dressing table sets. About three to four hundred pounds of scales in the moist form are necessary to make one barrel of scale water, which, in turn, produces about one pound of pearl essence."

Meanwhile, the wily processors lobbied the regulators in both California and Washington, D.C. to be allowed to "reduce" more and more of the catch. Without boring you with the details, over the years more and more reduction and take was allowed. By the time World War II began, various regulators just said, "The hell with it," and an essentially unregulated fishery commenced. Looking back, it was kind of unfortunate that the mid-1940s saw the wide-open fishery, for at just this time, the natural up and down cycle of the sardine population was heading, well, down, as falling average sea temperature resulted in poor sardine reproduction. And while it is quite possible that the population would have tanked even without overfishing, the combination drove the sardine population into the toilet. Most of the sardine fishing from Central California to British Columbia ended in the late 1940s, followed by a similar collapse a few years later in Southern California. While there were always a few sardine left in California waters, most of the Pacific Coast population retreated to central Baja California. It was not until the early 1980s, and the return of warmer water conditions, that the Pacific Coast population expanded northward and fisheries began again, albeit on a smaller scale.

Most of the sardine caught on the Pacific Coast are exported. For instance, sardine are sold to Japan for bait in their long-line fisheries and to Australia to feed reared tunas. I note that in the last few years fresh sardine, long a favorite of a cabal of fish lovers, have begun to appear on more restaurant menus and in fish market cases. Grilled sardine are a major treat. When sardine are abundant in California waters they can comprise a major part of the live bait used in the recreational fishery. Every skipper's goal is to have a tank full of pinhead northern anchovy for chum and medium-size sardine for the hooks. Pier fishermen also often catch them for bait.

ORIGINS AND RELATIONSHIPS: Fish in the genus *Sardinops* swam about in Late Miocene waters at least 5.3 million years ago. There don't seem to be any fossils of Pacific sardine in either Pleistocene and Pliocene deposits in California, so it may be that they are a relatively recent addition to the California Current fauna. In fact, Lecomte et al. (2004) present evidence that sardine did not live in the California Current until perhaps 200,000–250,000 years ago. Prior to that, going back to perhaps 300,000 years or more, winds off California may have been light and upwelling almost nonexistent and sardine might have entered the system when upwelling returned.

MISCELLANY: Two lemon-yellow Pacific sardine were taken in Monterey Bay.

REMARKS: Off California, sardine populations are, heh heh, extremely fluid. Baumgartner et al. (1992) were able to count the scales built up in seafloor sediments over the last 2,000 years and came to the conclusion that there were periods when these fish were very abundant and other times when they were just plain absent. It looks like there are, on average, something like 60-year cycles going on. What this means is that, while it might be emotionally satisfying to blame the disappearance of the sardine on overfishing, their populations are capable of crashing all by themselves. As Baumgartner et al. report: "An overriding lesson...is that in the past both sardine and anchovies experienced large natural fluctuations which were clearly unrelated to fishing, and that abrupt natural declines, similar to the collapse of the sardine during the 1940s, are not uncommon."

OTHER SPECIES

Etrumeus teres
(DeKay, 1842)
Round Herring

Round herring grow to 30.5 cm (12 in) TL. Circumglobal, on the West Coast they have been taken from Monterey Bay to Chile, including the Gulf of California. During some years, they are reasonably abundant as far north as Southern California. They are a pelagic, nearshore fish often found in or near the surf zone, and to depths of perhaps 200 m (656 ft), but mostly in 12.1 m (60 ft) or less. Along the West Coast, most reproduction seems to occur during summer and fall. These fish feed on such zooplankton as euphausiids and copepods.

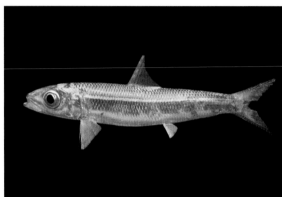
GERALD ALLEN

Opisthonema libertate
(Günther, 1867)
Deepbody Thread Herring

Deepbody thread herring grow to about 30 cm (12 in) TL and range from Port Hueneme (southern California) to Chile, including the Gulf of California. They are occasional visitors to Southern California. This is a nearshore, schooling species (frequently found in coastal lagoons and estuaries), found in 1 m (3 ft) or less to depths of at least 70 m (230 ft). Deepbodies are planktivores, feeding on copepods and diatoms, and also dinoflagellates, euphausiids, and ostracods.

GERALD ALLEN

FAMILY ARGENTINIDAE—Argentines

The argentines are pelagic marine fishes found throughout the world. Of the two genera and 23 species, one species is found within our range. They are oviparous and have pelagic eggs and larvae. Otoliths of members of this family have been recovered from Late Cretaceous (perhaps 71 million years old) strata. Fossil argentines have been found in a 7.6–8.6 million year old Southern California Miocene formation.

Argentina sialis

Gilbert, 1890

Pacific Argentine

ETYMOLOGY: *Argentina* means "silver" in Latin and *sialis* comes from the Greek word for "plump."

THE BASICS: Maximum Length: 22 cm (9 in) TL. The Ranges: Mouth of the Columbia River to the Gulf of California, and probably off northern Peru. 11–325 m (36–1,066 ft). Off Southern California, we see them mostly between about 170–220 m (553–722 ft). Eggs: 1.3–1.7 mm. Larvae: hatching length = 3.5–4 mm, flexion length = 1.1–1.5 cm (0.4–0.6 in), transformation length = about 3.5 cm (1 in). Length-weight parameters (SL, cm, gr): (sexes combined) $W = 0.003L^{3.306}$ (Rodriguez-Romero et al. 2009). Length-weight parameters (TL, cm, gr): $W = 0.0045L^{3.107}$ (Love unpubl.).

SALIENT CHARACTERS: Pacific argentines have that kind of typical smelt shape, along with a single (and tall) dorsal fin plunked in midbody, large eyes, adipose fin, and forked caudal fin. They have a slightly darker back, silvery sides and belly.

LIFE HISTORY: Young-of-the-year settle near the bottom at about 3.5 cm (1 in) SL. We usually see both juveniles and adults in schools, sometimes of only a few fish and sometimes containing hundreds of individuals, often near the bottom, and sometimes lying on the soft sediment.

An 18 cm (7 in) TL fish I aged was about 4 years old. Larvae are present off California throughout the year, although there may be a winter–spring peak. A few larvae have been captured from as far north as Point Reyes (Northern California), giving you some idea of how far north they may spawn. PAs may mature at around 12 cm (5 in) TL, but I have just examined a few, so who knows for sure? I examined a few fish at the Natural History Museum of Los Angeles County and these individuals had

JOHN BUTLER

eaten crustaceans. Pacific argentines are eaten by a variety of predators including bocaccio, California sea lions, harbor seals, common dolphins, and Humboldt squids.

ORIGINS: *Argentina* sp. fossils from the Eocene (at least 34 million years ago) have been found. Remains of Pacific argentines are known from 100,000-year-old strata in California.

FAMILY BATHYLAGIDAE—Deepsea Smelts

Bathylagids are marine pelagic fishes found throughout the world and generally in deep waters. There are eight genera and about 20 species, eight of which live within our range. Deepsea smelts are oviparous with planktonic eggs and larvae. Otoliths from bathylagids have been reported from the Late Cretaceous (perhaps 71 million years ago). The oldest-known fossil deepsea smelt in our region is *Paleobathygadus yaguinensis* from the earliest Miocene or Late Oligocene (at least 22 million years ago). *Bathylagus angelensis* also lived in the Miocene (at least 5.3 million years ago) of Southern California.

Leuroglossus schmidti
Rass, 1955
Northern Smoothtongue

ETYMOLOGY AND COLLOQUIAL NAME: *Leuroglossus* means "smooth" and "tongue" in Greek and *schmidti* refers to the Russian biologist P. Yu Schmidt (1872–1949). The species is called "sokoiwashi-rui" in Japanese.

THE BASICS: Maximum Length: At least 20 cm (8 in) SL. The Ranges: Northern Honshu to Bering Sea and to southern British Columbia, mostly north of the Strait of Georgia (British Columbia). They are very abundant in the Gulf of Alaska and Bering Sea. Near surface to 1,800 m (5,905 ft). Eggs: 1.7–1.9 mm. Larvae: hatching

R. HIBPSHMAN

length = 4–5 mm, flexion length = 1.3–1.8 cm (0.5–0.7 in), transformation length = 3.1–3.5 cm (1 in). Length-weight parameters (SL, mm, gr): (sexes combined) $W = 0.00000369L^{3.167}$ (Mason and Phillips 1985).

SALIENT CHARACTERS: Northerns are elongated, with a pointed snout, short dorsal and anal fins, and an adipose fin. The big characters are the small eyes and the radial striations on the gill cover. They are dark on the back and silvery on sides and belly.

LIFE HISTORY: Northern smoothtongues are epipelagic and mesopelagic fish. Researchers chasing about the northwestern Pacific, found that they are vertical migrators; they are found in 200–500 m (656–1,640 ft) at night and in 500–1,000 m (1,640–3,280 ft) during the day. On the other hand, Abookire et al. (2002) found them in near-surface waters during the daytime in an Alaskan fjord, so it's puzzling, isn't it? Northern smoothtongues observed underwater spent their time in a vertical position with their heads down.

Mason and Phillips (1985), working in the Strait of Georgia (British Columbia), provide the following intimate look at the biology of northern smoothtongues. For females, the estimated length at 50% maturity is 5.9 cm (2 in) SL. Tentatively, both sexes are mature as 2-year-olds, males seldom live beyond 4 years, and females may attain 5–6 years. Males may breed twice and females 3 or more times in a life. Spawning occurs from January–June, perhaps mostly in the late winter and early spring. In other locations, the spawning season may be longer. Larger females spawn earlier in the season. Spawning takes place over the continental slope. The highest density of eggs is in 200–260 m (656–853 ft) and as larvae hatch they migrate upward to depths of about 40–90 m (131–295 ft). Females (at least the larger ones) are multiple spawners, producing 2 or more batches per season. Fecundity has been estimated at 5,000–8,000 eggs. Northern smoothtongues feed on planktonic prey, particularly calanoid copepods, euphausiids, hyperiid amphipods, larvaceans, and arrow worms, but also pteropods, ostracods, ctenophores, medusae, polychaetes, and fish eggs. Predators include fishes (e.g., Atka mackerel, Chinook salmon, Greenland halibut, Pacific cod, Pacific hakes, various rockfishes and skates, spiny dogfish, and walleye pollock), seals, porpoises, and dolphins.

OTHER SPECIES

Leuroglossus stilbius
Gilbert, 1890
California Smoothtongue

California smoothtongues grow to 17.2 cm (7 in) TL and 31 gr (1 oz). They have been found from northern Oregon (45°52'N) to Colombia, including the Gulf of California. A subspecies, *Leuroglossus stilbius urotranus*, has been reported from Chile. California smoothtongues are epi- and mesopelagic fish; they live from near the surface to about 850 m (2,788 ft). Some researchers have found a discrete movement upward at night, while others have captured this species at the surface during the day.

California smoothtongues live to about 5 years old. They mature at about 3 years old and 8 cm (3 in) SL. While a few larvae have been taken in every month, most reproduction occurs in winter and spring. This species is planktivorous, feeding on larvaceans, pelagic tunicates, ostracods, copepods, crustacean larvae, arrow worms, and euphausiids. One study in Southern California found that while smoothtongues fed most intensively during the night in surface waters, there was also some feeding both day and night in middepths. Predators include albacore, Chinook salmon, king-of-the-salmon, various rockfishes, sablefish, walleye pollock, tufted puffins, California sea lions, common dolphins, Dall's porpoise, and Humboldt squids. Eggs: 1–1.2 mm. Larvae: hatching length = about 3 mm, flexion length = 3.5–15 mm, transformation length = 2.4–2.9 cm (1 in).

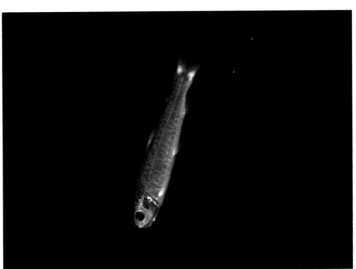

©2006 MBARI

TOTALLY UNRELATED RIFF #4 — BECAUSE WE HAD SOME SPACE TO FILL

PLUS ÇA CHANGE, PLUS C'EST LA MÊME CHOSE

So you think the moaning and groaning about workman's compensation by businessmen in California is a new phenomenon? Here's a statement by a representative of the Union Fish Company regarding the Pacific cod industry (Pacific Fisherman, 1914, Volume 12, Number 1) and headlined "San Francisco Cod Fish Market": "The workmen's compensation act will add another serious handicap to companies operating in California." Ironically, this was published while the dory Pacific cod fishery was robust and remained so for another 25 years.

ORDER SALMONIFORMES

FAMILY OSMERIDAE—Smelts

Well, let's start out by noting that fishes in the family Osmeridae are the "real" smelts. Other species that are called "smelt," like jacksmelt and topsmelt, are only pale, pale imitations. Historically, osmerids were called "whitebait" in California, which likely confused every one. The osmerids are found in marine, estuarine, and freshwater systems throughout the Northern Hemisphere. There are 11 genera and about 31 species, of which 10 occur along the Pacific Coast. All smelts are oviparous with planktonic larvae. The oldest fossil smelt, *Speirsaenigma lindoei*, comes from a freshwater Paleocene (56 million-year-old) site in Alberta (Canada). There is a key to most of the North American smelts in Mecklenburg et al. (2002).

Ever wonder where that cucumber-like odor found in all smelts comes from? Hmmm, well have you? Hey, look at me when I'm talking to you. Okay, it comes from all that *trans*-2-*cis*-6-nonadienal in the skin. Now why that stuff is in smelt skin is unknown.

Hypomesus pretiosus
(Girard, 1854)
Surf Smelt

KIRK LOMBARD

ETYMOLOGY AND COLLOQUIAL NAMES: *Hypomesus* comes from the Greek words "below" and "middle" (referring to the position of the pelvic fins located under the middle of the dorsal fin) and *pretiosus* means "precious" in Latin, referring to its flavor. The name "surf smelt" was bestowed by Swan (1880). "Day smelt" is a very popular name and "silver smelt" is also heard on occasion.

THE BASICS: Maximum Length: 30.5 cm (12 in) TL. The Ranges: Izembek Bay (Alaska Peninsula) and the Gulf of Alaska to Long Beach (Southern California). They are common at least from the Kodiak Island region down to southern Monterey Bay. Surf smelt live in shallow waters. Eggs: 1.1 mm. Larvae: hatching length = 3–5 mm, flexion length = 1.3–1.5 cm (0.5–0.6 in), transformation length = about 4 cm (2 in). Length-weight parameters (TL, mm, kg): (sexes combined) W = $0.000000000869L^{3.386}$ (RecFin 2009).

SALIENT CHARACTERS: An elongated fish with a rounded adipose fin, silver band along the side, a short lateral line, and a small mouth. "The surf smelt is olive on the back, light on the belly and sides, and has a silvery band along the region of the lateral line. The back of the male is darker than that of the female. It bears a distinct brownish tinge, whereas the female's back is a brighter green. The lower sides and belly of the male are yellowish; this region in the female is dead white. Breeding males differ from the females also, by the presence on the sides, side of the head, and fins of numerous minute tubercules" (Schaefer 1936).

LIFE HISTORY: This is a nearshore species that is found in the ocean, estuaries, and occasionally freshwater. Schools of juveniles and adults are common in eelgrass, kelp, and other aquatic vegetation. Adults are also found in areas without vegetation, including in offshore waters. Kind of interesting work by Kilambi et al. (1965) and Kilambi and DeLacy (1967) found that, based on blood groups and infection rates of larval anisakid nematodes, fish living in Puget Sound do not mix much with those dwelling on the outer coast of Washington.

Surf smelt are a relatively short-lived species; a few reach 5 years old. Many fish mature when around 1 year old and some a year later. The spawning season (at least when the entire geographic range of the species is examined) appears to extend throughout the year. Females produce 1,320–36,000 eggs per season, in more than one batch. Females spawn demersal, adhesive eggs on coarse sand and fine-gravel beaches (one study found the usual grain size to be 1–7 mm in diameter) near the high tide line. In the Puget Sound region (according to Penttila 1978), spawning usually occurs around "evening, night or morning high water slack periods. The spawning fish move into water a few inches deep along the water's edge. There

JAMES SWAN

In the mid- to late 19th century, James Swan spent many years among the Native American and First Nation tribes of the Pacific Northwest, and wrote of these peoples with a sense that is far more respectful than virtually any other observer of the time. In 1880, he discussed some of the beliefs that the Quillehute tribe of the northwestern tip of Washington embraced regarding some of their most important fishes: "The Quillehutes still retain the ancient superstition… relative to their fish, that the first ones must not be sold or given away to be taken to another place." Swan obtained some surf smelt and "No sooner did the Quillehutes learn that I was cooking some of their fish than two of the head chiefs came to see what I was doing, as they feared I would cut the fish with a knife; but I fried them whole, and when they saw me take the nice crispy smelts with my hand and eat them entire, without aid of knife or fork, they…allowed me to purchase as many as I wished to take away. But of salmon they would neither give or sell. They fully believed that if we took any salmon into our canoe, all the salmon would desert the Quillehute River…and if we had cut the smelts or salmon with a knife, they all would immediately disappear in the ocean and never return. I was unable to procure even a specimen of the salmon, but obtained enough smelts to forward some excellent specimens to Washington [to the Smithsonian Institution]."

the males and females arrange themselves side by side in groups of 3–4 [often with more than one male accompanying a female] and wriggle vigorously to and fro across the bottom, releasing eggs and sperm…Upon release, the eggs sink to the bottom and upon fertilization an adhesive outer membrane ruptures and turns inside out, anchoring the eggs…by tiny 'pedestals.'" Kirk Lombard, a serious smelt dilettante reporting from Central California, informs me that surf smelt there spawn during the day and not at night. As the tide recedes, the eggs are buried under a few inches of sand. At least in Puget Sound, a particular stretch of a specific beach will be utilized to the exclusion of nearby areas. These spawning sites are apparently used for a few months at about the same season each year. However, even within a small area like Puget Sound, different beaches are spawned upon at different times of the year. Schaefer (1936) observed: "The upper part of beaches used in the summer are usually shaded by overhanging trees…This modulates substrate temperatures. On most of them there is a seepage of freshwater which keeps much of the gravel moist." Eggs hatch in 9–56 days depending on water temperature.

Surf smelt feed on both water column and bottom species and their diets vary with location. In general, crustaceans are a major part of their diets. Commonly encountered foods include calanoid and harpacticoid copepods, isopods, gammarid and caprellid amphipods, cumaceans, shrimps, euphausiids, and crustacean larvae, as well as polychaetes, larvaceans, insects, and occasionally small fishes. Predators include Chinook and coho salmon, striped bass, bald eagles, common murres, rhinoceros auklets, various terns, and seals.

FISHERY: Surf smelt were a very important species to a number of indigenous peoples. Bean (1887b) wrote that they were a food fish in Yakutat Bay (Alaska). Swan (1880) noted that they were caught by the Quillehute tribe, just south of Cape Flattery (Washington) in nets made of stinging nettles: "On the first appearance of the fish the Indians rush into the surf and press the outer edge of the net down firmly on the sand or shingle, the swash of the breaker forcing the smelts into the net…I saw them take at least a bushel at a single swipe."

From the earliest days, the ease of capture (that means it was cheap to catch) and good flavor of surf smelt made them a valued commercial species and most were sold fresh. In general, these fisheries targeted spawning fish and used beach seines or dip nets. Today, this species supports relatively small commercial fisheries in the U.S. and little or none in British Columbia. Recreational fishermen catch substantial numbers. Many are taken using cast nets heaved into the surf, but others use a modified dip net called a "smelt rake" which is plied while standing tush deep in the water. A-frame nets are also utilized, while others are caught by hook-and-line from piers.

ORIGINS AND RELATIONSHIPS: Surf smelt remains have been found in 100,000-year-old strata in California. They are most closely related to delta smelt, *Hypomesus transpacificus*.

MISCELLANY: 1) Swan (1880) wrote,: "Captain Carroll, of the steamer Alexander Duncan, plying between the Columbia River and Puget Sound, informed me that, on the 24th of August, while on his passage from Astoria to Neah Bay, he ran through a school of smelts between Point Grenville and Quillehute which extended nearly forty miles [64 km], and at night their track was made visible by a bright phosphorescent light which emanated from them." 2) In both sexes, the gonads are asymmetrical with the left ones larger than those on the right. 3) Apparently, surf smelt contain an antifreeze compound in their blood. 4) In Central California, surf smelt and night smelt spawn on the same beaches, often on the same day. Occasionally at dusk both species spawn on a beach at the same time. 5) There is at least some evidence that surf smelt numbers, at least off British Columbia, have substantially declined.

REMARKS: *Hypomesus japonicus* from the western Pacific, previously thought to be a subspecies, is now considered a separate species.

Mallotus villosus
(Müller, 1776)
Capelin

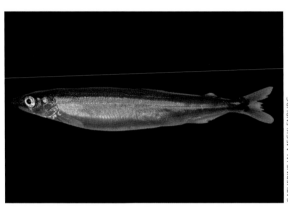

ETYMOLOGY AND COLLOQUIAL NAMES: *Mallotus* comes from the Greek word for "villous" (referring to the elongated and pointed scales of the males) and *villosus* is Latin for "hairy." Some folks up Nome (Alaska) way call them "cigar fish." The Japanese call them "Karafuto-shishamo."

THE BASICS: Maximum Length: 25.2 cm (10 in) TL. The Ranges: Circumglobal in northern boreal and arctic waters. In the eastern Pacific, they are found down to the Strait of Juan de Fuca. They are patchily abundant from the seas of Japan and Okhotsk to the central Gulf of Alaska and eastern Bering Sea, to the eastern Chukchi Sea and the Beaufort Sea, at least as far east as about Camden Bay. Surface down to at least 200 m (660 ft) or perhaps 300 m (984 ft), typically in the upper 100 m (330 ft) of the water column. Eggs: 1–1.1 mm. Larvae: hatching length = 3–7 mm, flexion length = begins at 1.1 cm (0.4 in). Length-weight parameters (FL, mm, gr): (sexes combined) W = 0.00000002L$^{4.2304}$ (Brown 2002).

SALIENT CHARACTERS: They have small scales and their adipose fin has a squared side. They can be differentiated from other Arctic smelt by the small teeth on their tongues, and the maxilla (upper jaw) not reaching past the middle of the eye. During the spawning season, males assume unique physical attributes, as their pectoral, pelvic, and anal fins and scales along the lateral line enlarge, skins thicken, and "hairs" grow along sides.

LIFE HISTORY: Juveniles can be found in very shallow and protected waters, often in areas without eelgrass or other plant life (although Scott Johnson and friends (2010) report a slug of fish taken in kelp). Adults form larger schools and, except when inshore for spawning, tend to live offshore a bit. In the Bering Sea, capelins live as much as 560 km (350 mi) from shore. Capelin schools may be more than 1 km (0.6 mi) long and 20 m (66 ft) or more thick. Aggregations of these schools may be 10 km (6 mi) long. Capelins have been found in waters between at least -2.1–14°C (30–57°F) and perhaps favor water that is 4°C (40°F) or colder. In some locations, capelins enter freshwater. See Remarks for word on capelin populations.

Prior to spawning, capelins form single-sex schools. Larger fish spawn earlier in the season and males usually reach the spawning grounds first. In the northeastern Atlantic, males stay just above the bottom and the females enter the area in large groups to mate. Males and females release milt and roe simultaneously, as the male digs into the substrate to bury the eggs. Eggs may reside on the surface or as much as 24 cm (10 in) below the seafloor. Regardless of bottom depth, capelins usually spawn over coarse sand and fine gravel (in the range of 0.1–25 mm diameter) but "favored" grain size varies with location. In the eastern Bering Sea and Gulf of Alaska, there is a tendency for spawning to occur, or at least begin, at night and around the highest tides. However, spawning can commence at any time of the day or night and has been known to continue over several days. Most spawning takes place in marine waters, although some occurs in brackish conditions. In general, capelins living in the northwest Pacific, eastern Bering Sea, and Chukchi and Beaufort seas spawn in very shallow waters, usually from the surf zone to depths of perhaps 10 m (33 ft). However, there is some evidence that spawning in the eastern Bering Sea, and perhaps Chukchi and Beaufort seas, may also occur somewhat deeper, although the maximum spawning depth is not known (it can be as deep as 280 m, 918 ft, in other areas). One study found that those capelins that spawn offshore always die after spawning, while beach spawners survive to spawn again.

Capelins live to 5 years old. Life span, growth rate, age at maturity, and fecundity vary between areas. Over all, females spawn at least from April (perhaps as early as March) to October. Spawning may take place later off British Columbia than in other areas of the Pacific Ocean or Bering Sea. Spawning occurs at least as far south as central Vancouver Island (on the eastern side) and in the Strait of Georgia. Taking in all of the studies from the Pacific, fecundity ranges between 3,020–53,200 eggs. Eggs reportedly hatch in 2 or 3 weeks. One report claims that after hatching at least some capelin larvae remain in the substrate for several days. Capelins primarily feed on calanoid copepods and euphausiids, but they will not reject other crustaceans (e.g., mysid shrimps, gammarid amphipods, and hyperiid amphipods), larval fishes, polychaetes, and arrow worms. One study found that they fed most heavily during afternoons and very little at night. Capelins are a major food source for a wide range of predators. There's not space here to list them all, but I found references to 25 fish species, 15 species of birds, five species of seals, five species of whales, various porpoises, and river otters. One study, examining the role of capelins in the diets of Pacific cod in the Bering Sea, found that, in many years, cod and capelins are kept apart by very cold water, with the cod to the south and the capelins to the north. However, in warm water years, cod are able to enter capelin country and feed heavily on this smelt.

FISHERY: Capelins have long been a part of various artisanal fisheries. On our side of the world (as opposed to in the Atlantic), they have never been terribly important as a commercial species. A while back there was a short-lived fishery for them in the Bering Sea and, apparently, there is currently one off Sakhalin Island in the Sea of Okhotsk.

ORIGINS AND RELATIONSHIPS: Capelins probably diverged from smelts of the genus *Osmerus* about 4 million years ago. Based on genetic analyses, capelins likely originated in the Pacific Ocean and perhaps made two separate dispersals across the Arctic into the North Atlantic over the past approximately 2.6 million years and now form four distinct populations. There is general agreement that North Atlantic fish are comprised of two populations, one in the northeast (perhaps from West Greenland to the Barents Sea) and one in the northwest (in Hudson Bay and the Canadian Atlantic). A third population exists in the Gulf of Alaska and may also include fishes from the western Pacific. Fish from the eastern Chukchi and Beaufort seas may form a fourth population that includes Bering Sea and western Pacific fish, but not those from the Gulf of Alaska.

Thaleichthys pacificus

(Richardson, 1836)

Eulachon

An oil-rich, anadromous fish that you can set on fire, assuming you are sufficiently pyropiscinic.

ETYMOLOGY AND SEEMINGLY ENDLESS COLLOQUIAL NAMES: *Thaleichthys* is composed of two Greek words for "rich" and "fish" (referring to their high oil content) and *pacificus* refers to the capture location of the first described individual. "Eulachon" appears to come from Chinook, a language composed of English, French, and First Nation words. Variants include "ulikon," "ooligan," "oolichan," "hooligan," and a myriad of similar names and also, let us not forget, "saak." I have recently seen "Pacific smelt" used. And, as Hart and McHugh (1944) noted: "It has been called candlefish because the flesh is so oily that the dried fish, when provided with a wick of rush-pith or strip from the inner bark of the cedar, burns with a steady flame, and was used as a candle by the natives." At one time they were also called "fathom fish" because dried ones were strung on thread and sold by the fathom (6 ft). The Japanese word for them is "yurakon."

THE BASICS: Maximum Length: 25.4 cm (10 in) TL. The 305 mm that you might see bandied about is likely incorrect. Maximum Weight: At least 138 gr (5 oz). The Ranges: Eastern Bering Sea, from west of St. Matthew Island and off Kuskokwim Bay and Nushagak River, and Bowers Bank (central Aleutian Islands), to Point Conception (Central California). They are common southward to at least the vicinity of the Klamath River (Northern California). A few have been taken in San Francisco Bay and a ripe male was taken in the Sacramento River. Surface waters to about 400 m (1,312 ft) and perhaps to at least 470 m (1,542 ft). Eggs: 0.8–1 mm. Larvae: hatching length = 4–8 mm. Willson et al. (2006) give age-length estimates from various sources. Length-weight parameters (SL, cm, gr): (sexes combined) W = 0.00667L$^{3.12}$ (Harvey 1987).

SALIENT CHARACTERS: This is a small, slim fish that is bluish or blue-silver on the back and silvery below, with tiny black dots on the back and sometimes on the caudal fin. There are circular grooves on the gill cover. At spawning time, the fish turn gray-brown, and males develop tubercles on heads and on the scales along the lateral line.

LIFE HISTORY: First of all, for a review of all things eulachon (assuming "all things" means in the vicinity of Washington, Oregon, and California), you might consider downloading Gustafson et al. (2010). On the other hand, the stuff below isn't exactly lugworm castings and you might get something out of it, who knows?

After entering the sea, young eulachon appear to school near the seafloor in the open ocean. As they grow, these fish often live in relatively deep waters, where they sometimes school with northern anchovy and Pacific herring. In general, you find juveniles and adults over the continental shelf in 20–150 m (66–492 ft). Along much of the Pacific Coast, eulachon from different rivers seem to mix less than one might expect (i.e., there is incomplete mixing of various river stocks). There is some evidence that fish in the southeastern Bering Sea are tending to move northward, likely in response to warming water temperatures. In the southeastern Bering Sea, fish have been taken at temperatures as cold as -1.8°C (29°F).

Eulachon are most often encountered during their spawning runs (with runs estimated to number somewhere between 30 and 60) ranging from watersheds on the Pribilof Islands, Bristol Bay, and the western end of the Alaskan Peninsula to the Russian River (Northern California). Some of the larger runs occur in the Klamath, Columbia, Fraser, and Nass rivers. Most of the major spawning rivers are characterized by a large spring runoff. Based on genetic data, Hay and Beacham (2005) stated: "Most eulachon stocks should be considered as genetically isolated, pending further information," a view reinforced by Beacham et al. (2005).

In many rivers, fish spawn within the tidal reaches; however they can go upstream a considerable way, for instance more than 160 km (99 mi) up the Columbia River. In some (but apparently not all) rivers, males are the first to reach the spawning grounds. Spawning temperatures vary widely from about 0–11°C (32–52°F) and sometimes occurs under ice. Spawning likely occurs at night and perhaps in the afternoon. The females lay their eggs mostly on sand and pea-sized gravel, but also on cobble, and sticks and other debris, in water depths of just a few centimeters to at least 8 m (25 ft) or more. The eggs are adhesive and the outer membrane, when fertilized, peels back and forms a cute little pedestal. The eggs are reported to hatch in 12–73 days (but perhaps mostly in 2–4 weeks) with hatching taking longer in colder waters. Young eulachon spend only a little time in freshwater before migrating downstream (apparently mostly at night) and entering the ocean. They do not return to freshwater until they are mature. It is likely that many eulachon return to natal spawning sites but site fidelity may be less than that of the various Pacific salmon.

Eulachon may live to be 9 years old, although figuring out the age of a eulachon has turned out to be an inexact science, so take that figure with a grain of salt. A few fish spawn when 1 year old. However, regarding size and age at maturity, Clarke et al. (2007) summarized thusly: "Southern populations of eulachon, Columbia River, Washington, USA, spawn after 2 years. Eulachon from the Fraser, Kemano, Skeena Rivers in British Columbia, Canada, generally mature after 3 years. Some Skeena River eulachon and most of the eulachon from the Copper River, Alaska, USA matured after 4 years. Spawning eulachon in the present study were at least 16 cm [6 in] FL and greater than 30 g, suggesting that eulachon spawn after reaching a minimum size. The age when fish reach the 16 cm threshold and mature varies with latitude: the Columbia River fish (the most southerly in latitude) spawn at the earliest ages, and the Copper River fish (most northerly in latitude) spawn at the oldest ages." Spawning occurs in rivers and streams from December to July. Note that the 28 November 1892 edition of the *Morning Oregonian* reports that eulachon were caught 50 miles up the Columbia River a few days previous, so spawning might even occur during that month. There appears to be a modest geographic pattern to the onset of spawning. For instance, fish living along the Alaska Peninsula tend to spawn latest. The onset of spawning varies between years even within a river and some watersheds have two runs per year. Most fish seem to die after spawning; however, some may spawn twice in a lifetime. Females produce between 3,242–67,510 eggs per season.

Eulachon eat phytoplankton and zooplankton. Euphausiids are popular, as are cumaceans, copepods, mysid shrimps, larvaceans, and fish larvae. These fish rarely, if ever, feed in freshwater. And predators? My goodness, almost everyone seems to like these little fat packets. Many fishes (e.g., Chinook and coho salmon, Pacific halibut, lingcod, sablefish, spiny dogfish, and white sturgeons), at least 34 species of birds, various seals, sea lions, whales, otters, minks, bears, and wolves all eat them. While many eulachon are eaten while at sea, major predation occurs when they gather to spawn. A number of animals, including numerous birds, as well as seals, sea lions, and whales, gather in anticipation of the upstream migration. In some

DISPATCHES FROM THE FRONT

Morning Oregonian (Portland), Thursday, 13 April 1922, p. 8, col. 2

Headline — Smelt Thick in Sandy, Autoists Congest Highway in Rush for Fish,
Calls for Assistance Cause Sheriff to Dispatch Entire Motorcycle Squad to District

Smelt scouts up the Sandy River evidently reported favorably concerning that stream as a spawning ground, for millions of the silvery little fish reached from bank to bank yesterday by the time autoists in any number began to gather in the vicinity of Troutdale.

More than 2,000 automobiles congested the Columbia River highway near the Sandy before noon and calls for assistance caused Sheriff Hurlburt to dispatch his entire motorcycle squad of six men and machines to the district to direct traffic and break the jam which had ensued.

Birdcages, lace curtains and many other substitutes for fish nets made their appearance and only a few minutes in the stream sufficed to supply any family with enough smelt for a reunion. All indications are that the run will last for a week or more and it is expected that the traffic will attain proportions by next Sunday which may make it necessary to employ traffic officers in addition to the sheriff's complement.

Morning Oregonian (Portland), Tuesday, 27 April 1920, p. 10, col. 6

Headline — Those Who Come and Go

When A. N. Ward gets back to the Hot Stove Club at Malden, Mass., [he] will have a fish story to tell that his fellow townsmen will probably not believe and will stamp it as a traveler's tale. When Mr. Ward recounts that he saw a river so filled with fish that the stream was virtually one solid mass of fish for miles, and contained millions of smelt, the Maldenites will sniff with suspicion. When he says that in five minutes he, or anyone, could gather enough fish from the Sandy River with his coat, or auto robe, or any old thing, to fill a car to overflowing, they'll be certain that he is drawing the long bow. And yet, those were the things which Mr. Ward saw when he toured the Columbia River highway yesterday. He saw the great smelt run and saw miles upon miles of parked cars, while their drivers were filling gunny sacks, cans, buckets, tubs, boxes and any container they could secure, with smelt. At home Mr. Ward is an undertaker, and with his wife he is at the Multnomah, returning from the profiteer belt of California.

Okay, I got the part about the smelt, but what is an undertaker from Massachusetts doing in the profiteer belt of California. Oh, and just where and what is the profiteer belt of California and is it available only to undertakers?

POTLATCH

Speaking of Native American (or in this case First Nation) practices, here is a rather telling quote I saw on the wall of the Museum of Anthropology at the University of British Columbia. It was written in 1918 by William Holliday, a Canadian Indian Agent. He was discussing the need for abolishing the potlatch, a traditional ceremony of the Haida, Tlingit, and other indigenous peoples: "During these gatherings they lose months of time, waste their substances, contract all kinds of diseases and generally unfit themselves for being British subjects in the proper sense of the word."

Hmmm, but given the current role model of British hooligans, how about being "British subjects" in the improper sense of the word?

instances, predators such as Steller sea lions only occupy certain haul out sites during eulachon migrations. Tens of thousands of predators may participate in an orgy of eulachon scarfing, a scene reminiscent of a Coney Island hot dog eating contest, albeit with less trans fat. In Alaska, as noted by Gende et al. (2001b), Steller sea lions appear to cooperatively forage for eulachon: "The line of Sea Lions [sic], comprised of about 200 to 300 individuals, was perpendicular to the shore and stretched nearly 0.75 km... Most individuals were no more than a few meters apart... All individuals in the line porpoised for 8 to 20 seconds before diving simultaneously for 4 to 9 minutes."

FISHERY: Eulachon, fatty and available during late-winter spawning runs, were just extremely important to indigenous peoples throughout the Northwest. Many of these people subsisted on dried fish throughout the winter, and as Ames and Maschner (1999) memorably put it: "A diet heavy in dried foods can lead to constipation and other digestive problems, as well as a crucial, even fatal, shortage of fats in the diet." Thus, the early appearance of nutritious laxatives-with-fins making spawning runs in coastal rivers was very welcome. As not all groups lived near spawning runs, many peoples traveled relatively far distances to capture these fish. For example, the Coast Tsimshian (in the Prince Rupert, British Columbia area) would travel by boat to the Nass River, 50 km (30 mi) to the north, for the run. Various kinds of nets and fish rakes were used to capture eulachon. Charles Gilbert, observing how the locals caught these smelt in the late 19th century, noted that: "Eulachon is caught by Indians by means of a rake with fine set teeth...The teeth were formerly made of wood—are now made of telegraph wire. One Indian paddles while another stands in front with rake which he cuts through the water on each side of the boat. As he passes through a shoal the fish are impaled and drawn in" (Pietsch and Dunn 1997). In general, the first fish caught were eaten fresh (that problem with 4 months of eating dried fish, as you remember) and some were then dried or smoked. But many were rendered for an oil that was consumed as a seasoning with almost every meal.

Today, eulachon are still rendered for their oil by local peoples and here is how they do it. Fish are taken with beach seines, placed in pits, and left to decompose for 8–14 days. Water is heated to about 76°C (170°F) in large wooden tanks, and the fish are soaked for about 30 minutes. After this, they are broken up with large wooden forks, which releases the oil. The oil is pushed to one side of the tank, scooped up and allowed to settle in large containers. Later, it is filtered through canvas and stored in dark bottles. In earlier days, it was stored in kelp floats, wooden boxes (which could weigh as much as 91 kg (200 lb)), fish bladders, or even in cleaned salmon skins. Eulachon oil, or "grease," was widely traded from the "have" tribes lucky enough to control spawning areas to "have-nots" living in the interior or away from the right rivers and streams. Irv Leask reports that there is still a brisk trade in eulachon grease, although the transactions smack of the 21st century. When his relatives travel up the Nass River to obtain the good stuff, the currency of choice is Sailor Boy Pilot Bread and Starbucks French Roast.

And how yummilicious is eulachon oil? Well, obviously the native peoples liked it. On the other hand, Stewart (1977) quotes the experience of the Rev. C. M. Tait "an itinerant minister" of the early 20th century in British Columbia: "I was immediately ushered into the chief's house, and his wife began to prepare food for me. A fresh lot of halibut had just come in and she began to cook. Out came her oolichan box, and the big horn spoon, a sort of great ladle made, I think, from the horn of the big-horn sheep. Of course the more grease—they value it—the greater the honour to the guest. I protested that I was unworthy of so much grease, but without avail. To my chagrin she was lavish, and simply showered her esteem on me by smothering the halibut in grease. I never acquired a taste for it. I am without hope that I ever shall." And one anecdote from Ms. Stewart:

"Stopping off at Hot Springs Island, in the Queen Charlottes, I once had an unexpected opportunity of tasting eulachon oil. A Haida family were staying in their summer cabin...and invited us to lunch and for the first time I tried steamed mussels and discovered how delicious they were. On the table was a jar of what, in our ignorance, we thought to be honey with its whitish, semi-crystalline appearance. Fortunately our hostess did not allow us to use it as honey, for it was eulachon oil. She did give us the opportunity of experiencing the taste but, like the good reverend, I am without hope that I could ever get to like it."

Eulachon have been the target of commercial fisheries for many years, although many of these fisheries have kind of come and gone. Early attempts (as early as 1877 on the Nass River of British Columbia) were made to ship eulachon oil to Europe, but with little success. Historically, the largest fisheries have been on the Fraser and Columbia rivers. In fact, all directed commercial fishing has been in freshwater, with fishermen using gill nets, otter trawls, and dip nets. Over the years, eulachon were used for fish meal, as mink food, have been sold fresh for food and for bait, particularly for sturgeons in the Columbia River. Jordan (1887) wrote that eulachon were a very popular pan fish in the Puget Sound region and around Victoria (British Columbia): "When absolutely fresh and not 'spent,' it is in my judgement the most delicious of all fishes—delicate, fragrant, saturated with an exquisite and readily digested oil...After the spawning season, however, the flesh become mealy and free from oil, although still excellent as food." Today, there are very modest fisheries for this smelt in a number of northeastern Pacific localities.

In the recreational fishery, they are taken with dip nets or are snagged with hooks.

RELATIONSHIPS: Eulachon are closely related to smelts of the genus *Spirinchus*.

MISCELLANY: 1) Apparently, some fish may be hermaphrodites. 2) Eulachon contain high levels of mono-unsaturated fatty acids, particularly oleic acids. Squalene is an important component. 3) "Dried, they serve as torches; when a light is needed, the tail is touched to the fire, and they will burn with a bright light for some time. No description can give an adequate idea of their numbers when ascending the river; the water is literally alive with them, and appears as if boiling" (Dall 1870). 4) Eulachon often resorb their teeth prior to spawning, with males losing more teeth than females.

REMARKS: There may be, I suppose, fishes that are as important a food resource for zillions of predators as the eulachon, but, oh my, there are not many. This makes even more serious the decline in spawning runs that have occurred from California to southeastern Alaska beginning in the mid-1990s.

OTHER SPECIES

Allosmerus elongatus
(Ayres, 1854)
Whitebait Smelt

Whitebaits grow to 22.9 cm (9 in) TL and are found from Vancouver Island to San Francisco, typically southward to at least Humboldt Bay. There is one questionable record from San Pedro (Southern California). This is a mostly nearshore and pelagic fish, found both in bays and off the open coast, living down to perhaps 103 m (338 ft) and perhaps to 131 m (430 ft). It feeds on zooplankton (such as euphausiids, mysid shrimps, copepods, and crustacean larvae), and small fishes. Various genetic analyses demonstrate that whitebaits are most closely related to members of the genus *Spirinchus*.

Osmerus dentex
Steindachner & Kner, 1870
Arctic Smelt

Arctics reach 31 cm (12 in) FL and live in the White and Barents seas, eastwards to Bathurst Inlet, Nunavut, and southward to the Sea of Japan and Heceta Head, Oregon, most commonly as far south as the Chukchi Sea. These are anadromous, nearshore fish, found from the surface to 150 m (495 ft) or more in estuaries, embayments, and nearshore waters. This species occupies a very wide range of temperatures (-2–13.5°C, 28–56°F) and from fresh to seawaters. Although tolerant of brackish conditions, in the Beau-

fort Sea region they tend to inhabit waters of 22 ppt or above and will avoid nearshore waters of lower salinities. While most fish enter freshwater only to spawn, landlocked populations are known. In the Beaufort and Chukchi seas, both juveniles and adults overwinter under ice in brackish river deltas and coastal waters. As the winter progresses, fish gather near spawning grounds and spawning takes place in the spring, just prior to ice break-up. Spawning occurs in many of the rivers entering the Chukchi and Beaufort seas and in at least one lake. Most takes place in the lowermost, but still fresh, parts of rivers, often very near the mouth. The sticky and stalked eggs are shed over gravel, sand, or plants in shallow, swiftly flowing waters and adhere to the substrate until hatching. Arctic smelt inhabit arctic and subarctic waters and live to at least 18 years. Throughout their range, age at first maturity appears to be highly variable and ranges from 1–10 years or more. On average, in the Chukchi and Beaufort seas, the fish mature at between 5–7 years old and perhaps 20–22.5 cm (8–9 in) FL. In these drainages, arctics spawn between about March–July, peaking in May and June. Arctic smelt feed heavily on small crustaceans (e.g., mysid shrimps and gammarid amphipods), insects, polychaetes, and small fishes. For many years, they have been of great importance to the subsistence fisheries in the Wainwright (northwestern Alaska) area. This species was, until just a moment ago (in geologic time), lumped with the rainbow smelt, *Osmerus mordax*, an Atlantic species.

Spirinchus starksi
(Fisk, 1913)
Night Smelt

Night smelt grow to 23 cm (9 in) TL and are found from Shelikof Bay (southeastern Gulf of Alaska) to Point Arguello (Central California), commonly to at least off San Simeon (Central California), and perhaps to off Pismo Beach, from the surface and surf to 128 m (422 ft). These fish appear to live about 2 years and the species may spawn from January–October, perhaps peaking in the summer. True to its name, spawning takes place from dusk into the dark on coarse sandy beaches. Although these fish may spawn on every tide and moon phase, Kirk Lombard, who is quite the aficionado, notes that recreational fishermen often target them around the high tides. Night smelt feed mostly on small crustaceans (e.g., calanoid copepods, gammarid amphipods, mysid shrimps, and crustacean larvae) and polychaetes, as well as larval fishes. Such predators as sea lions and cormorants often prey on them in shallow waters during spawning runs. Night smelt are an important food for a number of Native American tribes, are caught in recreational fisheries (usually with A-frame nets), and have been caught commercially and sold as food for fishes, birds, and mammals. I see the occasional catch for sale in San Francisco Asian fish markets. Night smelt are most closely related to longfin smelt. Length-weight parameters (TL, cm, gr): (sexes combined) W = $0.0495L^{3.101}$ (Kinnetic Laboratories 1980).

Spirinchus thaleichthys
(Ayres, 1860)
Longfin Smelt

Longfins grow to 20 cm (8 in) TL and are found from the Shelikof Strait (western Gulf of Alaska) to Monterey Bay, commonly southward to at least San Francisco Bay. They inhabit surface waters and the surf to depths of about 137 m (449 ft). Maturation occurs in the second year. These are anadromous fish; they ascend into freshwater to spawn. Based on larval catches in San Francisco Bay, longfins spawn from at least November–July, perhaps mostly in the winter and early spring. Most fish appear to die after spawning. Females lay single, adhesive eggs on vegetation or rocks. In a study in several Washington lakes, females contained anywhere from 535–23,624 eggs. Smelt eggs hatch (at 7–8 mm SL) after 40 days at 6.9°C (45°F). They feed both in the water column and near or on the bottom. Gammarid and hyperiid amphipods, euphausiids, mysid shrimps, calanoid copepods, cumaceans, and insects appear to be most important. Predators include Chinook salmon, cutthroat trout, striped bass, spiny dogfish, murres, seals, and porpoises. Recreational fishermen catch these with some regularity. Longfins are closely related to night smelt. Larvae: hatching length = as small as 5.3 mm. Length-weight parameters (SL, mm, gr): (sexes combined) W = 0.000002366L$^{3.373}$ (Dryfoos 1965).

FAMILY SALMONIDAE—Trout and Salmon

The salmonids (not just the salmon, mind you, but also the whitefishes, grayling, and the like) are a group of freshwater and anadromous (born in freshwater, spend some time in saltwater, return to freshwater to spawn) fishes that are native to the Northern Hemisphere. All of the salmon in the genus *Oncorhynchus* have been transplanted outside of their native ranges (like Chinooks to India and Madagascar) and Crawford and Muir (2008) are happy to tell you all about that. There are 11 genera and about 66 species, of which 14 inhabit our waters. All salmonids are oviparous. The earliest known salmon is *Eosalmo driftwoodensis*, from British Columbia and Washington. Apparently a strictly freshwater species, it lived in the Eocene (about 50 million years ago). The earliest known *Oncorhynchus* is *O. rastrosus* (previously known as *Smilodonichthys rastrosus*), the so-called "sabertooth salmon," a really big (to the tune of maybe 3–4 m, 10–13 ft, 305 kg, 1,000 lb) fish that lived in the Miocene, as much as 10–11 million years ago in the western U.S. It probably died out in the Late Miocene, prior to 5.3 million years ago. This species was anadromous and was most closely related to the modern pink, chum, and sockeye salmon. The positively svelte *Oncorhynchus* that we know and love evolved in the Late Miocene, at least 6 million years ago. Mecklenburg et al. (2002) provide keys to all of the western North American salmon and trout (and whitefishes, too).

Ray Troll's homage to the sabertooth salmon.

Historically, on the Pacific Coast, the word "salmon" meant one of the five species (Chinook, chum, coho, pink, and sockeye) in the genus *Oncorhynchus*. In recent years, the decision was made, by the usual cabal of systematists, that both rainbow (steelhead) and cutthroat trout were more closely related to the Pacific salmon then previously thought and thus they were moved from *Salmo* to *Oncorhynchus*. Perhaps it is best to think of both steelhead and cutthroat trout as salmon that are not so into reproduction that they have to die for the cause. And while we are on the subject, remember that "trout" and "salmon" have no biological meaning. In English, historically and colloquially, "trout" completed their life cycle in freshwater and "salmon" spent at least some time in saltwater. On the other hand, as pointed out by Stearley and Smith (1993), in French the two words had the opposite meaning.

For all kinds of reasons, the salmon have been damn important to the ecology and peoples of the northeast Pacific. After all, you can't exist in your millions in just about every watershed from Central California to the Chukchi Sea without having *some* effect on your surroundings. For instance, Gresh et al. (2000) estimated that back before the great runs came to an end, dead post-spawning salmon in the northeast Pacific contributed 6,850,000 kg of nitrogen and 810,000 kg of phosphorus to the ecosystem. As far as people are concerned, since around the time folks hit the North American shores and started exterminating the local megafauna, salmon have been important to many of those living in the Pacific Northwest. John Keast Lord (1819–1872), a British naturalist who visited British Columbia in the early 1860s, said it most bluntly: "Salmon is of the most vital importance to the Indians; deprived or by any means cut off from obtaining it, starve to death they must; and were we at war with the Redskins, we need only cut them off from their salmon-fisheries to have them completely at our mercy" (Lord 1866). *But we wouldn't do that, John, because it would be wrong. Right?*

Note that not all of these indigenous sea-coast peoples depended on the salmon. Ames and Maschner (1999) shake their metaphorical fingers and remind us: "Gregory Monks has used the humorous term *salmonopia* to describes this emphasis on salmon. Archaeologists and anthropologists afflicted with salmonopia can see only salmon, and are blind to the other resources that were crucial to the coast's Native economies." As an example, the peoples inhabiting the Queen Charlotte Islands of British Columbia, living in a relatively salmon-poor region, did not depend on salmon; Pacific halibut were far more important. But, with that caveat, it is true that way before white people came along, salmon were taken in just about every imaginable way, including some methods that clearly were devised by the Einsteins of the time. *Indian Fishing, Early Methods on the Northwest Coast* (Douglas and McIntyre, 1977) a simply lovely and lovingly crafted book by Hilary Stewart, is a tremendous resource if you want to know how First Nation and Native American peoples caught—and then preserved—salmon and other fishes.

As an example of the importance of salmon to some of the tribes, it was estimated that, even as late as the late 19th Century, the average native of Kodiak Island consumed at least 750 salmon annually. Of that amount, half was consumed fresh and half was dried for winter use. Dried salmon was extremely important for native peoples. Here is William Dall (see *Sebastes dalli* for some good gossip about this guy) commenting on the role that the dried product played for indigenous folk living on the Yukon in 1865: "At the mouth of the Yukon not less than two million salmon are dried every summer, and probably double that number. Words fail to describe their abundance...[At every village] Several acres of ground in front of the summer houses were literally covered with standards and stages bearing line after line of fish, split and hung up to dry...It is the principal staple of food, under the name of *ukali*, for all travelers, both men and dogs; being very light and portable, yet full of oil; of not the most agreeable flavor, it is at least strong if not strengthening. Occasionally one does get hold of a clean, well-dried ukali, that tastes very well when broiled over the fire; though in my own case the use of it invariably produced heartburn. The ration for a dog is one salmon weighing from a pound and a half to two pounds...They will travel on less, but the best policy is to feed your dogs well, and you may then, with proper attention, be sure that they will work well and rarely run away." *This last observation surely also applies to graduate students.*

On the other hand, Lucien Turner, hunkering down in the late 1870s on the Bering Sea, had a far more positive view of ukali. Describing the dried salmon of the same region (on the Yukon) as Dall, he writes: "The fish is hung up for several days, until it has dried out to a certain degree. The fish are so full of oil that among those people who have not the opportunity of procuring real oil...wooden vessels are placed under the fish to obtain the oil as it drips from the fish when drying. After the oil has dripped out and the fish is somewhat dried, the pieces are then separated and placed between layers of birch bark, formed so that the pressure of the fish and weight of stone, put on the pile of fish, squeezes out nearly all the oil. The fish, by this pressure, become very dry, yet not too much so. The process secures a first-rate article of ukali, which is much sought for by the traders" (Turner 1886). Ukali bought by the traders of that time was not cheap. Natives on the Yukon sold each dried salmon for one leaf of tobacco or 5–8 musket-balls.

While salmon flesh was, of course, the main target, almost all parts of the fish were consumed. For instance, the Coast Salish, of southwestern British Columbia and Puget Sound, would decompose salmon for the fishes' oil. Salmon eggs were also hugely popular. John Jewitt (see the minibiography under Pacific herring) made the following observation during his captivity in the early 1800s among a First Nation tribe on Vancouver Island: "The spawn of the salmon, which is a principal article of their provision, they take out, and without any other preparation, throw it into their tubs, where they leave it to stand and ferment, for though they frequently eat it fresh, they esteem it much more when it has ac-quired a strong taste...and whenever they took it out of these large receptacles, which they are always careful to fill, such was the stench which it exhaled, on being moved, that it was almost impossible for me to abide it" (Jewitt 1987). To be completely fair and not to take sides in this gustatory contretemps, one should always remember that Mr. Jewitt saw things through the prism of late 18th-century Great Britain, a prism just chock full of suet pudding, poorly refrigerated mutton, and kind of funky personal hygiene. Thus, even though partially rotted salmon eggs might arguably have been a flavor treat that was fun to eat, Mr. Jewitt might not have been in a cultural position to continence it.

Before we plunge into the life history of these fishes, there follows a number of riffs that to my mind are far more interesting than the kind of puny species accounts I saddle you with.

No One Likes a Cassandra (Except Maybe Cassandra's Significant Other)

Dr. Robert T. Lackey works for the Environmental Protection Agency and has thought about salmon restoration for a long time. In a series of papers, Lackey spells out what the state of salmon populations is today, what it is likely to be, and how really hard it will to bring them back. This is not because there are no solutions, but because what will have to be done is sufficiently unpalatable for enough people that it will not be done. So: "In California, Oregon, Idaho, Washington, and the Columbia River portion of British Columbia, many runs are reduced to less than 10% of their historical abundance. Some are much less than 10%. An unknown number have been extirpated...Other runs are dominated by hatchery-bred fish. Even for the Columbia, once the mightiest salmon-producing river south of Canada, over 80% of the total run comprises hatchery-bred fish." Lackey goes on to say that about the best that can be said is that: "Wild salmon runs in Alaska, Yukon, and northern British Columbia most likely will remain relatively healthy, or at least better off than those in the contiguous United States" (Lackey 2002).

What is It with These Names!?

Now, I would be first person to admit that I am not a salmon biologist. Lawsy, no. So, I don't have to deal on a daily basis with all of this *Oncorhynchus tshawytscha*, *gorbuscha* and *kisutch* stuff, those quill-twisting names that North Pacific salmon are stuck with. So, what's the story here? Whatever happened to honest Latin and Greek?

Well, the blame goes directly to Stepan Petrovich Krasheninnikov (1711–1755), a Russian scientist and, ultimately, Academician of the St. Petersburg Academy of Sciences. Between about 1737–1743, as part of Bering's second expedition to the region, he traveled around the then virtually unknown Kamchatka Peninsula. He later wrote *A Description of the Land of Kamchatka* (1751), the first work describing in detail the local tribes and their customs and cultures. And among the details he gave were the vernacular names of Kamchatka's (and our) five salmon species. In 1792, Johann Julius Walbaum (1724–1799) a German physician and naturalist, in an apparently misguided attempt to honor that which is local, used these names as the scientific names.

And, I might add that, along with making salmon names more difficult for us to handle, Walbaum was also the first person on record to use gloves in surgery. In 1758, it was recorded that he used the caecum of a sheep fitted over his hand for obstetric work.

Isn't This Illegal in Texas?

In his indispensable book *The Canning of Fishery Products* (1919), John Cobb (a man born deep, deep within the Victorian era) includes a section titled "Melt or Buckroe." Herein, he describes eating fish sperm without, of course, ever actually using the word "sperm." "The melts [*I'm sorry, what is that?*], or buckroe [*No, I don't know that term either*], as it is sometimes called (that part of the male which corresponds to the egg mass of the female) ["that part of the male that..."*oh, that part of the male*], of fishes are also excellent food, but have been almost totally neglected until within recent months" [*I don't actually want to know what had happened in that last few months*].

He goes on to note that the sperm had to be processed immediately after the salmon was killed, "as stale melt will not make a good canned product," a bit of advice we can all take to heart, or to any other organ for that matter.

How to Tell if a Salmon is Ripe

So, you think you can distinguish a salmon that is ready to spawn from one that is just thinking about it? Sorry, matey, you are probably self-delusional, for from the typing machine of John J. Brice's *A Manual of Fish-Culture Based on the Methods of the United States Commission of Fish and Fisheries* (Government Printing Office, Washington, D.C.,1898), we have this admonition that the early fish culturalists used "an indescribable ripe look, which is neither color, shape nor conditions of the organs, but a general appearance which shows at a glance that the fish is ripe and can be appreciated only by experience."

I believe at least one of the great cosmetic houses (was it Elizabeth Arden, I wonder?) tried to give their customers that "Indescribable Ripe Look" back in 1924.

Oh, Yes, I am a Grave Robber

During his stay in the American West, the 19th-century English naturalist John Keast Lord commented on the worn teeth of the peoples living on the Colombia River. He also noted that when these peoples dried salmon on the river banks, a great deal of sand blew on it and that when later consumed it "wears the teeth as if filed down, which I at first imagined them to be, until the true cause was discovered." Well, thus far all well and good, and a respectable job of sleuthing it was too. But then he goes on to say that, back in his digs in Fair Albion: "I have an under-jaw in my possession whereon the teeth are quite level with the bony sockets of the jaw, worn away by the flinty sand."

An under-jaw? Of one of the locals? Don't tell us you won it in a game of whist.

And now, at long last, we creep up to the species accounts. Of course, given the unholy amount of money that has been spent over the last 150 years on salmon research, there is enough information out there to cause even the most fanatic Onchorynchophile to rend his or her garments. I wouldn't even consider writing the definitive account of the Pacific salmon as they have already inspired hundreds of books, thousands of scientific papers, and, I shouldn't wonder, a musical comedy by Cole Porter [To the tune of "*You're the Top*"].

Music by
COLE PORTER
Words by
MILTON LOVE

Moderato

When you spawn   Oh salmon Pacific

Just at dawn   You know you're terrific

You're my sca - ly date   But my slim-y mate   don't

boast   for at   our consummation to our frustration we're   both toast.

Indeed, should you decide to continue your salmonic studies, and want to consume some concentrated information, you might try Groot and Margolis (1991), Moyle (2002), and Quinn (2005). There are many, many more books and you can find them on the web. On the other hand, here are a few of the quirkier ones:

Cobb, J. N. 1931. *Pacific Salmon Fisheries*. Report of the United States Commissioner of Fisheries for the Fiscal Year 1930. Appendix 13, Document No. 1092.

This is simply the bible regarding salmon fisheries as practiced to about 1930. Yes, it's all here: the history of the fisheries, how they caught them, who caught them, and what they did with them after that, all in simply excruciating detail. Direct from the days when there were still lots of salmon and written by a man whose writing style has the whiff of Dickens about it.

Iglauer, E. 1988. *Fishing with John*. Harbour Publishing, Madeira Park, British Columbia.

In the mid-1970s, Ms. Iglauer, mostly an East Coast urbanite writer, met and married John Daly, a British Columbia salmon fisherman. This book details their first year aboard their salmon troller fishing the British Columbia coast. I like the book, despite dialogue that is a bit too expository to ring completely true, and a distressing habit on the part of both protagonists to throw stuff (e.g., her: many issues of *The New York Times*; him: a bag containing two artichokes) into the sea.

Lyons, C. 1969. *Salmon: Our Heritage*. British Columbia Packers Limited. Printed by Mitchell Press, Vancouver, British Columbia, Canada.

Ms. Lyons worked for many decades as secretary to a succession of executives of British Columbia Packers, the largest of the British Columbia salmon canning companies. In the introduction, it is noted that Ms. Lyons was something of a "pack rat" who saved and collected: "Books, pamphlets and newspaper clippings [dealing with the British Columbia salmon canning industry], seemingly by the ton." Clearly, upon her retirement, she gathered all of this material to her bosom and the result is a year-by-year account of the salmon canning industry from its inception to the mid-1960s. Obviously a labor of love, *S:OH* details, from the cannery industry's perspective, the history of salmon canning in British Columbia. As far as I can tell, this book documents every machination of every steely-eyed cannery entrepreneur, every fisherman's strike, and every can of every species of salmon produced in every year. Bizarrely, interspersed among notes on the non-ratification of the Canadian-U.S. Sockeye Salmon Convention and the Fishermen's Indemnity Plan are bits of Canadian history, many of which have no apparent relationship to the canning industry. Thus, in the chapter covering 1940–1949, we read about the Massacre at Dieppe in 1942, where many Canadian soldiers died attacking German positions, followed within a page by a note that the sockeye run on the Fraser River was poor that year. Detailing 1917, Ms. Lyons writes that Canadians were fighting on the Somme and that: "During these anxious months the thoughts of the Industry were of the men who had absented themselves from British Columbia to ensure (amongst other considerations) that the great food resources of Canada's fisheries should not fall into alien control"; thus suggesting that World War I was fought, at least in part, to keep canned salmon away from the Hun.

The effect of all of this is rather disquieting. It's as if the treatise were written by a cannery worker channeling Prime Minister Margaret Thatcher in her prime.

McKervill, H. W. 1992. *Salmon People*. Whitecap Books, North Vancouver, British Columbia, Canada.

Early in his career, United Church minister McKervill was posted to Bella Bella, a coastal town north of Vancouver. He quickly discovered that during the summer salmon fishing season almost none of his First Nation parishioners were in town. And so, "In order to identify with the people I had come to help," he bought a gill-net vessel and for four summers went salmon fishing. Clearly, Reverend McKervill became entranced by salmon and the role they have played in the economy of western Canada. To that end, he wrote a marvelous book detailing the larger than life characters that were involved in the salmon fisheries and the canning industry. Included, too, is the story of how the World War II Canadian government ripped off the Japanese fishermen in a manner at least as repugnant as that of the United States.

Upton, J. 1977. *Alaska Blues*. Alaska Northwest Publishing Company, Anchorage, Alaska.

Just a wonderful and evocative book about one commercial salmon season in southeast Alaska. It's filled with green water over the bow, tramps through deserted and rotting canneries, the travails of chasing salmon, and lots of alcohol consumption (albeit ingested in a socially responsible way.)

Okay, now to the species accounts. And just to get us started, here is an overview of stuff most all *Oncorhynchus* do. There are always exceptions, of course, so please don't contact me with that triumphant exception to what below is a nice set of generalities. Indeed, the most important takeaway from the following homily is that species of the genus *Oncorhynchus*, perhaps more than almost any other group of fishes, are just incredibly plastic in their behavior, as they have had to adapt to the vagaries of hundreds of rivers and streams.

First: With a male hanging close and warding off other males, a female digs a hole in the gravel of (depending on species) a stream or lake bed; these nests are called *redds*. Larger salmonids tend to fancy larger gravel and somewhat faster-moving waters. After the eggs are deposited and the male sprays them with sperm, they are covered over by the female who then moves upstream and digs another hole. During this process, other territory-holding females may attack the female (or attendant male) and other males may attack the male. Females of species that die after spawning (Chinooks, cohos, chums, pinks, and sockeyes) (species termed *semelparous*) then guard the redds until they die. Females of species that may live to spawn again (*iteroparous* ones) like Dolly Vardens, steelhead, and cutthroats, do not guard their redds.

Then: The eggs hatch after a variable number of weeks and out pops the young fish, an *alevin*. Alevins stay within the gravel until they absorb their yolks and then emerge from within their rocky nursery as *fry*. Depending on species or even depending on which stock within a species, these fry may quickly migrate to the sea or to a lake or may just hang out in streams or rivers for as much as a few years. Fry that remain within freshwaters for a while develop dark bars and are call *parrs*.

Followed By: At some point all good things must come to an end and parrs begin to alter their physiology to allow for life in the sea, a process called *smoltification*, and they become, although I suppose we have already telegraphed this, *smolts*. Once at sea, movements are highly variable, and depend on species and geographic locations. Suffice it to say that some fish of some species stay in the sea for months and some for years; some migrate well offshore and some tend to hug the coast. For some species, such as chums and pinks, almost all fish remain at sea for a quite precise length of time. For others, like cohos and Chinooks, this sojourn is a bit more variable. And then there are *jacks*, males of a species that mature when younger than the youngest mature female. *Jills*, precociously mature females, are rare. Confusingly, in some instances, male parrs (fish that have not gone to sea) may also become mature (commonly among steelhead and cutthroats, less commonly in Chinooks, cohos, and sockeyes).

And Lastly: At some point, these fishes change from their silvery oceanic coloration to spawning plumage (termed "coloring up" by some) and migrate back to their home waters (although there is some straying to non-natal watersheds), and the process starts all over again.

Oncorhynchus clarkii

(Richardson, 1836)

Cutthroat Trout

ETYMOLOGY: *Oncorhynchus* comes from two Greek words for "hook" and "snout" and *clarkii* refers to William Clark (1770–1838), perhaps for putting up with the mercurial Meriwether Lewis from 1803–1806.

THE BASICS: Maximum Length: 99.1 cm (39 in) TL. The Ranges: Outer coast of Kenai Peninsula (northern Gulf of Alaska) to the Eel River (Northern California). Length-weight parameters (FL, mm, gr): (sexes combined) $W = 0.00000000507L^{3.14}$ (Wildermuth 1983).

SALIENT CHARACTERS: Probably the most obvious characteristic of this species is the orange or red streak on the lower jaw. A sea-run individual has a greenish-blue or blue back, a silvery side and belly, and lots of black spots on body and fins (although not on the pelvics). Freshwater individuals are often greenish on their backs. Another good character is the teeth on the back of the tongue; these are not found in steelhead or in Pacific salmon.

LIFE HISTORY: Interested in cutthroats? Sure you are and why shouldn't you be? There is just a ton of information on them in Hall et al. (1997).

Cutthroats are fish of smaller coastal rivers and streams (having perhaps evolved this trait to avoid competition with the larger steelhead and Pacific salmons). Some cutthroats are anadromous (spending time in the ocean before returning to freshwater), while others never leave their birth streams. Eggs hatch in 28–40 days and the newly hatched young stay under the gravel for 1–2 weeks. There is a wide range of freshwater residence periods for juveniles, reportedly anywhere from 1–9 years, with somewhere around 3 years being average. Juveniles and post-spawning adults enter the ocean in spring and summer (this varies with locality) and most return a few months later in late summer and fall (only a few return in midwinter and they rarely

WILLIAM CLARK

It is not too much to note that while Lewis was the primary Science Guy on the expedition, Clark was the one who made sure everyone had enough to eat, a place to sleep, and knew which direction to go. Mostly self-taught, Clark had a real ability to lead and part of this knack was the significant sympathy he exhibited for others, including on a number of occasions, Native Americans. There was even a period, when he was Superintendent of Indian Affairs in the Missouri area, when Clark attempted to prevent white settlers from taking over land provided to Native Americans by treaty. He also had a propensity for owning and beating slaves, for killing and exiling Native Americans, and for expropriating their lands. Later in his life, even after the death of his first wife, several children, and dozens of relatives, Clark wrote to his eldest son, Lewis; "View the world as it is, do not anticipate too much. The pleasant feelings of one day may never be realized in another, yet I hope many will be exceeded by you." Ultimately, he was a complex man, a kind of transitional American figure, with 1.8 feet planted firmly in Antebellum Virginia and the rest (perhaps three toes) dipping into the Enlightenment.

overwinter in the ocean). While at sea, fish may spend their days in estuaries or along the immediate coast (sometimes venturing at least as much as 250 km (155 mi) from their natal streams), or may venture out to sea as much as 50 km (31 mi) and slightly more. In some watersheds, a large percentage of first-returning fish do not spawn in that year. Returning fish tend to stay in the lower parts of the streams for a bit, then press on during fall and winter. Spawning occurs in fall and winter, at temperatures of 6.1–17.2°C (43–63°F). Most spawning occurs in small coastal streams in shallow waters and cutthroats rarely migrate more than 160 km (99 mi) upstream. Many cutthroats survive spawning and return in subsequent years. Genetic studies imply that cutthroats are characterized by a number of genetically distinct populations centered on individual streams. This species tolerates temperatures between about 6.1–26.1°C (43–79°F), preferring 8.9–12.2°C (48–54°F).

Life history parameters vary greatly among watersheds. For instance, while most cutthroats probably mature at 3–4 years, the span for wild fish is 2–10 years, and some hatchery fish are in there spawning after one year. Coastwide, fecundity seems to range from less than 100 to at least 4,420 eggs, but this also varies between watersheds. For instance, females are slightly more fecund (number of eggs per length or weight) in Washington than in Oregon. At sea, cutthroat trout mostly eat fishes. Also eaten are such zooplankton as euphausiids, gammarid amphipods, crustacean larvae, and insects. Harbor seals and likely bald eagles eat them.

FISHERY: Although not targeted by commercial fishermen, they are occasionally taken in the salmon fisheries. This is a very popular recreational species.

RELATIONSHIPS: An ancestor from the Miocene (at least 5.3 million years ago) may be the extinct species "*Salmo cyniclope*." Cutthroat trout are most closely related to steelhead and to the Western Pacific cherry salmon (*Oncorhynchus masou*).

MISCELLANY: Female steelhead in Washington sometimes mate, by accident, with male cutthroats. The male cutthroats are "sneakers," dashing in to fertilize steelhead eggs before steelhead males get a chance.

Oncorhynchus gorbuscha
(Walbaum, 1792)
Pink Salmon

ETYMOLOGY AND COLLOQUIAL NAMES: *Oncorhynchus* comes from two Greek words for "hook" and "snout" and *gorbuscha* refers to the name given by the locals in Kamchatka. "Humpback" is used a lot and the Japanese call them "Karafuto-masu." Humpback comes from the rather dramatic rounded back that males develop prior to spawning.

THE BASICS: Maximum Length: 76 cm (2.5 ft) TL. Maximum Weight: 6.8 kg (14.9 lb). The Ranges: North Korea and Japan to Siberia and to the Beaufort Sea (Sachs Harbor, Banks Island), and southward to La Jolla (Southern California). Small runs occur in a number of rivers and streams running into the Chukchi Sea (perhaps to about Barrow) and perhaps as far east as the Colville River in northern Alaska. They are abundant as far north as the Chukchi Sea (the most abundant of the salmon species that live there) and, in the Beaufort Sea, they are regularly caught at least as far east as Simpson Lagoon and in smaller numbers along the Alaska National Wildlife Reserve. Those few fish taken along the central Beaufort Sea coast have been captured near the Mackenzie River. Historically, pinks spawned in such California systems as the Russian and Sacramento rivers; these runs no longer exist. People of California, you are very naughty. Pinks are most abundant as far south as about Puget Sound and as far north as the Chukchi Sea. They are found from surface waters to depths of 96 m (315 ft).

SALIENT CHARACTERS: A pink can be distinguished from other Pacific salmon by the very large black spots on all of the caudal fin and back. Cohos have no black spots on the lower part of their caudal fins and Chinooks have small irregular black spots.

LIFE HISTORY: Fertilized eggs hatch after 4–8 months and the young spend a few weeks to several months in the gravel before emerging. Among Pacific salmon, pinks are the fish least dependent on freshwater, for after emerging (at about 3.5 cm, 1 in, TL), juvenile pinks quickly leave freshwater (migrating downstream at night) and may spend several months in nearshore areas (often in eelgrass) or may migrate 50 km (31 mi) or more offshore within a few days of entering seawater. At sea, pinks spend most of their lives in perhaps the upper 10 m (33 ft) of the water column and may stay a bit shallower during the night than during the day; they will, on occasion, descend to depths of at least 74 m (243 ft). While in the ocean, pinks are found in waters between at least 3–15°C (37–59°F), but most catches are in 4–11°C (39–52°F). During their ocean sojourns, pinks tend to migrate outward only as far as the Aleutian Islands, many more stay off Washington, British Columbia, and in the Gulf of Alaska. In general, fish spend one winter in the sea and return to spawn the following summer and fall, although the occasional male will mature at less than one year old.

Spawning usually occurs in the intertidal zone of coastal creeks or in freshwater close to the coast, although some fish migrate upstream as far as 700 km (435 mi). In Chukchi Sea drainages, pinks enter rivers in July and August and fish further southward spawn from August to as late as October. Spawning grounds are usually gravel beds in shallow areas of fast-flowing water and spawning most often takes place at 7.2–12.8°C (45–55°F). Larger fish, mostly males, usually reach the spawning grounds first. An unusual feature of pink salmon reproductive dynamics is a distinctive two-year abundance cycle where, in many watersheds, spawning success is significantly higher in either the odd or even year. Bonar et al. (1989) note: "Pink salmon have a 2-year life cycle, which is so invariable that fish running in odd-numbered calendar years are effectively isolated from even-year fish so that no gene flow occurs between them."

Apparently, the numbers of pinks that historically migrated up rivers were at times really large. Let's see what the Russian biologist I. F. Pravdin (quoted in *Pacific Salmon Life Histories*, 1991, University of British Columbia Press) has to say: "Although the water was calm...an extraordinary noise could be heard coming from the middle of the river...similar to the noise of boiling water splashing in a gigantic cauldron...Standing there, the fishermen feasted their eyes upon a tremendous school of fish... the noisy stretch of fish was at least one verse long [1,073 m, 3,521 ft] and not less than 100 m [31 ft] wide, so that the size of the school could be estimated at several million specimens." *See, I told you*. Most pinks live for 2 years, although a few live to 3 years. Females produce between 854–2,260 orange-red eggs that are about 4.7–6 mm in diameter. Pinks feed primarily on small planktonic crustaceans (e.g., cladocerans, copepods, hyperiid amphipods, and euphausiids), crustacean larvae, gelatinous zooplankton (like pteropods), small fishes, and arrow worms, and larger fish tend to eat larger prey. As you would expect of a diet dependent on the verities of oceanographic conditions, diets of pinks vary between years. Pinks feed both day and night and their diets can change between these two periods. Besides the usual terrestrial predators, aquatic ones include various lamprey species, coho salmon, Dolly Vardens, Greenland halibut, North Pacific daggertooths, Arctic smelt, salmon sharks, starry flounder, walleye pollock, bald eagles, spotted and northern fur seals, beluga, humpback, and sperm whales, Pacific white-sided dolphins, and orcas.

FISHERY: Pinks were often taken in various subsistence fisheries. Not a major object of commercial fishermen (due to pale flesh and kind of limp texture) until the overfishing of sockeyes, today pinks form a huge fishery in Alaskan waters, as well as off Russia and Japan. In North America, most pinks are canned. In addition, both the eggs and whole ovaries are salted and sold for *ikura* and *sujiko*, respectively.

"'I'm a spring [Chinook] salmon fishermen, primarily, although I catch a lot of coho, and if I hear there are sockeye around, sometimes I do change the gear for a short time. We don't see any dog salmon [*O. keta*] trolling, and I try to avoid humpies [pinks] as much as I can. Too much hard work; one big spring is the equivalent of about forty pinks, I really hate to clean humps. God, the blood! The fishermen call them 'slimers' because they are so slimy to clean." Fisherman John Daly quoted in Iglauer (1988).

Pinks are an important sport fish from Washington northwards. Most are taken from boats, but pier, jetty, and shore fishermen also catch some.

RELATIONSHIPS: Pink salmon are most closely related to chum salmon and the two species hybridize in nature.

REMARKS: In some years, the Alaskan pink salmon hatchery program (which releases hundreds of millions of fry annually)

YET ANOTHER TRIUMPH FOR WESTERN CIVILIZATION

In 1875, the Flemish Catholic priest Dr. A. J. Brabant (1845–1912) was assigned by his superiors to attend to the First Nation peoples of the west coast of Vancouver Island, a position he occupied for more than 30 years. In the course of his work he kept a diary, which was later published in book form by the Reverend Charles Moser as *Reminiscences of the West Coast of Vancouver Island* (Acme Press, 1926). In that diary, Dr. Brabant notes that the native peoples had a number of beliefs dealing with what could or could not be done with the fishes they caught. The general fear was that some behaviors would offend the fishes and they would leave the local waters. This led Dr. Brabant to pen the following entry on 10 November 1875: "I am having a great time here. Their [the local First Nation peoples] superstitions are so numerous and so absurd that they are almost incredible. Just think of it! They won't allow us again to have any salmon for fear that I might fry it in lard, or boil it in an iron pot! I will get the better of them anyway—to-morrow I will be out fishing myself, if the weather permits."

The next day Dr. Brabant went out and caught a salmon and brought it back to his house. At that point, "Quite a number of men and chiefs assembled in my house, and protested against my using a knife or frying-pan. I took no notice of their protestations and proceeded with my work, my only aim being to show that their superstitions were absurd and to try by all and every means to get them to give them up."

OF FOXES, HUMPIES, AND, IN A RATHER TANGENTIAL WAY, HERRING

What do foxes and pink (or humpback) salmon have in common? And just what role do Pacific herring play in this unlikely *ménage a trois*?

In 1921, Edward Tuerck and his wife, Josephine, established a fox farm on Nuka Island, just off the Kenai Peninsula of Alaska. And, to quote L. Cook and F. Norris, *A Stern and Rock-Bound Coast: Kenai Fjords National Park Historic Resource Study* (National Park Service, Anchorage, Alaska,1998): "The foxes were given a varied diet. To save on feed costs, they were provided as many locally caught products as possible; humpback salmon was a staple, supplemented by the meat of seals, sea lions, and even whales when they could be procured. When fish and marine mammals were scarce, the foxes were fed a cooked compote of rolled oats and rolled wheat, mixed together with soaked-out fish, seal oil, and cracklings. Josephine occasionally made the foxes hotcakes and provided eggs from the nearby hen house."

But there was another ichthyologic connection to this story. For in 1924, one year after Ed died (perhaps suffering from a lack of hotcakes and eggs), Josephine, desiring to stay in the fox trade and needing a man who would be "capable and willing to take care of the fur business," married Captain Peter "Herring Pete" Sather. Herring Pete was so named because "during the 1920s he fell overboard into a purse seine full of herring." Herring Pete was also involved in a curious piece of litigation. As noted in Cook and Norris, HP claimed to have "single-handedly started" a pink salmon run on a stream running through his property. "As part of his fox farming operation, he consistently cleaned the pink salmon he harvested in a stream that previously, in Sather's opinion, had had no salmon in it. By the early 1950s, the stream supported a significant pink salmon population. Other fishers discovered the run and attempted to harvest the resource. Pete, however, resisted; he reasoned that he had single-handedly created the run and should therefore have proprietary rights over the salmon. He took his case to the courthouse in Anchorage; the courts, however, ruled against him."

And thus was defeated Peter Pinksalmon Seed.

is perhaps too successful, and more pinks return to the area of a hatchery than can be utilized by canneries. In 1991, this resulted in the so-called "humpy dump," where millions of whole pink salmon carcasses were hauled out to sea and thrust overboard. Apparently learning from this experience, in at least a few subsequent years, millions of pinks were "roe stripped," their eggs removed for subsequent sale, and the carcasses ground up and, you guessed it, dumped at sea. While I guess roe stripping in this circumstance (it is usually illegal) is preferable to wasting the entire animal, there is something kind of, well, disrespectful about the whole process.

Oncorhynchus keta
(Walbaum, 1792)
Chum Salmon

ETYMOLOGY AND COLLOQUIAL NAMES: *Oncorhynchus* comes from two Greek words for "hook" and "snout" and *keta* refers to the vernacular name used by the fine folks of Kamchatka. Evermann and Goldsborough (1907) note: "Frequently the flesh is dirty red and soiled white alternately in broad bands, which, together with the banding on the surface, doubtless suggested the name calico salmon." The Russians call this salmon "hayko" or "lekai," while to the Japanese it is "sake." In 1866, J.K. Lord wrote of: "The large fanglike teeth, from which they derive the name of dog-salmon." And Ms C. Lyons commented in 1969: "In the early days of European settlement and during the [canning] Industry's first 20 years the *keta* was called 'chump salmon'. By about 1890 the final letter had fallen into disuse. Possibly the reason for the early name was suggested by the somewhat rounded shape of the fish, as in its original meaning 'chump' appears to have been applied to a thick end of meat (especially mutton), fish or wood."

THE BASICS: Maximum Length: 109 cm (43 in) TL. Maximum Weight: 20 kg (44 lb). The Ranges: Siberia west to Laptev Sea and east across Alaskan and Canadian Arctic to Kugluktuk [formerly Coppermine] (Nunavut) and also Korea and southern Japan, to Del Mar (Southern California). In North America, they are most abundant from the Chukchi Sea down to about Oregon and are the most abundant salmon in the Beaufort Sea. Spawning occurs from at least the McKenzie River (Canada) to (historically, but probably not today) the Sacramento River (California). At sea, they swim from the surface to 253 m (830 ft) or perhaps to 400 m (1,312 ft). Eggs: fertilized = 6–9.5 mm. Length-weight parameters (FL, cm, gr): (sexes combined) $W = 0.06252L^{2.6}$ (Bakkala 1970).

SALIENT CHARACTERS: Unlike most other Pacific salmon, chums do not have large black spots, rather they have tiny black speckling. Sea-run chums are metallic blue on their backs, with silvery bellies. Spawning individuals are blackish or dark olive on

JASON HESKEW

backs, reddish on sides, with dark bars or gray blotches (often described as a "calico" pattern).

LIFE HISTORY: Eggs hatch in about 1.5–6 months, when the young are as small as about 2.1 cm (0.8 in) TL. Most of these young fish leave freshwater within a short time (mostly traveling at night), although smaller numbers may remain in streams for a number of months. Upon entering saltwater, small juveniles often hug the coast and stay in somewhat brackish waters. Scott Johnson et al. (2005) caught over 65,000 juveniles in barely subtidal waters in southeastern Alaska, mostly in eelgrass, but also commonly over bedrock, some in kelp, and less commonly over bare seafloor. Within a few months, older fish from North America move somewhat offshore with highest densities in the Gulf of Alaska, although some fish are also found along the Aleutian Islands and in the Bering Sea. Regarding at-sea movements, I guess we can't do better than Beamish et al. (2005): "Chum salmon are distributed similar to sockeye salmon, except juveniles may remain in the coastal areas longer in their first year and more individuals may spend more than two winters in the high seas. Chum salmon from North America are not commonly reported from the western Pacific...Most chum salmon of North American origin spend 3 winters in the ocean, but a smaller percentage spend 4 winters and less than 5% spend five winters." At sea, they are found from less than 1 to 15°C (34–59°F), with highest catches in about 2–11°C (36–52°F). At sea, chums tend to stay relatively near the surface, mostly in the upper 10 m (33 ft), but they make occasional forays as deep as 253 m (830 ft). On homeward migrations, at least some

SALMON

The salmon's a fish so benighted,
For in getting its wish, it's shortsighted,
    It swims at full steam,
    To it's clear natal stream,
Then dies of a love *too* requited.

dive to considerable depths. There is genetic evidence that Japanese, Russian, and Yukon River fish form one population, and that this is different from fish from southeastern Alaska (another one), and from British Columbia (still another one).

On their return, chums enter natal rivers and streams primarily in the summer or fall, although some fish (such as in Puget Sound) enter freshwater in the winter. During the upstream migrations, fish may endure waters between nearly freezing and 21.1°C (70°F), with optimum spawning temperatures of 7.2–12.8°C (45–55°F) with a range of 4–16°C (39–61°F). In northern waters, spawning occurs as early as June, and to the south to as late as at least January. Most fish spawn from very near the coast (sometimes in intertidal waters) to within 200 km (124 mi) of the sea, but some populations travel considerable distances upriver. Some chums in the Yukon River, for instance, migrate over 3,129 km (2,000 mi) to spawn.

Female chums occasionally live as long as 7 years, although most fish die by 5 years old. At least a few males mature at 2 years old, but most fish are 3–5 years old at maturity. Females produce between 900–8,000 eggs; fecundity varies among areas and among years. For instance, in British Columbia, fish returning to Vancouver Island and the Queen Charlotte Islands were less fecund than those returning to mainland sites. Chums eat zooplankton, small fishes, and squids. Common prey include crustaceans (e.g., copepods, euphausiids, amphipods, and mysid shrimps), medusae, salps, larvaceans, arrow worms, insects, and fish larvae. One study found that fish feed more heavily shortly before sunset and sunrise. During spawning runs, at least some chums feed on salmon eggs. Like all salmon, chums are eaten by a wide range of predators. A short list includes Pacific halibut, Pacific sandfish, Pacific sleeper and salmon sharks, Arctic smelt, river lampreys, various sculpins, walleye pollock, horned puffins, rhinoceros auklets, harbor and northern fur seals, beluga, fin, and humpback whales, and orcas.

FISHERY: In bygone days, chums were widely used as subsistence food. Wolfe (1979) found: "One mail carrier [in the Yukon area] in 1920 kept 60 dogs, requiring 12 to 14 tons of dried salmon (about 15,000 to 20,000 small salmon) as dog food annually." Today, this species remains an important part of subsistence fisheries in a number of locations, particularly in the Arctic and Subarctic. Beyond that, chums have had just bad, bad, press. Turner (1886) started the drumbeat: "The flesh of this species is not good. It is coarse and without a decided flavor," while Evermann and Goldsborough (1907) piled on with: "As a food fish this species is inferior to all the other salmon...The inferiority, however, is more marked when the fish is canned than when otherwise utilized. The flesh is soft and spongy and does not lend itself readily to canning processes." Despite this opprobrium, overfishing of sockeye salmon in the mid-20th century led to greater fishing for chums after World War II. Much of the catch is frozen and exported, the eggs are salted and sold for *ikura* (salmon caviar), and the whole ovaries with eggs inside are sold as the salted and frozen product, *sujiko*.

© THOMAS KLINE

I note that, in the eternal attempt to put a fresh and new face on kind of funky fish names, chums are also often called "keta" salmon, which has a nice kind of ethnic ring. "Silverbrite" is another market name, although one should always beware of items whose names are intentionally misspelled.

Chums are a reasonably important sport fish. In places like Washington state, where runs of other salmon have tanked, recreational anglers have grudgingly started to target this species.

MISCELLANY: 1) A partially xanthic fish (yellow on dorsal area) was caught off Chignik (Alaska) and a hermaphroditic chum was taken in Tillamook Bay (Oregon). 2) There is some evidence that an occasional fish may not leave freshwater. A 36.5 cm (15 in) FL fish was taken in a British Columbia lake during the nonspawning season. The fish had not spawned and had small gonads. 3) Chums have a large baglike stomach that helps them digest gelatinous zooplankton.

RELATIONSHIPS: Unlike the modern chum salmon, the fossil relative, *Oncorhynchus ketaopsis*, found in 6–8-million-year-old Miocene strata, was perhaps a repeat spawner. Based on genetic analyses, chums are most closely related to pinks.

Oncorhynchus kisutch

(Walbaum, 1792)

Coho Salmon

ETYMOLOGY AND COLLOQUIAL NAMES: *Oncorhynchus* comes from two Greek words for "hook" and "snout" and *kisutch* is similar to the name used by Kamchatka indigenes. Some folks use "silver" or "blueback," and "cohoe" is an older spelling of the current name. The Japanese name is "ginzake."

THE BASICS: Maximum Length: 108 cm (43 in) TL. Maximum Weight: 11.8 kg (26 lb) for a native fish. On the other hand, the International Gamefish Association lists a 15.1 kg (33.3 lb) nonnative fish taken from the Salmon River in Pulaski, New York. What the hell are the Pulaskians putting in their water? The Ranges: North Korea and Japan to MacKenzie Delta, Northwest Territories, and to Bahia Camalu (northern Baja California). In North America, spawning occurs as far north as the Kukpuk River (entering the Chukchi Sea) and as far south (historically, alas no more) as the San Lorenzo River (Central California). At sea, cohos are most abundant as far south as about Monterey Bay. Surface to 247 m (820 ft). Egg: 4.5–6.9 mm. Length-weight parameters (TL, mm, kg): (sexes combined) $W = 0.00000000944L^{3.0}$ (RecFin 2009).

SALIENT CHARACTERS: Cohos have black spots on their backs and on the upper part of their caudal fins and their gums are white at the bases of the teeth. At sea, both sexes are blue on backs and silvery below. When they ascend rivers to spawn, males have a green back and red sides and sometimes blackish on bellies. Females are bronze to reddish on sides. A Chinook has black gums and spots throughout its caudal fin.

LIFE HISTORY: Embryos hatch under gravel at about 5–12 weeks after the eggs are fertilized and these young fish remain in the substrate for around 3–10 weeks after hatching. At the extreme, it takes some cohos living in the Big Qualicum River (British Columbia) almost 27 weeks to go from fertilized egg to juvenile fish emerging from gravel. Upon exiting the river floor, some fish head down stream to estuaries, while others remain in freshwater. Before entering the sea (mostly in March–May) cohos spend 1–4 winters (mostly 1–2) in fresh or brackish waters. Upon first entering marine

FRANK HILLSBERRY, an Altoona, Wash., gillnetter, this fall caught a Silver salmon with two distinct mouths, each furnished with tongue, teeth and gills—evidently one of the few monstrosities which lived to attain maturity.

PACIFIC FISHERMAN, 1933, 31(13):37

© THOMAS KLINE

waters, juveniles tend to hug the coast, frequently in just barely subtidal depths, often living in eelgrass, kelp, and filamentous algae. Once at sea, fish produced in California–British Columbia waters tend to move northward. Beamish et al. (2005) note: "Some coho have been observed in the Gulf of Alaska and even the western Pacific...However, coho are mainly a coastal species, not moving too far offshore [mostly staying over the continental shelf]. Coho spend one winter in the ocean...and return along the coast to spawn in the later summer and fall of the next year [16–18 months on average]." In the North Pacific, cohos have been caught in 5–15°C (41–59°F), with highest catches at 7–12°C (45–54°F). Cohos tend to spend most of their time in the top 10 m (33 ft) of the water column, although for at least some individuals excursions to a bit deeper depths happen on a daily basis. One tagged coho descended to 97 m (318 ft).

After hanging out in marine waters for maybe 1.5 years, most cohos arrive back at their natal rivers in later summer and fall (at the extreme, as early as April and as late as March). In general, fishes in the north return to freshwater earlier in the season than do those in the south. Upstream migrations (and these mostly during day) begin after the first heavy rains wash out the sand bars, allowing the fish to enter. Spawning occurs October–March (mostly November–January) in small coastal streams and the tributaries of larger rivers. Spawning tends to occur later in the season in the coastal streams. Although many spawning grounds are in the range of hundreds of kilometers from the sea, some fish spawn over 2,200 km (1,367 mi) from the sea in a branch of the Yukon River. Generally, males reach the spawning areas first.

Most cohos live to 3 years old, but smaller numbers live a few more years. A small percentage of males ("jacks") mature and return to spawn in freshwater after only 4–6 months at sea. Females produce between 1,400–7,600 eggs and, as one might expect, fecundity varies among areas and years. In general, a fish in the north, say off Alaska, produces more eggs per body length than do those to the south. On the other hand, cohos tend to be larger in the south. Cohos eat fishes and invertebrates. Larger fish eat larger prey, with juveniles focusing on smaller crustaceans and fishes. Among invertebrate prey, euphausiids, gammarid amphipods, mysid shrimps, cumaceans, polychaetes, and squids are commonly consumed. One fish was found to have eaten a sea bird, probably a petrel. During spawning runs, at least some cohos eat salmon eggs. Predators include black rockfish, North Pacific daggertooths, Pacific electric rays, Pacific and river lampreys, salmon sharks, Aleutian terns, common mergansers, common murres, rhinoceros auklets, harbor and northern fur seals, beluga whales, Pacific white-sided dolphins, and orcas.

FISHERY: Cohos are a major commercial species, taken by trolling, purse seines, and gill nets, primarily from Oregon northwards. Similarly, substantial recreational catches are made, mostly north of California waters. A few are caught from piers and jetties, some from the surf, and gobs from boats.

RELATIONSHIPS: Genetic analyses imply that cohos are most closely related to Chinooks.

MISCELLANY: Cohos occasionally hybridize with Chinooks. On 23 February 1927, a day that will live in infamy, a hermaphroditic adult was taken in the Chehalis River (Washington State). Although externally it had mature female characteristics, it contained both mature eggs and testes full of sperm.

Oncorhynchus mykiss
(Walbaum, 1792)
Steelhead

One of those iconic anadromous fish with highly variable life history strategies.

ETYMOLOGY AND COLLOQUIAL NAME: *Oncorhynchus* comes from two Greek words for "hook" and "snout" and *mykiss* is yet another vernacular name from the locals of Kamchatka, the same folks who gave you *keta*, *gorbuscha*, etc. Steelhead are rainbow trout capable of running to the ocean and David Starr Jordan claims that he was the originator of the common name "rainbow trout." In his book, *The Days of a Man* (World Book Publishing, 1922), Jordan writes: "[Spencer] Baird [of the Smithsonian Institution] asked to have common names attached to the different forms [of trout and salmon on the Pacific Coast]. For the trout of the coastwise streams...I naturally suggested 'Rainbow Trout.'" The anadromous form is typically called "steelhead," while freshwater populations are called "rainbow trout." Currently, our Russian colleagues are most likely to call this species *Parasalmo mykiss*. The Japanese call them "niji-masu."

THE BASICS: Maximum Length: 122 cm (48 in) TL. Maximum Weight: 19.2 kg (42.2 lb). The Ranges: Sea of Okhotsk, Kuril Islands, to Kuskokwim Bay and Port Moller (southeastern Bering Sea) to northern Baja California near Cuidad Durango. Historically, they ranged into waterways as far south as the Tijuana River (San Diego County) and are still in the close-by San Luis Rey River. Length-weight parameters (TL, mm, kg): (sexes combined) $W = 0.00000000637L^{3.063}$ (RecFin 2009).

SALIENT CHARACTERS: At sea, steelhead have bluish backs and silvery bellies, with small black spots on their backs and on dorsal and caudal fins. Spawning males have a small red or pink stripe along their sides. Salmon have 14 or more anal fin rays (compared to 9–12 in steelhead).

LIFE HISTORY: Steelhead life histories are quite plastic, so only generalities are presented below. Eggs hatch in 3–4 weeks (at water temperatures of 10–15°C, 50–59°F) and the young fish stay in the gravel for 2–3 weeks.

MARK CONLIN

Young fish remain in freshwater anywhere from less than one year to 4 years. Fish tend to spend less time in freshwater in the southern part of their range and those that leave in less than one year are less likely to survive and return to spawn. Juveniles migrate to sea at anywhere from 15–25 cm (6–10 in) TL, usually in the spring, but throughout their range there are fish entering the ocean in every month. Upon entering the ocean, steelhead appear to quickly move offshore. In the North Pacific, young steelhead were caught over 1,600 km (994 mi) from shore only a few months after the fish had left freshwater. Some fish born in North American waters migrate well westward and northward to the Aleutians and some almost to Kamchatka. Most steelhead probably stay in the upper 20 m (66 ft) of the water column.

Prior to first spawning, fish in the north likely spend more time at sea (overall this ranges from 1–3 years) than do those in the south; the average steelhead first returning to its home stream is 57.5 cm (23 in) TL at Santa Cruz (Central California), 65 cm (26 in) in Oregon, and 72.5 cm (29 in) in British Columbia. In southern Oregon and Northern California, many fish return to freshwater when still immature after only a few summer months at sea. After feeding throughout the fall and winter, they leave streams the following spring and again hang out in the sea. Depending on the stream, steelies may be "summer" or "winter" migrants. "Summer" fish ascend from about May–August (spending the warm months in cool, deep pools), while "winter" ones go up from about November–April. In some systems, males tend to swim up to the spawning areas before females. One study found that in Washington watersheds, males and females may mate with multiple individuals. In their study, the maximum number of mates for males was 10, and for females it was five. Most females mated with males that had already arrived and there was some evidence that resident rainbow trout often fertilized eggs from female steelhead. Regardless of when the migration occurs, most spawning takes place from March to early May. In the North Pacific, they have been caught at 5–15°C (41–59°F) with highest catches at 8 to about 11°C (46–52°F).

Population studies have yielded some interesting results. Based on genetic data, fish from the Fraser and Thompson rivers in British Columbia and the Columbia River in the U.S. form distinct groups. In the Nass River (British Columbia), winter-run fish are genetically distinct from those that run in the summer. A study in the Klamath-Trinity river complex found that there were many different "populations" among the tributaries implying that there is relatively little genetic interchange within this system.

Steelhead live to at least 8 and maybe to 10 years. Females produce between 200–12,749 eggs per season. This species eats large numbers of fishes and fish eggs and a wide range of invertebrates. Invertebrates include euphausiids, copepods, hyperiid amphipods and various crustacean larvae, squids, polychaetes, and pteropods. Steelhead do feed when they return to freshwater. Predators include Pacific lampreys, spiny dogfish, harbor and northern fur seals, California and Steller sea lions, beluga whales, and orcas.

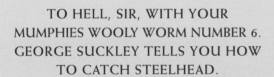

TO HELL, SIR, WITH YOUR MUMPHIES WOOLY WORM NUMBER 6. GEORGE SUCKLEY TELLS YOU HOW TO CATCH STEELHEAD.

In 1861, George Suckley, naturalist and lately a Civil War surgeon, penned a report on the salmon of North America. In this report (Suckley 1874), he included several descriptions of catching salmon and steelhead in the West, including this tip on angling for *"Salmo iridea"*: "Common raw meat is a very good bait for these trout—the tougher the better; we generally used the meat of a crow, killed for the purpose. This flesh combines redness and a rank smell with its proverbial toughness—all-important desiderata for 'killing' bait."

FISHERY: This was an important subsistence species for various indigenous peoples and was widely sold by locals to European settlers in, for instance, Sitka (Alaska). Called "salmon-trout" in the markets of 19th-century San Francisco, steelhead were preferred over Chinooks. A fairly robust commercial fishery existed in the early 20th century, with much of the production coming from the Columbia River and from British Columbia and almost all of it was frozen and shipped to Europe. "The French market, which takes a considerable portion of the frozen Steelhead...is said to insist upon round [uncleaned] fish because of the prejudice in the French mind, which conceives that if a fish has been dressed it is prima facie evidence that something was wrong and that the fish was dressed to conceal it" (Pacific Fisherman 1931). Smoked steelhead was held to be extremely tasty, but it has a light color compared to the salmon and it never seemed to catch on with the public. Today, directed commercial fishing for steelhead is banned, although some bycatch is allowed in certain regions and subsistence fishing is legal in some locales.

Steelhead are one of the most popular sport fish from Central California northward. They are caught mostly in rivers and streams, but some are taken by boat anglers and small numbers are taken off piers. I grew up reading outdoor magazines extolling the mystique, the wonder, and the glory of winter steelhead fishing. In the accompanying pictures I examined as a kid, there were always some sodden, bedraggled characters, standing neck deep in a freezing, torrential stream, with 3 inches of sleet piled up on their heads, looking like the snow monkeys that live in Japan. You remember, the ones sitting in hot pools with snow on their heads? But remember, the monkeys have enough sense to try to get out of the cold.

RELATIONSHIPS: Related to the steelhead lineage is *Oncorhynchus "Rhabdofario" lacustris* from the Miocene (at least 5.3 million years ago) of Idaho and Oregon. Steelhead are most closely related to cutthroat trout and cherry salmon (*Oncorhynchus masou*).

MISCELLANY: 1) A bisexual fish was taken from the Eel River, Northern California. 2) "Sneaker" male cutthroat trout will sometimes dash in and fertilize newly deposited steelhead eggs. 3) In Central California, adult steelhead are occasionally found in the kelp canopy.

REMARKS: Based on genetic data, steelhead might have found refuge from a Pleistocene ice age in the Gulf of California.

Oncorhynchus nerka
(Walbaum, 1792)
Sockeye Salmon

ETYMOLOGY AND COLLOQUIAL NAMES: *Oncorhynchus* comes from two Greek words for "hook" and "snout" and *nerka* refers to the name used way back when by inhabitants of Kamchatka. There are a host of variants on "sockeye," including "sawkeye," "suk-eye," "sukk-kegh," and "sau-qui." David Starr Jordan believed that "sockeye" was a corruption of the Chinook name "sukkegh." The species has long been "red salmon" in Alaska and "blueback" also has a long history. The Japanese word is "benizake."

THE BASICS: Maximum Length: To 84 cm (33 in) TL. Maximum Weight: 7.3 kg (16 lb). The Ranges: Northern Japan and the Sea of Okhotsk to Alaska to the Klamath River (Northern California), and along the Arctic Alaska and Canada coasts to Bathurst Inlet (Nunavut), and northward to the Sachs River estuary (Banks Island). In the ocean, they are common as far south as about

the Columbia River area. Their northern-most spawning site is in Kotzebue Sound (Chukchi Sea) and southernmost site is likely the Columbia River. Anadromous sockeyes are only rarely found in various watersheds south of the Columbia River are likely strays and do not represent spawning populations. They live from surface waters to 83 m (272 ft).

SALIENT CHARACTERS: In the ocean, a sockeye is blue-black on the top of its head, with a blue back and silvery sides. It does not have distinctive black spots on its dorsal and caudal fins (unlike Chinooks, cohos, and pinks). Spawning colors are a very distinctive, *très elegant* green head and bright red body (some females have green and yellow blotches on their bodies).

LIFE HISTORY: Sockeyes have both anadromous and fresh-water (never entering the sea) populations. What I have put down below deals with anadromous fish; if you are interested in the freshwater forms you are on your own.

MICHELLE PADDOCK

Nick Coroneos on his way to the Santa Barbara Summer Solstice Parade.

The young hatch out of eggs about 2–6 months after fertilization. After a period under the gravel, young fish emerge at night. Generally (but not always) juvenile sockeyes live for 1–3 years in lakes (mostly 1–2 years). However, some populations reside for only a few weeks in streams before they enter marine waters. After entering the sea in the spring or early summer, sockeyes spend several months in nearshore waters (sometimes in eelgrass and kelp) before migrating offshore in fall and winter, where they reside for 1–4 years (most spend 2 winters) before heading back to natal waters. The small fish spending only one year at sea are mostly males (called "jacks") only a few are females ("jills"). North American sockeyes often migrate way offshore, some almost to Kamchatka, where they mingle with Asian fish. While at sea, there is a tendency for fish to move northward as waters warm and southward as they cool. In the North Pacific, sockeyes have been caught in waters between less than 1–15°C (34–59°F), with peak catches in 2.5–9°C (37–48°F). Most fish spend their time in the upper 10 m or less (33 ft), although they do occasionally move downward to depths of at least 83 m (272 ft) or more. Sockeyes spawn between July–January, perhaps mostly in summer and fall. Spawning usually occurs either in waterways entering lakes or in the nearshore of lakes themselves, although sockeyes run in some streams (i.e., in western Washington) that have no lakes attached.

In the wild, sockeyes live, rarely, to 7 years old, although a nonnative one in a Connecticut lake lived to 8 years. Fecundity varies with area with females producing between about 2,000–5,000 orange-red eggs. Sockeyes feed primarily on a wide range of zooplankton (e.g., euphausiids, hyperiid amphipods, sergestid shrimps, copepods, and pteropods), but larger individuals will also consume small fishes and squids and there can be large differences in diets between areas within a year and between years. At least one study demonstrated that sockeyes feed during both day and night. Examples of their predators include cohos, Dolly Vardens, Pacific and river lampreys, Pacific sleeper sharks, other sockeyes, horned and tufted puffins, rhinoceros auklets, harbor and northern fur seals, beluga whales, Pacific white-sided dolphin, and orcas.

FISHERY: Turner (1886) reporting on Aleuts capturing river-run sockeyes on Attu Island, Aleutian Islands: "The young boys and girls have gone into the water some distance below [the traps], and with shouts and beating the water the fish seek the shelter near the weir. Those holding the seine then enter and soon have all the fish secured. They are thrown on the bank and cleaned. The fish are owned in common; any one who desires to work can do so, those not so desiring will of course be remembered, in the winter, when the fish are to be distributed. After the fish are dried they are carried on the backs of the women and children to the principal village and stored, in October, in sea-lion stomachs for winter's food. The stomachs of these animals are very large, and when fresh are inflated with air and stretched as much as possible...These skins make a

ON PREDATION

From the files of Gende et al. (2001a). They observed bears capturing and eating more than 20,000 sockeye, pink, and chum salmon in Alaskan streams. When salmon were abundant, the bears ate less of each fish, focusing on the more energy-rich parts, such as eggs in females and brains of males [no jokes please]. When times were tougher and salmon were scarce, the bears, as one might expect, ate more of each fish.

convenient receptacle for storing these fish, as they absorb just sufficient moisture to keep the contents in good condition and also prevent mold from spoiling them."

Today, sockeyes form a lively fishery and the meat is both canned and frozen. Ovaries with eggs are sold as the salted and frozen product *sujiko*.

RELATIONSHIPS: A related species, *O. salax*, lived during the Miocene (at least 5.3 million years ago) of Idaho. Fossil sockeyes found in 1-million-year-old strata in Washington have some of the characteristics of pink salmon, so divergence of the two species may have occurred around this time. Genetic analyses have demonstrated that sockeyes are most closely related to chums and pinks.

MISCELLANY: Evermann and Goldsborough (1907) state: "The red salmon is the neatest and most symmetrical of the salmon." Thus setting the stage, I expect, for telling us which species is the most slovenly and least symmetrical.

REMARKS: Busy researchers have come up with a very clever method to help figure out the origin of sockeyes caught at sea. After a long and diligent search, and probably through dissecting more salmon than is emotionally healthy, biologists have figured out that there are two parasites that can be used as indicators of a sockeye's origin. Sockeyes hatched in the Bristol Bay (Alaska) region have a larval tapeworm, *Triaenophorus crassus*, in their muscles, while Kamchatka fish have an intestinal worm, *Truttaedacnitis truttae*, in them. So the deal is, if you catch a salmon and it has one of these guys in it, you know where it came from. And if it doesn't? Hey, you are just out of luck.

Oncorhynchus tshawytscha

(Walbaum, 1792)

Chinook Salmon

ETYMOLOGY AND COLLOQUIAL NAMES: *Oncorhynchus* comes from two Greek words for "hook" and "snout" and *tshawytscha* refers to the name used by Kamchatka locals. Ever been bothered by this keyboard-twisting species name? Jordan and Gilbert (1883) were bothered too and tried to change the spelling to "chouicha." They wrote that "tshawytscha" was "a barbarous spelling of the word 'chouicha' which we thought proper to simplify." Well, obviously they were slapped down by the Dark Lords of Nomenclature. It seems that every town on the Pacific Coast had a different name for this species but "king," "spring," "tyee," "quinnat," and "blackmouth" were commonly used. It is called "masunosuke" in Japanese.

THE BASICS: Maximum Length: 160 cm (63 in) TL. Maximum Weight: 61.4 kg (135.1 lb). The Ranges: Naturally occurring from northern Japan to the Beaufort Sea at the Coppermine River, and to central Baja California at Bahia de Sebastian Vizcaino (27°54'N, 114°17'W). Planted successfully in New Zealand and the Great Lakes. At sea, Chinooks are common in some years in Southern California marine waters, but are more predictably found from the Bering Sea to Central California. Chinooks spawn in watersheds from Kotzebue Sound (Chukchi Sea) to the Central Valley of California. Surface waters to 344 m (1,128 ft). Length-weight parameters (TL, mm, kg): (sexes combined) W = 0.00000000944L$^{3.0}$ (RecFin 2009).

SALIENT CHARACTERS: At sea, Chinooks are bluish or greenish blue, gray, or (as they mature) black on backs and silvery below. Spawning fish are olive-brown to dark red, and small males may be yellowish. Most important in its identification are the black gums at the base of the teeth in the lower jaw and the irregular black spots on the back and all over the caudal fin.

MARK CONLIN

LIFE HISTORY: As with a number of other salmonids (such as steelhead), Chinooks display a rich assortment of life history patterns leading to the kind of sad and forlorn summary below.

Depending on water temperature, young Chinooks hatch under gravel between about 30–160 days after egg fertilization; warmer temperatures speed hatching time. Young fish tend to emerge from the gravel at night (after 4–6 weeks) and then quickly move downstream spending as little as a few weeks or as much as a year or more in freshwater. Many of the fish that quickly leave freshwater reside in estuaries for at least a few months, although length of residence varies annually and with location. At sea, as noted by Beamish et al. (2005), Chinooks "are virtually a coastal migrant, with very few fish found outside the 200-mile limits of Canada and the United States. [There are] 2 life history types. The ocean type enters the ocean in their first year in freshwater and migrate less in the ocean. The stream type spend one year in freshwater, enter the ocean in their second freshwater year, and tend to migrate further." There is a tendency for fish entering the ocean south of Cape Blanco (Oregon) to move south, while those entering north of the cape to move northwards. Along the Pacific Coast, ocean-dwellers tend to mostly stay deep in late fall and winter (commonly to 150 m, 492 ft) and rise into shallower waters in spring and summer. A tagged fish descended to at least 344 m (1,128 ft). Chinooks have been found in at least 2–16.9°C (7–63°F), perhaps mostly in 8–12°C (46–54°F). Chinooks in the Yukon River are genetically isolated from those of southeastern Alaska and British Columbia.

Upon re-entering freshwaters, Chinooks tend to move upstream during the day. Spawning occurs in gravel fields of natal watersheds from near intertidal waters to more than 3,200 km (1,988 mi) up the Yukon River in both large and small water-ways. Spawning months vary widely and range from as early as May to as late as January. Fish in the north generally spawn earlier than those to the south. However, even within a river system, such as the Sacramento, different populations may spawn at different times.

Chinooks live to at least 8 years old. Average age of maturity varies widely among watersheds and even among ocean-type and stream-type populations in the same watershed. In general, most fish mature at between 3–6 years old. Some runs harbor relatively large numbers of 2-year-old mature males (called jacks) and females (jills, of course). Males tend to mature at a slightly younger age than females and often the very oldest fish are females. A few males mature without ever entering

© UNIVERSITY OF WASHINGTON PRESS

FROM THE PEN OF R. RATHBUN, SALMON CRITIC

Yes, it's time to hear what R. Rathbun, the federal biologist who reported about the salmon of Alaska in 1893, has to say. So, let's listen in: "The red salmon [sockeye], according to Dr. Bean, is now the most important species for canning and salting in Alaska, and its flesh is so red as to win for it a reputation not warranted by its edible qualities. The largest and finest species is the king or quinnat salmon… The humpback [pink] is the smallest, most abundant, and most widely distributed of the Alaskan salmon. It is not taken for canning purposes, but being one of the most palatable species in the fresh-run condition it is destined to become of great importance in that connection. The silver salmon is used to some extent for canning, but far less than the red salmon, while the dog salmon [chum] is regarded by whites as one of the least important of the group."

the ocean. Some of these precocious 1-year-old fish may live to spawn in a subsequent year. Fecundity varies both among watersheds and between years within watersheds and females produce between 1,622–17,255 eggs. Juveniles feed on smaller fishes, along with euphausiids, calanoid copepods, hyperiid amphipods, mysid shrimps, copepods, pteropods, squids, and other water column organisms. Larger Chinooks will eat some of these prey, but really emphasize fishes. Adults will eat salmon eggs after their return to fresh waters. Predators include black rockfish, Chinook and coho salmon, North Pacific daggertooths, Pacific lampreys, Pacific sleeper sharks, spiny dogfish, striped bass, steelhead, common mergansers, common murres, least terns, harbor and northern fur seals, California sea lions, Pacific white-sided dolphins, Dall's porpoises, beluga whales, and orcas.

FISHERY: This is one of those really important species. Indigenous folks caught a lot of them and they are still really important to many subsistence fisheries in such places as the Yukon River. The first commercial salmon catches (these fish were netted) began as early as 1850 on the Sacramento and San Joaquin rivers. The Pacific salmon canning industry started with these guys in 1864, also on the Sacramento River. Parenthetically, canning California salmon was banned in 1934, leaving it to be sold fresh, salted, or smoked. Today, most of the commercial catch is sold fresh or frozen.

Unlike at least some other salmon species, the color of a Chinook's flesh is under genetic control. If a fish carrying the color gene eats prey (like euphausiids) that carry carotenoid pigments, the fish's flesh is pink or red. A few fish will have red muscle on one side of the body and the other side will be white; mottled-flesh ones are also known. If that fish does not carry the color gene, it can eat euphausiids until it explodes and its flesh remains white. At least some white-fleshed fish are found throughout all or most of the species' range, although some areas are hotspots and some watersheds have no white ones. In a study in Alaska and British Columbia, the greatest percentage of white-fleshed individuals was in the Fraser River of British Columbia, where 53.8% of fish were white. A study in British Columbia implied that white-fleshed Chinooks may grow larger, on average, than red-fleshed ones. Historically, white-meated Chinooks were worth less (and sometimes worth nothing) to commercial fisheries and these were often salted instead of canned. Food fashions being what they are, I note that supermarkets now may charge more for the white ones than for the red ones.

This is a big-time recreational species. While most folks fish for them from Central California northward, there are occasional years where fairly substantial numbers of fish reach into Southern California, even as far south as in the Newport Submarine Canyon. My favorite story about salmon sportfishing has got to be Rudyard Kipling's "American Salmon" (*American Notes*, R. F. Fenno, 1899). I mean Kipling was a glorifier of empire and just chock full of racial prejudices, but the dude could write. "American Salmon" is as evocative a piece about Oregon in another time and the joys of fishing as one can find.

RELATIONSHIPS: Fossils of fish possibly related to Chinooks were found in perhaps 3-million-year-old strata in Idaho. Genetic studies demonstrate Chinooks are most closely related to cohos.

JANA SUCHY

MISCELLANY: 1) A possible albino was taken on the Deschutes River, Oregon. 2) Chinooks will hybridize with coho salmon. 3) McCully (1956) reported that an adult male tagged 122 km (76 mi) up the Sacramento River was caught about 8 months later at the Farallon Islands. McCully notes that some fish tagged upriver are found down river later and then may go back upriver. This one went back to sea. 4) And lastly, from the exotic sex file: a bisexual Chinook, containing functional male and female parts, was captured off Fort Bragg (Northern California) a number of years ago.

REMARKS: Without putting to fine a point on it, a number of Chinook salmon stocks, like those of other salmon species, have just been trashed. In the early 21th century, this led to such drastic measures as closures of salmon fisheries along the California and Oregon coasts.

GEORGE SUCKLEY TELLS ALL

George Suckley was a naturalist who, well, naturalized his way along the Pacific Coast as part of the Pacific Railroad Survey. Here's what he wrote in 1861 (later published in 1874) about Chinook salmon in Oregon: "The *quinnat*, in an economical point of view, is by far the most valuable salmon of any species found in Oregon. The extreme richness and delicacy of its flesh cause it to be much preferred for salting, and were it not for the hitherto high prices of labor, barrels, and salt, it would have, ere this, been found a staple article of export from the Columbia. In numbers they seem to be inexhaustible, and are readily taken in nets and otherwise...The Indians on the Columbia take immense numbers, eating what they need while fresh, and drying thousands for winter consumption or for trade...During the height of the season it is not uncommon for a single man thus to take twenty or thirty fish in an hour...For subsequent consumption the salmon are split open and the entrails and back-bone taken out; they are then hung up in the lodges to dry in the smoke. When perfectly dry they are packed in bundles and kept in baskets or mats, and in some places, as along the river from Walla-Walla to Fort Colville, large stores are placed on platforms raised on poles some twelve or fifteen feet from the ground. This is to protect them from the ravages of the wolves. To guard against rain and the plundering propensities of crows, magpies, and ravens, they are covered with mats or strips of bark, and occasionally with rough-hewn boards. No salt is used by the savages in preparing the fish; nevertheless, the food thus preserved keeps in good order for several years."

Salvelinus malma
(Walbaum, 1792)
Dolly Varden

ETYMOLOGY AND COLLOQUIAL NAMES: *Salvelinus* comes from an old name for char and *malma* is based on a name used by the early inhabitants of Kamchatka. Other names include "Pacific brook char," "red-spotted trout," and "salmon trout." And regarding the common name "Dolly Varden," Jordan (1922) has this story to tell: "Another fine form with bright crimson spots–*Salvelinus malma*–had been sent to Washington from the upper Sacramento, with the comment that the land-lady at Upper Soda Springs declared it looked 'like a regular Dolly Varden.' This likeness to the 'plump, coquettish little minx' of Dickens' 'Barnaby Rudge' pleased [Spencer] Baird [of the Smithsonian Institution] and he remarked: 'That's a good name; call it Dolly Varden.' And Dolly Varden it remains to this day!" Inupiat names include "ahkalukpik," "iqaluqpik," and "iqalukpik" and the Tlingit name is "x'wáat." Locals also call them "trout."

THE BASICS: Maximum Length: 100 cm (39 in) TL or more. Maximum Weight: 9.5 kg (20.9 lb).

The systematics of this species are quite messy and complex. Most folks accept that there are two subspecies, *Salvelinus malma malma* (distributed from the Mackenzie River, Canada, to the Alaska Peninsula), and *S. malma lordi* (living along, and southward of, the Alaska Peninsula). Overall, Dolly Vardens are found from the Korean Peninsula and Japan to the Chukchi Peninsula, along Arctic Alaska to the Mackenzie River, and southward to northern Washington. There is also one (apparently anomalous) record of a Dolly caught in the Columbia River. However, as I was writing this book I saw something kind of interesting. Look above, under Etymology and Colloquial Names at what Jordan said. He reports having caught, and subsequently sent to the Smithsonian, a *S. malma* he took in the Sacramento River. So what is that all about? Char living east of the Mackenzie River are Arctic char, *Salvelinus alpinus*. Length-weight parameters (FL, mm, gr): (sexes combined) W = 0.00000389L$^{3.175}$ (Blackett 1968).

SALIENT CHARACTERS: Dolly coloration is highly variable and depends on race, age, and reproductive state. See McCart et al. (1972) and Armstrong and Morrow (1980) for lots of such details. The general color pattern, as described by Kitty Mecklenburg et al. (2002) is: "Olive green to dark blue or brown dorsally; yellow, orange, or red spots on side; largest spots usually smaller than pupil of eye; spots profuse, typically 60-80 below lateral line; pectoral, pelvic, and anal fins with white leading edge and black or red line behind; spawning males orange to red ventrally." Historically, Dolly Vardens and bull trout (*Salvelinus confluentus*) were thought to be the same species. Bull trout usually have 26–29 total branchiostegal rays and Dolly Vardens usually 21–23.

LIFE HISTORY: Dolly Vardens exhibit a wide range of behaviors including anadromous stocks, stocks with nonanadromous males but anadromous females (termed "facultative anadromous" by Peter Craig), and a variety of stocks where both sexes permanently live in streams, springs, or lakes. These and other frankly bewildering life history patterns are beyond anything I want to deal with, but, hey, check out Blackett (1968), Armstrong and Morrow (1980), Blackburn and Jackson (1982), and Crane et al. (2005).

On the other hand, to generalize, Dolly Vardens are anadromous fish living for most of the year in freshwater and occupying coastal waters during summer months. They have been found in waters ranging from 1–14°C (30–57°F). Between April and July, fry (at 8–12 mm, 0.3–0.5 in, FL) hatch under gravel in freshwater, emerging from the substrata at 2–2.7 cm (0.8–1.1 in) FL. These young fish remain in their natal waters from 1–5 years, with most first migrating to marine waters at ages 3–4. In Arctic watersheds, previous to their first seaward migration, these juveniles often overwinter in the only areas kept ice free, the few locations housing perennial springs. These are the same places adults overwinter. As noted previously, some of the offspring of anadromous Dolly Vardens do not migrate to the sea, but rather remain and mature in freshwater. These diminutive resident fish are mostly, although not always, males. Compared to anadromous individuals, resident fish grow more slowly, do not grow as large, and tend to mature when younger. Unlike anadromous Dolly Vardens, resident males spawn every year.

Outward migrations to the sea occur between May–July, with larger individuals leaving first. Dolly Vardens enter marine waters in June and July, where they form small schools. During the brief Beaufort Sea summer, smaller fish remain near the mouths of natal rivers while larger individuals disperse along the coast. Some fish living in drainages to the south may make longer marine excursions. As an example, 2 fish tagged on over-wintering grounds in the Wulik River (draining into the southeastern Chukchi Sea) were recovered well up the Anadyr River of Siberia with one of the

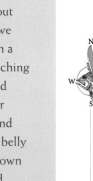

recoveries as much 1,690 km (1,050 mi) from the tagging site. It is likely that the Siberian recoveries were of Anadyr stock that had overwintered in the Wulik. This wide dispersal leads to a mixing of genetically distinct stocks in nearshore waters. Once in coastal waters many fish tend to inhabit shallow nearshore depths. Studies along the North Slope found that these fish tended to stay in the top 3–4 m (10–13 ft) of the water column, with occasional excursions down to 8 m (26 ft). In North American marine waters, most Dollies appear to stay close to shore, although a few have been taken in the central Bering Sea and one was caught way the hell out in the Gulf of Alaska.

Because Dolly Vardens overwinter in freshwater, they return to rivers and streams during the summer or early fall. As they make their return migrations into freshwater, their timing and behavior are quite complex and vary with location and with the state of maturity of individual fish. Spawning fish tend to enter freshwater first, followed by adult non-spawners, subadults, and juveniles. In some watersheds, for instance those draining into the Beaufort Sea, most fish overwinter in their natal waters. This is not true further south, where overwintering often occurs in non-natal waterways. Movements of adult fish in the southeastern Chukchi Sea drainages, for instance, are more complex and are detailed in DeCicco (1997). A major difference between these fish and those in Beaufort Sea drainages is that they may be either summer or fall spawners. Summer spawners, if they have overwintered in their natal rivers, do not migrate to the sea. Rather, in June and early July, they ascend rivers, spawn, and then descend to lower-river overwintering grounds. Summer spawning fish that have overwintered in non-natal rivers move into the Chukchi Sea in June and migrate directly to the spawning grounds and then descend to lower-river overwintering areas. In both instances, fish do not feed in the sea during the spawning year. Fall spawning fish behave more like their Beaufort Sea congeners, migrating to the sea in the summer, feeding, and then returning to freshwater in the fall. Armstrong and Morrow (1980) describe the even more complicated seasonal movements of fish in southeastern Alaska and, to be completely honest, I have neither the ability nor, *mea culpa*, the desire to figure out what they discerned. Please feel free to read it

yourself. Most Dolly Vardens appear to return to natal rivers and streams to spawn. Genetic studies have shown that there are multiple populations in drainages throughout their range, that these populations are centered on the various spawning watersheds, and that there may be more than one population occupying tributaries of a single river system. As far as the spawning itself, it is pretty typical of salmonids. Blackett (1968) has tonnage on Dolly Varden spawning behavior.

Dolly Vardens live to at least 18 years old although most fish die at 10 years old and less. Anadromous fish grow larger and may live slightly longer than resident individuals. A few anadromous individuals mature at 4 years old, most mature at between 6 and 8 years of age, and a few are not capable of reproducing until 10 years of age. Nonmigratory males mature at age 2–3 years old. Spawning generally occurs from August–December (apparently sometimes as early as June), and depending on area, it peaks from September–November. Some individuals spawn annually, while others spawn every other year, and apparently there are a few that may reproduce only every third year. A number of individuals spawn more than once in their lives. Fecundity of anadromous fish varies even between populations in adjacent watersheds and ranges between 650–16,291. When spawned, egg diameters range from 3.2–6 mm and fish in warmer watersheds may produce eggs of larger diameters. Dolly Vardens have the reputation for being major salmon eaters; however studies show that food habits vary greatly from place to place. In general, these char feed on various epibenthic and water column invertebrates (e.g., gammarid amphipods, mysid shrimps, euphausiids, insects and insect larvae, isopods, medusae, ctenophores, and larvaceans) and fishes. Important fishes include capelins, Pacific sand lances, Pacific herring, salmon (particularly juveniles) and their eggs, sculpins, and threespine sticklebacks. Fish migrating up rivers during spawning runs feed only occasionally. One study found that most feeding takes place during the day. Predators include Dolly Vardens, the usual terrestrial mammals, likely bald eagles, as well as ringed seals, polar bears, and beluga whales.

FISHERY: Today, Dolly Vardens are a very important subsistence species, particularly along much of the Alaskan Beaufort and Chukchi seas (although catches in the northeastern Chukchi Sea are small) to the Aleutian Islands, with some being taken as far southward as at least Sitka (Alaska). Depending on location, large numbers are taken both during the summer in coastal waters and at inland sites in fall and winter. Historically, Dolly Vardens were also used as dog food, their oil as medicine, and, as noted by Bean (1887b): "From the settlement of Port Clarence we obtained some dressed skins of the red-spotted trout (*Salvelinus malma*), which are used for making quite ornamental water-proof vests."

IN THE MATTER OF STINK-HEAD SOUP

My friend Irv Leask is a Tsimshian Native American from near Ketchikan, Alaska. He remembers that his grandmother was very fond of "Stink-head Soup," which depended for its fine, fine eating qualities on boiling salmon heads that had first been put in a sack and hung off a pier in the ocean for several weeks.

Admittedly, and assuredly, this is yet another example of my cultural imperialism, for the term "yum yummy" does not roll naturally off the tongue at times like this.

On the other hand, European settlers were not as entranced, although in the late 19th century, Dollies caught off Kodiak Island were salted and shipped to San Francisco and they were also a popular commercial fish in Puget Sound. The problem was that, over time, there developed the idea that far from being a resource to be fished, Dolly Vardens were bad juju and were a scourge to be disposed of. Cobb (1919) was a leader in this movement when he wrote: "Along our Northwest slope and in Alaska is found the Dolly Varden trout, also known as salmon trout, which is so abundant that it has become a serious menace to the salmon fisheries." Of course, it can be argued that the real menaces to salmon fisheries were too many fishermen and too much habitat destruction, but why deal with those issues when killing off Dolly Vardens was so much easier? One might as well suggest killing off peregrine falcons in order to protect the passenger pigeons. And thus it was that, in 1933, the State of Alaska placed a bounty on Dolly Vardens; the bounty was eliminated in 1941.

Dollies are commonly taken by recreational anglers.

ORIGINS AND RELATIONSHIPS: Fossil *Salvelinus* are known from the Late Miocene (at least 5.3 million years ago). There seems to be some consensus that Dolly Vardens are most closely related to Arctic char, *Salvelinus alpinus*.

MISCELLANY: A Dolly with two adipose fins, one to the right, and slightly behind, the other, has been taken. Another one, this one partially xanthic (yellow-colored) had two dorsal fins.

OTHER SPECIES

Salmo salar
Linnaeus, 1758
Atlantic Salmon

Atlantic salmon grow to 150 cm TL (59 in) TL and 46.8 kg (103 lb) and, although native to the north Atlantic Ocean, are now common in the Pacific Northwest to at least the Aleutian Islands due to accidental introductions via aquaculture facilities in Washington and British Columbia. Natural reproduction of *Salmo salar* occurs in at least a few of the rivers in British Columbia. There has not been much work on Atlantic salmon in the Pacific. The few fish that were

GILBERT VAN RYCKEVORSEL

examined had Pacific herring, Pacific sand lances, one Pacific salmon, and some shrimps in their guts. Regarding the escapement of many Atlantic salmon during pen-rearing operations, well, what the hell did you expect would happen? For those enamored with this species, Collette and Klein-MacPhee (2002) provide a very nice summary.

AND NOW … An Essay on Salmon Canning

In 1891, Alfred Carmichael (? -1961), more-or-less fresh off the boat from Belfast, took the Victoria steamer bound for the Windsor Cannery, located on the Skeena River in Northern British Columbia. He spent a season there and here is what he wrote about the experience. I thank the Royal British Columbia Museum, British Columbia Archives, where this manuscript resides, for permission to reproduce it. Oh, and I apologize for the, well, the racist undertones, but it was a different place and, one hopes, a different time.

"The canning season proper does not commence till the 15th of June, when fishing is begun, up to that date everything is being got ready. During the winter, while in Victoria, the manager makes a contract with a Chinese firm to do the following, 1st, make the cans, & 2nd, handle the salmon from first they are landed in the scow, which includes the cleaning, filling the cans, soldering, testing, boiling, putting on labels, and casing, the tools are all supplied by the company. When the fishing commences, the boss-Chinaman hires Indians to clean the fish, and their squaws to fill the cans. When the river gets clear of ice, the manager, boss-fisherman and Chinamen arrive.

"The nets are all made and old ones mended by the Klootchman as Indian women are called here, they are under a man named the net-boss, and when fishing commences, he superintends all work in this department and is required to be a very energetic man, one who has tact in handling the Indians…

"After the first of June all are busy, 20 white fishermen have come up from Victoria and are preparing for 6 weeks camping and fishing, 36 Japanese are bustling about making boxes, tables and stools, in fact everything required at the camps. We have three camps on an island 21/2 miles below us, another on a point 4 miles further, and a third 2 miles above us. These have each a camp-boss whose duties are to count the fish every tide and credit the same to the men, mend the snagged nets, and generally see after things. A steamer belonging to the company tows

the scow-loads of fish from the camps to the cannery. 45 boats are the total number licensed; to each boat there are two men, a fisher and a puller. The latter is hired by the former for either wages or halves. The fisher makes a contract with the manager…Now this brings us to the different species which are 'Spring' (red and white), 'Sockeye', 'Steelhead', 'Coho', 'Humback[sic]', and 'Dog Salmon'. The Springs as you see are of two, Red & White, the 'W' are discarded in canning, for it could not be sold in the London [England] Market [where most of the British Columbia canned salmon was destined], as your bigeted[sic] people could not be made to believe it was real genuine salmon, however the white are sweeter and very much more delicate than the red and considered by many more superior in flavour. It is a great pity when the men catch a majority of white in a tide as they do not get a cent for them.

"Now I think we have gone through all the needful preliminaries and we can safely describe the mode of canning a salmon as at present followed. At the first cleaning table it is bereft of its head and tail, also internal organs. It is slipped into the first washing tank where it is given a great scraping and scrubbing. All the fins are cut off and made respectable. At the second washer this is again done, the salmon is now perfectly clean and pure; water is constantly kept running through these troughs which keeps them always nice. They are now thrown into the drainer and again picked out by the cutter; 1 salmon if Spring, and two if Sockeye are placed lengthways in the machine. He now turns the lever and the salmon are cut into the desired size. This in turn comes under the hand of the chopper, who cuts it into the widths required. If a Sockeye he cuts the breast from the back on both sides, and chops the back in two.

"The salmon is now slid down an inclined shoot or drainer and caught in a bucket, two Indians are constantly kept busy here, one filling the buckets and the other taking them to the Klootchman, the fillers, who if they do their work properly put in each can one piece of back and one of the breast. If the chopper has done right, and if the Klootches have any brains, the salmon should slip beautifully in to the cans. Some were awfully self-willed and as it was my duty to see that they did not squash the salmon or put in nothing but back or skins, I would of course point out to them their mistake…I remember correcting one a dozen times for the same mistake, she got awfully angry and throwing the can on the floor, said 'Kahta miha halo mammuh,' in Chinook, she wanted to know why I did not fill cans, 'you work… '

"Each Klootch has a ticket for every tray of cans she fills, A Chinaman puts a hole in it. A tray holds 12 cans if flat, 24 if tall…when a tray is full it is taken to the weighing and cleaning table, a Klootch or two are weighing. Each can has to pass 6 cleaners before the lid is put on. These cleaners are all Indian children. They have pieces of net and just give a can one rub round and then pass it on to the next. 3 Chinese put on the lids which then go through the soldering machine, you must bear in mind that there is a small hole in the center of the lid for if there was no the air inside, [it] would be liable to burst the can open under the pressure to which it is exposed when passing through this machine [the upcoming cooker]. The cans now roll down the shoot to the bathroom, where Chinamen are picking them out, and placing them in coolers…[at the cooker the cans] are lowered down into it, just sufficient to cover the top of the cans. The steam is turned on and the water raised to boiling point."

[There follows an inordinate amount of detail about cooking, cooling, washing and labeling. He ends with a discussion of how the cannery is closed up for the year and then…]

"It was a curious sight to see 20 Indians [men] and 24 Klootchman coming to work in the morning flourishing their long knives. If you would pass they might make a pretend thrust at you, often watching your face to see if you were frightened."

J. E. Forester and A. D. Forrester, in their book *Fishing, British Columbia's Commercial Fishing History* (Hancock House, 1975), add one footnote to this essay. They note that Carmichael also wrote: "If the Klootchman had babies, which was quite often, they sat at the benches with babies on their laps. They would suckle them or attend to their toilet, then continue filling the cans with salmon. I protested to the manager that the process was hardly sanitary. He told me not to mind – 'It will be all sterilized in the cooking,' he said."

A Whole Columbia River Salmon, Sealed and Processed in 1875 in a Tin Made to Fit. Put up by the pioneer firm of J. W. & V. Cook, this fish was kept for many years on the desk of F. P. Kendall, general manager for the American Can Company in the Northwest, and is now in the possession of his son, Neal Kendall of the company's Portland office. The intention is to open it on the day it is 100 years old, provided it keeps that long. So far there has been no sign of deterioration, and if the tin resists corrosion for 46 years more there is no known reason why the contents should not be as good at the end of that time as when packed.

PACIFIC FISHERMAN, 1929, 27(7):30

ORDER STOMIIFORMES

FAMILY GONOSTOMATIDAE—Bristlemouths

The bristlemouths form another one of those ubiquitous groups of fishes (I don't actually have any other groups in mind, it just seems like the thing to say), this time in the mesopelagic and bathypelagic realm. Joe Nelson (2006) notes that fishes of the genera *Cyclothone* and *Vinciguerria* "have the greatest abundance of individuals of any vertebrate group in the world." This reminds me of a statement that Elmer Noble, my parasitology professor at UC Santa Barbara, made concerning nematodes. Paraphrasing Nathan Augustus Cobb (1859–1932), he noted that the number of nematodes in soil is so great that if you were to remove everything terrestrial (trees, rocks, lemurs, etc.) from the planet except nematodes, you could still see the outline of all of the continents. I'm loving that kind of thing.

There are five genera (although *Cyclothone* may be a synonym of *Gonostoma*, so stand by) and 23 species of these marine fishes, and 13 live within our range. Bristlemouths are oviparous and have pelagic eggs and larvae. What is perhaps a fossil bristlemouth was found in an Early Oligocene (at least 23-million-year-old) formation in the Caucasus region. *Cyclothone* cf. *solitudinis* is known from the Miocene (at least 5.3 million years ago) of Southern California. I know a bristlemouth when I see one, but I can't tell you why. On the other hand, Mecklenburg (2002) and Nakabo et al. (2002) can tell you why and will help you figure out what species you have in your hand.

Cyclothone acclinidens
Garman, 1899
Benttooth Bristlemouth

ETYMOLOGY: *Cyclothone* means "round" and "veil" in Greek. In his 1899 description of this species, S. Garman did not see fit to tell us what *acclinidens* meant, although the Latin word *acclivis* means "steeply ascending."

THE BASICS: Maximum Length: 7.1 cm (3 in). The Ranges: Circumglobal; Oregon to central Chile. 20–1,900 m (66–6,233 ft), mostly in 400–900 m (1,312–2,952 ft). Larvae: flexion length = about 5–6 mm, transformation length = about 1.3–1.4 to 2.2 cm. Length-weight parameters (SL, cm, gr): (sexes combined) W = $0.00000507L^{2.84}$ (De La Cruz Agüero and Cota Gómez 2006).

LIFE HISTORY: This is a pelagic species that may vertically migrate, but only to a limited degree. Benttooths live to 3 years old. Spawning appears to occur throughout the year, perhaps with a fall peak. They feed on such zooplankters as copepods, chaetognaths, and ostracods.

©2006 MBARI

FAMILY STERNOPTYCHIDAE—Marine Hatchetfishes

Those cute hatchetfishes are marine organisms found throughout the world. There are 10 genera and 67 species. We have nine species off our coast. At least some species vertically migrate into shallower waters during the night. Hatchetfishes are oviparous and have pelagic eggs and larvae. Otoliths of what might be hatchetfishes have been found in Late Cretaceous (at least 71 million years ago) strata. One of the first fossil *Argyropelecus* is from the Late Eocene (at least 34 million years ago). *Argyropelecus bullockii* lived in California waters during the Miocene (at least 5.3 million years ago). This or another species was also found in 7.6–8.6-million-year-old strata in Southern California. Hatchetfishes have compressed and hatchet-shaped bodies, large photophores (light-emitting structures) lining the belly region, and upturned eyes and mouths. See Baird (1971) and Nakabo (2002) for details on how to distinguish the various Pacific Coast species.

Although I picked *Argyropelecus sladeni* to exemplify our local hatchetfishes, *A. affinis*, *A. hemigynus*, and *Sternoptyx diaphana* are also abundant off our shores, and would have worked just as well, and likely have similar life histories.

Argyropelecus sladeni
Regan, 1908
Lowcrest Hatchetfish

ETYMOLOGY AND COLLOQUIAL NAME: *Argyropelecus* means "silvery" and "hatchet" in Greek and *sladeni* means...well, who the hell knows what *sladeni* means? In his description of this species, C. Tate Regan did not deign to give us the slightest clue. And that is peculiar because the name seems to refer to a person – I can't find any Greek or Latin word that comes close to this one. In addition, in Regan (1908), he names several other fishes after persons and then goes on to explain who they are. So, we seem to have here an Edwardian puzzle, second only to tracing down the names of all of Edward's mistresses. The Japanese name (for the fish, not for Edward's mistresses) is "teono-eso." Larvae: flexion length = about 7.5–9.4 mm, transformation length = about 8.2–13 mm.

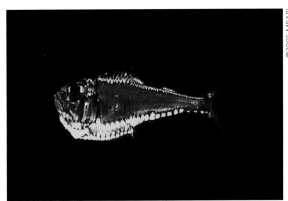

This is actually Argyropelecus affinis, *slender hatchetfish, but it's the best I could do.*

THE BASICS: Maximum Length: 6.7 cm (2 in). The Ranges: Circumglobal; Japan; western Bering Sea; British Columbia to Chile. The distribution of this species is perhaps antitropical. Primarily mesopelagic, at depths of 55–1,130 m (180–3,707 ft). Length-weight parameters (SL, cm, gr): (sexes combined) $W = 0.0266L^{2.89}$ (De La Cruz Agüero and V. M. Cota Gómez 2006) (I couldn't find a l-w relationship for this species. This one is for *Argyropelecus lychnus*, which is probably close enough).

LIFE HISTORY: This is a deeper-water pelagic species that probably exhibits a limited amount of vertical migration. Lowcrests live to about 3 years old. They appear to spawn throughout the year off Southern California, perhaps with a winter peak. Prey includes such zooplankton as copepods, ostracods, amphipods, and euphausiids. Predators are not well known, but they include longnose lancetfish and elegant terns.

FAMILY STOMIIDAE—Barbeled Dragonfishes or Dragonfishes

This is a marine family, found throughout the world, mostly in deep waters. The Stomiidae, formerly divided into six families, contain 28 genera and about 273 species, 19 of which live off our coast. These are oviparous fishes with planktonic eggs and larvae.

Chauliodus macouni

Bean, 1890

Pacific Viperfish

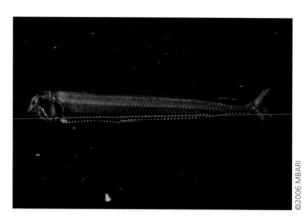

ETYMOLOGY AND COLLOQUIAL NAME: *Chauliodus* is Greek for "exserted" and "tooth" and *macouni* was named for John C. Macoun (1831–1920) of the Geological Survey of Canada. They are called "higashi-horaieso" in Japan.

THE BASICS: Maximum Length: 29.3 cm (12 in) SL. The Ranges: Southern Japan to Bering Sea (at least as far north about Saint Matthew Island) to central Baja California and Gulf of California. However, larvae have been taken as far south as Cabo San Lucas (southern Baja California). 25–4,390 m (82–14,403 ft) and mostly in 250 m (820 ft) and deeper. Eggs: 2.7–3.2 mm. Larvae: hatching length = at least 4.7 mm, flexion length = 1.8–2.2 cm (0.7–0.9 in), transformation length = about 3.3–4.9 cm (1.3–1.9 in). Length-weight parameters (TL, cm, gr): (females) $W = 0.000861L^{3.46}$; (males) $W = 0.00458L^{2.88}$ (Orlov and Binohlan 2009).

SALIENT CHARACTERS: Well, it's long, has fangs that hang out of the mouth, and has a very long first dorsal ray.

LIFE HISTORY: This is a deep-water pelagic species that may make limited vertical migrations. The long dorsal fin ray is probably used to lure in prey.

Pacific viperfish may live to at least 8 years old. Spawning occurs throughout the year, perhaps with a winter peak. They feed mostly on fishes and on the occasional copepod, amphipod, and euphausiid. Small ones tend to feed more on crustaceans. Predators include arrowtooth flounder, Pacific cod, Pacific halibut, sablefish, and various skates.

ORIGINS: A fossil species, *Chauliodus eximius*, is known from the Miocene (at least 5.3 million years ago) of Southern California.

OTHER SPECIES

Tactostoma macropus

Bolin, 1939

Longfin Dragonfish

Longfin dragonfish grow to 45.5 cm (18 in) SL. They range from Japan and the Sea of Okhotsk to the Bering Sea and down to Chile. This is primarily a mesopelagic and bathypelagic species, recorded from depths of 25 m or less to 2,000 m (82–6,562 ft). Longfins migrate into somewhat shallower waters at night. They live to at least

8 years of age (see Fisher and Pearcy 1983 for growth curves) and females may grow larger than males. Females mature at 5 or 6 years of age and at around 25–30 cm (10–12 in) SL. Spawning occurs mostly from May–September and females produce between 24,000–66,000 eggs. Dragonfish feed on crustaceans, such as euphausiids and sergestid shrimps, and fishes. Fish over about 20 cm (8 in) TL feed mainly on fishes, smaller individuals focus more on crustaceans. Chilipeppers and northern fur seals eat them. Length-weight (SL, mm, gr): (sexes combined) 50–about 220 mm individuals, $W = 0.00000054L^{3.08}$; 220–382 mm, $W = 0.0000000011L^{4.27}$ (Fisher and Pearcy 1983).

FAMILY SYNODONTIDAE—Lizardfishes

Lizardfishes are mostly marine (but occasionally estuarine) fishes that are found in tropical and temperate waters throughout the world. There are four genera and about 57 species; six occur within our range. Lizardfishes are oviparous and have pelagic eggs and larvae. Uncomfortable with your lizardfish identifications? Try Fischer et al. (1995), it has a key and descriptions of the various eastern Pacific species.

Parenthetically, I note that Asian lizardfishes of the subfamily Harpadontinae (and, in particular, *Harpadon nehereus*) are called "Bombay ducks." There are several, generally unsavory, theories on the derivation of that name; all of them referring to the intense smell the fishes develop when dried.

Synodus lucioceps
(Ayres, 1855)
California Lizardfish

ETYMOLOGY AND COLLOQUIAL NAMES: *Synodus* comes from a Greek word for an apparently unknown species of fish; it means "teeth meeting" (i.e., not shutting past each other like a scissors) and was appropriated for this genus and *lucioceps* means "pike" and "head" in Latin. An earlier name (but one I still hear) is "candlefish," not to be confused with the eulachon. In northern Baja California, it is called "chile."

THE BASICS: Maximum Length: 63.9 cm (25 in) TL. The Ranges: Cape Beal (British Columbia) to Guaymas (Gulf of California), mostly Southern California to at least the southern end of Bahia de Sebastian Vizcaino (central Baja California), and at least occasionally as far north as San Francisco. 1.5–229 m (5–751 ft), mostly in depths less than maybe 140 m (459 ft). Eggs: 1.2–1.5 mm. Larvae: hatching length = about 3 mm, flexion length = 8–11 mm,

"What though on hamely fare we dine, wear hoddin grey, an' a that." Is There for Honest Poverty, Robert Burns.

transformation length = 5–6.4 cm (2–3 in). Length-weight parameters (TL, cm, gr): $W = 0.0056L^{3.029}$ (Love unpubl.).

SALIENT CHARACTERS: These are cylindrical, elongate fish with small, lizard-like heads and mouths filled with good-size canine teeth. After capture, they are brown on backs and silvery on bellies with yellow fins. Underwater, they are also brown, but the backs and sides are often heavily barred and saddled with darker brown.

LIFE HISTORY: Lizardfish go through clear boom and bust years with astronomical numbers of small ones recruiting in one year and seemingly almost none the next. Young-of-the-year settle out of the plankton into shallow sandy areas (often nestling in bottom drift algae) at lengths as small as 3.5 cm (1 in) SL. However, Lavenberg and Fitch (1966) captured fish between 5.3–8.9 cm (2–4 in) SL in surface waters in the Gulf of California. Off Southern California, most settlement takes place in the spring and summer. Young-of-the-year can form huge schools—Jackie Patay, for instance, reports seeing a fast-moving school containing perhaps millions of individuals in 24 m (80 ft) along La Jolla Submarine Canyon during August 2010. You either see adult lizardfish buried in the soft seafloor with only their smile showing through the sediment or resting on the seafloor propped up on their pelvic and pectoral fins. While adults are partial to soft seafloors, they sometimes rest near rocks or other hard structure. Adult lizards may be most active at night. We see them in waters as cold as 10°C (50°F).

My data implies that these fish mature at between 30–36 cm (12–14 in) TL. Most spawning occurs from about June–December. California lizardfish feed primarily on fishes, as well as squids, mysid shrimps, and euphausiids. Predators include

California halibut, swordfish, California sea lions, and bottlenose dolphins. Steve Ross reports (and he sent the photo to prove it) catching a bunch of bonito off Ensenada, northern Baja California, that were stuffed with pelagic juvenile lizardfish.

FISHERY: Lizardfish are occasionally retained and sold by commercial fishermen. I have seen boxes of them in several Vietnamese markets in Orange County (Southern California). Anglers often catch them from piers (in some years in large numbers) and larger ones are taken from boats. Occasionally pier fishermen use the small ones as bait for California halibut and other species.

ORIGINS: A *Synodus* sp. is known from the Early Miocene (maybe 15–20 million years ago). California lizardfish have probably been in Southern California waters for at least 100,000 years.

KEVIN LEE

FAMILY ANOTOPTERIDAE—Daggertooths

Daggertooths (sometimes placed in the family Paralepididae) are found in the Pacific Ocean, north of the equator. The family has one genus and two species (one in our range). They are oviparous with planktonic larvae.

Anotopterus nikparini

Kukuev, 1998

North Pacific Daggertooth

TIM PERETTI

ETYMOLOGY AND COLLOQUIAL NAME: *Anotopterus* is Greek for "without" and "dorsal" (referring to the fin) and *nikparini* honors the Russian ichthyologist Nikolai (sometimes seen as Nikolay) V. Parin. North Pacific daggertooths were previously called *Anotopterus pharao*. The Japanese name is "mizu-uo-damashi."

THE BASICS: Maximum Length: 146 cm (58 in) TL. The Ranges: South of Japan to the southern Bering Sea and Gulf of Alaska to somewhere south of Baja California. An *Anotopterus* reported from the Gulf of California is likely this species. Near the surface (at night) to 2,750 m (9,022 ft). Larvae: hatching length = less than 8 mm, flexion length = 1.4–2.5 cm, transformation length = about 2.5 cm (1 in).

SALIENT CHARACTERS: Daggertooths are impressive-looking fish. As Welch and Pankhurst (2001) observe, they are "Slender snake-like fish with a reduced (almost glass-like) bone structure in both jaws and cranium." Daggertooths have no dorsal fin (they do have an adipose fin), no gill rakers, and canine teeth.

LIFE HISTORY: Daggertooths are open-water fish that are found from near the surface to great depths. They have been captured at temperatures of 0–14.8°C (32–59°F), but mostly at 3–6°C (37–43°F). It is hypothesized that these fish migrate northward to feed and return south to spawn. From scanty information, daggertooths at least spawn off southern Japan, around the Emperor Seamount, and off California. Shelekhov and Baginskii (2000) noted that there is a "current opinion that the daggertooth spawns just once and then dies."

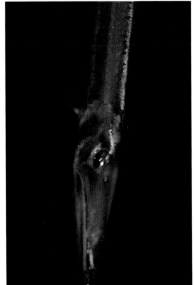

MBARI

North Pacific daggertooths are fish eaters; they apparently often attack their prey from below, causing a rather stereotypic slashing wound. Occasionally, the teeth of the predator's upper jaw will lock around the bones of larger prey (such as salmon) causing a daggertooth's jaw to be ripped off in the enthusing brouhaha. In some locations, daggertooths prey on relatively large numbers of Chinook and coho salmon, and smaller numbers of chums, sockeyes, and pinks. Even if salmon are not eaten, the slash marks left from unsuccessful attacks lower their commercial value.

MISCELLANY: Four toothless adults have been captured.

FAMILY ALEPISAURIDAE—Lancetfishes

The lancetfishes are pelagic deep-sea fishes found throughout the world. There are two genera and three species, one of which occurs within our range. These fishes are oviparous with planktonic larvae.

Alepisaurus ferox

Lowe, 1833

Longnose Lancetfish

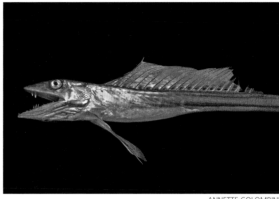

ANNETTE COLOMBINI

ETYMOLOGY AND COLLOQUIAL NAME: *Alepisaurus* means "without," "scale," and "serpent" in Greek and *ferox* means "ferocious" in Latin. They are "mizu-uo" in Japanese.

THE BASICS: Maximum Length: About 231 cm (91 in) TL. The Ranges: Atlantic and Pacific oceans; Japan and the Sea of Okhotsk to the southern Bering Sea to Chile. Near surface to 1,830 m (6,004 ft), commonly as deep as mesopelagic waters. While most fish seem to live well away from the coast, a fair number are taken in nearshore waters. Larvae: hatching length = less than 5 mm, flexion length = about 6–8.5 mm, transformation length = about 1.6–3 cm (0.6–1 in).

SALIENT CHARACTERS: A very large and arching dorsal fin, adipose fin, and big ol' dagger-like teeth distinguish this species.

LIFE HISTORY: Longnose lancetfish are another species for which the term "little is known" fits like a snug shoe. The fish are pelagic, yet have been taken with some regularity by Pacific halibut longline fishermen off British Columbia and Washington, so they apparently hang out near the bottom with some regularity. It is thought that lancetfish spawn in tropical and subtropical waters and that at least some individuals migrate northward as far as the Arctic to feed.

A study in the Atlantic implied that this species may be hermaphroditic. At least some fish off Southern California appear to spawn in the spring. Longnose lancetfish tend to focus on fishes and squids, but they disdain not the octopuses, hyperiid amphipods, pteropods, heteropods, and even polychaetes. Predators include albacore, bigeye tuna, dolphinfish, longnose lancetfish, Pacific pomfrets, striped marlins, swordfish, yellowfin tuna, bald eagles, common murres, Baird's beaked whales, and sperm whales.

FISHERY: Polovina et al. (2009) describe longnoses as "of limited commercial value" off Hawai'i, which kind of sums it up.

MISCELLANY: Longnoses are found on beaches along the Pacific Coast with depressing regularity. Orlov and Ul'chenko (2002) found a correlation between La Niña events and beaching occurrences and hypothesized that abrupt changes in water temperature were responsible for the strandings.

REMARKS: Giacomo Bernardi has a friend who ate one and found it mushy.

Longnose lancetfish sculpture by William Van Orden

FAMILY MYCTOPHIDAE—Lanternfishes

Goodness, but there are lots and lots of lanternfishes. This is a big, sprawling family of fishes, with 32 genera and somewhere in the vicinity of 240 species; 54 species grace our geographic range. All lanternfishes are marine and at least one member of the family can be found just about anywhere the water is salty and deep enough (but not too deep, mind). All are oviparous and have planktonic eggs and larvae. Many species appear to be vertical migrators, spending the night hours in relatively shallow waters and the day many hundreds of meters down. Some species (often called "dipnet myctophids") come to the surface at night. This is a very important group of fishes, if for no other reason that many fishes, sea birds, and marine mammals prey on them. All lanternfishes have blue-green light-emitting photophores (light-emitting structures); these look like little dots on various places on the body. The pattern of photophores varies between species and is often the only sure way of telling species apart. Otoliths from what might have been lanternfishes are known from the Late Cretaceous (at least 71 million years ago). Everyone (other than Special Creationists) seems to agree that the fishes were definitely around in the Eocene (as much as 55 million years ago) and that most genera had evolved by the Late Miocene (at least 5.3 million years ago).

I'm only presenting one species here because this is not the Big Book of Lanternfishes. If your favorite species was not included, think how lucky you were that a meteor has not yet hit you this day and go about your business. Fischer et al. (1995), Mecklenburg (2002), and Nakabo (2002) describe many of the Pacific Coast species.

Stenobrachius leucopsarus
(Eigenmann & Eigenmann, 1890)
Northern Lampfish

ETYMOLOGY AND COLLOQUIAL NAME:
Stenobrachius is Greek for "narrow" and Latin for "arm" and *leucopsarus* comes from two Greek words for "white" and "spotted" (probably referring to the luminous patches above and below the tail). The Japanese call them "kohire-hadaka." Larvae: hatching length = about 2 mm, flexion length = 6.5–8 mm, transformation length = 1.6–1.9 cm (0.6–0.7 in).
THE BASICS: 12.5 cm (5 in) TL. Southern Japan to southern Bering Sea, and Gulf of Alaska to northern Baja California (about 29°N, 115°W), common from parts of the Bering Sea to Southern California (to more than 322 km, 200 mi, off the coast). 30 m or less to at least 1,348 m (98–4,421 ft), reported to 2,896 m (9,500 ft).
LIFE HISTORY: Northern lampfish vertically migrate, but not all fish migrate every day. In addition, while it had long been assumed that if a northern lampfish

©2006 MBARI

migrated it spent the nights shallow (sometimes to near the surface) and the days deeper (in maybe 300–500 m, 984–1,640 ft), Abookire et al. (2002) found them in near-surface waters in the daytime in an Alaskan fjord. Genetic studies imply that fish throughout their range form one population without genetic structure.

Northern lampfish live to about 8 years old and mature at around 6 cm (2 in) SL. These fish spawn mostly in the winter and spring, although for what it is worth, a few larvae can be captured during any month of the year. They feed primarily on midwater crustaceans, including calanoid copepods, euphausiids, and gammarid and hyperiid amphipods. Other organisms occasionally eaten are fish eggs, crustacean larvae, arrow worms, mysid and sergestid shrimps, small fishes, squids, cteno-phores, medusae, and pelagic tunicates. Migratory individuals may feed mostly from dusk to midnight, while the non-migra-tory ones feed mostly during the day. Many organisms eat northern lampfish and a random selection includes albacore, blue sharks, flatfishes (four species), Pacific bluefin tuna, Pacific grenadiers, Pacific hakes, rockfishes (seven species), salmon (five species), murres, Leach's petrels, California sea lions, common dolphins, Dall's porpoise, and Humboldt squids.

ORIGINS: Based on fossil remains, northern lampfish were likely swimming off the coast at least 100,000 years ago.

MISCELLANY: The copepod, *Cardiodectes medusaeus*, infects the heart of this species by sticking its head in the bulbus arteriosus and leaving its butt end out in the sea. *Cardiodectes* drinks blood from its host. Infected fish are often sterile, and have likely been castrated by the parasite. Interestingly, parasitized fish grow faster than nonparasitized ones, likely because energy that would have gone into making eggs and sperm now goes into growth.

ORDER LAMPRIDIFORMES

FAMILY LAMPRIDIDAE—Opahs

Also called Lampridae, the opahs are singular (okay dualer) pelagic marine fishes comprised of one genus and two species (one within our range). They are oviparous, with pelagic eggs and larvae. The order Lampridiformes is known from the Late Paleocene/Basal Eocene Epoch (perhaps 56 million years ago).

Lampris guttatus
(Brünnich, 1788)
Spotted Opah

ETYMOLOGY AND COLLOQUIAL NAMES: *Lampris* is derived from a Greek word meaning "radiant" and *guttatus* means "spotted" in Latin. In Great Britain, I am informed, they are called "Jerusalem haddock," and no, I don't know why. They are also called "moonfish" and the Japanese refer to them as "akamanbo." Baja California commercial fishermen call them "opa."

THE BASICS: Maximum Length: 183 cm (72 in) TL. Maximum Weight: The largest fish taken off California weighed 74.1 kg (163 lb), but they are reputed to reach 270 kg (594 lb) or more. The Ranges: Circumglobal in temperate to tropical waters; Japan to Gulf of Alaska to Chile, and in the Gulf of California. They are reasonably abundant as far north as Oregon. Near surface to 736 m (2,414 ft).

SALIENT CHARACTERS: What would have happened if Picasso had drunk too many absinthes at Gertrude Stein's Paris flat in 1907? Yes, besides hitting on Georges Braque, he would have created this polka-dotted beauty. Opahs are one of those unique fish that can be confused with nothing else. They are oval, with bright vermilion lips, snouts, and fins. The dorsal areas are reddish-purple grading into reddish below. Oh, and they are covered in round silvery spots. Really, these fish are indistinguish-able from the typical attendee to a midnight screening of *The Rocky Horror Picture Show*. Holder (1913) opined: "[It] is a veritable moon, with a wonderful and ethereal investment of colours, a disc of silver veiled in old rose." Whoa, if that prose was more purple, it would be naval deep in the ultraviolet.

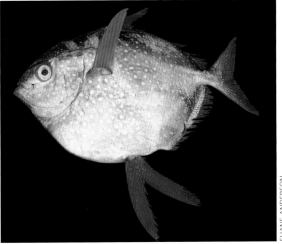

LIFE HISTORY: This is a perfectly lovely pelagic species that is usually found some distance from land. Although a number of California fish have been taken in surface waters, in other parts of the world many have been caught in deeper depths. In a study in the central North Pacific, opahs hung out in water between 28–736 m (92–2,414 ft), but rarely in shallower than 50 m or deeper than 400 m (164–1,312 ft). This translated to water temperatures of 5.2–25.6°C (41–78°F), mostly at 8–22°C (46–72°F), and averaging 14.7–16.5°C

SHANE ANDERSON

(59–62°F) (although elsewhere they have been recorded at temperatures as high as 26.6°C, 80°F). These fish tended to be found in shallower waters at night, but there was a lot of vertical movement throughout both day and night. Although their migration patterns are unclear, off California opah catches seem to increase following El Niño years. There appears to be a fairly large difference in the genetics of fish living in Japan and Mexico.

Not much is known about their biology. A 98.3 cm (39 in) TL fish was immature. Opahs feed on squids, fishes, and various crustaceans. The presence of some benthic fishes in the diet implies that they feed near the bottom on occasion. Cookie-cutter sharks attack opahs.

FISHERY: There is a fairly robust commercial fishery for opahs. They are caught in the drift gill net fishery off California and Baja California and they are also taken by commercial albacore and salmon trollers. Albacore sport fishermen also catch them. These are really yummy fish and you often see them in coastal fish markets.

ORIGINS: The oldest known member of

HOW THE OPAH GOT ITS NAME

The black Prince, and his Coufin, from *Anama-boe* on the Coaft of *Guinea*, and Mr. *Creighton*, formerly Governor of *Capo Corfo Caftle*, upon feeing this Fifh immediately knew it, and faid it was common on that Coaft, and is very good to eat. The Natives call it *Opah*, and the *Englifh* there call it the *King-fifh*. I fhall therefore retain the *Guinea* Name.

MORTIMER (1750)

the family Lamprididae is the giant (about 4 m, 13 ft, in length) *Megalampris keyesi* from the Late Oligocene (about 26 million years ago) of New Zealand. It was a highly evolved species, implying that the family had been around well before this time. In 1943, David described *Lampris zatima* from the Miocene (at least 5.3 million years ago) of Southern California. She noted that the species was "very similar" to *L. guttatus*.

REMARKS: Like some sharks and tunas, opahs keep their eyes and brains warmer than the surrounding sea water, 2.1–6.3°C warmer. Herald (1939) writes: "Formerly on the island of Madeira, the opah was held in such high esteem that every specimen taken was required by law to be carried to the governor of the island, without whose license it could not be sold in the market." Hey, this is just the kind of thing that leads to recall elections.

FAMILY TRACHIPTERIDAE— Ribbonfishes

Ribbonfishes are found throughout the world in marine waters. There are three genera, about 10 species, and four species live within our range. Trachipterids are oviparous with planktonic eggs and larvae.

Trachipterus altivelis
Kner, 1859

King-of-the-Salmon

ETYMOLOGY: *Trachipterus* is derived from two Greek words meaning "rough" and "tail" and *altivelis* is "high fin" in Latin.

THE BASICS: Maximum Length: 186 cm (73 in) TL. Maximum Weight: A 156.5 cm (62 in) TL fish weighed 4.1 kg (9 lb). The Ranges: Southeastern Bering Sea and Gulf of Alaska to Chile. Near surface to 1,189 m (3,900 ft). Eggs: 2.8–3.1 mm. Larvae: hatching length = about 7.2–7.4 mm, flexion length = more than 1.3 and less than 1.6 cm (0.5-0.6 in), transformation length = protracted

©2006 MBARI

and gradual, greater than 5.5 cm (2 in). Length-weight parameters (SL, mm, gr): (sexes combined) $W = 0.000204L^{2.06}$ (Shenker 1983).

SALIENT CHARACTERS: KOTS are compressed and extremely elongated, with a relatively deep head tapering to a tiny, and asymmetrical, caudal fin. They have no anal fin.

LIFE HISTORY: This is a little-known pelagic and mesopelagic species, although its food habits imply it must spend at least some time near the bottom. Adults are common from the nearshore out to more than 322 km (200 mi) from the Central and Southern California coasts. They may vertically migrate upward at night.

A 155 cm (62 in) TL fish was 7 years old. Spawning probably occurs throughout the year, but perhaps mostly in the winter and spring. King-of-the-salmon feed on a variety of fishes, amphipods, copepods, euphausiids, fish larvae, polychaetes, squids, and octopuses. Predators include albacore, bigeye and yellowfin tunas, longnose lancetfish, swordfish, northern fur seals, and Pacific white-sided dolphins.

FISHERY: Not as such, but KOTs are accidentally taken by salmon trollers and fishermen using purse seines to pursue various species. Regular folks are most likely to see dead ones washed up on beaches.

ORIGINS: *Trachipterus mauritanicus* is the oldest species known; it was found in Late Miocene strata (at least 5.3 million years ago) in Algeria.

REMARKS: The name king-of-the-salmon derives from a belief of the Makah people of the Straits of Juan de Fuca that this species led salmon to their annual fresh-water migrations. It was believed that killing this species harmed salmon harvests.

FAMILY REGALECIDAE—Oarfishes

The remarkable oarfishes are found throughout the world and comprise two genera, two or more species, and one occurs off the Pacific Coast. All are marine. The family is oviparous with planktonic eggs and larvae.

Regalecus russelii
(Cuvier, 1816) (probably)

Regalecus glesne
Ascanius, 1772 (perhaps)

Regalecus kinoi
Castro-Aguirre, Arvizu-Martinez & Alarcón-Gonzalez, 1991 (least likely)

Oarfish

Dude, if your fish is ribbony and has really long posterior dorsal fin rays and really, really long pelvic fin rays, and those rays are bright red, it's like an oarfish.

ETYMOLOGY: *Regalecus* means "king" and "herring" in Latin and *russelli* honors Patrick Russell (1727–1805). They are also known as "king of the herring," as at one time they were believed to precede or accompany herring shoals. Apparently, fishermen off Baja California call them "Pez dragon" and the Japanese name is "ryugunotsukai."

So, here's the deal. The status of this fish, particularly how many species there are, is in flux. For a while some authorities, for instance the American Fisheries Society, held that there might be one worldwide species, *R. glesne*. Others believed that there were at least three species, *R. russelii*, *R. glesne*, and *R. kinoi*. Tyson Roberts, who has extensively studied this group, states that there appear to be two species, *R. russelii*, found at least in the Pacific, and *R. glesne*, inhabiting Atlantic and Mediterranean waters, with *R. kinoi* identical to *R. russelii*. At this writing, those fish inhabiting Indian Ocean waters are being investigated. Given how little is known about any aspect of oarfish life and even which

PERHAPS HE THOUGHT HE WAS PROTECTING THE CORN LAWS

J. Hedley (1997) quotes from a 19th-century letter regarding the beaching of an oarfish on the Northumberland coast of Great Britain in 1845. The fish was found by a Preventive Service man (kind of like a customs official): "Its great length and unusual appearance at once raised the man's curiosity and excited his fears. On approaching it the creature bent itself around…and the man supposing it was about to dart upon him, drew his sword and struck it on the head." *It's just a fish, so why not back up a couple of feet?*

PATRICK RUSSELL

Dr. Patrick Russell was a physician and naturalist. Much of his career was spent in Aleppo (now Halab) in Syria where he became the "go to" guy for bubonic plague (not contracting it mind you, but researching it). This was particularly true during the great plague outbreaks of 1760–1762, when Russell took copious notes on when, who, and how the plague struck. The source of bubonic plague (now known to be transmitted by fleas) was unknown at the time and Russell, who noted that both fleas and the plague dissipated during the hot summer months, was not quite able to connect the dots. Hey, better luck in your next life, Pat. From Aleppo, Russell transferred to the East India Company, where he was stationed near Madras, India, and acted as the company's naturalist. It was during that tenure that he made major collections of plants and animals (particularly reptiles and fishes) of the region, culminating in his publishing *An Account of the Indian Serpents Collected on the Coast of Coroandel* and *Descriptions and Figures of Two Hundred Fishes Collected at Vizagapatam.* In his will, he stated that he was not to be interred in a church as this was "useless to the dead and prejudicial to the living" (Hawgood 1994).

species we have off our coast, I have chosen to kind of amalgamate whatever knowledge has been acquired worldwide (even if from at least two species), on the hope that it kind of applies to fish worldwide. This is probably incorrect, but there you have it.

THE BASICS: Maximum Length: 10.7 m (35 ft) TL. Maximum Weight: To at least 272 kg (598.4 lb). The Ranges: In eastern Pacific from Topanga Beach (Southern California) to Chile. Near surface to 1,640 m (5,380 ft).

SALIENT CHARACTERS: See the little italicized riff above.

LIFE HISTORY: Oarfish live in open water. Jonathan Bird observed a 2-meter-long one (7 ft) at Tongue of the Ocean, off Nassau, in the Caribbean. He writes that he was diving over several thousands of feet of water, about 12 m (40 ft) below the surface, when he saw a fish that was "positioned vertically in the water, with the anterior end pointed up. It had two long antennae with what looked like diamond-shaped fishing lures on the ends, as well as several along the length of each antennae. Its dorsal fin ran the length of its back, and undulated to propel the fish…As I approached within 3 meters of the fish, I noticed that its antennae were positioned horizontally, one pointing to the left and the other to the right, so that the animal resembled a cross." Soon after, the fish began to retreat and "It first rotated both antennae to vertical, above its head. Then, rather than turn around and swim down head first, the fish undulated its dorsal fin in reverse and swam 'tail first' back into the blue water."

Oarfish eggs (2.5 mm in diameter and red) and larvae have been found near the surface of the Mediterranean Sea in winter. A 3.5 m (11 ft) TL female *R. russelii* taken off Japan was mature. Two others, 2.9 m (10 ft) and 2.7 m (9 ft) long (and also from off Japan) were not. They eat such planktonic creatures as euphausiids, as well as fishes and squids.

FISHERY: Most of the oarfish that come to anyone's attention are those that wash up moribund or dead on beaches (quite a few on the beaches of the southern Gulf of California). Gill netters off Baja California catch them on occasion. Scandinavians report that oarfish flesh sucks big time and even dogs won't eat it. However, I imagine dogs would roll in it, big time.

RELATIONSHIPS: Morphological and molecular data implies that oarfish are most closely related to ribbonfish of the genus *Trachipterus*.

FAMILY OPHIDIIDAE—Cusk-eels

Cusk-eels are benthic marine fishes that are found throughout the world. There are 48 genera and about 223 species, 18 of which live within our range. These fishes are oviparous and have planktonic larvae with an extended pelagic juvenile stage. Otoliths that may be from early cusk-eels go back to the Late Cretaceous (at least 71 million years ago). The Atlantic species, *Ophidion marginatum*, produces sound (likely as part of courtship and mating behavior), so maybe our cusk-eels do too. Fischer et al. (1995) describes and has keys to the various tropical eastern Pacific species.

Chilara taylori
(Girard, 1858)
Spotted Cusk-eel

KEVIN LEE

ETYMOLOGY: *Chilara* is the modern Greek name for some Mediterranean cusk-eels and *taylori* refers to Alexander S. Taylor (1817–1876), who collected this fish in Monterey in 1857.

THE BASICS: Maximum Length: 39.6 cm (16 in) TL. The Ranges: Willapa Bay (Washington) to Punta Rompiente (27°43'N, 114°58'W) (southern Baja California) and Ecuador. They appear to be abundant to at least as far north as Mendocino (Northern California). One very large one was taken off central Ecuador; perhaps it had been transported as a pelagic prejuvenile across the Equator. Intertidal to 731 m (2,398 ft), but mostly in 30 to at least 190 m (98–623 ft). Larvae: hatching length = about 3.5 mm, flexion length = about 2.1–3 cm (1 in), transformation length = about 7–8.5 cm (3 in).

SALIENT CHARACTERS: Spotted cusk-eels are long, tapered fish with dorsal and anal fins that join at the tail. They are brown to ecru (so look it up) with lots of dark spots. They have long, filamentous pelvic fins. Four small "unspotted" specimens have been reported.

LIFE HISTORY: Young-of-the-year, at least as small as 4 cm (2 in) TL, recruit to soft seafloors. Cusk-eels of various sizes live in burrows in sand and mud. In shallow waters, you may find them both on the open coast and in bays (sometimes in eelgrass beds) and they occasionally hang out in estuaries. At Santa Catalina Island, Ted Hobson and Tony Chess (1986) watched as these fish emerged from the sand about 3 hours after sunset and returned to the sand about 3 hours before sunrise. They also come out during cloudy days. Bob Lea (1980) wrote: "Upon being approached these cusk-eels quickly disappear, tail first, into the sand. While out, the fish rest along the bottom with the pelvic fins oriented forward. The filaments are continuously moving, and apparently act as sensory appendages for detecting forage items." During our deeper waters surveys, we see them in 7.8–12°C (46–54°F) and mostly in 9.2–10.1°C (49–50°F).

In Southern California waters, a few larvae are found throughout the year, but it looks like most spawning is in the summer and fall. Spotted cusk-eels prey on bottom and near-bottom prey, as they spend much quality night-time swimming close to the seafloor probing the sand with their pelvic fins. Some of the more common food items include crabs, gammarid amphipods, euphausiids, and shrimps, along with some polychaetes, caprellid amphipods, mysid shrimps, and small fishes. A fairly wide range of animals eat spotted cusk-eels, including fishes (e.g., blue sharks, cabezons, California halibut, lingcod, longnose lancetfish, rockfishes, and white croakers), cormorants, sooty shearwaters, seals, dolphins, sea lions, and porpoises.

Oh, a cusk-eel once uttered
Or maybe just muttered,
"I'm sick of this burrow, where I spend my days.
'Cause by dawn I'm a-sleeping
And by dusk I'm a-creeping
I'd like to go out now and soak up some rays."

"But I'm just a-pondering
That if I am a-wondering
A sand bass will eat me before ere long
So I'll stay in the mud, now
The cold, dank, and crud, now
And strum on my pelvics and sing this, my song."

FISHERY: Native Americans only occasionally captured spotted cusk-eels. Historically, there has been no commercial fishery or market for this species, although Lockington (1879c) noted: "Although this fish is not sufficiently common to be of much value as an article of food, it is excellent eating." Cusk-eels caught as bycatch in commercial trawl fisheries were once used as mink food. They are caught very occasionally by recreational anglers.

ORIGINS: Otoliths from what are believed to be *Chilara* spp. have been found in Late Miocene or Early Pliocene deposits (around 5.3 million years ago). Remains of this species have been found in Late Pliocene (at least 1.8-million-year-old) deposits in Southern California.

OTHER SPECIES:

Ophidion scrippsae
(Hubbs, 1916)

Basketweave Cusk-eel

This species grows to nearly 28 cm (11 in) TL and lives from Central California (37°38'N) to southern Baja California (24°12'N, 111°21'W). Like its spotted cousin, this is a benthic species that maintains burrows in soft seafloors, from nearshore (occasionally estuarine) waters to at least 110 m (361 ft). It eats small crustaceans. Length-weight parameters (SL, cm, gr): (sexes combined) $W = 0.001L^{3.398}$ (Rodriguez-Romero et al. 2009).

The species name honors Ellen Browning Scripps (1836–1932), that remarkable newspaper woman and philanthropist. Ms. Scripps gave simply tonnage of dollars to a very wide range of causes and institutions, particularly those in Southern California.

In *More than Gold in California* (Berkeley, California, 1933), Mary Bennett Ritter tells this story about Ms. Scripps: "Perhaps this is a good place to tell a sombre joke on Mr. Scripps [E.W. Scripps, Ellen Scripps' brother]. When our first laboratory building [at what is now Scripps Institution of Oceanography] was under consideration he said to Mr. Ritter, 'Ritter, I want you to get my sister Ellen so deeply interested in this project that she will forget her age. She is seventy-one, and our family drop off at seventy-one or seventy-two years, and I know Ellen is thinking about it. I want her to become so absorbed in something that the next two or three years will pass before she realizes it. So I am going to urge her to build this laboratory in memory of our brother George'...He persuaded her to build the Memorial Laboratory for George H. Scripps who had had scientific tastes and thus hurdled her into an orgy of building and giving that caused her brother to utter words of warning later, all to no effect...She was still building Scripps College when she passed away at ninety-six years of age, while her brother followed the family tradition and was snapped out of life at seventy-two years."

ALEXANDER S. TAYLOR

My goodness, what to say about A. S. Taylor? He was born in Charleston, South Carolina, and came to Gold Rush California in 1849, by way of England, Southeast Asia, and China. One of the few legitimate jobs he held down was as the clerk of the U.S. District Court in Monterey (during which time he collected the cusk-eel that bears his name). In 1860, he married one of the daughters of the early American, and Santa Barbaran, settler Daniel Hill and his Californio wife Rafaela Olivera de Ortega. Alexander's new wife's fortune was perhaps not up to Alexander's hopes, and the family lived in Santa Barbara in what was described as a "somewhat primitive manner." Until his death, Taylor collected all manner of historical materials, from letters to newspapers, and wrote many, many articles of history, ethnology, and natural history, many of a dubious or spurious nature. Cowan (1933) summarizes his career thusly: "Many of his hypotheses were absurd and sundry of his deductions were fantastic or grotesque...His weirdest essay is titled: 'Sketches connected with California History: Prologue'...No historian has yet been able to sound its depths."

DAVID ANDREW

FAMILY BYTHITIDAE—
Livebearing Brotulas or Viviparous Brotulas

The brotulas are a group of benthic, marine fishes, found mostly in marine waters throughout the world. There are 37 genera and at least 107 species; four described and at least one undescribed species live within our range. Bythitids are viviparous with planktonic larvae. Otoliths of a fish identified as a bythitid have been found in Late Cretaceous (perhaps 71 million years ago) deposits. Fossils of brotulids go back to *Eolamprogrammus senectus*, a Late Paleocene or Early Eocene (about 55 million years old) fish of southern European Russia.

Brosmophycis marginata
(Ayres, 1854)
Red Brotula

ETYMOLOGY: *Brosmophycis* is a combination of "*Brosmius*" (an older name for a genus of cusks) and "*Phycis*" (an older name for the genus of codlings) and *marginata* means "edged" in Latin, referring to the bright red edging to the fins.

THE BASICS: Maximum Length: 46 cm (18 in) TL, reported to 50.8 cm (20 in) TL. The Ranges: Petersburg (southeastern Alaska) to Ensenada (northern Baja California). However, larvae have been taken along much of the northern and central Baja California coast, south to Punta Eugenia. 3–256 m (10–840 ft). Larvae: length at birth = less than 8 mm, flexion length = about 1.7–3.6 cm (1 in), transformation length = about 3.7–less than 8.1 cm (2–3 in). Burge and Schultz (1973) have a bit of age-length data. Length-weight parameters (TL, mm, gr): (sexes combined) $W = 0.00000437L^{3.0964}$ (Burge and Schultz 1973).

SALIENT CHARACTERS: Red brotulas have rounded heads, pelvic fins that attach to the throat, very long pelvic fin rays, long dorsal and anal fins, and a curious lateral line that is in two sections. Oh, also they are red.

LIFE HISTORY: Red brotulas are reclusive little fish that seem to spend most of their time in rock crevices. The smallest fish captured in a study off Central California (Burge and Schultz 1973) was 5.5 cm (2 in) TL. We usually see only a brief glimpse of a tail or head when we conduct submersible surveys. Andy Lamb and Phil Edgell (2010) mention that this species forms "mated pairs." They are perhaps nocturnal. A 30 cm TL (12 in) TL fish that I aged was about 12 years old. Fecundity ranges from at least 12,000–30,000 eggs. Based on the few fish I have studied and larval surveys from the usual gang of suspects, this species spawns from about March–August. From just a handful of fish, it looks like red brotulas feed on fishes, crustaceans (such as crabs), and snails. Predators include copper rockfish, Bonaparte's gulls, Brandt's cormorants, California sea lions, and harbor seals.

DANIEL HERSHMAN

ORDER GADIFORMES

FAMILY MACROURIDAE—Grenadiers or Rattails

Arguably, fishes of the family Macrouridae are one of the dominant groups in the deep marine waters of the world. There are 27 genera and about 350 species (at least 16 species within our range) and most live on or near the bottom in depths of 200–2,000 m (656–6,560 ft). They are oviparous and have planktonic larvae. There is speculation in the rattail research community that individuals of at least some species reproduce only once in their lives. Otoliths from what are believed to have been grenadiers have been found in Middle Oligocene (perhaps 30 million-year-old) deposits. David (1956) described scales from a number of macrourid species, the oldest of which may be *Homeomacrurus fernandensis* from the Miocene (at least 16 to as much as 22 million years ago) of Southern California. Other macrourid fossils have been found in Southern California Miocene formations of 7.6–8.6 million years old. Most of the North Pacific grenadiers are figured and described in Mecklenburg et al. (2002) and Nakabo (2002).

In the good old days, we used to call these fishes "rattails," which was nice and descriptive and good enough for simple, honest folks like us. Then, sometime after Sen. Joe McCarthy died, "rattail" became "grenadier" because, one assumes, the fish-buying public did not want to buy fishes that sound like they stick out of rodents' butts. On the other hand, according to *The Random House Dictionary of the English Language*, a "grenadier" is a "member of the first regiment of household infantry" in the British army. And, leaving aside for the moment the question of why any household has to have its own infantry, who would want to buy a fish named after a foreigner? And along these lines, I have also seen grenadiers for sale as "Pacific roughy."

Albatrossia pectoralis
(Gilbert, 1892)
Giant Grenadier

ETYMOLOGY AND COLLOQUIAL NAME: *Albatrossia* is an homage to the R/V *Albatross*, an early United States research vessel, and *pectoralis* refers to the pectoral fins (which are long and narrow). The Japanese call this species "mune-dara." Based on molecular research, this species should be placed in the genus *Coryphaenoides*.

THE BASICS: Maximum Length: 220 cm (87 in) TL. Maximum Weight: 41.8 kg (92 lb) or, just possibly, as much 86 kg (189.2 lb). The Ranges: Okhotsk Sea and northern Honshu to the Bering Sea and to Isla Guadalupe (central Baja California). They are most abundant from the Sea of Okhotsk, through much of the Bering Sea, and along the Aleutian Islands to the western Gulf of Alaska. They are still pretty common to perhaps Northern California. 140–2,189 m (459–7,182 ft), and mostly below about 300 to at least 1,200 m (984–3,936 ft) off North America and perhaps 1,800 m (5,904 ft) in the Russian Far East. Larvae: hatching length = about 5 mm. Length-weight parameters (TL, cm, gr): (females) W = $0.000735L^{3.3866}$; (males) W = $0.0001586L^{3.7045}$ (Orlov and Tokranov 2008a).

LIFE HISTORY: Juveniles tend to live above the bottom (settling to the seafloor at about 42–60 cm, 17–24 in, TL) and adults near or on it, although there is some evidence that adults feed well off the bottom. After settlement, juveniles tend to migrate into deeper waters. In at least some regions, males and females live more-or-less separately part of the year, with females mostly in less than 800 m (2,624 ft) and males deeper than that. Giant grenadiers inhabit a wide range of seafloor types, including everything from boulders and cobbles to fine sediment. Russian biologists have found that, in general, the species is found in the deepest part of its range during winter and early spring. There is a migration into shallower waters as the season progresses and by summer the fish are at their shallowest, although not all individuals seem to make a complete migration. Fishes in the more northern parts of their range may inhabit the shallowest waters. They are found in at least 0–8.7°C (32–48°F).

REBECCA REUTER

Giant grenadiers live to at least 58 years old. Females grow larger than males. In the Gulf of Alaska, 50% of females are mature at 26 cm (10 in) preanal length (from the tip of the upper jaw to about the anus) and about 23 years old. Females are batch spawners, with determinate fecundity, and spawning likely occurs throughout most or all of the year. Total annual fecundity ranges from 35,000–231,000 eggs. Juveniles feed on zooplankton and adults prey on a very wide range of organisms living both on the bottom and in the water column. Fishes are very important, and other commonly consumed prey include mysid shrimps, euphausiids, brittle stars, octopuses, shrimps, crabs, and sea cucumbers. Russian biologists believe most feeding takes place in the morning and evening. Predators include Greenland and Pacific halibut, sablefish, Pacific sleeper sharks, Baird's beaked whales, and sperm whales.

FISHERY: Giant grenadiers have just really, really soft flesh, the result of very high moisture content and low protein levels. How soft are they? Well, you know Dover sole, that kind of soft-serve ice cream of the fish world? Giant grenadier muscle is far softer than that of Dover soles. One taste panel (Matsui et al. 1990) found giant grenadiers had "exceptionally poor eating qualities." Kind of a badge of honor, that. Despite this, these are important commercial fish in the western Pacific. Most of the large catch off Alaska is bycatch in sablefish and Greenland halibut fisheries. Early 21st-century attempts in Alaska to market giant grenadiers either for surimi or as filets and roe met with despair and failure. However, there are so damn many of them there that someone will find a way to create a viable fishery.

REMARKS: This is a dominant species on the continental slope of the eastern North Pacific, Gulf of Alaska, and parts of the Bering Sea. Clausen (2008) reports that, off Alaska, there are two morphs, one with a larger eye than the other.

RELATIONSHIPS: This species appears to be very closely related to the Pacific grenadier.

Coryphaenoides acrolepis
(Bean, 1884)

Pacific Grenadier

ETYMOLOGY AND COLLOQUIAL NAME: *Coryphaenoides* means "resemblance" in Greek and *acrolepis* is "sharp" and "scale" in Greek. "Ibara-hige" is the Japanese word for this species.

THE BASICS: Maximum Length: More than 122 cm (48 in) TL. Maximum Weight: The 154.1 cm (61 in) TL. A 122 cm (48 in) one weighed 4 kg (8.8 lb). The Ranges: Sea of Okhotsk and the Pacific Ocean off Japan to the southern Bering Sea and Aleutian Islands to Isla Guadalupe (central Baja California). They are most common from the Sea of Okhotsk and northern Kuril Islands

to much of the Bering Sea and on down to Central California. While they have been reported in waters as shallow as 31 m (102 ft) and as deep as 2,825 m (9,268 ft), they are typically at depths of 1,000–2,500 m (1,968–8,202 ft). Larvae: transformation length = 9.4-–9.8 mm. Von Bertalanffy parameters (preanal length, cm): (sexes combined) L_∞ = 27.2, k = 0.041, t_0 = 0.25 (Drazen 2002). Length-weight parameters (preanal length, cm, gr): (sexes combined) W = $0.2555L^{2.697}$ (Drazen 2002).

LIFE HISTORY: Off the West Coast, young ones settle on soft substrate at around 8 cm (3 in) TL (at 9–12 cm, 4–5 in, TL in the Western Pacific). Generally, the smallest individuals are in the shallower parts of the overall depth range. Adults often swim well off the bottom (although they also lie on the seafloor). One study found that they commonly live at least 40 m (131 ft) above the seafloor and that in La Jolla Submarine Canyon (Southern California), the fish came into 200 m (656 ft) at night and retreated to 500 m (1,640 ft) during the day. They have been caught in water temperatures ranging from 1–18°C (34–64°F). Pacific grenadiers occupy a very wide range of habitats; really they will live in whatever type of seafloor you throw at them.

Pacific grenadiers live to at least 80 years old. Females grow larger than males. Andrews et al. (1999) used both total length (TL) and pre-anal fin length (PAF) [the distance between the tip of the snout and the base of the first anal fin] in estimating size and age at maturity. They found that females may grow larger than males and that the "Length at maturity is estimated to occur at approximately 50 cm (20 in) TL (about 17 cm, 7 in, PAF) for males (with the smallest mature ones 40 cm, 16 in, long) and from 46–65 cm (18–26 in) TL (about 15.3 to 23 cm, 6–9 in, PAF) for females...maturity may occur between 20 and 40 years for females and at 20 years for males." This species may spawn throughout the year, although in looking at a variety of studies one gets the sense that late winter through spring might be the peak period. Stein and Pearcy (1982) speculated that females may spawn only once every 2 years. Over their geographic range, females produce anywhere from 22,657–367,000 eggs annually. Pacific grenadiers feed both in the midwaters and on the bottom. Smaller fish eat mostly polychaetes, amphipods, cumaceans, and mysid shrimps, while larger ones eat more midwater prey (e.g., fishes, squids, and larger crustaceans). Predators include Greenland halibut, northern elephant seals, northern fur seals, and Baird's beaked and sperm whales.

FISHERY: This is a moderately valuable commercial fish. They are sometimes landed by commercial trawlers fishing for Dover soles on the U.S. West Coast and are also taken in the longline fisheries of the U.S. and Japan. In Pacific Grove, in 2003, "local grenadier" (likely this species) sold for $7/lb in a retail market. For those of you 100 years from now who are directly inputting this data into your cortex through your Sony-DutchShell-Fender Stratocaster Sensorium Input Device ("Now with Teflon Conduits for that Feeling of Bliss"), $7/lb was a fair amount of cash. Rattails have a mild, and kind of insipid, flavor.

RELATIONSHIPS: Pacifics appear to be closely related to giant grenadiers.

OTHER SPECIES

Coryphaenoides armatus
(Hector, 1875)
Abyssal Grenadier

Abyssal grenadiers reach 102 cm (40 in) TL. They are found in all oceans except the Arctic. Within our range, they dwell from the southeastern Bering Sea, and the Pacific south of the Aleutian Islands, to Chile. This is a deep-slope, upper-continental-rise species, found at depths of about 282–5,900 m (925–19,352 ft). Smaller abyssal grenadiers eat mostly benthic crustaceans, such as shrimps and isopods, but also polychaetes and sea cucumbers. Larger fish often feed off the bottom and target squids and fishes. Von Bertalanffy parameters (preanal length, cm): (sexes combined) L_∞ = 34, k = 0.0205, t_0 = 0.25 (Drazen 2002). Length-weight parameters (preanal length, cm, gr): (sexes combined) W = $0.129L^{2.944}$ (Drazen 2002).

©2006 MBARI

Nezumia stelgidolepis

(Gilbert, 1890)

California Grenadier

NOAA FISHERIES

CGs grow to a length of at least 50 cm (20 in) TL. They range from Vancouver Island to northern Chile (26°S). This is a benthopelagic species (we often see them slowly swimming about, just a meter or two off the bottom) that lives at depths of 277–909 m (909–2,982 ft). We mostly see them in about 400 m (1,312 ft) and more over mud or scattered boulders and mud. They live in temperatures of at least 6.0-8.4°C (43–47°F). Not much is known of their biology. Maximum age is poorly understood. A 34.5 cm (14 in) TL male was aged to 13 years and a female that was 27.3 cm (11 in) TL was 7 years old. A 38.2 cm (16 in) TL female was mature. These fish feed mostly on amphipods, mysids, shrimps, crabs, and polychaetes. They also consume snails, bivalves, cephalopods, cumaceans, isopods, hermit crabs, and a few fishes. Chinook salmon are known to eat them. Length-weight parameters (preanal length, mm, gr): (sexes combined) $W = 0.0000219L^{3.45}$ (Hoff et al. 2000).

FAMILY MORIDAE—Codlings

The codlings, not an improvisational comedy troupe, but mostly deep-water fishes, are found in marine waters (rarely in brackish conditions) throughout the world. There are 18 genera and about 105 species, only six of which live within our range. Fossil codlings from Miocene formations (at least 7.6–8.6 million years old) have been pried out of Southern California formations.

Antimora microlepis

Bean, 1890

Pacific Flatnose

ETYMOLOGY AND COLLOQUIAL NAME: *Antimora* comes from the Greek word for "opposite" and *Mora*, another genus of codlings. *Microlepis* is Greek for "small" and "mouth." The Japanese call them "kanadadara."

THE BASICS: Maximum Length: More than 73.3 cm (29 in) FL. Maximum Weight: At least 1.5 kg (3.3 lb). The Ranges: Pacific, off southern Japan (not in Japan Sea) to Sea of Okhotsk to Bering Sea and Gulf of Alaska to Gulf of California. About 68–3,144 m (223–10,312 ft), mostly in 500 m (1,640 ft) or more. Off California, adults live deeper than 400 m (1,312 ft).

SALIENT CHARACTERS: Flatnoses have a very characteristic depressed head, pointed snout, chin barbel, a shelf of bone reaching from above the mouth to under the eyes, and a long, anterior, dorsal ray. Both dead and live ones are various shades of dark.

LIFE HISTORY: Well, there is kind of nothing to say about this species. It lives on or near the bottom and we see individual fish mostly over soft seafloors, usually ambling just over the bottom. Off the West Coast, they have been captured in waters from 2.4–5.1°C (36–41°F). Baird's beaked whales eat them.

RELATIONSHIPS: Pacific flatnoses are closely related to *Antimora rostrata*, the blue antimora.

NOAA/OLYMPIC COAST NATIONAL MARINE SANCTUARY

FAMILY MERLUCCIIDAE—Merlucciid Hakes

Just up the road from the Gadidae, really right next door in the same dismal trailer park, are the hakes. There appears to be only one genus, perhaps 22 species worldwide, with two or maybe three species living within our range. These are marine fishes that are distributed throughout the world. Hakes are oviparous with planktonic eggs and larvae. The family Merlucciidae probably originated in the Paleocene (at least 55.8 million years ago). *Promerluccius venturaensis* is from the Southern California Miocene (at least 16 million years ago).

Merluccius productus
(Ayres, 1855)
Pacific Hake

LINDA SNOOK

ETYMOLOGY AND COLLOQUIAL NAMES: *Merluccius* is an ancient name for the European species and means "sea pike," while *productus* means "drawn out" in Latin. A while back, in a sad, sad, attempt to make this species more palatable, the federal government allowed Certain Parties to change this species' name to "Pacific whiting," but we are too smart for that, right kids? "Merluccio" (pronounced "merlooch") was the name used by Italian fishermen all along the Pacific Coast in the 19th century. At that time, they were also called "horse-mackerel" (as were sablefish).

THE BASICS: Maximum Length: 91.4 cm (36 in) TL. Maximum Weight: 3.9 kg (8.6 lb). The Ranges: Attu Island (Aleutian Islands) to Bahia Magdalena (southern Baja California) to Mexcaltitán (21°50'N) (southern Mexico), including Gulf of California, and Islas Revillagidedos. Pacific hakes are common from southeastern Alaska (at least periodically) to off northern Baja California. They have also been reported from the continental slope of the Bering Sea, but that evidence appears to be kind of sketchy. 12–1,400 m (39–4,593 ft), perhaps mostly in 50–500 m (164–1,640 ft). Eggs: 1.1-1.3 mm. Larvae: hatching length = about 2.4 mm, flexion length = about 8.5 mm, transformation length = about 3–3.5 cm (1 in). Regarding growth rates, every stock assessment worth the mention has one, but let's just be a bit retro and go with Dark (1975): Von Bertalanffy parameters (FL, cm): (females) L_∞ = 61.2, k = 0.3, t_0 = 0.01; (males) L_∞ = 56.3, k = 0.39, t_0 = 0.2. Length-weight parameters (TL, mm, kg): (sexes combined) W = $0.00000000633L^{3.03}$ (RecFin 2009).

SALIENT CHARACTERS: Pacific hakes are cod-shaped fish that are silvery with black speckles on the back and a black mouth lining. These fish have no fin spines and both the second dorsal and anal fins are deeply notched.

LIFE HISTORY: Let's start our discussion of hakes with a nice quote from John Field and Bob Francis (2006) that neatly summarizes much of what we should know about this species: "Pacific hake are also characterized by climate-induced variability in both production and distribution...A much greater proportion of the hake biomass extends north of the US/Canada border during warm years than cold years...Spectacular changes in abundance when recruitment conditions are good. In the early 1980s, two strong recruitment events (in 1980 and 1984) caused the stock biomass to nearly triple, from approximately 2 to 6 million metric tons...Pacific hake have been implicated as predators of juvenile salmon, inflict substantial predation pressure on commercially important pandalid shrimp and are voracious predators of krill, herring, and other forage fish."

Juveniles recruit from the plankton into relatively shallow waters in bays, estuaries, and on the open coast. Juveniles are rarely found in waters deeper than about 200 m (656 ft). Although they do not normally live among kelp beds, Bruce Leaman (1980) observed them at least occasionally in Barkley Sound (Vancouver Island) kelp beds at night. And although juveniles most often form large, midwater, schools, off Southern California I have seen lots of individuals lying on soft seafloors (they have very distinct dark vertical bars when they do that). Adults tend to be found in relatively deep waters, but they will, on occasion make inshore forays. For instance, in 2005, an apparent lack of food off Washington and British Columbia brought adult hakes into relatively shallow waters (to 30 m, 98 ft) to feed. Adults live mostly over soft sediment, but, on occasion, I have seen them near rocks. Pacific hakes can make extensive daily vertical movements. Stauffer (1985) noted that the fish undertake "strong diurnal migrations while on feeding grounds, apparently in response to the vertical movements of euphausiids...during the day the schools are densely concentrated between 100 and 250 m...At sunset the schools begin to disperse and rise toward the surface. At night (2200–0300 h) they are scattered from near the surface to 20 m [66 ft], moving quickly toward the bottom at dawn." Pacific hakes are often found in waters between 5–15°C (41–59°F) and as cold as at least 3.4°C (38°F).

Although it has been tweaked a bit since, the now-classic model of Pacific hake migrations is found in Bailey et al. (1982). In this model, hakes spawn off the coast between Central California and northern Baja California and juveniles stay in this area. As opposed to the very-easy-to-find feeding aggregations, spawning Pacific hakes are apparently spread widely along the California and Baja California coast (as much as 400 km (249 mi) off California) and are not easy to survey. Spawning occurs in at least 130–500 m (426–1,640 ft) of water, mostly over the continental slope, and schools at least 31.6 km (20 mi) long have been noted. For what it is worth, in the Strait of Georgia females tend to be found in shallower waters than males during the spawning season, so maybe that also

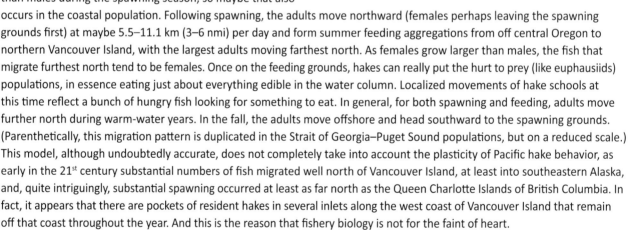

ANOTHER NAUGHTY PARASITE

The reason your average coastal Pacific hake gets all mushy when it dies is that the muscles of most fish are infected by the protozoan parasite *Kudoa paniformis*. This microscopic organism is found only in Pacific hakes. It is likely that *K. paniformis*, along with whatever else it does, continually produces proteolytic enzymes that can weaken muscle tissue but the hosts are continually removing the stuff through the blood stream. When a hake dies, the parasite continues chugging out the enzyme for a while and unless the fish is frozen pretty fast, you get a really soft product. More than 50% of the coastal Pacific hake population is infected and the amounts of these parasites that a hake can carry are impressive. In one study, several individuals had 80% of all their muscle fibers infected. Interestingly, Pacific hakes living in Puget Sound and the Strait of Georgia are not infected by this parasite and their meat remains relatively firm.

occurs in the coastal population. Following spawning, the adults move northward (females perhaps leaving the spawning grounds first) at maybe 5.5–11.1 km (3–6 nmi) per day and form summer feeding aggregations from off central Oregon to northern Vancouver Island, with the largest adults moving farthest north. As females grow larger than males, the fish that migrate furthest north tend to be females. Once on the feeding grounds, hakes can really put the hurt to prey (like euphausiids) populations, in essence eating just about everything edible in the water column. Localized movements of hake schools at this time reflect a bunch of hungry fish looking for something to eat. In general, for both spawning and feeding, adults move further north during warm-water years. In the fall, the adults move offshore and head southward to the spawning grounds. (Parenthetically, this migration pattern is duplicated in the Strait of Georgia–Puget Sound populations, but on a reduced scale.) This model, although undoubtedly accurate, does not completely take into account the plasticity of Pacific hake behavior, as early in the 21st century substantial numbers of fish migrated well north of Vancouver Island, at least into southeastern Alaska, and, quite intriguingly, substantial spawning occurred at least as far north as the Queen Charlotte Islands of British Columbia. In fact, it appears that there are pockets of resident hakes in several inlets along the west coast of Vancouver Island that remain off that coast throughout the year. And this is the reason that fishery biology is not for the faint of heart.

There are three or four Pacific hake populations. The highly migratory outer coast population ranges from Alaska to at least central Baja California. The fish living in the Strait of Georgia–Puget Sound region are currently considered to be two populations (Strait of Georgia and Puget Sound), based on different growth rates and discrete spawning locations; they tend to be smaller than the outer coast fish. It has been postulated that Pacific hakes entered the Strait of Georgia from the open coast about 15,000 years ago and split into the two populations about 2,500 years ago. And then there is the matter of what have been described as "dwarf" hakes, living off southern Baja California. There has been some debate as to whether these are 1) another Pacific hake population, 2) a new species, or 3) *Merluccius angustimanus*, a small hake species that primarily lives in the Gulf of California and points south. Funes-Rodriguez et al. (2009) present a fistful of evidence that suggests that this is a dwarf Pacific hake stock living off southern Baja California that is separate from the migratory, larger fish that live from central Baja California northward.

Most of what you find in this paragraph is taken from data on the outer coast population (although some is applicable to other populations). For stuff specifically on Strait of Georgia and Puget Sound fish, why don't you look up Kimura and Millikan (1977), McFarlane and Beamish (1985), Pedersen (1985), Gustafson et al. (2000), and King and McFarlane (2006)? Pacific hakes live to at least 25 years old. Females grow larger and faster (after about 4 years of age) than males. Estimates of size and age at maturity vary considerably, depending on the researcher and where the research was conducted. A summary of some of the estimates is given in Bailey et al. (1982) and Gustafson et al. (2000). On the outer

coast, it looks like most fish mature at 34–40 cm (13–16 in) TL and 3–4 years old. Most spawning occurs between January–April, although at least a handful of larvae have been taken during every month of the year. It is still a bit unclear whether females spawn only once per season, although that seems to be the current default. MacFarlane and Saunders (1997) did some research on Pacific hake fecundity. They found that the number of yolked eggs per female at any given length was similar between fishes living 1) offshore, 2) in the Strait of Georgia, and 3) in Puget Sound. Using this measure, hakes produce anywhere between around 100,000–2,000,000 eggs per season. They also discovered that females resorb a significant number of eggs (10–20% in the offshore fish and 38-58% in the Strait of Georgia ones) and, thus, just counting all the eggs in an ovary overestimates the "effective" fecundity, those eggs actually released and able to be fertilized. In a California study, the eggs were found between the surface and 250–300 m (820–984 ft), but mostly at 50–100 m (164–329 ft), the lower limit of the mixed layer and thermocline. Here, spawning occurred primarily between 2200–0600 hours. Hake eggs hatch in 5–6 days at 9–10°C (48–50°F) and 4–5 day hours at 11–13°C (52–55°F). While smaller larvae live mostly at depths of maybe 50–100 m (164-328 ft), larger ones, and particularly the pelagic juveniles, tend to live near the surface.

COURTESY OF MICK KRONMAN

OLD MR. SQUISHY

Marie De Santis fished commercially off California and in the following passage from *Neptune's Apprentice* (Presidio Press, 1984) Ms. De Santis gives us a pungent look at the relationship between salmon trollers and "Old Mr. Squishy." Having scored well on salmon the previous day and spreading the word to other fishermen, we find Ms. De Santis and her associates at dawn: "There was the normal twenty-minute radio silence as the sun rose while everyone was busy in the stern setting their gear. I was just barely getting the last line in the water when one of the gang yelled, 'Maruchis! Let's get the hell out of here.' It came out of the radio like a spit. Maruchi is Italian for hake, which in English is also pronounced like a spit, because of the strained nature of the relationships between the fishermen and the hake. Hakes are a school fish that attack the salmon bait like piranhas. When they show up in large enough numbers, it doesn't matter how many salmon are down here with them, you can forget about it. But thinking about the money they cost you is only part of the story. Their personal appearance has much to do with the fishermen's reaction as anything. These shit brown, jaundiced-eyed, bulging-bellied fish, which fall apart at the seams like mush whenever you handle them, had ended the show."

Because they are found in such large numbers, Pacific hakes are one of the most ecologically important fish species along the West Coast of North America. Young-of-the-year and somewhat older juveniles eat primarily euphausiids and calanoid copepods and minor amounts of other small crustaceans, such as gammarid amphipods and mysid shrimps, as well as small fishes and squids. Larger fishes, particularly those over perhaps 45 cm (18 in) FL, feed in both midwaters and near the bottom on euphausiids and on a very wide range of fishes. Sergestid and pandalid shrimps, and squids can also be quite important. In some years, particularly during periods of low food availability, there is a substantial amount of cannibalism. Best (1963) reported: "In some cases they chase their prey into the surf with such abandon that they have been stranded by a falling tide." Various studies give various results, but this species seems to feed during both day and night. Feeding either declines or ceases during the spawning period. At least 58 species are known to eat Pacific hakes, including 36 fish species, four species of birds, six pinnipeds, seven cetaceans, and Humboldt squids. The presence of Humboldt squids may cause hakes to scatter, resulting in less dense aggregations.

FISHERY: First Nation folks living in Barkley Sound (British Columbia) at least 5,000 years ago had a substantial fishery for this species. Hakes did not start out their commercial careers with panache. The problem is that, if coastal hakes are not frozen shortly after they die, the protozoan parasites in their muscles (see riff on page 170) cause their meat to liquefy. As Goode (1884) noted, they were "Scarcely salable in the markets of San Francisco" due to their soft flesh and ragged appearance. And indeed, for maybe 100 years, other than the occasional fresh fish sales, about the best that could be said was that there was some demand for hakes in the mink food industry.

And then, in about 1965, it all changed as Soviet and Japanese factory trawlers started fishing for hakes off Washington, Oregon, and California. Because these large vessels could quickly process and freeze the fish (unlike puny U.S. ships), muscle softening was not an issue. By 1977, when this strictly foreign fishery was closed down, Poland, East and West Germany, South Korea, Bulgaria, and Taiwan all had vessels out here. Under the Fishery Conservation and Management Act of 1976, only the USSR and Poland were allowed to fish for hakes in U.S. waters and, beginning in 1978, fish in the hake fishery began to be taken by U.S. vessels and then transferred to foreign processing vessels.

Well, things were cooking along pretty well, what with domestic vessels starting to get into the act, when lo and behold folks realized that Pacific hakes could be used as surimi. In 1986, the first American factory-fishing vessel made surimi, and happy days were here again, unless of course you were a hake. Surimi is processed fish flesh that is shaped and flavored into pretend seafood ("seafood analogues" as opposed, one supposes, to "seafood digitals"), including crab, lobster, and scallops. In the surimi process, fishes are mechanically filleted, the meat minced and then intensively washed in chilled water. The washing removes all sorts of gunk (e.g., blood, fat, and enzymes) and increases the amount of certain rather elastic proteins. The product is then dewatered in a press and the resulting flesh is white, odorless and, when extruded into various shapes, it has a texture, almost, but not totally unlike crab, lobster etc. Adding various flavors, colors, and additives completes the

COMRADE SQUISHINSKI

From 1978 to 1990, American fishing vessels caught Pacific hakes (and other species) and transferred them to Soviet factory ships for processing. The Soviet vessels needed American translators to communicate with the American trawl fleet and for a time Ms. Barbara Oakley worked as one of these translators. In *Hair of the Dog* (Washington State University Press,1996), Ms. Oakley lovingly details her experiences with chronically drunk captains of both nations, political commissars straight out of the gulag, accidents and general mayhem of all sorts, and the difficulties, even when sober, of life at sea. A classic piece is her recounting of an afternoon shepherding the crew of "her" Soviet vessel through deeper and darkest Portland. Ultimately, this study of high alcohol consumption and large hake catches is both charming and very poignant.

A most quotable quote concerns one character's observation regarding the American fishery observers who characterized the catches brought on board the Soviet vessels: "What person in their right mind would want to spend two months throwing up and cutting off fish noses in this filthy dump when they don't even speak the language?" And one more quote: "The trawls had slashed the heart out of the schools, and the remaining fish were wary and flighty. They hadn't yet had a chance to regroup, so the fish finders showed only small schools scattered here and there: 'hake fuzz', as the fishermen called them."

transformation. When you see seafood analogues in the market, they are usually called something like Kaptain Karl's Kustom Kooked Krab or Klassic Kolonial Kruztacian Kutlets, apparently based on the rather prevalent and long-held notion that mis-spelling a product gives one license to debase it. Most of the surimi the U.S. produces is exported; pretty good for a country that otherwise exports nothing but software and dreams. Today, there are pretty good-sized trawl fisheries off both Canada and the U.S. and the catch is mostly made into surimi, head and gutted products, and fillets.

Interestingly, from the late 19th century on, there has always been at least some commercial fishery for Pacific hakes in the Puget Sound and Strait of Georgia region. Part of this is because fish in that area do not contain the flesh-softening proto-zoan parasite in their muscles and don't turn to mush when you look at them sideways. I have also seen pretty good numbers of fresh coastal Pacific hakes sold at the Mercado Negro in Ensenada (northern Baja California).

This species is taken with some regularity from party vessels and, in some areas, from piers.

ORIGINS AND RELATIONSHIPS: The first *Merluccius* made its appearance in the Eocene (at least 34 million years ago). In western North America, *Promerluccius venturaensis* fossils were taken from Southern California Miocene deposits (at least 16 million years old). Pacific hake fossils have been taken from Pliocene deposits (at least 1.8 million years old) in Oregon and California. It is likely that the ancestor of all of the various eastern Pacific hake species came through the Panama Seaway in the mid-to-late Miocene. Pacific hakes are perhaps most closely related to *Merluccius gayi*, a species found on the west coast of South America, although no study has looked at its relationships to *M. angustimanus*, another species found in the eastern Pacific. Based on the estimated mutation rate of DNA, the divergence between *M. productus* and *M. gayi* took place between about 1.1 and 1.3 million years ago.

MISCELLANY: While examining more than 12,000 Puget Sound hake gonads, imagine their surprise when fisheries biolo-gists found a hermaphroditic hake. The fish had an ovary for a left gonad, while the right one had both sperm and eggs. Clearly this was a little reward they received for wading through more than 12,000 hake gonads. Mass strandings on beaches (of fish, not just their gonads) have been reported from Yaquina Bay (Oregon) and Northern California.

FAMILY GADIDAE—Cods

The cods are mostly marine, but sometimes estuarine, and even freshwater, fishes found throughout the world. The family is comprised of 16 genera and about 31 species, five of which live within our range. Cods are oviparous with pelagic eggs and larvae. Many members of the family have large lipid-rich livers that, one assumes, they use for both buoyancy and energy storage.

The family may have arisen with a fish of the genus *Protocodus* in the Early Paleocene (as much as 66 million years ago). This species may have been an early gadid or morid or merluciid or ancestor of all these. *Rhinocephalus*, from the Early Eocene (as much as 56 million years ago) of the United Kingdom, seems to be the more agreed-upon and most ancient of the cods. In western North America, a number of species including *Eclipes manni* and *E. verturnus* and *Progadus miocenicus* have been reported from Miocene formations (at least 5.3 million years ago) in California. This is all kind of peculiar, because ancestors of the current crop of Pacific Ocean gadids are thought to have invaded the North Pacific from the Atlantic about 3 million years ago. So, did all the Miocene ones go extinct?

Boreogadus saida
(Lepechin, 1774)
Arctic Cod

CATHERINE W. MECKLENBURG

ETYMOLOGY AND COMMON NAMES: *Boreogadus* means "northern" (in Greek) and "*Gadus*" and *saida* is the Russian name for this species. They have also recently been called "polar cod." Some Inupiat names are "ooack," "ovak" and "ogac," and the Japanese word is "hokkyokudara."

THE BASICS: Maximum Length: 40 cm (16 in) TL. The Ranges: Circumglobal in Arctic waters, perhaps to the North Pole. In our area, they live from Arctic Siberia to Cape Olyutorskiy (western Bering Sea) and from the Beaufort Sea to Bristol Bay (southeastern Bering Sea). They are abundant in the Beaufort and Chukchi seas and at least as far south as just below Saint Lawrence Island (northern Bering Sea). Barely subtidal, brackish waters to depths of 1,390 m (4,559 ft). In the Beaufort and Chukchi seas, they are abundant from surface waters to depths of at least 400 m (1,312 ft). Larvae: hatching length = about 5.5–6 mm. An age-length relationship is figured in Hop et al. (1997). Length-weight parameters (FL, mm, kg): (sexes combined) W = 0.000005398L$^{3.056}$ (Gillispie et al. 1997).

SALIENT CHARACTERS: Arctic cod are elongated, have a very small chin barbel, deeply forked caudal fin, and a lateral line that makes this curious wavy pattern as it runs under the second dorsal fin. They have a brown back with yellowish or purplish tones, and are covered in small black dots.

LIFE HISTORY: Arctic cod occupy a notably wide breadth of habitats. They can be found in any part of the water column, in estuaries and off river mouths, in shallow subtidal waters, and many hundreds of kilometers off the coast. These fish are often associated with ice, although they have been captured during spring and summer in the northern Bering Sea at least 300 km (186 mi) away from the nearest floe or pack ice and are abundant along the Chukchi and Beaufort seas in seasonally ice-free areas. However, they can be found in very large numbers under ice and are often seen in cracks, crevices, and in melt-water ponds on the ice. These fish have been taken in waters between -2.1–13.5°C (28–56°F) and from freshwater to salinities of 35 ppt. Several studies imply that fish tend to avoid temperatures below about -1.4°C (29°F) (although in the southeastern Bering Sea they apparently are routine down to -2.0°C, 28°F) and maximum preferred temperatures for adults have been variously estimated at between 0–4°C (32–39°F).

During the summer, larvae transform into juveniles at around 3 cm (1 in) FL. Some young-of-the-year recruit from the plankton directly into inshore habitat, but it is likely that others transform well offshore in near-surface waters. Adult fish are often found both on the bottom and in midwaters, and where ice is present they swim into surface waters. Jensen (1948) recorded the observations of a biologist in East Greenland who noted: "It is not seldom to see small cod (11–13 cm [4–5 in] long) swim briskly about just at the surface with uppermost part of the head above the water; if one tried to catch them they did not try at all to dive." Both juveniles and adults are found in very shallow, inshore waters in the Chukchi and Beaufort seas.

These are highly mobile and migratory fish, although their movements, particularly in the Chukchi and Beaufort seas, are very poorly understood. Throughout their range, fish are said to appear in nearshore waters in the summer, the precise time varying between locations and between years at the same location. However, studies on the diets of ringed seals in the nearshore of the Chukchi and Alaskan Beaufort seas imply that Arctic cod may be present throughout the year. In the nearshore, schools may move quickly through an area or may reside in the same location for weeks at a time. Along this coast, the abundance of cod varies greatly from year to year and even between adjacent sites within a year. This very large influx makes Arctic cod by far the most abundant fish in nearshore waters. Estimates of summer cod abundances have been as high as 12–27 million fish in Simpson Lagoon (Alaskan Beaufort

Sea) and 900 million fish in a small area off Cornwallis Island, in the Canadian Arctic. The amount of cohesion of summer fish schools is unknown, although in the Barrow Strait some schools stay together for at least 1–2 months.

The fall and winter behaviors of Arctic cod in the Chukchi and western Beaufort seas are very poorly known, although at least some fish spend winters under nearshore ice (presumably spawning). Whether the bulk of the population overwinters and spawns in shallow waters is unknown. Thus far, the most complete study of winter behavior was conducted by Benoit et al. (2008) in the eastern Beaufort Sea. They found that, after spawning during the early winter (perhaps over deeper waters in the Amundsen Gulf), very large numbers of fish either migrated to, or were passively carried into, waters primarily deeper than 180 m (590 ft) in Franklin Bay. Here they schooled in densities of up to at least 11.2 kg/m^2. From about late January through late April, cod remained in these depths, making diel migrations into 140 m (460 ft) or shallower. These cod did not feed during this time. Migration from these waters began with an abrupt upward movement and coincided with phytoplankton blooms and the beginning of feeding. The population characteristics of this species are unknown, although it has been speculated that there are a number of stocks in the Russian Arctic.

Arctic cod live to 7 or perhaps 8 years old in the Chukchi Sea and Canadian Arctic, and females may live longer than males. Relatively little work has been done on size and age at first maturity of this species, particularly in the Beaufort and Chukchi seas. In these waters, it appears that a few fish, possibly only males, are mature at Age-1 and around 10 cm (4 in) FL. Most fish mature at Age-2 and Age-3 (12 cm, 5 in, FL and larger) and it is possible that, on average, males mature about one year earlier than females. Spawning occurs under ice flows from November to at least April (and perhaps later), perhaps peaking in January and February in the Beaufort Sea. Females produce annually between 9,000–33,251 eggs, apparently in one batch. While it has been hypothesized that females do not spawn every year, in laboratory studies several females spawned in 2 successive years, implying that some fish are capable of spawning more than once in their lives and in sequential years. Ripe or fertilized, pelagic eggs are 1.3–1.9 mm in diameter, and stay at or near the surface. Eggs hatch in from 26–90 days. In the Canadian High Arctic, larvae are reported to develop only at temperatures below 3°C (37°F). The larval stage lasts about 2 months in the Russian Arctic. Although Arctic cod diets vary with location, epibenthic or pelagic crustaceans (e.g., mysid shrimps, isopods, copepods, gammarid and hyperiid amphipods, and shrimps), as well as larval fish, polychaetes, arrow worms, and small fishes (such as other Arctic cod) are important parts of the diet. Fish living under ice often target ice-associated crustaceans such as amphipods. Feeding by large schools of adults may be sufficiently intense as to cause localized depletion of zooplankton. Throughout much of their range, Arctic cod are an extremely important prey for a wide range of predators. In the Chukchi and Beaufort seas, they are eaten by at least eight fish species, 17 species of birds, and three species of marine mammals.

FISHERY: Turner (1886) notes that the native peoples at Saint Michael [Norton Sound on the Bering Sea] caught them through the ice during winter. They did not appear to be a major food source there. Historically, in the Chukchi Sea, this species was the basis of a very important winter ice fishery. It was eaten mostly by humans and was only occasionally cooked and fed to dogs.

RELATIONSHIPS: Genetic analyses imply that Arctic cod are most closely related to polar cod (*Arctogadus glacialis*).

MISCELLANY: Arctic cod blood contains antifreeze glyco-peptides.

REMARKS: A couple of quotes say it all. Hop et al. (1997): "This fish species is a central component of the Arctic marine food web...with larger schools of high fish density represent-ing important energy stores...such schools may be subject to intense predation pressure by seabirds and marine mammals." Gillispie et al. (1997): "Arctic cod...are one of the most abun-dant and widely distributed circumpolar fishes in the Arctic."

"Ah, for just one time I would take the Northwest Passage
To find the hand of Franklin reaching for the Beaufort Sea..."
Northwest Passage, Stan Rogers.

CRAIG GEORGE

Eleginus gracilis
(Tilesius, 1810)
Saffron Cod

ETYMOLOGY AND COLLOQUIAL NAMES: *Eleginus* is likely an unknown Mediterranean species that was mentioned by Aristotle and *gracilis* is Latin for "slender." Inupiats call them "Ogak" and similar-sounding names. The Japanese name is "komai" and the Russians call them "navaga." Up to the 19th century, "wachna" and similar words were used by both Inupiats and Russians and "tom-cod" (but not referring here to *Microgadus proximus*) was the English word. Based on genetic analyses saffrons are so closely related to Pacific tomcod that the genus *Eleginus* should be synonymized with *Microgradus*.

THE BASICS: Maximum Length: 60 cm (24 in) TL. The Ranges: Yellow Sea to the East Siberian Sea to the Bering, Chukchi, and Beaufort seas, eastward to Queen Maud Gulf (Nunavut) and northeast to Viscount Melville Sound (Northwest Territories), and in the Gulf of Alaska to Sitka (southeastern Alaska). They are common from the Sea of Japan to eastern Kamchatka, to the eastern Bering Sea, and northern Gulf of Alaska (to Prince William Sound), and patchily abundant all along the Chukchi and Beaufort seas to at least Kugluktuk [Coppermine] (Nunavut). Very shallow waters to 200 m (656 ft) or perhaps 360 m (1,181 ft), but typically in 50 m (164 ft) or less. Eggs: 0.8–1.7 mm (fertilized). Larvae: hatching length = 3.5–3.9 mm. An age-length rela-tionship is figured in Gudkov et al. (2005). Length-weight parameters (TL, cm, gr): (sexes combined) W = 0.005L$^{3.095}$ (Seaman et al. 1982).

SALIENT CHARACTERS: Saffrons have a slightly protruding upper jaw, a medium-sized chin barbel (not longer than the diameter of the eye pupil), and a lateral line that does not exist from under the second dorsal fin to the caudal fin. They are mottled brown to gray-green on back, lighter on sides and belly, and washed with yellow.

LIFE HISTORY: Saffrons are schooling, benthic, and midwater fish found in waters ranging from fresh to marine. Although they have been described as entering rivers and lakes, this species primarily lives in nearshore marine and brackish waters. They live over both soft and hard seafloors and, at least around Kodiak Island, Prince William Sound, and in the Sea of Japan, they often associate with eelgrass. Saffrons have been taken in waters between -2.0–14°C (28–57°F). In the Amundsen Gulf, a number of fish may have died when encountering 18°C (64°F) waters flowing out of the Coppermine River.

Young-of-the-year (YOY), at least as small as 3 cm (1 in) TL, recruit to very shallow nearshore waters in the summer. Around Kodiak Island, YOY and Age-1 fish are closely associated with nearshore eelgrass beds. However, off Hokkaido and the Kuril islands, YOYs are abundant to depths of at least 200 m (656 ft). Several studies found that large numbers of saffron cod move into the shallow waters of the Yukon Territory and southeastern Beaufort Sea in early summer and that fish in the northern Bering Sea may move northward into the Chukchi Sea in the summer. Young-of-the-year and Age-1 fish move into shallow eelgrass beds of Prince William Sound in the summer and leave in fall. Alongshore movements for many fish may be quite limited; in the 3 years a fish tagged off the North Slope of Alaska was at liberty, it moved 30 km (19 mi). The locations of overwintering grounds are not well known. Throughout their geographic range, some spawning occurs in shallow waters, although spawning behavior and locations are poorly understood. At least in the western Pacific, substantial spawning occurs in waters as deep as 32 m (105 ft). Saffron cod spawn over sand or small rocks, in high currents, at temperatures between at least -1.8–1.8°C (29–35°F). Water temperatures of more than 1.2°C (34°F) and salinities of less than 21 ppt are reportedly less favorable for egg and larval survival and all eggs die at temperatures of more than 8°C (46°F).

In the Beaufort Sea, saffron cod live to 19 years old. Maximum life spans are highly variable among geographic locations. For instance, fish in Neskynpil'gyn Lagoon (Siberian Chukchi Sea) live to 15 years. Off Asia, maximum life spans steeply decline to the south and fish living in Peter the Great Bay (Sea of Japan) only reach about 8 years old. Growth rates also vary with location. Very little research has been conducted on the age and length of maturation of this species off North America. As with maximum age, growth rates, fecundity, and age at first maturity all vary geographically. For instance, off Hokkaido, a few fish mature at as early as one year old and all are mature by Age-2, while in Neskynpil'gyn Lagoon, fish mature at Age-4 or Age-5. Overall, saffrons mature at 21–35 cm (8–14 in) FL. Off North America, spawning occurs from December to at least May, and off Kamchatka perhaps as late as June. Females

CATHERINE W. MECKLENBURG

produce between 4,900–690,000 demersal eggs annually, spawn once per year, and fecundity varies with location. Larvae hatch in 28–49 days and the eggs remain viable at water temperatures around -3.8–8°C (25–46°F).

Saffron cod tend to feed on or near the bottom on a range of invertebrates and fishes. Small fish, to perhaps 10 cm (4 in), appear to feed mostly on such water column zooplankton as larvaceans, copepods, and hyperiid amphipods. As the fish grow larger, polychaetes, shrimps, euphausiids, cumaceans, mysid shrimps, and fishes become more important. Small amounts of pteropods, bivalves, and echinoderms have also been noted in their stomachs. At least in the Chukchi and northern Bering seas, saffron cod feed throughout the year. During their spawning season, they often eat large numbers of eggs of their own species. Predators include Arctic char, great, plain, and thorny sculpins, Pacific cod, Pacific halibut, Arctic smelt, saffron cod, starry flounder, black-legged kittiwakes, common and thick-billed murres, spotted, ribbon, ringed, and bearded seals, Steller sea lions, beluga, fin, humpback, minke, and sperm whales, and harbor porpoises.

FISHERY: This was an extremely important species to the native folks residing along the Bering Sea of Alaska. Turner (1886) reported that these fish were commonly taken during spring, as soon as the ice melted from the nearshore, but were particularly important in November, when the pack ice returned. He noted: "When the ice in November has set, small holes of a few inches in diameter are cut through it...The hook used by the Eskimo consists of a piece of slightly curved bone, ivory, or deer horn. A small piece of metal is sharpened and firmly set in the concave side of the shaft of the hook. The bait used is generally a piece of fresh fish of any kind. The bait is secured to the hook by two little sinew threads which are fastened to the upper part of the hook. This keeps the bait from being taken off by the fish, as in winter it would be serious work to fasten on bait every few minutes...The Eskimo fisherman, or woman, goes out early in the morning to the hole...the line prepared and let down into the water. Ere many seconds one or two fish will be drawn out and slung high in the air; and, as they slap down on the ice they invariably become detached from the hook. The native is now in good humor...he takes off his glove and contentedly reaches behind his right ear for the quid of tobacco, which has lain there for the last twelve hours...and thrusting it far back between the teeth and cheek, calmly lets it soak while he pulls out dozens of Vakhni...During favorable times two or three bushels may be caught by a single fisherman. The number of fish of this species consumed by the inhabitants of Norton Sound is enormous. They are used as food for man and dog."

Today, this species is commonly taken in subsistence fisheries in the Chukchi, Beaufort, and Bering seas, usually through the ice by both hook and line and gill nets. There are also long-standing local fisheries in Amur Bay (Sea of Japan) that go back about 2,400 years. Russian trawl fisheries also take fair numbers of them.

MISCELLANY: Their blood contains antifreeze glycopeptides.

RELATIONSHIPS: Molecular evidence indicates that saffron cod are very closely related to Pacific tomcod.

Gadus chalcogrammus
Pallas, 1814

Walleye Pollock

"The theme is about staying alive. Life is a war of attrition. You have to stay alive on all fronts. It's one thing after another. I've tried to control a chaotic universe" Harvey Pekar.

ETYMOLOGY AND COLLOQUIAL NAMES: *Gadus* is the Latin name for the Atlantic cod and *chalcogrammus* is Greek for "brass" and "line." Back in the 19th century, the English settlers in Canada called them "coalfish." Other recent names include "whiting" and "bigeye." They are "suketo-dara" in Japanese. Previously called *Theragra chalcogramma*, this species is now known to be very closely related to both the Pacific and Atlantic cods, genus *Gadus*, so it makes sense to throw it into the same genus.

THE BASICS: Maximum Length: 91 cm (36 in) TL. Maximum Weight: At least 5.2 kg (11.4 lb). The Ranges: Pacific and Atlantic (the Atlantic *Theragra finnmarchica* is now thought to be *G. chalcogramus*). Seas of Okhotsk and Japan to off Cape Halkett (Beaufort Sea), Bering Sea, and Gulf of Alaska to Carmel (Central California). The Cape Halkett catches represented the most eastward stations of an arctic fish survey and it is highly likely that pollock live still further east. They are abundant from northern Japan, the Sea of Okhotsk, northern Kurils and southeast Kamchatka to at least the western-most Beaufort Sea, Bering Sea, and as far south as off Washington. However, the really big numbers are in the Sea of Okhotsk and eastern Bering Sea. In addition, they seem to be reasonably common in the Chukchi and at least westernmost Beaufort seas. Generally demersal, also taken pelagically near surface and in midwater, surf zone to depth of 1,200 m (3,936 ft). Often starts to fade out in waters deeper than about 300 m (984 ft), but in selected locations they are

BERNARD P. HANBY

abundant as deep as at least 800 m (2,624 ft). Eggs: about 1 mm; hydrated eggs = 1.2–1.8 mm. Larvae: hatching length = 3–4 mm, transformation length = 2.5 cm–about 4 cm (1–2 in). Von Bertalanffy parameters (FL, cm): (females) L_∞ = 71.57, k = 0.157, t_0 = -0.675; (males) L_∞ = 65.45, k = 0.182, t_0 = -0.569 (J. Ianelli, pers. comm.). Length-weight parameters (TL, mm, kg): (sexes combined) W = $0.00000000633L^{3.03}$ (RecFin 2009).

SALIENT CHARACTERS: Walleye pollock are olive-green or brown on back and silvery on sides; young ones have 2–3 yellow stripes on sides. They have three dorsal fins and two anal fins and either no chin barbel or a very small one. Pacific cod and Pacific tomcod have larger barbels.

LIFE HISTORY: This is a schooling fish found in vast numbers in the Bering Sea and parts of the Gulf of Alaska. Kevin Bailey (a man who apparently has made a Faustian bargain and can channel walleye pollock) and his associates (1999) summarized the species thusly: "Walleye pollock is a species with a very broad niche. Although commonly associated with the outer shelf and slope regions of oceanic waters, as a species it is capable of utilizing a wide variety of habitats including nearshore eelgrass beds, large estuaries like Puget Sound, coastal embayments, and open ocean basins such as the Aleutian Basin of the Bering Sea. Although adults of the species are often described as semi-demersal, in some areas they are strictly pelagic."

Depending on spawning location, eggs are released in near-surface waters to depths of over 400 m (1,312 ft). Halfway through their development, the eggs begin to rise in the water column. Young-of-the-year fish settle (at around 3 cm, 1 in, TL), often in the late spring or summer, in relatively shallow, nearshore waters, sometimes schooling in the barely subtidal, amid kelp, eelgrass, or over rocks and sand. Carlson (1995), observing a reef area in southeastern Alaska, found that young-of-the-year most often recruited in July and once in a while as late as November and noted: "The young fish formed shoals composed of hundreds to a few thousand loosely aggregated individuals within 1 m [3 ft] above the bottom or off rocky ledges at 20–30 m [66–98 ft]…As the juvenile pollock grew, they moved down the slope into deeper waters." By October or November, they were 10 cm (4 in) long and in 30 m (98 ft) or deeper during the day. At night, they would move into waters as shallow as 9 m (30 ft) or less and at dawn they would return down slope. In general, as pollock mature they tend to descend into deeper waters. At least some adults vertically migrate, apparently following zooplankton prey into near-surface waters at night.

Adults form extremely large schools and most frequently swim over mud, silt, or other soft bottoms, but they also occasionally live over rocks and boulders. Adults tend to live in deeper waters in the winter and shallower ones in the summer. Walleyes have been found in waters between -2.1–12.3°C (28–54°F), but apparently rarely enter waters less than 0°C (32°F) and over maybe 10°C (50°F). Spawning occurs in a number of discrete locations in the Strait of Georgia, Gulf of Alaska, Bering Sea, and in the western Pacific (illustrated in Bailey et al. 1999), and major spawning areas change over time. "Coastal stocks broadcast their eggs in deep inshore bays or in sea valleys and canyons that penetrate the continental shelf…in more oceanic stocks, they tend to spawn where currents are very weak" (Bailey and Ciannelli 2007). It is possible, although unclear, that fish return and spawn in those areas where they were born. Walleyes spawn in the water column at depths of at least 50 to 700 m (164–2,296 ft), depending on location, and in at least some spawning aggregations females tend to be higher in the water column than males. Observations of walleyes in an aquarium imply that these fish have a number of spawning-related courtship behaviors, including a great deal of males checking out every fish in the vicinity, apparently hoping that at least some are females.

Walleye pollock may form somewhat distinct stocks (although this is still unclear), and at one time or another as many as 12 different ones have been reported between Japan and southeast Alaska. For instance, Olsen et al. (2002) found that there was "significant genetic variation between North American and Asian populations. In addition, two spawning aggregations in the Gulf of Alaska, in Prince William Sound, and off Middleton Island [near Prince William Sound], appeared genetically distinct from walleye pollock spawning in the Shelikof Strait and may merit management as a distinct stock." In the western Bering Sea, the northwestern-most stock (in the Anadyr Gulf) may be genetically distinct from others in that area.

Pollock live to at least 33 years old. Females are larger at length than males. Very little attention has been given to maturation of males. Smith (1981) found that, in the eastern Bering Sea, a few males matured at 20 cm (8 in) (2 years old) FL, 50% were mature at 31 cm (12 in) (3 years old), and 100% were mature at 48 cm (19 in) (perhaps 7 years old). In a more recent study on females in the eastern Bering Sea (Stahl and Kruse 2008), size and age at maturity varied somewhat with location and year. On average, a few matured at 25 cm (10 in), 50% at 37.4 cm (15 in) (4 years), and virtually all by 56 cm (22 in). In this study, a few females were still immature at as large as 72 cm (28 in) long. Dorn et al. (2007) found that 50% of females in the Gulf of Alaska matured at 42 cm (17 in) and 5 years old.

Scanning his eyes throughout the species' range, Musienko (1970) reported that pollock spawn throughout the year. However in the Bering Sea and northeastern Pacific Ocean, spawning occurs from January–September, perhaps mostly from February–May. Spawning seasons tend to be short and to vary among areas. For instance, within the Gulf of Alaska, fish around Shumagin Island spawn from about 15 February to 1 March, from 15 March to 1 April in the Shelikof Strait, and mostly April to mid-May in the southeastern Bering Sea. Females are batch spawners (some

THE POLLOCK ARE COMING, THE POLLOCK ARE COMING!

Yes, just when you thought it was safe to be an arctic species, here come those crazy pollock. Trawl studies in the early 2000s have shown that there appears to be a substantial number of these voracious fish in the Beaufort Sea off Barrow, more of them than previously suspected. Are they spreading north and east in response to warming arctic seas? Stay tuned.

DID YOU KNOW?

It is estimated that humpback whales may consume as much as 3.26 x 10^6 kg of walleye pollock and 2.55 x 10^6 kg of capelins during their 5-month feeding season off Kodiak Island (Witteveen et al. 2006).

spawning at least 14 times per season), and produce pelagic, nonadhesive eggs. The spawning period of an individual female likely lasts less than one month. Fecundity ranges from about 60,000–1,400,000 eggs in the Bering Sea and eastern Pacific and may, on average, be lower off Asia. Eggs are typically found from near-surface waters to more than 400 m (1,312 ft) and larvae at depths of 20–60 m (66–197 ft). Eggs hatch in 2 weeks at 6°C (43°F). After hatching, larvae tend to ascend into surface or near-surface waters. In general, these larvae appear to make limited day-night vertical migrations, hanging in the shallowest waters at dusk and going deeper during daylight hours. However, and typically for anything having to do with marine science, Lew Haldorson et al. (1993) found that larvae in Auke Bay (Alaska) were slightly shallower during the day and migrated deeper at night.

Young-of-the-year and older juveniles feed heavily on such zooplankters as euphausiids, calanoid copepods, larvaceans, arrow worms, mysid shrimps, and gammarid amphipods. Larger fish also prey on these organisms, but additionally target pandalid and caridean shrimps, fishes, and squids. Fishes may dominate the diets of larger pollock. Diets may change with season and vary between years. Pollock are eaten by a vast assortment of fishes, birds, and mammals; thus far at least 78 species have been identified. Random examples include five species of salmon, nine species of flatfishes, Pacific cod, various sculpins

and skates, yelloweye rockfish, murres, shearwaters, puffins, murrelets, kittiwakes, six species of seals, Steller sea lions, six species of whales, and river otters. Great sculpins are reported to gather around nearshore reefs before young-of-the-year start to settle out of the plankton. Cannibalism by adults is a major source of juvenile mortality in the Eastern Bering Sea.

FISHERY: Bean (1887b) reported that walleye pollock were a major food fish in southeastern Alaska and Gulf of Alaska and they are still taken in subsistence fisheries. Pollock were first placed on the big-time commercial fishing radar when yellowfin sole abundance declined in the early 1960s and Japanese and other fishing interests had to find something to catch. For a number of years, walleye pollock have formed one of the world's largest commercial fisheries with annual harvests in the millions of tons (in some years forming 5% of the world's fish harvest). Most fish are taken with pelagic trawls, with a small percentage caught as bycatch in longline fisheries. Much of the catch is exported and the most important products are surimi [see the riff under Pacific hake], fillets, and roe, along with minced fish, and fish meal. Much of the fillets are exported to Europe and most surimi and roe go to Japan and South Korea.

Walleye pollock are common in the recreational catch, mostly from Washington northward.

ORIGINS AND RELATIONSHIPS: Otoliths of a fish of the genus *Theragra* (although whether of this species is unknown) have been reported from strata about 5.3 million years old. Genetic and morphological analyses imply that walleye pollock are most closely related to *Gadus morhua*, the Atlantic cod. Remains of this species have been found in 100,000-year-old strata.

WHEN LARVAE ATTACK

The Place: Shelikof Strait, Gulf of Alaska. The Time: 1981. Massive numbers of walleye pollock larvae (exceeding 100,000 larvae per 10 m²) ravage the zooplankton population like Ms. Pac-Man sucking up those little dots and gobbling fruit. Having eaten up all the good stuff, the larvae turn their maws to inferior foods such as invertebrate eggs, the nutritional equivalent of switching from ribeye steak to Pop-Tarts™. In 1981, few pollock larvae survive to become juveniles. And now you know the rest of the story. (Duffy-Anderson et al. 2002)

MISCELLANY: Wespestad et al. (2000) commented: "Strong year classes occur when juvenile pollock are transported inshore and away from adults in spring – conditions typical of warm years. In cold years, transport is reduced and juveniles remain on the outer shelf in proximity to adults." And a lot of chomping and silent screaming happens then.

Larval and early juvenile pollock often associate with medusae. In the Bering Sea, during the day, many of these small fish swim among the tentacles, while at night they move upward and away from the jellies and form dense near-surface aggregations. As many as 30 fish have been seen around a single medusae.

REMARKS: Walleye pollock form 70% of the groundfish biomass in the eastern Bering Sea. Bailey and Ciannelli (2007) note that pollock are not always the dominant species in the North Pacific. At the extreme, in Puget Sound, pollock were the "dominating groundfish populations in south Puget Sound in the 1980s and then becoming virtually extinct in the 1990s."

Gadus macrocephalus

Tilesius, 1810

Pacific Cod

BERNARD P. HANBY

ETYMOLOGY AND COLLOQUIAL NAMES: *Gadus* is the Latin name for the Atlantic cod and *macrocephalus* means "long" and "head" in Greek. Various other names have included "Alaska cod," "gray cod," and "true cod" (that last still in use and begging the question of which species might be the "false cod"). A Japanese name is "ma-dara." Bean (1887a) mentions that the Russians called them "tresk," the indigenous folks around Sitka (Alaska) used the term "sacht," and along the Aleutians they said "ah-mo-doc." Reportedly, the old Aleut name for this species translates to "the fish that stops" because its abundance varied so greatly over time.

THE BASICS: Maximum Length: 120 cm (47 in) TL. Maximum Weight: 20.2 kg (44.4 lb). Bean (1887a) noted that "a fish processor at Popoff Island said that one fish would "probably have weighed 50 pounds [22.7 kg]." The Ranges: Isolated population in the White Sea; Chukchi and Beaufort seas across Canada to west Greenland and to Gulf of Saint Lawrence (the fish from the Beaufort Sea eastward were previously called *Gadus ogac*). Also Yellow Sea to the Bering Sea, the Aleutian Islands, and in the Gulf of Alaska to Santa Monica (Southern California). Abundant off northern Japan, Sea of Okhotsk, northward throughout a considerable portion of the Bering Sea (but not in the northernmost portion), and southward to off Washington. Near surface waters and surf to depths of 875 m (2,871 ft), mostly in 300 m (984 ft) or less. Fertilized eggs: 1–1.1 mm. Larvae: hatching length = about 3–4 mm; transformation length = 2.5 cm (1 in). There are many, many, many studies dealing with P. cod growth and you probably know them better than I. As an example, Ormseth and Norcross (2009), summarizing others, give k and L_∞ von Bertalanffy parameters for 4 sites in the Pacific Northwest. Length-weight parameters (FL, mm, kg): (sexes combined) $W = 0.0000000138L^{2.96}$ (Wildermuth 1983).

SALIENT CHARACTERS: These are brown or gray fish, covered on back and sides with brown spots. They have 3 dorsal and 2 anal fins and a large, distinctive chin barbel (about as long as their eye diameter). Pacific tomcod have a smaller barbel (about one-half the eye diameter) and walleye pollock have no (or a minute) barbel.

LIFE HISTORY: Pelagic juvenile Pacific cod have been found near the surface in association with jellyfish. Young fish (when at least as small as 3.5 cm, 1 in, FL) settle in very shallow waters (often the intertidal or barely subtidal), over bare seafloor, bedrock, and such aquatic vegetation as kelp and eelgrass. Here they stay for a few months and then some start to seek slightly deeper waters. Young-of-the-year (although it is not clear if these are newly settled fish or somewhat older ones) have been reported to depths of at least 70 m (230 ft). Off Kodiak Island, Abookire et al. (2007) found young-of-the-year predominantly in 15–20 m (49–66 ft), while Laurel et al. (2009), also sampling around Kodiak, found most similar-aged fish in less than 3 m (10 ft). Young-of-the-year live over a range of substrates, often in kelp and eelgrass, but also over cobble and soft sediments. However, the most important habitat in the Abookire study was the seafloor mounds produced by sea cucumbers. In the Laurel study, Age-1 fish lived in 9–14 m (30–46 ft) (over soft sediments) during the day and moved shallower at night. While adults are perhaps most abundant over silt and mud, they also live on cobble and gravel, and occasionally over rocks, boulders, and such habitat-forming invertebrates as sponges and corals. Pacific cod are tolerant of at least mildly estuarine conditions.

In general, Pacific cod exhibit inshore-offshore migrations keyed to spawning in one area and feeding in another. However, as noted by Shimada and Kimura (1994): "Seasonal migrations of Pacific cod appear to be triggered by the desire to avoid temperature extremes that accompany the changing seasons." Pacific cod live in water temperatures ranging from at least -2.1–18°C (28–64°F) and preferred temperatures seem to be between 0–10°C (32–50°F) or, perhaps, even over a more narrow range. In northern waters, this means being offshore (and spawning) during winter, as nearshore waters get very cold, and inshore (and feeding) during summer. Further south on both sides of the Pacific (Puget Sound, Korea, and Japan): "Pacific cod migrate to deep offshore waters during summer months to avoid excessively heated…coastal waters. A returning inshore spawning migration occurs each winter" (Shimada and Kimura 1994). Of substantial interest is the work of Maschner et al. (2008) delving into the importance of Pacific cod to peoples living on Sanak Island, on the western tip of the Alaskan Peninsula. Delving into midden sites, they found that over the last 4,500 years there were periods when Pacific cod were clearly very abundant and others where these fish were scarce, probably reflective of oceanographic conditions.

While Pacific cod may extensively migrate inshore and offshore, it is less clear how much along-coast movements they perform. Over the years, various researchers have proposed a series of isolated or semi-isolated populations, culminating with Petr A. Moiseev's suggestion that there were a whopping 10 local stocks off Asia. On the other hand, Shimada and Kimura (1994) reported that Pacific cod living in the eastern Bering Sea, eastern Aleutian Islands, and the adjacent Gulf of Alaska may be well mixed. It does appear (based on a variety of tagging, spawning location, genetic, and otolith microchemistry data) that Puget Sound and Strait of Georgia fish may be a separate stock from fish living on the outer coast and that there is only limited dispersal even along the open coast with a major discontinuity between fish living in the northwest and northeast Pacific.

Pacific cod live to at least 17 years old (and perhaps to at least 25 years) and females may grow larger than males. Pacific cod growth rates and lengths at maturity appear to be endlessly mutable, making generalizations iffy. For instance, Welch and Foucher (1988), looking at fish off British Columbia, found that lengths at 50% maturity varied widely (as much as 10 cm, 4 in) between adjacent years. So what the hell are we to do? Well, we can say that the smallest mature fish on record was a 38 cm

William Helgeson longlining for codfish, Popof Island, Alaska, July, 1913.

NOW WE KNOW WHO PUT THE "DUMP" IN DUMPLINGS

While cod were prepared in all sorts of ways, the most memorable was probably a dish called "Scotch Dumplings" prepared at a fish processing station on Popoff Island in the 1870s. These dumplings were a mixture of chopped cod livers mixed with corn meal, then stuffed into cod stomachs, which were tied off and boiled.

(15 in) TL female and the largest immature fish was an 81 cm (32 in) TL female. In general, most fish seem to mature at, say, 4–6 years of age and somewhere between 50–70 cm (20–28 in) TL. It appears that, on average, cod living around Alaska grow more slowly and mature later, but reach a larger size and live longer, than those living off British Columbia and Washington. While their spawning seasons may vary a bit with locality, overall it is from December–July, often with a winter or spring peak. Spawning occurs primarily over coarse sand and cobble seafloors, on the continental shelf or shallow slope. Females produce only one egg batch per year and fecundity ranges from at least 225,000–6.4 million eggs. The eggs have been described as either "demersal" or "semidemersal" and "not adhesive" or "weakly adhesive," so take your pick. Hatching after fertilization takes 8–28 days.

Pacific cod are big-time opportunistic feeders, operating in both the water column and near or on the bottom; they seemingly eat just about whatever is common in their environment. In general, smaller fish feed more on crustaceans and larger ones begin to add healthy amounts of fishes to their diets. Major prey include many, many species of fishes, various shrimps (e.g., pandalids and crangonids), crabs (e.g., Tanner and snow), caprellid and gammarid amphipods, copepods, euphausiids, squids, octopuses, clams, hermit crabs, sea cucumbers, polychaetes, mysid shrimps, and echiurans. Rocks are found in a fair percentage of stomachs in some locations. Feeding tends to increase in the summer and decrease in winter and diets change from year to year. In a study off Kamchatka, feeding seemed to occur least between about 5 p.m.–1 a.m. Many animals feed on Pacific cod. These include, but are by no means limited to: arrowtooth flounder, Chinook salmon, various Irish lords, Pacific cod, Pacific halibut, Pacific lampreys, sablefish, walleye pollock, yellowfin soles, bald eagles, horned and tufted puffins, rhinoceros auklets, bearded, harbor, and ribbon seals, northern fur seals, Steller sea lions, beluga, fin, humpback, minke, and sperm whales, river otters, and orcas.

FISHERY: Pacific cod formed a substantial part of the diet of a number of coastal peoples and are still often taken in subsistence fisheries. This species was extremely important to many of the villagers living along the eastern tip of the Alaskan Peninsula, for instance, extending back at least 4,500 years. Data from an excavated Tlingit site in southeastern Alaska implies that there was heavy use of Pacific cod during the late winter and early spring (Bowers and Moss 2001). During that period, fresh fish were likely at a premium as stored food started to suck by that time. Bower and Moss quote Mr. Henry Katasse, a Tlingit, on how fish were treated after capture. After the fish were cleaned and split by the adults, the kids would take over: "We dug an indentation about 6 inches deep. Others were bringing hemlock branches, and lining this shallow area with hemlock branches. We hauled the fish and laid them close together on top of the branches, flesh down toward the branches. When the area was filled, another layer of branches was thrown on top of the other and another layer of cod went on top etc. until the cod were all gone. The final stages were to cover the last layer of fish with a thick layer of branches so it will get some air. We would cover it and leave it for four days and three nights...The reason for going to all the trouble of getting hemlock boughs was to get rid of the worms inside the flesh of the cod."

From its inception, and for many decades after, most of the commercial catch of cod was salted or occasionally dried. Cod liver oil was also quite valuable. I've read several stories detailing the origins of the Pacific cod commercial fishery, all of them giving somewhat different versions of dates and events. However, the one I like best (and one that was written reasonably close to the events in question) is the account of C.M. Scammon in 1870 and Tarleton Bean in 1887. It appears that until the early 1860s, the presence of large quantities of Pacific cod in the North Pacific was unknown to anyone save, of course, for the indigenous peoples and, probably, the Russkies who lived there. In Bean's version, the large-scale commercial cod fishery in the North Pacific had its naissance in 1863. In that year, the sailing vessel *Timandra*, lately out of San Francisco, found itself becalmed off Sakhalin Island in the Sea of Okhotsk near Siberia. When the crew, likely bored with whittling and spitting (well at least with whittling), put out a few fishing lines, cod started hurtling over the rails. Later, back in San Francisco, the *Timandra*'s captain and some of the venture capitalists of the time saw the economic potential and, within 2 years, seven vessels were cod fishing in Alaskan waters, and the catch was approaching a half-million fish. In later years, catches approached 2-million fish.

For the next 70+ years, well into the 1930s, the fishery remained more or less unchanged. Fishing was conducted from about April–November, in Alaska and, to a certain extent, in British Columbia and further south. However, the area around the Shumagin Islands, near the southwest corner of the Alaska Peninsula, and later the Bering Sea, were the major fishing grounds. For the most part, fish were taken by hook and line from small (14 or 15 foot long) dories which were, early on, powered by sail or oar and later by outboard motors. Some cod were also taken by setlines laid on the bottom. Fishermen either lived aboard the schooners or in fish stations ashore. While there was a relatively small Canadian catch, primarily destined for domestic markets, most of the cod were taken by fishermen who rode sailing schooners that traveled to Alaska from San Francisco and Seattle. Fishing often took place during the early morning. A dory fisherman used two handlines, baited with a variety of baits, sometimes salted herring carried from San Francisco or Seattle, or herring, salmon, Pacific halibut, sculpins, Atka mackerel, pollock, octopuses, or clams caught near the fishing site. A typical dory would hold 200–320 cod, depending on fish size, and weather conditions. A full cargo for the vessel would be about 120 tons (75,000 fish), and it usually took about 3 months to fill the cargo hold. Fishermen would usually return to the vessel to unload only when the dory was full. While 400–500 fish in a day was considered an excellent catch, the record appears to be held by one Billy Lund, working out of the schooner *Sophie Christenson*, who on one fateful day in 1935, hauled in a remarkable 1,062 cod. Good going, Billy.

On some vessels, and on some of the shore stations set up for processing cod, fishermen caught the cod in the morning and spent the afternoon preparing the fish for salting or drying. On larger vessels, there was a separate crew who did nothing but clean fish. Whoever did the preparation, that crew was divided into specialists. There was the "throater" who cut the fish's throat and opened the belly; the "header" who cut off the head and took out the entrails; the "blackskinner"

whose job was to remove the black membrane inside the cod's gut cavity; and the "splitter" who, not surprisingly, split the fish open and removed part of the backbone. The guy who then put salt in the fish was called, to no one's intense surprise, the "salter." Clearly, there was a refreshing candor about these job titles. Today, the "throater" would be the "thoracic esthetician," the "header" a "cephalic manipulator," the "splitter" a "separational lumbar expeditor," and the "salter" would answer to "sodium chloride dispersal engineer."

Particularly in the 19th and early 20th centuries before icing or freezing of fishes was the norm, there was a very high demand for salt cod in San Francisco (the major population center along the West Coast) and to a lesser extent in

Resigned workers making codfish bricks.

various other West Coast cities. While initially all of the salted cod were consumed locally, markets later developed throughout the western U.S., the West Indies, and Central America. Unlike many other fisheries, the salt cod industry never employed hundreds of vessels, it always remained an industry pursued by a relatively few, and obviously hardy, individuals. Before leaving the world of salt cod it should be noted that one San Francisco firm of the 1880s marketed their salt cod under the rather puzzling label "Extra George's Codfish." So, did this mean that the codfish had been produced by Extra George and if so, what kind of first name is Extra? Or did it mean that it was George's codfish and it was "extra"? But extra what? Extra yummy, extra expensive, extra salty, or extra full of codfishy goodness?

After 1937, no boat from San Francisco went to fish for cod. In that year, the San Francisco packing plant burned down and the demand for dried cod was so low that it was not deemed financially wise to start up again. Seattle sent a few vessels up until 1942, when you could have gotten shot up out there. Some dory fishing lasted until 1950. However, following World War II, the rise of the frozen "Fish Stick" industry led to a massive fishery, and Pacific cod became one of the most important trawl-caught species. The fishery changed radically in 1954 with the Bering Sea trawl fishery (followed closely thereafter by Soviet trawlers in 1958). Today, Pacific cod are still a very important commercial species, with decent landings made as far south as Washington (and occasionally Oregon). They are taken with trawls, longlines, pots, and jig gear. Although most of these fish are sold as headed and gutted or fillet product, there is also some production of whole or salted fish. The roe is also often saleable. Much of the U.S. catch is exported to such countries as Japan, China, and Portugal.

Pacific cod are a common catch of recreational anglers from about Washington northward.

ORIGINS AND RELATIONSHIPS: Otoliths of what might be this species have been found on the Miocene-Pliocene Boundary (about 5.3 million years ago).

MISCELLANY: The remarkable Russian Orthodox priest Ioann Veniaminov (born Ivan Evseyevich Popov, but that is another story) recorded that, following earthquakes in 1825 and 1826, large numbers of dead cod were observed floating around the waters of Unalaska Island (Alaska). While we can't be sure these were Pacific cod, there is certainly a decent chance of it.

NORTH PACIFIC HALIBUT COMMISSION

Microgadus proximus
(Girard, 1854)

Pacific Tomcod

ETYMOLOGY AND COLLOQUIAL NAMES: *Microgadus* is
Greek for "small" and "*Gadus*" refers to the cods, and *proximus*
means "near" in Latin, referring to its close relationship to
Microgadus tomcod, the Atlantic tomcod. "Pacific tomcod" goes
back at least to the 1880s. It was called "whiting" at that time by
settlers in Victoria (British Columbia), while 19th-century San Francisco restaurants listed them "smelt" on the menu.

THE BASICS: Maximum Length: 37 cm (15 in) TL. Maximum
Weight: At least 344 gr (0.8 lb). The Ranges: Southeastern Bering
Sea and eastern Aleutian Islands to Point Sal (Central California),
commonly in the eastern Bering Sea and Gulf of Alaska (at the
western end of the Alaskan Peninsula) to about Monterey Bay. Surf
and surface (young fish) to 275 m (905 ft), mostly in 100 m (328 ft)

KIRK LOMBARD

or less. Eggs: 3 mm. Larvae: flexion length = 8–15 mm, transformation length = 2.2–2.8 cm (1 in). Length-weight parameters
(TL, cm, gr): (sexes combined) W = 0.0408L$^{3.268}$ (Kinnetic Laboratories 1980). Wildermuth (1983) presents length-weight data
from Puget Sound fish.

SALIENT CHARACTERS: These are small fish with three dorsal fins, two anal fins, and a small chin barbel. They tend to
be greenish or brown on back with a white belly. Pacific cod usually have a larger barbel and spots and walleye pollock usually
have no barbel and a slightly projecting lower jaw.

LIFE HISTORY: Pacific tomcod are schooling fish that are found both near the bottom and in midwaters. Young-of-the-year
recruit into shallow, nearshore waters at as small as 2.7 cm (1 in) SL. Juveniles live in brackish to marine waters, in bays, estuaries, and on the open coast. Smaller fish live around eelgrass and kelp and over soft seafloors and are often found in midwaters and near the surface. In at least some areas, juveniles begin to leave the shallow nursery grounds in the fall and winter of
their first year. Larger fish also live over soft seafloors, but mostly in somewhat deeper waters (perhaps 50–100 m, 164–328 ft),
although there are a few that live in the shallow channels of places like Humboldt Bay. Tomcod are quite tolerant of a wide
range of salinities, as well as temperatures: they have been taken in waters from 1.4–18°C (35–64°F). In Puget Sound (and one
assumes other locations), tomcod move inshore at night.

Apparently no one has seen fit to tell us anything about tomcod growth rates or life span. For shame, sirrah, for shame.
Tomcod spawn from at least February–May and possibly a bit later. They feed on planktonic, near-bottom, and bottom prey.
Young-of-the-year fish seem to feed almost completely on water-column zooplankton and one study found that juveniles in
general were more likely to feed in midwater than were adults. In certain instances, fish will probe the seafloor for food. Overall, small crustaceans (gammarid amphipods, mysid shrimps, caridean shrimps, harpacticoid copepods, and cumaceans) are
very important, and polychaetes, crabs, and fishes are also consumed. In at least some areas, these fish appear to feed during
both day and night. Predators include a wide range of fishes, sea birds, and various mammals. Examples include albacore,
black rockfish, lingcod, sand soles, spotted ratfish, spiny dogfish, Brandt's cormorants, common murres, horned and tufted
puffins, harbor and northern fur seals, California sea lions, porpoises, and river otters.

FISHERY: In at least some places, for instance around Elkhorn Slough (Central California), tomcod appear to have been eaten
by Native Americans in pretty good numbers. In the 19th century, they were a major part of the paranzella trawl catch off San
Francisco. However, by the early 1930s, laws restricting small mesh trawl nets pretty much ended the fishery. In general, their
small size makes them a not terribly marketable fish. Recreational anglers commonly take them.

ORIGINS AND RELATIONSHIPS: Otoliths of fish in the genus *Microgadus* have been found on the Miocene-Pliocene
Boundary (about 5.3 million years ago). Fossil Pacific tomcod have been found in Late Pliocene (at least 1.8-million-year-old)
deposits in Oregon and Southern California. This species is very closely related to saffron cod.

ORDER BATRACHOIDIFORMES

FAMILY BATRACHOIDIDAE—Toadfishes

Toadfishes are mostly marine (although some enter estuaries and a few species live in freshwater) fishes found throughout the world. With few exceptions, these fishes live over soft seafloors, often burying themselves in sand or mud. There are 25 genera and about 78 species, four of which live within our range. Those nasty little opercular spines on plainfins and specklefins may or may not be venomous. While spines on the tropical genera *Daector* and *Thalassophryne* are nasty, it does not look like there has been much effort to examine eastern Pacific *Porichthys*. The photophores (those little button-like light-emitting structures) found on plainfins and specklefins produce a bluish-green light. An extinct batrachoidid, *Holabatrachus didactylus*, lived during the Miocene (at least 5.3 million years ago) of Algeria.

Porichthys notatus
Girard, 1854
Plainfin Midshipman

Plainfins live most of their lives in relatively deep water, spending their days buried in the sand, with only their beady little eyes and toothy mouths exposed, looking like the Cheshire Cat facing a Congressional probe.

ETYMOLOGY AND COLLOQUIAL NAMES: *Porichthys* means "pore" and "fish" in Greek and *notatus* is Latin for "spotted."

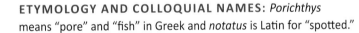

SCOTT GIETLER

A 19th-century name was "silver-spangled toadfish" and they have also been called "northern midshipman."

THE BASICS: Maximum Length: 40 cm (16 in) TL. Maximum Weight: 765 gr (1.7 lb). The Ranges: Smith Sound (southern British Columbia) to southern Baja California (about 24°12'N, 111°21'W), commonly from perhaps the Strait of Georgia (British Columbia) to Puget Sound, and from Humboldt Bay (Northern California) to at least Bahia Magdalena (southern Baja California). Interestingly, this species appears to be absent from between about Cape Vizcaino (Northern California) and Puget Sound. Intertidal to 383 m (1,256 ft), although the species pretty much poops out around 250 m (820 ft). Eggs: 4–6 mm x 4–8 mm. Larvae: hatching length = 7–8 mm, flexion length = occurs before hatching, transformation length = juveniles detach about 1.6–1.9 cm (0.6-0.7 in). Von Bertalanffy parameters (SL, mm): (females) L_∞ = 199, k = 0.61, t_0 = -0.24; (males) L_∞ = 273, k = 0.324, t_0 = -0.67 (Sak 1990). Length-weight parameters (TL, cm, gr): W = $0.004L^{3.282}$ (Love unpubl.).

SALIENT CHARACTERS: Another distinctive species, plainfins have scale-less bodies, large, flattened heads, upturned mouths filled with sharp teeth, a sharp spine on each gill cover, and rows of dot-shaped photophores on their sides and belly. In this species, the throat photophores form a inverted V. Specklefin midshipmen have spots on their dorsal and pelvic fins and their throat photophores form an inverted U.

LIFE HISTORY: Juveniles remain attached to rocks for a number of weeks and, once unbuttoned, remain in shallow waters for perhaps six months. You can see juveniles on the sand or in eelgrass, and they burrow into the seafloor during the day. Older fish live in deeper waters and they, too, bury in soft sediments during the day and emerge to feed in the water column at night. These fish inflate their swim bladders at dusk and deflate them at dawn. Plainfins are tolerant of estuarine conditions (but are mostly found at 15 ppt and higher). Both sexes make inshore spawning migrations, males arriving on the nesting grounds first. These migrations occur mainly in the late winter or early spring. Nesting occurs at depths from the intertidal to, reportedly, 81 m (265 ft).

Males seek out sites on sandy or muddy bottoms around rocks or other hard stuff. Then, using their mouths or fins as scoops, they proceed to excavate hollows for nesting sites. After excavation is complete and, one assumes the stars are aligned, the fish begin to hum (by vibrating muscles that are attached to their swim bladders), hoping to attract females. The humming, which only occurs at night, can last uninterrupted for from a few seconds to more than an hour. At some point,

BERNARD P. HANBY

apparently stimulated by the sound, a female will enter the nest of her own accord. Occasionally, males grab passing females and try to force them into the nest (just a sad, sad commentary), although this is most often unsuccessful. Almost immediately after a female enters the nest, the male stops humming, and the female begins to lay eggs, plastering them to the walls or ceiling. It may take up to 20 hours for the female to lay all her eggs, with the male fertilizing them as they are put in place. After laying is completed, the male drives the female out of the nest (she has laid all her eggs and swims back to deep water), commences guarding the eggs (as well as brushing and fanning them), and starts humming again, hoping to get lucky. A single nest may harbor as many as 2,000 eggs from a number of females. When the nests are exposed to air at low tides the males may splash about, causing water to be thrust upwards, bathing the eggs. During this time, the males eat very little, maybe noshing on a few midshipmen eggs or larvae or the occasional crab or shrimp. While guarding nests, males, on average, lose about 3% of their body weight (but sometimes as much as 24%). Reportedly, it takes maybe 40–45 days for newly fertilized eggs to develop into young and for the young to detach themselves from the substrate. One male in Tomales Bay (Northern California) spent 131 days in the intertidal guarding a succession of egg clutches. Apparently, some males may return in the subsequent year and guard more eggs.

Now that we have the basics down, here is the nitty gritty of plainfin reproduction, and folks, you are going to love this. It turns out there are two kinds of plainfin males, cleverly referred to as Types I and II. Type I males are the typical nest-creating hummers. They are relatively large and have small testes (about 1.2% of their body weight). Type II males do not have the ability to hum, are relatively small, do not hold territories, and their testes are, well, huge, about 8.3% of their body weight. In any given nesting area, about 90% of the males are the stolid Type 1s. Type IIs are "sneakers" and fertilize eggs in two ways. One way is to stealthily enter a nest and either act like a female or hide in some crevice, and then give the eggs a good spritz when they are laid by the real female. Another method is to hang out just outside the nest opening and emit sperm toward the nest while fanning water toward the eggs. As Brantley and Bass (1994) note: "Type II males appear to be obligate sexual parasites of the nest-building, mate-calling, and egg-guarding Type I males."

Plainfins live to at least 5 years old and perhaps to as much as 7 years. A few males are mature by at least as small as 13 cm (5 in) SL and a few females at 7 cm (3 in) and as young as 6 months old. Most males are mature at 16 cm (6 in) (2–3 years) and females at 13 cm (5 in) (about 2 years). Conventional wisdom holds that most spawning occurs May–September, although some Tomales Bay males were observed guarding nests from March–December. It's a bit unclear how many eggs per season a female will produce, although it appears to be somewhere between maybe 70–200. Fecundity varies between years at the same site and plainfins off the Washington-British Columbia area may produce more and larger eggs than those living in Southern California. The eggs are light yellow when first laid, becoming orangish or brownish as they mature. These are nocturnal predators that feed primarily (although not exclusively) on midwater crustaceans. Depending on locality, important foods include euphausiids, gammarid amphipods, mysid shrimps, ostracods, and copepods. Squids, crabs, polychaetes, and fishes are also consumed. You would think those sharp opercular spines would dissuade potential predators but this is clearly not the case. It's probably like lacing your lasagna with habanero sauce. A random sample includes fishes (e.g., arrowtooth flounder, barred sand bass, blue and leopard sharks, lingcod, longnose skate, sablefish, speckled sanddabs, spiny dogfish, striped bass, various rockfishes, and white sturgeons), birds (e.g., Bonaparte's gull, Brandt's cormorants, common murres, and sooty shearwaters), seals, sea lions, dolphins, porpoises, pygmy sperm whales, and Humboldt squids. For the minks of British Columbia, midshipmen may be the dominant food during summer months. Leopard sharks eat the eggs.

FISHERY: Midshipmen remains are commonly found in Native American middens in California (and sometimes in those of First Nation folks, like in Barkley Sound, British Columbia), so there must have been some midshipmen dining action back then. And later? Lockington (1879c) notes: "It can scarcely be entitled a food fish, yet it is eaten in considerable numbers by the Chinese, and is occasionally brought to market. The ugly head, dark-colored scale-less body, and altogether bizarre appearance of this fish are probably the principal reason for its rejection by white people. Doubtless the Chinese are as good judges of fish as we are, but their ideas of beauty possibly differ." Later on, trawl-caught plainfins were sold to mink farmers for animal food.

Mike McCorkle, a commercial fisherman in Santa Barbara, claims he has filleted midshipmen and sold them at the Saturday fishermen's market. They are fairly frequently caught by sport fishermen and some anglers harvest them for shark and ray bait.

ORIGINS: Remains of what are apparently plainfins have been found in Late Pliocene (at least 1.8-million-year-old) deposits in Southern California.

MISCELLANY: 1) Bass et al. (1999) report that plainfins produce at least three sounds: A) the aforementioned "hum," B) a "grunt" (often in the form of "grunt trains"), and C) "growls." While only Type I males produce hums and growls, grunts (likely an aggressive sound) are produced by both forms of males and by females. Parenthetically, "Grunt Trains" is the perfect title for a 1936 New York agit-prop theater production involving a boy, a dog, the ghost of Andrew Carnegie, and Leon Trotsky. 2) Plainfins are capable of aerial respiration. If kept moist, they can stay alive out of water for at least 8 hours. 3) Males guarding eggs in aquaria have been noted to bark or croak at passersby. 4) At least some males may die after guarding their young as they get to look pretty ragged at the end of the spawning season. 5) The sperm of plainfins actually swim faster under low oxygen conditions (as would be found in tide pools at low tide) than when in more oxygenated water. 6) The sonic muscles attached to the swimbladder (these create the humming) vibrate at some of the fastest speeds found in nature (like 6,000 times a minute).

The first mention of the plainfin midshipman in its natural surroundings (rather than in a jar full of alcohol) comes from W.N. Lockington in *Walk Round San Francisco—The Bay Shore* (American Naturalist, 1878, vol. 12, p. 505–512). In this rather poetic paean to a long-gone bay, Lockington notes the abundance of these fish under intertidal rocks in July. He makes a few misjudgments, saying that the females are guarding the young and that the belly photophores are used to produce mucous (remember, they produce light), but he makes up for it with a nice example of a Victorian nature essay. The second mention of a midshipman's ability to croon comes from the notebooks of Charles Gilbert, one of the Grand Old Men of Ichthyology. In 1880, as part of a survey of fish and fisheries of the Pacific Coast, Gilbert found himself in Port Townsend, Washington, where he was informed that there was a local species of fish that "sang." As he noted in his notebook: "June 7: Heard of [a] wonderful singing fish & resolved to do or die. June 8: Mr. Hadlock...and [I] went to head of Bay and procured 'singers' alias *Porichthys*" (quoted in Pietsch and Dunn 1997). And then there is Holder (1910a) murmuring: "An acquaintance while walking on the sands of San Diego Bay, very early in the morning, heard a singular murmuring sound. It evidently proceeded from the water, and presently so increased in volume that the listener stood for some time trying to trace it. Finally, with the aid of a boat, he discovered that the sounds came up from the sea, and emanated from a school of midshipman."

REMARKS: One of the more illuminating (heh, heh) facts about the midshipmen is that they produce their own light. A typical plainfin has more than 700 photophores (light-emitting organs) on its head and body and these little buttons emit a blue-green light. Interestingly, plainfins living in Puget Sound, although they have perfectly functional photophores, do not produce light. So, like, what's going on? It turns out that luciferin, a chemical needed by plainfins for light production, is produced by the planktonic ostracod, *Vargula hilgendorfi*. If that animal is absent from the diet, plainfins, even plainfins with the best of intentions, cannot produce light. While *Vargula* lives along the California coast, apparently more commonly the further south you go, it does not live in Puget Sound. Juvenile plainfins, even before they begin to feed on *Vargula*, can produce light. They get a jolt of luciferin in their yolk, enough to keep them glowing for their first 6–15 months.

Researchers have posited several possible functions of plainfin light production, including as a warning display or to attract prey. A nice experiment by Harper and Case (1999) demonstrated that countershading is at least one of these functions. In laboratory experiments, these folks found that plainfins are able to match their bioluminescence to the light coming in from above. In effect, then, a predator looking upward at a plainfin sees similar light coming both from the fish and from the environment, effectively camouflaging the fish.

> ### MIDSHIPMAN
>
> Male plainfin midshipmen create nests in shallow rocky areas, then hum loudly to attract females. The noise is so loud that people who live on boats in San Francisco Bay report they can't sleep.
>
> The midshipmens' come hither call,
> Might hold all their ladies in thrall,
>   But to those in their bunks,
>   These are slimy-skinned punks,
> And their harmonies soon start to pall.

OTHER SPECIES

Porichthys myriaster
Hubbs & Schultz, 1939
Specklefin Midshipman

Specklefins grow to 51 cm (20 in) TL and 1.4 kg (3 lb). They range from about Point Arguello (California) to at least Bahia Magdalena (southern Baja California) and have also been reported in northern Peru. The fish live anywhere from the intertidal to 126 m (414 ft), mostly in 60 m (197 ft) or less. During El Niños, they tend to retreat into slightly deeper waters. Specklefins are common in bays and estuaries, but are also found on the open coast. Nocturnal predators, they feed on crustaceans (e.g., mysid shrimps, gammarid amphipods, crabs, and shrimps), small fishes, cephalopods, and the occasional bivalve. These are mostly spring–summer spawners, in nearshore waters. Fossil remains have been taken from Late Pliocene (at least 1.8-million-year-old) deposits in Southern California. Length-weight parameters (TL, cm, gr): W = 0.005L$^{3.183}$ (Love unpubl.).

ORDER LOPHIIFORMES

FAMILY ANTENNARIIDAE—Frogfishes

Those cute frogfishes are marine fishes that usually hang out in tropical and subtropical waters. The roughjaw frogfish (see below) is one of the exceptions; it occasionally makes it up to warm temperate conditions. There are 13 genera and 40 species, only one of which is found north of Cabo San Lucas (Baja California). Moser (1996) notes that the family is oviparous and that: "[They] presumably [have] eggs contained within an elongate, floating gelatinous mass; larvae are planktonic." The family evolved in the Eocene (which ended 33.9 million years ago) or perhaps earlier. Froggies have that little flap at the tip of their first dorsal spine that they wriggle about when trying to lure in fishes. Ted Pietsch and David Grobecker (1987) go into exhaustive, one might say punishing, detail about this fine group.

Antennarius avalonis
Jordan & Starks, 1907
Roughjaw Frogfish

ETYMOLOGY: *Antennarius* comes from the Latin for a "feeler" or "tentacle" and *avalonis* notes that the first specimen was taken near Avalon, on Santa Catalina Island.
THE BASICS: Maximum Length: 35.8 cm (14 in) TL. The Ranges: Santa Catalina Island to Iquique (Chile), including the Gulf of California. Roughjaws are rare in California waters. Intertidal to 300 m (984 ft). Larvae: hatching length = less than 2.2 mm, flexion length = about 3 mm, transformation length = greater than 3.6 mm and less than 13.7 mm.
SALIENT CHARACTERS: If it looks like a walking piece of mung, that is a good start. Add a little lure fashioned from the first dorsal spine, an upturned mouth, and an orange eyespot on the rear of the dorsal fin, and you likely have a roughjaw.
LIFE HISTORY: Hey, not much is known about this one. This little cryptic species lives in cracks, crevices, and benthic algae and eats small fishes. Their larvae have been mostly collected from August–October.
REMARKS: Fish of the genus *Antennarius* lived in the Late Eocene (at least 34 million years ago).

ORDER MUGILIFORMES

FAMILY MUGILIDAE—Mullets

The widely distributed mullets (really found throughout the world in tropical and temperate climes) are mostly marine and estuarine, although there are some freshwater species. Most of the marine species are nearshore, soft-seafloor dwellers. There are about 17 genera and 72 species, and six inhabit waters within our range. Mullets are oviparous with planktonic eggs and larvae. A fossil mullet has been discovered in the middle-ish Miocene (about 16 million years ago) from Kern County (Southern California). Various eastern Pacific mullets are described in Fischer et al. (1995).

Mugil cephalus
Linnaeus, 1758
Striped Mullet

ETYMOLOGY AND COLLOQUIAL NAMES: *Mugil* come from the Latin word "to suck" and *cephalus* is derived from the Greek word for "head." Host to a wide range of colloquial names, I would only mention "lisa" in Mexico and my personal favorite, from the Gulf of Mexico, "Biloxi bacon." Genetic studies strongly imply that "*Mugil cephalus*" is actually a group of closely related species. Thus the species living along our coast is likely a separate one from those dwelling in other parts of the world.

THE BASICS: Maximum Length: 135 cm (53 in) TL. Maximum Weight: 4.7 kg (10.4 lb). The Ranges: Circumglobal; in western Pacific to southern Kuril Islands; San Francisco Bay to Chile, mostly from Southern California southward. Intertidal to 122 m (400 ft). Eggs: 0.7–1 mm diameter. Larvae: hatching length = about 2.2 mm, flexion length = 3.9–4.4 mm, transformation length = 7.5–12 mm. Length-weight parameters (TL, mm, kg): (sexes combined) $W = 0.00002L^{3.0213}$ (RecFin 2009).

SALIENT CHARACTERS: Striped mullet are heavy-bodied, yet elongated, fish with a depressed head, two widely spaced dorsal fins, and a series of dark stripes along the sides. They are greenish on back and silvery on sides and belly.

LIFE HISTORY: After drifting about in the plankton, juveniles recruit (at least as small as 2.1 cm, 1 in, SL) to the shallow waters of sheltered lagoons, mangrove forests, tide pools, and bays. Julianne Kalman collected quite small ones in October in a Southern California salt marsh. While these young fish will come into the intertidal at high tide, they are not a classic tide pool species. Schools of adults are also usually found over soft seafloors in quiet coastal areas, estuaries, and in freshwater. These are tough fish, they can tolerate temperatures of at least 12–25°C (54–77°F) and hypersalinities of 100 ppt. In California, there are substantial numbers of them in San Diego Bay and apparently pretty good numbers in a few other harbors and the like. For instance, Scott Gietler has seen at least one school in one of the canals in Venice (Southern California) and I have seen them jumping in the Ventura River near its mouth. They are also found at Santa Catalina Island. You can often see striped mullet leaping out of the water – why they do this is unclear.

OCTAVIO ABURTO-OROPEZA

Various genetic studies imply that there is relatively little gene flow between various populations throughout the world and that, indeed, these "populations" probably represent different species. However, until all of this is made official, let us pretend that all is one. Thus, while folks have researched this "species" in other parts of the world, not much is known about the biology of this species along the West Coast, so I will just throw in stuff from other parts of the world. Ibåñez Aguirre and Gallardo-Cabello (2004) found that for Gulf of Mexico fish, 50% of both sexes were mature at about 37 cm (15 in) TL and 6 years old. They also present a range of values from other papers for size and age at maturity. Along our coast, ripe fish or larvae have been observed between August–December, but really no one has looked hard at this species. Bettaso and Young (1999), working in the lower Colorado River, speculate that the mullet there probably spawn in freshwater in some years. Researchers from other areas have noted salt water spawning. From work in other parts of the world, striped mullet are reportedly single clutch spawners and females produce between 250,000–2,200,000 eggs. These fish feed heavily on diatoms and detritus, but various other tiny prey, like forams, copepods, ostracods, amphipods, snails, and invertebrate eggs are also consumed. One study found that fishes were also occasionally eaten. While it is likely that a wide range of animals eat them, thus far I can only find mention of California sea lions and sailfish as predators in the eastern Pacific.

FISHERY: Way back in the late 19th century, mullet were occasionally seen in San Francisco markets, however all of these fish were caught near Santa Cruz (Central California). Jordan (1887) observed that it was an important commercial species in the fresh fish markets in San Diego Bay and that they were taken by beach seines. Collins (1892) dittoed that for Santa Barbara. Sometime in the early 20th century, demand kind of dried up, and mullet became sort of an afterthought, mostly taken by a few fishermen working in San Diego Bay. In other parts of the world, striped mullet are very important, and even in the Mercado Negro fish market in Ensenada (northern Baja California), you will see pretty hefty numbers.

On some piers in Southern California, folks in the commercial end of things use snaglines to catch mullet for sale, a process that, while legal, tends to drive the sport folks wild.

RELATIONSHIPS: Striped mullet are most closely related to the Atlantic species, *Mugil liza* and *M. platanus*.

REMARKS: And in Roman medical news, here is what Pliny the Elder's *Natural History* says about combating ear diseases: "Most beneficial to the ears is the fresh gall of the skate, but also when preserved in wine, the gall of grey mullet and also that of the star-gazer with rose oil poured into the ears, or beaver oil poured into the ears with poppy juice." Gee, if the latter procedure becomes popular, will Medicare cover beaver oil and poppy juice, I wonder. And are we going to have to pay exorbitant rates for it in the U.S. or can we get the cheap version from Canada?

SEAPICS

OTHER SPECIES

Mugil curema
Valenciennes, 1836
White Mullet

Similar to *Mugil cephalus*, "*Mugil curema*" probably represents a number of closely related species. However, because this has not been well worked out, I have just jammed data from these various species into one, thinking that what works for one probably works for them all. Reaching 91 cm (36 in) TL, within our range, this fish ranges from Newport Bay (Southern California) to Chile, including the Gulf of California. It is at least occasional in Southern California backwaters and lives in the intertidal and down to 25 m (82 ft). In the Gulf of Mexico, white mullet spawn from February–May. White mullet feed on a variety of sediment-dwelling organisms, including filamentous algae, diatoms, small mollusks, foraminifera, snails, and insect eggs and larvae. In Mexico, these fish are of great economic importance and are consumed fresh and smoked; the roe is also popular. Von Bertalanffy parameters (FL, cm): (sexes combined) $L_\infty = 34.5$, $k = 0.144$ (Warburton 1979). Length-weight parameters (FL, cm, gr): $W = 0.0097L^{3.095}$ (Warburton 1979).

ORDER ATHERINIFORMES

FAMILY ATHERINOPSIDAE—New World Silversides

The silversides, often mistaken for and called "smelts," are marine, estuarine, and freshwater fishes found in the Western Hemisphere. There are 11 genera, about 108 species, and six species live around here (if here is defined as anywhere from the Beaufort Sea to Cabo San Lucas). All of the silversides are oviparous with planktonic larvae. J.D. Stewart reports that there are fossil atherinids from Middle Miocene strata (10 million years ago or more) in Southern California. Based on a gene mutation rate model, it has been estimated that at least some of the genetic divergence that has occurred between silverside genera in North and South America occurred about 40 million years ago. Silversides (it's hard to tell the species apart from their bones) are commonly found in Native American middens.

HEMINGWAY, EAT YOUR HEART OUT

It appears that W.W. Boyd of Santa Cruz holds the record for most silversides caught by a recreational angler on hook and line in one day, as back in December 1930 he landed nearly 500. As noted in the *San Francisco Call-Bulletin* of 15 December 1930, Boyd would chum the fish to the surface using cans of condemned sardines, then use worms for small fishes and beef hearts for the big ones. Then, to quote arch-fisherman Boyd: "One of the chief factors involved is the ability to get the fish off the hooks, rebait and get the hooks back in the water in the shortest time possible while the fish are bunched up and biting. On the day of my good catch, they just happened to be there. I started early and they patronized me, sometimes 1, sometimes as many as 5 at one time. I quit at 2:30 p.m. A reporter happened along and asked me how many I had. I told him 500. I had not counted them then but later when I did count them, I found that there were 497" (Bonnot 1931).

Atherinops affinis

(Ayres, 1860)

Topsmelt

DAVID ANDREW

ETYMOLOGY AND COLLOQUIAL NAMES: *Atherinops* comes from two Greek words, "*Atherina*," a word for a genus of related silversides, and "like," and *affinis* is Latin for "related." The name "top smelt" goes back at least to the 1890s, although "bay smelt" was also commonly used until relatively recently. Italian fishermen called them "panzarotti," which means "broken belly."

THE BASICS: Maximum Length: 38.8 cm (15 in) TL. Maximum Weight: 379 gr (0.8 lb). The Ranges: Sooke Harbour (Vancouver Island) to Gulf of California. They are abundant from at least Tillamook Bay (Oregon) to Ojo de Liebre (central Baja California). On the outer coast of Baja California, larvae have been taken as far south as southern Baja California, below Bahia Magdalena (23°30'N). Intertidal and surface to 26 m (85 ft). Eggs: 1.4–1.7 x 1.5–1.8 mm. Larvae: hatching length = 4.3–5.4 mm, flexion length = about 7.7–10.5 mm, transformation length = about 1.4–2.1 cm (0.5–0.8 in). Length-weight parameters (TL, mm, kg): (sexes combined) $W = 0.0000000557L^{2.59}$ (RecFin 2009).

SALIENT CHARACTERS: Topsmelt are green or bluish on back, with silvery stripes and often yellow splotches on the sides. The anal fin begins below the first dorsal, there are 5–8 scales between the dorsal fins, and the jaw teeth are forked. This contrasts with jacksmelt, with an anal fin beginning behind the dorsal, 10–12 scales between the dorsal fins, and un-forked jaw teeth.

LIFE HISTORY: Young topsmelt settle to quiet nearshore waters at lengths as small as 0.6 cm SL. Much of that recruitment occurs in spring and early summer. You can find this species in just great abundance in estuaries (sometimes in freshwater), coastal bays, and on the open coast. As an example, Larry Allen and co-conspirators (2002) estimated that there were 10 million topsmelt in San Diego Bay, which is one passel of topsmelt. Schools of topsmelt are very common in such aquatic vegetation as eelgrass, surfgrass, and giant kelp, but they also swim well away from the weeds. Single-sex schools have been noted. Mostly you see them near the surface, often creating a very characteristic dimple in the water (as opposed to the "flip" made by northern anchovy). On the other hand, Swift et al. (1993) noted: "During certain months, particularly in the spring and fall, schools of large individuals are observed 'rooting' in the sand at depths up to 12 meters." One study found that while topsmelt tended to aggregate close to kelp forests by day, at night most larger individuals moved away from the kelp, dispersing just beneath the water's surface over adjacent deeper water. On occasion, topsmelt school with sardine and jack mackerel. Topsmelt are just really tough animals, as they can survive in anywhere from freshwater to at least 80 ppt (salinities nearly three times that of the ocean) and temperatures between 8–33°C (46–91°F). Movements, if any, are not well known. Phillips (1932a) reported that fish in Monterey Bay appeared to live in inshore waters from about October–February, then reside offshore during the rest of the year. How far offshore was not noted.

Topsmelt live to perhaps 8 years old. Fish in the northern part of the range seem to grow larger than those to the south. It's funny, but there seems to be no definitive study on the age and size at maturation of this extremely abundant species. A few fish mature at 1 year old and around 10 cm (4 in) TL, but most mature at 2–3 years old and as large as 15 cm (6 in). Females produce between at least 200–1,000 eggs per season. It appears that topsmelt may spawn during almost any month of the year (perhaps not in November and December), although it mostly occurs late winter to early fall in Southern California and perhaps mostly spring and summer further north. Large females may spawn earlier in the season than smaller ones. As Feder et al. (1974) noted: "Spawning observed over a shallow reef consisted of a female followed by several males making repeated passes through a clump of red algae containing many eggs. The relatively large eggs have short adhesive filaments that tangle on bits of seaweed." Spawning substrate includes a wide range of aquatic vegetation. Croker (1934), anchored up in a cove at Santa Catalina Island, observed topsmelt spawning in very nearshore vegetation at night on a nearly full moon. He wrote: "The constant splashing sounded like the rustle of leaves in a wind" and, "occasionally individuals stranded themselves on the beach." The eggs, like the fish, are very tough and hatch at salinities as high as 72 ppt and at temperatures between less than 12.8° to about 27°C (55–81°F).

Topsmelt prey on a wide variety of both water column and substrate-oriented organisms. Diatoms, detritus, algae, small crustaceans (e.g., ostracods, copepods, and amphipods), foraminifera, polychaetes, clam siphons, insect larvae, fish eggs, and occasionally very small fishes are all consumed. Topsmelt diets often vary with location. For instance, because their diets appear to be dependent on what foods are readily available, estuarine fish may eat more detritus, benthic crustaceans and macroalgae, while kelp-bed fish may concentrate on zooplankton. Most fish feed during day rather than at night. Topsmelt are eaten by such predators as barred sand bass, California halibut, gray smoothhounds, kelp bass, leopard sharks, shovelnose guitarfish, staghorn sculpins, striped bass, yellowtail, cormorants, terns, murres, pelicans, loons, and grebes, gulls, dolphins, California sea lions, and harbor seals. Eggs likely are eaten by leopard sharks and brown smoothhounds.

FISHERY: Even back in the 19th century, when people seemingly would eat just about anything that commercial fishermen brought in, topsmelt were not particularly popular (although jacksmelt were). Later on, some commercial guys would go for them using roundhaul nets and circle gill nets, but few were those who based their careers on this species. They are caught in great numbers by pier and shore fishermen, whence they are often used as bait for larger species.

ORIGINS AND RELATIONSHIPS: An *Atherinops* sp. was found in Late Miocene deposits (7.6–8.6 million years ago) in Southern California. Topsmelt remains occur in 100,000-year-old strata in California. Based on allozyme studies, topsmelt are most closely related to silversides in the genus *Colpichthys*. By erecting several species and a host of subspecies, ichthyologists as far back as the 19th century have attempted to deal with the morphological differences that topsmelt seem to delight in. Thus, according to those who walk the splitter side of the street, topsmelt are divided into at least seven subspecies.

MISCELLANY: 1) Topsmelt in Laguna San Ignacio (southern Baja California) clean tissue and whale lice appendages from gray whales. 2) MacGinitie (1935) notes that at night: "If the direct rays of a flashlight were turned on one of these smelt it would remain perfectly quiet and could be lifted out of the water with a small hand net." *More tales from the "topsmelt whisperer."*

Atherinopsis californiensis
Girard, 1854

Jacksmelt

ETYMOLOGY AND COLLOQUIAL NAMES: *Atherinopsis* comes from two Greek words, "*Atherina*," a Greek word for a genus of related silversides, and "resembling," and *californiensis* refers to its first being recognized from a catch near San Francisco. The word "jacksmelt" goes back to at least 1884. At that time "California smelt" was also heard. Small jacksmelt (and all topsmelt) were called "panzarotti" by Italian fishermen.

THE BASICS: Maximum Length: 48.6 cm (19 in) TL. Maximum Weight: 0.7 kg (1.5 lb). The Ranges: Yaquina Bay (Oregon) to at least Bahia Magdalena (southern Baja California), and in the Gulf of California. They are abundant from at least Coos Bay (Oregon) to at least Bahia San Juanico (26°15'N) (southern Baja California). Surf, rarely rocky tide pools (juveniles), and surface to at least 29 m (95 ft). Eggs: 1.9–2.5 mm. Larvae: hatching length = 6–9 mm, flexion length = 9.8–12.8 mm, transformation length = 1.8-about 2.5 cm (1 in). Length-weight parameters (TL, mm, kg): (sexes combined) W = 0.000000000988L$^{3.354}$ (RecFin 2009).

SALIENT CHARACTERS: These fish are greenish-blue on back, with silver stripes on sides. The anal fin begins behind the first dorsal fin, there are 10–12 rows of scales between the dorsal fins, and the jaw teeth are unforked. Compare that to topsmelt, and see what you think.

LIFE HISTORY: Jacksmelt are schooling fish, often found in and near kelp and other structures. While they are perhaps most abundant on the open coast (and often swim at least as far as 5 km, 3.1 mi, offshore), they also live is estuaries and in hypersaline ponds (with salinities at least as high as 52 ppt). These fish school (often with sardine and jack mackerel) during the day and appear to disperse at night. Very little is known about their movements. Phillips (1932a) reported that fishermen believed the fish in Monterey Bay moved inshore from about April–October and then somewhat offshore during fall and winter. Eigenmann (1892) observed that jacksmelt were very abundant in San Diego Bay in the fall and then left sometime after January.

Jacksmelt live to at least 11 years old. They mature at about 15–20 cm (6–8 in) TL long and 2–3 years old. Taking in all of their geographic range, it looks like they spawn throughout the year, albeit perhaps with a winter–spring peak. Females attach masses of orange eggs via long filaments to various floating material, particularly aquatic plants. The females are batch spawners, perhaps spawning every couple of weeks. Jacksmelt feed on a variety of small prey including various crustaceans (e.g., euphausiids, copepods, and gammarid amphipods), diatoms, algae, fish eggs, polychaetes, and small fishes. Jacksmelt primarily feed during the day and there is some evidence that they may partially cease feeding during their reproductive season. Some jacksmelt predators include bluefin tuna, broadnose sevengill sharks, California halibut, Chinook salmon, kelp bass, leopard sharks, spiny dogfish, striped bass, yellowtail, cormorants, sooty shearwaters, seals, sea lions, and dolphins. Leopard sharks and brown smoothhounds likely eat the eggs.

FISHERY: Historically jacksmelt and topsmelt comprised most of the "smelt" landed in Central and Southern California (true smelt, family Osmeridae, were far more important from Northern California northward). While early records did not differentiate between the two species, it was noted that, at least in the Monterey Bay commercial fishery, jacksmelt comprised 90 percent of all "smelt" landed. One of the earliest records of the California commercial catch reported that, in the 1880s, silversides (likely mostly jacksmelt) were one of the most important fresh fish in the markets of San Diego. And from the 19th well into the 20th centuries, jacksmelt were caught in very large numbers by gill nets strung in nearshore waters, often in kelp beds. Perhaps the best-documented silverside fishery was that in Monterey, as reported by the redoubtable Julius Phillips in a 1932 report. He noted that there was a fair-sized commercial fishery, with most of the fish taken by roundhaul nets (lampara and purse seines). Looking back, it appears that the period up to and including World War II might be termed the Golden Age of the Silverside Fishery because catches declined rapidly after that, as changing tastes and low prices pretty much marginalized this fishery. Today, the jacksmelt fishery is just a pimple on the rump of the commercial fishing business. Pier, jetty, and shore anglers catch lots and lots of them. They are popular both as a food fish and are used for bait by pier fishermen.

ORIGINS AND RELATIONSHIPS: Remains of *A. californiensis* have been found in Late Pliocene deposits (at least 1.8-million-years-old) in California. One study implied that jacksmelt are most closely related to grunions.

REMARKS: Something else to freak out about: A jacksmelt caught during a bloom of the dinoflagellate, *Pseudo-nitzschia*, was found to contain simply a tubful of domoic acid (see the exposé under northern anchovy for an acid trip.)

Samuel Marsden Brookes, 1816–1892
Salmon Trout and Smelt, 1873
Oil on canvas, 40 3/8 x 32 1/8 (102.6 x 81.6 cm)
Fine Arts Museums of San Francisco, Gift of Collis P. Huntington, 7115

The only painting of jacksmelt I know of.

Leuresthes tenuis

(Ayres, 1860)

California Grunion

That iconic symbol of unbridled friskiness.

DOUG MARTIN/GRUNION.ORG

ETYMOLOGY: *Leuresthes* comes from the Greek for "smooth" and "to eat" (referring to the toothless jaws) and *tenuis* means "slender" in Latin.

THE BASICS: Maximum Length: 19 cm (8 in) TL. Maximum Weight: 41 gr (1 oz). The Ranges: Tomales Bay (Northern California) to Bahia Magdalena (southern Baja California). Spawning runs occur from Tomales Bay southward. These fish are fairly common as far north as Central California, very abundant in Southern California, and substantial catches have been made as far south as Bahia Tortugas (southern Baja California). Surf zone and tide pools to 18 m (60 ft). Eggs: 1.5–2.2 mm. Larvae: hatching length = 6.5–7 mm, flexion length = about 8–9.5 mm, transformation length = about 1.5–2 cm (0.6–0.8 in). Age-length relationship is figured in Clark (1925). Length-weight parameters (SL, cm, gr): (sexes combined) $W = 0.0089L^{3.0}$ (Clark 1925).

SALIENT CHARACTERS: Grunions are small, slender fish, greenish on back with a silver-blue stripe on sides. They have few or no teeth, and their anal fin begins below the first dorsal fin.

LIFE HISTORY: Other than their one big trick, grunions are kind of boring, like the accountant who can balance a banana on her nose. What can we say about a fish that comports on shores in scenes out of an X-rated beach party movie? Grunions are schooling fish. Precisely where they live when not spawning is unknown. They have been taken or observed in near-surface waters, in the nearshore open coast, in bays, tide pools, and rarely in estuaries and freshwater. Within California waters, they form one genetically congruent population.

Okay, now for the one big trick. In general, grunions spawn well out of the water on sandy beaches, often sandy beaches in areas of freshwater flow (e.g., creeks and river mouths). Spawning takes place at night on the highest tides of the second, third, and fourth nights following the new and full moons. Just after the highest parts of these tides, the fish (sometime by the many, many thousands) storm up the beach as far into the upper intertidal as their little flippy bodies will take them. Using her tail, a vertically oriented female then digs a hole (maybe 5 cm, 2 in, deep) and deposits her eggs (several hundred to several thousand) under the wet sand. Males, observing this, flounce over, curl around her, and spray sperm in her general direction; some of it runs down her body, into the sand, and on to the eggs. There is no relationship between the size of the female and the number of males that attend her. On average, sperm from about four males (sometimes perhaps as many as nine) fertilize the eggs in a typical nest. Because the Universe abhors nice and neat stories, there is one exception to this tale (or might it be tail?). In San Francisco Bay, grunions do not leave the water to spawn, rather they deposit their eggs right at the water margins. Elsewhere, individual fish may come onshore more than once a run or repeatedly over a spawning season. The first fish hitting the beach tend to be males and they may just kind of take a look around and not spawn on that go-round. Runs may last for just a few minutes or go on for an hour or more, with the whole beach just alive with the drumming of flopping fish.

For several days after spawning, the tides further bury the eggs and they wind up 15–20 cm (6–8 in) under the sand. At 18°C (64°F), eggs are ready to hatch in about 10 days, around the time of the next set of high tides. However, these eggs will not hatch until they are agitated by seawater, when the next set of high tide roils the encasing sand. Smyder and Martin (2002) note: "The California grunion is the only vertebrate known to have eggs that do not hatch unless they are mechanically stimulated...In the absence of a hatching trigger, grunion embryos extend incubation and remain metabolically active...At 18°C [64°F], grunion eggs have enough yolk to extend incubation up to 35 days after fertilization." Lab experiments demonstrate that the eggs will hatch at 14–28.5°C (57–83°F) and that maximum egg survival and hatching occurs at 16–27°C (61–81°F).

California grunions may live to be 5 years old and they mature at about their first birthdays. Females produce anywhere between 1,559–3,579 orange eggs per season (the eggs become silver as the embryos develop). Spawning occurs from February to perhaps September, peaking April–June, and the largest individuals spawn earliest in the season. Intriguingly, at least a few larvae have been captured in every month, so there might be some unofficial spawning going on during the putative "off" season. Females appear to spawn all of their eggs at one go, but then may raise up a new batch and spawn again that season (perhaps as many as six times). Males spawn more than once per summer. Grunions eat zooplankton (one study found that mysids were particularly favored) but do not feed prior to spawning. Predators include various fishes (e.g., California corbinas, common thresher sharks, kelp bass, shovelnose guitarfish, spotfin croakers, thornback rays, and white croakers), an array of birds (e.g., black-crowned night herons, black skimmers, double-crested cormorants, elegant terns, godwits, great blue herons, gulls, least terns, night herons, and snowy egrets), seals, sea lions, dolphins, and cats. Fishes and Humboldt squids often beach themselves while chasing after grunions. Ruddy turnstones, sanderlings, western gulls, godwits, ants, beetles, and worms seek the eggs.

FISHERY: In the late 19th century, grunions were often found in the fish markets of San Diego; they formed a very small part of the "smelt" fishery in Southern California well into the 1930s. Today, it's illegal to catch them for commercial purposes; they can only be caught by recreational people with their hands.

ORIGINS AND RELATIONSHIPS: Grunion remains are known from as far back as 100,000 years ago. It is likely that California grunions have been separated from their kissing cousins (they will hybridize with them in the laboratory) *Leuresthes sardina*, a Gulf of California species, for 400,000–3,000,000 years.

THE AWFUL TRUTH

Now a grunion may look *innocente*
And it may try to act *impotente*
   But it's really quite randy,
    When it gets where it's sandy,
And you catch it quite in *enflagrante*

The Good Book says, "Don't spill your seed,"
That's against every good grunion's creed,
   "If we tried penetration,
    There'd be no next generation,
To our natures we just have to heed."

BILL HOOTKINS

"You pulled me like the moon pulls on the tide
You know just where I keep my better side
What days have come to keep us far apart
A broken promise or a broken heart
Now all the bonny birds have wheeled away
I need you at the dimming of the day."

I Need You at the Dimming of the Day,
Richard Thompson

FAMILY BELONIDAE—Needlefishes

The needlefishes are near-surface, marine and freshwater fishes found from tropical (occasionally into warm temperate) waters worldwide. There are 10 genera and 34 species. Five species are found in our range, but only one reaches southern California. Needlefishes are oviparous. The family Belonidae may have evolved as far back as the Middle Eocene (around 40 million years ago) or Early Miocene (as recently as about 23 million years ago). Tropical eastern Pacific species are figured and described in Fischer et al. (1995).

And This Just In From Our Man in the Maldives

Jamie McKenzie, a physician who worked in the Maldive Islands (in the Indian Ocean) following the devastating tsunami of 2005, reports on a needlefish-caused injury. He notes that many lobster fishermen are towed behind small vessels at night: "Four large floodlights light up the area of water and the seabed. Lobsters are more active at night and therefore more vulnerable to capture. They are caught by Snorklers [sic] free diving to depths of up to 30 metres…Needlefish are found usually in large shoals just below the water surface…They are attracted and seem to be sent into a frenzy by bright light, skittering and leaping across the surface of the water traveling at speeds of up to 30 mph. There are a few reports of fatalities when accidentally impaling fishermen." Well, we can see where this story is heading. A needlefish, startled by the bright lights on a lobster boat, skittered across the water and rammed into the neck of one of the lobster fishermen being towed in the water. After some minor surgery, the fisherman was released and a month later, he was back in business. Dr. McKenzie notes that the fishermen "have developed a primitive warning system…A fisherman stands at the bow of the Dhoni as a look out, a floodlight is directed forward and on spotting a shoal of needlefish the fisherman strikes the bar onto which the ropes pulling the fisherman are attached. On this signal the fishermen dive to 5 metres below the surface in an attempt to avoid the passing shoal" (McKenzie 2005).

Strongylura exilis
(Girard, 1854)
California Needlefish

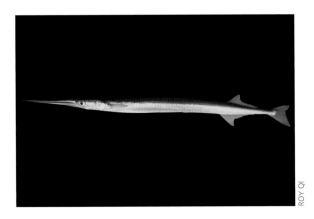

ROY QI

ETYMOLOGY: Van Hasselt (1824) does not mention what *Strongylura* means and *exilis* is Latin for "slender." On the Pacific side of Mexico, they are called "aguja," "agujón," and "sierrita."
THE BASICS: Maximum Length: 91.4 cm (3 ft) TL. The Ranges: San Francisco to Chile, and in the Gulf of California. They appear to be at least reasonably common as far north as perhaps Marina del Rey (southern California). Intertidal to depths of 100 m (328 ft). Eggs: 2.3–2.8 mm. Larvae: hatching length = 6.2–9.3 mm, flexion length = occurs before hatching, transformation length = about 3.2–6.8 cm (1–3 in). Length-weight parameters (TL, mm, kg): (sexes combined) W = $0.000000002L^{3.0}$ (RecFin 2009).
SALIENT CHARACTERS: Needlefish are skinny, with a mouth elongated into a toothy beak. They are bluish-green on the back, merging into silvery below. Among species that might cause confusion, needlefish have one dorsal fin, while barracuda have two, and halfbeaks have only the lower jaw elongated.
LIFE HISTORY: California needlefish are schooling, nearshore animals, usually living near the surface in quiet backwaters and estuaries. A 75 cm (30 in) TL fish was reported to be 5 years old. They seem to spawn from at least April–August, with

females attaching eggs to floating objects. There is not much data on what they eat, but way back in 1891, Eigenmann wrote that they ate small fishes. Predators include sailfish, smooth hammerheads, swordfish, and least terns.

FISHERY: In Mexico, California needlefish are taken in artisanal fisheries. In Southern California, recreational anglers, particularly those fishing in San Diego and Mission bays, catch a few, particularly when pitching small lures.

MISCELLANY: There is a report of a needlefish, apparently in good health, with a broken-off bill.

RELATIONSHIPS: California needlefish are most closely related to an Atlantic species, *Strongylura marina*, and to an undescribed Brazilian species.

FAMILY SCOMBERESOCIDAE—Sauries

Sauries are small, epipelagic marine fishes found in cold temperate to tropical seas worldwide. There are only two genera and four species; only one species lives off the Pacific Coast. Sauries are oviparous with pelagic larvae. An extinct member of the family, *Scomberesox edwardsi*, is known from the Miocene (at least 5.3 million years ago) of Southern California.

Cololabis saira
(Brevoort, 1856)
Pacific Saury

ETYMOLOGY AND COLLOQUIAL NAME: *Cololabis* is kind of clever and means "curtailed" and "forceps" in Greek (an allusion to the short beak) and *saira* is Japanese for "spearfish." They are called "sanma" in Japan and "saira" in Russia and the commercial name "mackerel pike" is often seen in Asia. The Chinese characters used in both the Chinese and Japanese names mean "autumn knife fish," an allusion to this species' body shape and the peak season of abundance over there.

MAKOTO OKAMOTO

THE BASICS: Maximum Length: About 44 cm (17 in) TL. Maximum Weight: 180 g (0.4 lb). The Ranges: Yellow Sea, seas of Japan and Okhotsk, and Pacific Ocean off Japan to Olyutorskiy Bay (western Bering Sea) and southeastern Bering Sea to Islas Revillagigedo (Mexico). Off North America, perhaps mostly from Vancouver Island southward. Surface to 229 m (751 ft) and perhaps to 295 m (968 ft). Eggs: 1.5–1.8 mm x 1.6–1.9 mm. Larvae: hatching length = about 5–7 mm, flexion length = occurs before hatching, transformation length = about 2.1–3 cm (1 in). Von Bertalanffy parameters (knob length, mm): (sexes combined) L_∞ = 342.4, k = 0.41, t_0 = -0.72 (Hughes 1974). Knob length is the distance from the tip of the lower jaw to the posterior end of the knob at the caudal fin base.

SALIENT CHARACTERS: Sauries are slender fish, with a pointed snout, and—this is really important—a series of finlets behind the dorsal and anal fins. Sauries are blue or green on back and silvery on sides and belly. Most any species you might confuse with a saury, like a silverside or sardine, has no finlets.

LIFE HISTORY: Juveniles reportedly may associate with drifting seaweed. With the occasional exception, both juveniles and adults mostly hang at or near the surface. You can find them both well out to sea or pretty close to shore (in the surf zone in Japan) and they are occasionally cast up on beaches. Limbaugh (1955) observed sauries under kelp canopies in Southern California. Saury schools may be up to at least 32 km (20 mi) long and several miles wide. These schools can be kind of noisy, what with all that leaping, splashing, and slapping, and can be heard perhaps 500 m (1,640 ft) away. Along the Pacific Coast, sauries occasionally school with small halfmoons, smelts (the Osmeridae kind), and Pacific herring. In the eastern Pacific, sauries migrate northward in the summer to feed, and then head southward in the winter to spawn off Baja California and California. Pacific sauries are not divided into populations. Taking their entire geographic range into consideration, they live in waters between at least 6–24°C (43–75°F) and, in the north Pacific, perhaps mostly in 12–17°C (54–63°F). At least one saury was caught in the Carquinez Strait (San Francisco Bay) in estuarine conditions.

Some research implies that Pacific sauries live for about 4–6 years and mature when 2–3 years old. However, fish kept in aquaria live for only slightly more than one year and mature at 6–8 months old. Sauries apparently spawn throughout the year, although with definite peaks, and these peaks may vary with year. Larger fish begin to spawn earlier in the season. Females are batch spawners and fecundity has been estimated at 225–4,500 eggs per batch. Kramer and Smith (1970) nicely summarized spawning in the eastern Pacific, to wit: "Major centers of the spawning populations of the Pacific saury can first be located in January in a relatively small area about 150–200 miles [93–124 km] offshore from southern California and northern Baja California…In February and March, the centers of spawning spread inshore and northward to Point Conception and, in April, May and June, to San Francisco. Although eggs may be found as far south as Magdalena Bay, the major spawning centers seldom extend much farther than northern Baja California…The saury is a repetitive spawner in 2-month intervals during the year…Saury eggs are adhesive [to each other and on drifting material] and often collected in clumps of 20 or more." The eggs are colorless early on, reportedly becoming blue a few days before they hatch. Eggs hatch in about 17 days at 13.5–15.7°C (56–60°F). Pacific sauries eat both zooplankton (e.g., euphausiids, amphipods, copepods, and pteropods) and fishes. Sauries are a major food for a virtual Who's Who of ocean predators. Suffice it to say that at least 46 species of fishes, sea birds, mammals, and invertebrates have been found to eat them. A random selection includes albacore, blue and shortfin mako sharks, California halibut, Chinook salmon, North Pacific daggertooths, Pacific bonito, Pacific hakes, shortspine thornyheads, skipjack tuna, yellowtail rockfish, striped marlins, swordfish, rhinoceros auklets (although it was reported that the chicks sometimes suffocate on large sauries), tufted puffins, sooty shearwaters, western gulls, California sea lions, Dall's porpoises, fin, sei, and sperm whales, and squids.

FISHERY: There has never been much of a saury fishery off the Pacific Coast. Before World War II, some were taken in purse seines and shipped to Japan. In 1947, the Hovden Food Products Company, of Monterey, ever on the lookout for products to titillate the discerning palate, and probably beginning to freak out because the sardine were starting to give out, packed a few half-pound oval cans of sauries in oil. Tasters liked the product better than sardine, but the little run of sauries gave out and no further attempt at canning was attempted. Then, between 1969 and 1971, the Japanese tried fishing for them off the U.S. West Coast and British Columbia, but the fishery was not successful. Both catches and fish were small, and many of the fish were infected with parasites, making the fish unsuitable for human consumption. Today, sauries remain very popular in Asia, but the fishery for them tends to be in the central and western Pacific. Most Asian markets carry canned sauries; try them, you may like them. Once in a while a recreational angler catches one and is rightly mystified.

MISCELLANY: Those dark, thick, "threads" hanging off saury bodies are the parasitic copepod, *Pennella* spp. The parasites stick their heads into the musculature and the rest of their bodies hang off in the water.

REMARKS: As noted previously, Pacific sauries are major forage fish for a wide range of species. People who do this sort of thing for a living estimate that there are 56.1 billion sauries in the North Pacific.

FAMILY EXOCOETIDAE—Flyingfishes

Flyingfishes are marine forms found all over the world, from the tropics into the cold temperate zone. There are eight genera and about 52 species, 10 of which live along our coast, and three reach into Southern California or points north. The group is oviparous, the eggs attach to floating objects or to each other, and the larvae are planktonic. Flyingfishes are known from as far back as the Middle Eocene (40 million or more years ago). There is a key, and descriptions, of the eastern Pacific flyingfishes in Fischer et al. (1995).

Way back in 1840, F.D. Bennet noted that flying fish glide, they do not fly: "When disturbed by the passage of a ship, or pursued by predaceous fish, they rise from the water in dense flocks, and present a beautiful spectacle as they glide through air, the broad silvery 'wings' and blue bodies glittering beneath the rays of a tropical sun. Their tour through the air must be regarded rather as a leap than a flight; their expanded pectoral fins, or wings, being projected horizontally, but having very little movement during this evolution." As noted by Bureau of Marine Fisheries (1949): "The pectoral fins are extremely long and are capable of great expansion till they resemble the wings of a monoplane. The fish picks up its initial speed in the water. Breaking through the surface it extends its pectoral fins into sails and adds to its speed by rapidly sculling with the lower lobe of the tail fin. When soaring speed is attained, the tail is completely withdrawn from the water and the fish can soar from 50 to 200 feet through the air. As the speed slackens the fish loses altitude and if it wishes to continue in the air it will once more lower the tail into the water and scull very rapidly, gaining a fresh burst of speed for another long soar and can make as many as four soaring trips before settles in the water."

Cheilopogon pinnatibarbatus

(Bennett, 1831)

Smallhead Flyingfish

ETYMOLOGY AND COLLOQUIAL NAME: Well, I have no idea what either *Cheilopogon* or *pinnatibarbatus* signifies. *Cheilo* is Greek for "lip" which is fine, while *pogon* is Greek for "bearded" which, because this species does not have a beard, is not so fine. *Pinnatibarbatus* is Latin for "feather" or "finned" and "barbel." Again, I must be misunderstanding something, because, like, where is the barbel? These were known for many years off our coast as "California flyingfish."

THE BASICS: Maximum Length: 48 cm (19 in) TL. Maximum Weight: about 0.6 kg (1.4 lb). The Ranges: If you include the various subspecies, this species is likely circumglobal. Western Pacific, north to southern Kuril Islands; eastern Pacific, Astoria (Oregon) to southern Baja California, including Gulf of California. Typically from at least Southern California southward. Surface waters, perhaps to 10 m (33 ft). Eggs: 1.6–2.4 mm. Larvae: hatching length = about 4–5 mm, flexion length = occurs before hatching, transformation length = about 1.8–2.2 cm (0.7–0.9 in). Length-weight parameters (TL, mm, kg): (sexes combined) $W = 0.00000001744L^{2.793}$ (RecFin 2009).

DAN RICHARDS

SALIENT CHARACTERS: Like almost all flyingfish species, smallheads have large pectoral fins, although this species has really long ones (if you press them against the body, they will extend beyond the rear of the dorsal fin). The head of *C. pinnatibarbatus* is also on the short side; the snout length, for instance, is about equal to the diameter of the eye.

LIFE HISTORY: These are pelagic animals that make inshore forays to spawn in kelp beds. Smallheads live to at least 5 years old. Off California, they spawn in the summer and early fall. Larvae hatch about 16 days after fertilization at 17–18.1°C (63–65°F). Smallheads eat zooplankton. They are eaten by various pelagic fishes (e.g., albacore, blue sharks, various billfishes, and yellowtail), pinnipeds (e.g., California sea lions), and cetaceans.

FISHERY: Historically, there was a small gill net fishery for smallheads around Santa Catalina and some of the other Southern California islands. The nets were set in kelp beds during the spawning season and the fish were sold as bait for billfishes.

While there has not been any organized angling for flyingfish, we must credit Charles Holder (1910b) for at least trying to think of a novel way to kill them: "The sportsmanlike way to take it is to shoot it with a shotgun. This I have accomplished by seating myself in the bow of a fast launch, and as the flying fish rises on either hand shooting it either to the right or left. A good dog might be trained to spring and retrieve flying fish." Actually, a sportsmanlike way to shoot a flying fish is to stretch a rubberband along a finger, and as the flying fish rises on either hand, release the band either left or right. Parenthetically, I must say that my friend Merit McCrea has trained Arthur, his Chesapeake Bay retriever, to leap from small vessels and retrieve rockfishes that get off the line and are floating away (see photo below).

MERIT MCCREA

MISCELLANY: Flyingfish always remind me of taking the SS *Catalina*, the Great White Steamer, to Catalina as a youth in the 1950s. How well I remember the excitement of docking in Avalon and of seeing the young boys swim out to meet the ship and beg for coins to be tossed. Of course, my favorite memory is of throwing them slugs (those coin-shaped worthless metal disks used in vending machines) and hearing their cries of rage and frustration. Of such memories are our lives built.

And another timeless quote from Holder (1910a): "Noticing a charge of tunas and albacores upon a school of flying fishes one day off Santa Catalina I rowed my boat into the line of march and carnage...coming slowly on was a mass of white caps that covered several acres...Flying fishes were darting toward me like arrows...The tunas were magnificent creatures six or seven feet in length...but the most astonishing display was caused by their efforts to capture the flying fishes in the air, to accomplish which the tunas would dash out of the water rising to a height of ten feet."

FAMILY HEMIRAMPHIDAE—Halfbeaks

Halfbeaks are marine and freshwater fishes, found in tropical to warm temperate waters around the world, usually near the surface. There are 12 genera and about 109 species, and eight occur within our range. Halfbeaks are oviparous and all the species are presumed to attach eggs to a spawning substrate, followed by a planktonic larval stage. Fossil halfbeaks are knows from as far back as the Middle Eocene (maybe 45 million years ago or so).

Hyporhamphus rosae
(Jordan & Gilbert, 1880)
California Halfbeak

ETYMOLOGY: *Hyporhamphus* means "below" and "beak" in Greek and *rosae* honors Rosa Smith Eigenmann (1858–1947), arguably the first major female ichthyologist.

THE BASICS: Maximum Length: 20 cm (8 in) TL. The Ranges: Off the Santa Ana River (Southern California) to the Gulf of California, and in Bahia Nonura (Peru). They are common as far north as San Diego Bay. At and near surface. Larvae: transformation length = 1.9 to about 3 cm (0.7–1.2 in).

SALIENT CHARACTERS: Another easy one. The lower jaw of this species is very long, much longer than the upper one. This species has a red-tipped beak and is green on the back and silvery below.

LIFE HISTORY: Well, no one wants to catch them, so no one has done much work on this species. They school, live in coastal lagoons, mangrove areas, in bays, and will occasionally enter freshwater. Jerry McGowen (1977) captured some of their larvae in San Diego Bay in April, June, October, and November. Their one known predator (likely one of many) is the least tern.

ROSA SMITH EIGENMANN

A remarkable woman, Rosa Smith Eigenmann grew up in San Diego and early on developed an intense interest in nature, and fishes in particular. In a time when few women were encouraged to professionally pursue these interests, she published papers on fishes in her own name and collaborated with her husband, Carl Eigenmann, on a number of others.

ORDER CYPRINODONTIFORMES

FAMILY FUNDULIDAE—Topminnows

Topminnows form a group of exceedingly tough little fishes. A number of species are capable of thriving over a very wide range of salinities, some from freshwaters to levels seen only in theater popcorn or in those strange little gobbets of deep-fried pork rinds that people seem to enjoy while watching automobiles race around tracks. Ocean-dwelling species live in nearshore and protected waters. All of the family is found in North America, Bermuda, or Cuba. There are four genera and 50ish species. Only one species (California killifish) is native to our range, but the rainwater killifish, *Lucania parva*, has been introduced into a few estuaries. This is yet another example of "If you import them, they will be released eventually into the wild, creating what havoc we can only speculate." Fundulids are oviparous.

Fundulus parvipinnis
Girard, 1854
California Killifish

MILTON LOVE

ETYMOLOGY: *Fundulus* means "bottom" in Latin (referring to the benthic habitat of some species) and *parvipinnis* means "small" and "fin" in Latin. Historically, they were also called "Pacific killifish" and "California mud-fish."

THE BASICS: Maximum Length: 10.8 cm (4 in) TL. The Ranges: Morro Bay (Central California) to Bahia Magdalena (southern Baja California). At the more northern part of their range, they are common both at Goleta Slough (near Santa Barbara) and in Morro Bay, but do not seem to occur between these sites. Shallow waters, rarely in more than 3 m (10 ft). Eggs: 2.3–2.8 x 2.4–2.8 mm. Larvae: hatching length = 5.6–6.8 mm, flexion length = occurs before hatching, transformation length = about 1.1–1.4 cm (0.4–0.6 in). Von Bertalanffy parameters (TL, mm): (sexes combined) L_∞ = 94.7, k = 0.93, t_0 = 0.01 (Pérez-España et al. 1998). Length-weight parameters (SL, cm, gr): (sexes combined) W = $0.02L^{3.08}$ (Ruiz-Campos et al. 2006).

SALIENT CHARACTERS: These are very pretty, thick-bodied fish with a characteristic more-or-less squared off caudal fin. They are olive-green on back and sides and yellow-brown on belly. Males have a series of black bars on sides. Breeding males turn dark brown on back with yellow suffusing the belly, pelvic and pectoral fins, and the lower part of the head.

LIFE HISTORY: California killifish are schooling, mostly estuarine fish that are only rarely found on the open coast. They often live among eelgrass and over mud flats. Limbaugh (1955) reported that killifish occasionally are found in the kelp canopy (really, I am not making that up). Talley (2000) noted that this species is "A numerically dominant resident fish in wetlands of southern and Baja California representing as much as 80% of the individuals captured during studies." Pérez-España et al. (1998) estimated that there were between 32.7 and 44.2 million killifish in Ojo de Liebre Lagoon (central Baja California). In some estuaries, densities of over 2,000 fish per m² have been calculated. Small fish tend to be found in shallower waters than larger ones. One study in Anaheim Bay (Southern California) found that killifish move into channels on ebbing tides and reverse this on flood tides, eventually spreading out over vegetated flats. Reportedly, killifish will burrow into mud or use crustacean burrows when frightened. Younger fish appear to school more than older ones. These are really, really tough fish, able to tolerate everything from essentially freshwater to 128 ppt (about four times the salinity of salt water). Once, when I was sampling fishes in Goleta Slough (near UC Santa Barbara), I absent mindedly put a killifish in the pocket of my pea coat. An hour later, having forgotten the fish was there, I put my hand in that pocket, it wriggled, and I had to promptly wash my pants. I mean, these fish are tough. Bernardi and Talley (2000) found that: "Morphological differences across Punta Eugenia (Baja California) were accompanied by large genetic differences...Gene flow was in general very reduced over the range of the species with a strong break at Punta Eugenia."

This is a short-lived species, as only a few California killifish live to 30 months old, with most living about 18 months. California killifish mature at 11–12 months old and 4.6 cm (2 inches) SL or larger. They spawn from April–September, with females producing between 61–439 eggs. The eggs are demersal and attached to the substrate with filaments that are universally described as "weakly adhesive," so I guess they are. Males are said to die within a month of spawning and females live only a little longer. Fish appear to spawn within 2–3 days of the full or new moon, on high tides, and the spawning occurs at night. It is likely that vegetated shallows and intertidal pools are used for spawning. The eggs successfully hatch at between 16.6–28.5°C (62–83°F) and the larvae hatch out in anywhere from 46 days at 17.2°C (63°F) to 14 days at 28.5°C (83°F). After hatching, the larvae hang out in very shallow waters within the estuary. California killifish feed throughout the water column on various arthropods (e.g., gammarid amphipods, harpacticoid copepods, ostracods, crabs, shrimps, dipteran insects, and spiders), as well as polychaetes, clam siphons, snails, fish eggs, small fishes, detritus, and algae. The fish feed both day and night, although it is unclear whether feeding is heavier during one time of the day over another. Predators include California halibut, longjaw mudsuckers, staghorn sculpins, walleye surfperch, least terns, and light-footed clapper rails.

ORIGINS AND RELATIONSHIPS: An extinct species, *Fundulus eulepis*, is known from Miocene deposits (at least 5.3 million years ago) of eastern California. Based on genetic analysis, California killifish are most closely related *to F. lima*, a freshwater species found in central Baja California.

MISCELLANY: My associate Kevin Lafferty, along with Aaron Morris (1996), found that *Euhaplorchis californiensis*, a digenetic trematode worm, alters the behavior of the California killifish. During its life, each worm has three hosts: snails, fishes, and birds. Adult worms, that live in various estuarine birds, shed eggs that wind up on estuary mudflats. These eggs are then eaten by the horn snail, *Cerithidea californica*, where the eggs develop. Worm larvae leave the snail, swim about in the water, and enter a killifish, winding up in the fish's brain. And finally we come to the good part, because a brain-infected killifish is more likely to behave in ways that are liable to get themselves eaten by birds, the final host of the trematodes. The worms actually alter the normal behavior of these fish, causing them to come to the surface, while vibrating, jerking, and contorting; all ways of saying to your local cormorant: "I'm in show biz, eat me."

ORDER STEPHANOBERYCIFORMES

FAMILY MELAMPHAIDAE—Bigscales

Melamphaids are deep-water marine fishes (mostly bathypelagic) that are found throughout much of the world. There are five genera and 36 species, 17 of which live within our range. Bigscales are oviparous. In California, the family goes back at least to the Early Miocene (perhaps 30 million years ago).

Poromitra crassiceps
(Günther, 1878)
Crested Bigscale

ETYMOLOGY AND COLLOQUIAL NAME: Hmmm, lessee, Jordan and Evermann (1896) say that *Poromitra* is Greek for "pore" and "stomacher." And what, pray tell, is a stomacher? Well, the Oxford English Dictionary gives several definitions, all of them of little-used words, and all having to do with a waistcoat or other covering of the chest, often medicated or covered with jewels. Hart (1973) adds that it may also refer to a head-band. *Crassiceps* is Latin for "thick" and "head." They are called "kabutouo" in Japanese.

THE BASICS: Maximum Length: 189 cm (8 in) SL. The Ranges: Circumglobal; Japan to southern Bering Sea to Chile. 532 m (1,745 ft) to at least 4,000 m (13,120 ft) and perhaps as shallow as 282 m (925 ft); juveniles shallower, one record from 150 m (492 ft). Larvae: hatching length = < 3 mm, flexion length = 7.2–10.7 mm, transformation length = about 1.8–2.2 cm (0.7–0.9 in).

SALIENT CHARACTERS: Crested bigscales have a sculptured and crested head, stout body, and large, easily dislodged scales. They are black.

LIFE HISTORY: Crested bigscales are mesopelagic and bathypelagic. Off Southern California, adults usually come no shallower than about 400 m (1,312 ft), and do not seem to undergo daily vertical migrations. They live to about 9 years old and may only reproduce once, in their last year of life. Fossil *Poromitra* are known from the Late Oligocene (at least 23 million years ago).

R. HIBPSHMAN

ORDER BERYCIFORMES

FAMILY ANOPLOGASTRIDAE—Fangtooths

Fangtooths are deep-water marine fishes that are found throughout the world. There are only two species in one genus and one species within our range.

Anoplogaster cornuta
(Valenciennes, 1833)
Longhorn Fangtooth

Alone do you cast as you drift on your way,
A dark, brooding shade on the jubilant day.
　　　　　　　 – Storm-Cloud, Alexandr Pushkin

ETYMOLOGY AND COLLOQUIAL NAME: *Anoplogaster* is Greek for "unarmed" and "belly" and *cornuta* is Latin for "horned." They are called "oni-kinme" in Japanese.

THE BASICS: Maximum Length: 16 cm (6 in) SL. The Ranges: Nearly circumglobal; northern Japan and Sea of Okhotsk; southern British Columbia to northern Chile (18°26'S). Adults at 75–4,992 m (246–16,378 ft), juveniles as shallow as 2 m (7 ft).

SALIENT CHARACTERS: An idiosyncratic species with 1) a head that looks like Gaia (after playing Fuzzy Duck with Bhuvaneshwari, Njord, Huixtocihuatl, and a nearly infinite amount of beer) went about hitting it with a ball-peen hammer, 2) a cavernous mouth, and 3) large, sleek teeth. The adults are brown to black. Juveniles are light gray.

LIFE HISTORY: Not much to say here. Juveniles start off in relatively shallow waters and descend as they mature. They become adults at about 8 cm (3 in) SL and eat crustaceans and fishes.

"For it's only when dreaming that I see you gleaming down in the dark, deep…" Farewell to the Gold, Paul Metsers

ORDER GASTEROSTEIFORMES

FAMILY AULORHYNCHIDAE—Tubesnouts

The tubesnouts, as cute a group of fishes are ever was eaten by a barred sand bass, are nearshore marine fish found only in the North Pacific. There are only two genera, each with its special species. Tubesnouts are oviparous.

Aulorhynchus flavidus
Gill, 1861
Tubesnout

A nearshore species that is pencil-shaped, needle-nosed, small-spined, and other words that can be hyphenated.

ETYMOLOGY: *Aulorhynchus* comes from the Greek for "tube" and "snout" and *flavidus* is Latin for "yellow."

THE BASICS: Maximum Length: 18.8 cm (7 in) TL. Maximum Weight: 13.4 gr (0.5 oz). The Ranges: Pavlof Bay (southwest Alaska Peninsula) and Kodiak Island to Punta Rocosa (central Baja California). Abundant from at least Prince William Sound (Gulf of Alaska) to northern Baja California. Surface to at least 37 m (130 ft), typically in 20 m (66 ft) or less. Eggs have been described as either 1.4 by 1.2 mm, or about 2 mm in diameter. Larvae: hatching length = about 5.5–8 mm. Length-weight parameters (TL, mm, gr): (sexes combined) $W = 0.0000001622L^{3.43}$ (Bayer 1980).

SALIENT CHARACTERS: The well-named tubesnouts are rigid, needle-like fish with tubular mouths. You see them in brown, green, or bluish on back (sometimes with white flecking and dark barring), silvery sides and belly. Breeding males have blue spots, blue snouts, and red pelvic fins.

Tubesnout eggs balance on an algal float.

JAN KOCIAN

SCOTT GIETLER

LIFE HISTORY: Tubesnouts are schooling fishes that tend to live in the midwaters of heavily vegetated (like eelgrass and kelp), sometimes rocky, nearshore waters, although they will also school well away from shelter. They are found along the open coast, in bays, and estuaries. Although you often see them in small schools of up to maybe 100 individuals, schools of 2,000 fish have been observed. One school off Santa Rosa Island was estimated to be 0.4 km (0.3 mi) long and extended from depths of 9–21 m (30–70 ft). Adults tend to occupy a wider depth range than do juveniles. In Puget Sound, they reportedly move into surface waters at night. Strangely, given what we thought we knew of its habitat preferences, Russian researchers report commonly taking these more than 322 km (200 mi) from the Central and Southern California coast. Tubesnouts tend to be found in more inshore and shallow waters to the north and some may move offshore a bit during the winter. They are found in waters at least as cold as 1.4°C (35°F). In Southern California, young tubesnouts may school with señoritas.

Tubesnouts live to at least 9 years old and probably mature when less than 1 year old. When you add up all the months that various researchers have found tubesnout nests, it looks like they (the tubesnouts, not just the researchers) spawn throughout the year. Females lay eggs on vegetation (in egg masses 1.3–3.3 cm, 0.5–1.3 in, in diameter, and containing 150–600 eggs) and, writes Limbaugh (1955) who found nests in 5–37 m (17–120 ft) of water, the male: "Binds seaweed together with a very thin thread which is extruded from the urogenital region. The seaweed chosen is often new growth of the giant kelp. The eggs are deposited around the seaweed by the females and are closely guarded by the male." The bit about laying eggs on new plant growth (although not necessarily giant kelp) and the guarding male has been observed by others, although the thing about the extruded thread has not. But wait! Jan Kocian writes me that he has recently been observing tubesnout nests in Puget Sound and that, indeed "the eggs seem to be found only on the bull kelp floats, and then only on the young plants which do not reach to or are no where near close to the surface." Well, that matches what others have seen, but then Jan goes on to observe: "The guarding I have read about in other accounts was not a norm at all here at Keystone. Most of the egg clusters are unattended." In checking dozens of egg nests, Jan observed only two tubesnouts anywhere near eggs. Proving, once again, that Science does not necessarily March On. Rather, sometimes it kind of wobbles like a Lindy Hop dancer doing the Suzie Q (and yes, that is one of the more esoteric references in a book filled with same). Jeff Marliave (1976), who tends to have interesting theories about almost everything, noted that fish spawning on "fragile plant material may have evolved not only so that egg masses would break free easily, but also in order that some plant material would remain with the egg mass." This would allow dispersal of eggs. Males often guard clutches from as many as six females. All of the eggs from one clutch are the same color, but that color varies between females and ranges from pale brown through reddish-amber. Eggs become pale yellow or greenish-yellow with development and take 10 days–6 weeks to hatch. Tubesnout larvae have an extremely brief planktonic stage, maybe 30 minutes long. The larvae then form schools near the bottom, in quiet nearshore waters, around rocks and vegetation. Tubesnouts feed throughout the water column on a variety of small crustaceans (e.g., calanoid and harpacticoid copepods, gammarid amphipods, cladocerans, and mysid shrimps), polychaetes, and fish larvae. They are eaten by barred sand bass, California scorpionfish, cabezons, California halibut, kelp bass, staghorn sculpins, widow rockfish, gulls, and Steller sea lions. Barred sand bass eat their eggs.

FISHERY: Tubesnouts are a very rare catch in sundry recreational fisheries.

ORIGINS: Fish in the genus *Aulorhynchus* may have lived as long ago as the Eocene (34 million years ago).

DIANE O'LEARY

FAMILY GASTEROSTEIDAE—Sticklebacks

Sticklebacks are small fishes found in marine, estuarine, and freshwater in the Northern Hemisphere. From a taxonomic standpoint, this is a nasty, nasty group of fishes, as several of these species (threespine and ninespine sticklebacks come to mind) exhibit a breathtaking range of physical characters. Currently, researchers seem to be in a "lumper" mood and thus only five genera and eight species are recognized. Two species live within our range.

Gasterosteus aculeatus

Linnaeus, 1758

Threespine Stickleback

RICHARD BELL

ETYMOLOGY AND COLLOQUIAL NAME: *Gasterosteus* means "belly" and "bone" in Greek (for the bony belly plate) and *aculeatus* means "spined" in Latin. They are called "itoyo" in Japanese.

THE BASICS: Maximum Length: 10.2 cm (4 in) TL. The Ranges: In the ocean, North Atlantic, Arctic Europe, Asia, and North Pacific. In the North Pacific from the Korean Peninsula to Seas of Japan and Okhotsk, and to the Bering, Chukchi, and Beaufort seas, and Gulf of Alaska to Monterey Bay. In freshwater, they live as far south as Rio Rosario (northern Baja California). Sticklebacks are abundant from the Sea of Japan to about the Kotzebue area (southern Chukchi Sea), and southward to Rio Rosario. Intertidal and surface to about 27 m (90 ft). Eggs: 1–2 mm. Larvae: length at hatching = 4.2–5.5 mm. Length-weight parameters (SL, cm, gr): (sexes combined) $W = 0.01L^{3.61}$ (Ruiz-Campos et al. 2006).

SALIENT CHARACTERS: These small fish have three isolated spines before the single, soft-rayed dorsal fin. While threespines are often totally or partially covered with bony plates, there are populations composed of naked ones. During the nonbreeding season, threespines tend to be drably colored, with a dark dorsal area, vague dark bars on the flanks, and lighter belly. During the spawning season, males usually develop red throats, belly, and sometimes flanks. On the other hand, the males of some populations in California, Washington, and the Queen Charlotte Islands (British Columbia), turn black during the breeding season. In at least some populations, the degree of redness in the males correlates with the amounts of carotenoids in their diet.

LIFE HISTORY: Gee, I would not even attempt to claim that this discussion covers all the coolness that is the threespine stickleback. For that you should turn to Bell (1976), Wooton (1976), Moyle (2002), and Östlund-Nilsson et al. (2007). But, just to give you a little *forshpeis*, as my mother would say, a little appetizer, here are some basic life history details.

Way back in the Miocene (13 million years or more), threespines were originally a marine fish that today come in three flavors: freshwater, anadromous (spending most of their lives in salt water), and strictly marine. Among populations, there is just a ton of morphological variation (often in such things as the number of, or even presence of, bony plates on the sides), perhaps caused by marine fish repeatedly entering various freshwaters and becoming somewhat genetically isolated. For whatever reason, this has led perfectly sincere taxonomists to create a flock of species. At the height of the madness, back in the 19th century, as many as 30 species were thought to exist. Well, all of that is in the faintly embarrassing past and today dedicated sticklebackers tend to view *G. aculeatus* as a "superspecies," formed of many populations with a variety of different morphological, color, and behavioral characteristics.

Threespine sticklebacks are fish that usually, except for the breeding season, spend their lives in schools. For the anadromous and marine forms, both juveniles and adults are often found in the intertidal zone or in the shallow subtidal, among eelgrass, kelp, and other plants, as well as around rocks and over mudflats or sand. Although they spend much of their time resting on, or hovering just over, the bottom, juvenile and adult sticklebacks also occupy midwaters and seeing them at the surface is not uncommon. While fish occupying marine waters more usually live very near the coast, threespines have been captured as much as 805 km (500 mi) offshore. Stickleback movements in marine waters are poorly understood; at least some fish migrate in the fall into coastal waters to overwinter, although others may overwinter in deep water. Surveys in Puget Sound imply that both juveniles and adults can rise into, and inhabit, surface waters at night.

Spawning occurs, depending on stickleback flavor, all the way from freshwater lakes to marine tide pools. Some watersheds harbor both anadromous and strictly freshwater populations. During breeding season in the Little Campbell River of British Columbia, for instance, freshwater sticklebacks live mostly in the upper parts, with the anadromous form in the lower parts. As breeding season approaches, mature males leave their schools (small mature ones tend to leave first) and set up territories, where they create nests. A nest usually starts as a little pit or tunnel (maybe a few inches long) excavated in the sediment (the digging is done by mouth) and often located in sheltered areas near the roots of a water plant. Once the initial excavation is complete, the male then carries over a variety of nesting materials (e.g., bits of plants) with which he covers the pit and forms something of a sphere with a tunnel running through it. Males will often try to find shiny, brightly colored bits of stuff to use for their nests and red-colored material is a favorite. The male glues all this together with a sticky, antimicrobial secretion called *spiggin* (after *spigg*, the Swedish name for the threespine stickleback) formed in his kidneys. Spiggin puts me to mind of every product at Ikea, all with names like the Klubbo coffee table, Knubbig table lamp, Krabb and Figgjo mirrors, and need we add, the Luftig Hoo exhaust hood. Yes, it's the Spiggin napkin cozy, perfect for those frosty winter days when only a cozy napkin will do.

The nest now being complete (in Central California it takes 1.5–4 hours), it's time to entice a female to enter and lay some eggs, and this the male does with a courtship dance (see Östund-Nilsson 2007). Eggs laid, the female is unceremoniously kicked out of the nest and the male spends the next week, or three, fanning and guarding the eggs against both predators and other males and females. Well, he spends much of the time fanning and guarding, because sometimes, perhaps out of ennui, who knows, males will also raid other nests and there will fertilize, steal, or eat eggs and take additional nest material. A male tends one egg batch at a time and after the eggs hatch, he entices another female, thus collecting up to 20 batches per season.

Threespines live to at least 3.5 years, although maximum life spans vary with area and can be as little as one year. Growth rates also vary with area. Some fish mature after 1–2 years. Females are batch spawners, laying 50–200 eggs at a time, with overall fecundity ranging from 65–1,300 eggs. In Alaska, females spawn every 2–8 days, although elsewhere there may be 10 days between spawnings. Ovulation, occurring mostly during morning hours, may occur as much as 48 hours before spawning. Spawning usually occurs in the spring and summer, but Ruiz-Campos et al. (2000) reported ripe adults from November–April in northern Baja California. The eggs take 5–20 days to hatch. Threespine sticklebacks feed throughout the water column, mostly on small crustaceans (e.g., copepods, amphipods, euphausiids, and mysid shrimps) and also on polychaetes, larvaceans, insects, fish eggs, and the occasional small fish. Sticklebacks are eaten by a fairly diverse crowd of fishes, birds (in particular), and mammals. Predators include, but are not limited to, copper rockfish, other threespine sticklebacks, Arctic smelt, steelhead, striped bass, various skates, white sturgeons, mergansers, guillemots, cormorants, shearwaters, murres, herons, grebes, minks, river otters, northern fur seals, harbor seals, and three species of whales.

FISHERY: Stickleback remains are fairly common in the middens of some Native Americans (for instance those around Elkhorn Slough, Central California). Recreational anglers only rarely catch them.

ORIGINS: Sticklebacks likely evolved during the Miocene and thus far the earliest example is from marine deposits of the Miocene (13–13.3 million years ago) in California. Fragmentary fossils of what may be threespines have been found in somewhat older strata (16 million years old), but they are too funky to identify with complete certainty.

REMARKS: And from the Mind-Meld Department: *Schistocephalus solidus* is a tapeworm. Adults of *S. solidus* live in the digestive tract of birds and one of the larval stages lives in sticklebacks. The only way the larvae can become an adult is if its intermediate host (the stickleback) is eaten by a bird. It turns out that, compared to uninfected fish, sticklebacks infected with the larval tapeworm tend to live in shallower waters, shelter and school less, and more often feed in the presence of potential predators. In other words, they tend to engage is "riskier" behavior, which makes them more likely to get eaten.

YES WE CAN

So, Zbinden et al. (2003) had some males in an aquarium and these males were just about to fertilize some eggs. And just before that happened, these researchers presented these males with computer images of potential competitor males, so the test males thought that someone was about to horn in on the action. And what happened then? It turns out that these freaked-out males were able to increase the number of sperm they ejaculated compared to males that were not shown pictures of competing males. Do you just love natural selection, or what?

FAMILY SYNGNATHIDAE—Pipefishes and Seahorses

The syngnathiids are marine, estuarine, and freshwater fishes found throughout the world. There are 52 genera and about 233 species; eight pipefish species and one species of seahorse inhabit our waters. All members of this family are oviparous and, after a stylish courtship ritual, females transfer unfertilized eggs to male brooding pouches, or to areas located under the tails or abdomens. Males fertilize these eggs and lug them around until the eggs hatch. The earliest known *Syngnathus* are apparently from the Eocene (about 50 million years ago) of the famous Monte Bolca formation of Italy. Two species, *S. emeritus* and *S. avus*, have been described from the Upper Miocene (at least 5.3 million years ago) of California. Extensive keys and descriptions to the eastern Pacific species are found in Fritzsche (1980).

Hippocampus ingens
Girard, 1858
Pacific Seahorse

SCOTT GIETLER

ETYMOLOGY: *Hippocampus* comes from the Greek word for "seahorse" (derived from the words for "horse" and a type of sea monster) and *ingens* means "gigantic" in Latin.

THE BASICS: Maximum Length: 30.5 cm (12 in) TL. The Ranges: Point Conception (Southern California) to Chile, including the Gulf of California. While they are likely common from about central Baja California southwards, at least periodically there is a little colony of them in San Diego and Mission bays. There is an old, and seemingly poorly documented, record from San Francisco Bay. 1–107 m (3–351 ft). Larvae are about 7 mm long when released. Length-weight parameters (TL, cm, gr): (females) $W = 0.05748L^{2.1308}$; (males) $W = 0.02937L^{2.3286}$ (Ortega-Salas and Reyes-Bustamante 2006).

SALIENT CHARACTERS: I don't know—they look like seahorses. Check out Lourie et al. (1999) if you want to tell the various species apart. Pacific seahorses can be red, yellow, or green, with black or brown mottling, small white or dark spots, and white bands.

LIFE HISTORY: Pacific seahorses live in calm, nearshore waters, both over reefs and among such vegetation as eelgrass and brown algae. Males have elaborate courtship displays involving bobbing, weaving, and other fancy stuff. Scott Gietler has seen males release young in Southern California waters.

In captivity, Pacifics mature at 10–12 months. In a study in Bahia Magdalena (southern Baja California) seahorse larvae were captured in February, May, July, and November. Males reportedly carry 400–1,600 young and these develop for 14–15 days. The young are 1 cm at birth. Pacific seahorses feed on small epibenthic crustaceans. They are eaten by such predators as porcupinefish, sailfish, and yellowfin and bluefin tunas.

FISHERY: Pacific seahorses are of some economic importance as a dried ornament and are apparently shipped to China in the medical trade. Certainly, you can see just a whole bunch of dried seahorses of various kinds in Chinese herbal shops.

ORIGINS AND RELATIONSHIPS: There are just not many seahorses in the fossil record, although it is likely they evolved perhaps 20 million years ago. Pacific seahorses are most closely related to the Atlantic species *Hippocampus reidi* and *H. algiricus*.

REMARKS: This is the only species of seahorse found within our range. Kristen Darrow, observing this species at the Cabrillo Marine Aquarium, reports that when the lights are turned on in the morning, Pacific seahorses ritualistically link up in pairs to greet each other. She also notes that individuals can quickly change color.

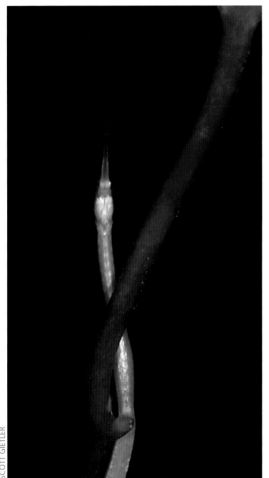

I can't tell one pipefish species from another, so here are a bunch of pictures.

Syngnathus leptorhynchus
Girard, 1854

Bay Pipefish

ETYMOLOGY: *Syngnathus* means "together" and "jaw" in Greek and *leptorhynchus* means "slender" and "snout" in Greek.
THE BASICS: Maximum Length: 38.5 cm (15 in) TL. The Ranges: Prince William Sound (northern Gulf of Alaska) to Bahia Santa Maria (southern Baja California). They are very abundant from Prince William Sound to Bahia San Quintin (northern Baja California). Intertidal to 18.3 m (60 ft), abundant down to 18.3 m. Eggs: 1–1.5 mm. Larvae: hatching length = 4.5–5 mm. Length-weight parameters (SL, mm, gr): (sexes combined) W = 0.0000000329L$^{3.955}$ (Mahan 1988).

SALIENT CHARACTERS: Differentiating the various pipefish species involves such abstrusities as the number of rings on the trunk. For these, Fritzsche (1980) and Eschmeyer and Herald (1983) are the places to go. Bay pipefish come in at least 14 color variants.

LIFE HISTORY: Young-of-the-year recruit to nearshore waters at lengths at least as small as 1.5 cm (0.6 in) SL. All life stages are found mostly in bays and estuaries (occasionally in freshwater) and usually around aquatic plants. Eelgrass seems to be a particular favorite, although they will not disdain kelp and filamentous algae. They also occasionally swim over gravel, sandy, or muddy bottoms. These are pretty tough little fish, able to withstand everything from freshwater to marine conditions, and temperatures as low as at least 4.7°C (40.5°F). At least in Puget Sound, they often seem to swim in near-surface waters at night. Genetic analysis imply that fish off San Diego seem to be somewhat isolated from populations off Oregon, Washington, and Alaska. However, this isolation occurred quite recently. Even more interestingly, within Barkley Sound (British Columbia) there appears to be two genetic subpopulations (within a distance of 3.8 km). Bay pipefish may remain in the same eelgrass bed for at least two months at a time.

Many, or perhaps most, bay pipefish live only one year, but some may live as long as two. Fritzsche (1980) found a fully mature male that was 11.4 cm (5 in) SL, the smallest mature fish for which I can find a record. The smallest mature male and female in Mahan's (1988) study were about 16 cm (6 in) SL. Bay pipefish (particularly those in relatively warm waters) likely spawn throughout the year, although the peak period is probably in the spring and summer. Fish in more northerly areas (e.g., Alaska and British Columbia) probably have a more constrained spawning season. Females produce between 79–721 eggs and males may simultaneously carry eggs from as many as three females. In one laboratory study, the eggs hatched in from 39–50 days. Bay pipefish eat small crustaceans (e.g., isopods, gammarid amphipods, copepods, and small shrimps), and fish larvae. Predators include brown smoothhounds, spotted sand bass, and elegant terns.

RELATIONSHIPS: Bay pipefish may be most closely related to barcheek pipefish (*Syngnathus exilis*).

REMARKS: At least in San Diego Bay, male bay pipefish hybridize (carry the fertilized eggs of) female barred pipefish.

OTHER SPECIES

Syngnathus auliscus
(Swain, 1882)
Barred Pipefish

Barred pipefish grow to 19 cm (8 in) TL and are found from the Santa Barbara Channel (Southern California) to Puerto Pizarro (Peru), including in the Gulf of California. They appear to be at least occasionally common as far north as about Newport Bay (Southern California). This is a fish of intertidal and shallow inshore bays and lagoons, to depths of 20 m (66 ft). They are usually found amid such vegetation as eelgrass, mangroves, and sargassum. In Southern California, they appear to be spring–fall spawners. Males simultaneously carry eggs from as many as three females. Female barred pipefish will, on occasion, put their eggs in the pouches of male bay pipefish. These eggs are duly fertilized, but the fate of hybrid offspring is unknown. Length-weight parameters (SL, cm, gr): (sexes combined) $W = 0.0002L^{3.29}$ (Gonzalez-Acosta et al. 2004).

Syngnathus californiensis
Storer, 1845
Kelp Pipefish

Kelp pipefish reach a total length of 49.5 cm (20 in) TL. They are found from Bodega Bay (Northern California) to Bahia Santa Maria (southern Baja California) from the intertidal to 15 m (48 ft), commonly down to at least 12.1 m (40 ft). True to their name, kelp pipefish are very abundant in the canopy and mid-depths of giant kelp beds. They are also found in eelgrass, surfgrass, and around drifting kelp mats. While they are most abundant on the outer coast, this species is also a habitué of bays, and even the occasional estuary. They spawn from at last June–October. Kelp pipefish eat mostly mysid and other shrimps, but also slurp down the occasional gammarid and caprellid amphipods. Predators include blue sharks, kelp bass, kelp rockfish, gulls, and northern fur seals. Eggs: 1.1–1.3 mm. Larvae: 2.1 cm when recently released. Length-weight parameters (SL, mm, gr): (sexes combined) $W = 0.00000000163L^{3.955}$ (Quast 1968a).

ORDER SCORPAENIFORMES

FAMILY SCORPAENIDAE—Rockfishes or Scorpionfishes

And thus we come, in our stately progress through the fishes of the Pacific Coast, to the Scorpaenidae. This is a swashbuckling assemblage of fishes, mostly marine (a few freshwater), that are found over much of the globe. There are at least 56 genera and at least 421 species. Within our range, 85 species (including two undescribed rockfishes) dwell. Some species (like the scorpionfishes and thornyheads) are oviparous, and some (like the rockfishes) are viviparous. The family Scorpaenidae perhaps arose during the Late Paleocene or Early Eocene (about 55 million years ago). In California, fossil rockfishes are known from later Miocene deposits of about 7.6–8.6 million years ago.

Most or perhaps all members of this family harbor venomous spines. The venom ranges from the truly horrific (e.g., stonefishes, genus *Synanceia*) to the bad (e.g., California scorpionfish), to the relatively benign (e.g., our friends the rockfishes, genus *Sebastes*). In the rockfishes, the venom is contained in tissue that lines grooves in the dorsal, anal, and pelvic spines (but not the spines on the cheeks or top of head). In some species, all dorsal, anal, and pelvic spines have this tissue, and in others only some spines do. It is unclear whether some rockfish stings hurt worse than others, although bocaccios are sometimes pointed to as a leading contender.

In this section, I give you just the deep-fried golden nuggets you will need to hold your own in any gabfest on rockfishes. In *The Rockfishes of the Northeast Pacific* (University of California Press, 2002), Mary Yoklavich, Lyman Thorsteinson, and I simply flog the rockfish thing. Anyone who is really, really into rockfishes should consult that tome. Shameless self-promotion, you say? Oh my, yes. Fischer et al. (1995) is a good source of information for the more tropical scorpaenids of the eastern Pacific.

Scorpaenidae or Not Scorpaenidae, That is the Question.

The rockfishes are in the family Scorpaenidae. I know, I know, Ishida (1994) put them in the family Sebastidae, but he was wrong. And the fact that so many of you have seen fit to slavishly follow his lead does you no credit. Why was he wrong? Well, if you look at the genetic relationships of the entire Scorpaeniformes order, as did Smith and Wheeler (2004), it is clear that many of the genera that Ishida scattered among a number of families, including *Dendrochirus* and *Pterois* (Scorpaenidae), *Sebastes* and *Sebastolobus* (Sebastidae), and *Setarches* (Setarchidae) are actually relatively closely related to one another. At the same time, other genera he thought were closely related to some of these, such as *Scorpaena* and *Iracundus* (he placed these in the Scorpaenidae) are actually not that closely related. So I say, what the hell, why don't we retain the rockfishes and thornyheads in the family Scorpaenidae?

THE ROCKFISH ANTHEM

(Try singing this to Robert Burns'
Is There For Honest Poverty)

Oh here's to you who live alone,
And here's to you who school,
And here's to you who have a home,
Though that is not a rule.

Oh rockfish, this is our wish,
We hold your banner high,
Though they might eat you
Raw or steamed, or even deep fried.

Scorpaena guttata
(Girard, 1854)
California Scorpionfish

ETYMOLOGY AND COLLOQUIAL NAMES: *Scorpaena* comes from the Ancient Greek word for the scorpionfishes and *guttata* is Latin for "speckled." Although the official name is California scorpionfish, most fishermen call them "sculpins." Back in the 19th century, they were called "scorpenes" by Italian fishermen in California. In Mexico, fishermen call them "lupón."

THE BASICS: Maximum Length: 47 cm (19 in) SL. Maximum Weight: 2 kg (4.4 lb). The Ranges: Santa Cruz (Central California) to the Gulf of California. This species is abundant from the Santa Barbara Channel to Todos Santos (southern Baja California). Tide pools (rarely) to 183 m (600 ft), typically in about 10–85 m (33–279 ft). Eggs: 1.2 x 1.2–1.3 mm. Larvae: hatching length = 1.9–2 mm, flexion length = 4.5–5.7 mm, transformation length = greater than 1.3 cm (0.5 in). Von Bertalanffy parameters (TL, cm): (females) L_∞ = 44.3, k = 0.13, t_0 = -1.9; (males) L_∞ = 36.3, k = 0.12, t_0 = -3.86 (Love et al. 1987). Length-weight parameters (TL, cm, gr): (females) W = $0.0196L^{3.0102}$; (males) W = $0.0205L^{3.0045}$ (Love et al. 1987).

SALIENT CHARACTERS: California scorpionfish are spiny, thick-bodied fish, with lots of spines and flaps on the head, and large flexible fins. Their colors are extremely variable, ranging from reds, oranges, browns, to lavenders, in blotches and saddles, all often covered in dark brown spots.

LIFE HISTORY: Young-of-the-year fish (at least as small as 1.1 cm, 0.4 in, SL) recruit to bottom drift algae, sand dollar beds, and other low relief in nearshore waters. Both older juveniles and adults are common on hard and mixed hard-soft bottoms, often around kelp, eelgrass, sand dollar beds, and on the shell mounds around oil platforms. I have, on a number of occasions, observed them out on sand and mud (even occasionally semi-buried). Although they tend to hang near or lie on the bottom during the day, they can range well up in the water column, even to surface waters, at night. A tagging study I conducted demonstrated that this species moves around a bit. Certainly some fish living in Southern California waters move throughout this area. California scorpionfish spawn in large aggregations over discrete spawning grounds, grounds that some individuals return to year after year. These grounds are in at least 18 to at least 110 m (60–360 ft), often over mixed soft and hard substrate. Known spawning sites include near Anacapa Island, in Santa Monica Bay, off Long Beach, Dana Point, Islas Las Coronados, and Cortes Bank (John Ugoretz saw this last one). On one of our manned submersible fish surveys, Merit McCrea observed just an immense number of scorpionfish around the bottom of an oil platform off Long Beach (Southern California). Here, scorpionfish were so crammed as to be virtually on top of one another.

Taylor (1963) observed California scorpionfish as they spawned in an aquarium over a number of days during June of 1962. He wrote that during this period the back of the head and dorsal area of a male became dark while many females turned pale. When releasing eggs, females "darted along the bottom, swooped upward, ejected a single egg mass, and returned to the bottom...The egg masses rose directly to the tank surface, unfolding quickly into characteristic hollow bilobed structures. During the spawning one or more males were suddenly on the scene swooping up with the female."

Females live to at least 21 years old and males to at least 15 years old. Females grow larger than males. A few fish of both sexes mature at as small as 14 cm (6 in) TL (one year old), 50% of fish mature at 17–18 cm (7 in) (2 years), and all at 22 cm (9 in) (4 years). This species is oviparous, spawning occurs from at least May–August and larvae are pelagic. California scorpionfish eat lots of small crustaceans (particularly crabs, but also shrimps, caprellid amphipods, and isopods), octopuses, squids, and fishes. I have occasionally found them with pebbles in their stomachs. While they are often nocturnal,

---

BUT I WILL WEAR MY HEART UPON MY SLEEVE FOR DAWS TO PECK AT

Go sit in the back seat, Othello. In 2009, lawyer Marc Dreier pleaded guilty to eight counts involving various forms of securities fraud. Regarding his culinary habits, the *Wall Street Journal* quoted the events manager of the sushi restaurant Tengu: "Dreier 'liked exotic things,' she added, especially live California scorpion fish...He would eat one 'on a stick, with its heart still beating.'"

scorpionfish will also feed during daylight hours. Predation on scorpionfish, particularly larger individuals, is likely to be quite low, although one individual was found in the gut of a leopard shark.

FISHERY: In the 19th century, this was a fairly important commercial species, particularly for fishermen plying Santa Catalina waters (and selling their fishes in Los Angeles). On the other hand, Eigenmann (1892) noted that the species was not popular in San Diego because of its appearance and because of the erroneous rumor that its head spines were poisonous. California scorpionfish remained a fairly important commercial species throughout the 20th century; they were mostly caught by a few fishermen targeting summer spawning aggregations and were also taken as a bycatch in the rockfish fisheries. They were an early part of the live fish fishery that took Southern California by storm in the 1980s and remain popular in some Asian markets and restaurants. On most days you can see them for sale in the Mercado Negro in Ensenada (northern Baja California).

A herd o' scorpionfish, probably a spawning aggregation, on the shell mound around Platform Edith, Southern California.

With the decline in abundance of a number of rockfish species and more stringent recreational fishing regulations, there has been a large increase in the California scorpionfish catch. They are most often taken by boat fishermen, but fairly large numbers are caught from piers, jetties, and rocky shorelines.

REMARKS: The sharp spines on the dorsal, anal, and pelvic fins are quite venomous (however, the head spines, while quite sharp, are not). Getting stung by a California scorpionfish is not fun, unless you are into pain. Stings from this fish are relatively common; fishermen and others who routinely handle this species are most likely to get nailed. Following the puncture, there is rapid pain and the pain tends to radiate out from the puncture site. All sorts of associated nastiness, including nausea, weakness, and headaches may accompany the pain, which often lasts for a number of hours. In most spinings, while there may be swelling and tenderness for a few days, no more severe effects will occur. However, in a few instances, hospitalization is necessary. Treating the wound with hot water will often give a great deal of relief.

A DECKHAND "FESTER" STORY

When I was a kid in 1950s and 1960s, I lived in the Southern California seacoast town of Santa Monica. I had no life other than fishing and lived much of every summer and every weekend on the sportfishing partyboats that ran from the Santa Monica Pier. I occasionally helped out on the boats and, in contravention of the law, sold the fishes I caught in order to pay for more trips. Later, during my college years, part of my doctoral work involved surveying what fishes were caught on a partyboat berthed in Santa Barbara. So, I am confident that I have a fairly accurate picture of the people, particularly the deckhands, who work on these vessels.

Every deckhand I have ever met has a storehouse of what I call "fester" stories. These usually involve some sort of awful accident that occurred while working on a partyboat and usually involve hooks caught in various body parts or fish spines breaking off in these same parts. Almost inevitably, the wound becomes infected, swells up, and festers. Rarely does the deckhand, poorly paid and uninsured, seek medical help. Rather, determined not to miss a day of work, the suppurating wound is cut open with a filleting knife and allowed to drain, while the gallant deckhand keeps on gaffing fish and untangling lines.

Dr. Findlay Russell is one of the world's authorities on venomous animals and here is his contribution to this folk art, with a story of his experiences with California scorpionfish (Russell 1965): "As a 'bait boy' on the Billings [sportfishing] Barge off Ocean Park, California during the 1930s, I received numerous stings from this fish. I recall that some of them were so painful that they caused me to vomit and on several occasions precipitate episodes of migraine. My fingers were often swollen for several days following an envenomation. I do not recall that I ever became immune to the pain produced by the venom, even though I suspect I must have been stung at least twenty times over a 4-year period.

On some days, two of us cleaned as many as seventy-five of these fish during a single afternoon, and at least one person was stung every day or so while handling, or mishandling, *Scorpaena guttata*. The pain following the stinging of this fish is more severe than that experienced following a stinging by *Urolophus halleri* [now *Urobatis halleri*, round stingray] or *Trachinus vipera* [weeverfish]. I do not think it is as painful as that produced by *Pterois* [lionfish], although on this point I cannot speak from experience."

This is an excellent, and really quite subtle, fester story. Not only did young Russell actually throw up after being stung, he also got a migraine, and his fingers were swollen for days after. However, note that despite these really awful reactions, he apparently just kept on working.

Sebastes

STUFF ABOUT ROCKFISHES THAT EITHER I DON'T WANT TO REPEAT OVER AND OVER OR THAT DIDN'T FIT ANYWHERE ELSE

HOW MANY SPECIES ARE THERE? Obviously there are a lot of rockfish species and they seem to be speciating at a frightening rate. This leads to extremely similar-appearing species that, while the differences are obvious to the fishes, escape the notice of biologists. This is a situation that biologists just dread. Here we were, happily thinking that there was a species called the "rougheye rockfish," when all this time the "rougheye rockfish" were thinking there were "rougheye" rockfish and "blackspotted" rockfish. So, all of that lovely information that researchers acquired over the years on one species is likely an amalgam of data on two species. So, right now, your tax dollars are going to play catch up and figure out what these two species are really doing.

ABOUT NAMES. Just so I don't have to repeat this in the etymology of each species, *Sebastes* means "magnificent" in Greek. In 1822, Father Jose Señán, writing to his superiors from his mission in Ventura (Southern California) called red rockfishes "chimuya," the oldest reference I can find to a local name. In the 1850s, San Francisco fishermen called them both "rock fish" and "rock cod," so these names also go way back.

REPRODUCTION. As long ago as Jordan (1892), some researchers held that rockfishes were viviparous. Over the years this notion changed to rockfishes being ovoviviparous (internal fertilization but the mother supplied no nutrients, other than the yolks, to the young). It was not until the advent of George Boehlert and Mary Yoklavich (first in Boehlert and Yoklavich, 1984) that it was shown that, indeed, rockfishes have both internal fertilization and a transfer of nutrients from mother to embryos in utero, and hence that these fishes are viviparous. John Hyde and company (2008) provided evidence that female rockfishes of a number of species may mate successfully with more than one male per season, and thus embryos within a brood may have more than one father. In a number of papers, Steve Berkeley, Sue Sogard and colleagues, have shown that larger female rockfishes produce larvae that are better able to withstand the rigors of a pelagic existence. So, don't kill all the big ones, kids.

SOUND PRODUCTION. It is likely that most or perhaps all rockfishes produce sounds; certainly they all have the apparatus (muscles attached to the swim bladder) to do it. Although this research is in its infancy, these sounds (and there are a number of them, bocaccios produce three discrete kinds) are used at least in aggressive interactions and, perhaps, as chick and dude attractors.

USE BY INDIGENOUS PEOPLES. Although it is clear that both Native Americans and First Nation peoples heavily utilized rockfishes, I do not discuss their use under each species. This is because I am not convinced that midden muckers can always differentiate rockfish species based on otoliths, vertebra, and other remains. Hey, no offense meant, I just think it's too difficult. Russel Barsh once told me that when the indigenous folks in Puget Sound got sick of eating sockeye salmon, they might have gone out and caught a few rockfishes "for lunch." Turek et al. (2009) report that rockfishes, particularly yelloweyes, were important foods for the Tlingit of the Sitka area during the winter and spring, when halibut were not available. They go on to note that the indigenous folks at Nanwalek and Port Graham (Gulf of Alaska) would walk the beaches after storms, picking up fishes tossed on shore by large swells.

ECOLOGICAL IMPORTANCE. Pelagic juvenile rockfishes are very important to a number of species of fishes, sea birds, and marine mammals. When these young fishes are not abundant, a lot of young birds die of malnutrition.

WHAT'S WITH THOSE BLACK BLOTCHES ON THEIR SKINS? These are abnormal growths (technically hyperplastic and neoplastic lesions) of melanophores, the black skin color cells. While they are found in many rockfish species, they seem to be particularly common in bocaccio, chilipepper, olive, widow, and yellowtail rockfishes. It is not clear if this condition is damaging to the fish. Yellowtail rockfish also develop the lesions in the cells controlling yellow and red. Fish with these abnormalities are still OK to eat.

> ## THE ROCKFISH AFFIRMATION
> "If Nature didn't like me, she would not have given me a protrusible upper jaw."

Sebastes alutus
(Gilbert, 1890)
Pacific Ocean Perch

ETYMOLOGY AND COLLOQUIAL NAME: *Alutus* is Greek for "unwashed," referring to the speckled coloration. If you are in with the in crowd, you call them "POP." "Arasuka-menuke" is the Japanese name.

THE BASICS: Maximum Length: 75 cm (30 in) FL. Maximum Weight: 2.7 kg (5.9 lb). The Ranges: Southern Japan and Sea of Okhotsk to the Bering Sea (Navarin Canyon) and along the Aleutian Islands to Punta Blanca (29°08'N, 115°26'W) (central Baja Cali-

REBECCA REUTER, NOAA FISHERIES

fornia). They are most abundant in the northern Kurils and Kamchatka Peninsula, along the Aleutian Islands, in a few places in the southern Bering Sea, and southward to British Columbia, after which they slowly decline in abundance. Larvae and juveniles may drift into the Chukchi Sea. Near surface waters to 825 m (2,707 ft), and mostly in 100–400 m (328–1,312 ft). Von Bertalanffy parameters (FL, mm): (females) L_∞ = 414, k = 0.175, t_0 = 0.58; (males) L_∞ = 392, k = 0.19, t_0 = -0.62 (Malecha et al. 2007). Malecha et al. found significant differences in growth rates among a number of different sites in Alaskan waters. Length-weight parameters (TL, cm, gr): (sexes combined) W = $0.009L^{3.133}$ (Love et al. 2002).

SALIENT CHARACTERS: These are fairly elongated fish with a prominent, forward-thrusting lower jaw. Colors and markings are quite variable and range from pale, almost white to dark red, with a variety of darker saddles and dorsal patches.

LIFE HISTORY: Juveniles are found mostly in mixed sand and boulders and they really seem to like corals and sponges. Juveniles live mostly in perhaps 70 to at least 220 m (262–722 ft) (the smallest ones in the shallowest part of that range). As POP grow, they tend to move into deeper waters. Adults often live over soft seafloors that are covered in sea whips, as well as over boulders and cobbles, in waters between 2.6 and 11.1°C (37–52°F). Schools rise up off the bottom well into the midwater (to at least as high as 60 m, 197 ft), where they may contain both northern and dusky rockfishes. POP are variously reported to either stay near the bottom during the night and then ascend into the water column during the day or, alas, the reverse.

During summer and fall, males and females live together in relatively shallow waters. Following mating, females migrate into deeper waters (mostly on the continental slope) to give birth, and then return to join the males on the summering grounds. While there do not appear to be discrete populations in the Gulf of Alaska and Bering Sea, there is some genetic structure among fish in that region.

POP live to at least 104 years old. Females grow larger than males. Growth rates and size at maturity vary with area. Size at 50% maturity ranges from 22–27 cm (9–11 in) in the Bering Sea to 33–35 cm (13–14 in) off British Columbia and 4—10 years of age. Females release larvae from January–October, peaking in February–May, and larger females tend to release larvae earliest in the season. Females produce between 2,000–505,000 eggs and they may mate with as many as four males per season. POPs eat a lot of euphausiids. Indeed, in some locations, these crustaceans may form 90% of a fish's diet. Copepods, mysid shrimps, squids, and fishes can also be important, and shrimps, gammarid amphipods, arrow worms, and polychaetes are also consumed. Fishes are more important in the diets of larger individuals. One study found that smaller POPs fed most intensively in the spring. Feeding appears to be heaviest during daylight and early evening hours. Females do not seem to feed much during the parturition season. Predators include arrowtooth flounder, Chinook salmon, Pacific cod, Pacific halibut, sablefish, rhinoceros auklets, northern fur seals, and sperm whales. Albacore eat pelagic juveniles.

FISHERY: POPs are taken in subsistence fisheries along the Aleutians. Historically, in the 1960s, when Russian and Japanese trawlers took massive amounts, this was one of the largest fisheries in the Gulf of Alaska and off British Columbia. Even after foreign fishermen were excluded from territorial waters, fairly large numbers were caught between Northern California and the Bering Sea. Today, POP stocks in many locations are depleted, but substantial numbers are still taken in some areas. Recreational anglers only rarely catch them.

RELATIONSHIPS: POPs are most closely related to the Atlantic rockfishes, and more distantly related to such species as yellowmouths, darkblotcheds, and northerns. The separation between POPs (or its ancestor) and the Atlantic species seems to have occurred around 3 million years ago.

Sebastes atrovirens
(Jordan & Gilbert, 1880)
Kelp Rockfish

ETYMOLOGY AND COLLOQUIAL NAMES: *Atrovirens* is Latin for "black" and "green." "Garuppa" was used by fishermen of the 19th century and "sugar bass" is sometimes used today.

THE BASICS: Maximum Length: 42.5 cm (17 in) TL. The Ranges: Fort Bragg (Northern California) to Bahia San Carlos (29°36'N, 115°12'W), and Islas San Benito (28°19'N, 115°35'W) (central Baja California). Kelps start to poop out somewhere north of Point Reyes (Northern California). Barely subtidal to 82 m (269 ft), typically down to about 30 m (98 ft). Larvae: birth length = 4.4–4.9 mm, flexion length = begins at 6.1–6.9 mm and completed at about 8.6 mm. Von Bertalanffy parameters (SL, cm): (females) L_∞ = 285, k = 0.29, t_0 = -0.03; (males) L_∞ = 281.9, k = 0.3, t_0 = -0.01 (Romero 1988). Length-weight parameters (TL, cm, gr): (sexes combined) W = $0.0239L^{2.862}$ (Love et al. 2002).

SALIENT CHARACTERS: Kelps are moderately deep-bodied fish, with relatively large head spines, and large, diaphanous pectoral fins. They are often tan or brown, but you might see them in blackish, greenish, reddish, or even nearly white. Dark flecking on back and sides is the norm.

LIFE HISTORY: Young fish remain in the plankton for 2–3 months. Young-of-the-year recruit to kelp beds (mostly), but also to such structures as oil platforms, at lengths as small as around 2 cm (1 in) TL. Settlement may occur as early as April, although it is more likely to take place in the summer or early fall. After recruiting to the kelp canopy and forming kind of loose aggregations, juveniles slowly work their way down to subsurface stipes and by fall they are in bottom crevices. Larger juveniles and adults live throughout kelp beds, rocky reefs, and such human-made habitat as oil platforms and breakwaters. Although often seen as solitary individuals, kelps can ball up in groups of several hundred. Among the rockfishes, kelps seem to be among the least concerned about remaining upright, as you can see them lying sideways or even upside down, often with their lacy pectoral fins extended and lazily undulating in the current. When females are carrying larvae, they reportedly retire to caves and crevices. There appears to be little population structure between Santa Cruz (Central California) to Point Loma (Southern California). At least some kelp rockfish remain within circumscribed areas, as Brad Mongeau observed a black-faced one (named Mr. Splotch) living in the same Southern California boulder field for at least 3 years. In a study off Central California, home ranges averaged about 700 m² but ranged as large as 3,000 m² and home range size decreased with increasing depth.

Kelp rockfish live to least 25 years old. There appears to be conflicting data on size and age at maturity in Central California fish. In the first study, a few females matured at 15.8 cm (6 in, 3 years) SL, 50% at about 17 cm (7 in), and 100% at 23.3 cm (9 in, 6 years). In the second study, females matured at between about 21.8 cm (9 in, 5 years) TL and larger than 32 cm (13 in). In this study, a few males were mature at 24.6 cm (10 in) and the largest immature fish was 33.8 cm (13 in). Females produce between at least 10,000–340,000 eggs, may mate with 2 or more males in a season, and release their larvae between February–August (and all in one batch). Young-of-the-year kelp rockfish eat zooplankton. Larger fish eat these same prey, but also add fishes, along with shrimps, isopods, crabs, pelagic red crabs, euphausiids, and snails. Small kelp rockfish are eaten by young-of-the-year bocaccios and likely by other rockfishes.

FISHERY: Kelps are not particularly important to commercial fishermen in California (although they are landed in the live fish fishery), but they are frequently seen in the Mercado Negro fish market of Ensenada (northern Baja California). They are a common recreational catch, mostly taken from boats, but also from jetties and around a few piers. Because you can just about swim up to a kelp rockfish and give it a big hug, they are quite important in the sport diver catch.

RELATIONSHIPS: Genetic studies demonstrate that kelps are most closely related to black-and-yellow, copper, gopher, and quillback rockfishes.

MISCELLANY: For whatever it is worth, fish in the northern part of their range tend to have fewer tympanic head spines than those living to the south.

DAN RICHARDS

Sebastes auriculatus
Girard, 1854

Brown Rockfish

ETYMOLOGY AND COLLOQUIAL NAMES: *Auriculatus* is Latin for "eared" (for the black blotch on the operculum). "Bolinas" (for Bolinas, Northern California) is still widely used and "chocolate bass" is also commonly heard.

THE BASICS: Maximum Length: 56 cm (22 in) TL. Maximum Weight: 2.7 kg (5.9 lb). The Ranges: Prince William Sound (Gulf of Alaska) to Bahia San Hipolito (26°50'N, 113°55'W) (central Baja California). They are reasonably abundant from the southernmost part of southeastern Alaska to Puget Sound, and from Bodega Bay (Northern California) to Bahia Tortugas (southern Baja California). Intertidal to 287 m (941 ft) and perhaps to 294 m (964 ft). In Southern California, we see them mostly down to depths of about 70 m (230 ft), while off Oregon they are reportedly reasonably common down to about 122 m (400 ft). Larvae: birth length = about 5.5 mm, flexion length = about 6.5–8.5 mm. Von Bertalanffy parameters (TL, cm): (sexes combined) L_∞ = 51.4, k = 0.16, t_0 = -0.55 (Love and Johnson 1998). Length-weight parameters (TL, cm, gr): (sexes combined) W = $0.044L^{2.74}$ (Love and Johnson 1998).

SALIENT CHARACTERS: This is a relatively heavy-bodied species with fairly prominent head spines. Both dead ones and those underwater are colored various shades of brown, with lots of dark mottling. Characteristically, there is a dark blotch on the rear part of the gill cover.

LIFE HISTORY: From April–September, at 2.5–3 months old, young-of-the-year recruit to mixed sand-rock areas in nearshore waters. Most of these fish recruit to rocks and other hard substrata, bits of drift algae, eelgrass, submarine canyon walls, and (rarely) tide pools; we frequently see them on the shell mounds that surround oil platforms. Newly settled individuals may be as small as about 3 cm (1 in) TL, although 4.1 cm (2 in) SL fish may still reside in the water column. This is kind of a generalist species; you can find them on or near the bottom over reasonably high relief, but also on low-lying structure, on adjacent soft bottoms, and around such material as oil platforms, breakwaters, pipes, and piers. They are perhaps most abundant in relatively quiet and kind of turbid waters. In Puget Sound, fish living on high relief have relatively small home ranges and tend to stick around for extended periods. On low relief, browns wander about more. Adults may, on occasion, be weakly territorial, as Wayne Palsson saw two of them locking jaws. Browns are tolerant of estuarine conditions and can be abundant in salinities down to about 25 ppt. Genetic studies imply that there is somewhat limited dispersal of larvae along the coast.

Brown rockfish live to at least 34 years. Females may grow larger, but the sexes appear to have similar life spans and growth rates, and mature at about the same age and length. In general, a few fish are mature at 19 cm (8 in, TL, 3 years), 50% at 24–31 cm (10–12 in, 4–5 years), and all are mature at 38 cm (15 in, 10 years). Females produce between 55,000–339,000 eggs and release larvae from December–August, generally later in the season to the north. In at least some locales, females spawn their larvae in at least two batches. Brown rockfish feed primarily on fishes, shrimps, and crabs. They also consume isopods, clams, polychaetes, starfish, and fish eggs. Predators include Chinook salmon, leopard sharks, and rhinoceros auklets.

FISHERY: Browns were a major commercial species in late 19th-century San Francisco. Today, they are an important part of the live-fish fishery in California, are often sold on ice in places like San Francisco's Chinatown, and you see them all the time in the Mercado Negro in Ensenada (northern Baja California).

This is an important recreational species. Poke-polers and other fishermen catch them from rocks and jetties and pier fishermen and boat anglers also catch large numbers.

THE HYBRID'S LAMENT

Oh, my father was a quillback,
My momma, she's a brown,
It's hard to show my face, I fear,
In any part of town.

The other rockfish snicker,
They say, "Hide your head in shame,
'Cause it is so very obvious,
That mongrel is your name."

But I've got that hybrid vigor,
Because I am a mutt,
And if anybody questions that,
I'll bite them on the butt.

RELATIONSHIPS: Various genetic studies show that browns are most closely related to grass rockfish.

MISCELLANY: 1) A pugheaded fish was caught in San Francisco Bay. 2) Several studies have found that, in Puget Sound, browns hybridize with quillback and coppers. Remember those Olympia beer commercials, touting that "it's the water?" Well, maybe it is.

Sebastes brevispinis
(Bean, 1884)
Silvergray Rockfish

ETYMOLOGY: *Brevispinis* is Latin for "short" and "spine."

THE BASICS: Maximum Length: 74.4 cm (29 in) FL. Maximum Weight: At least 4.7 kg (10.4 lb). The Ranges: Southeastern Bering Sea to Bahia de Sebastian Vizcaino (central Baja California); commonly west to about Shumagin Island (Alaska Peninsula) and southward probably to someplace along British Columbia. Surface to 580 m (1,902 ft) or more, and mostly at 100–300 m (328–984 ft). Von Bertalanffy parameters (FL, mm): (females) $L_\infty = 623$, $k = 0.093$, $t_0 = -1.68$; (males) $L_\infty = 572$, $k = 0.11$, $t_0 = -1.68$ (Malecha et al. 2007). Length-weight parameters (TL, mm, kg): (sexes combined) $W = 0.00000000583L^{3.09}$ (RecFin 2009).

SALIENT CHARACTERS: Silvergrays are relatively slim fish, with reduced head spines. They have a relatively large mouth and a prominent symphyseal knob at the end of the lower jaw. Rick Stanley avers that the white spot on the upper front part of the lower jaw is a good diagnostic character. Despite their name, silvergrays are dark gray, green, or brown on back, with silvery or tan flanks.

LIFE HISTORY: Juveniles tend to be found in relatively shallow waters (often as shallow as maybe 25 m, 82 ft, or less), sometimes in kelp beds, and they move into deeper waters with age. Juveniles have also been found associated with drifting algae. This is a schooling fish that favors rugged bottoms of rock ridges, boulders, and vertical walls, but also occasionally cobble seafloors. Fish in British Columbia waters may move into shallower depths in the spring and then migrate back into deeper waters in the fall. In one study, fish tended to have peak densities at around 7.2°C (45°F). In a trawl study off Alaska, silvergrays were taken in 4.1–12.3°C (39–54°F), but mostly in 5.0–6.6°C (41–44°F).

RICK ROSENTHAL

Silvergrays live to 82 years old. Females grow larger and faster than males. A few females are mature at 9 years old, 50% at 10 years (45 cm, 18 in, FL), and nearly all at 18 years (maybe 49 cm, 19 in); a few fish are resolutely immature into their 30s. Similarly, a few males are mature at 6 years old (about 40 cm, 16 in), 50% at 10 years (45 cm, 18 in), and almost all at 13 years (about 47 cm, 19 in). Females produce 181,000–1,917,000 eggs and release larvae from at least February–October, with a May–July peak. Very little is known about their diet, although they do eat fishes, along with euphausiids, copepods, crab larvae, shrimps, and arrow worms.

FISHERY: As far back as Bean (1887b), silvergrays were noted as food fish at Port Althorp (southeastern Alaska). Currently, they form a moderate part of the trawl and hook-and-line commercial fisheries, from northern Washington to the Gulf of Alaska. Similarly, they are common, but not overwhelmingly so, in sport catches as far north as the Seward/Valdez area.

RELATIONSHIPS: One study found that silvergrays may be most closely related to redstripes, while another determined that they were not closely related to any extant species. This latter work proposed that silvergrays are a relatively old species, evolving perhaps 3 million or more years ago.

Sebastes carnatus
(Jordan & Gilbert, 1880)
Gopher Rockfish

ETYMOLOGY AND COLLOQUIAL NAMES: *Carnatus* is Latin for "flesh-colored." "Gopher" was used at least since the 1930s and "garrupa" goes back to the 19th century.

THE BASICS: Maximum Length: 39.6 cm (16 in) TL. Maximum Weight: The International Game Fish Association record is 2.9 kg (6.3 lb), which seems kind of heavy to me, but whatever. The Ranges: Cape Blanco (Oregon) to Punta San Roque (27°12'N, 114°26'W) (southern Baja California). They are common from Northern California to at least off Bahia San Quintin (northern Baja California). Tide pools to 86 m (282 ft), typically from about 12–50 m (39–164 ft). Larvae: birth length = about 4.3 mm. Von Bertalanffy parameters (females, TL, mm): (females) L_∞ = 341, k = 0.253, t_0 = 0.1; males: L_∞ = 329, k = 0.275, t_0 = 0.1 (Lea et al. 1999). Length-weight (TL, cm, gr): (sexes combined) W = $0.0186L^{2.957}$ (Love et al. 2002).

SALIENT CHARACTERS: Gophers are another of the heavy-bodied, spiny, bottom-oriented rockfishes. They are patchily olive-brown to reddish-brown alternating with white or pink.

LIFE HISTORY: Young-of-the-year recruit (from May–August) at 1.5–1.8 cm (0.6–0.7 in) SL, to the canopies of nearshore algae beds and, over time, larger juveniles slide downward and become demersal at between about 4–5 cm (2 in). Both juveniles and adults love that high relief, although juveniles will occasionally frequent eelgrass beds. These are highly territorial fish and fairly frequently you can see them locking jaws during turf battles. During the day, gophers tend to hide away in sheltering holes, and then emerge at dusk.

Gophers live to 24 years old. At least a few females mature at as small as 20.7 cm (8 in) TL, and males at 23.7 cm (9 in). Off Central California, females release larvae between January–July. Young-of-the-year gophers eat mostly calanoid copepods. Larger fish shift to a broad diet of mostly benthic-oriented crustaceans (crabs, shrimps, mysid shrimps, isopods, and gammarid amphipods) and fishes, and lesser amounts of squids, octopuses, snails, polychaetes, brittle stars, and fish eggs. Young-of-the-year gophers are eaten by juvenile bocaccios and likely by other fishes.

FISHERY: Historically, gophers were a minor part of the rockfish catch brought into the important 19th-century ports of San Francisco and San Diego. Today, gophers are very important in the California live fish fishery (and a fair number are also taken in Oregon), as they can be caught in shallow waters and then survive fairly well in captivity. Recreational anglers catch lots of them, mostly from vessels, and occasionally from rocks and piers.

RELATIONSHIPS: Gophers are very, very closely related to black-and-yellows. Narum et al. (2004) classified them as "incipient species" with black-and-yellows and that seems pretty reasonable. What we seem to see here (as with several other instances among the rockfishes) is speciation in action. If we came back 500,000 years from now the genetic differences between gophers and black-and-yellows would be more distinct. Gophers are also fairly closely related to kelp rockfish.

KAWIKA CHETRON

Sebastes caurinus

Richardson, 1844

Copper Rockfish

ETYMOLOGY AND COLLOQUIAL NAMES: *Caurinus* is Latin for "northwestern," from the word *caurus*, the northwest wind. "Garrupa" was a 19th-century name; "whitebelly" and "chucklehead" were used when I was a kid, and "toro" is what they are called in northern Baja California.

THE BASICS: Maximum Length: 66 cm (26 in) TL. Maximum Weight: 4.5 kg (10 lb). The Ranges: Western Gulf of Alaska (east of Kodiak Island) to Islas San Benito (central Baja California). They

are most common from southeastern Alaska to at least off Bahia San Quintin (northern Baja California). Intertidal to at least 310 m (1,017 ft), and mostly from the shallow subtidal (particularly to the north) to about 70 m (230 ft). Larvae: birth length = about 5.3 mm, flexion length = about 7–8 mm. Von Bertalanffy parameters (FL, cm): (sexes combined) L_∞ = 45.6., k = 0.1, t_0 = -3.7 (Love et al. 2002). Length-weight parameters (FL, cm, gr): (sexes combined) $W = 0.0172L^{3.018}$ (Love et al. 2002).

SALIENT CHARACTERS: A deep-bodied and spiny species, coppers come in a very wide range of colors, from olive, brown, and copper-pink, to scarlet and almost black. Regardless of color pattern, blotches in some form are always present and the light-colored lateral line is usually there.

LIFE HISTORY: From April–July, young-of-the-year recruit (at as small as 1.2 cm, 0.5 in, SL) to such very shallow nearshore structures as algae (e.g., giant kelp canopy and various benthic macrophytes), eelgrass, pilings, floats, and oil platforms. They also recruit, once in a while, to drifting algae and to tide pools. Within a few months (at 4–5 cm, 2 in), these juveniles descend to the bottom where you often find them among bottom drifting algae or along rock-sand interfaces. Particularly in more

"Copper Rockfish" Terry Pyles http://www.alaskanart.net

northern waters, juveniles can occupy very shallow, almost intertidal waters, most often where there is a lot of cover. Adults are almost always found around some sort of complex structure, including rocks, oil platforms, and piers, and usually close to, or on, the bottom. They will co-occupy giant Pacific octopuses dens when so allowed.

Coppers probably do not move about much (Clinton Bauder, for instance, has seen an adult living in the same rock pile for five years), although there has been speculation that some fish living in exposed areas may move into slightly deeper waters with the coming of winter

storms. Jeff Marliave, working around some nearshore rocks in the southern Strait of Georgia, says that they retreat into deep crevices when conditions get funky from November–April. Coppers tend to have home ranges and on low relief (likely of less quality) these home ranges tend to be larger than on high relief. While they can be solitary fish, you often see them in small groups (sometimes with such congeners as quillback), and sometimes in small schools. Wayne Palsson reports that they can be weakly territorial. They seem to be most active during the day. Genetic data demonstrate that connectivity between areas may sometimes be limited. For instance, there are substantial genetic differences between fish living in Puget Sound and those in the Canadian Gulf Islands and between Puget Sound fish and those on the outer West Coast.

Coppers live to 50 years old. Females release their young earlier in the season off California (January–April), then further north (March to perhaps July off Alaska). Females produce between about 16,000–650,000 eggs and larger fish release their young earlier in the season. Females release their larvae in one batch. Coppers are opportunistic feeders on benthic, epibenthic, and pelagic animals. Fishes, all kinds of crustaceans (e.g., crabs, shrimps, gammarid amphipods, euphausiids, mysid shrimps, isopods, and cumaceans), squids, octopuses, painted greenling eggs, and occasionally tunicates, brittle stars, clams and polychaetes are part of their diets. As you might expect, virtually any fish that they can swallow is fair game. Coppers seem to feed most heavily around dawn and dusk. Predators include Chinook and coho salmons, Rhinoceros auklets, and California sea lions. Young-of-the-year are eaten by juvenile bocaccios and perhaps other juveniles.

FISHERY: In the late 19th century, coppers were a common sight in the fresh fish markets of both San Francisco and San Diego. Bean (1887b) noted that they were an important food fish in Sitka (southeastern Alaska). They are frequently seen in Asian markets all up and down the coast, both live and on ice. British Columbia hook-and-line commercial fishermen, in particular, take a lot of them. Coppers are commonly taken by boat, pier and, to a certain extent, rocky shore recreational anglers (mostly small ones in the nearshore, although there is an occasional toad near the rocks).

RELATIONSHIPS: Several genetic surveys imply that coppers are closely related to kelp, quillback, and China rockfishes. In Puget Sound, coppers may, on occasion, mate with browns or quillbacks.

COPPER ROCKFISH

Some copper rockfish in Puget Sound mate with other species of rockfishes.

There once was a fish from the Sound,
Who figured out something profound,
* "Sex with one's own is just fair,*
* But it just can't compare,*
With interspecies fooling around."

"Ae fond kiss and then we sever." Robert Burns

TOM SHELDON

MISCELLANY: 1) Jeff Marliave has seen a black-faced one for 2 years running at the same spot. 2) Eigenmann (1892) reported on something that has been noted by deckhands on sportfishing partyboats for many decades; this species is very hardy and takes a long time to die in a sack. The challenge for a deckhand is, as the vessel leaves the fishing grounds, trying to fillet dozens of coppers that are still flopping around without getting spines driven into flesh and, thus, embarrassing oneself in front of the passengers.

Sebastes chlorostictus
(Jordan & Gilbert, 1880)
Greenspotted Rockfish

JOHN BUTLER

ETYMOLOGY AND COLLOQUIAL NAMES: *Chlorostictus* is Greek for "green" and "spotted." "Boscos," "Santa Marias," "scrubs," and "chuckleheads" are still heard on occasion.

THE BASICS: Maximum Length: 53.4 cm (21 in) FL. E.J. Dick reports that several port sampler databases list a number of fish larger than 53.4 cm, with one as large as 63.1 cm (25 in) FL. But, given the possibilities of confusion with greenblotched rockfish, we will just have to live with uncertainty. Maximum Weight: A 48.2 cm (19 in) FL fish weighed 2 kg (4.4 lb). The Ranges:

Vancouver Island (49°04'N, 126°49'W) to southern Baja California (25°32'N, 113°04'W). They are common from Central California to at least off Bahia San Quintin (northern Baja California). 30–379 m (98–1,243 ft), mostly in 100–200 m (328–656 ft). Von Bertalanffy parameters (FL, mm): (sexes combined) L_∞ = 457, k = 0.062, t_0 = -1.16 (Benet et al. 2010). Length-weight (FL, mm, gr): W = 0.00001032L$^{3.108}$ (Benet et al. 2010).

SALIENT CHARACTERS: Another of the patented squat and spiny species, greenspotteds are heavily dotted with green spots on back and head. Underwater, they are various mixtures of yellows, whites, and pinks; dead ones tend to be deeper pink and yellow. There are 3–5 white or pinkish-white blotches on the back.

LIFE HISTORY: We have seen 5 cm (2 in) TL ones in waters between 60–240 m (197–787 ft), so young-of-the-year recruit out of the plankton to a wide depth range. Both juveniles and adults seem to prefer mixed mud-rock bottoms (and commonly in brachiopod beds), although you will also see them fairly often on rocks and boulders. They are also quite abundant around the bottoms of some oil platforms. While greenspotteds are basically solitary animals, they will kind of bunch up in little groups on occasion. This is a benthic species; they only rarely rise more than a meter above the seafloor, and often are found within caves and crevices. A tagging study in a submarine canyon in Central California demonstrated that greenspotteds are fairly sedentary, moving at most a few kilometers along the canyon walls. During our submersible surveys, we have seen them at 8.2–13°C (47–55°F), mostly at 9.5–11°C (49–52°F).

Greenspotteds live to at least 51 years old. Off Southern California, a few males are mature at 20 cm (8 in) TL, 50% at 22 cm (9 in), and all by 28 cm (11 in). A few females release larvae at 15 cm (6 in), 50% at 22 cm (9 in), and all reproduce at 32 cm (13 in). Off Central California, females first mature at 18 cm (7 in, about 6 years) FL, 50% are mature at about 26 cm (10 in, 12 years), and 100% by 40 cm (16 in, about 19 years). Females produce between about 14,000–760,000 eggs and fish off Central California are slightly more fecund than in Southern California. Larval release is from February–September and tends to occur earlier in the season off Southern California and later further to the north. In Southern California, females produce several broods of larvae per season.

FISHERY: As far back as 1892, they were a major part of the commercial catch in the San Diego area and they have remained moderately important in Central and Southern California. They are almost always sold whole. You see lots of them in the big Mercado Negro fish market in Ensenada (northern Baja California). Smaller individuals taken by trawlers in the 1960s were sold for mink food. Greenspotteds are important in the recreational catch in Central and Southern California.

RELATIONSHIPS: Greenspotteds are most closely related to greenblotched and also to pink rockfishes.

Sebastes chrysomelas
(Jordan & Gilbert, 1881)
Black-and-Yellow Rockfish

ETYMOLOGY AND COLLOQUIAL NAMES: *Chrysomelas* is Latin for "gold" and "black." Along with *S. carnatus*, these were call "garrupa" and "gophers" in the old days.

THE BASICS: Maximum Length: 38.7 cm (15 in) TL. The Ranges: Cape Blanco (Oregon) to Isla Natividad (27°51'N, 115°10'W) (central Baja California). Black-and-yellows are reasonably common from Fort Bragg (Northern California) to at least northern Baja California. Tide pools (occasionally) to 37 m (120 ft), typically from 2–15 m (6–50 ft). Larvae: birth length = 4.4–4.8 mm. Von Bertalanffy parameters (SL, cm, Central California): (females) L_∞ = 25.2, k = 0.22, t_0 = -0.45; (males) L_∞ = 24.7, k = 0.24, t_0 = -0.32 (Love et al. 2002). (Southern California): (females) L_∞ = 21.5, k = 0.21, t_0 = -0.72; (males) L_∞ = 19.9, k = 0.28, t_0 = -0.28 (Love et al. 2002). Length-weight parameters (TL, cm, gr): (sexes combined) W = $0.0081L^{3.257}$ (Love et al. 2002).

SALIENT CHARACTERS: B&Ys are heavy-bodied and spiny. Like gophers, their bodies are covered in alternating patches, in this case olive or black alternating with yellow.

LIFE HISTORY: From about June–September, young-of-the-year recruit at 1.5–1.8 cm (0.6–0.7 in) SL to nearshore algae. At around 4–5 cm (2 in) SL, these fish have made their ways down to the seafloor and they hang out around kelp holdfasts and the like. Older fish live among rocks and other high relief, where they hold territories. However, Brad Mongeau shot an image of 6 fish over low relief, all very near each other. At least some individuals feed during both day and night.

B&Ys live to at least 30 years old. Fish appear to grow larger off Central California compared to those in Southern Califor-

nia. Males and females grow to about the same maximum size and mature at the same length and age. Off Central California, a few males mature at 14 cm (6 in) SL, half at 16–17 cm (6–7 in), and all at 18 cm (7 in). For females, these values are 16 cm (6 in), 17 cm (7 in), and 21 cm (8 in). A few Southern California males are mature at 13 cm (5 in) and all at 15 cm (6 in); a few females at 14 cm (6 in) and all at 17 cm (7 in). All of this translates to 3–6 years of age. Females produce between 25,000–450,000 eggs and release their young in one batch from January–May. Black-and-yellows focus their attention on benthic organisms. Crabs and shrimps are perhaps most important, but fishes, gammarid amphipods, isopods, snails, chitons, octopuses, hydrozoans, bryozoans, and kelp fragments are also consumed. Young-of-the-year are eaten by juvenile bocaccios and undoubtedly by other species. Older fish are nailed by cabezons.

FISHERY: As one of the more brightly colored rockfish, black-and-yellows have always been an easily sold fish, even back in the 19th century,

DAN RICHARDS

although landings were not large. Black-and-yellows are a large part of the lucrative live fish fishery in California (and many are also taken in a similar fishery in southern Oregon). They are commonly taken by rocky shore, jetty, and boat fishermen.

RELATIONSHIPS: Black-and-yellows are just so very, very closely related to gopher rockfish.

MISCELLANY: My associate, Mike Moss, saw a black-and-yellow jaw-locking with a gopher rockfish.

Sebastes constellatus
(Jordan & Gilbert, 1880)
Starry Rockfish

Another species Gaia has seen fit to paint in striking colors.

ETYMOLOGY: *Constellatus* is Latin for "starred." "Corsair," an Azorean name, goes back to the 19th century.

THE BASICS: Maximum Length: 46 cm (18 in) TL. The Ranges: Off the mouth of the Russian River (Northern California) to off Todos Santos (23°24'N, 110°14'W) (southern Baja California). They have also tentatively been identified from photographs taken at Rocas Alijos (about 25°N, 115°45'W). Starries are abundant from Central California to at least off Bahia Tortugas

JOHN BUTLER

(southern Baja California). 15–274 m (50–900 ft) and mostly in 75–135 m (246–443 ft). Larvae: birth length = about 4 mm, flexion length = about 7 mm. Von Bertalanffy parameters (TL, cm): (females) L_∞ = 45, k = 0.09, t_0 = -3.11; (males) L_∞ = 38, k = 0.09, t_0 = -1.07 (Love et al. 2002). Length-weight parameters (TL, cm, gr): (sexes combined) W = $0.0097L^{3.16}$ (Love et al. 2002).

SALIENT CHARACTERS: Well, first, you can't mistake the juveniles; they are the only lemon-yellow juvenile rockfish. Adults are relatively squat, with quite rounded heads, and orange to orange-brown bodies profusely splattered with light spots. Typical of their subgenus, they also have 3–5 light blotches on the back.

LIFE HISTORY: We have seen newly recruited young-of-the-year over rocks and oil platform

shell mounds, at depths between 30–170 m (98–558 ft). In general, both adults and juveniles are found at the same depths and often in the same habitats (boulders fields, rock ridges, and occasionally cobblestones). These are solitary animals that rarely ascend more than a meter or so into the water column. In our Southern California fish surveys, we have seen starries in 8.3–16.4°C (47–62°F), although most were in 9.5–11.8°C (49–53°F).

Starries live to at least 32 years old. The sexes have similar life spans. Off Southern California, a few males are mature at 18 cm (7 in) TL and 4 years, and all are mature at 27 cm (11 in) and 12 years. Male starries further north mature at a larger size; a few males are mature at 28 cm (11 in, 6 years) and all are mature at 36 cm (14 in, 12 years). Similarly, a few Southern California females mature at 21 cm (8 in, 6 years) and all are mature by 29 cm (11 in, 14 years), while off Central and Northern California these values are 23 cm (9 in, 5 years) and 34 cm (13 in, 9 years) respectively. In Southern California, females release larvae January–July and as late as November off Isla Guadalupe (central Baja California). Females produce between about 33,000–228,000 eggs and release their larvae in one batch. Starries feed on shrimps, crabs, euphausiids, and fishes. Lingcod eat them.

FISHERY: Starries were a moderately important commercial species in the San Francisco fish markets of the late 19th century and remained an occasional catch until the advent of monofilament gill nets in the 1970s. At that time, fishermen lay their nets on top of previously inaccessible boulders and rock ridges and a ton of starries were caught. With that nice, bright color, you always see this species sold whole, as like other brightly colored rockfishes, starries command a premium price. I have also seen numbers caught by artisanal fishermen as far south as off Bahia Tortugas (southern Baja California). Sport fishermen catch a lot of them.

RELATIONSHIPS: The starry rockfish is a relatively recent species that has closest affinities to the Southern Hemisphere species, *S. capensis* and *S. oculatus*.

Sebastes crameri

(Jordan, 1897)

Darkblotched Rockfish

ETYMOLOGY AND COLLOQUIAL NAMES: *Crameri* refers to Frank Cramer (1861–1948), a student of David Starr Jordan who tried to use head spines in rockfish taxonomy. They were also called "black-mouth rockfish" and the Japanese use the word "yotsujimamenuke."

THE BASICS: Maximum Length: 59.5 cm (23.4 in) TL. Maximum Weight: 2.8 kg (6.2 lb). The Ranges: Eastern Bering Sea southeast of Zhemchug Canyon, and Aleutian Islands off Tanaga Island, to near Santa Catalina Island and Laguna Beach (Southern California); per-haps most commonly from Yakutat (Gulf of Alaska) to Northern or perhaps Central California. 29–915 m (95–2,985 ft). Fish in

ROBERT LAUTH

Southern California may, on average, live in deeper waters than those to the north. Larvae: hatching length = about 5.7 mm, flexion length = 8–9.3 mm, transformation length = 1.6–2.1 cm. Von Bertalanffy parameters (FL, cm): (females) L_∞ = 41.8, k = 0.16, t_0 = -1.0; (males) L_∞ = 37.4, k = 0.21, t_0 = -0.59 (Love et al. 2002). Length-weight parameters (TL, cm, gr): (sexes combined) W = $0.0295L^{2.824}$ (Love et al. 2002).

SALIENT CHARACTERS: This is a deep-bodied, perch-shaped species, with a downward-directed symphyseal knob on the tip of the lower jaw, a dark blotch on the rear of the gill cover, and 3–5 dark saddles on the back. Dead ones are orange or pink, while underwater they can be that color or quite light.

LIFE HISTORY: Some young-of-the-year recruit to low-relief and mud bottoms at as small as 4.8 cm (2 in) SL, while others stay in the water column until at least 6.2 cm (2 in). These young fish recruit to bottom depths of 55–200 m (182–660 ft), and many appear to move into deeper waters as they mature. We often see juveniles perched on sponges or other promontories. Both juveniles and adults are found mostly over mixed rock-mud seafloors; however, you do see them out on the mud and occasionally over high relief. These appear to be relatively solitary fish, although we don't see enough of them to be sure about that. They usually stay near the bottom and are often partially sheltered by rocks. They live in at least 4.4–11.1°C (40–52°F).

Darkblotcheds live to 105 years. Females grow larger than males and may live longer. Size and age at maturity may vary among areas (see the summary in Love et al. 2002). Length at 50% maturity (taking into consideration that some measurements were in TL and some FL) ranges from about 27–39 cm (11–15 in) and maybe 8–9 years old. Females produce 20,000–610,000 eggs and larvae are released between November–June in one batch. Darkblotched rockfish mostly eat larger planktonic organisms, such as euphausiids, amphipods, and pelagic tunicates. They occasionally consume fishes and octopuses. Pelagic juveniles are eaten by albacore, Chinook salmon, and rhinoceros auklets.

FISHERY: Historically, darkblotcheds were an important part of the commercial trawl fisheries of the Northwest, both as food for humans and such animals as minks. As often happens, the fishery was not well regulated and the species has been declared overfished. Darkblotcheds are not an important sport species.

RELATIONSHIPS: Darkblotcheds are most closely related to yellowmouth rockfish and they perhaps came on the scene about half a million years ago.

Sebastes dallii
(Eigenmann & Beeson, 1894)
Calico Rockfish

ETYMOLOGY AND COLLOQUIAL NAME: *Dalli* is named for William Healey Dall (1845–1927), a Smithsonian Institution zoologist. They are called "flea cod" off San Diego.

THE BASICS: Maximum Length: 25.4 cm (10 in) TL. The Ranges: San Francisco to Bahia de Sebastian Vizcaino (central Baja California). They are common from at least Santa Cruz (Central California) through Southern California (but rare around many of the islands and offshore banks). Intertidal–305 m (1,000 ft) and mostly at maybe 45–70 m (148–230 ft). Larvae: hatching length = 5 mm, flexion length = 6.2–8 mm, transformation length = less than 2 cm (0.8 in). Von Bertalanffy parameters (SL, cm): (sexes combined) L_∞ = 16.2, k = 0.12, t_0 = -2.95 (Love et al. 2002). Length-weight parameters (TL, cm, gr): (sexes combined) W = 0.0067L$^{3.182}$ (Love et al. 2002).

SALIENT CHARACTERS: This one is easy. They have reddish-brown bars slanting obliquely front-back and the bodies sometimes are profusely marked with dark brown spots.

LIFE HISTORY: Young-of-the-year recruit to nearshore waters from at least May–July, some at as small as 2.5 cm (1 in) SL. Settlement occurs over low-lying hard surfaces (such as the shell mounds surrounding oil platforms), sand-rock interfaces, and soft substrata. Juveniles and adults inhabit a wide range of habitats, but mostly live on a mixture of low-hard relief and the surrounding sand and mud. We see them in large numbers on some of the shell mounds surrounding oil platforms. This is a mostly benthic species; they rarely ascend more than a meter or two above the bottom. They are found as solitary individuals or in small aggregations. In Southern California, we see them in 9.9–15°C (50–59°F) and mainly in 10.8–11.8°C (51–53°F).

KEVIN LEE

While calicos have been aged to 12 years, I would wager they grow somewhat older. Males and females mature at the same size; a few are mature at 7 cm (3 in) SL, 50% by 9 cm (4 in), and all by 14 cm (6 in). Females produce between 3,900–18,000 eggs per season and release their young in one batch between November–May, peaking in about February. Calico rockfish feed to a considerable extent on benthic and epibenthic crustaceans (e.g., copepods, shrimps, mysid shrimps, gnathiid isopods, and hyperiid amphipods). They also consume smaller numbers of crabs, fishes, bivalves, and octopuses.

FISHERY: This small species has never been part of the commercial catch. Although not a targeted species, they are pretty commonly caught in recreational boat catches.

RELATIONSHIPS: Calicos are most closely related to brown and grass rockfishes.

OH, I'M AN AMERICAN AND I'M OKAY—WILLIAM HEALEY DALL

For sheer down-and-dirty *uber*American hubris, it is hard to beat William Dall's *Alaska and its Resources*, published in 1870. This undeniably riveting account of his 2 years in Russian-owned Alaska, filled with really quite exquisite verbal pictures of the land and its inhabitants, is also a bulging psycho-social potpie filled with enough national and racial stereotypes to please even the most discriminating nativist. In Dall's Alaska, a handful of heroic Americans deal the best they can with drunken and corrupt Russians, filthy, thieving, and murderous Inupiats and Indians, and effete Brits. Oh, and did I mention that he doesn't like Jews or the Greek Orthodox Church? Well, he doesn't. Oh, and did I mention that he stole an Indian skull from a grave? Well, he did.

Here is the setup to my favorite quote from the book. Dall mentions that some of the natives of the lower Yukon had killed a number of Russians. The Russians had then retaliated, killing every man, woman, and child in the offenders' village. Dall then writes: "The result was wonderful. From that day to this not a native on the Lower Yukon has lifted his hand against the whites. The bloody lesson was not thrown away. The strong hand, which alone commands the respect of savages, was worth a thousand missionaries."

And here is my second favorite quote from Mr. Dall's work. Discussing the colonies of Vancouver Island and British Columbia, he writes: "There can be but little doubt but that annexation to the United States would be hailed with joy by the majority of the inhabitants of this region, who have already taken to celebrating the Fourth of July with a heartiness not surpassed by the citizens of the United States." Now, before you happy jingoists out there start pouring the champagne I should tell you that I asked Rick Stanley of the Canada Department of Fisheries and Oceans about this and he says it ain't so.

Sebastes diploproa
(Gilbert, 1890)

Splitnose Rockfish

ETYMOLOGY AND COLLOQUIAL NAME: *Diploproa* means "double" and "prow" in Greek. "Rosefish" was a common name a while back.

THE BASICS: Maximum Length: 45.7 cm (18 in) TL. Maximum Weight: 1.1 kg (2.4 lb). The Ranges: Sanak Islands (western Gulf of Alaska) to Isla Cedros (central Baja California), typically from British Columbia to at least Southern California. 45–924 m (148–3,031 ft), maybe mostly from 200–350 m (656–1,148 ft). Larvae: birth length = about 4.4–5.2 mm, flexion length = about 6.5–7.7 mm, transformation length to pelagic juvenile = about 2 cm (0.8 in). Von Bertalanffy parameters (FL, cm): (females) L_∞ = 34.1, k = 0.1, t_0 = -4.45; (males) L_∞ = 29.9, k = 0.16, t_0 = -2.01 (Love et al. 2002). Length-weight parameters (TL, cm, gr): (sexes combined) $W = 0.0195L^{2.927}$ (Love et al. 2002).

SALIENT CHARACTERS: Splitnoses are deep-bodied, large-eyed, kind of pointy-snouted, and there is a deep notch in the center of the upper jaw. Dead ones are red or pink on backs and silver on sides. Underwater, they are white, pink, or sometimes orangy-red, with a number of red, pink, or orange blotches.

LIFE HISTORY: Splitnose have an interesting beginning to their lives. At 1–5 cm (0.4–2 in) SL, the young recruit to drifting kelp mats and other material and here you will find them in large schools, ever ready to dash into the fronds if disturbed. By the time they are 3–5 cm (1–2 in) long and a year old, most of these fish have left surface waters (mostly in spring and summer) and are living on soft seafloors. While most of these newly recruited fish are in relatively deep waters, often maybe in 90–200 m (295–656 ft) and more, they do recruit to shallow depths. Mike Moss, for instance, observed some in 9 m (30 ft) of water, living at the base of a kelp plant at Anacapa Island. Both older juveniles and adults are found primarily on mud-rock and mud bottoms, usually right on the seafloor (on mud, they often sit in divots of their own making). On the other hand, I have seen large ones on rocks; schools will swim well into the water column (reportedly as much as 100 m, 329 ft) above the seafloor. They live at temperatures of at least 5.2–10.9°C (41–52°C).

Splitnoses live to at least 103 years. Females grow larger and faster than males, and fish in the northern part of the range grow faster than do those to the south. Off Central and Northern California, males mature at 20–29 cm (9–11 in) TL (about 7–10 years old) and females at 18–23 cm (7–9 in) (6–9 years). Off British Columbia, 50% of both males and females are mature at 27 cm (11 in). Splitnoses appear to release young throughout the year, although most of that action seems to occur from the summer to early winter. Females produce anywhere from about 14,000–255,000 eggs. These fish feed almost entirely on midwater and epibenthic crustaceans, translating to a diet heavy in euphausiids and copepods. Food items that are usually less important are pelagic tunicates and pteropods. When very young, the young-of-the-year that live under drifting algae eat copepods, cladocerans, and other plankters, then switch to feeding on animals living on the plants (e.g., gammarid amphipods and small shrimps) as they grow. Predators include bocaccio, Chinook salmon, lingcod, longnose lancetfish, longnose skate, California and Steller sea lions, and Humboldt squids.

FISHERY: Historically, splitnoses have been of varying importance in the trawl fisheries from British Columbia to Central California. For much of that time, most of the catch was sold for animal food, but some of the catch was landed in fish markets. Splitnoses are almost never taken in the recreational catch.

RELATIONSHIPS: Genetic studies of this species give equivocal results regarding its relationships to other rockfishes. One study found that splitnoses are most closely related to semaphore rockfish, as well as to several species (*S. cortezi*, *S. sinensis*, and *S. peduncularis*) that live in the Gulf of California. Another found them to be closely related to greenstriped rockfish. So, you pays your money and you takes your choice.

Sebastes elongatus

Ayres, 1859

Greenstriped Rockfish

JOHN BUTLER

ETYMOLOGY AND COLLOQUIAL NAMES: *Elongatus* is Latin for "elongated." Other names include "strawberry," "reina" ("queen" in Portuguese), "serena" ("serene appearance" in Italian and Spanish), and "poinsettia" (a personal favorite of mine).

THE BASICS: Maximum Length: 47 cm (19 in) FL (about 48.6 cm, 19 in, TL). Maximum Weight: 980 gr (2.2 lb). The Ranges: Chirikof Island (western Gulf of Alaska) to Isla Cedros (central Baja California), mostly from Yakutat (Gulf of Alaska) to at least Bahia San Quintin (northern Baja California). 12–1,145 m (39–3,756 ft). In southern California, they are typically in 130–205 m (426–672 ft), and in the Gulf of Alaska at about 180–250 m (590–820 ft). Von Bertalanffy parameters (FL, mm): (females) $L_\infty = 374.5$, $k = 0.079$, $t_0 = -3.465$; (males) $L_\infty = 300.8$, $k = 0.108$, $t_0 = -3.273$ (Shaw and Gunderson 2006). Hicks et al. (2009) has more VBs for your viewing pleasure. Length-weight parameters (TL, cm, gr): (sexes combined) $W = 0.00793L^{3.127}$ (Love et al. 1990) (for Southern California), but note that fish south of 42°N may be lighter at length than those to the north (Hicks et al. 2009).

SALIENT CHARACTERS: This is a slim species with four horizontal green stripes. The bodies of both live and dead ones may be suffused with red.

LIFE HISTORY: Young-of-the-year recruit at as small as 2.6 cm (1 in) SL to low-hard relief (e.g., cobbles or shell mounds around oil platforms), and to mud, at bottom depths of at least 70–240 m (230–787 ft). Both juveniles and adults are mostly solitary animals that live primarily over mixed mud and low-relief rocks (often those covered with brachiopods) and shell mounds. Not uncommonly you will also observe them on both mud seafloors and boulders. I rarely see greenstripeds above the bottom and, in fact, most of the time they seem to lie right on the substratum. Surveys along Alaska and the West Coast demonstrate that they live at 4.1–11.9°C (39–53°F). There is little genetic variation along the entire West Coast.

Greenstripeds live to 54 years old. Females grow larger than males and fish off Oregon and Washington grow relatively slowly but reach a larger size than those to the south. Greenstripeds in Southern California mature when smaller than do those off Oregon and Washington. Off Southern California, a few fish mature at 15 cm (6 in, about 3 years) TL, 50% at 18 cm (7 in, about 5 years), and all at 26 cm (10 in, 9–12 years). For the study off Oregon and Washington, I have taken the data from

Shaw and Gunderson (2006) that is in FL and converted those lengths into TL. In this study, a few males mature at 15.6 cm (6 in) (about 4 years), 50% maturity at 23.5 cm (9 in) (10 years), and 100% is reached at 30.9 cm (12 in). For females, the respective values are 15.6 cm, 21.4 cm (8 in) (7 years), and 28.8 cm (11 in). Mating occurs from December–February and larval release takes place January–July. Greenstripeds feed both on water column and benthic prey. Midwater shrimps (sergestids), euphausiids, fishes, crabs, and shrimps are often most important, while other foods include hyperiid amphipods, copepods, mysid shrimps, crustacean larvae, and squids. Predators include lingcod and California sea lions. Chinook salmon eat pelagic juveniles.

FISHERY: Back in the 19th century, Eigenmann (1892) reported that greenstripeds were not commercially valuable in San Diego, but were very popular in San Francisco. Over the years, their small size has made them of only small interest as a commercial species, although they were an important part of the animal food industry in California during the 1950s and 60s. Today, they are often seen in Asian markets in Southern California. Recreational anglers often catch, but usually discard, them.

RELATIONSHIPS: While one genetic study found that greenstripeds are a very old species (going back 5 million years or so) and not closely related to any living rockfish, another found them perhaps related to splitnose rockfish.

Sebastes emphaeus
(Starks, 1911)
Puget Sound Rockfish

MARC CHAMBERLAIN

ETYMOLOGY: *Emphaeus* is Latin for "display."
THE BASICS: Maximum Length: 19 cm (8 in) TL. The Ranges: Outer coast of the Kenai Peninsula and Prince William Sound (northern Gulf of Alaska) to Point Sur (Central California). They have been tentatively identified and photographed from off Monterey. 3–455 m (10–1,492 ft), and perhaps to 470 m (1,542 ft), typically in about 10 m (33 ft) and deeper. Von Bertalanffy parameters (FL, mm): (females) L_∞ = 170.7, k = 0.53, t_0 = -0.46; (males) L_∞ = 137.4, k = 0.7, t_0 = -0.32 (Beckmann et al. 1998). Length-weight parameters: (sexes combined) W = $0.000058L^{2.687}$ (Beckmann et al. 1998).

SALIENT CHARACTERS: A dwarf species, Puget Sounds are brown, pinky, or orangish underwater, and kind of brown when dead. There is usually a dusky, brown, or orangey stripe running below the lateral line.

LIFE HISTORY: Young-of-the-year recruit to nearshore reefs in January and February at about 2.5–3 cm (1 in) TL. Fish of all sizes live over very rugged bottoms and along vertical walls. They often aggregate in large schools (sometimes in the thousands) in the water column by day and are inactive at night, spending that time singly or in small groups huddled among rocks. Pregnant females are said to remain near the bottom, often in hiding. At least in southeastern Alaska, Pugets live in relatively shallow waters (although rarely less than 11 m, 36 ft) during the summer and then retreat into water deeper than 25 m (82 ft) for the winter.

Puget Sounds live to at least 22 years. Females may mature as small as 11 cm (4 in) FL and from 1–2 years old. All females are mature by 13 cm (5 in) and produce between about 3,300–58,000 eggs per year. Females release larvae between June–September. Puget Sounds feed most heavily on zooplankton (e.g., copepods, crustacean larvae, arrow worms, siphonophores, amphipods, and pelagic tunicates). However, they also deign, on occasion, to eat benthic prey, including lingcod eggs and caprellid amphipods. Predators include black, copper, quillback, silvergray, and yelloweye rockfishes, and lingcod.

FISHERY: This species is not of commercial importance and is only occasionally taken by anglers.

RELATIONSHIPS: Puget Sounds are most closely related to pygmy and harlequin rockfishes.

REMARKS: In some parts of the Northwest Pacific, this is a dominant species over relatively shallow reefs.

Sebastes ensifer

Chen, 1971

Swordspine Rockfish

ETYMOLOGY: *Ensifer* means "sword-bearing" in Latin.

THE BASICS: Maximum Length: 30.5 cm (12 in) TL. The Ranges: San Francisco to Banco Ranger (28°25'N, 115°32'W) (central Baja California). They are abundant as far north as the Santa Barbara Channel. 50–433 m (164–1,420 ft), and most commonly in 90–140 m (295–459 ft). Von Bertalanffy parameters (SL, cm): (sexes combined) L_∞ = 17.6, k = 0.14, t_0 = -1.04 (Love et al. 2002). Note that these values come from reading whole otoliths, so I would be cautious. Length-weight parameters (TL, cm, gr): (sexes combined) W = $0.0132L^{2.97}$ (Love et al. 2002).

SALIENT CHARACTERS: True to their names, swordspines have a very long second anal spine. These are slim fish, with 3–5 light blotches on the back, and pink, orange, or bronzy back and sides, and light belly.

LIFE HISTORY: Swordspines are mostly found over cobble, flat bedrock, and small boulders. Although we usually see them either lying in crevices (maybe as many are eight will cram into a small space) or hovering just above the substrate, they will at times ascend a few meters above the bottom. Young-of-the-year are found in the same habitat as adults. In Southern California, we have seen swordspines in 7.9–13.4°C (46–56°F), with most in 9.1–10.6°C (48–51°F).

Swordspines live to at least 43 years. A few individuals mature at as small as 11 cm (4 in) TL and 3 years. Females produce between 12,200–38,000 eggs per season and release larvae between December–July, peaking in March. In southern California, females often produce two batches of larvae per season. I have found mostly euphausiids and copepods in their stomachs. In turn, they are eaten by California sea lions.

FISHERY: Swordspines are caught in very large numbers by recreational anglers, who usually toss them back as seagull food.

RELATIONSHIPS: Swordspines are most closely related to rosethorn and pinkrose rockfishes.

Sebastes entomelas

(Jordan & Gilbert, 1880)

Widow Rockfish

ETYMOLOGY AND COLLOQUIAL NAMES: *Entomelas* is Greek for "within" and "black," referring to the black-lined peritoneum. Other names include "brownie" and the rather militant "brown bomber."

THE BASICS: Maximum Length: 62 cm (24 in) TL. Maximum Weight: 3.0 kg (6.6 lb). The Ranges: Albatross Bank (western Gulf of Alaska) to Bahia de Todos Santos (northern Baja California). Widows are common from at least southeastern Alaska to the Santa Barbara Channel, and on the outer banks of Southern California. Both juveniles and adults come to the surface on occasion. Young-of-the-year only rarely enter tide pools and adults are found in as much as 800 m

CLINTON BAUDER

(2,625 ft). In Southern California, we see widows mostly in 80–125 m (262–410 ft), while northward they can be abundant from fairly shallow waters to 200 m (656 ft) or more. Larvae: hatching length = 4.5–4.6 mm, flexion length = 9.9–12.9 mm, transformation length = 2.2–3.1 cm (1 in). Von Bertalanffy parameters (FL, cm): North of 43° Latitude - (females) L_∞ = 50.5, k = 0.14, t_0 = -2.68; (males) L_∞ = 44, k = 0.18, t_0 = -2.81. South of 43° Latitude - (females) L_∞ = 47.6, k = 0.2, t_0 = -0.17; (males) L_∞ = 41.5, k = 0.25, t_0 = -0.28 (He et al. 2009). Length-weight parameters (TL, cm, gr): (sexes combined) W = $0.0164L^{2.942}$ (Love et al. 2002).

SALIENT CHARACTERS: Widows are slim and streamlined, with reduced head spines. When dead or swimming in the water column, they tend to be brown, brass, or orangey, with diffuse barring or speckling. When they sit on the bottom, they become heavily and darkly blotchy or barred. Unusual among the rockfishes, the peritoneum (body cavity lining) is black.

LIFE HISTORY: Among the rockfishes, pelagic juveniles tend to be found at deeper depths than many other species, often in at least 100 m (328 ft). Young-of-the-year recruit from the plankton, at as small as 4 cm (2 in) SL, to such subtidal structures as rocks, kelp, and oil platforms, and, very rarely, to tide pools. Not all pelagic juveniles recruit that small; some fish remain pelagic until 8.1 cm (3 in) long and 5 months old. Widows recruit over a wide depth range, as I have seen very small fish on the bottom in waters from a handful of meters deep to depths of at least 150 m (489 ft). Settlement occurs from at least May–September (we saw some really small fish at a platform on 3 May, so they might have recruited in April). Both juveniles and adults usually live over high relief (some in crevices and often well above the bottom) and they can form very large schools of thousands of individuals. As they mature, fish that have recruited shallow tend to move into somewhat deeper waters, although mature individuals can be found at the surface, particularly from Central California northward. It is unclear how much movement these fish make, although they very likely move from rock pile to rock pile. Interestingly, while juveniles and subadults are very abundant in Southern California (particularly around oil platforms and pinnacles), only rarely do we see adults, and I have wondered if many fish migrate northward to Central California.

Widows live to at least 60 years. Females grow larger and probably live longer. A few males are mature at 26–32 cm (10–13 in) TL, 50% at 32–37 cm (13–15 in), and all are mature at 37–41 cm (15–16 in). A few females may mature at lengths of 29–34 cm (11–13 in), 50% at 35–38 cm (14–15 in), and 100% at 36–43 cm (14–17 in). Off Central and Northern California, both sexes mature at between 3–8 years old. Females produce about 95,000–1,113,000 eggs per season and release larvae from December–April (and perhaps rarely into May). Females off Oregon and Washington produce more eggs per body length than do those to the south. Widow rockfish feed on water column animals and their diets vary with season, location, and year. In general, fishes, pelagic tunicates, natanthian shrimps, hyperiid amphipods, and euphausiids are extremely important. Also consumed in some numbers are ctenophores, polychaetes, squids, octopuses, mysid shrimps, isopods, larvaceans, and arrow worms. Young widows are eaten by Chinook salmon and rhinoceros auklets. Other predators include California and northern sea lions.

FISHERY: Because they dwell over rocks (and hence are not susceptible to more primitive trawls and gill nets), and are not as readily taken by hook and line as some other rockfishes, widow rockfish were not very important in early commercial fisheries. With the discovery that they were readily taken with midwater trawls, widows became an important species from British Columbia–Central California. Along with being a targeted species, they can be a significant bycatch in the Pacific hake fishery. All of this led, almost by definition, to their being declared overfished in U.S. waters. Widows are a fairly important recreational species, particularly off California.

RELATIONSHIPS: Widows are very closely related to the two species of blue rockfishes.

Sebastes flavidus
(Ayres, 1862)
Yellowtail Rockfish

ETYMOLOGY AND COLLOQUIAL NAME: *Flavidus* is Latin for "yellow." They are frequently called "greenies" (but not, as one might expect, "yellowies").

THE BASICS: Maximum Length: 66 cm (26 in) TL. Maximum Weight: 4.2 kg (9.3 lb). The Ranges: Eastern Aleutian Islands (south of Unalaska Island) to Isla San Martin (northern Baja California). They are abundant as far south as Central California and reasonably common southward to the western Santa Barbara Channel, San Miguel and Santa Rosa islands, and to the outer banks of Southern

JANNA NICHOLS

California. Commercial fishermen in the central Baja California area around Isla San Martin report catching them with some frequency. Surface waters and tide pools (for young-of-the-year fish) to a depth of 549 m (1,801 ft), typically in about 90–180 m (295–590 ft). Larvae: hatching length = 4.5 mm, transformation length = 2.4–2.7 cm (0.9-1.1 in). Von Bertalanffy parameters (FL, cm): (females) L_∞ = 52.2, k = 0.17, t_0 = -0.75; (males) L_∞ = 47.6, k = 0.19, t_0 = -1.69 (Love et al. 2002). Length-weight parameters (TL, cm, gr): (females) $0.0287L^{2.822}$; (males) W = W = $0.0359L^{2.745}$ (Love et al. 1990).

MARCOS PERREAU GUIMARAES

SALIENT CHARACTERS: This is another of the more streamlined midwater rockfishes. Dead ones tend to be a uniform brassy, brown, or greenish-brown with yellow fins. Underwater, they can be brown or greenish-brown, with light and dark blotches on the back, and a suffusion of yellow, particularly below the lateral line. If you look closely, particularly in juveniles and smaller adults, you will notice that every scale contains a little dab of orange-brown.

LIFE HISTORY: Young-of-the-year (after about 3.5 months in the plankton) recruit to nearshore waters (occasionally in estuaries) from April–August, settling among kelp and other algae, as well as eelgrass, around oil platforms, and (apparently very rarely) in tide pools. These fish can recruit at as small as 2.8 cm (1 in) SL, but may also remain in the water column until at least 6.3 cm (3 in). Older juveniles (although not adults) are reported to be active at night. Schools of juveniles may remain in the nearshore until fall, when storms drive them deeper. In general, yellowtail migrate into deeper waters as they mature. However, in such areas as southeastern Alaska, a relatively few mature fish live in the nearshore (less than 18 m, 60 ft). Yellowtail mostly live over high relief; they love them rock ridges and boulder fields. While they occasionally rest on the bottom, most often they are well up in the water column, frequently in large schools, which may rise as much as 70 m (230 ft), sometimes to the surface. Fish along the West Coast live in waters as cold as 5.2°C (41°F).

In several ways this is a quite motile species. For instance, and apparently unlike many other rockfishes, individuals often make rapid, frequent, and extensive ascents and descents (at least 40 m, 131 ft). This species also exhibits a very strong homing tendency. If you remove them from a reef and stick them many kilometers away, they will often find their way back. It is unclear to what extent these fish migrate. Certainly juveniles migrate out of Puget Sound to the open coast and some adults have made extensive movements along the Pacific Coast. However, whether this is the norm is not clear. Fish on either side of Cape Mendocino are somewhat, but not completely, isolated from one another.

Yellowtail live to at least 64 years. Females grow larger than males and, after maturation, are larger at age. Fish off Washington and Oregon grow faster than do those off California. This leads to wide variations of size at first maturity. A few males mature at 30–35 cm (12–14 in) FL, 50% at 32–44 cm (13–17 in), and all at 37–54 cm (14–21 in). For females, these values are 27–36 cm (11–14 in), 36–54 (14–21 in), and 38–50 cm (15–20 in), respectively. Larvae are released between January–July. Females produce between 56,000–1,992,700 eggs and fecundity may vary between years. Yellowtail rockfish mostly, although not exclusively, eat midwater prey, including euphausiids, squishy zooplankton (such as medusae, pelagic tunicates, and pteropods), fishes, other large zooplankters (e.g., hyperiid amphipods), but also some benthic shrimps. Chinook salmon, pelagic cormorants, pigeon guillemots, and rhinoceros auklets eat pelagic juveniles and lingcod consume older fish.

FISHERY: Yellowtail were one of the principal commercial rockfish species in 19[th-] century San Francisco and Monterey. Today, it remains a major commercial species, mostly taken in midwater and benthic trawls, and mostly from British Columbia to Central California. They can form a significant bycatch in the Pacific hake fishery, and in 2007 this led to a closure of that fishery. In some locations, these fish are taken in the live fish fishery. This is an important part of the recreational rockfish catch and most are taken from vessels, with small ones caught from piers.

RELATIONSHIPS: Yellowtail are most closely related to black and olive rockfishes.

MISCELLANY: Here's an interesting bit of fluff. During a severe storm off Monterey, yellowtail were left stranded on shore by giant waves.

REMARKS: Unlike most or all other rockfish species, yellowtail seem to be able to quickly release the expanding gasses that accompany a swift ascent into the water column (like when you catch them and quickly haul them in). Because of this, they are much more likely to head straight down when released and avoid becoming seagull food.

Sebastes goodei
(Eigenmann & Eigenmann, 1890)

Chilipepper

JOHN BUTLER

ETYMOLOGY: *Goodei* refers to George Brown Goode (1851–1896).
THE BASICS: Maximum Length: 59 cm (23 in) TL. Maximum Weight: 2.3 kg (5.1 lb). The Ranges: Pratt and Durgin seamounts (eastern Gulf of Alaska) to off Bahia Magdalena (southern Baja California), typically from Cape Mendocino (Northern California) to at least Punta Colnett (northern Baja California). Near surface (young) to 515 m (1,689 ft), mostly in 75–325 m (246–1,066 ft). Larvae: hatching length = about 4.5–5.8 mm, flexion length = about 6.5–8.8 mm, transformation length = about 2.2 cm (1 in). Von Bertalanffy parameters (FL, cm): (females) L_∞ = 52.2, k = 0.17, t_0 = -0.75; (males) L_∞ = 47.6, k = 0.19, t_0 = -1.69 (Love et al. 2002). Length-weight parameters (TL, cm, gr): (sexes combined) W = $0.0076L^{3.12}$ (Love et al. 2002).

SALIENT CHARACTERS: A streamlined species, chilis are one of those rockfish that can very quickly change color and pattern. When dead, or when swimming in the midwater, a chili is brownish on the back, and pinky on flanks, with faint dark markings. However, within a few seconds of settling on the seafloor, the same fish becomes darker, highly blotched, and patterned.

LIFE HISTORY: After a pelagic life of 3.5–5.5 months, young-of-the-year settle onto the seafloor at 3–8.2 cm (1–3 in) SL. Little is known about settlement patterns of these young fish. We know they can recruit to Central California kelp beds, where they quickly form large schools. On the other hand, some fish were reported to have settled on bottom drift kelp in 12 m (40 ft) off La Jolla (Southern California). Regardless of location, chilis leave these very shallow waters within a few months and begin a several year movement into deeper waters. We see adults over rocky bottoms and also on soft seafloors near reefs. Although they often school up, we do see the occasional single individual. Chilis can swim well up into the water column or sit on the bottom. Trawl surveys along the West Coast catch them in at least 5.3–10.8°C (42–51°F).

Don Pearson, who has aged a bone-chilling 40,000-plus chilis, says that they live to 39 years old. Females grow considerably larger than males. Off Central and northern California, a few females are mature at 22 cm FL (9 in, 3 years old), 50% at 26 cm (10.2 in, 3 years old), and almost all at 40 cm (16 in, 8 years old). These parameters are pretty similar for both males and females off southern California. Females produce 18,000–538,000 eggs and release larvae August–June, although mostly during the winter. Chilis appear to feed more-or-less exclusively in the water column. Fishes, euphausiids, and squids make up most of their diets. Predators include blue sharks, bocaccio, other chilipeppers, and California sea lions. Pelagic juveniles are eaten by Chinook salmon.

FISHERY: Chilis have long been an important commercial species; way back in 1880s San Francisco, the fish markets were full of them. With the rise of the semiballoon trawl in the 1940s, chili catches skyrocketed and this fish has remained important ever since. Similarly, they are important in the sport catch in both Southern and Central California.

ORIGINS AND RELATIONSHIPS: Genetic studies imply that chilis are an old species, going back perhaps 5 million years or more, and are distantly related to shortbelly rockfish and bocaccio.

GEORGE BROWN GOODE

From Roppel (1982) we find that Dr. Goode was an early fish hatchery enthusiast: "He believed it was better to expend a small amount of public money to make fish so abundant that they could be caught without restriction and serve as cheap food for the people at large, than to expend a much larger amount to prevent people from catching the few fish that remained." David Starr Jordan wrote: "Although one of the chief builders of the science of Oceanic Ichthyology, Goode was equally interested in the history of Zoology... He also delighted in setting things in order; the striking characteristic of his scientific papers was scholarly accuracy and good taste." *Thus leading one inevitably to ponder what a scientific paper rife with "bad taste" would be like.*

JOHN BUTLER

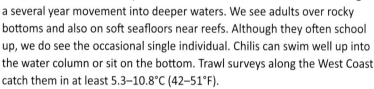

Sebastes helvomaculatus

Ayres, 1859

Rosethorn Rockfish

JOHN BUTLER

ETYMOLOGY: *Helvomaculatus* is Latin for "light yellow" and "spotted."

THE BASICS: Maximum Length: 43 cm (17 in) FL. Maximum Weight: 1.5 kg (3.3 lb). The Ranges: Western Gulf of Alaska (east of Sitkinak Island) to Banco Ranger (28°33'N, 115°25'W) (central Baja California). Rosethorns are common from about Yakutat (Gulf of Alaska) to Central California. 16–1,145 m (52–3,756 ft), typically in 80–350 m (262–1,148 ft). Larvae: birth length = 4.1 mm, flexion length = 7.7–8 mm, transformation length = 1.2–1.9 cm (0.5–0.7 in). Von Bertalanffy parameters (FL, cm): (females) L_∞ = 28.7, k = 0.1, t_0 = -2.77; (males) L_∞ = 27.9, k = 0.11, t_0 = -2.07 (Love et al. 2002). Length-weight parameters (TL, cm, gr): (sexes combined) W = $0.0166L^{2.994}$ (Love et al. 2002).

SALIENT CHARACTERS: This is a small, semi-squat, spiny species. There are 4–5 lighter blotches on the back. Dead ones range from red-orange through orange-yellow, sometimes with a green or yellow wash. Underwater, they come in pinks, yellow, greens, or reds. When doing deeper-water fish surveys, I admit I have a lot of trouble telling this species apart from the pinkrose rockfish.

LIFE HISTORY: Rosethorns live over all kinds of habitats. If you had to generalize, mixed rock/mud bottoms would win out, but they will also occupy boulder fields and plop themselves onto muddy bottoms. These are mostly solitary fish, although a few will often snuggle together in a crevice. We never see them more than a meter or so above the bottom and, in fact, a kind of Theravada-like meditative state seems to characterize them. Trawl surveys off Alaska and the West Coast catch them in at least 4.1–9.1°C (39–48°F).

Rosethorns live to at least 87 years. Males and females mature at about the same size and age. A few fish mature at 20 cm (8 in) TL, 50% at 21–22 cm (8–9 in), and all are mature at 27 cm (11 in). Females release larvae from February–September, peaking in April–June. Rosethorns have a varied diet. Crabs are very important, and they also eat midwater and benthic shrimps, fishes, hyperiid amphipods, copepods, euphausiids, squids, and pelagic tunicates. Among their predators are lingcod and yelloweye rockfish.

FISHERY: Rosethorns were commonly seen in the fish markets of San Francisco at least as early as 1859. Recently, they have been landed in moderate numbers as bycatch in both trawl and longline fisheries along much of the Pacific Coast. Recreational anglers dipping their lines into deeper waters often catch them.

RELATIONSHIPS: As one might expect (if one were at all observant), rosethorns are most closely related to pinkroses and secondarily to swordspines.

Sebastes hopkinsi

(Cramer, 1895)

Squarespot Rockfish

ETYMOLOGY AND COLLOQUIAL NAMES: *Hopkinsi* recognizes Timothy Hopkins (1859–1936). "Belinda bass" and "spotted rockfish" are two other names.

THE BASICS: Maximum Length: 29 cm (11 in) TL. A 28 cm (11 in) fish weighed 275 gr (10 oz). The Ranges: Southern Oregon to northern Baja California (30°19'N, 116°06'W) and Isla Guadalupe (central Baja California), typically from Central California to at least off Bahia San Quintin (northern Baja California). 18–305 m (60–1,000 ft) and mostly in 55–115 m (180–377 ft). Von Bertalanffy parameters (TL, cm): (females) L_∞ = 25.3, k = 0.18, t_0 = -3.36; (males) L_∞ = 24.7, k = 0.06, t_0 = -10.33 (Love et al. 2002). Length-weight parameters (TL, cm, gr): (sexes combined) W = $0.0146L^{2.984}$ (Love et al. 2002).

SALIENT CHARACTERS: Squarespots are shaped like the more elongated seaperch. Both living and dead ones can be brown, tan, or yellow-brown on back and sides and lighter underneath, usually with those characteristic, somewhat-square, dark blotches. Confusingly, these blotches may be indistinct or even missing in fish viewed underwater.

LIFE HISTORY: After a pelagic juvenile phase of 3.5–4 months, young-of-the-year (when at least as small as 4.3 cm, 2 in, SL) settle out over rocks and other structures. My associate, Scott Clark, has found them with some regularity in depths as shallow as 21 m (70 ft). Juveniles and adults live almost entirely over hard bottoms, ranging from boulder fields and rock ridges to cobbles, as well as around wrecks and oil platforms. This is a schooling species that often ascends 10 m (33 ft) and more into the water column, although at times they will spend the day sheltered in crevices. They are quiescent and hide away at night. Squarespots often school with adult pygmies and halfbandeds, as well as with young widows and speckleds. The over 21,000 squarespots we observed in our Southern California submersible surveys lived in 8.8–16.4°C (48–62°F), primarily in 9.7–12°C (49–54°F).

Juveniles swarm around an oil platform.

Squarespots live to about 19 years old. Females grow much larger than males. A few males are mature at 13–15 cm (5–6 in, 4 years) TL and all are mature by 16–17 cm (6–7 in, 5 years). Females first mature at 14–17 cm (6–7 in, 3–5 years) and all are mature by 15–21 cm (6–8 in, 4–7 years). Squarespots living north of Southern California may be slightly larger when they mature. Females develop between 9,000–39,000 eggs and release larvae from January–April. Many of those in Southern California release their larvae in two batches.

Squarespots are planktivores; they mostly eat copepods, hyperiid amphipods, euphausiids, crustacean larvae, and larval fishes. While I would bet that a variety of larger fishes eat them, so far their reported predators are Chinook salmon, California sea lions, and rhinoceros auklets.

FISHERY: There is no commercial fishery for this species. On the other hand, Southern California recreational anglers catch large numbers, primarily because many reefs have been denuded of most larger fishes.

RELATIONSHIPS: Squarespots are most closely related to speckled rockfish and, more distantly, to bank rockfish. No surprise there. Of more interest, perhaps, is that they also appear to be fairly closely related to dwarf-red and whitespotted rockfishes.

REMARKS: Arguably, this is the most abundant fish on medium-depth Southern California reefs. We see just zillions of them.

TIMOTHY HOPKINS

In a somewhat convoluted tale, Mr. Hopkins, an orphan from Maine, was, as an adult, adopted by Mary Hopkins, widow of railroad magnate Mark Hopkins (and wipe that smirk from your face). Timothy Hopkins became a wealthy and respected businessman and philanthropist. Among his better-known achievements was helping to create (along with Leland Stanford) the city of Palo Alto (home of Stanford University). It was at Palo Alto that Hopkins, allegedly at Stanford's request, wrote a liquor sales ban into all of the deeds, thus helping to ensure that generations of Stanford University students would revile his name. In 1892, Hopkins provided extensive funding for the building and equipping of Stanford University's Seaside Laboratory of Natural History at Pacific Grove, later renamed Hopkins Marine Laboratory. Mr. Hopkins also underwrote Barton Evermann's salary, allowing for the completion of the seminal work *The Fishes of North and Middle America* by Jordan and Evermann. When it came time to name the squarespot rockfish, Frank Cramer, student of Stanford University's President David Starr Jordan, paid back this largesse.

So here's my deal: if you build a marine lab for me, I will name a fish after you.

Oops, I almost forgot. It is quite possible that Hopkins was involved in the cover–up of a murder. For all the details, see the discussion regarding David Starr Jordan, under petrale sole, *Eopsetta jordani*.

Sebastes jordani
(Gilbert, 1896)
Shortbelly Rockfish

JOHN BUTLER

This is what happens when natural selection takes a dumpy, spiny, bottom-dwelling ancestral rockfish and over millions of years metaphorically squeezes the tar out of it. Voila, a mackerel-shaped midwater species.

ETYMOLOGY AND COLLOQUIAL NAMES: *Jordani* honors David Starr Jordan (1851–1931), one of the great ichthyologists, blah, blah, blah. See the petrale sole (*Eopsetta jordani*) section for all the usual panegyrics about Jordan, plus a bonus section dealing with some kind of sketchy stuff that he apparently was involved in. "Steamer rockfish" and "slim rockfish" are older names.

THE BASICS: Maximum Length: 35 cm (14 in) TL. Maximum Weight: 0.3 kg (0.6 lb). The Ranges: Perhaps eastern Bering Sea and north of Graham Island, British Columbia to southern Baja California (23°28'N, 110°43'W). Shortbellies are most abundant between Point Reyes (Northern California) and the Northern Channel Islands (Southern California). Adults at depths of about 91–491 m (300–1,611 ft), typically from 150–270 m (492–886 ft), with fish tending to live deeper in Southern California. Larvae: birth length = 5.4 mm, flexion length = 8–10 mm, transformation length = 2.7–3 cm (1.1–1.2 in). Schnute/von Bertalanffy parameters (FL, mm): (females) L_{min} = 154, L_{max} = 258, k = 0.198; (males) L_{min} = 153, L_{max} = 243, k = 0.2 (Field et al. 2007). Length-weight parameters (TL, cm, gr): (sexes combined) $W = 0.0056L^{3.16}$ (Love et al. 2002).

SECOND

I LIKES TO EATS EUPHAUSIIDS

I likes to eats euphausiids
    Crunch on they carapace
And nibbling legs is, oh, so nice
    But 'specially they face.

'Cause euphausiids gots them pointy heads
    And gots them googly eyes
They waves them left and right, you see,
    When they be so surprised.

See, copepods they has their place
    And likewise polychaetes
But euphausiids with them googly eyes
    They makes my day completes.

SALIENT CHARACTERS: Shortbellies are shaped like mackerels, with slender bodies and deeply forked tails. Dead ones are usually pink or brown-pink, and most lack any patterning. The best character when you have one in hand is the position of the anus, which is located well anterior of the anal fin. Underwater (where anus spotting would be a competitive sport), when in the water column, shortbellies range from silvery to bronze or pink and may have mottling and spots. When sitting on the bottom, shortbellies are always high patterned.

LIFE HISTORY: Young-of-the-year, at as small as 3 cm (1 in) SL, recruit to such hard structure as kelp beds, rock piles, oil platforms, and other human-made structures, from at least May–July. As an example, during the summer of 2005, there were just huge numbers of newly recruited individuals on the *Yukon*, a vessel intentionally sunk in about 30 m (98 ft) of water off Mission Bay (Southern California). These young fish may recruit as shallow as kelp bed depths, but I have also seen very small fish in as deep as 120 m (394 ft). Juveniles quickly form large, actively moving, schools. As these fish mature, they tend to migrate into deeper waters. While this is a schooling species (we have often seen many thousands of fish in polarized aggregations), it is not uncommon to spot a lone individual just kind of poking along the bottom. I don't know how wedded shortbellies are to a particular seafloor type, most of the time we see them either lying on, or swimming over, soft and steep seafloors. On the other hand, I have observed them over boulder fields and other high relief, although my sense is that they were just kind of passing through. At least one study found that these fish hang near the bottom during the day and then at night rise up 20–70 m (656–230 ft) to feed. Adults can come to within 30 m (98 ft) of the surface. Shortbellies are fully capable of going through "boom and bust" periods of population increase and decrease without any fishery influence. In Southern California, and not including newly settled fish living in very shallow waters, we see them in 7.7–13.2°C (46–56°F), and mostly at 8.7–11.1°C (48–52°F).

Shortbellies live to at least 32 years old, but rarely past 20. Females grow larger and faster and probably live longer than males. Off Central and Northern California, males and females mature at the same lengths and ages. A few are mature at 12 cm (5 in, 2 year) FL, 50% are mature at 14 cm (6 in, 2 years), and all are mature at 19 cm (8 in, 4 years). Females produce

241

Beaucoup de petits poissons.

DAVID STARR JORDAN REFLECTS

Here's DSJ, perhaps reflecting his times, commenting on a bit of California history: The Spanish missionaries and their actions toward the Native Americans of California: "These men were effective. Not in religion merely, but sociologically. They taught over 75,000 naked, indolent, houseless savages, who had not a single industry this side the stone age, to live in villages; to build such architecture as the missions, and houses for themselves; to farm, raise stock, spin, weave, to be masons, carpenters, plasterers, soapmakers, blacksmiths, millers, bakers, brickmakers, saddlers, etc. If their regime had continued, ninety per cent of these people might have been developed into self-supporting, decent citizens" (Jordan 1905). Actually, what he meant was that the small fraction that survived cholera, measles, and enslavement would have done OK.

as many as 50,000 eggs. Off Oregon, a few fish were observed to produce two batches of eggs per season. Parturition occurs from November–May, mostly January–April, although a few larvae can be found throughout most of the rest of the year. Shortbellies forage in the water column. Day in and day out, euphausiids are the most important prey, although large numbers of copepods are sometimes eaten. Also taken are larval crustaceans, gammarid and hyperiid amphipods, and arrow worms. Occasionally a small fish is nabbed. Shortbellies are important prey for a number of animals. Predators include, but are certainly not limited to, blue and other rockfishes, Chinook salmon, lingcod, longnose lancetfish, longnose skate, Pacific hakes, sablefish, steelhead, common murres, pelagic cormorants, rhinoceros auklets, northern fur seals, fin and sei whales, common dolphins, and Humboldt squids.

FISHERY: There is no commercial fishery for shortbellies. Folks keep thinking about ways to make money off them, but their small size keeps defeating these venture capitalists. On the other hand, it is likely that in the heyday of the foreign trawl fisheries, in the 1960s and 1970s, thousands of tons were taken.

RELATIONSHIP: This may be a very old species, having evolved perhaps 5 million years ago. It is likely most closely related to bocaccio.

MISCELLANY: Once in a while, large numbers of shortbellies, wafted toward shore by atypical southerly winds, pile up on the beaches of Northern California.

REMARKS: As noted previously, this is food for a host of other animals. For instance, it is a major murre food at the Farallon Islands, where it is thought these birds will eat shortbellies in preference to other species. So, when I hear about plans to create fisheries for them, the term "no bueno" comes to mind.

Sebastes levis
(Eigenmann & Eigenmann, 1889)

Cowcod

ETYMOLOGY AND COLLOQUIAL NAMES: *Levis* is Latin for "fantastic." "Roosterfish," "cowfish," and "gallo" (rooster, in several Romance languages) are other names.

THE BASICS: Maximum Length: 100 cm (40 in) TL. Maximum Weight: at least 13.2 kg (29 lb). The Ranges: Norther Oregon (45°44'N, 124°40'W) to Banco Ranger (central Baja California) and Isla Guadalupe (central Baja California). However, larvae have been reported far further southward, to just south of Punta Eugenia (Baja California). They are most typical from Central California to at least off Bahia San Quintin (northern Baja California). Juveniles as shallow as 17 m (55 ft); adults 15–491 m (50–1,610 ft), and mostly at about 130–215 m (426–705 ft). Larvae: birth length = 5 mm, flexion length = 7.6–10.4 mm, transformation length to pelagic juvenile = about 1.9 cm (0.7 in). Von Bertalanffy parameters (FL, cm): (sexes combined) L_∞ = 858, k = 0.06, t_0 = -1.3 (Love et al. 2002). Length-weight parameters (TL, cm, gr): (sexes combined) $W = 0.01L^{3.093}$ (Love et al. 2002).

SALIENT CHARACTERS: With their large heads and mouths, small eyes, and deeply incised dorsal fins, cows are one of the more iconic rockfishes. Dead, they are usually red, orange, or pink, with some faint darker barring and blotching. Underwater, you find them in all kinds of colors, from white and cream to yellow, salmon, and pink. Living fish can rapidly change color – I observed one go from orange to white in 20 seconds.

LIFE HISTORY: Young-of-the-year recruit at at least as small as 4.9 cm (2 in) SL (100 days old), although pelagic juveniles more than 6 cm (2 in) SL have been captured. These juveniles mostly settle out on such hard/low relief as cobble, cobble-small boulder, pipelines, and the shell mounds that surround oil platforms, in depths from at least 17–330 m (55–1,082 ft). As these fish grow, they move into high relief and adults are almost always found in complex habitats (e.g., rock ridges, boulder fields, and the bottom of oil platforms) containing sheltering sites. I often see cows deep within crevices with only an eye showing or fish with their heads in caves and the rest of their bodies flapping in the current. Because cowcod have been so severely overfished, we tend to see only isolated individuals. However, on the one unfished reef anyone has surveyed, the adults were gregarious, often snuggling up together in cracks and crevices. Only rarely will cows rise more than a few meters into the water column. In Southern California, we observed them in 7.7–12.4°C (46–54°F), but mostly in 9–10.7°C (48–51°F).

Cowcod and bocaccio are friends.

MARCOS PERREAU GUIMARAES

Cowcod live to at least 55 years old. Males and females grow at the same rates, although females may grow to a larger maximum size. A few fish mature at about 32 cm (13 in) TL. Off Southern California, 50% of males are mature at 44 cm (17 in), and all are mature at 48 cm (19 in). Fifty percent of females are mature at 43 cm (17 in), and all are mature at 52 cm (21 in). Females produce between 181,000–1,925,000 eggs per season and release their larvae (in several broods in Southern California) between November–May (peaking in the winter). Juvenile cowcod eat copepods, shrimps, mysid shrimps, gammarid amphipods, hydroids, and a few small fishes. Larger individuals tend to stick to fishes, octopuses, and squids, although I did see a bunch of euphausiids in an 80 cm (32 in) TL fish; so who knows? Young cowcod have been found inside chilipeppers.

This is very cool—a pelagic juvenile. BRETT TISCHLER

FISHERY: Cowcod were reasonably important commercial fish as far back as the late 19th century, when fishermen working off San Diego caught them almost daily. Today, commercial fishermen receive premium prices for them. Back in the 1970s, one of my fish processor acquaintances would have his people fillet cowcod and he would then sell them as "white seabass." I kind of miss those days.

The fact that cows are the size (and shape) of Volkswagen Beetles made them a popular species in the Central and Southern California recreational fishery. Some anglers would target cows on party and private vessels, using whole, large fishes as bait. When I was a kid, constantly fishing on partyboats and the avatar of every rockfish's nightmare, I found that cows really liked to bite on black lures.

RELATIONSHIPS: Genetic studies imply that cowcod are an old species, going back perhaps 6 million years, and are not closely related to any living rockfish species.

Sebastes maliger
(Jordan & Gilbert, 1880)

Quillback Rockfish

ETYMOLOGY: *Maliger* is Latin for "mast" and "I bear," referring to the high dorsal spines.

THE BASICS: Maximum Length: 63.6 cm (25 in) TL. Maximum Weight: 3.3 kg (7.2 lb). The Ranges: Kodiak Island to Anacapa Passage (Southern California). They are most abundant from southeastern Alaska to Central California. Intertidal to 274 m (899 ft) and mostly from perhaps 10–130 m (33–426 ft). Von Bertalanffy parameters (FL, cm): (females) L_∞ = 41.8, k = 0.07, t_0 = -6.8; (males) L_∞ = 39.5, k = 0.09, t_0 = -5.5 (Love et al. 2002). A number of other VB parameters are presented in Love et al. (2002). Length-weight parameters (TL, cm, gr): (sexes combined) W = $0.1L^{2.5}$ (Love et al. 2002).

KAWIKA CHETRON

SALIENT CHARACTERS: Another of the more dramatic rockfish, quillback have very long, very deeply incised dorsal fins. They are brown or brown-black with orange or white mottlings and often have a profusion of dark or orange spots.

LIFE HISTORY: In late spring and summer, young-of-the-year recruit (at as small as 2.2 cm, 0.4 in, TL) to nearshore waters, particularly in areas of heavy algae coverage or other complexities. Buckley (1997) theorized that some young-of-the-year settle in slightly deeper water on bottom-drifting bits of algae and move into shallow waters over time. In general, juveniles live around such habitats as rocks, eelgrass, kelp, and cloud sponge gardens. Over time, juveniles begin to move into somewhat deeper waters and most adults live in 20 m (66 ft) or more. Adults live mostly over high relief and next to vertical walls and are often solitary, but will sometimes aggregate in little groups, sometimes with copper rockfish. Lynne Yamanaka and Rick Stanley saw an aggregation of perhaps 100 fish in the Queen Charlotte Islands. Quillback occupy home ranges that are relatively small when on high relief (some as small as 10 m²), but larger over low and less productive reefs. At times, quillback are territorial and will lock jaws over pieces of property. You mostly see them either on the seafloor or hovering 0.5–3 m (1–10 ft) above the bottom, although feeding fish will, on occasion, rise as much as 12 m (40 ft) into the water column. Quillback appear to be most active during the daylight hours.

Quillback live to 95 years. Males and females seem to grow to the same size and males mature somewhat earlier than females. In British Columbia, a few females are mature at 20 cm (8 in, 5 years) FL, 50% at 29 cm (11 in, 11 years), and almost all at 38 cm (15 in, 22 years). In southeastern Alaska, 50% of both males and females are mature at around 35 cm (14 in) FL. Females release larvae from March–July. Quillback eat just about anything they can catch. Fishes are important, as are a vast array of crustaceans (e.g., crabs, shrimps, gammarid amphipods, mysid shrimps, and euphausiids), lingcod and painted green-ling eggs, snails, and pelagic tunicates. Predators include lingcod, yelloweye rockfish, Steller sea lions, and orcas.

FISHERY: Quillback were singled out by Jordan (1887) as an important commercial species around Victoria (British Colum-bia), were noted as an important food fish at Sitka (Alaska) by Bean (1887b), and were often sold in San Francisco markets of that time. Today, they are commercially important throughout much of their range and are a major part of the live-fish fishery. Quillback are often taken in the recreational fishery, particularly from Oregon northward.

RELATIONSHIPS: Among their closest relatives are China, copper, and kelp rockfishes. In Puget Sound, quillback hybridize with coppers and browns.

Sebastes melanops
Girard, 1856

Black Rockfish

ETYMOLOGY AND COLLOQUIAL NAMES: *Melanops* is "black" and "face" in Greek. In the 19th and early 20th centu-ries, they were variously called "black rock cod," "Sitka black bass," and "black bass" among other sobriquets. The Tlingit of southeastern Alaska call them "lit.isdúk." In 1949, the California Department of Fish and Game noted that this species had no official name and that "priestfish" was the official name in Canada. They decided to give that a try. This was a complete failure and one wonders if our cousins to the north were just having a little fun with us. Black rockfish are still widely called "black sea bass."

THE BASICS: Maximum Length: 69 cm (27 in) TL. Maximum Weight: 6 kg (13.3 lb). The Ranges: Southern Bering Sea and Amchitka Island (Aleutian Islands) to northern Baja California. They are most abundant from at least Kodiak Island to Central California. Surface to 366 m (1,200 ft) and mostly in 73 m (240 ft) or less. Larvae: birth length = about 4 mm, flexion length = about 5.7–7.7 mm, length at transformation = 2.3–3.1 cm (0.9–1.2 in). Von Bertalanffy parameters (FL, mm): (females) L_∞ = 442, k = 0.33, t_0 = 0.75 (Bobko and Berkeley 2004). Length-weight parameters (TL, cm, gr): (sexes combined) W = 0.0043L$^{3.362}$ (Love et al. 2002).

SALIENT CHARACTERS: Black rockfish are relatively streamlined fish with almost no head spines. The basic body color is black, although there is usually a light streak (of various widths) running along the flanks and white blotches on the back. This species seems to be particularly prone to developing some orange or yellow on fins and body.

LIFE HISTORY: Young-of-the-year recruit to shallow, nearshore (often intertidal), rocky areas, kelp beds, algae, eelgrass,

MARK LOMELI

and bottom drift algae (mostly at 2.5–4 cm, 1–2 in, SL) from March–September. Settlement takes place both on the open coast and in bays (sometimes fairly estuarine ones). Once settled, juveniles form aggregations, on occasion mixing with other rockfishes. Young black rockfish are one of the few rockfish species that can be predict-ably found in tide pools, where they may stay for a month or more. Mark Lomeli estimated that there were at least 1,000 young-of-the-year black rockfish in a Northern California tide pool. He saw the first ones in mid-June and by the end of August they had departed. In high-energy, open-coast situations (i.e., Central California kelp beds), juveniles may depart the shallowest subtidal waters with the first winter storms. Generally, as these fish mature, they seek deeper water, although always around high relief. However, this does not preclude large schools from coming to the surface and sometimes

Young-of-the-year occupy a Northern California tide pool.

KAWIKA CHETRON

leaping out of the water when chasing prey. Working off southeastern Alaska, Rick Rosenthal and his bunch (1982) found that males tended to be in shallower waters than females. Although black rockfish spend a lot of time schooling in the water column, you can often find them perched on rocks. They are inactive at night. Off Oregon, Parker et al. (2007) observed black rockfish making lots of vertical movements from the bottom to the midwaters and sometimes to the surface. Generally, vertical movements were less in the winter, when the fish spent more time on the bottom. Both genetic studies and otolith microchemistry imply that fish off Oregon and Washington move little and that their larvae may not disperse very far. However, there are the occasional fish that just get up and boogie, as a number of females have been caught way off shore. For instance, two running ripe females were taken more than 1,000 km (621 mi) from shore in central Gulf of Alaska. So what is that about?

Black rockfish live to 56 years old. Females grow larger than males. A recent study has it that females off Oregon mature at around 34.5 cm (14 in, about 5 years) FL, 50% are mature at 40–42 cm (16–17 in, 7–8 years), and all are mature by 45 cm (18 in, 10–15 year). A study from southeastern Alaska found similar results for both sexes. A few fish mature at as small as 25 cm (10 in, 3 years). Females produce between 283,618–1,135,457 eggs. Females release larvae from January–March and larger females release larvae earlier in the season. Black rockfishes appear to feed primarily in the water column. Younger fish feed mostly on zooplankton and as the fish grow they begin to target fishes in a big way. Zooplankton prey include all kinds of crustaceans (euphausiids, gammarid amphipods, copepods, and crustacean larvae), pteropods, and polychaetes, along with such benthic organisms as octopuses, isopods, caridean shrimps, and the occasional rock. Predators include Chinook salmon, lingcod, bald eagles, pigeon guillemots, rhinoceros auklets, Steller sea lions, and minks.

FISHERY: Way back in the 19th century, black rockfish was one of the most important species in San Francisco markets and was noted as an important food fish as far north as Kodiak Island. The black rockfish is still taken in various subsistence fisheries as far north as the Gulf of Alaska, and has remained an important commercial species (taken mostly by hook-and-line, but sometimes in trawls), from the Chignik area of Alaska to Central California, and finding particular favor in the live fish trade. Sport fishermen catch lots of them from piers (mostly juveniles), rocky shores, jetties, and vessels.

Evermann and Goldsborough (1907) evinced a rather cavalier attitude toward the sporting qualities of the black rockfish with: "They are therefore a 'boy's fish,' which will not appeal strongly to the experienced angler, but they are good food fish." *So, what's a "girl's" fish?*

RELATIONSHIPS: Black rockfish are closely related to olive and yellowtail rockfishes.

REMARKS: Steve Berkeley and associates (see Berkeley et al. 2004) came up with the Big Old Fat Female (BOFF) concept when studying black rockfish. The BOFF observation (now shown to be true for at least some other rockfishes) is that older females produce larvae with higher levels of lipids than small females. This allows larvae of older females to 1) grow faster and 2) resist starvation.

Sebastes melanostomus
(Eigenmann & Eigenmann, 1890)
Blackgill Rockfish

JOHN BUTLER

ETYMOLOGY: *Melanostomus* is Greek for "black" and "mouth."

THE BASICS: Maximum Length: 61 cm (24 in) TL. Maximum Weight: 3.4 kg (7.4 lb). The Ranges: Northern British Columbia (off the west coast of the Queen Charlotte Islands) to Isla Cedros (central Baja California), typically from Northern California to at least Southern California. Pelagic juveniles have been taken as far south as Punta Abreojos (26°06'N, 114°05'W) (southern Baja California), strongly implying that adults live in southern Baja California. 88–768 m (289–2,520 ft), mostly in 200–600 m (656–1,968 ft). Larvae: Hatching length: 4.5 mm, flexion length: 6.2–7.2 mm, transformation length: about 1.6 cm (0.6 in). Von Bertalanffy parameters (TL, cm): (females) $L_\infty = 55.4$, $k = 0.04$, $t_0 = -4.66$; (males) $L_\infty = 46.7$, $k = 0.06$, $t_0 = -2.98$ (Love et al. 2002). Length-weight parameters (TL, cm, gr): (sexes combined) $W = 0.0122L^{3.042}$ (Love et al. 2002).

SALIENT CHARACTERS: Blackgills are heavy-bodied and spiny. Dead ones are usually red with dark overtones on the back. Underwater, they tend to be red or pink, often with white blotches or dark saddles on the back, and white-tipped dorsal spines. There are black streaks on the rear edge of the gill cover, in the mouth, and in the fold above the upper jaw.

A mound o' blackgills.

COURTESY OF MICK KRONMAN

LIFE HISTORY: Young-of-the-year (at between 3 and 7 months old) settle out of the plankton at around 3.6 cm (1 in) SL in 200 m (656 ft) or more. I have seen newly settled juveniles on sand near rocks in over 300 m (984 ft). We see older juveniles over rocks and other structures and over mud. Adults live on high relief and crevice-filled rocks and these fish often are kind of tucked away in holes and caves. They live in at least 4.7–10.2°C (40–50°F).

Blackgills live to at least 90 years old. Females grow larger and may live longer than males. Off California, the smallest mature fish are 29 cm (11 in) TL, 50% are mature at 34 cm (13 in), and all are mature at 39 cm (15 in). Fish off Oregon seem to be a bit larger as 50% of males are mature at 37 cm (15 in) and 50% of females at 41 cm (16 in). These fish mature at between 13–26 years old. Females produce between about 152,000–769,000 eggs and release their larvae from January–June. The few blackgills that have been checked ate fishes.

FISHERY: In the days of lots of rockfishes, commercial fishermen pretty much ignored blackgills. They live in deep water and who wants to dump a lot of gear in deep water? In the 1970s and particularly by the 1980s, most of the shallow rockfish spots in Southern and Central California (down to maybe 274 m, 900 ft) had been hit hard, and those deeper-water fish started to look pretty good. The good news was that, with their nice red skin, blackgills proved very popular in Asian markets. Here is Mick Kronman (unpublished) describing this hook-and-line fishery: "Blackgills' suicidal behavior, however, was both good news and bad news. Sure, you could milk a single pinnacle for dozens of tons of fish before it expired, but when the foam settled, every last fish on the spot was gone. 'Absolutely kamikaze,' says Tim Athens [commercial fisherman], describing blackgills' eating habits. 'After fishing'em I became convinced that you can completely decimate a rockfish spot with hook-and-line. Don't let anybody ever tell you it can't be done, because I've done it.'"

Similarly, until the 1990s, blackgills were a very minor part of the rockfish recreational catch in Southern California. But, as shallower water species were heavily fished, fishermen began targeting blackgills.

RELATIONSHIPS: Genetic studies imply that blackgills are a relatively old species, going back 6 million years and more, and are not closely related to any living rockfish.

Sebastes miniatus
(Jordan & Gilbert, 1880)
Vermilion Rockfish

Our old friend genetics has shown that the "vermilion" rockfish is actually two closely related species. But, since most previous work assumed one species, we can't tell which study refers to which species. So, I have just said the hell with it and placed almost all of the data under one bailiwick.

A kind of older juvenile.

ETYMOLOGY AND COLLOQUIAL NAMES: *Miniatus* is Latin for "vermilion." John Hyde has given the new (and at this time undescribed species) the name S. *crocotulus*, "sunset rockfish." "Vermilion rockfish" was used at least as far back as the late 19th century. Vermilions are most often referred to as "red snapper," but both "rasher" and "barracho" were commonly used in the early 20th century.

THE BASICS: Maximum Length: 76 cm (30 in) TL. Maximum Weight: 6.8 kg (14.9 lb). The Ranges: Zaikof Bay, Montague Island (Prince William Sound, Alaska) to Islas San Benito (central Baja California). They are fairly common at least as far northward as the southern Strait of Georgia and the west coast of Vancouver Island, and really abundant from Northern California to at least off Bahia San Quintin (northern Baja California). Juveniles in shallow water, adults in 12–439 m (39–1,440 ft). In Southern California, subadults and adults are typically in 40–105 m (131–344 ft). Adult sunsets are usually found in deeper waters than vermilions. Scattered adults come into shallow depths (sometimes into kelp beds) in colder water areas. Length-weight parameters (TL, cm, gr): (sexes combined) W = 0.0216L$^{2.923}$ (Love et al. 2002).

SALIENT CHARACTERS: Newly settled fish are dark, with a light caudal fin. Within a few months they become red or red-brown, with various light and dark mottling. Adults are various shades of red and orange-red, often with gray and black mottling, although the presence of two species (each perhaps with a typical color pattern) makes it difficult to generalize.

LIFE HISTORY: Young-of-the-year recruit at as small as 1.3 cm (0.5 in) SL (but mostly at maybe 2.5–3 cm, 1 in) from at least August–April, to a range of nearshore habitats, out to depths of at least 40 m (131 ft). Little reds recruit to a wide range of reasonably low relief structures, such as sand dollar beds, tubeworm colonies, eelgrass, cobble, and the sandy areas just outside kelp forests. Within a year or less, most of the juveniles that have settled in the shallowest depths begin to move into slightly deeper waters, and over the years (particularly south of Point Conception), most continue to move deeper as they mature. Juveniles and subadults begin to target high-relief areas and adults are most often found where there are crevices, caves, and other sheltering spots. Boulder fields, rock ridges, and the bottoms of some oil platforms are typical spots. Juveniles and adults will school (sometimes in aggregations of 100 or more), both in the water column (as much as 9 m, 30 ft, above the seafloor), or near the bottom. While their activity patterns are poorly understood, juveniles can be active at night. We don't know much about their movement patterns, although

A more or less newly settled juvenile.   KIM MITCHELL

juveniles and subadults may be quite motile. On the other hand, Dave Kushner reports that several very large ones living in the shallow water around San Miguel Island may have stayed in the same area for at least a decade. John Hyde and Russ Vetter (2009), working with vermilions (the real vermilions, *S. miniatus*, mind), found that there were barriers to complete genetic dispersal along the Washington coast, as well as across Cape Mendocino, Point Conception, Santa Monica Bay, and Punta Colnett.

Vermilions live to at least 60 years. Females grow larger than males. A few fish mature at around 31 cm (12 in, 4 years) TL, 50% are mature at about 37 cm (15 in, 5 years), and all are mature by 47 cm (19 in, 9 years). Females release larvae almost throughout the year, with a fall peak. Fecundity ranges from about 63,000–2,600,000 eggs. Vermilions feed on crustaceans (mostly euphausiids, copepods, and mysid shrimps) and fishes, as well as amphipods, caridean shrimps, octopuses, and squids. California sea lions eat them.

FISHERY: Vermilions were very important in the commercial fisheries of 19th-century San Francisco and San Diego. Throughout the 20th century, their bright red color (and hence high demand) made vermilions a real take home pay fish for commercial fishermen fishing with hook and line and later with gill nets. The prices were good, the fish were abundant, and they bit a hook real well. The redoubtable Mick Kronman, who seems to have interviewed just about every commercial fisherman in Santa Barbara, quotes veteran fisherman Red Allen as noting that while fishing the reefs between Point Conception and Point Arguello: "He remembers

Vermilions, kelps, and a copper.   KAWIKA CHETRON

hauls as great as five tons of vermilions in a single day" (Kronman, unpublished). Reds are still an important species both as dead fish on ice and, when the fishermen can pull it off, as live product. I also see large numbers of them in the Mercado Negro of Ensenada (northern Baja California). This is a really important recreational species because everyone loves to catch those reds.

RELATIONSHIPS: As noted above, "vermilion" rockfish are comprised of two species. Both are closely related to canary rockfish.

MISCELLANEY: Kim Anthony (2009) caught some at platforms in the Santa Barbara Channel, moved them 11–18 km (7–11 mi) away to Anacapa Island, and a number of them promptly moved back to the rigs.

This is likely a sunset rockfish.   JOHN BUTLER

THAT'S THE WAY THE WORLD GOES ROUND

When I was a commercial fisherman we got 12 cents a pound for brightly colored rockfishes (e.g., vermilions, cows, flags, and greenspotteds), all termed "reds," and 6 cents a pound for drabber species (e.g., chilis, bocaccio, and widows), all called "junk." This was because people would rather buy the more colorful species and is a perfect example of how cultural factors influence what fish we purchase. The reality is that, despite small differences in texture and flavor, once rockfishes hit the plate, it's all about the same.

Sebastes mystinus
(Jordan & Gilbert, 1881)
Blue Rockfish

There appear to be two species of "blue" rockfish tentatively called "blue-blotched" and "blue-sided."

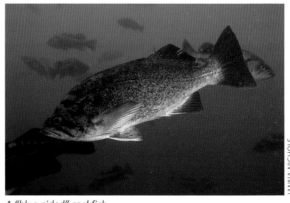

A "blue-sided" rockfish.

ETYMOLOGY AND COLLOQUIAL NAMES: *Mystinus* means "priest" in Greek, a reference to the dark color of both fish and professional clothing. Many, many folks call them "blue bass" and no sin there. Early on, they were often called "priestfish."

As with "vermilion rockfish" and "rougheye rockfish," it now appears that the "blue rockfish" is actually two, likely very closely related, species. Because researchers have been previously unaware of this distinction, at this time it is not possible to differentiate previously completed research conducted on the two species. So, as I have done on several occasions, I have lumped all "blue rockfish" research together, on the likely overly simplistic notion that, basically, these two species do things similarly, so the information can't be too wrong.

THE BASICS: Maximum Length: 53.3 cm (21 in) TL. Maximum Weight: 1.8 kg (3.9 lb). The Ranges: Chatham Strait and Kruzof Island (southeastern Alaska) to Santo Tomas (31°30'N) (northern Baja California). The northernmost range appears to be uncertain, at least partially due to this species' resemblance to the dark rockfish (*S. ciliatus*). It is likely that all "blue rockfish" recorded from the Bering Sea and the western Gulf of Alaska refer to dark rockfish. Blues (likely two species remember) are fairly common at least as far north as Ohiat Islet, Barkley Sound (British Columbia) and very abundant from some place along the Oregon coast to Southern California. Surface to about 549 m (1,800 ft), including intertidal zone, commonly from barely subtidal waters to about 55 m (180 ft). Larvae: birth length = about 3.8 mm, transformation length to pelagic juvenile = larger than 2.1 cm (0.8 in). Von Bertalanffy parameters (FL, mm): (females) L_∞ = 400, k = 0.149, t_0 = -1.34; (males) L_∞ = 329, k = 0.195, t_0 = -0.95 (Laidig et al. 2003). Length-weight parameters (TL, cm, gr): (sexes combined) W = $0.0158L^{2.988}$ (Love et al. 2002).

Here's a "blue-blotched" one.   ROBERT LEE

SALIENT CHARACTERS: Both species are somewhat oval with reduced head spines. Blue-blotcheds are, as the name implies, blotchy on the sides, and tend to have a deeper body. Blue-sideds are slimmer, have a more even, and often darker coloration, and have a more prominent and elevated lateral line.

LIFE HISTORY: After 3–6 months in the plankton (when at least as small as 3.1 cm, 1 in, SL), young-of-the-year recruit between April–July to nearshore reefs, kelp beds, and oil platforms, as well as deeper tide pools and occasionally bays and estuaries (often in eelgrass). Linda Snook saw a few, very small fish on a reef in 63 m (207 ft), but based on our surveys maximum settlement depth is usually 40 m (131 ft) and shallower. Little blues first form bottom-oriented schools, sometimes in association with olive and black rockfishes. As these fish mature, their schools ascend higher into the water column, although almost always over hard and high relief seafloors. Acoustic tagging studies in Northern California kelp beds (Jorgensen et al. 2006) suggest that adult blues typically do not move more than 100 m (328 ft) from a central core zone. Results from this study also suggested that for these fish "where kelp is abundant, blue rockfish may prefer it to adjacent areas without kelp." Schools of adults may number in the thousands of individuals and often mix with olive rockfish or blacksmiths. At night, both juveniles and adults generally hunker down in crevices and other shelters.

Because they have internal fertilization, one would imagine that rockfishes have some kind of courtship behavior. This has only rarely been observed in West Coast rockfishes (although Japanese researchers not only frequently observe it, they have very nice images of it). In several cases, a blue rockfish male has been seen swimming by the head of a female while kind of thrusting his ventral area near her snout. Of course, in no instance has mating actually been observed among blue rockfish, so whether this approach actually works or if it's merely an unrequited fetish is unknown. Cope (2004) noted some genetic differences between fish living north and south of Cape Mendocino (Northern California). However, given the potential confusion between the two species, these findings should remain provisional.

Blue rockfish live to at least 44 years old. A few fish are mature at 22 cm (9 in, 4–5 years) TL and all are mature by 32–35 cm (13–14 in, 9–11 years). Females produce at least as many as 525,000 eggs and release larvae between October–March, but mostly in January and February. Both juveniles and adults feed primarily on water column organisms, particularly crustaceans (e.g., copepods, mysid shrimps, gammarid amphipods, and various larvae), gelatinous zooplankton (e.g., pteropods, siphonophores, medusae, and larvaceans), arrow worms, and polychaetes. Larger blues add fishes and squids to this diet. Some individuals also eat hydroids and algae. Blue rockfish, and particularly their young-of-the-year, are eaten by a very wide range of critters, including gopher, kelp, and olive rockfishes, kelp greenlings, lingcod, pigeon guillemots, and California sea lions. Pelagic juveniles are food for Chinook salmon and a number of sea birds.

KAWIKA CHETRON

FISHERY: Wearing that rather drab mantle and with a reputedly short shelf life, blues were never a terribly popular commercial species, although in the 19th century they were the most abundant rockfish in the markets of San Francisco. And until recently blues were classified with such "junk" rockfish as bocaccio and chilipepper and brought only low prices to commercial fishermen. However, the rise of the live fish fishery, where any rockfish brought in alive is worth more than most rockfishes dead, has earned blues a moderate place among sought-after species.

On the other hand, this is a major sport species. They are primarily taken in California, with lesser numbers off Oregon and Washington. Although caught mainly on recreational vessels, substantial numbers of mostly young ones are captured by anglers fishing from rocky shores, jetties, and piers. In such areas as the Big Sur coast, adult fish can be taken from the rocky shoreline.

RELATIONSHIPS: Blues are closely related to widow rockfish.

REMARKS: During years when they are fortunate enough to survive the rigors of a pelagic existence and recruit heavily to nearshore reefs, young-of-the-year are a really important food for many predators.

Sebastes nebulosus
Ayres, 1854

China Rockfish

Another dramatic fish.

ETYMOLOGY: *Nebulosus* is Latin for "clouded."

THE BASICS: Maximum Length: 45 cm (18 in) TL. Maximum Weight: 1.9 kg (4.2 lb). The Ranges: Kodiak Island to Redondo Beach and San Nicolas Island (Southern California), typically from at least as far north as British Columbia to Central California. 3–128 m (10–420 ft), most fish live in 10 m (33 ft) and greater. Length-weight parameters (TL, cm, gr): (sexes combined) $W = 0.0548L^{2.715}$ (Love et al. 2002).

SALIENT CHARACTERS: Chinas are compact and spiny. They are black or blue-black, mottled with yellow and sometimes white, and usually with a simply grand yellow stripe that runs from about the third dorsal spine down to and along the lateral line. Some individuals are liberally sprinkled with yellow spots. Chinas that were almost completely yellow, and others totally black, have been observed.

LIFE HISTORY: Young-of-the-year may settle out in shallow waters during the summer, but precisely when and in what habitat(s) is unclear. Chinas almost always (or perhaps always, but we are trained never to use that word) live in complex structure, like boulder fields or kelp beds. A study from the west coast of Vancouver Island found that Chinas are solitary animals that likely have both home ranges and territories. They tend to stay put during the day and stray just a bit (a few

ROBERT LEE

more meters) at night. Giant Pacific octopuses and Chinas sometimes occupy the same crevice, sometimes in an amicable manner. Most fish stay right on the bottom or only a few meters above it; they may be most active during evening hours.

Chinas live to at last 79 years. Males and females mature at about the same size and age. A few fish are mature at about 26 cm (10 in) TL and all will reproduce by 30 cm (12 in). Females release larvae from January–August. Benthic invertebrates, particularly brittle stars and crustaceans (e.g., crabs, shrimps, and caprellid amphipods) are favored, but fishes can also be important. Other invertebrate prey include bryozoans, hydroids, nudibranchs, snails, various abalones, octopuses, and hermit crabs.

FISHERY: Chinas, blessed with that bright coloration, were readily salable in 19th-century fish markets. Today, the big money for this species is as live product, wherever that is legal, from British Columbia southward. Recreational anglers catch good numbers from Central California all the way up to the Gulf of Alaska.

RELATIONSHIPS: Chinas may be one of the older living species of the *Pteropodus* subgenus, the spiny group made up, along with Chinas, of quillback, coppers, and the like.

Sebastes paucispinis
Ayres, 1854

Bocaccio

ETYMOLOGY AND COLLOQUIAL NAMES: *Paucispinis* is Latin for "few" and "spines." When I was a kid, everyone called them "groupers" or "salmon groupers."

THE BASICS: Maximum Length: At least 98.1 cm (39 in) TL. Maximum Weight: 10.7 kg (23.6 lb). The Ranges: Western Gulf of Alaska, south of Shumagin Islands, and Alaska Peninsula to Punta Blanca (29°05'N, 118°13'W) (central Baja California). However, larvae have been taken further southward to about 26°N (southern Baja California). Bocaccio are most abundant from Northern California to at least Bahia San Quintin (northern Baja California), are less common along the Oregon and Washington coasts, with high-density pockets off British Columbia. Juveniles near surface and in inshore waters (rarely in tide pools), adults at about 20–475 m (66–1,578 ft). In Southern California, we see most adults in 95–225 m (312–738 ft) of water. Larvae: birth length = 4–5 mm, flexion length = 7.2–9.7 mm, transformation length to pelagic juvenile = about 1.5–3 cm (0.6–1.2 in). Von Bertalanffy parameters (British Columbia) (FL, cm): (females) L_∞ = 78.3, k = 0.163, t_0 = -1.2; (males) L_∞ = 69.98, k = 0.108, t_0 = -8.46 (Stanley et al. 2009). (Central and Northern California) (FL, cm): (both sexes) Length@A_{min} = 26, (females) Length@A_{max} = 67.8, k = 0.22; (males) Length@A_{max} = 58.9, k = 0.27 (Field et al. 2010). Length-weight parameters (TL, mm, kg): (sexes combined) W = $0.000000005833L^{3.0941}$ (RecFin 2009).

SALIENT CHARACTERS: Bocaccio are elongate and laterally compressed fish with a very large mouth and few head spines. Their lower jaw extends out beyond the upper and is tipped with a prominent knob. Juveniles are red-brown to brown and may have saddles, bars, and spots. Dead adults are dark on the back and salmony elsewhere, often with many small dark spots and some with vague mottling. Underwater, fish in the water column are colored similarly to dead ones; fish sitting on the bottom are covered with bright white and dark blotches and spots. Folks have found a variety of color variants, including (most commonly) bright orange fish, along with pink-orange, and gray ones.

LIFE HISTORY: Unusual for the rockfishes, juveniles may remain pelagic until they are at least 11 cm (4 in) SL and 5.5 months old. Young-of-the-year recruit mostly to nearshore waters (at as small as 0.9 cm, 0.4 in, TL) from January–August, perhaps mainly in May and June. I have seen what appeared to be newly settled juveniles near the bottom at depths as great as 80 m (262 ft) and Mary Yoklavich saw what looked like new recruits in more than 274 m (900 ft). Juveniles recruit to the kelp canopy, other nearshore algae, eelgrass, rocky reefs, drifting kelp mats, piers, tide pools (rarely), and the midwaters of oil platforms (here they can form extremely large schools). Within a few months to about one year, juveniles begin to retreat into deeper waters, a process that may take several more years. Older juveniles and adults are pretty much structure-oriented and are most often found where there are such sheltering sites as caves and crevices. Both juveniles and smaller adults will move well off the bottom (as much as 30 m, 98 ft), but those old ones with the big potbellies tend to stay in caves. On shallow-cresting pinnacles, such as Cordell Bank (Northern California), adults will come close to the surface when chasing food. Juveniles and subadults may be fairly mobile, moving from reef to reef, while older fish may be more sedentary. Bocaccio have been caught in waters as cold as 5.3°C (42°F). In Southern California, we see them mostly in 9.5–12°C (49–54°F) and as warm as at least 16.6°C (62°F). Although genetic studies have kind of implied that bocaccio form one unit along the Pacific Coast, it is likely that there are two "demographic clusters," from Central California southward and along British Columbia, as this species is relatively uncommon along Oregon and Washington.

STEVE MURVINE

THE ROCKFISH LONGLINER

Tim Thomas interviewed an elderly Monterey fisherman and here is what he found out: "When Vince Giamanco's family came to Monterey at the turn of the 20th century, the sardine fishery was in its infancy and the bay was pristine. The Giamanco's plied the bay for rockfish and albacore; they were long-liners and hook & line fishermen. Mr. Giamanco would say, 'You never starve when you hook & line.'

"Vince Giamanco was 5 years old when he started to fish rockfish with his father, Antonino (in the Sicilian community a boy is considered a man at 7.) A typical day would begin at 2 am when Vince and his older brother, along with their dad, would walk the 3 blocks from their home to the Monterey Wharf, often times just steps ahead of the truant officer. From there they would board their small 32-foot jig boat that would take them to the fishing grounds, usually between the Bixby Creek Bridge and Point Sur. This area was known to the Monterey fishermen as the 'Ranch.' If Vince was lucky, he could get some sleep during the four to five hour trip. The boat had no radio, depth finder, or fish finder, Mr. Giamanco didn't need them; he had decades of experience fishing these same waters.

"At dawn, they would start to lay out their longline gear, anywhere from 10–15 baskets with 250 hooks each. For the next eight hours they would pull in rockfish—chilipeppers, black cod [sablefish], and in the spring, bocaccio. Vince says, 'Sometimes you would have a chili on every hook and a bocaccio trying to eat it—two fish on one hook. The bocaccio could weigh 7–8 pounds and the chili 2–3 pounds; in no time at all, you had the boat loaded.' Other times when the fish were biting, they would lay out 25–30 lines and leave them alone. When the fish stopped biting, they would pull in 400–500 pounds of fish per line. It was not unusual to bring in 4 tons on a single trip.

"On the way home, Vince and his brother would "pin" (place the hooks) and bait the baskets for the next day, a process that could take the whole five hour trip. Once back in Monterey, they would sell their catch to the local fish markets on the Wharf, and if they were lucky, be home by five. This routine was repeated five–six days a week throughout the winter and spring. They made a very good living. As Vince grew up, so did the fishing industry. Vince likes to say, 'Those were the old days. I don't think you can catch 10 fish in the same area today.'

"The biggest change came, he believes, in the form of gear—nylon nets and drag boats changed the rockfish fishery, and not for the better. The weighted nylon nets were often lost in the bay. Vince says, 'In my opinion, that would kill fish forever and ever; the nylon net never deteriorates.' The drag boats pounded the sandy bottom in 80–90 fathoms outside the rock-beds. Four or five boats working everyday, disturbing the natural habitat. 'It disturb them so bad that we couldn't fish there anymore.'"

Bocaccio live to at least 58 years old. Females grow larger than males. Size at maturity varies greatly with geographic area. Off Southern California, 50% of both males and females are mature at 35–36 cm (14 in) TL and all are mature at 42–44 cm (17 in). Off Central and Northern California, 50% of females are mature at about 39.9 cm (16 in, about 3–4 years old) FL and 95% are mature at 48.1 cm (19 in, 5–6 years old). Fish off British Columbia mature when much larger than those further southward; 50% of females are mature at about 55 cm (22 in) FL (6 years old). Females may release larvae throughout the year, although most occurs from October–July, with a January–February peak. Multiple releases of larvae by a female frequently occur off Southern California, but are unusual further northward. Females produce between 20,000–2,298,000 eggs. Bocaccio, with their preternaturally large mouths, are effective fish predators; hoo boy, don't you know. Even young-of-the-year prey on small fishes, including smaller bocaccio, along with such zooplankters as euphausiids. Larger bocaccio prey almost completely on fishes and squids, although an occasional shrimp may be consumed. Predators include blue and leopard sharks, lingcod, seals, and sea lions. Pelagic juveniles are eaten by such predators as Chinook salmon and rhinoceros auklets.

FISHERY: Back in 19th-century San Francisco, bocaccio was an important commercial species. In the late 1940s, along the California coast, catches really ratcheted up as the semiballoon trawl (able to be towed over low rocks) caught on. Historically, this was one of the major rockfish species in the sport fishery of Central and Southern California. Bocaccio remained a mainstay of both fisheries in California until too many folks caught too many fish. Bocaccio have been declared overfished by the federal government.

Survivorship through the pelagic juvenile phase for young bocaccio is very erratic and good year classes occur, on average, only every decade or so. When survivorship is good, however, inshore reef areas can be just flooded with young fish. During these years in the good old days, before game wardens were too finicky, young-of-the-year bocaccio supported very large pier fisheries in Central California. I remember my folks taking me to the Cayucos Pier (located just above Morro Bay) in the 1950s, and seeing dozens of farm families from the San Joaquin Valley catching thousands of young bocaccio. As some family members were catching four fish at a time (often on bare hooks), others would be cleaning and bagging them for use during the winter.

RELATIONSHIPS: Based on genetic studies, bocaccio go back a long ways, perhaps 5 million years and more. They are at least distantly related to shortbelly rockfish.

MISCELLANY: I think bocaccio have a very distinctive, kind of sickly-sweet odor, quite different from other rockfishes. If you have hung around party or commercial vessels long enough, you can just tell when they have loads of bocaccio. In fact, even their swim bladder gas tastes different from other rockfishes. I spent a good part of my college career tagging rockfishes. When they are caught from waters deeper than perhaps 30 m (98 ft) their swim bladders expand and they must be deflated to allow them to return to depth carrying their tag. A quick way to deflate them is to stick a hypodermic needle into their bladders and quickly suck the gas out. Even with my eyes closed, by the taste of that gas, I could always tell when I was deflating a bocaccio.

REMARKS: The Puget Sound/Georgia Basin segment of the bocaccio population has been declared endangered by the National Marine Fisheries Service under the Endangered Species Act. That is just one step away from kissing their anal fins goodbye.

Bocaccio are capable of producing at least three different low-frequency and short-duration sounds.

Sebastes pinniger
(Gill, 1864)

Canary Rockfish

ETYMOLOGY AND COLLOQUIAL NAMES: *Pinniger* is Latin for "large-finned." In the 19th century, they were called "orange rockfish" (they still are) and "flianum." In my youth, we called them "red snappers."

THE BASICS: Maximum Length: 76 cm (30 in) TL. Maximum Weight: 6.7 kg (14.7 lb). The Ranges: Western Gulf of Alaska south of Shelikof Strait to Punta Colnett (northern Baja California), typically from at least British Columbia to Central California. Young fish in shallow waters (occasionally in tide pools); adults about 18–838 m (59–2,749 ft) and mostly from 80–200 m (262–656 ft). Larvae: birth length = 3.6–4 mm, flexion length = less than 7.8 mm, transformation length = 1.3–2 cm (0.5–0.8 in). Von Bertalanffy parameters (FL, cm): (females) L_∞ = 56.9, k = 0.163, t_0 = 0.561; (males) L_∞ = 52.9, k = 0.174, t_0 = 0.32 (Stanley et al. 2009, British Columbia). Length-weight parameters (TL, cm, gr): (sexes combined) $W = 0.012L^{3.056}$ (Love et al. 2002).

SALIENT CHARACTERS: Basically, canaries are orange or yellow fish heavily marked with gray. The lateral line sits in a gray zone and the anal fin is pointed and slants anteriorly.

LIFE HISTORY: From April–July, young-of-the-year recruit to nearshore areas, mostly at lengths of 2.3–3 cm (1 in) SL. These fish settle on the bottom, often along the edges of rocks and kelp (and rarely in tide pools). Young fish begin to move into somewhat deeper waters within a few months. Older juveniles and adults are found most often around high-relief structures, such as rock ridges and boulders, but also on cobble and on mud-rock habitats. This is a schooling species that, while usually found near the bottom, will ascend well up into the water column. Canaries have been taken in waters down to at least 5.2°C (41°F) and we have observed them in waters as warm as 12.2°C (54°F).

Canaries live to at least 84 years. Females grow larger than males. Off British Columbia, a few females are mature at perhaps 37 cm (15 in, 7 years) FL, 50% at around 50 cm (20 in, 14 years), and all at about 54 cm (21 in, about 20 years). Females produce between 260,000–1,900,000 eggs and release their young November–March. Young-of-the-years are planktivores, targeting euphausiids, calanoid and harpacticoid copepods, crustacean larvae, mysid shrimps, and gammarid amphipods. Older juveniles and subadults prey on euphausiids, gelatinous zooplankton, caridean shrimps, pelagic red crabs, and a few fishes. Larger individuals add still more fishes to their diets. Pelagic juvenile canaries are eaten by Chinook salmon and pigeon guillemots. Lingcod and yelloweye rockfish eat larger individuals.

FISHERY: Canaries have been an important commercial species since at least the late 19th century, and for many years they were a major commercial trawl and hook-and-line species from Central California to British Columbia. Declared overfished in U.S. waters, catches there are relatively small, although they have remained relatively robust in British Columbia waters.

This is a major sport species, particularly from Central California northward.

RELATIONSHIPS: Canary rockfish are most closely related to the two vermilion rockfish species.

Sebastes polyspinis
(Taranetz & Moiseev, 1933)

Northern Rockfish

JOHN BUTLER

ETYMOLOGY AND COLLOQUIAL NAME: *Polyspinis* means "many spines" in Latin, referring to the extra dorsal spine this species bears. The Japanese call them "kitanomenuke."

THE BASICS: Maximum Length: 48 cm (19 in) TL. Maximum Weight: 2.1 kg (4.6 lb). The Ranges: North Pacific off Kuril Islands to Bering Sea at Pervenets Canyon, and Commander–Aleutian chain to Graham Island (northern British Columbia). They are common all along the Aleutian Islands and Alaska mainland, perhaps to about the Yakutat area, and are one of the most abundant rockfish in the Gulf of Alaska and much of the Aleutian Islands. 10–740 m (33–2,428 ft), mostly in 75–200 m (246–656 ft). Von Bertalanffy parameters (FL, mm): (females) L_∞ = 376, k = 0.178, t_0 = -0.31; (males) L_∞ = 357, k = 0.205, t_0 = -0.04 (Malecha et al. 2007). Length-weight parameters (FL, cm, gr): (sexes combined) W = $0.0136L^{3.04}$ (Love et al. 2002).

SALIENT CHARACTERS: This is a streamlined species and the only abundant eastern Pacific rockfish with 14 dorsal spines (other species have 13). They are red with brown or dark gray mottling, and have three dark bars radiating backward from the eye.

LIFE HISTORY: Young fish tend to live in shallower waters and then move deeper as they mature. Northerns live over high-relief bottoms, where they may school by themselves or with POP as much as 40 m (131 ft) or more above the seafloor. At night, northerns tend to retreat to the sea floor. Russian researchers report that fish in the Bering Sea tend to live in shallower waters in the summer. They can tolerate waters from at least -0.2–10.6°C (32–51°F). There is some genetic structure to northern assemblages in the eastern Bering Sea and Gulf of Alaska.

Northerns live to at least 88 years. Females grow larger than males. Fish along the eastern Aleutians and Gulf of Alaska are larger at age than those from the western Aleutians, and probably reach a larger maximum size. In the central Gulf of Alaska, a few females mature at 27 cm (11 in, 6 years) FL, 50% at 31 cm (12 in, 8 years), and 100% at 36 cm (14 in, 13 years old). Females release larvae from April–June. Northerns are primarily, but not exclusively, planktivorous. Euphausiids and copepods tend to make up a majority of their diets, but they also consume such water column and benthic-oriented prey as polychaetes, larvaceans, pteropods, gammarid and hyperiid amphipods, shrimps, hermit crabs, squids, octopuses, and brittle stars. Larger individuals add fishes to their diets. Little is known of their predators, but these include other northern rockfish.

FISHERY: Northerns form the basis for a large and valuable trawl fishery. The fish are headed, gutted, and frozen and then exported, mostly to Japan and South Korea. Because northern rockfish are not the bright red color that the Japanese, in particular, are fond of, these fish do not command as high a price as do the more florid Pacific Ocean perch. In the Gulf of Alaska, most of the catch is directed to this species and is retained. In the Aleutian Islands, most of the northern catch is bycatch in the Atka mackerel fishery and most is discarded—an unfortunate event, I would posit. They are only rarely taken in sport catches in Alaska.

RELATIONSHIPS: Northerns are most closely related to dark and dusky rockfishes.

REMARKS: Susanne McDermott (the Atka mackerel's best friend) notes that Atka mackerel and northern rockfish share very similar ecological niches. It appears that Atka mackerel maybe feed more during the day and northerns perhaps more at night, but they hang out together and both feed on euphausiids and copepods.

Sebastes rastrelliger

(Jordan & Gilbert, 1880)

Grass Rockfish

DAN RICHARDS

ETYMOLOGY AND COLLOQUIAL NAMES: *Rastrelliger* is Latin for "rake" and "I bear," referring to the small gill rakers. "Grass rockfish" goes back to the 19th century, as does "garrupa." People often call them "grass bass."

THE BASICS: Maximum Length: 55.9 cm (22 in) TL. Maximum Weight: 2.9 kg (6.4 lb). Commercial fisherman Bill James says that some of his associates claim to have caught them to 4.1 kg (9 lb). The Ranges: Ucluelet (Vancouver Island) to Bahia Playa Maria (28°50'N) (central Baja California). They are pretty abundant as far southward as central Baja California. Tide pools and to 46 m (150 ft), and commonly from the intertidal to 15 m (50 ft). Larvae: birth length = 4.3 mm, flexion length = about 6–8 mm, transformation length = less than 2.7 cm (1.1 in). Von Bertalanffy parameters (TL, cm): (sexes combined) L_∞ = 51.3, k = 0.11, t_0 = 12.4 (Love and Johnson 1998). Length-Weight (TL, cm, gr): (sexes combined) W = 0.045L$^{2.77}$ (Love and Johnson 1998).

SALIENT CHARACTERS: Like most bottom-dwelling rockfishes, grasses are spiny and heavy bodied. They range from greens to almost black, with a constellation of black spots and blotches. Some fish exhibit a dark blotch on the gill cover. Confusingly, grasses can change color fairly rapidly as, after putting one in a white bucket, I saw one go from green to white rather quickly.

LIFE HISTORY: Young-of-the-year recruit to tide pools and shallow subtidal waters around rocks and algae and to oil platforms and other human-made structures, from at least May–September. Most juveniles settle at 2.9 cm (1 in) SL or smaller. Both juveniles and adults live around hard, complex structure, as well as kelp beds and other plant life. These are solitary, bottom-hugging fishes. Larger fish tend to be found in slightly deeper waters, although my friend Rich Lee caught a 2.7 kg (6 lb) one in a deep tide pool the size of your bed. Studies demonstrate that there are some geographic genetic differences among grass rockfish, implying that larval dispersal may be limited.

Grass rockfish live to 23 years old and growth rates, size, and age at maturity, are similar for both sexes. Off Southern California, a few fish are mature at 22 cm (9 in) TL, 50% at about 24 cm (9 in), and all at 28 cm (11 in) (between 2–5 years old). Fish in Central California are larger at maturity; a few females are mature at as small as 29.2 cm (12 in) and males at 35.9 cm (14 in). Females produce between 80,000–760,000 eggs and release larvae from January–March. Grasses feed on fishes, along with crabs, shrimps, hermit crabs, octopuses, snails, gammarid amphipods, and isopods. Predators include barred sand bass.

FISHERY: Grass rockfish were a popular commercial species at least as far back as San Francisco of the 1880s. Catches declined for most of the 20th century due to the fishermen's inability to efficiently catch large numbers of these shallow-water fish. However, with the coming of the live fish fishery, and the need to keep fish...well, alive, grasses clearly fit the bill, and today they are a major part of that industry. Grasses are a very important species for rocky shore fishermen; both for poke polers and more traditional anglers. Those who fish from piers and boats also catch good numbers.

RELATIONSHIPS: Grasses are most closely related to brown and calico rockfishes.

REMARKS: Brad Mongeau reports feeding one, then returning 3 weeks later and the same fish (with a characteristic notch in the tail) followed him all over the reef.

Sebastes rosaceus
Girard, 1854
Rosy Rockfish

ETYMOLOGY AND COLLOQUIAL NAME: *Rosaceus* is Latin for "rosy." Fishermen in the 1880s called them "corsairs."

THE BASICS: Maximum Length: 36 cm (14 in) TL. The Ranges: Strait of Juan de Fuca (Washington) to Bahia Tortugas (27°30'N, 114°50'W) (southern Baja California), typically from at least Cordell Bank (Northern California) to Punta Colnett (northern Baja California), and on Banco Ranger (central Baja California). 7–263 m (24–864 ft); in Southern California most commonly in 50–90 m (164–295 ft). Von Bertalanffy parameters (SL, cm): Central California - (females) L_∞ = 32.9, k = 0.12, t_0 = -0.7; (males) L_∞ = 30.2, k = 0.16, t_0 = -0.1; Southern California - (sexes combined) L_∞ = 20.2, k = 0.17, t_0 = -1.13 (Love et al. 2002). Length-weight parameters (TL, cm, gr): (sexes combined) W = $0.0052L^{3.386}$ (Love et al. 2002).

SALIENT CHARACTERS: Rosies are small, spiny, and brightly colored. There are 4–6 small, white blotches on the back. Typically, rosies are orange or red-orange liberally marked with purple. However, underwater, they can also have very extensive white patches on backs and fins.

LIFE HISTORY: Young-of-the-year settle out on low/hard relief, such as small rocks and the shell mounds around platforms, and mostly in 27 m (89 ft) and more. Juveniles and adults live mostly over high-relief bottoms, as well as over cobble. These are mostly solitary fish, although they will form little groups on occasion. They tend to either lie right on the seafloor or hover

This is the more usual looking rosy.

This is the less frequently seen pattern.

a meter or two above it. The over 3,600 rosies we have observed in Southern California waters resided in 9.3–16.2°C (48–61°F), the vast majority in 10.2–12.4°C (50–54°F).

Not much is known about their growth rates, although Don Pearson found one rosy he thought was 40 years old. They mature at between 12–25 cm (5–10 in) TL, with fish off Northern and Central California maturing at a larger size than those in Southern California. Rosies release larvae from January–September (peaking around May). In Southern California, females may release larvae twice in a season and produce 12,600–95,000 eggs per year. Rosies feed on both benthic and midwater prey, including shrimps, euphausiids, gelatinous zooplankton, and small fishes.

FISHERY: Rosies were an important species in the San Francisco fish markets of the 19th century. On the other hand, consumers living in San Diego at the same time tended not to purchase small fishes, and rosies were not popular. Today, rosies are only a small part of the commercial rockfish trade, albeit you often see them in Asian markets. They are caught in large numbers by recreational anglers and, although historically relatively rarely kept by most recreational anglers, Kirk Lombard notes that retention rates seem to be increasing.

RELATIONSHIPS: Rosies are perhaps the oldest of the living species of the subgenus *Sebastomus*, those rockfishes having 3–5 lighter blotches on their backs.

Sebastes rosenblatti
Chen, 1971
Greenblotched Rockfish

ETYMOLOGY: *Rosenblatti* honors Richard Rosenblatt (1930–), hotshot ichthyologist at Scripps Institution of Oceanography.
THE BASICS: Maximum Length: 54 cm (21 in) TL. Maximum Weight: 2.7 kg (5.9 lb). The Ranges: Point Delgada (40°04'N) (Northern California) to Banco Ranger (central Baja California), and typically from Central California to Banco Ranger and Isla Guadalupe. 55–491 m (180–1,610 ft), in Southern California mostly in 170–270 m (558–886 ft). Von Bertalanffy parameters (TL, cm): (females) $L_\infty = 58$, $k = 0.05$, $t_0 = -2.47$; (males) $L_\infty = 56.1$, $k = 0.06$, $t_0 = -2.1$ (Love et al. 2002). Length-weight parameters (TL, cm, gr): (sexes combined) $W = 0.011L^{3.106}$ (Love et al. 2002).

SALIENT CHARACTERS: Greenblotcheds are deep-bodied and spiny. They have 4–5 light blotches on the back. Dead ones are pink, orange, and yellow with green vermiculations on the back and head. Vermiculations on larger dead fish are often difficult to see. Underwater, they are pinkish, orange, reddish, or white, and the vermiculations can be brown, green, or olive.

LIFE HISTORY: Greenblotcheds recruit to low/hard relief and to soft seafloors at as small as 3 cm (1 in) SL. I have seen newly recruited fish down to depths of 200 m (656 ft) and slightly larger ones at depths between 50–240 m (164–787 ft), so this species recruits to fairly deep water. Larger fish live on rocks, boulders, and mixed rock-mud bottoms; the bottoms of several oil platforms have high densities of them. This is a solitary or semi-solitary species that usually sits right on, or barely above, the bottom, but may ascend a few meters. In Southern California, we see greenblotcheds in 7.9–12°C (46–54°F), but mostly in 8.9–10.4°C (48–51°F).

Greenblotcheds live to at least 58 years old. A few fish are mature at 16 cm (6 in, 4 years) TL, 50% are mature at about 29 cm (11 in, 10 years), and all are mature at 34 cm (13 in, 15 years). Females release larvae between December–July, peaking in April. Many greenblotcheds release two batches of young per season; females produce between about 30,000–655,000 eggs per year. Greenblotcheds feed on calanoid copepods and gammarid amphipods when small, and when larger add shrimps, fishes, and squids.

FISHERY: Moderate numbers of this species are taken in both the commercial and recreational catches.

RELATIONSHIPS: Greenblotcheds are most closely related to greenspotted and pink rockfishes.

Sebastes ruberrimus
(Cramer, 1895)

Yelloweye Rockfish

ETYMOLOGY AND COLLOQUIAL NAMES: *Ruberrimus* is Latin for "very red." "Tambor," a Portuguese name, was commonly used in the 19th century. You still often hear "red snapper" and "goldeneye." The Tlingit of southeastern Alaska use "léik'w" and slightly further north they are "ushmaq" in Alutiiq.

THE BASICS: Maximum Length: At least 91.4 cm (36 in) TL. Maximum Weight: At least 12.6 kg (27.8 lb). The International Gamefish Association lists a world record yelloweye of 103.5 cm (41 in) TL and 17.8 kg (39.3 lb). However, when I reviewed a picture of that fish, I could not discount it being a shortraker rockfish.

THE RANGES: South of Umnak Island (Aleutian Islands) to Ensenada (northern Baja California), and common from perhaps the western end of the Alaska Peninsula to Central California. They are occasional at San Miguel Island and on those outer Southern California banks bathed by the California Current. My friend, Jorge Rosales-Casián, has also seen them landed as far south as off Bahia San Quintin (northern Baja California). Given the relatively cold waters in that area, that seems plausible. 11–549 m (36–1,800 ft), typically from 91–180 m (300–590 ft). Adults tend to live in shallower water in the north (as shallow as 18 m, 59 ft, in southeastern Alaska). Von Bertalanffy parameters (FL, cm): (females) L_∞ = 65.9, k = 0.04, t_0 = -11.7; (males) L_∞ = 64.4, k = 0.05, t_0 = -5.44 (Love et al. 2002). Length-weight parameters (TL, cm, gr): (sexes combined) W = $0.0074L^{3.222}$ (Love et al. 2002).

SALIENT CHARACTERS: One of the largest rockfishes, this species has yellow eyes, red-orange or orange-brown bodies, and a raspy top of the head. Newly settled juveniles are red-orange and have two horizontal bright white stripes, one on each side of the lateral line. As these fish mature, they lose the striping and larger fish often have several light blotches on the back.

LIFE HISTORY: Although the early life history of this species in poorly understood, juveniles are found in high-relief, often algal-ridden, nearshore areas. Off Monterey, Clinton Bauder sees fair numbers of newly settled fish in around 46 m (150 ft). Adults spend much of their time sheltering in crevices, although they will often venture a few meters above the seafloor.

CLEO BRYLINSKY

While we usually see them as solitary individuals, it is unclear as to whether this is their normal behavior. As with such species as cow-cod, because they have been so heavily overfished, some aspects of their sociability may be masked by their current low densities. For instance, when Lynne Yamanaka and Rick Stanley surveyed fishes at Bowie Seamount (British Columbia), a less-heavily fished site well off the coast, they observed aggregations of 30 or more adult yelloweyes. An occasional yelloweye is found in waters as cold as at least 4.7°C (40°F).

A juvenile.

Yelloweyes are one of the older-living species in the eastern Pacific, some surviving to a stunning 147 years. In general, 50% of fish are mature at 40–54 cm (16–21 in) FL (around 20 years old). Females release larvae from March–September, with a late spring–early summer peak. Females produce 1,200,000–2,700,000 eggs per season. Yelloweyes feed primarily on fishes, crabs, shrimps, squids, octopuses, and the occasional snail and euphausiid. Pelagic juveniles are eaten by Chinook salmon and older individuals by other yelloweyes, Steller sea lions, sperm whales, and orcas.

FISHERY: The role that yelloweyes might have played in the lives of some native people is shown by the name given to a site on the Queen Charlotte Islands. It is called "Skung Gwaay 'Linagaay" by the Haida or "Red Cod Island Town." Today, yelloweyes are still an important subsistence species for a number of local peoples. As early as the 1880s, yelloweyes were an important commercial species in the markets of Victoria (British Columbia) and San Francisco, although markets were not always friendly to yelloweyes (see below). Today, yelloweyes bring premium prices to commercial fishermen. Similarly, they are an important sport species, mostly from Central California northward.

Yelloweyes have been declared overfished in the U.S. and the Committee on the Status of Endangered Wildlife in Canada (COSEWIC) has given this species Special Concern status.

RELATIONSHIPS: Genetic analyses imply that this is a relatively old species, going back perhaps 4 million years or more. The closest living relative is likely the Mexican rockfish.

REMARKS: Interestingly, in 1892, Collins reported that they were fairly important in the San Diego fish markets and Eigenmann and Eigenmann (1889) reported that in the same markets it was: "Not rare, usually large individuals brought into market." Most of the rockfish fishery of that time was conducted near the coast. Thus, these observations imply that there was a fairly large population of these fish along a mainland where, today, they are essentially absent. Given their lifespan of well over 100 years, it seems likely that, even if successful recruitment events were rare, substantial unfished populations of yelloweyes built up in Southern California waters.

GOSH, THIS IS DEPRESSING

In *Spilsbury's Album* (Harbour Publishing, 2001), Canadian writer, businessman and painter Jim Spilsbury writes about commercial lingcod fishermen who worked out of Lund, British Columbia (north of Vancouver) about the time of World War I: "At that time there was no market for red snapper [yelloweye rockfish], but the average boat caught three or four red snappers for every ling cod [sic]. The fishermen simply threw them overboard as they caught them. Red snapper usually come up from very deep water, and as they approach the surface they cannot stand the decompression. Their stomachs come out of their mouths and choke them. I can recall seeing long strings of these bloated red fish floating away from the stern of every codfishing boat—miles of them."

So, let's do the math. If every yelloweye was, say, 100 years old, and there was *only* one mile of yelloweyes behind a boat, and there was one yelloweye every 50 feet (with a slow drift that would be an underestimate), that would be, lessee here, 105.6 yelloweyes, but we'll be conservative and call it 105 yelloweyes, and that times 100 years, gives us 10,500 years of yelloweyes for one boat for one day.

Sebastes rubrivinctus

(Jordan & Gilbert, 1880)

Flag Rockfish

"From fairest creature we desire increase, That there by beauty's rose might never die."

Sonnet 1, William Shakespeare

ETYMOLOGY AND COLLOQUIAL NAMES: *Rubrivinctus* is Latin for "red" and "banded." We called them "barber poles" when I was a kid. At first blush, the derivation of the name "flag" rockfish appears to be a bit obscure. Historically, however, the name given by fishermen (and noted in Santa Barbara in 1880 by David Starr Jordan) was "Spanish flag." This, too, is a little tough to understand, as the current Spanish flag contains *yellow* and red stripes. However, the current flag of Cantabria, a region located in northern Spain on the Bay of Biscay, has one white and one red horizontal stripe, and the Cross of Burgundy, an older flag of Spanish origin, is a white and red "X." Just as appropriate, perhaps, fishermen off northern Baja California call them "payaso," which means "clown."

THE BASICS: Maximum Length: 44 cm (17 in) TL. Maximum Weight: 1.8 kg (4 lb). The Ranges: Heceta Bank (Oregon) to southern Bahia de Sebastian Vizcaino (central Baja California), typically from Central California to at least off Bahia San Quintin (northern Baja California). 30–418 m (100–1,371 ft), in Southern California mostly in 80–115 m (262–377 ft). Length-weight parameters (TL, mm, kg): (sexes combined) W = 0000000234L$^{3.0213}$ (RecFin 2009).

SALIENT CHARACTERS: Those four bright red or orange bands alternating with white separates flags from all other species except the redbanded rockfish. The snouts of flags are narrower and the first red bar reaches well down the gill cover (it just barely crosses on to it in redbandeds). At the depths where they are found, the red bars appear to be black (red light does not penetrate to the depths where flags live) giving them a zebra-in-tall-grass look.

JOHN BUTLER

LIFE HISTORY: Young-of-the-year recruit to hard substrate at as small as 2 cm (1 in) TL. Juveniles recruit to drifting kelp mats, oil platforms, and other hard substrate in waters from at least 30–170 m (984–558 ft).

Most settlement appears to take place in the fall and winter. Adults favor areas with caves and crevices, smaller ones can be found over cobble. Very occasionally, you will see two or more together, and around several platform bottoms relatively large numbers will aggregate. Most fish stay close to the seafloor, but they will rise up maybe 4 m (13 ft) above the bottom. Flags may be immune to the stinging cells of sea anemones, as they will nestle right into the tentacles. In Southern California, they live at least in 7.9–12.6°C (46–55°F) and mostly in 9.6–11.4°C (49–53°F).

Flags live to at least 38 years old and probably longer. Off Southern California, a few males mature at 18 cm (7 in) TL, 50% are mature at 21 cm (8 in), and all are mature by 26 cm (10 in). For females, first maturity is as early as 22 cm (9 in), while all are mature at 26 cm (10 in). Fish farther northward may mature when larger. Females release larvae from May–November, which is out of sync with most other rockfishes. Flags feed on fishes, shrimps, copepods, amphipods, euphausiids, and hermit crabs.

FISHERY: Flags are of moderate importance to the commercial rockfish fishery. Their bright colors ensure that they are sold whole and at premium prices. They are also commonly taken in the recreational industry.

RELATIONSHIPS: Flags are most closely related to treefish and also to tigers and redbandeds.

Sebastes rufus

(Eigenmann & Eigenmann, 1890)

Bank Rockfish

ETYMOLOGY AND COLLOQUIAL NAMES: *Rufus* is Latin for "red." These are often called "red widows," "bank perch," or "Floridas."

THE BASICS: Maximum Length: 55.2 cm (22 in) TL. Maximum Weight: A 54 cm (21 in) fish weighed 2.5 kg (5.5 lb). The Ranges: Queen Charlotte Sound (British Columbia) to central Baja California (29°02'N, 118°13'W) and Isla Guadalupe. 31–512 m (102–1,680 ft), in Southern California most often in 195–275 m (640–902 ft).

Larvae: hatching length = 4.3–4.7 mm, flexion length = 6.2–7.6 mm. Von Bertalanffy parameters (TL, mm): (females) L_∞ = 594, k = 0.04, t_0 = -6.96; (males) L_∞ = 488, k = 0.048, t_0 = -8.37 (Watters et al. 2006). Length-weight parameters (TL, cm, gr): (sexes combined) W = $0.0078L^{3.147}$ (Love et al. 2002).

SALIENT CHARACTERS: Banks are oval and have small head spines. Dead ones tend to be brown with a red cast or reddish, usually with black spots, and a reddish lateral line. Underwater, these fish can be a myriad of colors and patterns, from almost white to brown, red-brown, and almost black, with a variety of light and dark saddles and blotches, and dark spots. There is a dark "<" mark behind the eye.

LIFE HISTORY: We have seen 5 cm (2 in) TL fish, clearly newly settled, over rocks in 90–290 m (295–951 ft). Banks live mostly over high relief, in boulder fields and steep rocky slopes, and only occasionally over mixed rock-mud. This is a fairly reclusive fish. Even at relatively high densities, they tend to mostly line crevices or perhaps emerge in small to medium schools (I have seen as many as maybe 50 fish in a small stampede) to as much 5 m (17 ft) into the water column. In Southern California, we see them in 7.7–11.8°C (46–53°F) and mostly in 8.9–9.6°C (48–49°F).

Banks live to at least 53 years and may live to 80 years old. Females grow larger than males. A few fish are mature at 28 cm (11 cm, 10 years) TL, 50% at around 33 cm (13 in, 16 years), and all are mature at 39 cm (14 in, 20+ years). Females release larvae from December–May, perhaps with a winter peak. Females produce between about 65,000–608,000 eggs. The few banks that I have examined had fed on gelatinous zooplankton, euphausiids, and fishes. Banks are eaten by California sea lions and Humboldt squids. Rhinoceros auklets eat the pelagic juveniles.

FISHERY: Banks are an important commercial species in California waters, with lesser amounts coming out of southern Oregon. Historically, most fish were taken with trawls and gill nets, but hook-and-line fishermen caught a fair amount. Recreational anglers catch substantial numbers, particularly off Southern California.

RELATIONSHIPS: This appears to be a relatively old species, going back perhaps 4 million years. Its closest relatives are the somewhat more recently evolved speckled and squarespot rockfishes. One study implied it was also closely related to both dwarf-red and whitespotted rockfishes.

Sebastes saxicola

(Gilbert, 1890)

Stripetail Rockfish

ETYMOLOGY: *Saxicola* is Latin for "rock" and "I inhabit." Ironically, of course, stripetails only rarely are seen among rocks. So take that, Charles Gilbert.

THE BASICS: Maximum Length: 41 cm (16 in) TL. Maximum Weight: 0.7 kg (1.5 lb). The Ranges: Yakutat Bay (eastern Gulf of Alaska) to Punta Rompiente (27°41'N, 115°01'W) (southern Baja California), commonly from British Columbia to at least Southern California. 25–547 m (82–1,795 ft), off Southern California mostly in 180–270 m (590–886 ft). Von Bertalanffy parameters (TL, cm):

(females) L_∞ = 33, k = 0.06, t_0 = -4.63; (males) L_∞ = 17.4, k = 0.19, t_0 = -3.78 (Love et al. 2002). Length-weight parameters (TL, cm, gr): (females) W = 0.0248L$^{2.805}$; (males) W = 0.0379L$^{2.619}$ (Love et al. 1990).

SALIENT CHARACTERS: Stripetails are relatively slim fish (although not as slim as the closely related halfbanded). Dead ones are pink-red to yellow-pink, sometimes with dark saddles. Both dead and living ones have brown or green stripes on the caudal fin rays. Underwater, stripetails range in color for almost white to red-brown, and the light and dark mottling may be faint or extremely intense.

LIFE HISTORY: Pelagic juveniles are least occasionally associate with drifting algae. After 2–3 months at sea, young-of-the-year, at as small as 2.4 cm (1 in) SL, recruit to the seafloor between February–October. Some pelagic juveniles stay in the water column until they are at least 5.2 cm (2 in) SL. Settlement can occur in waters as shallow as 12 m (29 ft) (in tubeworm/red algae beds) and I have seen very small fish on the bottom in as deep as 110 m (361 ft) and only slightly larger ones in 290 m (951 ft). Juveniles are found on sand, as well as over sea pens, tubeworms, and other low relief. Fish that recruit to kelp beds and other shallow habitats tend to migrate into slightly deeper waters within a few months. Usually solitary fish, stripetails mostly lie on the bottom or hover just above it, and older juveniles and adults live over soft and soft-low rock habitats. I often see them on the shell mounds surrounding oil platforms. In Southern California, stripetails retreat to somewhat deeper waters during warm-water periods. Stripetails live in waters between at least 6.7 and 11.8°C (44–53°F).

Stripetails live at least 38 years. Females grow larger than males and after maturation are larger at age. As an example, a 17 cm (7 cm) TL male caught off Southern California was 28 years old, while the average female from that area of about the same size was about 9 years old. Off Southern California, a few fish are mature at 9 cm (4 in, 2 years), while off Central and Northern California a few are mature at 15–17 cm (6–7 in, 2–3 years). All female stripetails off California are mature at 18 cm (7 in, 9 years old in Southern California and 4 years old further north). Females produce between 15,000–230,000 eggs and release their larvae from November–March. Stripetails are planktivores, feeding primarily on euphausiids and calanoid copepods, and occasionally on pelagic tunicates, ctenophores, and other planktonic animals. They are eaten by bocaccio, Chinook salmon, lingcod, longnose lancetfish, longnose skate, Pacific hakes, and rhinoceros auklets.

FISHERY: Stripetails have never been particularly important in either the commercial or recreational fishing industries. However, they are taken in large numbers as bycatch in trawl fisheries and are sometimes landed. During the 1960s, they were sold for animal food.

RELATIONSHIPS: Work by John Hyde implies that there are two populations or perhaps two species of "stripetails." The closest relative of these fish(es) are halfbandeds.

Sebastes semicinctus
(Gilbert, 1897)
Halfbanded Rockfish

ETYMOLOGY: *Semicinctus* is Latin for "half" and "banded."
THE BASICS: Maximum Length: 25 cm (10 in) TL. The Ranges: Strait of Juan de Fuca (Washington) to Bahia Asuncion (southern Baja California) and abundant from at least Central California to Southern California. It is almost certainly abundant farther southward, but the proper studies have not been done down there. 15–402 m (48–1,320 ft). In Southern California, they are mostly in 60–135 m (197–443 ft). Von Bertalanffy parameters (TL, cm): (females) L_∞ = 18,1, k = 0.37, t_0 = -1.37; (males) L_∞ = 14.6, k = 0.45, t_0 = -1.46 (Love et al. 2002). Length-weight parameters (TL, cm, gr): (females) W = 0.0152L$^{2.94}$; (males) W = 0.0127L$^{3.016}$ (Love et al. 1990).

SALIENT CHARACTERS: These are slim fish with very distinctive diamond-shaped red-brown or dark marks on sides. Schooled fish tend to be light, almost white, while those lying on rocks can be very dark and red with dark bands, speckles, and other markings.

LIFE HISTORY: Beginning in May, young-of-the-year recruit all the way from kelp beds to depths of 220 m (722 ft). A few of these fish are at least as small as 2.2 cm (1 in) SL, but some stay at sea until at least 4.8 cm (2 in). Juveniles recruit to low-relief rock and sand, and to the shell mounds surrounding oil platforms. Adults are most abundant over mixed soft and hard low-relief bottom (like cobble beds), although they can also be found over rocks and boulders and over mud seafloors.

I see them both as individuals lying on rocks (big ones are sometimes in crevices) or in little divots on mud, and singly or in schools some meters into the water column. Schools of juveniles, in particular, ascend 21 m (70 ft), or more, above the seafloor. Halfbandeds often school with pygmy and squarespot rockfishes and with pink seaperch. We have observed over 15,000 of them in our submersible surveys and they all were in waters between 8.4–20.7°C (47–69°F), but mostly at 9.6–11.6°C (49–53°F).

Halfbandeds live to 15 years old. Female grow larger than males. A few fish are mature at 10 cm (4 in, 1 year old) TL, 50% are mature at 11 cm (4 in, 1–2 years), and all are mature by 14 cm (6 in, 3–6 years). Females release larvae from December–April, peaking in February. Females produce 3,000–31,000 eggs and release all of their larvae once per season. Water column zooplankters (e.g., euphausiids, copepods, and larvaceans) comprise their diets. Predators include lingcod, rhinoceros auklets, and California sea lions.

A clearly urban halfbanded shaking its booty at a mildly non-plussed cusk-eel.

FISHERY: In the U.S., there is no commercial fishery for this species, although I have seen them for sale in the Mercado Negro fish market in Ensenada (northern Baja California). Halfbandeds are taken with some frequency by recreational anglers, particularly in Southern California, although they are rarely retained.

RELATIONSHIPS: Halfbandeds are mostly closely related to stripetail rockfish. Halfbandeds may have evolved as much as 3 million years ago.

Sebastes serranoides

(Eigenmann & Eigenmann, 1890)

Olive Rockfish

ETYMOLOGY AND COLLOQUIAL NAME:
Serranoides comes from "Serranus" (a genus of basses) and the Greek word for "resemblance." "Johnny bass" is still a popular name.

THE BASICS: Maximum Length: 61 cm (24 in) TL. Maximum Weight: 2.7 kg (5.9 lb). The Ranges: Southern Oregon to Islas San Benito (central Baja California), and most abundantly from about the San Francisco area to Southern California. Surface and intertidal to 172 m (564 ft), typically in 55 m (180 ft) and shallower. Larvae: length at birth: 4.8–5.4 mm. Von Bertalanffy parameters (TL, cm): (females) L_∞ = 51.9, k = 0.18, t_0 = -1.57; (males) L_∞ = 43.3, k = 0.27, t_0 = -1.03 (Love and Westphal 1981). Length-weight parameters (TL, cm, gr): (females) $W = 0.111L^{3.063}$; (males) $W = 0.0152L^{2.964}$ (Love and Westphal 1981).

SALIENT CHARACTERS: Olives are streamlined and have virtually no head spines. They are dark brown or green-brown on the back and somewhat lighter brown or greenish on sides. Combined with those light blotches, they can only be confused with yellowtail rockfish. Yellowtail have a red-brown fleck on each scale and usually have more yellow on their fins.

TO THE OUT OF STEP OLIVE ROCKFISH

Now you may be randy and filled with great vim,
And it's just like sweet candy, just thinking of him,
But always remember when you are in need,
It's June, not December, and you cannot breed.

Lord, pity the odd fish who strangely, off season,
Is feeling its hormones expressed, without reason,
For always remember when lust draws a bead,
This isn't December and you may not breed.

For 12 million years of evolution, selective,
Has made it quite clear, this is not an elective
Yes listen, remember, to these words you must heed,
This isn't December and you must not breed.

LIFE HISTORY: Young-of-the-year settle to nearshore structures (e.g., kelp and eelgrass beds, rocks, oil platforms, and piers, and rarely to tide pools) from March to perhaps September, at as small as 3 cm (1 in) SL. On the other hand, some pelagic juveniles stay out in the open ocean until as large as 5.4 cm (2 in). Older juveniles can be found throughout the water column, always close to some kind of structure. Adults are schooling fish that live over high relief. You often see them mixed in with larger numbers of blue rockfish. On rare occasions, I have seen olives break the surface when chasing prey.

Olives live to at least 30 years old. Starting at maturation, females grow larger and tend to be longer at any age. A few fish are mature at 29–30 cm (11–12 in, 3 years) TL, 50% at 33–35 cm (13–14 in, 5 years), and most at about 39 cm (15 in, 8 years). Females release larvae in one batch from December–March, peaking in January. Females produce 30,000–490,000 eggs. Young-of-the-year olives eat such zooplankters as calanoid and harpacticoid copepods, euphausiids, and crustacean larvae. When slightly larger they begin to feed on more benthic-oriented prey (e.g., gammarid and caprellid amphipods, and isopods). Larger fish eat fishes, squids, and octopuses, as well as the usual zooplankton and epibenthic crustaceans. I have found parasitic copepods in the stomachs of juveniles, which might be evidence of their cleaning other fishes. At least some adults feed at night and there is evidence that fish between about 6–15 cm (2–6 in) TL are primarily nocturnal. Predators include black-and-yellow rockfish, Chinook salmon, and California sea lions.

KAWIKA CHETRON

FISHERY: Relatively minor in the commercial catch (some are taken in the live fish fishery), olives are very important in the recreational vessel catches of Southern and Central California. They are also occasionally taken from piers, jetties, and rocky shores.

RELATIONSHIPS: Intrepid researchers have determined that olives are most closely related to black rockfish and secondarily to yellowtail rockfish. Based on appearance, I would have put my money on the opposite, but there you go.

KEVIN LEE

Sebastes serriceps
(Jordan & Gilbert, 1880)
Treefish

ETYMOLOGY AND COLLOQUIAL NAMES: *Serriceps* is Latin for "saw" and "head." The name "treefish" goes back at least to the late 19th century and, no, none of us know where that name came from. Referring to other names, Ed Roberts, California Fish and Game biologist, noted that one gentleman called them "Tijuana donkeys." He continued: "A picture of those tourist donkeys on the street corner in Tijuana, painted up to look like a zebra, came to mind." Other names are "convict bass," "lipstick fish," and, in Mexico, "payaso" (clown).

THE BASICS: Maximum Length: 41 cm (16 in) TL. Maximum Weight: 1.9 kg (4.2 lb). The Ranges: San Francisco to Isla Cedros (central Baja California). Treefish are common from Southern California to northern Baja California. Barely subtidal waters to 97 m (320 ft); mostly in 50 m (165 ft) and less. Von Bertalanffy parameters (TL, cm): (sexes combined) L_∞ = 30.6, k = 0.233, t_0 = -1.167 (Colton and Larson 2007). Length-weight parameters (TL, cm, gr): (sexes combined) W = 0.014L$^{3.081}$ (Colton and Larson 2007).

SALIENT CHARACTERS: This unmistakable species has 5–6 vertical bars, two oblique bars on the head radiating from the eyes, and adults have pink, orange, or red lips. The bars may be brown, black, or dark green, interspersed with yellow or green. Some individuals are simply strewn with tiny light dots.

GREG SANDERS

LIFE HISTORY: Young-of-the-year settle out (at as small as 2.5 cm, 1 in, TL) to nearshore waters (at least to as deep as 16 m (52 ft), but probably considerably deeper) from June–October, mostly in the summer. We see these young ones in nearshore rocky areas and around oil platforms, and they also seem to recruit to buoys and drifting kelp mats. Both juveniles and adults prefer to live in hard and complex substrate. Treefish are benthic, often quite secretive, but once in a while they surprise us. For example, Douglas Klug reports that he saw numerous adult fish in the water column of a kelp bed in September at Anacapa Island. Treefish can be very territorial and you can often see typical agonistic displays, where two fish face off, jaws gaping, or even jaws grasping. On the other hand, periodically they will gather together in small groups (sometimes of 20 or more), in, or near, caves and crevices.

Treefish live to 25 years old. Females may live slightly longer than males. A few females mature at 19 cm (8 in, TL, 4 years) and all at 23 cm (9 in, 5 years). A few males mature at 19.7 cm (8 in, 3 years) and all by 25 cm (10 in, 7 years). Females release larvae from March–July. About 70,000 eggs were found in a 28.5 cm (11 in) fish. Treefish are predominantly nocturnal or crepuscular (early morning or late evening) feeders. They primarily target benthic crustaceans, like shrimps and crabs, along with fishes. Isopods, gammarid and caprellid amphipods, octopuses, and squids round out the diet. Fish larger than perhaps 20 cm (8 in) eat mostly fishes.

FISHERY: Trees were a valuable rockfish in the commercial stalls of San Francisco in the late 19th century. Today, they are often part of the live-fish fishery. They are an important recreational species, mostly taken from boats, but are not an unusual jetty, pier, or even rocky coast catch.

RELATIONSHIPS: Trees are most closely related to flag rockfishes, but are also related to both tiger and redbanded rockfishes.

Sebastes umbrosus

(Jordan & Gilbert, 1882)

Honeycomb Rockfish

ETYMOLOGY: *Umbrosus* is Latin for "shady."

THE BASICS: Maximum Length: 28.5 cm (11 in) TL. The Ranges: Point Pinos (Central California) to near Punta San Juanico (25°48'N) (southern Baja California). They are abundant from about Santa Monica Bay southwards. 18–270 m (60–891 ft), perhaps typically between 45–70 m (148–230 ft). Length-weight parameters (TL, cm, gr): (sexes combined) $W = 0.0067L^{3.319}$ (Love et al. 2002).

SALIENT CHARACTERS: Like many of their close relatives, honeycombs have 4–6 light blotches on their back. Their key character is the crosshatching of brown or olive-green that gives them that honeycomb appearance. Note that this crosshatching is faint in small fish. An occasional individual is blotchy white with brownish saddles and kind of pinky or reddish blotches.

LIFE HISTORY: Young-of-the-year settle to the bottom (around rocks or other shelter) in 27–54 m (90–180 ft). Both juveniles and

Typical coloration.   CHRIS GROSSMAN

adults live mostly over boulders or cobble. These are solitary fish that most often shelter in crevices, but will sometimes ascend 3–4 m (10–13 ft) above the reef. In Southern California, we see them in 9.5–14.3°C (49–58°F) and mostly in 10.8–11.9°C (51–53°F).

Atypical coloration.

Honeycombs live to at least 31 years old. A few fish are mature at 12 cm (5 in, 3 years) TL, 50% at about 15 cm (6 in, 5 years), and all are mature at 18 cm (7 in, 8 years).

FISHERY: The only place I commonly see honeycombs is in Asian markets in Southern California. I have seen them caught with some regularity in the artisanal fishery along the Baja California coast, to as far south as Bahia Tortugas (southern Baja California). Although these are commonly caught by recreational vessel anglers, they are not usually retained.

RELATIONSHIPS: Honeycombs are most closely related to freckled rockfish.

Sebastolobus

Thornyheads are oviparous and the eggs are released in hollow, bilobed, gelatinous masses that float in surface waters.

Sebastolobus alascanus

Bean, 1890

Shortspine Thornyhead

ETYMOLOGY AND COLLOQUIAL NAMES: *Sebastolobus* is derived from "*Sebastes*" and the Greek word for "lobe" and *alascanus* for "Alaskan." Other names include "channel rock," channel rockcod," "idiotfish," "hardhead," and, in Japanese, "arasuka-kichiji."

THE BASICS: Maximum Length: 82.6 cm (33 in) FL. Maximum Weight: to at least 6.6 kg (14.5 lb). The Ranges: Seas of Okhotsk and Japan to the Pacific Ocean and Bering Sea off Kamchatka (as far north as Navarin Canyon) and the Aleutian Islands to Boca de Santo Domingo (25°32'N, 113°04'W) (southern Baja California). They are reasonably abundant from the northern Kuril Islands, through the

JOHN BUTLER

Aleutians, in some areas of the Bering Sea, and southward at least as far as Southern California. 17–1,524 m (56–5,000 ft). Characteristic depth ranges vary with location, but most fish are found in about 200 to maybe 800 m (656–2,624 ft). Fish in the northern part of their range tend to live in shallower waters than do those to the south. Eggs: 1.1 x 1.2 mm. Larvae: hatching length = about 2.6 mm, flexion length = 6–7.3 mm, transformation length = pelagic juvenile = about 2 cm. Von Bertalanffy parameters (TL, cm): (sexes combined) L_∞ = 70, k = 0.03, t_0 = -1.45 (Love et al. 2002). Length-weight parameters (TL, cm, gr): (sexes combined) W = $0.0039L^{3.357}$ (Love et al. 2002).

SALIENT CHARACTERS: Like other thornyheads, shortspines have a very obvious spiny ridge running across each cheek. Dead ones are pink-red or red, with some dusky patches. Underwater, they are usually red, although there are often big patches of white, some have a bit of black, and many have white-tipped dorsal spines. Underwater, the pectoral fins are lined in bright white that really flash when the fish is swimming. Underwater, I have trouble telling these apart from longspine thornyheads, although if a fish erects its dorsal spines and the third spine is not noticeably longer than the rest, it is a shortspine.

LIFE HISTORY: After drifting about in the plankton for maybe 13–15 months, young-of-the-year (at about 2.2–2.7 cm, 1 in, FL) settle to relatively shallow waters (still deep, mind you, 100–600 m, 330–1,980 ft) and then migrate deeper as they mature. Juveniles are found most often over mud bottoms, sometimes near small rocks and other solid objects, usually in little divots they probably dig for themselves. We see adults on mud (often near rocks or debris), and over low-hard relief, or even, rarely, over boulder fields. They are usually solitary (often quite evenly spaced) and almost always lying right on the seafloor. Although little is known about gender distribution, Zenger (2004) noted that in the Aleutian Island-southern Bering Sea region, females were much more abundant in the 101–200 m (331–656 ft) depth zone, while males were more numerous in 301–500 m (987–1,640 ft).

Interestingly, off the West Coast of the U.S., large females were found to live in deeper waters than males. So that is not very satisfying, is it? Along the West Coast, shortspines live in waters at least between 2–10.2°C (36–50°F). It is unlikely that shortspines make much in the way of organized migrations (although there has been some speculation that fish that settle out off Washington make their way southward) and there appears to be relatively little genetic divergence in the northeast Pacific.

MATT SOAVE AND COREY SHEREDY

Shortspines live to at least 133 years old and researchers have speculated that some individuals may live much longer than that. Females grow larger than males. Fifty percent of females living off Alaska are mature at 21.5 cm (9 in) FL, while 50% of females living along the Washington–California coast are mature at 18.2 in (7 in). Shortspines living off the Kuril Islands and around Kamchatka reportedly mature when considerably larger (50% maturity at 45–49 cm, 18–19 in, FL). Spawning occurs between December–July and fish in the south may tend to spawn earlier in the year than those to the north. These oviparous females produce between 10,000–2,000,000 eggs per season, with all of the eggs spawned in a single batch. Larger females spawn earlier in the season than do smaller ones. Smaller fish tend to eat more shrimps, mysid shrimps, polychaetes, and amphipods, with larger ones shifting to fishes and larger crustaceans. Other prey includes squids, octopuses, brittle stars, hermit crabs, copepods, and arrow worms. Diets vary with location. Predators include arrowtooth flounder, Pacific hakes, Pacific sleeper sharks, sablefish, shortspine thornyheads, California sea lions, and harbor seals.

FISHERY: Thornyheads were really not caught in any great numbers until the early 1930s, when California longline sablefish fishermen encountered these fish. For the next 40 years or so, moderate numbers were caught by trawlers and sold as animal food (although foreign trawlers working in the Gulf of Alaska targeted them for human food). Fortunately for commercial fishermen, and unfortunately for *Sebastolobus*, thornyheads are a very popular, and quite expensive, delicacy in Japan. The Japanese, having overfished their major species, the broadfin thornyhead, began importing thornyheads from the U.S. and, later, Canadian waters, and the fishery blossomed. Today, both shortspine and longspine thornyheads are taken in commercial fisheries along much of the northeast Pacific. Most of the catch is made with trawls and longlines, although there are also some pot fisheries. Because thornyheads lack swim bladders, they can be brought up from deep water with little internal damage and thus are sometimes sold live. Recreational anglers occasionally catch shortspines, but almost never catch longspines.

ORIGINS AND RELATIONSHIPS: Shortspines are most closely related to longspine thornyheads. Both share an ancestor with broadfin thornyheads at about 4–5 million years ago and shortspines are believed to have diverged from longspines about 1.3 million years ago.

MISCELLANY: A black one was taken off Oregon.

SOMETHING WORTH THINKING ABOUT

Tarleton Hoffman Bean was the gentleman who described the shortspine thornyhead. One only wonders the heights I could have achieved had I been named Tarleton Love or, for that matter, Bean Love. For many years, Bean (1846–1916) was curator of fishes at the United States National Museum. Here is what Bean (1887b) wrote regarding the fishes of Alaska: "The Territory of Alaska has seventy-five species of food-fishes, seven-eighths of which are strictly adapted to the use of man, the balance being more suitable for bait.

What does "strictly adapted to the use of man" mean? Does it mean that these species are only adapted for our use? What happens if a bear eats one? Will the bear go to Hell? What happens if, say, a yelloweye rockfish doesn't want to be eaten by anyone? What if it just wants to hang out in its crevice, eat the occasional sand lance, quietly engage in internal fertilization, and then die at the age of 129 years? Will it go to Hell? And what about this "strictly" thing? Was Dr. Bean, out there in his igloo, into some sort of "ichthyological bondage"? Will he go to Hell? And is Ichthyological Bondage a good name for a scientific journal?

OTHER SPECIES

Scorpaenodes xyris
(Jordan & Gilbert, 1882)
Rainbow Scorpionfish

Rainbow scorpionfish grow to 15 cm (6 in) TL and are found from Anacapa and Santa Barbara islands to Islas Chincha (Peru), including the Gulf of California. They are occasional around San Clemente and Catalina islands. This species inhabits caves and crevices from the intertidal to about 50 m (164 ft).

Sebastes aleutianus
(Jordan & Evermann, 1898)
Rougheye Rockfish

Sebastes melanostictus
(Matsubara, 1934)
Blackspotted Rockfish

Formerly believed to be one species,
now known to be two.

Rougheyes reach at least 72.6 cm (29 in) TL and blackspotteds grow to at least 69 cm (27 in) TL. Rougheyes range from at least the eastern Aleutian Islands, off Unalaska Island, to the eastern Bering Sea at Pribilof Canyon at 55.7°N, south to southern Oregon at 43.9°N, and perhaps into Northern California, at depths of 45 to at least 439 m (158–1,440 ft). They are abundant at least throughout the Gulf of Alaska, particularly in 200–500 m (656–1,640 ft). Larger individuals tend to occupy deeper depths. Blackspotteds have been taken from the Pacific coast of Japan, (at about 35°N), north through the Kuril Islands, Aleutian Islands, and the Bering Sea to 60.5°N, and south to Southern California on Coronado Bank (at 32.6°N), at depths of at least 84–490 m (276–1,607 ft). They, too, are abundant at least in the Gulf of Alaska and mostly at 300–500 m (984–1,640 ft). Again, larger fish are found in deeper depths. There appears to be only limited gene flow among blackspotteds in the North Pacific and Bering Sea.

Rainbow scorpionfish

KEVIN LEE

Rougheye rockfish

SCHON ACHESON

Blackspotted rockfish

REBECCA REUTER

Not much is known about either species and what was thought to be understood is now muddied by this two-species situation. Nevertheless, here are a few things that may be valid: These fishes live in association with boulders and other complex habitats. Small fish may school, while larger ones are either solitary or form small aggregations. Fish in the northwest Pacific may aggregate more in the fall and winter. Kristen Munk aged one individual (she tentatively thinks it was a *S. melanostictus*) to a whopping 205 years old. Crangid and pandalid shrimps are often the most important foods. Fishes are also very important, particularly in individuals over 30–40 cm (12–16 in) long. Other prey include gammarid amphipods (mostly in smaller individuals), other crustaceans (e.g. euphausiids, mysid shrimps, isopods, and crabs), polychaetes, and octopuses. Pacific lampreys parasitize them. They are taken primarily by bottom trawl and longlines. Alaska and British Columbia commercial fishermen catch substantial numbers of this species complex. Rougheyes/blackspotteds are only occasionally taken in the recreational catch. Rougheyes and blackspotteds hybridize on occasion. These species are most closely related to shortrakers.

The growth rate estimate is likely comprised of both species, so beware. Von Bertalanffy parameters (FL, mm): (sexes combined) L_∞ = 496, k = 0.108, t_0 = 0.63 (Malecha et al. 2007). Length-weight parameters (FL, mm, gr): *Sebastes aleutianus* (females) W = 0.000007562L$^{3.121}$; (males) W = 0.000008619L$^{3.095}$: *Sebastes melanostictus* (females) W = 0.000004684L$^{3.195}$; (males) W = 0.000005543L$^{3.166}$ (Szaley et al. 2010).

Sebastes aurora
(Gilbert, 1890)
Aurora Rockfish

Auroras grow to 41 cm (16 in) TL and at least 1.1 kg (3.4 lb). They live from west of Langara Island (about 54°15'N, 133°10'W) (British Columbia) to Isla Cedros (central Baja California), and are common from northern Oregon to at least Southern California. Larvae have been taken off Bahia Magdalena and Banco Thetis (24°40'N, 112°18'W) (southern Baja California) strongly implying that this species lives considerably farther south than its current southern-most record. This is a benthic species, mostly found on mixed hard and soft bottoms, in 81–893 m (266–2,930 ft) (perhaps mostly in 260 m, 853 ft, and deeper), and in waters between at least 5.4 and 9.3°C (42–49°F). I observed what appeared to be a young-of-the-year aurora under a boulder in 504 m (1,653 ft) off southern California. Females live to 118 years old and males to 81 years. Males grow faster and reach a smaller maximum size. A few females mature at 24 cm (9 in) FL and 11 years old, 50% are mature at 26 cm (10 in) and 13 years, and a few individuals may wait until 31 cm (12 in) and 32 years old. However, it is possible that these older fish do not spawn every year and that researchers had sampled these mature fish during an off year and were thus misled. It has been estimated that 50% of males are also mature by 26 cm (10 in). Females with developed embryos have been collected from March–June. However, larvae have been taken throughout the year, with heaviest densities in January–June. Predators include Humboldt squids, California sea lions, and for pelagic juveniles, Chinook salmon. Auroras are of some importance in trawl fisheries from Washington to Central California and are also taken in small numbers in sablefish pots as far south as Southern California. Unbelievable as it may sound, despite their usually living in unwholesomely deep water, auroras are occasionally taken by sport fishermen, perhaps an indication of how deep some anglers are going for a little rockfish action. Auroras are most closely related to chameleon rockfish. Larvae: birth length = about 4 mm, flexion length = 6.7–8.6 mm, transformation length = about 1.3 cm. Length-weight parameters (TL, cm, gr): (sexes combined) W = 0.0244L$^{2.832}$ (Love et al. 2002). Von Bertalanffy parameters (FL, cm): (females) L_∞ = 36.9, k = 0.06, t_0 = -5.45; (males) L_∞ = 33.6, k = 0.092, t_0 = -1.91 (Thompson and Hannah 2010).

Sebastes babcocki
(Thompson, 1915)
Redbanded Rockfish

Also called "barberpoles," "bandits," and "red bandits." Redbandeds grow to 71 cm (28 in) FL and 5 kg (11 lb). They occur from the Bering Sea, at Zhemchug Canyon, and Amchitka Island (Aleutian Islands) to San Diego. They are perhaps most abundant from about the Kodiak Island area eastward and fairly common as far south-ward as Central California (inhabiting the *Montebello*, a tanker sunk on 23 December 1941, by the Japanese submarine I-21). Found in 31–1,145 m (102–3,756 ft), almost the entire population inhabits waters between 150–450 m (492–1,476 ft). Redbandeds live in waters ranging at least down to 4.1°C (39°F). Pelagic juveniles often live under drifting kelp mats. We see larger juveniles and adults most often on rocky reefs, although they also inhabit low/hard bottoms. While they are most often solitary, they can also hang out in small groups. Redbandeds live to at least 106 years old. Females grow larger than males. Size and age at maturity may vary dramatically with area (or someone's data is incorrect). For instance, off British Columbia, 50% of both males and females are mature at 19 years and 42 cm (17 in) FL. Off California, a few males mature at 27 cm (11 in) TL, 50% at 31 cm (12 in), and all are mature at 36 cm (14 in). For females, the values are 32 cm (13 in), 34 cm (13 in), and 41 cm (16 in), respectively. Females release larvae from March–September. Redbandeds feed mostly on crabs, shrimps, and fishes. Euphausiids, isopods, cephalopods, and gammarid amphipods are also consumed. Predators include Steller sea lions. This is a moderately important commercial species (quite important in the British Columbia hook-and-line fishery) that is particularly popular in Asian markets, due to its bright red bars. They are occasionally caught by recreational anglers. Redbandeds are most closely related to the three other vertically barred species: treefish, flag, and tiger rockfishes. However, despite a similarity in appearance to flags, redbandeds seem to be most closely related to tigers. Length-weight parameters (TL, cm, gr): (sexes combined) W = $0.0206L^{2.943}$ (Love et al. 2002).

Sebastes baramenuke
(Wakiya, 1917)
Brickred Rockfish

This species grows to 51.7 cm (20 in) TL and lives from the Sea of Japan, off the Korean Peninsula, and the Pacific Ocean off Honshu to Kiska Pass, western Aleutian Islands, at depths of 100–760 m (328–2,493 ft). It is very rare within our range. Brickred rockfish feed on, at a minimum, fishes, euphausiids, and shrimps.

Sebastes borealis
Barsukov, 1970
Shortraker Rockfish

DAIJI KITAGAWA HOKKAIDO NATIONAL FISHERIES RESEARCH INSTITUTE

Shortrakers grow to 120 cm (47 in) TL and can weigh as much as a pudgy 30.6 kg (67.3 lb). They range from the Okhotsk Sea and the Pacific off northern Hokkaido to Kamchatka, and thence to the western Bering Sea at Navarin Canyon and to the Aleutian Islands and southward to Point Conception (California). They are reasonably common from the northern Kuril Islands and southeastern Kamchatka Peninsula to Cape Olyutorskiy in the western Bering Sea and at least to British Columbia. You find them at 25–1,200 m (82–3,937 ft), mostly at perhaps 300–600 m (984–1,640 ft). Fish off Asia appear to settle to the bottom at around 10 cm (4 in) TL and perhaps 2 years old. Shortrakers are bottom-oriented and generally solitary (although they will form small aggregations). They live over rocks and either rest on the bottom or hover as much as 10 m (33 ft) in the water column. Larger individuals may live in somewhat deeper waters. Fish in the western Bering Sea may migrate into slightly shallower waters in the summer and return in the winter. Along the Aleutian Islands and in the Northeast Pacific, fish

CLEO BRYLINSKY

tend to be slightly larger in the east. A genetic study in this same area found little evidence of discrete populations. Shortrakers can live just a very long time, to at least 160 years old. Females grow larger than males. Sizes at maturity have been variously estimated at between about 30–60 cm (12–24 in) TL. A relatively recent study (Hutchinson et al. 2007), estimated that 50% of females are mature at 21–23 years old and around 45 cm (18 in) FL. Females release larvae from at least March–July and maybe later. Smaller short-rakers feed mostly on shrimps, gammarid amphipods, and other crustaceans. At around 30–40 cm (12–16 in), their diets change and fishes become more important. Other prey include mysid shrimps, isopods, crabs, polychaetes, squids, and octopuses. Alaska skate, likely among other fishes, eat them. This is a moderately important commercial species in both the trawl and longline fisheries of the North Pacific, but are only rarely taken in the sport catch. One genetic study found that they were most closely related to rougheyes, while another discerned a close link to *S. flammeus* and *S. iracundus* from the western Pacific. Von Bertalanffy parameters (FL, cm): (sexes combined) $L_\infty = 84.6$, $k = 0.03$, $t_0 = -3.62$ (Hutchinson et al. 2007). Length-weight parameters (FL, mm, gr): (females) $W = 0.00000663L^{3.143}$; (males) $W = 0.000008303L^{3.105}$ (Szaley et al. 2010).

Sebastes ciliatus
(Tilesius, 1813)
Dark Rockfish

PAULINE RIDINGS

Darks grow to a length of 47 cm (19 in) FL. They have been found off the western Aleutian Islands and in the eastern Bering Sea to Johnstone Strait (British Columbia), in 5–160 m (17–528 ft). This is a species of complex relief. Small fish can inhabit very shallow, almost intertidal, waters. Older and larger fish often live around sponges and boulders. Dark rockfish live to at least 67 years old. Females re-lease larvae at least between May and July. While fishes dominate their diets, they also eat a fairly wide array of other prey, includ-ing cnidarians, polychaetes, euphausiids, hermit crabs, crustacean larvae, snails, and the occasional cephalopod. Pacific halibut eat them. Darks are most closely related to dusky rockfish (the split occurring perhaps less than 500,000 years ago) and also to northern rockfish. They are a common sport species, at least as far north as Kodiak Island.

Sebastes eos
(Eigenmann & Eigenmann, 1890)
Pink Rockfish

JOHN BUTLER

Pink rockfish grow to 56 cm (22 in) TL and range from central Oregon (44°33'N) to southern Baja California (25°24'N, 113°01'W), mostly from Southern California southward. They live at depths of 45–366 m (150–1,200 ft), typically as solitary individuals over rocky reefs. We haven't seen many of them, but the ones we have ob-served live in 8–11.2°C (46–52°F). I aged one that was 51 cm (20 in) TL at about 52 years old. Larval release occurs between April–June. Length-weight parameters (TL, cm, gr): (sexes combined) $W = 0.0186L^{2.957}$ (Love et al. 2002).

JOHN BUTLER

Sebastes gilli
(Eigenmann, 1891)
Bronzespotted Rockfish

Often called "Arkansas reds," and "warthogs," bronzespotteds grow to at least 85 cm (34 in) TL and can weigh as much as 6.6 kg (14.5 lb). They are found from Monterey Bay to off Punta Colnett (northern Baja California), at depths between 75–413 m (246–1,354 ft). Interestingly, bronzespotteds do not appear to be particularly abundant anywhere, leading one to wonder if they have been horribly overfished. They are more-or-less predictably seen from about Anacapa Island southwards, including out at such offshore banks as Tanner-Cortes. This is a cave-dwelling species that lives to at least 60 years old and probably longer. Larval release likely occurs in the winter. Commercial and recreational fishermen catch them on occasion. Based on genetic analyses, it appears that bronzespotteds are a relatively old species (stretching back perhaps 3 million years), that has no close relatives, although both aurora and chameleon rockfishes are distantly related. Bronzespotteds also may be somewhat closely related to *S. nivosus* and *S. taczanowski*, species found in the western Pacific. Length-weight parameters (TL, cm, gr): (sexes combined) W = 0.0177L$^{2.981}$ (Love et al. 2002).

Sebastes lentiginosus
Chen, 1971
Freckled Rockfish

Freckleds grow to about 23 cm (9 in) TL and are found from Point Conception (34°36'N) (California) to Punta San Roque (27°08'N, 114°26'W) (central Baja California), and Isla Guadalupe (and rarely north of Santa Monica Bay, Southern California) at depths of 22–290 m (73–951 ft). We see them over both high and low relief reefs,

JOHN BUTLER

either as solitary individuals or maybe 2–3 lying near each other. This is a benthic species that rarely ascends even a meter above the seafloor. In Southern California, they live in 9.6–12.2°C (49–54°F). They live to at least 22 years. Females probably release larvae in the spring.

Sebastes macdonaldi
(Eigenmann & Beeson, 1893)
Mexican Rockfish

They are called "rubies," "Arkansas red," "Arkansas black," and "Arkansas traveler." Mexican rockfish grow to 66 cm (26 in) TL and range from Point Sur (Central California) to southern Baja California (23°24'N, 111°11'W), and in the central Gulf of California. They are not terribly abundant in most of Southern California, although by the time you get to around the U.S.-Mexico border, their numbers begin to pick up. Based on larval densities, relatively large populations exist as far north as about 30°N (central Baja California). There apparently is extensive gene flow between Pacific Coast fish and those living in the Gulf of California. Bottom-oriented, rocky-reef dwellers, they can be found at depths of 76–350 m (249–1,148 ft). Larvae are released from November–May, perhaps peaking in April. Mexican rockfish form a minor part of the Southern California commercial rockfish catch. They are more important in Baja California commercial and artisanal fisheries. California anglers catch a few of them. Several genetic studies imply that this is a relatively old species and may be related to yelloweye rockfish or perhaps chilipeppers. Larvae: hatching length = 4–5 mm, flexion length = 7.7–9 mm, transformation length to pelagic juvenile = about 1.5 cm. Settlement occurs at around 6 cm (2.4 in) SL. Length-weight parameters (TL, cm, gr): (sexes combined) W = 0.0446L$^{2.664}$ (Love et al. 2002).

Macdonaldi refers to Marshall MacDonald (1835–1895), a Confederate army officer, professor at Virginia Military Institute, and United States Commissioner of Fisheries, and kind of a pushy guy. Here is David Starr Jordan writing about describing a new species of trout from Colorado (Jordan 1922): "To my delight we caught some half-dozen fine large specimens weighing from eight to ten pounds. At a hint from Marshall Macdonald, then the excellent United States Commissioner of Fisheries, we named the new form for him [*Salmo macdonaldi*, now known to be the cutthroat trout, *Oncorhynchus clarkii*], though the appellation I had originally in mind would have forever associated it with the high cliffs and eternal snow of the Saguache range, several peaks of which exceed 14,000 feet." *Gee, nice going Marshall. You already had a rockfish named after you, but was that enough? Nooo.]*

Sebastes melanosema
Lea & Fitch, 1979
Semaphore Rockfish

This species grows to 39 cm (15 in) TL and lives from the Santa Barbara Channel and possibly central Oregon (44°41'N, 124°48'W) to Punta San Pablo (27°13'N, 114°30'W) (central Baja California), at depths of 97–490 m (318–1,607 ft). We see them on rocks, almost always sitting real still.

JOHN BUTLER

JOHN BUTLER

Sebastes moseri
Eitner, Kimbrell, and Vetter 1999
Whitespotted Rockfish

A dwarf species, they grow to 20.6 cm (8 in) TL and have been seen or captured between Big Creek (36°03'N, 121°36.8'W) (Central California) to off Punta Colnett (northern Baja California) and Isla Guadalupe (central Baja California), at depths of 50–220 m (165–726 ft). This is a very abundant (to at least as far north as the southern part of Southern California), schooling species that lives over rocky reefs. In Southern California, we have seen them in 9.3–11.9°C (49–53°F).

Sebastes nigrocinctus
Ayres, 1859
Tiger Rockfish

Tigers reach 61 cm (24 in) TL and a weight of 3.4 kg (7.5 lb). They are found from Unalaska Island (Aleutian Islands) to Tanner and Cortes banks (Southern California), typically from southeastern Alaska to Northern California. They have been found in 9–298 m (30–978 ft); adults commonly are in 30 m (98 ft) and deeper. From about June–August, young-of-the-year settle (starting at around 2.4–2.8 cm, 1 in, TL) to drifting algae, floats, or other material. Little is known about juvenile settlement to benthic habitat, although juveniles do live among shallow rock piles. Adults are often solitary,

MARCOS PERREAU GUIMARAES

mostly reclusive, and live in crevice-filled high-relief rocks. In southeastern Alaska, tigers might move out of shallower waters in winter. Tigers live to 116 years old. Females release young at least from February–June. Tigers fancy bottom-oriented prey, such as crabs, hermit crabs, caridean shrimps, brittle stars, and hydroids. Although not taken in huge numbers, these are popular and valuable in hook-and-line commercial fisheries, for both the dead and (particularly) the live fish trade. Recreational anglers catch pretty good numbers, particularly from the Gulf of Alaska to Washington. Several genetic studies imply that tigers are closely related to the three other barred species (flag and redbanded rockfishes, and treefish), perhaps most closely to redbandeds. Length-weight parameters (TL, cm, gr): (sexes combined) W = 0.009L$^{3.205}$ (Love et al. 2002).

Sebastes ovalis
(Ayres, 1862)
Speckled Rockfish

Speckleds grow to 56 cm (22 in) TL. They range from Northern Washington (47°38'N) to Arrecife Sacramento (29°40'N, 115°47'W) (central Baja California), typically from Central California to at least Punta Colnett (northern Baja California). Distributed in 30–366 m (100–1,200 ft), in Southern California they are mostly in 90–140 m (295–459 ft). Also in Southern California, they live in at least 9.1–12.7°C (48–55°F) and mostly at 9.5–11.3°C (49–52°F). This is a schooling species that lives around rock ridges and in boulder fields. Speckleds live at least 37 years. Females grow larger than males. Off Southern California, a few fish mature at 23 cm (9 in) TL, 50% at 24 cm (9 in), and all are mature at 32 cm (13 in) (4–12 years old). Further north, fish mature between 28 and 30 cm (11–12 in, 4–5 years old). Females release larvae from September–May (peaking January–February). Speckleds feed mostly on water column prey, such as calanoid copepods, euphausiids, amphipods, larval fishes, and such gelatinous zooplankton as siphonophores. Pelagic juveniles are eaten by Chinook salmon and rhinoceros auklets. This is a minor commercial species and is taken in fairly large numbers by recreational fishermen. Speckleds are most closely related to squarespots, banks, and perhaps dwarf-red and whitespotted rockfishes. Larvae: hatching length = 4.9–5.1 mm, flexion length = about 6.8 mm. Von Bertalanffy parameters (TL, cm): (females) $L_\infty = 50$, $k = 0.05$, $t_0 = -4.94$; (males) $L_\infty = 35.9$, $k = 0.06$, $t_0 = -10.25$ (Love et al. 2002). Length-weight parameters (TL, cm, gr): (females) $W = 0.0084L^{3.137}$; (males) $W = 0.0052L^{3.217}$ (Love et al. 1990).

Sebastes phillipsi
(Fitch, 1964)
Chameleon Rockfish

Chameleons reach 52 cm (21 in) TL. They have been found from Point St. George (41°34'N) (Northern California) to the Nine Mile Bank (32°39'N, 117°28'W) (Southern California), at depths of 174–300 m (570–984 ft). A fish found over high relief (occasionally on soft substrata next to reefs), chameleons are common at least as far north as Monterey Bay. They live to at least 53 years old. I found that chameleons eat euphausiids.

    Phillipsi honors Julius B. Phillips (1904–1995), the California Fish and Game biologist who was one with the rockfishes.

Sebastes proriger
(Jordan & Gilbert, 1880)
Redstripe Rockfish

Redstripes reach a length of 61 cm (24 in) TL and a maximum weight of 1.7 kg (3.7 lb). They are found from Pribilof Canyon (southeastern Bering Sea) and Amchitka Island (Aleutian Islands) to southern Baja California (26°46'N, 114°07'W), typically from southeastern Alaska to Oregon, and at depths of 12–524 m (40–1,719 ft) and perhaps to 598 m (1,932 ft), mostly from 55–300 m (180–984 ft). Along Alaska and the West Coast, they have been taken in waters from at least 4.5–11.9°C (40–53°F). Redstripes school around boulders and rock ridges, but you can also see them on cobbles and pebbles. Schools reportedly rise up off the bottom at night. Redstripes live to at least 70 years. Females grow larger than males. Redstripes mature at between 22–33 cm (9–13 in) FL. Females release larvae from April–July. Prey items include euphausiids, shrimps, and small fishes.

Historically an important food fish, today redstripes are an important part of trawl fisheries from the eastern Gulf of Alaska to Oregon. They are occasionally taken in recreational fisheries. Redstripes do not appear to be too closely related to any extant species, but there does seem to be some relationship with sharpchins and pygmies. Length-weight parameters (TL, cm, gr): (sexes combined) $W = 0.0331L^{2.681}$ (Love et al. 2002).

Sebastes reedi
(Westrheim & Tsuyuki, 1967)
Yellowmouth Rockfish

Yellowmouths grow to about 58 cm (23 in) TL and at least 2.8 kg (6.2 lb) and are found from the Gulf of Alaska (58°54'N, 140°54'W) to near San Francisco. They live over rocky seafloors at depths of 75–430 m (246–1,410 ft) and perhaps to 445 m (1,460 ft), typically at 100–400 m (328–1,312 ft).

A reasonably long-lived species, yellowmouths can live to at least 100 years old. A few fish mature at 31 cm (12 in) FL and 50% are mature at around 38 cm (15 in). Females release larvae from February–June. Limited studies show that yellowmouths eat midwater fishes, shrimps, and squids. Yellowmouths are an important trawl commercial species, particularly from British Columbia to Oregon. Von Bertalanffy parameters (FL, cm): (females) L_∞ = 46.4, k = 0.25, t_0 = -2.14; (males) L_∞ = 45.18, k = 0.22, t_0 = -1.09 (Love et al. 2002). Length-weight parameters (TL, cm, gr): (sexes combined) W = $0.0187L^{2.97}$ (Love et al. 2002).

Sebastes rufinanus
Lea & Fitch, 1972
Dwarf-red Rockfish

This species grows to 17 cm (7 in) TL and inhabits the offshore banks and islands off Southern California, as far northwest as San Miguel Island, at depths of 58–220 m (363–722 ft). We have observed them in 8.8–14.5°C (48–58°F), mostly in 9.5–11.8°C (49–53°F). Dwarf-reds live over high-relief reefs and we usually see them in small schools near the bottom.

Sebastes simulator
Chen, 1971
Pinkrose Rockfish

Pinkroses reach a length of 42.1 cm (17 in) TL. They are found from at least Carmel Submarine Canyon (Central California) to Cabo Colnett (northern Baja California), and at Isla Guadalupe (central Baja California), most commonly from Southern California southward. They have been taken at depths of 99–450 m (325–1,476 ft). Off Southern California, we see them mostly in 205–290 m (672–951 ft), always on the bottom on low (but hard) or high relief. I have aged them to as old as maybe 36 years old. Most fish seem to be mature by about 19 cm (7 in) TL. Female sims release larvae from at least February–July

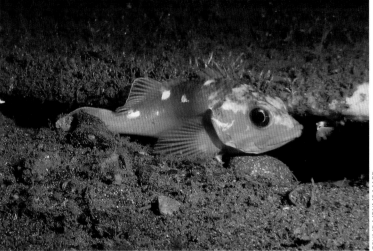

and produce 20,88–63,700 eggs. I find mostly galatheid crabs in their stomachs. Pinkroses are most closely related to rosethorns and a little more distantly to swordspines. Although small in stature, they have big mouths and are taken fairly often in the recreational catch. Length-weight parameters (TL, cm, gr): (sexes combined) W = $0.00564L^{3.27}$ (Love unpubl.).

Sebastes variabilis

Pallas, 1814

Dusky Rockfish

Duskies reach a length of 59 cm (23 in) FL and at least 3 kg (6.6 lb). They have been found from Hokkaido and eastern Kamchatka to about 60°N in the Bering Sea and along the Aleutian Islands to Oregon (44°24'N, 124°47'W) (and less commonly south of around Sitka, Alaska), in 6–675 m (20–2,228 ft), perhaps mostly in 100–300 m (328–984 ft). Smaller individuals live in the shallower depths. Duskies live over both high/hard and low/hard relief in waters at least between 2.8 and 10°C (37–50°F). They live to at least 76 years old. In the Gulf of Alaska, 50% of females are mature at 36.5 cm (14 in) FL and about 9 years old. Also in the GOA, females release young from April to perhaps July. Duskies are mostly planktivores, and euphausiids may be their most important prey. They also eat copepods, larvaceans, gammarid amphipods, arrow worms, shrimps, cephalopods, and fishes. Genetic analyses imply that dusky rockfish are most closely related to dark rockfish (the split occurring perhaps less than 500,000 years ago) and to northern rockfish. Von Bertalanffy parameters (FL, mm): (females) L_∞ = 470, k = 0.235, t_0 = 1.23; (males) L_∞ = 455, k = 0.253, t_0 = 1.28 (Malecha et al. 2007). Length-weight parameters (FL, mm, gr): (sexes combined) W = $0.0088L^{3.11}$ (Chilton 2010).

Sebastes variegatus

Quast, 1971

Harlequin Rockfish

Harlequins grow to 38 cm (15 in) TL, at least 966 gr (2.1 lb), and live between the southeastern Bering Sea and Aleutian Islands, at Bowers Bank, to 95 km (59 mi) southwest of Newport (44°32'N, 124°39'W) (Oregon), commonly as far south as at least Dixon Entrance (between Alaska and Canada). They have been taken at depths of 6–558 m (20–1,831 ft), mostly between 50–300 m (164–984 ft) and between at least 3–9.6°C (37–49°F). These are high-relief reef dwellers. Harlequins live to at least 47 years old. Fifty percent of fish are mature at 22–24 cm (9 in) FL. Females release larvae around June. Von Bertalanffy parameters (FL, mm): (females) L_∞ = 323, k = 0.11, t_0 = -3.26; (males) L_∞ = 306, k = 0.091, t_0 = -4.76 (Malecha et al. 2007).

Sebastes wilsoni

(Gilbert, 1915)

Pygmy Rockfish

Pygmies grow to 24 cm (9 in) TL and range from the outer coast of the Kenai Peninsula (northern Gulf of Alaska) to at least Cortes Bank (Southern California). Pygmies are quite abundant as far south as Southern California. Because they are hard to capture, it is likely that the currently known range of this species is incorrect and that it is also found off Baja California. Young-of-the-year settle out of the plankton at depths between 30–200 m (98–656 ft). Found between 29–383 m (95–1,256 ft), most fish live in 60–150 m (197–492 ft). At least a few fish live at temperatures as low as 4.5°C (40°F). In Southern California, we see them in 8.8–12.1°C (48–54°F) and mostly in 9.5–11°C (49–52°F). These are schooling fish whose adults are usually found over structure and often over high relief. We have observed that young-of-the-year often school over sand or mud near rocks. In Southern California, adults often school with squarespots and halfbandeds. Pygmies live to at least 26 years old. Females probably release larvae from July–October. Pygmies are planktivores, mostly eating euphausiids, along with some copepods, amphipods, and other zooplankton. Chinook salmon and California sea lions definitely eat them and they are probably consumed by rockfishes and a bunch of other fishes. There are no commercial or recreational fisheries for this species. Pygmies are most closely related to harlequin and Puget Sound rockfishes. Larvae: flexion larvae = 8 mm or less, transformation length = 1.8–2.3 cm (0.7–0.9 in), and some remain in the water column to at least 3.5 cm (1.4 in).

CHARLES BRANCH WILSON

Wilsoni refers to Charles Branch Wilson (1861–1941). He was first appointed Professor of Science at the State Normal School in Gorham (Maine) and later at the State Normal School in Westfield (Massachusetts). Given the symmetrical nature of the Universe, one then wonders who got these positions at the two New England State Abnormal schools. In 1899, Wilson began research on the parasitic copepods of common fishes of the New England region. In 1901, the United States National Museum gave Wilson its entire parasitic copepod collection for identification. This is similar to the owner-operator of the Aegean Stables turning over the contents of that building, complete with shovel, to Hercules. Nonetheless, Wilson did a good enough job that, in 1933, he was named Honorary Collaborator by the Museum, a title that seemingly was held in high esteem, at least until Vidkun Quisling kind of put the tarnish to it.

Sebastes zacentrus
(Gilbert, 1890)
Sharpchin Rockfish

Sharpchins reach a length of 49 cm (19 in) TL and a weight of 1.1 kg (2.4 lb). They range from Saint George Island (eastern Bering Sea), and Attu Island (Aleutian Islands) to San Diego and are abundant from maybe Kodiak Island to Central California. They live on the bottom, at depths of 25 to 610–660 m (83 to 2,001–2,164 ft), but mostly from perhaps 200–300 m (656–984 ft). Trawl surveys have caught them in waters between at least 3.8 and 12.3°C (39–54°F). Sharpchins occupy a wide range of habitats, but most often live on hard (both high and low relief) or mixed hard-and-soft seafloors. Sharpchins live to 73 years old. Size at maturity is variable and fish to the north appear to be larger at maturity. Fifty percent maturity has been variously estimated to range from about 21–28 cm (8–11 in) (about 6–10 years old). Larval release occurs from March–July and is likely to be in the later part of that season in more northerly waters. Sharpchins feed on fishes, euphausiids, copepods, pteropods, midwater and benthic shrimps, hermit crabs, and cephalopods. Predators include Chinook and coho salmon and Pacific cod. They are most closely related to such dwarf species as Puget Sounds and pygmies. Larvae: birth length = about 4.3 mm, flexion length = 7.4–8.5 mm, transformation length = 1.4–2 cm. Von Bertalanffy parameters (FL, mm): (females) L_∞ = 350, k = 0.122, t_0 = -0.75; (males) L_∞ = 284, k = 0.167, t_0 = -0.48 (Malecha et al. 2007).

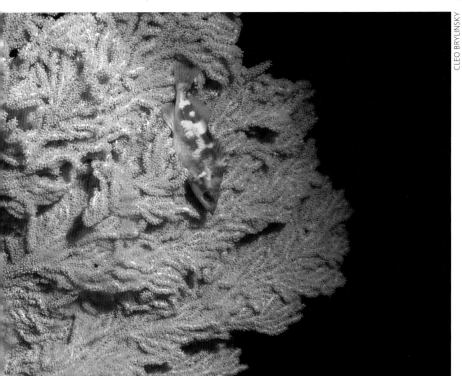

CLEO BRYLINSKY

JOHN BUTLER

Sebastolobus altivelis
Gilbert, 1896
Longspine Thornyhead

Longspines reach 38 cm (15 in) TL and at least 668 gr (1.5 lb). They range from the Shumagin Islands (western Gulf of Alaska) to Cabo San Lucas (southern Baja California), and mostly from Vancouver Island to at least Southern California. While found from 194–1,756 m (636–5,760 ft), they are typically in 500–1,300 m (1,640–4,264 ft). Adults are found in deeper water in the southern part of their range. At 18–20 months old, young-of-the-year settle from the plankton to soft seafloors at about 4.2–6 cm (2 in) FL, usually in water between 600–1,200 (1,980–3,936 ft). Unlike shortspines, longspines do not tend to migrate into deeper waters as they mature, but rather settle in adult habitats. Most longspines live over mud, often near bits of hard stuff like rocks or sponges, in waters of at least 2–8.1°C (36–47°F). These are solitary and sedentary fish, you almost always see them resting on the seafloor. Genetic analyses imply that there are no discrete populations. Longspines live to at least 65 years old. Fifty percent of females are mature at around 17.8 cm (7 in) FL. Females spawn their eggs (between 3,000–106,000) in one batch between at least January–May. Longspines are opportunistic feeders that feed on or near the bottom. Pelagic juveniles feed on euphausiids and other planktonic creatures and benthic juveniles feed on such small invertebrates as gammarid amphipods and polychaetes. As they grow, they work their way up to fishes, shrimps, crabs, squids, octopuses, and brittle stars. Predators include North Pacific daggertooths. Longspines are most closely related to shortspine thornyheads. Both share an ancestor with broadfin thornyheads from about 4–5 million years ago and longspines diverged from shortspines perhaps 1.3 million years ago. Eggs: 1.1 x 1.2 mm. Larvae: hatching length = about 2.6 mm, flexion length = 6–7.3 mm, transformation length = pelagic juvenile = 2.2 cm (1 in). Von Bertalanffy parameters (TL, cm): (sexes combined) L_∞ = 30, k = 0.07, t_0 = -1.9 (Love et al. 2002). Length-weight parameters (SL, mm, gr): (sexes combined) W = $0.0101L^{3.28}$ (Wakefield 1990).

GOOD NEWS FOR BRITTLE STARS

From Smith and Brown (1983), we learn that "only 0.007% of the [brittle star] population per day would be assimilated by the *S. altivelis* population."

Sebastolobus macrochir
(Günther, 1877)
Broadfin Thornyhead

Broadfins grow to 38 cm (15 in) TL. They live from the seas of Japan and Okhotsk to the Bering Sea and to the Pacific Ocean just south of the Aleutian Islands at depths of 100–1,504 m (328–4,934 ft). They are very abundant in the seas of Japan and Okhotsk to as far east and north as the northern Kurils and southeastern Kamchatka, perhaps most commonly in 200–800 m (656–2,624 ft). A handful have been taken in US waters. In the Kuril Island region, juveniles may settle to the sea floor at perhaps 7 cm (3 in), at depths of 400–650 m (1,312 ft).

ALEXEY ORLOV

Broadfins live to at least 34 years old and fish mature at anywhere from 15 to 32+ cm (6–13 in). Most studies imply that spawning occurs in winter and spring. Brittle stars and small crustaceans (e.g., amphipods and shrimps) seem to be a big part of their diets, along with occasional polychaetes, fishes, and squids. Greenland halibut and sablefish eat them. There have been substantial trawl and bottom gill net fisheries for this species. For those who keep track of such things both melanistic (black-colored) ones and an albino fish have been caught. Broadfins are most closely related to longspine and shortspine thornyheads and appear to share an ancestor with these two species that lived about 4–5 million years ago. Length-weight parameters (TL, mm, gr): (sexes combined) W = $0.01742L^{3.141}$ (W. Wakefield, pers. comm.).

FAMILY TRIGLIDAE—Searobins

The Triglidae are tropical and temperate marine fishes found throughout the world. There are 10 genera and at least 105 species of these benthic fishes. Eight species live within our range, but only one reaches as far north as California. Searobins are oviparous, with planktonic eggs and larvae. Unsure about that searobin in your hand? Not to worry, Fischer et al. (1995) has both keys and illustrations of eastern Pacific species.

Prionotus stephanophrys

Lockington, 1881

Lumptail Searobin

ROSS ROBERTSON

ETYMOLOGY AND COLLOQUIAL NAMES: *Prionotus* means "saw" and "back" in Greek and *stephanophrys* is "crown" and "eyebrow," also in Greek. In Mexico, they are called "angel," and "lapón."
THE BASICS: Maximum Length: 43 cm (17 in) TL. The Ranges: Off the Columbia River to Chile, including the Gulf of California, and mostly south of Bahia Magdalena (southern Baja California). On occasion, for instance during some El Niño years, they are fairly common as far north as Southern California. 2–255 m (7–836 ft) and mostly at maybe 10–110 m (33–361 ft). Eggs: 1–1.2 mm. Larvae: hatching length = about 1.9 mm, flexion length = about 5–8 mm, transformation length = 9 mm. Von Bertalanffy parameters (SL, mm): (sexes combined) L_∞ = 379, k = 0.138, t_0 = -0.0812 (Schmitter-Soto and Castro-Aguirre 1991). Length-weight parameters (SL, mm, gr): (sexes combined) $W = 0.000025L^{2.9729}$ (Schmitter-Soto and Castro-Aguirre 1991).
SALIENT CHARACTERS: A fairly unforgettable species with a bony and spiny head, and very large pectoral fins whose three lowest rays are not connected to the rest of the fin. They tend toward a gray, purple, or dark back with darker mottling.
LIFE HISTORY: No one has paid much attention to this searobin. Young-of-the-year recruit to soft sediment at as small as 1.1 cm (0.4 in) SL. Lumptails are sedentary fish that appear to spend most of their time resting on soft seafloors. A 28 cm (11 in) SL fish was 9 years old. Spawning occurs at least from September–February. They are eaten by California sea lions.
FISHERY: These are of only small economic importance in some artisanal fisheries in, for instance, central Pacific Mexico.
ORIGINS: The oldest *Prionotus* has been found in the Pliocene deposits (1.8 million years ago) of North Carolina. Fossils of lumptail searobins have been found in 100,000-year-old sediments in Southern California.

FAMILY ANOPLOPOMATIDAE—Sablefishes

The family Anoplopomatidae is made up of a modest group of fishes (well, there are only two species, truth to tell) that live in the North Pacific. Both species are oviparous, with planktonic eggs and larvae and both are found within our range.

MBARI

Anoplopoma fimbria

(Pallas, 1814)

Sablefish

ETYMOLOGY AND COLLOQUIAL NAMES: *Anoplopoma* is Greek for "unarmed" and "operculum" and *fimbria* means "fringe" in Latin. In the 19th century, "horse mackerel," "candle-fish," "Spanish mackerel," and "black-cod" were the popular names. In the Queen Charlotte Islands, white folks called them "coal-fish," while local Haida called them "skil," and the Makah of the Olympic Peninsula used "beshowe." By the early 20th century, "sablefish" was in use, although "blackcod" continues to be popular. They are "gindara" in Japanese.

N
W E
S

Emil Carlson, *Still Life*, 1891. Courtesy of the Oakland Museum of California

THE BASICS: Maximum Length: 116.8 cm (46 in) FL. Maximum Weight: A 25.5 kg (56 lb) fish was taken off Fort Bragg (California) in 1930. Historically, fish larger than 22.7 kg (50 lb) were rare. The Ranges: Central Honshu to Aleutian Islands, and Bowers Bank to Bering Sea south of St. Lawrence Island (Alaska), and to Islas San Benito and Isla Cedros (central Baja California). They are particularly common from the eastern Aleutian Islands and eastern Bering Sea to about Banco Ranger (central Baja California). There are fair numbers of fish off southern Kamchatka and the northern Kuril Islands; however, these fish may not reproduce successfully and may be migrants from further eastward. Surface to 2,740 m (8,989 ft). Juveniles at surface, most adults live at depths of maybe 300–1,000 m (984–3,280 ft), but optimum depth varies with locality. A mature fish was taken right next to the beach in Puget Sound, so they come in close on occasion. Eggs: 1.8–2.2 mm. Larvae: hatching length = 4.4–6 mm, flexion length = 10.3–16.1 mm, transformation length = about 3.5–7 cm (1–3 in). Growth rates are highly variable between locations and depths. As an example, see Sigler et al. (1997) for a number of von Bertalanffy growth parameters, just from Alaskan waters. Length-weight parameters (TL, mm, kg): (sexes combined) $W = 0.0000000224L^{2.8408}$ (RecFin 2009).

SALIENT CHARACTERS: Sablefish are sleek and fusiform. Pelagic juveniles are blue and blue-back on back with white belly; larger juveniles are greenish or grayish with faint stripes on back. Adults are dark gray, greenish-gray, bluish-green, or blackish, sometimes with a latticework pattern on back, and dirty gray belly. Back in 1885, Swan wrote that sablefish were "Dark olive brown or sepia on the back, with grayish sides and belly." We still can't beat that, although we are sad that the term "sepia" seems to have gone to whatever reward is waiting for words that have passed their prime. Sablefish have two dorsal fins and two anal fins.

LIFE HISTORY: Young-of-the-year are pelagic; you can sometimes find them right at the surface, sometimes even breaking the water. I have seen them hanging around drifting kelp mats and other debris. Based on work in the Bering Sea, Kulikov (1965) stated that juveniles smaller than about 30 cm (12 in) FL are always pelagic and that by 60 cm (24 in) all individuals are demersal. Rutecki and Varosi (1997) reported: "Older juveniles (ages 1 and 2) [one year old fish are about 30 cm, 12 in, FL] were caught on or near the bottom." They are also occasionally found in slightly estuarine conditions. Juveniles have been found at least as deep as 411 m (1,348 ft). After recruiting to the seafloor, sablefish tend to slowly move into deeper waters (fish tend to get larger with depth). The percentage of females also gets larger with depth and, in some areas, by about 1,300 m (4,264 ft) most individuals are females. Adults are found over a wide range of habitats, including boulders, cobbles, and just plain sediment. They are often seen either resting on the seafloor or moving just above it, but they reportedly will range 40 m (131 ft) or more off the bottom. Kulikov (1965) believed that at least some adult sablefish were vertical migrators, occupying the water column during the day and hanging out near the bottom at night. These fish really like the oxygen minimum layer and highest densities are often found in these waters. In general, there are relatively few large sablefish in Southern California waters, implying that either 1) the fish do not grow large there or 2) the larger ones mostly move northward. Sablefish tend to spawn in deeper waters in winter and then move into shallower depths in summer. On the seafloor, they have been taken in waters of 2–12.6°C (36–55°F).

Frankly, trying to figure out movements of sablefish is just a thankless task. McFarlane and Saunders (2006) found that tagged juveniles off the Queen Charlotte Islands tend to move north and west into Alaska, while those tagged off the west coast of Vancouver Island tended to move little. Maloney and Heifetz (1997), working in the eastern Gulf of Alaska, noted: "Over three-fourths of all tags were recovered in the EGOA [eastern Gulf of Alaska], most of them in or adjacent to the original release area. Chatham Strait, with its high density of mature fish and low rate of tag recovery outside the EGOA, appears to have a high proportion of nonmigrating fish. Of the fish recovered outside the EGOA, more small fish (<57 cm FL when tagged) moved north and westward, and more large fish (>66 cm FL when tagged) moved south and eastward." Not to be outdone, Maloney (2004) found that small numbers of adult sablefish are found on offshore seamounts [and likely form separate stocks] in the Gulf of Alaska. These fish come from adult fish living in slope waters that swim to the seamounts. Maloney, citing several other papers, stated: "Most sablefish undertake a migration from eastern areas of the Gulf of Alaska to western areas, including the Aleutian Islands and the Bering Sea, during their younger years, and most return eastward along the continental slope after reaching maturity." So, it's all kind of confusing, isn't it?

Kimura et al. (1998) state that there are two overlapping populations in North America: "An Alaska population ranging from the Bering Sea, including the Aleutian Islands and extending down through the Gulf of Alaska to northwest Vancouver Island, Canada; and a west coast population extending from southwest Vancouver Island to Baja California. Tag recoveries indicate that these 2 populations mix off southwest Vancouver Island and northwest Washington, and to a lesser extent off southern Washington and Oregon." They further note that the Alaska population tends to move about more than West Coast fish.

Sablefish live to at least 113 years old, but they are notoriously hard to age, so all we can do is hope for the best. Females grow larger than males. Growth and maturation rates appear to be very plastic, as the size and age at maturity varies between fish in different decades, and at different depths and locations, even in relatively small areas. As an example, let's look at the length at 50% maturity of female sablefish living in the Barkley Sound area of Vancouver Island (Saunders et al. 1997). In deep waters, 50% are mature at about 48 cm (19 in) FL. All well and good, except that in the shallow waters of the same place, 50% of the females are mature at about 61 cm (24 in) FL. Similarly, comparing various locations off British Columbia, female average age at 50% maturity can vary from 2–5.5 years and males from 1–5 years. On a less fine scale, Macewicz and Hunter (1994), working off Oregon, found that 50% of females were mature at 54.8 cm (22 in) FL. So look, if you want to know something about growth and maturity of sablefish, look at Mason et al. (1983), Macwicz and Hunter (1994), and Saunders et al. (1997). Various studies have found spawning to occur between October–July, and when you read all of these reports it is hard to generalize about peak spawning seasons. However, fish off California seem to spawn mostly in the fall and winter. Spawning of pelagic eggs tends to occur in relatively deep waters over the continental slope, usually in at least 200 m (656 ft)

SABLEFISH DO NOT RUST

Yes, despite your perhaps well-founded misgivings, sablefish do not rust. Steel girders on the Neligh Mill Bridge (Antelope County, Nebraska) might rust. Old Chevy Novas heaped up in a junkyard just outside of Indianapolis might rust. Bits of German shell casings hurled at Republican forces during the Spanish Civil War and lying buried under a battlefield in Catalonia might rust. But sablefish, bless their stainless steel hearts, do not rust. How do we know? Well, in a section of *Report on Black Cod of the North Pacific Ocean*, written in 1885 by James Swan, we find a section titled "The Black Cod Does Not Rust." In it, Swan reports that in 1883, he gave a bunch of salted sablefish to George Vienna, a fish seller in Victoria on Vancouver Island. Three months later: "I examined the same fish, which had been exposed to the weather in the stall all the time, and it was perfectly sweet. Mr. Vienna said it never would rust; it was too well salted."

and in some areas mostly in deeper than 800 m (2,624 ft) of water. Females spawn 3–4 egg batches per season and produce between 51,000–1,300,000 eggs per year. Fish off the west coast of the U.S. may produce more eggs per body length than those off British Columbia, but folks don't seem to know if this perceived difference is real or an artifact of different research methods. Off Central California, peak spawning occurs at night. Sablefish eggs hatch in about 300 hours at 6°C (43°F). Pelagic young-of-the-year eat a wide range of zooplankton, along with a few fishes and squids. Once the fish start living near the sea-floor, they are opportunistic feeders, and prey on fishes, crustaceans (euphausiids, shrimps, crabs, and gammarid amphipods), squids, octopuses, gelatinous zooplankton, polychaetes, and offal. As sablefish become larger, fishes become more important in the diet. Juvenile sablefish may be a significant source of mortality of juvenile salmon. Diet varies by fish size, geographic location, season, and year, and in at least some northern areas, feeding is heaviest in the spring, declining in fall and winter. Many species prey on sablefish and a condensed list includes albacore, arrowtooth flounder, big skate, blue, salmon, and soupfin sharks, Chinook and coho salmon, Pacific cod, Pacific hakes, Pacific halibut, Pacific sleeper sharks, sablefish, steelhead, widow and yellowtail rockfishes, storm-petrels, cormorants, auklets, puffins, California and Steller sea lions, harbor and northern elephant seals, Dall's porpoises, sperm whales, orcas, river otters, and Humboldt squids.

FISHERY: Swan (1885) noted that most northwestern indigenous peoples did not specifically fish for sablefish because the species was taken at a relatively great depth, one difficult to fish from canoes. This was particularly the case in light of the great abundance of more easily captured species, such as Pacific halibut, eulachon, herring, the various salmons, and rockfishes. Nevertheless, sablefish were caught accidentally and were widely consumed. Swan notes that the Haida (of British Columbia) would boil the fish for their oil. Swan credits himself with introducing the fish to most of the white folks in the Northwest through his determined efforts to send boxes of salted sablefish to Victoria (Vancouver Island) and other cities.

By the late 19th century, sablefish were of some commercial importance in the Puget Sound and San Francisco region and a reasonably large setline fishery for them commenced off Washington and British Columbia in the 1890s. This expanded up and down the coast and there was a moderate demand for this species for a number of decades. The fishery expanded again during World War I, again in the 1930s, and during World War II (for both meat and livers). Throughout this time, most of the fish were sold fresh or, in substantial quantities, smoked, and also sold for animal food. However, the fishery just sputtered along until the Japanese and Soviet Union started fishing them in the late 1950s and early 1960s. With their entry (followed soon after by a number of other nations), sablefish gained considerable respect as a commercial product. Today, sablefish form a major fishery in both the U.S. and Canada. Most of the fish are frozen and shipped overseas, primarily to Japan, but also to the Republic of Korea, Hong Kong, and various other Asian and European nations. In Japan, most sablefish are sold as either steaks or fillets and consumed fresh. Sablefish are often made into stews and are prepared as "kasuzuke," fish marinated in rice wine. It is also consumed raw in sashimi. I have been told that sablefish are graded for sashimi by their oil content (the higher the better) and that deeper-dwelling fish have more oil. Most of the fish are taken by trawls, longlines, and in fish traps. While there is some commercial fishing for sablefish in Southern California, the number of large fish (preferred by processors) is not large and most of the fishery takes place from Central California northward. An exploratory commercial fishery for sablefish along northern and central Baja California in the late 1970s (with fish taken down to about Isla Cedros, central Baja California) lasted only a few years. Oh, at least in California, they are also landed alive for the live fish market. Sablefish liver is apparently a semi-treat, as I am starting to see it in a few fish markets. Apparently there is considerable enthusiasm for sablefish farming in British Columbia and considerable fear about that possibility. Whether this will turn out to be a major industry remains to be seen.

In the recreational catch, small ones are taken from piers, mostly from Central California northward, and larger ones are fairly important in vessel catches from Southern California northward. In years with good recruitment of young sablefish to nearshore waters, catches from piers can be epic. As an example, between 11 July 1947 and 26 July 1947, anglers on the municipal pier in Monterey caught an estimated 100 tons.

MISCELLANY: 1) Orcas and sperm whales, working their way down commercial longlines, seem particularly fond of sablefish. Sperm whales will preferentially eat sablefish, ignoring other species. 2) Sablefish have large amounts of fat and they store this in their muscles and bones. 3) Interestingly, larval sablefish have not been caught off Baja California or in the western Pacific, perhaps implying that fish do not spawn in those waters. 4) Beauty Tip: Off southeastern Alasaka, fish in shallow waters have firmer flesh than do those in deeper waters.

OTHER SPECIES

Erilepis zonifer
(Lockington, 1880)
Skilfish

Skilfish grow to 183 cm (72 in) TL and 91 kg (200.2 lb), and have
been found from central Honshu to the Gulf of Alaska and to Monterey Bay. Juveniles live near the surface, while adults stay close to
the bottom at depths of 200–1,030 m (656–3,379 ft). Skilfish do not
appear to be abundant anywhere, as catches (made by accident
with trawls, gill nets, and long-lines) throughout their range have
been quite small. Not much is known regarding their life history. They live to at last 20 years (that fish was 155 cm, 61 in, long).
Japanese researchers have hypothesized that spawning occurs off central Japan in the winter and spring. Adults eat squids
and octopuses. Length-weight parameters (TL, cm, kg): (sexes combined) W = 0.000038L$^{2.8247}$ (Mitani et al. 1986).

FAMILY HEXAGRAMMIDAE—Greenlings

The Hexagrammidae is a North Pacific family, comprised of temperate water, mostly benthic fishes. All of the Hexagrammidae (or at least the greenlings, lingcod, and Atka mackerel, I don't think we know how the combfishes do it) have
demersal and adhesive eggs and planktonic larvae. There are five genera and 13 species in this family, and nine species
occur within our range. A fossil greenling, *Hexagrammos achrestus*, has been recovered from the Miocene diatomite
beds (at least 5.3 million years old) of Lompoc (Central California). Based on evidence from genetic studies, Karen Crow
et al. (2004) found that the family Hexagrammidae contains some species that really are not that closely related to one
another. In their view, the family should probably only contain the genera *Hexagrammos* (the greenlings) and *Pleurogrammus* (Atka mackerel). The painted greenling and the combfishes appear to belong in a separate family, presumably
the Zaniolepidae. Lingcod present a whole different problem. They are not closely related to any of these species and, in
fact, in Karen's study seemed to be a kissing cousin of the sculpins, and particularly cabezon. So, are lingcod some sort
of *uber*-sculpin? Right now it's too early to tell as not enough sculpin species have been examined to allow comparisons.
Mecklenburg et al. (2002) provides characterizations and keys to the North Pacific species.

Hexagrammos

Back in the 19th century, the Russians called them "terpugh," "tar-poog," or other similarly spelled words
(meaning "file"), Aleuts said "idyajuk," and folks inhabiting Vancouver Island used "tath-le-gest." Fishermen often
call them "seatrout."

Nineteenth-century naturalists, as was their wont, were often enthusiastic about the appearance of various
fishes. And thus we have John Keast Lord (*The Naturalist on Vancouver Island and British Columbia*, V. 1, 1866,
Richard Bentley), clearly taking a page if not an entire chapbook, from Wordsworth, waxing poetical over
greenlings: "On the fish-stalls in Victoria and San Francisco markets the visitor may generally see, lying by the
side of the dingy, spiny rock cod, a handsome, shapely fish...Its sides, though somewhat rough, rival in beauty
many a tropical flower: clad in scales, adorned with colours not only conspicuous for their brilliancy, but grouped
and blended in a manner one sees only represented in the plumage of a bird, the wing of a butterfly, or the
petals of an orchid...We might as reasonably attempt to describe, the flushing changing colors of the Aurora
Borealis...as to hope by word-painting to give the faintest conception of the colourings that adorn the chirus: red,
blue, orange, and green are so mingled, that the only thing I can think of as a comparison is a floating flower-
bed." Yes, in the mind's eye we can clearly see a young Oscar Wilde, years before his extremely unfortunate day
in court, strolling through Covent Garden, holding a daffodil in one hand and a greenling in the other.

Kelp and whitespotted greenlings (and probably all members of the genus *Hexagrammos*) have five lateral lines, but only one of these structures is functional. This is, one assumes, kind of a useless fashion statement like those pantsuits introduced by Courrèges in the 1960s.

Hexagrammos decagrammus
(Pallas, 1810)
Kelp Greenling

*They look like those lushy, roundy,
fin de siècle ladies of Alphonse Mucha.*

A female.

STEVE MURVINE

ETYMOLOGY AND COLLOQUIAL NAMES:
Hexagrammos is Greek for "six" and "line" and *deca-grammus* means "ten" and "line" in Greek. "Boregata" was a name bestowed by Italian fishermen in Puget Sound and Japanese names appear to be "ainame-rui" and "arasuka-ainame." They are often called "sea trout" or "kelp trout." By the mid-20th century, the common name for the kelp greenling had kind of settled down to "greenling" north of California and "seatrout" in California. This posed some problems in California waters because not only is a greenling not a trout, nor a seatrout, but in Southern California "sea-trout" was also a name for small white seabass (which is, of course, neither a bass nor a trout) and sablefish (which is not a sable, but is a fish). In an attempt to find some compromise common name, the California Department of Fish and Game tried kind of jamming all the names together, did a little judicious pruning, and came up with the name "greenling seatrout." This pleased no one and was relegated to the Recycling Bin of Failed Words (where the letters in the words are recycled and put in new words).

THE BASIC: Maximum Length: 62.9 cm (25 in) TL. Maximum Weight: 2.1 kg (4.6 lb). The Ranges: Attu Island (Aleutian Islands), and Gulf of Alaska to La Jolla (Southern California). They are common at least as far west as about Kiska Island (Aleutian Islands), and as far to the southeast as Central California. Matarese et al. (2003) report fairly high densities of larvae in the southern Bering Sea, so maybe they are relatively common there, too. During some years, for instance 1999, kelp greenling young-of-the-year will recruit strongly well into Southern California. Intertidal to 130 m (426 ft); reported but not confirmed to 242 m (794 ft). They are most common from the intertidal to about 100 m (328 ft). Larvae: hatching length = 7–9 mm, flexion length = 1.5–1.8 cm (0.6–0.7 in), transformation length = about 3 cm (1 in). Von Bertalanffy parameters (TL, mm): (sexes combined) L_∞ = 398.6, k = 0.88, t_0 = 0.919 (Moulton 1977). Von Bertalanffy parameters (FL, cm): (females, Oregon) L_∞ = 38.98, k = 0.3, t_0 = -2.46; (females, California) L_∞ = 43, k = 0.2, t_0 = -2.5; (males, Oregon) L_∞ = 37.1, k = 0.4, t_0 = -1.21; (males, California) L_∞ = 39.5, k = 0.3, t_0 = -1.4 (Cope and MacCall 2005). Length-weight parameters (FL, cm, kg): (females) W = $0.00000445L^{3.3194}$; (males) W = $0.00000828L^{3.1442}$ (Cope and MacCall 2005).

SALIENT CHARACTERS: Kelp greenlings are elongated, yellow-eyed, with a long fourth lateral line (extending to about the end of the anal fin, and two cirri above each eye (one near the eye, the other, smaller one, further up the head). Describing kelp greenling coloration is messy, as males and females have different colors and patterns, and these change during the reproductive season. Young kelp greenlings seem to come in three colors—reddish, yellow-brown, and kind of gray and heavily dark mottled. The basic male pattern is brown-orange and red-purple with bright blue spots. Courting males are often uniform gray, again with the blue spots. The rule is, if it has blue spots, it is a male. Females tend to be gray or brown with brown or yellow spots. Among variants of this basic pattern are 1) gray bodies covered in orange and yellow spots and yellow fins, and 2) females with large and numerous dark-brown blotches. Ed DeMartini (1986) discusses this stuff at length.

LIFE HISTORY: Kelp greenlings are solitary reef fish that mostly inhabit shallow and nearshore waters. Juveniles settle to intertidal or shallow subtidal waters at 3 cm (1 in) FL or larger (some wait until they are about 7 cm, 3 in, TL). Older juveniles live in both the rocky intertidal and the shallow rocky subtidal, mostly in maybe 10 m (33 ft) and less, but occasionally to at least 23 m (76 ft); almost always in eelgrass, kelp, and other plant life. Adults can be found in the intertidal, but they are more common in subtidal waters and they, too, are virtually always over rocks of various sizes and shapes and among plant life. Although these fish are most abundant in kind of cool temperate waters, at least a few hang out in waters down to 4°C (39°F). Kelp greenlings spend the vast majority of their time within a few meters (let's say 10 ft) of the bottom. Several researchers (for instance Rick Rosenthal, 1980, in Prince William Sound) have noted that, at least during certain times of the year, the sexes tend to stay apart. In Larry Moulton's (1977) encyclopedic doctoral thesis on the reef fishes of Puget Sound, he notes that in relatively shallow waters males tended to be found at an average of 3 m (10 ft) deeper than females and that all fish below 15 m (49 ft) were males. While they are almost always solitary, kelp greenlings will, on occasion, form small groups. Males, particularly during nesting season, are very territorial, females (throughout the year) less so. In Central California, kelp greenlings generally have home ranges of about 500–3,000 m² (averaging around 1,000 m²) and female home ranges tend to be larger than those of males. The size of home ranges may increase with depth. In Central California, red algae appears to be an important constituent of a kelp greenling's habitat, as the more red algae there is, the smaller is the home range. These fish are inactive at night. Kelp greenlings are able to withstand at least slightly estuarine conditions.

Females lay adhesive eggs in nests that are located from barely subtidal waters to at least as deep as 17 m (56 ft). The bluish, gray, pink, green, or purple egg masses are usually deposited on encrusting material, like barnacle or scallop shells, or worm tubes, but also on hydrocorals, algae, and occasionally bare rock. Mature eggs turn silvery as the larvae become

A male.   JAN FREIWALD

pigmented. Males guard as many as 11 egg masses (ranging in size from golf to tennis balls) and many males guard eggs from more than one female in nests that may be as large as 7 m². Some males are "sneak spawners." These are non-territorial males that hang around egg nests and squirt sperm on the eggs when the territorial male is not paying close attention.

Kelp greenlings live to at least 25 years old. Females grow larger than males. A few fish mature at perhaps 26 cm (10 in) FL, 50% at about 30 cm (12 in), and all at maybe 32 cm (13 in). Females produce between 28,500–125,000 eggs per season and spawn between July–January. Females are batch spawners and produce three or more batches per season. Kelp greenlings are extremely opportunistic feeders and most of their prey is bottom-oriented. Common food items include brittle stars, crabs, gammarid and caprellid amphipods, polychaetes, and shrimps. Also frequently consumed are various fishes, fish eggs, copepods, snails, chitons, hermit crabs, and some algae. Larry Moulton reports that individual greenlings seem to target one food type, as he would find one fish loaded with snails, another filled with crabs, and so on. Predators include, but are not limited to, black rockfish, cabezons, lingcod, various salmon, skates, auklets, guillemots, murres, puffins, Steller sea lions, harbor seals, and minks.

FISHERY: Kelp greenling remains are commonly found in Native American middens. In the 19th century, this species was a prominent part of the commercial fish trade from the Aleutian Islands to Central California. By the 20th century, kelp greenlings had become a relatively minor part of the fresh fish commercial fishery. The species' kind of small size, relatively solitary habits, and poor shelf life made it a side catch of fishermen targeting lingcod or rockfishes. Indeed, few were the fishermen who proudly flew the *Hexagrammos* flag when steaming into port with a hold filled with greenlings destined for the Tables of America. And then, because they stay alive real well, along came the live fish fishery and all things old were new again. Fishermen who once turned up their zinc oxide-slathered noses in disdain found a reason to love our little five lateral-lined friends.

Rocky shore recreational anglers catch them in large numbers. You can catch a pretty big one in a relatively small tide pool.

RELATIONSHIPS: Kelp greenlings appear to be the most ancestral of the greenlings and are probably most closely related to rock greenlings.

MISCELLANY: Fairly often you will find a kelp greenling with blue flesh.

Hexagrammos lagocephalus
(Pallas, 1810)
Rock Greenling

ETYMOLOGY AND COLLOQUIAL NAMES: *Hexagrammos* is Greek for "six" and "line" and *lagocephalus* means "hare" and "head" in Greek. Older names include "rock trout," "sea trout," "boregat," and "bodieron," and the Japanese call them "usagi-ainame."

THE BASICS: Maximum Length: 61 cm (24 in) TL. Maximum Weight: 2.1 kg (4.7 lb). The Ranges: Yellow, Japan, and Okhotsk seas to the Commander–Aleutian chain and to Point Conception (Central California). They are occasional at least as far south as about Morro Bay (Central California) and more abundant north of San Francisco. A few larvae have been collected as far south as Santa Monica Bay (Southern California), so the species may live down there as well. Intertidal area and shallow waters, recorded to depth of 80 m (262 ft) in the eastern Pacific and to 596 m (1,955 ft) in the western Pacific. Off North America, they appear to be most abundant from the intertidal down to about 20 m (66 ft). Eggs: 2–3 mm. Larvae: hatching length = 9 mm, flexion length = 1.2–1.5 cm (0.5–0.6 in), transformation length = about 2.9 cm (1.1 in). Length-weight parameters (TL, mm, kg): (sexes combined) W = 0.000000026L$^{2.8928}$ (RecFin 2009).

SALIENT CHARACTERS: Rock greenlings have red eyes, only a single, large cirrus above each eye and, unlike kelp greenlings, the fourth lateral line is short, perhaps reaching just past the midpoint of the anal fin. The basic body color is brown or greenish with extreme red or orange mottling in males and blue or light spots in females. There is often a dark spot above the base of the pectoral fin and the mouth cavity is usually blue.

LIFE HISTORY: A conundrum, indeed. When you read the scientific literature on research on rock greenlings from Asia and North America, the behavior described for this "species" is sufficiently different that one wonders if there is not more than one species here. I realize that genetic studies imply that the former *Hexagrammos superciliosus* is no more and that it is now thought to be identical with *H. lagocephalus*, but how do you explain the following? Zolotov and Tokranov (1991) and Gomelyuk (2000), reporting from eastern Kamchatka and the Sea of Okhotsk, respectively, state that rock greenlings often form schools (sometimes dense ones) and show little or no territoriality. On the other hand, Rosenthal (1980), reporting from Prince William Sound, and Simenstad (1971), from Amchitka Island, both note that the species is mostly solitary and quite

territorial. In addition, Zolotov and Tokranov observed a spring-summer migration into shallow waters, while this kind of movement has apparently not been reported from North America. Orlov (2005) reports taking substantial numbers of these fish off the northern Kuril Islands and southeastern Kamchatka at depths of 100–300 m (328–984 ft). No one working off North America has reported any rock greenling from these depths.

So, look, I am kind of nervous about all this. And in light of this, what I describe below is entirely based on research from fish off North America, because, well, I'm nervous.

Young-of-the-year settle out of the plankton in late spring and summer to intertidal and subtidal algal beds and rocky bottoms. Juveniles remain particularly abundant in intertidal or barely subtidal waters, most often around eelgrass or other plants, often over cobble bottom. Simenstad (1971), observing adult rock greenlings near Amchitka Island, found that they were concentrated in "the sublitoral regions of dense algal growth" and that "During periods of high tide, when water covers the intertidal bench, the greenling is found abundantly over the bench...often rising to the surface and producing a 'rippling-popping' sound."

Okay, I changed my mind. Because there is so little known about age, growth and reproduction of North American rock greenlings, here is some stuff about both western Pacific fish and North American ones even though, as I mentioned above, the two populations seem to do some things differently. In the western Pacific, females live to at least 11 years old, males to 8 years old, and the sexes appear to have similar growth rates. The fish mature when 29–35 cm (11–14 in) (probably SL, Gorbunova, 1970, is a little vague on this point) long. Throughout their range, females produce as many as three batches of demersal, adhesive eggs per season, laying these eggs mostly on algae in shallow waters (intertidal to 27 m, 89 ft), from June–September. Females produce between 5,794–103,000 bluish, purple, gray, or light brown eggs per season. Rosenthal (1980) states that males guard the eggs and Simenstad et al. (1977) relays that both sexes do the guarding. Males are reported to be either territorial throughout the year or only during the spawning season. The eggs take about 30 days to hatch at 6–10°C (43–50°F). Jeff Marliave believes that, off British Columbia, the timing of spawning seems to be keyed to algal growth rather than temperature, day length, or salinity changes.

Simenstad et al. (1977) note: "After the juvenile rock greenling hatch in the summer, they form pelagic schools and apparently move into offshore oceanic waters and into the epipelagic community. Although juvenile rock greenling were seldom captured in Amchitka's inshore waters, the purse seine catches...65 to 95 km [40 to 60 mi] off Kagalaska Island often included significant numbers of juvenile rock greenling. After 2 to 3 years, they apparently migrate back into the inshore areas."

Like other greenlings, rock greenlings appear to eat just about everything available, feeding both near the bottom and in the water column. Important prey include crustaceans (particularly gammarid and caprellid amphipods, crabs, shrimps, isopods, and mysid shrimps), fishes, snails, octopuses, bivalves, polychaetes, and algae. Also consumed are brittle stars, chitons, limpets, sea cucumbers, insects, tunicates, pteropods, and sea anemones. During spawning seasons, fish eggs, such as those of Atka mackerel and yellow Irish lords, are very important. At least one study found that rock greenlings feed both day and night, but may leave the protection of benthic algae more at night. Predators include coho salmon, great sculpins, Pacific cod, other rock greenlings, Arctic and Aleutian terns, bald eagles, horned and tufted puffins, rhinoceros auklets, Steller sea lions, and probably by river otters.

FISHERY: Various indigenous peoples commonly harvested rock greenlings in the past, and their descendants continue to do so today. Back in 1868, Swan noted that the Makah of Washington state ate them and also commented on the color of greenling flesh. "Its flesh varies in color with the locality where it is taken...and may be found with shades ranging from a pure white to a greenish-blue--the latter color being very disagreeable to most of the white men, who regard it as produced by a poisonous agency. I have eaten freely of this fish, and found that the color of the flesh made no difference either in flavor or quality." Today, there seem to be small artisanal fisheries for them, but no large commercial enterprises. Shore, jetty, pier, and boat anglers commonly take them, particularly north of about San Francisco.

RELATIONSHIPS: The previously accepted species *Hexagrammos superciliosus* is now thought to be this species. Rock greenlings appear to be one of the more ancestral of the greenlings.

Hexagrammos octogrammus
(Pallas, 1814)
Masked Greenling

DAIJI KITAGAWA

ETYMOLOGY AND COLLOQUIAL NAME: *Hexagrammos* is Greek for "six" and "line" and *octogrammus* means "eight" and "line" in Greek. In Japan, they call these "suji-ainame."

THE BASICS: Maximum Length: 31.8 cm (13 in) TL. Maximum Weight: 1.5 kg (3.3 lb). The Ranges: Okhotsk and Japan seas to the Commander–Aleutian chain and St. Lawrence Island, northern Bering Sea, to Banks Island (northern British Columbia). They are abundant from the Sea of Japan and Sea of Okhotsk to at least as far north as the Pribilof Islands (eastern Bering Sea) and fairly common southward to about southeastern Alaska. 6–26 m (20–86 ft), mostly from barely subtidal to about 10 m (33 ft). Eggs: 1.5–2.5 mm. Larvae: hatching length = 6–9 mm, flexion length = about 1.2–1.5 cm (0.5-0.6 in), transformation length = about 3 cm (1 in). An age-length relationships is figured in Shestakov and Nazarkin (2006). Length-weight parameters (FL, mm, kg): (sexes combined) $W = 0.00000374L^{2.0275}$ (Recfin 2009).

SALIENT CHARACTERS: Compared to other greenlings, this species has a deep caudal peduncle, a short fourth lateral line (not extending past the pelvic fin), and a first lateral line that reaches back to the posterior part of the soft dorsal fin. Pelagic juveniles are dark green on back and silvery-white on sides. The basic body color is green or brown, with darker spots and mottling, the cirrus above the eye is black, and the eyes are red. In the northwest Pacific, preguarding and guarding males are mostly dark brown with small silvery spots on the head and front part of the torso, and the undersides and pelvic and anal fins are very dark.

LIFE HISTORY: Young-of-the-year recruit (at about 3.2–4 cm, 1–2 in, FL) from May–August amid shallow algae, eelgrass, and other plant life. Both juveniles and adults live in nearshore eelgrass, kelp, and other algae and among rocks in lagoons and other protected habitats. These are solitary fish that spend most of their time within a meter (3 ft) of the bottom. At least in the Western Pacific, juvenile masked greenlings are reported to be territorial (occupying areas of 1.5–2.5 m²) and to guard sheltering sites. Gomelyuk (2000) observed that when a masked greenling in a shelter is approached by another masked greenling it will sometimes start to tremble and when it can't escape, it sways its front area back and forth in a 30° arc. In this same location, adult fish were not territorial. This species appears to be active only during the day. Fish living around Kodiak Island live in waters as cold as 1.4°C (35°F).

Masked greenlings live to at least 5 years old and perhaps to 12 years. Females are larger at age than males. Most males mature at around one year old, most females at 2 years old, and everyone seems to be mature at 3 years old. Maturation occurs at maybe 15–17 cm, 6–7 in, TL). Spawning occurs at least June–December, in shallow water (mostly 0.7–7 m, 2–23 ft). Females lay adhesive eggs (in masses 2–9 cm, 1–4 in, wide) on various types of algae and on rocks, producing 1,604–7,998 eggs per season, perhaps deposited in two batches. The eggs have been described as "brownish mauve" and "violet with an orange spot." Males guard multiple egg masses (sometimes as many as 20). Guarding males spend a lot of time ventilating the eggs, often using a technique Markevich (2004) dubbed "fidgeting." In this behavior, "a fish performs rather active movements with a caudal peduncle, and its body moves several centimeters alternately forward and backwards. However, at the same time, the pectoral fins work actively directing the water flow to the egg mass." Males guard nests until the eggs hatch, (about 31–54 days). Nests may occur at high densities, as often the nests are separated by less than one meter (3 ft), and there seems to be little aggressive behavior between guarding males. Some mature males are "sneakers," as they don't guard eggs, but rather sneak in and fertilize eggs masses when the territorial male's head is turned. Maskeds are the archetypal generalist feeders. One study from the Sea of Japan found 70 different food items in their diets. Overall, crustaceans (e.g., crabs, gammarid and caprellid amphipods, harpacticoid copepods, caridean shrimps, and isopods), polychaetes, fishes, and fish eggs may be most important. On the other hand, they are reported to feed on mussels by ripping off pieces of mussel mantle until the bivalve can't keep its shell shut. Folks who have watched them say they spend a lot of time picking up chunks of turf and winnowing out amphipods and other smaller organisms. Predators include great and plain sculpins, starry flounder, Steller sea lions, and river otters. The eggs occasionally are eaten by sea urchins and sea stars.

FISHERY: Bean (1887b) noted that they were a food fish along the Aleutian Islands and Chereshnev et al. (2001) write that whitespotteds form an important local commercial fishery in the northern Sea of Okhotsk. Other than that, the species seems to be of rather limited commercial value. They are taken by sport fishermen in the Sea of Japan and, one assumes, other locations.

RELATIONSHIPS: Masked greenlings seem to be most closely related to the western Pacific species, *Hexagrammos agrammus* and *H. otakii.* In the Sea of Japan, they hybridize with both species.

Hexagrammos stelleri
Tilesius, 1810
Whitespotted Greenling

ETYMOLOGY AND COLLOQUIAL NAMES: *Hexagrammos* is Greek for "six" and "line" and *stelleri* refers to Georg Wilhelm Steller (1709–1746), a supreme naturalist, and something of a professional grump. Rutenberg (1970) pointed out that the original name, *Hexagrammos asper* Tilesius, has priority, but that in 1884 Jordan called the species *H. stelleri*. In Puget Sound of the 1880s, Italian fishermen called them "boregata" and the Native Americans at Cape Flattery (Washington) used "tsebarqua." The Japanese name is "ezo-ainame."

THE BASICS: Maximum Length: About 48 cm (19 in) TL. Maximum Weight: 1.6 kg (3.5 lb). The Ranges: Japan Sea to Commander–Aleutian chain and southern Chukchi and Bering seas to Puget Sound. There are unconfirmed reports of fish being taken in Simpson Cove, Beaufort Sea, and in the Chukchi Sea northwest of Wainwright. They are most abundant from the seas of Japan and Okhotsk, and the eastern Bering Sea, to at least the Kodiak Island–Cook Inlet area, but not rare as far south as Puget Sound. Intertidal waters to 275 m (902 ft), mostly shallower than 100 m (328 ft). Eggs: 1.6–1.9 mm. Larvae: hatching length = about 7–9 mm, flexion length = about 1.2–1.5 cm (0.5–0.6 in), transformation length = about 3 cm (1 in). An age-length relationship is figured in Shestakov and Nazarkin (2006). Von Bertalanffy parameters (FL, mm): (sexes combined) L_∞ = 730, k = 0.12, t_0 = -0.51 (Barker 1979). Length-weight parameters (FL, mm, kg): (sexes combined) W = 0.00000000102 (Wildermuth 1983).

SALIENT CHARACTERS: Whitespotteds appear to be noticeably slimmer than other greenlings, have a fourth lateral line that just extends past the base of the pelvic fin, a slender caudal peduncle, and a prominent black spot on the anterior part of the dorsal fin. These are brownish or greenish animals (males are golden during spawning season), often washed in yellow, that have small white spots. Ed DeMartini (1986)

reported that males guarding nests had noticeably dusky pelvic and anal fins. Ed also noted that these males had the dark spot on the front of their dorsal fin, implying that other whitespotteds did not, which may mean that the black spot is associated with gender and reproductive state.

LIFE HISTORY: Around Kodiak Island, young-of-the-year settle to shallow algal beds, mostly from May–August (and into September in the Sea of Japan), at lengths as small as 4 cm (2 in) FL. Juveniles as large as 7.2 cm (3 in) SL have been taken in surface waters. At least in the western Pacific, juveniles are pelagic for about one year. Both juveniles and adults are common in nearshore waters, around eelgrass and algae and, less commonly, over rocks. In the Sea of Okhotsk, they are reported to live only where sheltering sites are available and to stay in these at night. On the other hand, Tack (1970), working in Izembek Lagoon (eastern Bering Sea), found that adults: "Move into shallow eelgrass at night to feed when the tide is high and water deep" and considered juveniles as resident in eelgrass and adults as transient in eelgrass and resident in deeper channels. They can tolerate at least slightly estuarine conditions and there is one report of a whitespotted taken in a freshwater lake

in British Columbia. In some areas, adults appear to migrate into deeper waters in the winter, even onto the shallow continental slope (to 275 m, 902 ft) in the Sea of Japan. They have been taken in waters from -1.5°C (29°F) to at least 11.7°C (53°F). Fish in the Sea of Okhotsk are reported to be mostly solitary, although in the evenings they occasionally form schools of perhaps a dozen individuals. This same study found that whitespotteds tended to stay within 1.5 m (5 ft) of the bottom, with occasional forays 5–6 m (16–20 ft) into the water column. They have also been reported to be fairly agonistic toward one another.

RICH ZADE

Whitespotteds live to at least 5 years old and likely longer. Females are larger at age than males. These fish apparently mature at as small as about 15 cm (6 in) FL, but mostly by 20 cm (8 in) FL, and mostly about 2 years old. When do whitespotteds spawn? Oh, depending on which study you read, you can sort of pick your month. DeMartini (1986) saw them spawning in October in Puget Sound, Rogers et al. (1983) found ripe females around Kodiak Island from June–August, and Busby et al. (2000) reported winter and spring spawning in Puget Sound. In the Bering Sea, Musienko (1970) states they spawn during the summer, and in September off the more southern parts of their Asian range. That's all I know, now go talk among yourselves. Females are batch spawners and lay green, blue, violet, brown, or gray eggs in nests (often in or on algae but also, apparently, on rocks) and these are guarded by males. Most nests are built in quite shallow waters, like barely subtidal to maybe 8 m (26 ft). Males often guard more than one (and sometimes at least as many as 7) egg masses at a time and these can be from different females. Ed DeMartini (1986) reports that guarding males are quite aggressive and that "One male was noted attacking another male. Four fish circled me aggressively; and two males bit my face mask." The eggs hatch in about a month. In one study in Puget Sound, these egg clutches contained between 1,200–5,200 embryos. In the Sea of Okhotsk, fecundity was reported to be at least 1,070–12,397 eggs.

Like other greenlings, whitespotteds feed on many, many things. And while much of their feeding takes place on the bottom, predation in midwaters is not slighted. Pelagic juveniles eat zooplankton, while newly recruited benthic young-of-the-year tend to eat mostly crustaceans. In some locations, whitespotteds feed over both hard and soft substrata, often rooting about in the sand after shrimps and the like. Important prey include crustaceans (e.g., gammarid and caprellid amphipods, caridean shrimps, and crabs), along with polychaetes, snails, bivalves, fishes, and fish eggs. Predators include Dolly Vardens, Arctic and Aleutian terns, horned and tufted puffins, and river otters. And here's something from Turner (1886): "During the winter time the foxes of the Aleutian Islands catch many...as they are left in the shallow lagoons or rock crevices by the receding tides. The fox is quite expert in catching the fish. He will watch them for a long time until they wander into the shallower water, upon which the fox springs, even immersing his entire head to seize the fish."

FISHERY: Whitespotteds have always been important in various artisanal fisheries. As in example, in 1886, Turner noted that they were a substantial part of the diets of the local peoples of the Aleutian Islands and that women spent considerable time fishing for them. There is also an important local fishery for them in the northern Sea of Okhotsk. Recreational fishermen catch them fairly commonly from Washington northward.

RELATIONSHIPS: Whitespotteds are perhaps most closely related to masked greenlings.

GEORG WILHELM STELLER

As a youth, Steller first studied for the Lutheran ministry at the University of Wittenberg only to soon transfer to Halle University, where he pursued studies in botany and medicine. Given his remarkable insensitivity to the needs and desires of others, his world-class lack of humility, and his real genius as a naturalist, this move saved some congregation a lot of grief. At the age of 25, Steller looked around his native Bavaria, populated mostly, one expects, by trichinosis-redolent sausage-eaters, heard a loud sucking sound, and went off to Seek His Fortune in the Big City, in this instance, St. Petersburg. In young Georg's case, Fortune was to consist of 1) ingratiating himself with the Russian Imperial Academy, 2) marrying a woman best described as having the most impressive attributes of both Madonna and the Wicked Witch of the East, 3) veritably forcing his way onto Vitus Bering's expedition to discover Alaska, 4) managing to offend every one on the ship with his overbearing smugness and know-it-all attitude, even though he was often quite correct, which led to 6) his advice being routinely ignored by the ship's officers, particularly on how to avoid scurvy, then 7) being shipwrecked for nearly a year on a desolate island off Kamchatka surrounded by scurvy-ridden Russians and feces-eating foxes, 8) nursing some of these sailors back to health, helping to build a ship, and sailing back to port, 9) and dying several years later of, well who knows what people died of in an age of extreme alcohol consumption and less than no personal hygiene. Along the way, *naturellement*, Steller was also the consummate naturalist, describing in his journal lovely details of every damn animal and plant he came across, even while semi-starving on the island of feces-eating foxes. Among Steller's descriptions were those of the Steller jay, Steller sea eagle, Steller sea lion, and Steller sea cow, and although it was not published in his lifetime, the whitespotted greenling.

Among his observations of various and sundry marine and terrestrial animals and plants, Steller's journal also contains a fascinating description of a creature often referred to as "Steller's Sea Ape." This creature, described in Steller's journal of 10 August 1741 from south of the Semidi Islands, was about 5 feet long, had a head like a dog, with long whiskers, a tail divided in two with the upper lobe longer than the lower, and apparently no forefeet or other fins. The animal, as described, is like nothing anyone had seen before or, for that matter, since, and it has engendered lots of comment, both by those folks who wear aluminum foil hats to ward off transmissions from Alpha Centuri and by curious biologists.

Ophiodon elongatus
Girard, 1854

Lingcod

ETYMOLOGY AND COLLOQUIAL NAMES: *Ophiodon* means "snake" and "tooth" and *elongatus* is Latin for "elongate." "Cultus cod" was a common name in the 19th and early 20th centuries, although the name had changed to "Pacific cultus" by the 1930s. "Cultus" means "of little worth" in Chinook. "Bastard cod" was also popular in Washington in the early days, as was "green rock cod" in San Francisco. In Mexico, they are called "bacalao."

A juvenile one.

THE BASICS: Maximum Length: 152 cm (60 in) TL. Maximum Weight: Females grow to 37.5 kg (82.6 lb) and males to at least 10 kg (22 lb). The Ranges: The well-documented range is the Shumagin Islands (south-western Gulf of Alaska) to off Punta San Carlos (central Baja California). However, Fall et al. (2007) report that lingcod are taken in the eastern Bering Sea, at least as far north as the Yukon-Kuskokwim Delta, in the Pacific halibut subsistence fishery. They appear to be most abundant from about the Kodiak Island area to at least off Punta San Antonio (central Baja California). Lingcod larvae have been taken much further south, off Bahia Tortugas (southern Baja California), and I wonder if lings are also common off this cold, upwelling-bathed area. Intertidal waters and to depth of 475 m (1,558 ft), most commonly from nearshore waters to perhaps 200 m (656 ft). Contrary to what you see further north, adult lingcod rarely enter shallow waters in Southern California. Eggs: 2.9–3.5 mm. Larvae: hatching length = about 9 mm, flexion length = 1.1–1.5 cm (0.4–0.6 in), transformation length = about 3 cm (1 in). Von Bertalanffy parameters (FL, cm): (Washington and Oregon) (females) L_∞ = 130.2, k = 0.104, t_0 = -2.85; (males) L_∞ = 91.8, k = 0.149, t_0 = -3.097; (California) (females) L_∞ = 112.8, k = 0.145, t_0 = -1.573; (males) L_∞ = 81.7, k = 0.223, t_0 = -1.435 (Jagielo and Wallace 2005). Length-weight parameters (TL, mm, kg): (sexes combined) W = $0.0000000116L^{2.99}$ (RecFin 2009).

SALIENT CHARACTERS: These are elongated fish with one lateral line and large mouths filled with canine teeth. Lings come in a vast assortment of colors, from black, or brown, to green, with darker mottling and spotting on back and sides. They often have orange or yellow spots. My favorite variety is colored a kind of burnt sienna with burnished copper sides—very tasteful indeed.

LIFE HISTORY: Most young-of-the-year appear to recruit between April–July at 7–8 cm (3 in) TL to nearshore waters, although Jeff Marliave (1975) found that in aquaria some young fish settled at as small as 5.5 cm (2 in). Regardless of size, fish fresh out of the plankton often settle onto open sand, sometimes sand containing a little complexity, such as ripples, shells, or small pebbles. On this open territory, I have seen these little lings huddling next to octopuses. Within a few months, many of these fish begin to nestle among slightly more complex, but still low habitats, like small rocks, sea pens, or eelgrass. Linda Snook reports that if you dive in the ocean in Monterey Bay—right off the Pebble Beach golf courses—along with lots of golf balls, you will see young-of-the-year lingcod snuggled up to many of the Titleists. My research demonstrates that the shell mounds surrounding some California oil platforms harbor very high densities of young lingcod. Juveniles appear to remain in a

JAN KOCIAN

Striped seaperch and sea stars dining on lingcod eggs.

relatively circumscribed area for months at a time and they are somewhat tolerant of estuarine conditions. In Southern California, we see juveniles as small as 15 cm (6 in) TL in waters as deep as almost 200 m (656 ft), but most of these small fish are in less than 100 m (328 ft). As lingcod mature they tend to move from low relief to more complex rocky bottoms. However, although boulders, rock ridges, and other high relief areas seem to be preferred habitats, adults can be found over nearby soft seafloors, particularly where adult densities on reefs are high. Although adults do not school, in areas where they are not fished they can be found in very high densities, sometimes even stacked on top of each other. Lingcod may be most active at night.

Lingcod are most often found lying on the bottom, although sometimes you see them a meter or so above the substrate, usually when they are in their traveling mode. When of a mind to be still, nothing can be as inert as this fish. They can lie there stiff as a board or be drooped over rocks in a kind of boneless way. Often they sit on the most prominent piece of real estate in the area, such as a sponge or rocky promontory. At Platform Grace (in the Santa Barbara Channel), Mary Nishimoto saw a lingcod lying on the seat of a chair that had fallen from the platform

and landed upright. Wayne Palsson reports seeing lingcod sitting on soft bottom near hard structures, having apparently dug small (maybe 15 cm, 6 in deep) troughs around themselves.

Numerous tagging studies imply that, in general, lingcod do not move about much. Oh, there can be some seasonal inshore and offshore migrations, particularly of fish living deeper than nesting depths, and there is the occasional fish that wanders a considerable distance. But as Rick Starr et al. (2005) wrote, in summarizing their work on movements of lingcod living on a remarkable pinnacle off southeastern Alaska: "Net movements of fish are minimal, but most fish frequently move short distances, and some move great distances." Lingcod are also able to home back from considerable distances. Kim Anthony (2009) caught 10 at Platform Gail (in the Santa Barbara Channel), moved them to Anacapa Island (about 11 km, 7 mi, away), and 9 returned to the platform, one within about a day. Marko et al. (2007) found that, despite pelagic young drifting about for as much as 3 months, there seems to be limited connectivity among groups of Pacific Coast lingcod and fish in the Puget Sound region seem to be the most isolated from other groups.

Prior to spawning, males migrate to nesting areas and begin to defend territories. Generally, these are high current sites (from intertidal waters to at least 97 m, 318 ft, and perhaps to as deep as 126 m, 413 ft). Nests are often in crevices or under overhangs, but some are on exposed surfaces. Lingcod may live in caves with wolf-eels and the males create nests inside these caves. A particular male may return to the same nesting area year after year. For instance, one fish (nicknamed "Bob") came back at least 4 years in row to the same patch at the Edmunds Underwater Park in Puget Sound. Most spawning occurs at night, although apparently impatient couples have been seen doing that kind of thing during the day. Females enter the nesting area somewhat later than the males, lay sticky eggs in large masses, and then often leave the area. However, Tory O'Connell (1993), observing fish nesting in somewhat deep waters (30–97 m, 98–318 ft) off southeastern Alaska, found that females sometimes remained in the spawning area after they laid their eggs. She speculated that females may leave nesting sites in shallow waters because there is not enough to eat, whereas prey may be more available in deeper waters, and thus there would be no need to migrate away from the nesting site. Jeff Marliave has a nice rule of thumb for estimating the age of a female that laid a particular egg mass, even when you can't find the female. He says that if the clutch is the size of a grapefruit, the females is 3 years old, a cantaloupe equals a 4-year-old, and a female producing a watermelon is 5 years and up. Egg masses weigh as much as 14 kg (30.8 lb). Larger and older females may spawn earlier in the season than younger and smaller ones.

The males guard the eggs until they hatch and hatching takes about 24 days at 14°C (57°F), 48 days at 8°C (46°F), and hatching as much as 72 days after deposition has been recorded. All of the eggs within a mass hatch in 1–7 days of each other.

The eggs have been described as "pearly pink" when deposited, changing to white shortly after. In a study in Puget Sound, spawning occurred when water temperatures fell below 9°C (48°F). Males often guard more than one egg mass (as many as 6 masses have been noted) and the masses can be at least as much as 7.5 m (25 ft) apart. Males often either lie on the eggs, sit very close to them, or sit atop high relief "observation posts" as much as 10 m (33 ft) away, where they can get a good view of the action. Guarding males, often (but not always), can be quite aggressive, chasing and biting intruders, including divers. By the same token, some males are fairly low-key about this whole guarding thing. Interestingly, the level of aggression a male exhibits may be genetically fixed, as this trait seems to be exhibited year after year for each individual. Guarding males (often dark with little or no mottling) often look pretty tattered, what with their various wounds and shredded fins, and this may be the result of fighting between males or with other fishes. Guarding males apparently do not feed, although they often swallow several species of snails that attempt to eat the eggs. While the males actively chase after a number of fish species (e.g., various greenlings and perch), they do not seem bothered by others (e.g., prowfish). Within an egg cluster, eggs begin to hatch from the outside inwards. The guarding males apparently ignore newly hatched larvae, as predators have been observed eating the young with impunity. Not all mature males are territorial and guard nests. Some males are "sneakers," who dash into a newly laid nest, spray sperm, then ditch out before the guardian male can respond. Even neighboring guardian males may fertilize the eggs of adjacent guardian males. An egg clutch may have as many as 5 fathers. In some instances where a guarding male was removed, another male, perhaps one not involved in their fertilization, took up guardianship of the now-unguarded eggs.

Lingcod live to at least 36 years old and females grow larger than males. Length at maturity seems to vary by area and fish in the more northern part of their range (like off British Columbia) appear to be larger (although not particularly older) at maturity than fish from, say, off California. Silberberg et al. (2001) found that for Northern and Central California, a few

CLEO BRYLINSKY

females were mature at 43.7 cm (17 in, FL, 2 years), 50% at 55.7 cm (22 in, 4 years), and 100% at 75 cm (30 in, 9 years). For males, these values were 30 cm (12 in, 2 years), 46.1 cm (18 in, 3 years), and 69 cm (27 in, 8 years) respectively. This is not grotesquely different from estimates made by, for example, Cass (1990) from British Columbia. Casting an inquiring eye along their entire range, lingcod spawn from November–June, with something like a January–March peak. Females may spawn all of their eggs at one time and they produce between 97,000–490,000 eggs per season. The eggs are about 3.5 mm in diameter when they hit the water. The larvae and pelagic juveniles stay in the water column for as much as 3 months. Pelagic juveniles and small benthic fish (less than perhaps 20 cm, 8 in, TL) feed on euphausiids, small fishes, copepods, and crustacean larvae. Larger fish focus on other fishes. They are one of the few fish that will eat a spiny dogfish. Also consumed are shrimps, octopuses, squids, hermit crabs, fish eggs, and hydroids. Kirk Lombard reports that a reliable source found a common murre in the stomach of one fish. Arguably, at high densities, lingcod are one of the dominant fish predators, able to reduce the number of local prey fishes. Lots of animals eat lingcod, a list too long for this book. Here are some predators that I basically list at random: Chinook and coho salmon, canary, black, and copper rockfishes, lingcod, spiny dogfish, white sharks, bald eagles, common murres, harbor seals, California and Steller sea lions. Lingcod eggs appear to be easy pickings for a range of predators, including sun stars, shrimps (which have been observed carrying eggs away and then eating the larvae as they emerged), various snails, sea urchins, crabs and fishes (e.g., cabezons, lingcod, rockfishes, and sea perch).

FISHERY: Lingcod were quite important in the diets of many of the native Northwest inhabitants. First Nation peoples utilized the lingcod's well-known habit of following hooked fishes to near the surface. They devised several types of lures (many resembled shuttlecocks in badminton) out of wood or feathers that took advantage of this behavior. A fisherman in a boat would push the lure to the bottom with a pole or spear, then with a quick motion, release the lure to float back to the surface. When the lingcod followed the lure upward it was speared or netted. Among some of these peoples, lingcod were a particularly important winter food, a source of fresh fish when some other species (such as the salmon) were not available.

This species was also a very important market fish along the Pacific Coast, at least as far back as the 1860s (in British Columbia). By the late 19th century, lings were extensively harvested around most of the major ports from Alaska to California. While most of the catch has always been sold fresh, there was a liver fishery (the livers are very high in vitamins A and D) during the 1930s and 1940s (with livers going for $2/lb) and the fish were also sold to mink raisers as food for their animals. Lingcod cheek (the muscles that control jaw movement) was a specialty item in Seattle markets in the 1930s. Today, lingcod are a solid part of the commercial fishery and are taken primarily by hook-and-line and trawl from Kodiak Island to northern Baja California. There is a substantial live fish fishery for them in various places.

As noted in the admirable *Sutebusuton: A Japanese Village on the British Columbia Coast* by Mitsuo Yesaki (Peninsula Publishing, 2003), at the turn of the 20th century, Japanese fishermen in British Columbia figured out a way of maximizing their lingcod profits. Although Vancouver City was the major market for fish, some of the best lingcod grounds were located across the Strait of Georgia, a long way from port in the small vessels of the time. To compensate, these fishermen would catch lingcod by hook-and-line and then store them live in floating wooden pens that were moored close to the fishing grounds. Periodically, a steamer would collect the fish and haul the product to market. In the days before ice or refrigeration, this allowed fishermen to fish well away from major markets.

My associate, the late Scott Boley, owned a fish market in Oregon. He noted that about 20% of all of the lingcod they processed were green-meated, actually sometimes almost turquoise in color. He charged premium prices for those. Markets in California during the 1940s also sold green-colored lingcod meat for premium prices. Har, creative marketing at its finest.

The lingcod is a major recreational species along much of the coast. While most folks catch them from boats, a surprising number are taken from piers, jetties, and even from rocks. I have seen pretty large individuals pulled out of tidal channels by poke-polers.

Lingcod have been overfished in a number of places and fears of at least localized overfishing were voiced at least as early as the 1940s. Cass et al. (1990) note: "Toivo Lane, who fished lingcod in the Strait of Georgia from 1944 to 1985 observed that reefs that became overfished during his early years as a fisherman never regained their original level of productivity even after the decline in fishing effort after the 1940s." Smith et al. (1990) argue that, in the Strait of Georgia, the sport fishery was likely the main human cause of the "continuing decline in lingcod landings." Just something to think about when you are blaming commercial fishermen for all overfishing.

ORIGINS AND RELATIONSHIPS: The University of California Paleontological Museum lists a fossil *Ophiodon* sp. from Miocene deposits (at least 5.3 million years ago) from Northern California. Lingcod fossils, apparently from *O. elongatus*, have been found in 100,000-year-old deposits in California. As noted in the introduction to the Hexagrammidae, genetic analyses implies that lingcod are not closely related to other members of the family and, in fact, seem to be more closely related to some sculpins.

MISCELLANEY: 1) Tory O'Connell sent me a picture of xanthic (yellow) lingcod from Alaska. 2) Hart (1967) noted that fish taken from newly discovered concentrations in Canada were "notably poor and 'all head.'"

Oxylebius pictus
Gill, 1862
Painted Greenling

ETYMOLOGY AND COLLOQUIAL NAMES: *Oxylebius* means "sharp" in Greek and *Lebius*, a synonym for *Hexagrammos*, (so it means "sharp *Hexagrammos*," for the pointed snout) and *pictus* is Latin for "painted." When I was a kid, we called this species a "convict fish." See, it has these vertical stripes and the convicts in the Keystone Cop movies wore clothes that had stripes and...well, you get the picture. And not just me, but lots of people, even biologists like Conrad Limbaugh called them convict fish. So, who the hell

KEVIN LEE

decided to change its name? I mean if this is another example of political correctness, who were we offending—the convicts? Did the lifers in the Ichthyology Club at San Quentin write a nasty letter? Did the Fish Man of Alcatraz go on a protest hunger strike? And why would they be offended? And, as much to the point, why is this greenling any more "painted" than a kelp or rock greenling? In fact, I submit that *O. pictus* is *less* painted than a male rock greenling, which looks like someone ready to play the grand lady herself on the 100th birthday of Dolores del Rio float [sponsored by the United Fruit Company] at the Rose Parade.

THE BASICS: Maximum Length: 25.4 cm (10 in) TL**.** The Ranges: Kachemak Bay and Prince William Sound (northern Gulf of Alaska) to Bahia San Carlos (29°36'N, 115°35'W) (central Baja California), commonly from at least southeastern Alaska to Punta Banda (northern Baja California). Larvae have been taken into southern Baja California at about 27°N. Intertidal and to depth of 225 m (738 ft), reported to 249 m; typically shallower than 50 m (164 ft). Eggs: 1.3–1.4 mm. Larvae: hatching length = less than 3.5 mm, flexion length = 7–9 mm, transformation length = 1.6–2 cm (0.6–0.8 in). Von Bertalanffy parameters (TL, mm): Seattle (sexes combined) L_∞ = 214, k = 0.43267, t_0 = -0.513; Monterey (sexes combined) L_∞ = 184, k = 0.31968, t_0 = -1.488 (DeMartini and Anderson 1980). Length-weight parameters (TL, mm, kg): (sexes combined) W = $0.00000000182L^{3.384}$ (RecFin 2009).

SALIENT CHARACTERS: These fish have an elongated and pointy head, on top of which sit two pairs of cirri. Painted greenlings are one of the few fish on the Pacific Coast with alternating bars on their sides. These red or red-brown bars alternate with gray, tan, orange-red, or white. Some individuals are heavily sprinkled with tiny white spots and have yellow throats and jaws. Males turn real dark and are peppered with light spots at spawning time. Ed DeMartini (1985) discusses colors and patterns at record length.

LIFE HISTORY: Young-of-the-year settle to hard structure or to the interface between hard and soft seafloors, at sizes as small as 3 cm (1 in) TL. At least some level of settlement appears to occur throughout the year. Although most settlement takes place in relatively shallow waters, I have seen very small juveniles at depths as deep as 70 m (230 ft). Most fish live over hard bottom, such as caves and crevice-ridden boulder fields, tubeworm mats, and the cross beams and around the bottoms of oil platforms. A few have been taken from drifting kelp mats. When not nipping at each other (even young one seem to gather together so that they can nip at one another), painted greenlings tend to sit motionless on the substrate. When disturbed, this species has a very characteristic little flutter, causing it to sort of leap into the water a short distance above the bottom before settling back down.

Painted greenlings appear to be immune to the stinging cells of sea anemones, and both juveniles and adults (but most often juveniles) are often found around or on them. As many as 7 individuals can make a single anemone a home. However, not all anemone species are acceptable. For instance, off British Columbia, the strawberry anemone (*Urticina lofotensis*) is most often occupied, although a few fish settle for *U. piscivora*. Other anemones are ignored. The tightest associations occur at night, when this species tends to hunker down, and an individual may return to the same anemone night after night for many months. Elliot (1992) reports that, when disturbed, juveniles will dive into the gut cavity of anemones. Large individuals often forsake anemones and shelter in crevices and caves. In particular, larger males have been observed keeping females and juveniles away from premier boulder areas. Adults tend to live within fairly restricted homes ranges of 10^2 m or less.

A little one in an anemone.

JOHN YASAKI

Regarding gene flow, Giacomo Bernardi writes to me: "I think that there is much gene flow in *Oxylebius pictus*, but during the glaciation (which one I don't know) much of the northern population disappeared. The southern extreme did fine (Punta Banda) and a refugium in Puget Sound survived the glaciation. Secondary contact after the glaciation occurred and because of high gene flow, there is much mixing. Yet genetic signatures for both northern and southern populations exist. Importantly, an ecological break does exist in Oregon and Washington, but it does not translate into a genetic break there." So, that is cool.

During the spawning season, males stake out spawning territories in high

A female and a male.

relief areas. Where prime habitat is sparse, these territories will be jammed cheek to jowl. Limbaugh (1955) notes, "Off La Jolla, an individual was observed to attack a sheephead almost a hundred times its own weight, apparently as a territorial display in defense of a nest." Ed DeMartini (1985) writes: "Females preferentially court smaller males…consistent with the hypothesis that larger females…choose (since females visit males, not vice versa) vigorous males, often smaller than themselves, that are less likely to cannibalize spawn…Female *O. pictus* also cannibalize spawn, but to a relatively minor extent." Females lay walnut-shaped clutches (composed of up to 5,000 eggs) and males often simultaneously guard more than one female's clutch (actually as many as 10 different clutches). A male may go through several guarding cycles before saying the hell with it for the year. As males don't go in for that fancy fanning stuff, guarding does not involve much more than trying to keep the eggs from being eaten until the larvae hatch.

Painted greenlings live to at least 8 years old. In one study, males and females grew at the same rates, although fish near Seattle grew faster than those from Monterey Bay. In this work, Monterey males matured at 2 years, at an average of 12.3 cm (5 in) TL, and 14.3 cm (6 in) in Puget Sound. Females matured at 3 years and 14 cm (6 in) at Monterey and 17.1 cm (7 in) at Seattle. It seems likely that the spawning season for this species extends throughout the year, albeit perhaps with a winter–spring or early summer peak. A female may spawn 3 times or more per season (seasons last about 3 months per female) and the mature eggs are pink-orange. Females in the Seattle area may produce eggs that are slightly larger than fish in Monterey Bay. Eggs hatch in 17 and 20 days at 12° (54°F) and 10°C (50°F) respectively. Painted greenlings primarily eat small crustaceans (e.g., caprellid and gammarid amphipods, isopods, shrimps, crabs, and harpacticoid copepods) along with hydroids and poly-chaetes. Males occasionally eat both their own or other painted greenling eggs. Painted greenlings are eaten by such fishes as cabezons, kelp rockfish, and treefish and by Brandt's cormorants. Their eggs are preyed upon by striped seaperch, various rockfishes, and sculpins.

FISHERY: Painted greenlings are rarely taken by recreational anglers.

REMARKS: Genetic analysis demonstrates that painted greenlings are most closely related to the combfishes and, with them, probably form a family separate from lingcod and greenlings.

Pleurogrammus monopterygius
(Pallas, 1810)
Atka Mackerel

A reef species that has always been faintly embarrassed about being called a "mackerel."

ETYMOLOGY AND COLLOQUIAL NAMES: *Pleurogrammus* is Greek for "side" and "line" (Bob Lauth speculates perhaps for the multiple lateral lines) and *monopterygius* means "one" and "fin" (and this for the single dorsal fin?). Regarding the name "Atka mackerel," in 1918 John Cobb wrote: "As the fish is not a mackerel at all, and bears no resemblance to one, it having acquired the name because of a fancied resemblance in flavor to the real mackerel, the U. S. Bureau of Fisheries has suggested Atkafish as a more appropriate name for it." Well, Johnnie, that is one bit of Big Brother Meddling that went just nowhere. "Yellowfish" was a commonly applied name in the 19th century. The Japanese call them "kitano-hokke" and my favorite name, coming to us from Korea, is "dan-gi-im-yon-soo-eo."

THE BASICS: Maximum Length: 54 cm (21 in) FL. Maximum Weight: At least 2.1 kg (4.6 lb).

THE RANGES: Seas of Japan and Okhotsk to Commander–Aleutian chain and Bering Strait to Redondo Beach (Southern California). They are abundant at least off the northern Kuril Islands and Kamchatka, along the Aleutian Islands, and in the eastern Bering Sea, with numbers dropping off precipitously east of Kodiak Island and Prince William Sound. Lower intertidal to, reportedly, 720 m (2,362 ft) (although this maximum depth is probably too deep. It is likely that this was a trawl-caught fish that was swimming in midwaters and was taken when a bottom trawl was being pulled up through the water column. Hey, it happens, what can I say?). Commonly from surface waters to perhaps 225 m (738 ft). Eggs: 2.1–2.8 mm. Larvae: hatching length = 0.8–1.1 cm, flexion length = about 1.4–1.9 cm (0.6–0.7 in), transformation length = about 3 cm (1 in). Growth rates vary with location and Lowe et al. (1998) present a number of von Bertalanffy growth parameters. Length-weight parameters (FL, mm, gr): (sexes combined) W = $0.000011L^{3.013}$ (Zenger 2004).

SALIENT CHARACTERS: Atka mackerel have an unnotched dorsal fin and a deeply forked caudal fin. Atka body coloration is quite variable and Bob Lauth et al. (2010) deal with this extensively. Suffice it to say here that during the spawning period males that hold territories become bright yellow or orange and the dark vertical bars, lower half of the pectoral fins, and the entire pelvic and anal fins become black. Nonterritorial adult males are plain yellow with dark blotches, while females and nonbreeding males are mottled gray-blue with white blotches on the head and back and dark vertical stripes. There are also variations on this theme for fish that are up in the water column, territorial males that have been displaced from their nests, and the like.

LIFE HISTORY: Atka mackerel are schooling reef fish found in great abundance along the Aleutian Islands, usually in areas with high currents. Young-of-the-year settle to the bottom at around 8 cm (3 in) SL. Juveniles have been reported off shore in surface waters and the upper water column of the western Bering Sea and along the Bering Sea shelf. Presumably, these fish settle in more coastal waters during their second year and enter the adult habitat at age-3. Atka mackerel do not move about extensively although they are capable of homing at least 3.2 km (2 mi) when displaced. On the other hand, during the day these fish make extensive vertical movements to feed (routinely up to 50 m (164 ft) or more above the bottom and even to the surface) and start to head back to the reef in the afternoon. Note that males guarding nests do not vertically migrate. Nights are spent huddling in the rocks. Atkas live in water temperatures between at least 2–8.7°C (36–48°F). Several studies imply that there is one stock stretching from Japan to the Gulf of Alaska.

Come the summer spawning season (starting in June), adult males are the first to aggregate in nesting colonies (rocky areas bathed by currents) where they set up nesting territories. Females are ready to spawn about 1.5 months later and there follows lots of courtship behavior involving a male swimming vertically into the water column, turning sharply downward, and descending back toward the nest with some nifty tail wags and more stuff after that (see Bob Lauth 2007 for all the details). Females then lay their eggs on rocks (in oblong irregularly shaped masses) and the males guard the eggs until they hatch. A male will often guard eggs from more than one female and females spawn with more than one male. There are two types of adult males, Type I (territorial egg-guarders) and Type II (nonterritorial, not egg-guarders that likely dash by a nest and spray sperm on it). In North America, nests have been found at depths of 15–144 m (49–472 ft) along the Aleutian Islands and as far east as Unga Island (lower Alaska Peninsula). Because eggs can take as much as 3 months to hatch, males that start guarding a batch at the end of the spawning season in October could still be at it in January.

Atka mackerel live to at least 15 years old (but apparently rarely over 12 years). Growth rates vary among local aggregations along the Gulf of Alaska and Aleutian Islands, with fish growing faster in the far east. A few fish are mature at 29 cm (11 in) FL (2–3 years old), with 100% at 45 cm (18 in) (around 7 years old). Length at 50% maturity varies with location; it becomes smaller as we move from the Gulf of Alaska (38.2 cm, 15 in) to the western Aleutian Islands (33.6 cm, 13 in), however, 50% maturity for fish occurs between their third and fourth years. Along the Aleutians, spawning occurs from July to at least October (and as early as June in Asia). Females produce from less than 1,000–100,000 adhesive eggs per season (although later in the season many of these eggs disintegrate, *in utero*), in batches of about 3,000–12,000. The eggs are light green when laid and become reddish-brown with age. The average female spawns 4–5 times per season. Egg incubation times range from 44 days at 9.9°C to 100 days at 3.9°C (50–39°F) and the larvae are pelagic. Atka mackerel feed both in midwater and on the bottom on such crustaceans as copepods, euphausiids, and hyperiid amphipods, along with fishes, arrow worms, snails, medusae, and squids. AMs also eat large quantities of their own eggs. Thus far, at least 30 species of predators are known to eat Atka mackerel. These include arrowtooth flounder, Pacific cod, Pacific halibut, rough rockfish, sablefish, at least five species of skates, shortspine thornyheads, puffins, shearwaters, harbor seals, northern fur seal, Steller sea lions, and four species of whales.

FISHERY: Wherever Atka mackerel were abundant, indigenous folks caught a lot of them and, along the Aleutians, still do. Early European fishermen used them for bait for Pacific cod and they (the Atka mackerel, not the fishermen) were also salted in large numbers (fishermen were *salty* in large numbers). Trawl fisheries for them along the Aleutian Islands began in the early 1970s and have continued to this day.

RELATIONSHIPS: Atka mackerel are most closely related to the greenlings of the genus *Hexagrammos*. There is substantial evidence that this species is genetically separate from *Pleurogrammus azonus*, a closely related species of the western Pacific.

MISCELLANY: In 1958, over one million Atka mackerel eggs were collected off southeastern Kamchatka and airlifted thousands of kilometers westward across Siberia to near Murmansk (northern Russia). The eggs were hatched and the larvae were released, with the goal of establishing these fish in the Barents Sea. Nothing came of this transplantation experiment, so one assumes that Gaia was not pleased. In fact, we note that Nikolai Bulganin (1895–1975), who was Prime Minister of the Soviet Union when this plan was hatched (pun intended), lost power in the same year this experiment took place. In fact, in September 1958, *the month the larvae were placed in the Barents Sea*, Bulganin was forcibly removed from the Soviet Central Committee and sent to live in Stavropol, a city in southwestern Russia whose sister city is Des Moines (Iowa). Clearly, Gaia was *really* not pleased.

REMARKS: This extremely abundant species is really quite important to a number of fishes, birds, and mammals. For instance, Atka mackerel are the main prey for Steller sea lions living along the Aleutian Islands.

Zaniolepis

Julianne Kalman, who has handled many, many thousands of fishes in her relentless pursuit of external parasites, reports that combfishes have a peculiar "grassy" smell. After being scooped up in a trawl, hauled up from the depths, and dumped on deck, both shortspine and longspine combfishes very typically curl up into tight little half moons. When we see them underwater, however, they tend to be arrow straight. The combfishes are closely related to the painted greenling and with them probably form a separate family.

Zaniolepis frenata
Eigenmann & Eigenmann, 1889
Shortspine Combfish

ROSS ROBERTSON

ETYMOLOGY AND COLLOQUIAL NAME: *Zaniolepis* is Greek for "comb" or "card" and "scale" and *frenata* means "bridled" in Latin. The Japanese word is "ainame-rui."

THE BASICS: Maximum Length: 25 cm (10 in) TL. The Ranges: Southern Oregon to Bahia San Cristobal (27°22'N, 114°37'W) (southern Baja California), and in the Gulf of California. They are abundant from at least Central California to central Baja California (about 28°24'N). 55–244 m (180–800 ft); reported but not confirmed at 7–450 m (23–1,476 ft). They are perhaps most abundant at maybe 100–215 m (328–705 ft). Eggs: 1.4–1.6 mm. Larvae: hatching length = 2.5 mm, flexion length = about 6–9 mm. Length-weight parameters (TL, cm, gr): W = 0.0033L$^{3.277}$ (Love unpubl.).

SALIENT CHARACTERS: Shortspines are very slender and elongated, with tiny scales that give them a rough feeling. All of the dorsal spines are relatively short, compared to the long number two dorsal spine in longspine combfish. Dead ones are kind of tan or pink with darker diffuse markings. Underwater, they have a series of dark saddles on the back and various blotches and spots on sides and a dark mark across the eye. Shortspines sitting in complex habitat are more densely marked and heavily pigmented than those on soft sediment.

LIFE HISTORY: Based on our manned submersible studies, young-of-the-year shortspines recruit out of the plankton to soft seafloors at depths of at least 90–120 m (295–394 ft). Bottom trawls have taken fish as small as 4.2 cm (2 in) SL. Shortspine combfish are benthic fish found mostly on mud and low-hard relief (e.g., pebbles and cobbles). We usually see them sitting on the bottom, but they rise into the water column at dusk. The over 5,000 shortspines we have observed lived in 7.8–12.7°C (46–55°F), mostly in 9.1–10.8°C (48–51°F).

I have found that shortspines mature at around 14 cm (6 in) TL. Shortspines spawn at least from August–February, however larvae have been taken as late as May. Based on surveys of only a few fish, females produce between at least 767–959 eggs. Shortspine combfish eat a variety of small benthic and epibenthic prey. Important foods include gammarid amphipods and mysid shrimps, along with gnathiid isopods, calanoid copepods, shrimps, polychaetes, euphausiids, cumaceans, and fish eggs. Predators include California halibut, longnose lancetfish, Brandt's cormorants, and California sea lions.

Zaniolepis latipinnis
Girard, 1858
Longspine Combfish

JOHN BUTLER

ETYMOLOGY: *Latipinnis* means "broad" and "fin" in Latin.

THE BASICS: Maximum Length: 30.5 cm (12 in) TL. The Ranges: Vancouver Island to southern Baja California (25°45'N, 112°23'W) and fairly abundant from at least as far north as off San Francisco Bay to Bahia de Sebastian Vizcaino (central Baja California). They are very abundant in Southern California. 37–201 m (120–660 ft); reported but not confirmed at 7–421 m (23–1,381 ft), and mostly from perhaps 50–205 m (164–672 ft). Larvae: hatching length = about 3 mm, flexion length = about 6.5–9 mm. There is a table with age-length data in Johnson and Adams (1970). Length-weight parameters (TL, cm, gr): W = 0.0027L$^{3.353}$ (Love unpubl.).

SALIENT CHARACTERS: As with the shortspine combfish, longspines are elongated with sandpapery skin. However, unlike shortspines, the first three dorsal spines are very long. Underwater, longspines are usually silvery or gray, with a black streak across the eye, often dark saddles on the back, and frequently several rows of orangey-brown spots and markings along the sides.

LIFE HISTORY: This is a benthic species; we often see them sitting in little divots that they appear to create. Young-of-the-year settle on soft seafloors at lengths as small as at least 4.4 cm (2 in) SL, at depths of 60–245 m (197–804 ft). Most longspines occupy either muddy or low, hard-relief seafloors. As longspines grow larger they tend to migrate into deeper waters. This species also moves deeper during warm water decades. Despite their mostly sedentary habits, longspines frequently rise several meters into the water column to feed.

Longspines live to at least 7 years old and fish mature at about 12–14 cm (5–6 in) TL. Ripe females have been collected during all seasons. Females are batch spawners, producing as many as 3 clutches per year, and as many as 6,530 eggs per season. Longspine combfish eat a wide range of benthic and epibenthic organisms, such as gammarid amphipods, mysid shrimps, isopods, and polychaetes, and lesser numbers of scallops, snails, fishes, hydroids, shrimps, nudibranchs, copepods, and crabs. Predators include California halibut, longnose lancetfish, longspine combfish, Brandt's cormorants, and California sea lions.

FISHERY: Not as such.

ORIGINS AND RELATIONSHIPS: The two combfish species are very closely related to the painted greenling.

FAMILY RHAMPHOCOTTIDAE—Grunt Sculpin

The Family Rhamphocottidae is composed of one species, the frighteningly cute grunt sculpin. Despite what was previously believed, genetic analyses demonstrate that this family is not really all that closely related to the large and funky family Cottidae.

Rhamphocottus richardsonii

Günther, 1874

Grunt Sculpin

A small cold-water and solitary fish that, with the possible exception of the Pacific spiny lumpsucker, is the cutest fish on the West Coast.

ETYMOLOGY AND COLLOQUIAL NAME: *Rhamphocottus* means "snout" (in Greek) and "*Cottus*" and *richardsonii* honors John Richardson (1787–1865), British Arctic explorer and one of the best naturalists of his time. The Japanese call them "kuchibashi-kajika."

THE BASICS: Maximum Length: 9.3 cm (4 in) TL. The Ranges: Japan; Unimak Pass (Gulf of Alaska) to Santa Monica Bay (Southern California) and Tanner Bank (32°38'N, 119°09'W). They are common from at least the Alaska Peninsula to Cape Mendocino (Northern California). Tide pools and shallow water to depth of 258 m (846 ft), possibly deeper. Eggs: 2.5–2.8 mm. Larvae: hatching length = 6–7 mm, larval flexion length = 8.4 mm.

SALIENT CHARACTERS: Grunt sculpins have silly-shaped deep bodies, very pointed snouts, and lots of body prickles. These little fish are colored like a tropical species, with a base color of cream or tan, and with brown streaks. The big tip-off is the bright red or orange streak on the caudal peduncle.

MARC CHAMBERLAIN

VALERIE LYTTLE

Female guarding eggs.

LIFE HISTORY: Fish settle to the bottom at as small as 1.4–1.5 cm (0.6 in) SL. Grunt sculpins live over rocks and algae, usually in or near small crevices. They can withstand mildly estuarine conditions.

These live to at least 13 years in captivity. It is not clear when this species spawns, but at least January–April seems reasonable. In captivity, they may spawn throughout the year. Eggs are yellow or orange and are laid in nests guarded by females. They eat a variety of small crustaceans, such as harpacticoid copepods, gammarid amphipods, shrimps, isopods, mysid shrimps, and crabs, as well as polychaetes and the occasional insect. In turn, they are eaten by Pacific halibut, quillback rockfish, pigeon guillemots, and river otters.

REMARKS: These sweet little fish always remind me of one of those kinetic sculptures you see in the museum in Ferndale (Northern California).

JOHN RICHARDSON

Acting as a physician and naturalist, John Richardson was involved in three epic expeditions to the Canadian Arctic, expeditions that were recorded in a series of books, notably *Fauna Boreali-Americana*, which described a number of animals new to science. In addition to *Fauna*, Richardson wrote extensively on the Arctic and on British fishes. It was on the first expedition to the Northwest Territories that Richardson showed his truest grit. His moment of truth came as evidence mounted that one of the expedition's scouts, Michel, had likely killed two of the company, and perhaps chopped one up for dinner. In true Brit fashion, Richardson discussed the matter with his surviving companion and promptly shot the scout. Nothing that your typical ichthyologist would not do today, but a display of mettle nonetheless.

TOTALLY UNRELATED RIFF #5 — BECAUSE WE HAD SOME SPACE TO FILL

A RANT BY DAVID STARR JORDAN

In 1880, David Starr Jordan, even then one of the premier ichthyologists in North America, conducted an extensive survey of the fisheries of the Pacific Coast of North America. In this effort, he concentrated his attention on San Francisco, then the only population center north of perhaps Valparaiso, Chile. Let's look in on Jordan (1887) and see what he has to say: "The San Francisco fishermen constantly violate the State law concerning the size of mesh in their seines...The men are mostly Italian, Greek, and Spanish. Like all other fishermen of these nationalities they are improvident, spending their money as soon as earned. But, although without money, they have plenty to eat, drink, and wear, and seem to have a good time... Scarcely any are Americans or of Germanic races. Few of them can read...The drag-nets destroy and waste immense quantities of fish, doubtless amounting to several hundred tons per year...For many years the bay has been systematically overfished with nets of such small mesh that probably the bay does not contain one-twentieth the number of fish that it did twenty years ago."

Okay, as rants go it wasn't much. Certainly not up to the level of demagogic radio personalities who think global warming is some ganja-induced fantasy. But, hey, it's David Starr Jordan, not Ambrose Bierce.

FAMILY COTTIDAE—Sculpins

Sculpins are freshwater and marine benthic fishes, found in the Northern Hemisphere and way down in eastern Australia and environs. There are about 70 genera and at least 275 species. There are a breathtaking 92 species within our range. Seemingly, all of the sculpins produce sounds via muscles that attach on the skull and onto other bones. As to how they reproduce, let us look in on Petersen et al. (2005) and see what they have to say: "[In] the marine cottids a variety of care patterns has been documented, including male care, biparental care and no care...In addition to several forms of parental care, both external fertilization and internal gamete association are known to occur in cottids. Internal gamete association differs from the more typical internal fertilization in fishes in that sperm enters the ovary, and although it may enter the micropyle does not penetrate the ooplasmic membrane and initiate fertilization and development until eggs are released. True internal fertilization has not been documented in the cottids." I note that claims for internal fertilization, for instance in *Chitonotus pugettensis*, *Clinocottus analis*, and *Oligocottus maculosus*, are still out there. All cottids are oviparous.

Look, I'll level with you. I can't tell most sculpins apart and it would be the height of hubris for me to pretend that I can. Not that I wouldn't indulge in that if I could get away with it. If I have to key one out, I go to Miller and Lea (1972), Eschmeyer and Herald (1983), Mecklenburg et al. (2002), Nakabo (2002), and Lamb and Edgell (2010).

The word "sculpin" was first used on the Atlantic Coast for members of the genus *Cottus*. Most sculpins were called "catfish" by both fishermen and fish sellers in 19th-century San Francisco.

A fossil of a fish tentatively identified as a cottid was found in the Middle Eocene deposit (around 50 million years old) of Monte Bolca (Italy). David (1943) described *Lirosceles elegans* from the Miocene (at least 5.3 million years old) of Southern California. She wrote: "The fish may very well be related to *Scorpaenichthys.*"

Artedius

Named for the Swedish ichthyologist, Peter Artedi (1705–1735). Artedi, with excellent reason, is often called the Father of Ichthyology (although it is likely that no one ever called him that to his face). The position of Mother of Ichthyology is still vacant.

As happens to so many of us, Artedi, who was originally destined for the church, early on came under the spell of the piscine world. Switching to medicine, and more particularly natural science, Artedi began a rather lonely existence at the University of Uppsala, an institution with almost no professors and few students in that subject. Thus, it was probably with great relief when, after 4 years, Artedi met the younger Carolus Linnaeus, a newly arrived student with similar interests. The two young men had many interests in common and quickly formed a lifelong bond.

It was at dear old Uppsala U that Artedi, recognizing that fish systematics was in a dismal state, began a massive revision of the classification of the fishes, a work that eventually became the seminal *Ichthyologia*. Suffice it to say that the underlying systematic concepts that Artedi developed (e.g., using such physical characters as gill rakers and lateral line scales to discriminate genera and species) have been used by biologists ever since. Ultimately, much of the classifications Artedi established, such as many of the genera names that we still enjoy (e.g., *Syngnathus*, *Clupea*, *Xiphias*, *Scomber*, and *Balistes*), remain unchanged to this day.

In 1834, Artedi traveled to London, where he continued to revise his still unpublished monograph. In 1835, before this massive work could be published, the nearly penniless Artedi moved to Amsterdam. Here he was hired to catalogue and describe the fishes in the collection of Albertus Seba, a wealthy merchant and pharmacist. Ironically, Artedi, apparently after a night's partying at Seba's house, fell into a canal and drowned. Hearing the news, Linnaeus rushed to Amsterdam only to find that Artedi's landlord claimed the young man owed him money and refused to give up the manuscript of *Ichthyologia*. After a period of confusion and uncertainty, Linnaeus was able to ransom Artedi's manuscript and see to its publication.

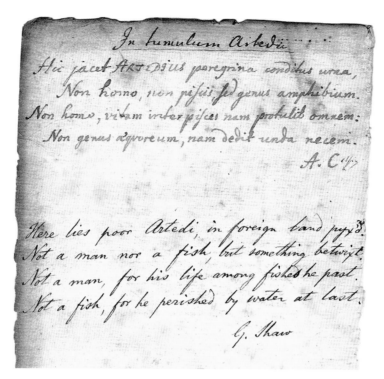

Apparently as a memoriam to Artedi's watery demise, the Swedish astronomer Anders Celsius (1701–1744) penned this elegiac poem on the flyleaf of Linnaeus's copy of Ichthyologia. English botanist and zoologist George Shaw (1751–1813) added an English translation:

Here lies poor Artedi, in foreign land pyx'd
Not a man nor a fish, but something betwixt,
Not a man, for his life among fishes he past,
Not a fish, for he perished by water at last.

Artedius fenestralis
Jordan & Gilbert, 1883
Padded Sculpin

RICH ZADE

ETYMOLOGY: *Artedius* is named for Peter Artedi (see above) and *fenestralis* means "with a window" (referring to the small pore-like slit behind the fourth gill) in Latin.

THE BASICS: Maximum Length: 14 cm (6 in) TL. The Ranges: Unalaska Island (Aleutian Islands) to north side of Alaska Peninsula at Herendeen Bay and to Diablo Cove (Central California), most commonly from perhaps Kodiak Island and Prince William Sound to about Sonoma County (Northern California). Tide pools to 55 m (180 ft), reported to 122 m (402 ft), variably common (depending on location) in the intertidal and subtidal to at least 10 m (33 ft) or more. Larvae: hatching length = 3.5–3.8 mm, flexion length = 5.9–6.9 mm.

SALIENT CHARACTERS: Paddeds are small fish with rounded heads, scales almost continuous between the dorsal fin base and the lateral line, and all along the body onto the caudal peduncle and under each eye. They are orange, yellowish, or greenish, with dark saddles. Petersen et al. (2005) note: "Males had more colorful dorsal fins, with red to yellow coloring throughout most of the spinous dorsal fin, and 2 dark areas on the anterior and posterior margins of the fin."

LIFE HISTORY: Padded sculpin larvae occur from near-surface waters to a depth of more than 50 m (164 ft), sometimes only a few meters from shore. Small ones settle to substrate from the plankton at as small as 1.2–1.3 cm (0.5 in) SL. This is a benthic species that rests on a wide range of habitats, including pavement rock, boulders, cobble, sand and gravel, eelgrass, kelp, and mud. They can tolerate fairly brackish waters. Densities as high as 1.4/m² have been noted.

Males appear to grow larger than females. Padded sculpins may practice both internal gametic association (see introduction to the Cottidae) and external fertilization. In northern waters, fish spawn at least from February–May. In Southern California, larvae have been found from March–October (peaking March–May), so the season may be longer down there. Spawning occurs under rocks in the lower intertidal and shallow subtidal. The eggs are laid in globular, adhesive masses and males guard multiple egg clutches (from different females). Each egg mass is uniformly colored, but masses can be gray, light blue, maroon, or purple. Females prefer to mate with males that are already caring for eggs. Males usually do not guard eggs at low tide, apparently preferring to hang out in deeper waters ogling some floozy snapping shrimp. Padded sculpins are bottom and near-bottom feeders. Gammarid amphipods, crabs, shrimps, and isopods are often most important; the fish also consume other small crustaceans, polychaetes, and benthic tunicates. They are eaten by coho salmon and probably by river otters.

RELATIONSHIPS: Padded sculpins are most closely related to bonyhead sculpins.

FISHERY: They are occasionally caught off rocks and piers by recreational anglers.

Artedius harringtoni
(Starks, 1896)
Scalyhead Sculpin

ETYMOLOGY: *Artedius* is named for Peter Artedi (see above) and *harringtoni* honors Mark Walrod Harrington (1848–1926), a president of the University of Washington.

THE BASICS: Maximum Length: 11.2 cm (4 in) TL. The Ranges: Unalaska Island, (Aleutian Islands) to San Miguel Island, most commonly as far south as Diablo Cove (Central California). Larvae are most abundant from the easternmost Aleutian Islands to Northern California. Tide pools to 40 m (131 ft), mostly subtidal, in some areas common to 21 m (70 ft) or more. Larvae: hatching length = less than 3 mm, flexion length = 5.2–6.4 mm.

GREGORY JENSEN

SALIENT CHARACTERS: Scalyheads have orange gill membranes, a flattened, two-forked spine on the posterior of the operculum, lots of little hair-like things along the lateral line and from the back of the jaw along the lower preoperculum, and a band of scales on the dorsal area. Males have a bushy cirrus above each eye. Underwater, scalyheads are dark olive-green or brown, with much mottling on body, and 5–7 dark saddles. Ragland and Fischer (1987) report: "During breeding season, males possessed a bright orange branchiostegal membrane, red-brown spots inside the mouth, and a brown anal fin with small yellowish-white spots that resembled eggs in color, shape, and size."

LIFE HISTORY: Young-of-the-year settle out of the plankton when at least as small as 0.8 cm (0.3 in) SL. This is a bottom dweller that, in some locations, shelters next to anemones (although they are not immune to the stinging cells), particularly to the strawberry anemone, *Urticina lofotensis*. You can also find them among barnacles and over rocks, sometimes in densities up to 4/m². Bruce Leaman (1980) found that in Barkley Sound (Vancouver Island), the nearshore aggregations had sex ratios of 484 females to 1 male. He speculated that scalyhead sexes are either separated by depth or are seasonally isolated. He also noted that they are "generally obvious and aggressive, being attracted to any disturbance in its vicinity." They are inactive at night and can tolerate slightly brackish waters. Ragland and Fischer (1987) report on courtship behavior thusly: "The male, which was not guarding eggs, responded by rolling its head in a circle and flaring the orange branchiostegal membranes." Jeff Marliave (2003) observed what appeared to be haremic behavior in this species, where the males guard both a nest site and some females. He "observed several rotund fish, presumed females, dart inside the empty shell of a giant barnacle, immediately followed by a much larger individual, presumed male, which curled its body and spread its fins to close off entry to the barnacle shell."

Females probably mature at around 5.4 cm (2 in) TL and 1 year old. Males seem to grow larger than females. Scalyheads practice internal gametic association (see the introduction to the Cottidae). Spawning likely occurs from January to perhaps June, peaking in the spring, although sexual activity was noted in an aquarium in December. Females may spawn more than one batch of eggs per season. Males guard as many as 10 egg clutches and the eggs hatch in 12–18 days. In a miasma of irony,

"He ne'er is crowned for immortality who fears to follow where airey voices lead." John Keats

males will sometimes eat some of the eggs they are guarding. Along with dining on the kids, scalyhead sculpins eat a wide variety of benthic and water column animals, including harpacticoid and calanoid copepods, crabs, gammarid and caprellid amphipods, shrimps, euphausiids, polychaetes, mysid shrimps, arrow worms, hydroids, snails, fishes, and lingcod eggs. Predators include copper rockfish, pigeon guillemots, and Steller sea lions.

RELATIONSHIPS: Scalyhead sculpins are closely related to...well, other species in the genus *Artedius*.

REMARKS: Jan Kocian reports that scalyheads clean lingcod, even venturing into their hosts' mouths (see image above).

MARK WALROD HARRINGTON

Harrington had kind of a checkered life. He 1) worked at the University of Michigan Museum of Natural Science, 2) was an astronomer's assistant for the U.S. Coast and Geodetic Survey in Alaska, 3) was a professor of astronomy in Beijing, 4) directed the Detroit Observatory, and 5) was chief of the United States Weather Bureau. At this point, his life seemed to have gotten a bit sketchy, as, within a few years, he was fired over concerns with his management. After a short stint at the University of Washington (from 1895 to 1897), Harrington and family moved back east where he briefly again worked for the weather bureau, but soon retired due to failing physical and mental health. At about this time, he left from home to attend a dinner and kind of disappeared. Well, actually, he was not seen again for 10 years. His wife finally found him when she read a newspaper article about a brilliant patient known as "John Doe No. VIII," who resided at the State Hospital in Morristown, New Jersey. His wife always believed that a lightning strike at the University of Washington led to his mental problems. Personal injury lawyers and our current litigious society did not exist in 1908, and that is pretty much the end of the story.

Artedius lateralis

(Girard, 1854)

Smoothhead Sculpin

GREGORY JENSEN

ETYMOLOGY: *Artedius* is named for Peter Artedi (see above) and *lateralis* means "pertaining to the side" in Latin.

THE BASICS: Maximum Length: 14 cm (6 in) TL. The Ranges: Sanak Island (western Gulf of Alaska) to Punta Baja (29°58'N, 115°49'W) (northern Baja California), most commonly from at least southeastern Alaska to Central California, and along northern Baja California, from about Punta Clara to Punta Baja. Intertidal zone to at least 15 m (49 ft), but perhaps as deep as 70 m (228 ft); typically from the mid-intertidal to at least 10 m (33 ft). Eggs: 1–1.2 mm. Larvae: hatching length = 3.9–4.5 mm, flexion length = 5–6.3 mm, transformation length = 9.5–10.5 mm.

SALIENT CHARACTERS: Smoothheads have that nice flattened head that always makes me think of a wolf. They have a single, forked spine on the rear end of gill cover, no scales on the head, a single band of scales along back, and thick scales along the lateral line. "Generally dark maroon or brown with two or more darker, irregular saddles and frequently a light patch of varying size on the caudal peduncle. The body was occasionally speckled or spotted with pink or white, or vertically banded with two or more alternating dark and light bands in shades of green and brown. One nearly pure white individual was collected" (Cross 1981). "Males tended to have more pink or red colouration around their head" (Petersen et al. 2005).

LIFE HISTORY: Larval smoothheads apparently mostly live within a few meters of shore. Juveniles and adults live in a variety of habitats including rocky tide pools, cobbles, pebbles, and sand. You can find them among brown, red, and coralline algae, eelgrass, and surfgrass. On occasion, they will come to the surface at night. One study found them to be more abundant in relatively quiet waters. Maximum densities are at least 0.5/m². On Vancouver Island, tide-pool fish displaced as much as 40 m (131 ft) homed back to their original sites.

    We don't know much about these fish. Two fish about 8.5 cm (3 in) SL were 3 years old. They may mature at about 3.2 cm (1 in) TL, in their first year. Males grow larger than females. Like some other *Artedius*, this species may have both internal gametic association and external fertilization. Smoothheads spawn from at least December–June, although a few larvae have been found as early as October. The eggs are adhesive, can be yellow, orange, or red, and they are laid in clusters in the lower intertidal under rocks. Males guard the eggs and, even when the eggs are exposed at low tide, males kind of hang in there. The eggs hatch in 11–12 days at 16°C (61°F). Smoothhead sculpins, like some of the other *Artedius*, are small fish with wide diets. Depending on which study you read, gammarid amphipods, shrimps, small fishes, and crabs tend to be most important, with isopods, polychaetes, hermit crabs, mysid shrimps, and algae also consumed. One fish had 23 parasitic isopods in its gut. Predators include kelp greenlings, red Irish lords, and northern clingfish.

RELATIONSHIPS: Coralline sculpins are the smoothheads' closest relative.

FISHERY: They are taken fairly often from piers and such by recreational anglers.

Ascelichthys rhodorus

Jordan & Gilbert, 1880

Rosylip Sculpin

GREGORY JENSEN

ETYMOLOGY: *Ascelichthys* means "without," "leg," and "fish" (no pelvic fins) in Greek and *rhodorus* is "rose" and "margin" in Greek (for the red-edged spiny dorsal fin).

THE BASICS: Maximum Length: 16.8 cm (7 in) TL. The Ranges: Prince William Sound (Gulf of Alaska) to Pillar Point (Central California), common to the Bodega Bay area (Northern California) and perhaps a bit further south. Intertidal to 15.2 m (50 ft), typical both in the intertidal and shallow subtidal. Eggs: 1.7–2 mm. Larvae: hatching length = 6 mm, flexion length = 8.8–11 mm, transformation length = 1.2–1.5 cm (0.5–0.6 in).

SALIENT CHARACTERS: No pelvic fins, curse you, no pelvic fins. No scales, one preopercular spine, and...no pelvic fins. "Black or greenish-black, either solid or subtly banded with two or more lighter areas. The margin of the spinous dorsal fin was etched with red; the lips often bore the same marking, hence the name rosylip. A different color pattern was observed at night. When resting exposed on a rock encrusted with coralline algae, they were pale gray" (Cross 1981).

LIFE HISTORY: Young ones settle out of the plankton at 1.4 cm (0.7 in) SL. A benthic species, rosylips are found around and under various-sized rocks, in kelp beds, other algae, and surfgrass, and over sand and mud. Smaller individuals tend to live in tide pools (sometimes way up in the intertidal) and larger ones in lower pools or in the slightly subtidal. You can often find them in the dens of giant Pacific octopuses. They can breath air, so they also spend time out of the water. They also show some ability to home back to a favorite pool.

Rosylips spawn from January–April and practice external fertilization; larger females likely reproduce earlier in the season than smaller ones. Females lay their eggs (blue or purple, and then brown as embryos advance) under rocks in the mid or lower intertidal. An egg mass typically contains clutches from a number of females; one was reported to have had more than 200 clutches in it. Unlike many other sculpins, males are not territorial during the spawning season (although they do hang around their clutches) and do not really guard their eggs. Because a male is not aggressive and does not dominate an area, there is likely intense sperm competition, as males likely spray sperm all over the place. Not only do males not appear to guard the eggs, they sometimes eat them, particularly toward the end of the spawning season, when the females have left and boredom has set in. An experiment that removed males from a nesting site did show that just the presence of males, even males who just sat there looking decorative, probably has some deterrent effect on egg predators. Eggs hatch in about 24 days at 10°C (50°F), larvae develop schooling behavior within 2 weeks of hatching and some settle to the bottom beginning at 55–60 days of age. Rosylips feed on small, benthic-oriented prey, such as gammarid amphipods, isopods, polychaetes, shrimps, crabs, and mysid shrimps. Minks eat them.

Chitonotus pugetensis
(Steindachner, 1876)
Roughback Sculpin

ETYMOLOGY: *Chitonotus* means "chiton" and "back" and *pugetensis* refers to Puget Sound.

THE BASICS: Maximum Length: 22.9 cm (9 in). The Ranges: Mears Pass (55°17'N, 133°11'W) (southeastern Alaska) to Bahia Santa Maria (southern Baja California), commonly from perhaps Vancouver Island to northern Baja California. Intertidal to 144 m (474 ft). In Southern California, they are most abundant in perhaps 30–70 m (98–230 ft), while to the north they move into more nearshore waters. Eggs: 1–1.1 mm. Larvae: hatching length = 2.9–3 mm, transformation length = greater than 1.6 cm (0.6 in). Length-weight parameters (TL, cm, gr): W = 0.005L$^{3.268}$ (Love unpubl.).

SALIENT CHARACTERS: The back and head of roughbacks are almost completely covered by large scales. They have large, antler-like spines on their cheeks, an elongated first dorsal spine, and a deep notch between the third and fourth dorsal spines. They come in browns and grays, with dark saddles and blotches. The first dorsal fin is black-edged and a red blotch may appear on the sides during spawning season.

LIFE HISTORY: Roughbacks are most common over sandy bottoms, although you can find them on mud, gravel, low-lying rocks, or in eelgrass. They appear to be most active at night.

Females mature at as small as 6.6 cm (3 in) SL. In Southern California, they likely spawn throughout the year, albeit with a late winter to early spring peak; further north, spawning seems to occur almost entirely in the late winter and early spring. Misitano (1980) claimed to have found fertilized eggs inside a female, meaning this species has internal fertilization. As this has not, apparently, been confirmed, I have no idea if this is correct. Eggs are demersal and deposited on worm tubes and other low-lying material. In Southern California, females are batch spawners, producing as many as three batches per year, with an average batch running about 3,100 eggs. The eggs are pink or red and hatch in 14 days at 12°C (54°F). Roughback sculpins feed on or near the bottom and they consume crustaceans (e.g., crabs, shrimps, and gammarid amphipods), a few fishes, polychaetes, and larvaceans. Predators include Brandt's cormorants, pigeon guillemots, California sea lions, and harbor seals.

ORIGINS: Otoliths of roughback sculpins have been found in Pliocene (1.8 million years ago or more) deposits in Oregon and California.

Clinocottus acuticeps
(Gilbert, 1896)
Sharpnose Sculpin

ETYMOLOGY: *Clinocottus* is formed from two words for other genera, "*Clinus*" and "*Cottus*" and *acuticeps* means "sharp" and "head" in Latin.

THE BASICS: Maximum Length: 6.4 cm (3 in) TL. The Ranges: Attu Island (Aleutian Islands) to off Big Sur River (Central California). Abundant at least from Amchitka Island (Aleutian Islands) to Northern California. Intertidal to 20 m (66 ft), including tide pools. Perhaps most abundant in the intertidal and often in the mid to high intertidal. Eggs: 1–1.2 mm. Larvae: hatching length = 3–4 mm, flexion length = 5.5–7.3 mm, transformation length = 1.3–1.5 cm.

SALIENT CHARACTERS: I don't know, compared to some other sculpins, this species just does not seem to have a particularly sharp nose. Probably better characters are 1) the dark spot on the membrane between the first few rays of the first dorsal fin, 2) the light, kind of silvery, cheek patch or line extending diagonally backward from the eye, 3) a small cirri above each eye, 4) no scales, and 5) a single spine on each cheek. These fish can be gray, brown, or green and Jeff Cross (1981) saw one change from dark to light gray almost instantaneously when it moved from under a rock to open sand.

LIFE HISTORY: Sharpnoses are found in marine and brackish conditions, and occasionally freshwater. In many areas, they are particularly common among green algae, eelgrass, and surfgrass (and sometimes over gravel, cobble, larger rocks, and sand). One study found that they grow faster in vegetated areas than in rock/cobble and sand. They have been found in waters as cold as 1.4°C (35°F).

They spawn from at least January–April. Jeff Marliave (1981a) reports from British Columbia that spawning occurs in the high intertidal, mostly on smooth rock surfaces—ones that are overlaid with algal blades at low tide. These blades tend to keep the eggs, which would otherwise be exposed to the air, damp. The eggs are laid in a single layer (18–96 eggs in a mass) in a circular shape. Eggs are amber or olive-green when first laid, becoming gold, green, or red when they contain eyed larvae. It is assumed that this species does not guard the eggs. Sharpnose sculpins feed mostly on gammarid amphipods and isopods, as well as on some insects and copepods. Staghorn sculpins eat them.

RELATIONSHIPS: Interestingly, sharpnoses are apparently most closely related to members of the genus *Artedius* and not to *Clinocottus*. If true, I would think a genus change is in order.

Clinocottus analis
(Girard, 1858)
Woolly Sculpin

ETYMOLOGY: *Clinocottus* is formed from two words for other genera, "*Clinus*" and "*Cottus*" and *analis*, Latin for "anus," an allusion to the large anal papilla.

THE BASICS: Maximum Length: 17.8 cm (7 in) TL. The Ranges: Cape Mendocino (Northern California) to Punta Abreojos (southern Baja California). They are a dominant high intertidal tide-pool fish from about Duxbury Reef (Northern California) to about Bahia Tortugas (southern Baja California). Intertidal to 18 m (60 ft), mostly in the intertidal but in some areas also common in the very shallow subtidal. Eggs: 1.2–1.3 mm. Larvae: hatching length = 3.1–4.5 mm, flexion length = about 5.2–less than 8.4 mm, transformation length = 1–1.2 cm (0.4 in). Von Bertalanffy parameters (TL, mm): (females) L_∞ = 96.3, k = 1.0, t_0 = -0.07; (males) L_∞ = 119, k = 0.71, t_0 = -0.1 (Wells 1986). Length-weight parameters (TL, mm, gr): (females) W = $0.0000346L^{2.793}$; (males) W = $0.0000159L^{2.988}$ (Wells 1986).

SALIENT CHARACTERS: Woollies are densely covered with cirri and prickles on back, head, and there are 1–2 cirri at the rear of upper jaw. The upper preopercular spine has 2–3 points. These fish come in a very wide variety of colors (e.g., green, green-black, brown, and reddish), specklings, and mottlings. Fish living in deep pools are darker than those living in shallow ones.

WALTER HEIM

LIFE HISTORY: Young-of-the-year (at as small as at least 0.9 cm SL) settle from November–May, perhaps peaking in November–February. They settle into the upper intertidal in small and shallow pools and move to increasingly larger and lower intertidal pools as they mature. Juveniles less than 2.5 cm (1 in) are rarely found in pools inhabited by adults. Fish occupy home pools in the lower intertidal at low tide, rising upward as the tide advances, and retreating as it ebbs. Wooly sculpins associate with a variety of substrates, including sand, gravel, small rocks, and bedrock, often sitting on vertical rock faces, or on top of rocks. Larger fish tend to inhabit pools with moderate to heavy cover (such as algae, caves, and crevices). Maximum temperature for this species seems to be about 22°C (72°F) and they can tolerate salinities down to at least 24 ppt for short periods. Densities of larger fish can reach 27/m². These fish are active during both day and night.

Males live to at least 8 years old and females to at least 6 years old. Males grow both faster and larger. Sexual maturity occurs near the end of the first year. Some fish mature when as small as 5 cm (2 in) TL and all fish over 6 cm (2 in) are mature. Spawning takes place throughout the year, although the peak period seems to vary between years and areas. On average, spawning may be heaviest from spring–fall, but don't hold me to it. Fertilization is said to be internal and females can store sperm for at least 2 months; at least some produce several batches a year. Egg colors vary (e.g., greenish-yellow, brown, dark red, and lavender) and a female may have different colored eggs in her ovaries at the same time. Fecundity ranges from about 50–1,300 eggs and may vary geographically. Larvae hatch in 12–20 days (more slowly at lower temperatures) and will develop at temperatures ranging from about 6 to perhaps 24°C (43–75°F). Larvae drift about for 25–40 days before they settle out of the plankton. Wooly sculpins feed on a wide range of crustaceans, mollusks, and other small benthic and epibenthic prey. Some of the more important foods are gammarid amphipods, isopods, crabs, harpacticoid and calanoid copepods, shrimps, pycnogonids, sipunculids, polychaetes, barnacle cirri, limpets and other snails, and the occasional abalone, insect, sea urchin tube feet, fish, algae, and fish egg.
RELATIONSHIPS: Wooly sculpins may be most closely related to lavender sculpins and only secondarily to other *Clinocottus*.
MISCELLANY: The blue-green blood serum of this species is likely caused by a build-up of biliverdin, a by-product of the breakdown of hemoglobin. Wooly sculpins can breathe air (at least partly through their skins).

BREATHLESS BETWEEN THE TIDES

A sculpin, a good friend of mine
In a tide pool she sure walked the line
At high tide, she was covered
But she soon discovered
She was exposed for the rest of the time.

Oh, she's breathless between the tides
Oh, she's breathless between the tides
But she still requires
That she must respire
Yet she's breathless between the tides.

So in air she did all that she could
Even though her gills were no good
In response, instantaneous
She respired, quite cutaneous
She always knew that she would

[Refrain]

Like a sculpin caught up in the tide
This fact simply can't be denied
Exposed or quite hidden
It happens unbidden
We're just simply along for the ride

[Refrain]

We're all breathless between the tides
We're all breathless between the tides
Yes, we still require
That we must respire
But we're breathless between the tides.

Clinocottus globiceps
(Girard, 1858)
Mosshead Sculpin

GREGORY JENSEN

ETYMOLOGY: *Clinocottus* is formed from two words for other genera, "*Clinus*" and "*Cottus*" and *globiceps* is Latin for "globe" and "head."

THE BASICS: Maximum Length: 19 cm (8 in) TL. The Ranges: Chernabura and Kodiak islands to Gaviota (Southern California). A common species from about San Francisco northward. Intertidal and shallow subtidal areas, mostly in tide pools, often in the mid and higher ones. Eggs: 1.5–2 mm. Larvae: hatching length = 5.1–5.4 mm, flexion length = 6.2–8.1 mm, transformation length = 1.3–1.4 cm. However, note that Mgaya (1995) reported collecting a settled juvenile that was 5 mm SL. Gompertz parameters (SL, mm): (sexes combined) L_0 = 26.7, G = 1.58, g = 0.3 (Mgaya 1995). Length-weight parameters (SL, mm, gr): (sexes combined) W = $0.0000159L^{3.16}$ (Mgaya 1995).

SALIENT CHARACTERS: I like mossheads because, for a smarmy little sculpin, they are pretty easy to identify. They have a rounded, blunt head, and a single, rounded preopercular (cheek) spine. Best of all, they have lots of cirri on their head (between the eyes). Mossheads come in a wide range of colors, from solid black to reddish-brown to olive-green. They often have irregular white patches or vertical bands.

LIFE HISTORY: Larvae are found in coastal waters, perhaps mostly 2–20 km (1–12 mi) from shore. Off Washington, larvae survive better (larval settlement is larger) in years when upwelling begins later in the spring. Young-of-the-year settle to tide pools (usually small ones) from April–October, generally peaking in May. Mossheads are found mostly in rocky tide pools and occasionally on cobble beaches. Smaller fish tend to live higher in the intertidal than larger ones. This fish can home back to favored pools (from at least 44 m, 144 ft, away) and their home ranges seem to encompass more than one pool. Mossheads can stay in the same little area for at least 6 months. In at least some areas, mossheads undergo boom and bust cycles.

Mossheads live to 6 years old. They probably spawn from February–June. Eggs are demersal and larvae likely hatch 15–20 days after the eggs are laid. Settlement occurs 25–40 days after hatching. Mosshead sculpins, unlike most other sculpins, simply dote on eating sea anemone tentacles, particularly those of the green anemone, *Anthopleura elegantissima*. These fish prefer tentacles that contain zooxanthellae (the brownish tentacles), rather than zoochlorellae (the green tentacles), or no algae symbionts at all (the white tentacles). Other prey include algae, harpacticoid copepods, polychaetes, nemertean worms, ostracods, and insects.

RELATIONSHIPS: Mosshead sculpins are most closely related to bald and calico sculpins.

GREGORY JENSEN

Enophrys bison
(Girard, 1854)
Buffalo Sculpin

ETYMOLOGY: *Enophrys* means "on" and "eyebrow" in Greek and *bison* refers to the American buffalo (for the species' horns).

THE BASICS: Maximum Length: 37.1 cm (15 in) TL. The Ranges: Uyak Bay, Kodiak Island to Monterey Bay. They are typical from around Kodiak Island to at least Cape Mendocino (Northern California), then patchy to San Francisco Bay. Intertidal to 43 m (141 ft), reported to 137 m (450 ft). Eggs: 1.7–2 mm. Larvae: hatching length = about 5 mm, flexion length = 5.2–7 mm, transformation length = 7.6–9.5 mm. Length-weight parameters (TL, mm, kg): (sexes combined) W = $0.0000000179L^{2.896}$ (RecFin 2009)

SALIENT CHARACTERS: That very long upper preopercular (cheek) spine is a key character. The lowest cheek spine (near the jaw) is small and points downwards. These fish are scaleless except for a bunch of large, thick ones along the lateral line. Colors of these rather remarkable sculpins are black to green, often with three dark saddles across the back.

LIFE HISTORY: Juveniles are found in shallow waters in eelgrass, kelp, and various rock bottoms. Adults are found a little deeper, in high currents, on steep walls or gravel-cobble seafloors. These fish can tolerate brackish conditions and water at least as cold as 1.4°C (35°F). Most spawning sites (from the intertidal to depths of 15–20 m, 49–66 ft) are located where currents are strong: on rocky headlands, reef crests, and such structures as piers, and among invertebrates (e.g., barnacles and mussels). The egg masses are multilayered, roughly circular, and 7–14 cm (3–6 in) in diameter. They contain eggs from more than one female (a male mates with as many as 9 females in a season). Males guard the nests (except at low tide), lying next to or on top of the eggs, and staying there for as long as 39 days. Eggs are purple, pink, yellow, orange, red, or tan, and all the eggs in a female are of a single color. Nests can be as close as 1.3 m (4 ft) from each other, but average 3 m (10 ft).

Displaying all the unruffledness of a fish with a brain the size and shape of a lima bean, a buffalo sculpin studiously ignores the caresses of a sea star.

The spawning season lasts from at least January–April. Females apparently spawn twice per season and total fecundity ranges from 16,000–43,100 eggs. Eggs are often exposed at low tide but are apparently not eaten by terrestrial predators—so are they bad tasting? However, the eggs are eaten by striped sea-perch. Buffalo sculpins feed on a wide range of benthic and epibenthic organisms. Crustaceans (e.g., crabs, gammarid and cap-rellid amphipods, and mysid shrimps) are important, as are snails, fishes, and algae. Also consumed are mussels, polychaetes, insects, nudibranchs, and hydrozoans. Predators include fishes, seals, and river otters.

FISHERY: Pier and shore anglers commonly take buffalos.

Hemilepidotus hemilepidotus

(Tilesius, 1811)

Red Irish Lord

ETYMOLOGY AND COLLOQUIAL NAME: *Hemilepidotus* means "half" and "scaled" in Greek (for the 2 scale bands on the upper sides). "Honyokosujikajika" is the Japanese word.

THE BASICS: Maximum Length: 50.8 cm (20 in) TL. Maximum Weight: 1.5 kg (3.2 lb). The Ranges: Commander–Aleutian chain and southeastern Bering Sea to Mussel Point (Monterey Bay). They appear to be common around the Pribilof Islands (Bering Sea) and at least Amchitka Island (Aleutian Islands) to off Northern California, perhaps almost to San Francisco. Intertidal (including tide pools) to at least 88 m (289 ft) and reported to 168 m (552 ft), common in nearshore waters. Eggs: 1.5–1.7 mm. Larvae: hatching length = about 5–6 mm, flexion length = about 9.1 mm, transformation length = about 1.9–2.3 cm. Length-weight parameters (TL, mm, kg): (sexes combined) $W = 0.0000000358L^{2.896}$ (RecFin 2009).

SALIENT CHARACTERS: Two distinct scale bands help differentiate RILs from other sculpins. There are two major bands, one above the lateral line (4–5 rows wide), and one below the lateral line (up to 10 rows wide). Look also for the single dorsal fin that has two notches and a fringed cirri in the nasal area. They come in a variety of colors, often red, with black, white, and brown spots and blotches mixed in. Males have black and white pelvic fins and females have white ones.

LIFE HISTORY: Young-of-the-year red Irish lords settle to near-shore areas when at least as small as 2 cm (0.8 in) SL. Juveniles are found in quite shallow waters, mostly in eelgrass, some in kelp, and occasionally on cobble and bare seafloors. Most adults inhabit the subtidal, resting on rock, gravel-cobble, and sand/shell bottoms. They also hide in algae and occasionally rise into the kelp canopy. These are solitary fish that usually remain motionless. Although they don't appear to defend territories, larger fish may remain in the same general area for months at a time. One study found them living in the dens of giant Pacific octopuses. Eggs are deposited on rocks, mussels, barnacles, or other hard surfaces, usually in high current areas. DeMartini and Patten (1979), reporting from Puget Sound, note that the depth of spawning can range from the intertidal to about 5 m (16 ft), but mostly just around the lower low

RICH ZADE

tide line. The eggs masses are "roughly circular, 100–200 mm in diameter, and 20–40 mm thick. The eggs adhered to one another…Embryogenesis (time to hatching) required 22–26 days in the field…Some individuals of both sexes spawned within the same general breeding area during successive years." Usually females, but occasionally males, guard the eggs and this often takes the form of sitting on top of them. Females and males may switch off guarding duties. Eggs laid in the intertidal can be exposed for up to 4 hours.

Males grow larger than females, and fish reach maturity at 4 years old. Prior to spawning, males, having nothing better to do, start to hang out in the spawning areas. Females get there a day or two before spawning begins. Females spawn from October–March and males may breed with more than one female per season. Females produce one batch of pink eggs per year and fecundity ranges from 59,000–126,000 eggs. Red Irish lords feed heavily on crabs, mussels, hermit crabs, shrimps, barnacles, gammarid and caprellid amphipods, polychaetes, brittle stars, sea urchins, snails, octopuses, small fishes, sipunculids, nudibranchs, and euphausiids. These fish are nocturnally active and likely feed mostly at night. Predators include fishes (e.g., Pacific cod, various greenlings, sculpins, salmon, and snailfishes), bald eagles, minks, and river otters.

FISHERY: Historically, sculpins in the genus *Hemilepidotus* were fairly important food fish for various indigenous peoples and they still taken in some numbers. Given that they can reach a reasonable size, there is not much meat on Irish lords, and, hence, little commercial interest, although a few are brought alive to the fish markets of British Columbia. Red Irish lords are often taken in recreational catches from boats, piers, and shore.

MISCELLANY: Did you ever look at the blood serum of this species? Well, it's blue-green, and likely caused by a build-up of biliverdin, a by-product of the breakdown of hemoglobin.

Icelinus quadriseriatus
(Lockington, 1880)
Yellowchin Sculpin

NICK HARLING AND DAN ITUARTE

ETYMOLOGY: *Icelinus* is likely a reference to Icelus (also known as Phobetor), a Greek god of nightmares, and *quadriseriatus* means "four-rowed" in Latin.

THE BASICS: Maximum Length: 11 cm (4 in) TL. The Ranges: Sonoma County (Northern California) to Cabo San Lucas (southern Baja California), most commonly from about Monterey Bay to Bahia Sebastian de Vizcaino (central Baja California). Intertidal to 201 m (660 ft), typically in perhaps 20–100 m (66–328 ft). In Southern California, these fish tend to retreat into deeper waters during warm-water episodes. Eggs: 1.1–1.2 mm. Larvae: hatching length = 2.6–3.4 mm, flexion length = 5–7.4 mm, transformation length = greater than 1.1 cm and less than 1.6 cm (0.4–0.6 in). Length-weight parameters (TL, cm, gr): W = 0.0036L$^{3.43}$ (Love unpubl.).

SALIENT CHARACTERS: These are perky little fishes, with a double row of scales on their sides running from near the beginning of their dorsal fins to near their tail. Their back is brown or olive-green and lined with various brown saddles and lines. Males have bright yellow chins. When you catch one, they flare out their cheek spines, making it difficult to pry them free of the net.

LIFE HISTORY: It is assumed that larvae drift about in the plankton for 2 months before young-of-the-year take up residence on soft seafloors. The smallest mature female in one study was 5.1 cm (2 in) SL. In southern California, females produce an average of 284 eggs per batch and may produce three batches per year. Eggs reportedly are pale green and adhesive. Spawning occurs throughout the year and peaks in the winter and spring. Larvae hatch in 12–13 days at 13–16°C (55–61°F). Yellowchin sculpins feed mostly on seafloor animals. These include ostracods, burrowing and tubiculous gammarid amphipods, polychaetes, crabs, shrimps, cumaceans, caprellid amphipods, mysid shrimps, small fishes, and fish eggs.

ORIGINS: Yellowchin remains have been reported in 100,000-year-old strata in California.

Jordania zonope
Starks, 1895

Longfin Sculpin

ETYMOLOGY: *Jordania* honors David Starr Jordan (1851–1931) (see petrale sole, *Eopsetta jordani*, for all the gory details about DSJ) and *zonope* means "zone" and "window" (referring to the banded eye).

THE BASICS: Maximum Length: 15 cm (6 in) TL. The Ranges: Danger Island, Prince William Sound (northern Gulf of Alaska) to Diablo Canyon (Central California); reasonably common southward to at least Point Arena (Northern California). Intertidal areas, including tide pools, to at least 117 m (384 ft) and perhaps to 126 m (413 ft), most typically in subtidal waters down to at least 40 m. Von Bertalanffy parameters (TL, mm): (sexes combined) L_∞ = 130.4, k = 0.3715, t_0 = -0.83 (Moulton 1977). Length-weight parameters (TL, mm, gr): (sexes combined) W = 0.000006109L$^{3.022}$ (Moulton 1977).

SALIENT CHARACTERS: This one is long and slender, with long dorsal and anal fins, scales covering the body above the lateral line, and plate-like scales below the line. Also, look for the three dark bars under each eye. They are olive-green with red marks, dark saddles, and dark bars across the cheek. Reportedly, adults are darker during spawning season.

LIFE HISTORY: Young-of-the-year settle out of the plankton at around 2.3–3 cm (1 in) SL. Longfins are solitary, highly territorial (with territories of 0.3–0.5 m²), and benthic fish that rarely swim more than 0.5 m (1.6 ft) above the bottom. At least in the Puget Sound region, they tend to leave the shallowest waters in the winter. You find them mostly on rocks (in caves and crevices) or around barnacles, hydroids, and the like. They often sit on vertical walls using their pelvic and pectoral fins to shuffle around. Elliott (1992) found longfins living in British Columbia sheltering next to strawberry anemones, *Urticina lofotensis*, and (rarely) *U. piscivora*, at night. These sculpins are not immune to the anemones' stinging cells, just (one supposes) careful. Longfins are inactive at night. In areas of high abundance, densities can reach 1.6 fish per m². Females lay amber-colored egg masses in rocky crevices and, apparently, both males and females have been observed guarding these eggs.

LINDA REISINGER.

A male and a female.

An 11.7 cm (5 in) SL fish was 5 years old. Spawning is in the spring Longfins have a very diverse diet, one that focuses on benthic organisms. More important prey include polychaetes, gammarid amphipods, harpacticoid copepods, caridean shrimps, barnacle cirri, snails, hydroids, lingcod and painted greenling eggs. One study found that these fish foraged over an area of 4–9 m². Predators include smoothhead sculpins.

REMARK: Both Linda Reisinger and Jan Kocian have observed longfins cleaning lingcod. See the one balancing on a lingcod head on the previous page.

Leptocottus armatus

Girard, 1854

Pacific Staghorn Sculpin

SCOTT GIETLER

ETYMOLOGY AND COLLOQUIAL NAME: *Leptocottus* means "slender" (in Greek) and "cottus" and *armatus* means "armed" in Latin. They are often called "bullheads."

THE BASICS: Maximum Length: 48 cm (19 in) TL. The Ranges: Pribilof Islands and Port Moller (southeastern Bering Sea) to Bahia San Quintin (northern Baja California), commonly from the Pribs to Bahia San Quintin. Intertidal to 150 m (492 ft), but perhaps to 188 m (618 ft). Common in very shallow waters to perhaps 9 m (30 ft).

In nearshore marine waters and seasonally in brackish water and freshwater, including lower portions of coastal rivers and streams. Eggs: 1.4–1.5 mm. Larvae: hatching length = 3.9–4.8 mm, flexion length = about 8 mm, transformation length = 1.5–2 cm (0.6–0.8 in). Length-at-age data are shown in Jones (1962) and Weiss (1969). Length-weight parameters (TL, mm, gr): (sexes combined) W = 0.00000571L$^{3.134}$ (Weiss 1969).

KEVIN LEE

SALIENT CHARACTERS: Staghorns are green-brown or gray fish, scaleless, with depressed, flattened heads, and long, branching cheek spines. They are usually kind of mud-colored with white or yellow mixed in.

LIFE HISTORY: Young-of-the-year settle (when at least as small as 1.2 cm, 0.5 in, SL) to very shallow waters. Juveniles, in particular, can tolerate freshwater. Staghorns also live in hyper-saline pools of up to about 53 ppt. Both juveniles and adults usually spend much of their time partially buried in muddy or sandy bottoms. Areas with eelgrass and other vegetation are particular favorites, although they also frequently inhabit bare seafloors and will enter rocky tide pools.

A study in Puget Sound found that both juveniles and adults will rise up into the water column at night. Off Kodiak Island, they have been taken in waters as cold as 1.4°C (35°F).

Remember Ed Ricketts? Sure you do, he was the model for "Doc," that lovable beer milkshake-swilling character in John Steinbeck's *Cannery Row* and *Sweet Thursday*. I like Ricketts because, as one observer noted, he was "half saint and half satyr" (my goal for next year is to be three-quarters satyr and one-quarter saint). Ricketts and Steinbeck wrote a book about their marine life collecting expedition to the Gulf of California (*Log from the Sea of Cortez*) and they planned on doing another one based on collections made in the Vancouver Island–Queen Charlotte Islands area. Unfortunately, Ricketts died before that occurred, but he left extensive notes on preliminary trips he made up that way. These, along with lots of other writings, were published in *Breaking Through* (edited by Katharine Rodger, University of California Press, 2006). In these notes, we find Ricketts writing about the staghorn sculpins he observed on a mud flat at Masset in the Queen Charlotte Islands. "All the Masset specimens so far have been in old tin cans. Apparently that's where they hide when the tide's out." *Hey, artificial reefs for staghorns.* I have also seen staghorns bury themselves in mudflats at low tide and have observed blue herons subsequently dig them out.

Staghorns live to at least 10 years old. In Anaheim Bay (Southern California), fish mature at the end of their first year; females at a minimum of 12.4 cm (5 in) SL and males at 11 cm (4 in). Looking across the geographic range of this species, spawning may occur throughout the year, albeit with different peaks in different areas and between years. There is also evidence for two spawning peaks in some areas. Their eggs are adhesive, and white, pale yellow, or orange. A female spawns once per season and, at least in Northern California, produces between 2,000–11,000 eggs. Males may guard eggs, although no one seems to be quite sure. In one laboratory study, eggs hatched in 10 days. Staghorns feed on a wide range of benthic and epibenthic organisms. Prey include crabs, gammarid and caprellid amphipods, shrimps, algae, fishes, mysid shrimps, clam siphons, snails, harpacticoid copepods, fish eggs, clams, polychaetes, and terrestrial insects. There is some evidence that staghorns feed more at night than during the day. Butter clams often sequester paralytic shellfish toxins in their siphons. Staghorn sculpins will prey on siphons that do not contain the toxin, but avoid siphons with the toxin. Predators include a wide range of fishes (e.g., brown smoothhounds, shovelnose guitarfish, and white sturgeons), birds (e.g., cormorants, great blue herons, and terns), seals, sea lions, minks, and river otters.

FISHERY: Staghorns were a common food of those indigenous folks living near sloughs and estuaries. Commercial fishermen, eyeing the bait trade, land modest quantities. They are caught in huge numbers by anglers. Some pier and shore fishermen target staghorns and then use them for bait for California halibut, sharks, and striped bass. Historically, they were caught by Chinese fishermen in San Francisco Bay, then dried and shipped to China. Goode (1884) wrote that these fishermen considered them "the poorest of all dried fishes." So, there you go.

ORIGINS AND RELATIONSHIPS: Staghorn sculpin fossils have been found in Pliocene deposits (at least 1.8 million years old) from Oregon and California. One molecular study implied that this species is most closely related to *Cottus kazika*, a Japanese species, while another pointed to northern sculpins.

MISCELLANY: Staghorns are capable of breathing air. That spine on their cheek is kind of sharp but not venomous.

REMARKS: Hmmm, MacGinitie (1939) claims that on a number of occasions, he saw staghorns taking large pieces of food to shrimps and then eating the small pieces that were created when the crustaceans broke up the food material. The maunderings of a fevered mind? We wonder.

Myoxocephalus polyacanthocephalus
(Pallas, 1814)

Great Sculpin

ETYMOLOGY AND COLLOQUIAL NAME: *Myoxocephalus* means "dormouse" and "head" in Greek and *polyacanthocephalus* is Greek for "many," "spine," and "head." The Japanese name is "togekajika."

THE BASICS: Maximum Length: At least 79 cm (31 in) TL. Maximum Weight: 10 kg (22 lb). The Ranges: Okhotsk Sea and eastern Japan Sea to Commander–Aleutian chain to Chukchi Sea off Point Hope (68°20'N, 167°06'W) and to southern Puget Sound. They are very abundant from the Sea of Japan to the eastern Bering Sea and to about Prince William Sound (northern Gulf of Alaska). They are then locally common as far south as Puget Sound. Postlarvae have been taken from the Chukchi Sea, off Point Hope (68°20'N, 167°06'W). Intertidal to 825 m (2,707 ft), perhaps most abundant to about 200 m (656 ft). Length-weight parameters (TL, cm, gr): (sexes combined) $W = 0.0123L^{3.08}$ (Orlov and Binohlan 2009).

SALIENT CHARACTERS: A nice full-bodied, big-mouthed, expansive-finned fish is the great sculpin. Really, this is a sculpin's sculpin, the kind of iconic cottid that your armorhead, woolly, and yellowchin sculpins can only hope to be in their next lives. Great sculpins have small ridges behind each eye, a very long, straight, and single preopercular spine, and warty things on the top and sides of head. They are usually brown or gray, often with yellow or orangey mottling, and some dark saddles.

LIFE HISTORY: Off Amchitka Island (Aleutian Islands), young-of-the-year (at maybe as small as 1.1 cm, 0.4 in) SL settle in the spring to tide pools and the shallow subtidal. They remain there for a few months, migrating somewhat deeper in the fall. Juveniles live over a wide range of very shallow habitats, including eelgrass, kelp, cobbles, and soft seafloor. Adults inhabit rocks, algae, and sandy bottoms. Off Kamchatka, they have been found in waters from 0.5–12°C (33–54°F), mostly at 8°C (46°F) or lower. Off Alaska, they are taken down to -1.7°C (29°F). They can tolerate slightly brackish conditions. In the Okhotsk Sea, trawlers have taken as much as 4 tons per hour.

Great sculpins live to at least 16 years old. Most research on this species has been off Kamchatka. Here great sculpin females live to 13 years and males to 9 years. A few males mature at 5 years and 33–34 cm (13 in) TL, 50% at 6 years and 40 cm (16 in), and all are mature at 8 years old and 50 cm (20 in) long. Similar parameters for females are 7 years and 49–50 cm (19–20 in), 8 years and 55 cm (22 in), and 9 years and 65 cm (26 in), respectively. Off Kamchatka, spawning occurs in January and February in about 120–210 m (394–689 ft), at temperatures of 0.8–1.9°C (33–35°F). Off Kodiak Island, larvae were likely taken in April and May. In the Sea of Japan and Okhotsk Sea, fish may spawn well down the continental slope. Spawning areas are sandy bottoms with small stones; the eggs are adhesive and yellowish-orange to red. Females produce 48,000–423,000 eggs. Great sculpins feed on anything that is not bolted to the seafloor. In the western North Pacific, this species feeds most intensively in the summer (when waters warm to 0.01–1°C, 32–34°F). Crabs, shrimps, and gammarid amphipods are more important in smaller individuals and fishes in larger ones. Other food organisms include caprellid amphipods, isopods, hermit crabs, snails, fish eggs (including their own species), octopuses, brittle stars, sea urchins, echiuroids, polychaetes, euphausiids, bivalves, ascidians, and sand dollars. Predators include fishes (e.g., great sculpins, Pacific cod, Pacific halibut, and rock greenlings), pigeon guillemots, seals, sea lions, minks, and probably river otters.

FISHERY: Bean (1887b) reported that this was an important food fish along the Alaskan coast to the Chukchi Sea. Artisanal fishermen along the Aleutian Islands still catch them with some frequency and they are occasionally taken by recreational anglers. Currently, there is no directed fishery for them, although they are often part of the Russian trawl fishery bycatch.

RELATIONSHIPS: Great sculpins are related to the frog sculpin, *Myoxocephalus stelleri*.

REMARKS: Unlike Arctic (*M. scorpioides*) and shorthorn sculpins, with their blue or green blood serum, the serum of this species is clear. Burger et al. (2007) found that some great sculpins living around Adak Island (Aleutian Islands) had fairly high levels of some heavy metals.

Oligocottus maculosus
Girard, 1856
Tidepool Sculpin

Like the pestilence of multilingual puns in Finnegans Wake, *this is the über-dominant species in the intertidal of much of the northeast Pacific.*

ETYMOLOGY: *Oligocottus* is composed of two words "small" (in Greek) and "*Cottus*" and *maculosus* is Latin for "spotted."

THE BASICS: Maximum Length: 8.9 cm (4 in) TL. The Ranges: Pribilof Islands (southeastern Bering Sea); Shumagin Islands (western Gulf of Alaska) to Palos Verdes Peninsula (Southern California). They are very common from at least Cook Inlet (Gulf of Alaska) to the San Francisco area, and fairly abundant well into Central California. Intertidal and shallow rocky areas, including tide pools, but they have been observed down to the -9 m (-30 ft) level on a dock piling. Eggs: 1.1–1.5 mm. Larvae: hatching length = 4.2–4.5 mm, flexion length = 7.2–7.6 mm, transformation length = 0.8–1 cm. Age-length regressions are figured in Craik (1978). Length-weight parameters (SL, mm, gr): (sexes combined) W = $0.0000056L^{2.991}$ (Pierce and Pierson 1990).

SALIENT CHARACTERS: Tidepools have no scales—an excellent beginning. They have a single preopercular (cheek) spine and it is usually forked (but occasionally cleaved in thirds). In adult males, the first 3–4 rays of the anal fin are extra large. There are often 2–5 darker saddles or vertical bands on the body. And color? Ah, well there we have a problem, dontcha know? Tidepools can change their colors to match their backgrounds, so expect gray, green, brown to be common, along with stripes and speckles in white, tan, green, black etc. etc.

LIFE HISTORY: Larvae likely stay very close to shore, apparently often within a few meters of land. During this stage, larvae are very susceptible to being swept offshore by large waves (these create jets and other offshore-moving currents) and years with a lot of large waves in the spring are years with fewer young fish settling out. Settlement occurs 25–40 days after larvae hatch. Young-of-the-year (at maybe 1 cm, 0.4 in, SL) settle in small pools (often in June–August) in the upper intertidal and later migrate just a bit deeper throughout the intertidal and shallow subtidal. Tidepools are found in a wide range of habitats, including rocks, cobbles, coralline algae, eelgrass, mussels, and sand. These are tough little fish; they can live in nearly freshwater for a few days and in 7.5 ppt indefinitely. Fish larger than about 3 cm (1 in) TL begin to settle down in one or a few pools and by 5 cm (2 in) have developed the ability to home back to that site if displaced (as much as 100 m, 328 ft). Fish in calmer waters seem to become more attached to home pools than those in more turbulent areas. Interestingly, a tidepool sculpin's sense of smell seems to be a more important factor in homing than its sight. At low tide, they will sit out of the water in a damp place.

A high and semi-dry sculpin waits for the tide to come in. Greg Jensen thinks this is either a mosshead or bald sculpin.
DONNA MCCOY

Here is what Atkinson (1939) wrote of their mating behavior in an aquarium: "The males began to pursue the female in quick jerks or hops and by sudden movements of their pectoral fins. They appeared to keep their bodies well above the bottom of the tank by supporting themselves with rigid ventral fins and with the caudal peduncle. At times, the male would mount the female by placing one pectoral fin in the notch between her two dorsal fins. The posterior part of the body of the male curved upward slightly with the caudal fin expanded and rigid...After several seconds, the female would suddenly dart away and the male would either pursue her or fight the other male in the aquarium. Both males participated in the courting activity and on two occasions both mounted the female at the same time (one on each side)."

GREGORY JENSEN

Tidepool sculpins live about 5 years and females mature when about 1 year old and as small as 2.4 cm (0.9 in) SL. Growth rates vary between sites. Reproduction is thought to be by internal gametic association (see introduction to the Cottidae), although fertilized eggs have been found inside females, suggesting some internal fertilization. The spawning season varies between years and areas, but ranges from December–August, likely peaking in late winter and early spring. The eggs are green, bluish-green, red, or maroon, sometimes within the same egg clutch. Females that lay maroon eggs on exposed rocks in one year have laid green ones in captivity the following year. So what is that about? Eggs are deposited on rocks and other substrates, down to a depth of about 3 m (10 ft), and there is no parental care. Females spawn as many as 3 times per year, and clutch sizes range from 40–242 eggs. Tidepool sculpins really, really like gammarid amphipods, but they don't say no to isopods, harpacticoid copepods, polychaetes, shrimps, barnacles, and the occasional insect. Predators include smoothhead sculpins, blue herons, Steller sea lions, and probably river otters and minks.

RELATIONSHIPS: Tidepools are most closely related to fluffy and rosy sculpins.

MISCELLANY: Tidepool sculpins show an alarm response when they detect chemicals that come from the broken skin of other *O. maculosus*. Alarmed fish tend to hide, reduce their movements, and feed less.

REMARKS: Man, you do not want to be a tidepool sculpin. This species has been the subject of more experiments than any other. The number of fish that have been poked, prodded, tagged, dyed, observed, and for all I know, smoked, is just astronomical. It seems like every clueless undergraduate who can't think of any other summer project takes out his or her frustrations on tidepool sculpins.

BERNARD P. HANBY

Green one.

Oligocottus snyderi
Greeley, 1898
Fluffy Sculpin

ETYMOLOGY: *Oligocottus* is composed of two words "small" (in Greek) and "*Cottus*" and *snyderi* honors John Otterbein Snyder (1867–1943), a student of D.S. Jordan and C.H. Gilbert at Stanford. Snyder was eventually head of the Department of Zoology at Stanford. He worked extensively on salmon and steelhead, and was a major force in freshwater fisheries conservation.

THE BASICS: Maximum Length: 7.6 cm (3 in) SL, about 9.2 cm (4 in) TL. The Ranges: Chernabura Island (western Gulf of Alaska); Samsing Cove, near Sitka (southeastern Alaska) to Punta Cono (29°06'N, 114°42'W) (central Baja California). They are most common from about Vancouver Island to Central California, but appear to also be patchily abundant in southern California and northern Baja California. Tide pools and shallow rocky areas to 6 m (20 ft) or more. Eggs: 1.2–1.3 mm. Larvae: hatching length = 4.5 mm, flexion length = 6.2–8.4 mm, transformation length = 1.1–1.3 cm and perhaps smaller. Length-weight parameters (SL, mm, gr): (sexes combined) $W = 0.0000253L^{2.991}$ (Freeman et al. 1985).

SALIENT CHARACTERS: These are pretty little fish that usually come in red, lime-green, and grayish-green morphs (additional colors include orange, brown, and reddish green). They have smooth bodies without scales and prickles. Look for the forked preopercular (cheek) spine and the cirri along the base of the dorsal fin and along the lateral line. Fluffies seem to be able to change color.

LIFE HISTORY: Larvae drift in the plankton for 25–40 days before settling out in tide pools. Young-of-the-year settle (at as small as 0.7 cm SL, and often in June–August) to mid-intertidal tide pools and adults are common in the mid- and lower intertidal zone (and occasionally in the high intertidal and shallow subtidal). Fluffies prefer habitats with lots of rocks and cobbles, usually with algae or surfgrass cover, but they also can be found over sand. Older fish eventually find a pool or series of pools to park in and they can return back to this home from at least 76 m (250 ft) away. Fluffies are capable of breathing air at least for a short period.

Not green one.

Fluffies live for 2 years. Now, what I am about to tell you may not be proper for impressionable youths. So, if you are under 18 years old, please close your eyes. Are your eyes closed? Are you sure? Okay, for the adults in the audience, male fluffies have a well-developed clasping device and fertilization is internal (although whether this is an example of internal gametic association is, it appears, unknown. See the introduction to the Cottidae for more on IGA). Okay, you can open your eyes now. Spawning occurs throughout the year, but seems most intense in late winter and spring and varies with year and area. Females probably produce 2–4 clutches of red, orange, yellow, or green demersal eggs (eggs tend to be the color of the mother) per year. Wherever they live, gammarid amphipods are an important part of their diet. In addition, harpacticoid copepods, polychaetes, isopods, crabs, sipunculids, shrimps, hermit crabs, sea anemones, barnacle cirri, caprellid amphipods, snails, bivalves, bryozoans, beetles, and algae are eaten. Minks are likely one of their predators.

RELATIONSHIPS: Fluffies are closely related to rosy sculpins.

REMARKS: And this from Morris (1956), based on aquarium observations: "Copulation took place in an atmosphere of carefree promiscuity." *One assumes that is in opposition to "careworn promiscuity."*

Scorpaenichthys marmoratus

(Ayres, 1854)

Cabezon

A phlegmatic fish with barely enough qi to get by.

ETYMOLOGY AND COLLOQUIAL NAMES: *Scorpaenichthys* comes from the Greek for "Scorpaena" and "fish" and *marmoratus* is Latin for "marbled." The oldest reference to the name "cabezon" appears to come from a letter written in 1822 by Father José Señán, head of the Mission San Buenaventura in Southern California. When not complaining about the naughty Chumash Indian acolytes, or requesting more snuff, Father Señán wrote this about what

fish were caught for the Mission: "Near the [Channel] Islands many cabezón are caught. This too is an excellent fish, either fresh or dried." Cabezón (in various publications also called "cabezone" and "cabezona") is Spanish for "bigheaded." Other names include "blue cod" and (both still in the rotation) "bullhead" and "marbled sculpin."

THE BASICS: Maximum Length: 99 cm (39 in) TL. Maximum Weight: At least 11.5 kg (25.2 lb) and perhaps to 13.6 kg (30 lb). The Ranges: Southeastern Alaska (near Sitka) to Punta Abreojos (central Baja California). They are common from perhaps the Queen Charlotte Islands to Bahia Playa Maria (central Baja California). Larvae (but apparently no benthic juveniles or adults) have been collected from the western Gulf of Alaska east of Kodiak Island. Intertidal to 231 m (758 ft), commonly to perhaps 73 m (240 ft). Eggs: 1.4–1.9 mm. Larvae: hatching length = 4–6 mm, flexion length = 7.5–10 mm, transformation length = 1.4–1.5 cm (0.6 in). Von Bertalanffy parameters (TL, cm): (females, Oregon) L_∞ = 68.8, k = 0.2, t_0 = -2.26; (females, California) L_∞ = 61.5, k = 0.17, t_0 = -1.19; (males, Oregon) L_∞ = 59.1, k = 0.25, t_0 = -1.26; (males, California) L_∞ = 41.5, k = 0.45, t_0 = -1.22 (Cope and Punt 2005). Length-weight parameters (TL, cm, kg): (females, Northern California) W = $0.0000092L^{3.187}$; (females, Southern California) W = $0.00001236L^{3.113}$; (males, northern California) W = $0.00001163L^{3.118}$; (males, Southern California) W = $0.00001989L^{2.997}$ (Cope and Punt 2005).

SALIENT CHARACTERS: Cabezons are large, scaleless, brown, red, or green fish covered in darker mottlings. They have a skin flap on their snout and long, branched flaps over each eye. Juveniles are sometimes bright red. O'Connell (1953) found that almost all adult males were reddish and almost all adult females were greenish. On the other hand, some folks at the Oregon Department of Fish and Wildlife didn't see a sex-color relationship, so maybe the jury is out.

LIFE HISTORY: Young drift in the plankton for 3–4 months and slim and silvery young settle to tide pools, quieter shallow subtidal areas, and oil platforms at 3–5 cm (1–2 in) TL. In the Santa Barbara Channel, young-of-the-year settle March–August, mostly from April–July. Juveniles live from tide pool depths to at least 30.5 m (100 ft) around rocks, eelgrass, and attached and drift algae. While adults occasionally live in tide pools, most are found in somewhat deeper waters. And while mature fish are most abundant over rocks, in algae, and on the cross beams of oil platforms, they can be surprisingly common along rock-mud or cobble-mud interfaces. In Monterey, they have been found in densities as high as 41/hectare (16.6 fish/acre). Cabezons probably do not migrate long distances, although they do move into the intertidal as waters rise. John Stephens (1983) reported that fish in King Harbor (Southern California): "May undergo an offshore migration in Fall-Winter," although how far they might travel is anyone's guess. For management purposes, the federal government breaks the contiguous western states' population into 3 stocks: southern California, the rest of California, and Oregon. It is unclear how separate these "stocks" are. One genetic study (Villablanca and Nakamura 2008) came up with sufficiently opaque results that the Oracle at Delphi would have looked faintly puzzled. Cabezons are tolerant of somewhat brackish waters. Kim Mitchell reports that young ones are active at night.

Cabezons live to about 19 years old. After they mature, females are larger than males at any age. Generally, fish off Oregon are larger at age than those off California. A few females mature at about 32 cm (2 years), 50% at about 35 cm (3 years), and all at about 41 cm (7 years). Cabezons spawn throughout the year, with most of the effort in winter and spring; spawning may peak off California in January and February and in March–April in Puget Sound. Females are batch spawners (57,000–152,000 eggs per batch), producing white, pink, maroon, crimson, or blue-green adhesive eggs, which become olive as they mature. The adhesive eggs are laid in large masses (up to 46 cm, 18 in, in diameter, and 5 cm, 2 in, thick) on exposed rock surfaces and in crevices from tide pool depth down to at least 20 m (65 ft). These spawning areas may be used year after year. Males guard the nests, even hanging with them in the intertidal. In Puget Sound, fertilized eggs incubate from 25–49 days (averaging 34 days) before the eggs hatch. The eggs are toxic and even when exposed at low tide are not eaten by such likely predators as ravens, gulls, minks, and raccoons. Cabezons eat whatever lives near or on the bottom and fits in their mouths. Juveniles feed primarily on small crustaceans (e.g., copepods, isopods, gammarid amphipods, and mysid shrimps). Fish more than perhaps

30 cm (12 in) TL start to focus on larger crustaceans (crabs, hermit crabs, and lobsters), fishes, mollusks (abalone, limpets, chitons, clams, snails, nudibranchs, octopuses, and squids), polychaetes, and fish eggs. As an example, one 58.8 cm (24 in) fish contained one red Irish lord, several seaperch, 3 species of crabs, shrimps, and about half a pound of fish eggs. Predators include fishes (e.g., copper rockfish, coralline sculpins, sablefish, various salmon, steelhead, threespine sticklebacks, and white sharks), birds (e.g., bald eagles, cormorants, pigeon guillemots, rhinoceros auklets, and sooty shearwaters), harbor seals, river and sea otters.

FISHERY: Cabezons were commonly eaten by Native Americans and First Nation peoples all along the Pacific Coast, to at least as far southward as Isla Cedros (central Baja California). As an example, Swan (1868), commenting on the fish's importance to the Makah of the Cape Flattery (Washington) region notes: "The cottoids are very plenty and of several varieties, all of which are eaten. The largest, which is called tsa-daitch, measures twenty-seven inches in length. It is an uncouth, repulsive-looking fish, dark greenish-brown, the body larger in proportion to the head than other sculpins; but it is of good flavor, either boiled or fried." Parenthetically, "repulsive" and "uncouth" seem like rhetorical overkill, just the sort of salmon-centric thinking that seems to infect all who dwell in the Northwest. At worst, the cabezon is a species that appears to have taken up a Goth sensibility a little too intensely.

Cabezons were first mentioned by a European in Captain George Vancouver's journals, where he described fish caught in Puget Sound in 1792: "A large sort of sculpin, some weighing

The most optimistic cormorant in the world.   KAWIKA CHETRON

six or eight pounds, with a greenish colour about their throat, belly, and gills; these were very coarse, but no ill effects were consequent on eating them" (Pietsch and Dunn 1997). Early commercial fishermen, for instance those in late 19th-century San Diego, could not sell cabezons because of their funky appearance. Indeed, the species never found too much favor in commercial markets (it was always a small bycatch in the rockfish and lingcod fisheries) until the live fish fishery came along in the 1980s. The fishery went through the roof once folks caught onto the facts that 1) cabezons live through almost anything and 2) they taste great. Cabezons have always been a fairly popular recreational species. They are particularly avidly sought after by rocky shoreline anglers. Poke polers, in particular, catch pretty fair numbers.

REMARKS: Cabezons have toxic eggs; don't eat them. Carl Hubbs (Hubbs and Wick 1951) reported: "An unhappy gastronomic experience of the senior author and his wife...indicate rather definitely that there is some toxic constituent in the roe of the cabezon...On January 14, 1923...the senior author and his wife partook of the roe...The two who ate the eggs awoke in misery about four hours afterward and were violently ill throughout the rest of the night, with rapidly alternating chills and fever and with frequent vomiting and diarrhea." The toxin is a phospholipid called lipostichaerin that damages the liver. Interestingly, the same toxin is also found in *Stichaeus grigorjewi*, a prickleback found in the northwest Pacific.

And what's with that blue-colored skin and muscle? That flashy hue is caused by high levels of a bile pigment called biliverdin, which causes the blood serum of the fish to be blue-green (or occasionally purplish) and which also finds its way into the muscles. The source of this pigment (which is also found in a number of other sculpins) is unclear, although the most likely source is the breakdown of heme (as in hemoglobin) or other molecules called porphyrins. Why these fish should carry such a high concentration in their blood is unknown. Also possible is that the color comes from the fish's diet, as some invertebrates store bile pigments from the algae they eat. The levels of biliverdin found in cabezon blood serum are higher than those found in humans with jaundice and how these fish cope with nominally toxic levels of this material remains a mystery.

Arrgh, me smells a thesis here, matey.

Artedius corallinus

(Hubbs, 1926)

Coralline Sculpin

Coralline sculpins grow to 14 cm (6 in) TL and live from Orcas Island (Washington) to Isla San Martin (northern Baja California) in the lower intertidal and to 70 m (230 ft). They live in rocky areas, usually under boulders or in crevices. Fishes and some shrimps have been found in their stomachs. They are closely related to smoothhead sculpins.

Artedius notospilotus

Girard, 1856

Bonyhead Sculpin

Growing as large as 25.4 cm (10 in) TL, bonyheads range from Puget Sound to Punta Rocosa (28°45'N, 114°24'W) (central Baja California). They are rocky reef dwellers, found from the intertidal to depths of 52 m (170 ft). The few fish that have been examined had eaten crabs. Remains of bonyheads have been found in Late Pliocene deposits (at least 1.8 million years old) in California. Smoothhead sculpins are close relatives.

Clinocottus embryum

(Jordan & Starks, 1895)

Calico Sculpin

Calicos grow to 7 cm (3 in) TL and are found from Attu Island (Aleutian Islands) to Punta Banda (northern Baja California), commonly southward to at least Mendocino County (Northern California). Larvae are found in coastal waters, perhaps mostly 2–20 km (1–12 mi) from shore. Off Washington, larvae survive better (larval settlement is larger) in years when upwelling begins later in the spring. They live in the intertidal and shallow subtidal, typically in tide pools, among rocks, coralline algae, and shell fragments. The fish will home back to pools from as far away as 30 m (98 ft). Young-of-the-year settle from May–September, generally peaking in June. Calico sculpins feed on such small benthic and epibenthic organisms as gammarid amphipods, isopods, barnacle cirri, polychaetes, insects, copepods, and mollusks. They are most closely related to bald and mosshead sculpins. Larvae: hatching length = about 4 mm, flexion length = 6.4–9.6 mm, transformation length = 1.3–1.4 cm.

Clinocottus recalvus
(Greeley, 1899)
Bald Sculpin

Baldies grow to 13 cm (5 in) TL. They are found from Mill Beach (southern Oregon) to Punta Rompiente (central Baja California), are particularly common in Northern and Central California, and do make something of a showing in selected parts of southern California and northern Baja California. They live in the rocky intertidal and shallow subtidal. Fish about 9 cm (4 in) TL are 2 years old. Reproduction is through internal gametic association (see introduction to the Cottidae) and parents do not guard the eggs. Females spawn from March–August, probably peaking May–July. Eggs hatch in about 18 days at 16°C (61°F) and the larvae drift about for 25–40 days before settlement. Feeding heavily on diatoms, bald sculpins are mostly herbivorous. They also eat small crustaceans, sipunculids, sea urchin tube feet, and beetles. Bald sculpins are able to aerially respire. Wright and Raymond (1978) note that the fish can be seen "either with just their heads emerged, or totally emerged up to 10 cm [4 in] from the pool." Some individuals will stay out of water for at least 90 minutes, after which they gulp air, go underwater, and stay down for 1–3 minutes, then expel air through their gill openings, and repeat the cycle. Bald sculpins are most closely related to mosshead and calico sculpins. Eggs: 1.3–1.4 mm. Larvae: hatching length = 4.6–4.7 mm, flexion length = 6.5–9 mm, transformation length = 0.9–1 cm.

Enophrys diceraus
(Pallas, 1788)
Antlered Sculpin

CATHERINE W. MECKLENBURG

Antlered sculpins grow to 38 cm (15 in) TL and 760 gr (1.7 lb) and range from Japan and Okhotsk seas to the Commander–Aleutian chain, the Bering and Chukchi seas to Point Franklin (undocumented report further up to Point Barrow), and to Fort Tongass (southeastern Alaska). They are fairly common from perhaps the Chukchi Sea at least to Prince William Sound (northern Gulf of Alaska). These are rocky bottom dwellers, living at depths of 2–120 m (7–394 ft) and perhaps to 395 m (1,296 ft). Fish may mature at about 18 cm (7 in) TL, spawning takes place nearshore, and males guard nests. Spawning may occur anywhere from November–May (and maybe into July).

Antlered sculpins feed on small crustaceans (e.g., gammarid amphipods, small brachyuran crabs, and hermit crabs), small mollusks (e.g., limpets), green sea urchins, ctenophores, and brittle stars.

Gymnocanthus galeatus
Bean, 1881
Armorhead Sculpin

R. HIBPSHMAN

Armorheads grow to maybe 36 cm (14 in) TL. Females reach 1.2 kg (2.6 lb) and males 0.6 kg (1.3 lb). They range from the northern Japan Sea to the Bering Sea and to Wales Island (British Columbia). They appear to be common from the northern Kuril Islands and southeast Kamchatka to the eastern Bering Sea and Kodiak Island, and not unusual at least to southeastern Alaska. They are found from the nearshore to 579 m (1,900 ft), possibly to 625 m (2,050 ft), and typically at 50–165 m (164–541 ft). Juveniles are found in very shallow waters, mostly on bare bottom, occasionally in kelp beds, and in eelgrass. Adults live deeper than kids. Armorheads are able to tolerate at least mildly brackish waters. Off Kamchatka, they are found mostly in 0–4°C (32–39°F) and in Alaska in waters as warm as 5.5°C (42°F). Females live to 13 years and males to 11 years. Females grow larger than males and males mature when somewhat smaller than females. Off Kamchatka, they spawn at least during December, in 1.1–1.5°C (34–35°F), on sandy-gravel bottoms. Females produce between 12,000–48,000 eggs. Armorheads feed on benthic and epibenthic prey, including gammarid amphipods, polychaetes, echiuroids, sea anemones, isopods, bivalves, fishes, copepods, larvaceans, brittle stars, shrimps, ascidians, and sipunculids. Predators include great sculpins, Pacific cod, Pacific halibut, red Irish lords, and bald eagles. Bean (1887b) reported that this species was caught and consumed by folks on Unalaska Island. Currently, there is no commercial fishery for them, although they are taken as bycatch in Russian flatfish and cod trawl fisheries. Mean lengths at age are given in Tokranov (1988). Length-weight parameters (FL, cm, gr): (sexes combined) $W = 0.005726L^{3.1958}$ (Tokranov 1988).

Gymnocanthus pistilliger
(Pallas, 1814)
Threaded Sculpin

This species reaches 31 cm (12 in) TL and 240 g (0.5 lb). They live in the Seas of Japan and Okhotsk to the Aleutian Islands and Bering Sea (to Port Clarence) and to Oliver Inlet, Stephens Passage (southeastern Alaska) and commonly from at least the seas of Japan and Okhotsk to the eastern Bering Sea (and perhaps even as far north as Port Clarence) and to Kodiak Island. They inhabit shallow waters (including tide pools) and have been reported to 456 m (1,496 ft); in the northeastern Pacific and Bering Sea, mostly in 100 m (328 ft)

Female

and less. Threaded sculpins live over sand and mud. Around Kodiak Island, juveniles settle in June, when at least as small as 2 cm (0.8 in) FL. At least off Russia, these sculpins migrate inshore during the spring and offshore in the fall. Jerry Hoff (2000) found that in a June survey females tended to be mostly in the shallower parts of the species' range and might migrate to

deeper waters in late winter or spring, although probably to not much deeper than 50 m (164 ft). While they have been found from -1.5–12°C (29–54°F), it appears that perhaps 8°C (46°F) is as warm as they usually tolerate. In the eastern Bering Sea, they live to at least 10 years old and females grow faster than males. Off Kamchatka, this species lives to 13 years old. Males reportedly mature earlier than females. Three mature males collected around Kodiak Island were 16–20 cm (6–8 in) TL. Off Kamchatka, threaded sculpins spawn in December–January; while around Kodiak Island, ripe individuals have been found during March. Females produce between 5,000–41,000 eggs, the eggs are adhesive and, off Kamchatka, fish spawn over sandy bottoms at temperatures of 1–1.2°C (34°F). Threaded sculpins feed on a broad range of benthic and epibenthic

Male

animals although polychaetes, mysid shrimps, and echiuroids, shrimps, and fishes are often most important. Predators include great sculpins and Steller sea lions. Von Bertalanffy parameters (TL, mm): (females) $L_\infty = 223.8$, $k = 0.228$, $t_0 = -0.23$; (males) $L_\infty = 165.5$, $k = 0.375$, $t_0 = -0.07$ (Hoff 2000). Length-weight parameters (TL, mm, gr): (sexes combined) $W = 0.0000024L^{3.307}$ (Hoff 2000).

Hemilepidotus jordani
Bean, 1881
Yellow Irish Lord

Yellows grow to about 52 cm (21 in) TL, at least 2.4 kg (5.3 lb), and are found from the Okhotsk Sea off Hokkaido to the Commander–Aleutian chain, Bering Sea to Bering Strait and to Port Conclusion (southeastern Alaska). They are most abundant westward from the Kodiak Island-Cook Inlet area. Young-of-the-year settle to nearshore waters in summer and fall when no larger than 3 cm (1 in) TL. A shallow-water and nearshore species, they live in tide pools (juveniles) to a depth of 917 m (3,008 ft), mostly at less than 150 m

CATHERINE W. MECKLENBURG

(492 ft), and over a wide range of habitats. Yellows live in waters of -1.5–10°C (29.3–50°F), mostly at 0–8°C (32–46°F), and they will inhabit slightly estuarine waters. Over the years, there has been a slow northward distribution shift of this species in the southeastern Bering Sea. These fish live to at least 28 years; a few mature at 28 cm (11 in) TL (4 years), 50% at about 36 cm (14 in) (6 years), and all at 40 cm (16 in) (8 years). Fish make inshore spawning migrations to shallow waters in the summer. In Russian waters, they spawn in August and September, and around Kodiak Island, in June–August. The bright green to yellow eggs are demersal and adhesive, and attached to rocks. Fecundity is 25,000–241,000 eggs. On their spawning grounds, a male is territorial during the spawning season and may guard fertilized eggs produced from more than one female. Males appear to eat large quantities of the eggs they are guarding. Yellow Irish lords have very broad diets that vary with location. Important prey include crabs, fishes, fish eggs, brittle stars, hermit crabs, medusae, sea anemones, polychaetes, snails, clams, squids, octopuses, isopods, amphipods, euphausiids, and sea stars. Historically, YILs were eaten by various indigenous peoples (and are still important in places like the Aleutian Islands); there is one report of a developing commercial fishery for them off Kamchatka. The species is sexually dimorphic; the body and fins of males are brighter than the females' and they are deep brown in males, while green-gray in females. Males have numerous regular dots on the abdomen.

Hemilepidotus spinosus
Ayres, 1854
Brown Irish Lord

BERNARD P. HANBY

Brown Irish lords reach 33 cm (13 in) TL and are found from the southern Bering Sea to Santa Barbara Island, and on the mainland to Ventura (Southern California). They appear to be common as far south as Central California. They live from tide pools (rarely) to at least 131 m (430 ft) and perhaps to 151 m (495 ft). This is a rock dweller. A 21 cm (8 in) SL fish was 7 years old. Spawning may occur at least at low levels throughout the year, with a likely peak in winter and spring. Brown Irish lords eat crustaceans (crabs, hermit crabs, isopods, and gammarid amphipods), octopuses, polychaetes, fishes, and snails. They are occasionally caught from vessels and piers. Larvae: hatching length = about 5 mm, flexion length = 7.6–10.1 mm, transformation length = about 1.9 cm (0.7 in). Burge and Schultz (1973) have some age-length data. Length-weight parameters (TL, mm, kg): (sexes combined) W = 0.0000000358L$^{2.9}$ (RecFin 2009).

Icelinus borealis

Gilbert, 1896

Northern Sculpin

Northern sculpins reach a length of 11.4 cm (5 in) TL and range from the Pribilof Islands and Bristol Bay (eastern Bering Sea) and Attu Island (Aleutian Islands) to southern Puget Sound, at depths of 2–450 m (7–1,476 ft). This is a benthic species whose juveniles and adults live over both rock and gravel, amid aquatic vegetation (particularly eelgrass), and occasionally on mud. In at least a few areas, such as along southeastern Alaska, northern sculpins

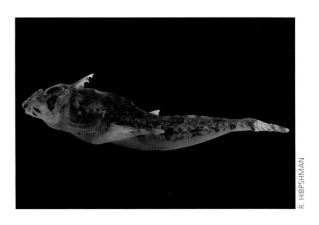

are very abundant in barely subtidal waters. They are tolerant of slightly estuarine conditions. Northerns feed on a range of benthic and epibenthic organisms, such as gammarid amphipods, harpacticoid copepods, shrimps, crabs, mysid shrimps, and polychaetes. Predators include Pacific cod, Pacific halibut, and pelagic cormorants.

Icelinus filamentosus

Gilbert, 1890

Threadfin Sculpin

Threadfins grow to 27 cm (11 in) TL and have been found from near Chirikof Island (western Gulf of Alaska) to Cortes Bank and Point Loma (Southern California). They live on mud or mud-pebble bottoms, at depths of 18–421 m (60–1,381 ft), and perhaps to 1,201 m (3,940 ft). In Southern California, we tend to see them in 160–265 m (525–869 ft).

DIANE O'LEARY

GREGORY JENSEN

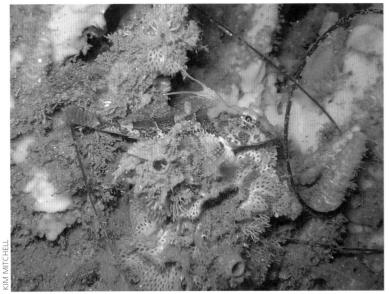

KIM MITCHELL

Icelinus tenuis
Gilbert, 1890
Spotfin Sculpin

Spotfins grow to 15.9 cm (6 in) TL and are found from near Ketchikan and west of Noyes Island (55°24'N, 134°48'W) (southeastern Alaska) to the Islas San Benito (central Baja California). They appear to be common as far south as northern Baja California. Spotfins live at depths of 7–373 m (23–1,224 ft), mostly in maybe 60–100 m (197–328 ft). A 13.3 cm (5 in) TL fish I aged was 2 years old. We see them on coarse sand, shells, and small rocks where they feed on benthic and epibenthic organisms (e.g., amphipods, polychaetes, clam siphons, shrimps, isopods, cumaceans, and small fishes). They spawn at least in April.

Leiocottus hirundo
Girard, 1856
Lavender Sculpin

Lavender sculpins grow to 25.4 cm (10 in) TL. They are found from Gaviota (Southern California) to Punta Banda (northern Baja California), and in 2–37 m (8–120 ft), perhaps most often at 3–21 m (10–70 ft). You usually see them resting immobile on sand, and near rocks, eelgrass, and algae. Various benthic prey, including gammarid amphipods, polychaetes, clams, sea cucumbers, and snails are consumed and feeding occurs during both day and night. Their blood serum is lavender- to wine-colored and appears to contain a red chromoprotein that may be a breakdown product of heme or other porphyrins. Lavenders may be most closely related to woolly sculpins.

MARC CHAMBERLAIN

Megalocottus platycephalus
(Pallas, 1814)
Belligerent Sculpin

Belligerents grow to 42 cm (17 in) TL and 1.1 kg (2.4 lb), and are found from Peter the Great Bay to the Okhotsk Sea, in the western Bering Sea to the Chukchi Sea off the Chukchi Peninsula and Point Barrow, and south to Herendeen Bay (eastern Bering Sea). This is a nearshore species that often enters the lower reaches of rivers and lives down to depths of 30 m (98 ft). Smaller belligerents feed on algae, copepods, cumaceans, amphipods, and mysid shrimps; larger

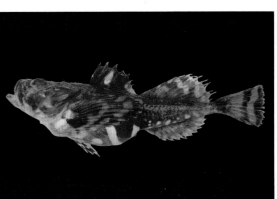

JAMES W. ORR, ALASKA FISHERIES SCIENCE CENTER

ones add small fishes to this diet. Both Bean (1887b) and Turner (1886) note that this species was an important food fish for Inupiats. Turner states: "The Eskimo prize the flesh very highly, though they have so many subcutaneous parasites that I could not induce myself to touch the flesh."

Myoxocephalus jaok
(Cuvier, 1829)
Plain Sculpin

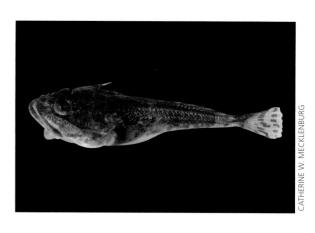

This species reaches a respectable 70 cm (28 in) TL and at least
8 kg (17.6 lb). They range from the Japan and Okhotsk seas, to the
eastern Chukchi Sea (at least as far north as Point Belcher), to the
eastern Gulf of Alaska at Limestone Inlet and Glacier Bay. They are
common from eastern Sakhalin Island and the Bering Sea (at least
as far north as Norton Sound) to at least as far east as the Kodiak
Island–Cook Inlet area. Small ones occupy the intertidal zone and
adults are found down to 680 m (2,231 ft). Young-of-the-year settle out of the plankton in shallow waters at as small as 1.3 cm
(0.5 in) SL. Juveniles and adults live mostly on soft seafloors. This species must occasionally pack in pretty tightly, with a ton
or more taken per hour of trawling. Plain sculpins are found from less than -1.5–12°C (29–54°F). Fish in the western Pacific
(and, who knows, maybe throughout their range) migrate into shallow waters in the summer and retreat to the deeper shelf
and upper slope for the winter. For instance, off western Kamchatka, plain sculpins live mostly at depths less than 50 m (164
ft) during the summer and in 150–400 m (492–1,312 ft) in the winter. Females (15 years) live longer than males (12 years). In
Asia, females grow faster than males. Is this true in good ol' North America? Only time, and some hapless graduate student,
will tell. A few males mature in the fourth year of life and most are mature by Age 6. A few females are mature in their sixth
and most by their eighth year. On the Asian side, plain sculpins spawn from December–March in shallow waters. Males guard
eggs that have been laid on mussels and algae, larvae hatch in April, and settlement occurs around June. Off Kodiak Island,
larvae have been found from April–June and recruits noted as early as May. Plain sculpins feed more heavily in summer than
in winter. This species eats a wide variety of organisms and crustaceans (e.g., crabs, shrimps, gammarid amphipods, and
hermit crabs), fishes, cephalopods, brittle stars, sea urchins, snails, and fish eggs dominate their diets. Predators include great
sculpins and probably river otters. Both Bean (1887b) and Turner (1886) noted that they were commonly eaten by the folks
who lived in the eastern Bering Sea. Turner wrote: "They are caught principally by the old women and men who are not able
to go great distances to procure other food." You can cob together a growth pattern from a table in Panchenko (2002).

Myoxocephalus scorpius
(Linnaeus, 1758)
Shorthorn Sculpin

Shorthorns grow to 90 cm (35.4 in) TL and are circumpolar in their
geographic range. In our area, they are found in the Chukchi (where
they are abundant) through Bering seas, the Commander–Aleutian
chain to Kamchatka Bay (Russia), and to northern British Columbia,
in the intertidal to 550 m (1,804 ft), but mostly in 70 m (230 ft)
and less. You will find them on a range of substrates, from soft and
muddy to rocky and vegetated. Their maximum age is 15 years.
Females grow larger than males. Ages at 50% maturity are 5 years
for males (around 30 cm, 12 in, TL) and about 6 years for females
(about 35 cm, 14 in). They spawn in November and December (and perhaps into early spring) in shallow water; females go
deeper after spawning, and then return in late spring. Males guard eggs that have been spawned on rocks and may spawn
with more than one female. Females produce 4,000–6,100 eggs. At 0°C (32°F) the eggs hatch in 3 months and both larvae and
younger juveniles are pelagic. Shorthorns eat almost anything that is available, either on the bottom or in the water column.
Prey includes fishes, crabs, gammarid amphipods, shrimps, snails, polychaetes, clams, sea urchins, brittle stars, and sea cucumbers.

Oligocottus rimensis
(Greeley, 1899)
Saddleback Sculpin

Saddlebacks grow to 6.5 cm (3 in) TL and range from Kakul Narrows (southeastern Alaska) to northern Baja California (typically southward to Central California). They inhabit rocky tide pools and the rocky subtidal, as well as eelgrass and algal beds down to 8 m (26 ft). Saddlebacks feed on gammarid and caprellid amphipods, harpacticoid copepods, isopods, and polychaetes. Saddlebacks are most closely related to other species in the genus *Oligocottus* and perhaps also to snubnose sculpins.

PHIL EDGELL

Oligocottus rubellio
(Greeley, 1899)
Rosy Sculpin

Rosies grow to 10 cm (4 in) TL and range from Fort Bragg (Northern California) to Punta Baja (northern Baja California) (mostly as far southward as northern Baja California), from lower intertidal tide pools to depths of about 6 m (20 ft). Rosies feed on a variety of small organisms, including gammarid amphipods, hermit crabs, polychaetes, brachyuran crabs, shrimps, and occasionally algae. Fluffy sculpins are close relatives.

CHRIS GROSSMAN

Orthonopias triacis
Starks & Mann, 1911
Snubnose Sculpin

Snubnoses grow to 9.6 cm (4 in) TL and are found from Solander Island (northwest Vancouver Island) to Bahia Tortugas (27°38'N, 114°51'W) (southern Baja California), and are apparently abundant at least from Central California to northern Baja California. They live from the intertidal to 30 m (100 ft), typically in 5–21 m (15–70 ft). Snubnoses prefer algae-covered rocks, where they tend to sit motionless. A 7.6 cm (3 in) SL fish was 2 years old. The smallest mature female in one study was 4.4 cm (2 in) SL. Spawning may occur throughout the year, likely with a winter or spring peak. The eggs are adhesive and range from colorless to pale yellow or pinkish-brown. Females are batch spawners, each batch containing 124–194 eggs. Eggs are laid on the bottom and parents probably do not guard them. Like most other nearshore sculpins, snubnoses really fancy gammarid amphipods, but also dig polychaetes, snails, caprellid amphipods, shrimps, ostracods, copepods, pycnogonids, pelecypods, and algae. Genetic analyses imply that this species is closely related to members of the genus *Oligocottus* and should probably be in that genus. Eggs: 0.9–1.1 mm. Larvae: hatching length = 2.9–3.8 mm, flexion length = 4.2–4.7 mm, transformation length = between about 9.2 and 1.3 mm. Length-weight parameters (TL, mm, gr): (sexes combined) W = $0.0000258L^{3.011}$ (Burge and Schultz 1973).

Ruscarius creaseri
(Hubbs, 1926)
Roughcheek Sculpin

Roughcheeks grow to 7.6 cm (3 in) TL and range from Carmel Bay (Central California) to Punta San Pablo, Islas San Benito, and Isla Cedros (central Baja California). They are abundant from Southern California to about Isla San Martin (central Baja California). Roughcheeks live on rocks, from the intertidal to a depth of 27 m (90 ft), but they are most abundant in perhaps 6–15 m (20–50 ft) of water. A 5.5 cm (2.2 in) SL fish was 2 years old. Females as small as 3.8 cm (1.5 in) TL are mature. Spawning seems to take place from about January–July. The few fish that have been examined had eaten shrimps. Roughcheeks are most closely related to Puget Sound sculpins.

Ruscarius meanyi
Jordan & Starks, 1895
Puget Sound Sculpin

This species grows to 5.9 cm (2 in) TL and has been found from Fillmore Island (southeastern Alaska) to Arena Cove (Northern California). However, its larvae have been collected from the eastern Aleutian Islands and western Gulf of Alaska, suggesting a wider distribution of adults. They live in rocky areas in the intertidal and subtidal, at depths of 1.5–82 m (5–269 ft). Puget Sounds feed on such items as gammarid amphipods, isopods, crabs, snails, and lingcod eggs. Roughcheek sculpins are their nearest genetic neighbors.

EDMOND STEPHEN MEANY

Meanyi honors Edmond Stephen Meany (1862–1935). Meany was an historian, writer, state legislator, and professor at the University of Washington. In 1879, Meany was also a founding member of the Young Naturalists Society of Seattle. The Society met in the home of young naturalist, and later rich guy, Charles Latimer Denny (1861–1919). Some of the early papers read at the society's gatherings were…well, kind of primitive. Here is part of one written early on by member Jesse O. Young (1863–1923) titled "Woman": "Woman was created from the ribs of a young man by the name of Adam. This division took place some six thousand years ago, that is as far as we are able to trace back. The first few years of her life was [sic] spent in comparative seclusion. The first event of any importance that happened to this young woman, Eve by name, was the memorable encounter with the Devil in the Garden of Eden" (Pietsch and Dunn 1997). On the other hand, the young gentlemen (and, somewhat thereafter, young ladies) turned out to be spot-on in collecting fishes and other curiosities in Puget Sound, and wound up with a substantial collection, a collection that eventually served as a basis for the Burke Museum on the UW campus.

Synchirus gilli
Bean, 1890
Manacled Sculpin

Manacleds reach a length of 6.9 cm (3 in) TL. They range from Unalaska Island (Aleutian Islands) to San Miguel Island, from the intertidal to depths of 14 m (46 ft) or more. Not a lot is known about this interesting little fish. They settle out of the plankton when at least as small as 1.2 cm (0.5 in) SL in shallow subtidal waters. Juveniles and adults usually cling to all kinds of aquatic vegetation. You can find these fish all the way from near-surface waters to right next to the bottom, at temperatures at least as cold as 6.2°C (43°F). They spawn at least in July and August, the eggs are pink, and apparently they are laid on plant material. Jeff Marliave (1986) found their larvae within a few meters of the British Columbia shoreline. In one study, manacled sculpins ate mostly harpacticoid copepods, along with lesser amounts of mysid shrimps and amphipods. Predators include kelp and rock greenlings. Larvae: hatching length = less than 5.2 mm, flexion length = 6.5–8.5 mm, transformation length = about 1.7 cm. Of particular interest are the pectoral fins that are joined. The males grip the females using their pelvic fins and their lower jaw. Krejsa (1964) reported: "There is a definite symphyseal pad on the lower jaw. This pad plus the very notice-able wrinkling of the skin in the hyoid [throat] region of the open-mouthed male probably serves as a nonskid device when holding the female." Krejsa went on to note that a male that was forcibly separated from a mating pair tried to mate with his right index finger, a behavior many of us can relate to.

DAVE WASHBURN

FAMILY HEMITRIPTERIDAE— Sailfin Sculpins or Sea Raven

The hemitripterids are benthic, marine fishes that live in the North Pacific and Northwest Atlantic. There are three genera, eight or more species, and seven species live within our range. A fossil species, *Hemitripterella granulata*, is known from the Miocene (at least 5.3 million years ago) of Sakhalin Island.

Blepsias cirrhosus
(Pallas, 1814)
Silverspotted Sculpin

What happens when Evolution takes up netsuke.

ETYMOLOGY AND COLLOQUIAL NAMES: *Blepsias* is derived from the Greek word for "look," apparently in reference to an old fish name, although Cuvier (who coined the name) was kind of coy about this. *Cirrhosus* means "bearing cirri" in Latin. The Russians and Japanese call this the "littledragon sculpin" ("isobatengu" in Japanese), a very nice name, indeed.

THE BASICS: Maximum Length: 20 cm (8 in) SL. The Ranges: Okhotsk and Japan seas to western Bering Sea near Cape Olyutorskiy (59°44'N, 170°20'E), Commander–Aleutian chain and Pribilof Islands (Bering Sea) to San Simeon (Central California). Common from the Sea of Japan to Kuril Islands and eastward to the eastern Bering Sea and to Central California. Intertidal to 95 m (312 ft), mostly in the nearshore, but reported common to perhaps 60 m (197 ft) in the Sea of Japan. Eggs: 3–4 mm. Larvae: flexion length = less than 11 mm. Length-weight parameters (TL, cm, gr): (mostly females) $W = 0.000005L^{3.1454}$ (Kolpakov and Dolganova 2006).

SALIENT CHARACTERS: Gee, this is just a precious little species. Silverspotteds are compressed, have a high and deeply notched dorsal fin, and a number of little doodads hanging off their face. Body colors range from browns (that is the color I usually see them) to greenish with reddish or yellow bellies, and silvery marks on the flanks and fins. Kolpakov and Dolganov (2006) report that, in the western Pacific, females turn red-brown or purple with a bright yellow abdomen during the breeding season.

LIFE HISTORY: Young-of-the-year settle at 2.1 cm (0.8 in) SL or smaller. Juveniles and adults live primarily in the subtidal, but are occasionally found in tide pools. They are particularly common over rocks, cobble, eelgrass, and kelp, often on the boundary between hard and soft substrata. Belying their appearance, this species frequently swims in midwaters or near the surface. Silverspotteds are probably nocturnal. In the Sea of Japan, this sculpin reportedly migrates into shallow waters in the spring (occasionally into tide pools), then migrates in the fall into depths of 30–40 m (98–131 ft). They can tolerate brackish waters and around Kodiak Island they were taken at temperatures as cold as 1.4°C (35°F).

Silverspotteds live to 6 years old. Their spawning remains clouded in confusion. Off Japan and Russia, they spawn in June and July. On the other hand, Jeff Marliave (1975) reports taking larvae off British Columbia from February–April, and Hart

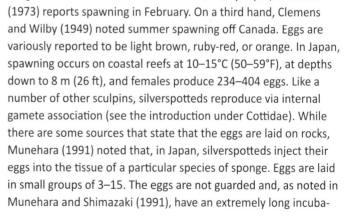

A young one.

(1973) reports spawning in February. On a third hand, Clemens and Wilby (1949) noted summer spawning off Canada. Eggs are variously reported to be light brown, ruby-red, or orange. In Japan, spawning occurs on coastal reefs at 10–15°C (50–59°F), at depths down to 8 m (26 ft), and females produce 234–404 eggs. Like a number of other sculpins, silverspotteds reproduce via internal gamete association (see the introduction under Cottidae). While there are some sources that state that the eggs are laid on rocks, Munehara (1991) noted that, in Japan, silverspotteds inject their eggs into the tissue of a particular species of sponge. Eggs are laid in small groups of 3–15. The eggs are not guarded and, as noted in Munehara and Shimazaki (1991), have an extremely long incubation time. So putting them inside sponges: 1) puts them in something almost inedible to other organisms, 2) the antibacterial and antifungal agents in the sponge probably protects them against infections, and 3) there is a rich source of oxygenated water. From the sponge's perspective, however, this fascinating behavior is faintly irritating, as its tissue seems to be somewhat damaged in the process. Once laid, fertilized eggs take a mind-boggling long time to hatch; apparently about 200 days in the laboratory and 250 or more days in the sea (at 10–11°C, 50–52°F). Silverspotteds feed mostly on epibenthic, and occasionally midwater, crustaceans, particularly gammarid, caprellid, and hyperiid amphipods, isopods, shrimps, euphausiids, and mysid shrimps, along with polychaetes and small fishes. Predators include Dolly Vardens and rock greenlings, along with Aleutian and Arctic terns.

Nautichthys oculofasciatus
(Girard, 1858)
Sailfin Sculpin

ETYMOLOGY: *Nautichthys* is Greek for "sailor" and "fish" (referring to the high dorsal fin) and *oculofasciatus* is Latin for "eye" and "banded."

THE BASICS: Maximum Length: 20.3 cm (8 in) TL. The Ranges: Kodiak Island to San Miguel Island. Common from at least Cook Inlet (Gulf of Alaska) to Central California. Duane Stevenson reports that there is one record of a specimen being taken from the eastern Bering Sea (at 57°N, 169°W), but that this fish was not retained and thus its identity cannot be confirmed. Intertidal to 110 m (360 ft), but mostly subtidal. Eggs: 2–2.5 mm. Larvae: hatching length = 9 mm, flexion length = about 9–11 mm, transformation length = 1.8–2.5 cm (0.7–1 in). Length-weight parameters (TL, mm, gr): (sexes combined) W = $0.000112L^{2.7137}$ (Burge and Schultz 1973).

SALIENT CHARACTERS: A very, very high first 4–5 rays of the first dorsal fin and a dark band through the eye and on to the cheek are good things to look for. Sailfins can be brown or silvery, usually with black blotches somewhere about.

LIFE HISTORY: Sailfin biology remains mostly unplumbed. Young-of-the-year settle when at least as small as 2.3 cm (0.9 in) SL. These are nocturnal and benthic fish, that usually live on rocky reefs, and in kelp and eelgrass beds. Underwater observations imply they spend most of their time hidden away under algae or in caves and crevices, including caves occupied by giant Pacific octopuses or wolf-eels. They can tolerate slightly estuarine conditions.

At least some sailfins spawn in the intertidal from January–May. Eggs are red or orange and laid on the undersides of rocks and there is no parental care. Jeff Marliaeve (2003) described their reproduction as internal gametic association (see introduction to the Cottidae) and went on to write: "Extrude...eggs into interstitial spaces among mussels in the intertidal over a period of weeks during winter. The female must migrate into shallow water during high tides in order to reach the mussel beds, where the eggs are periodically exposed to air but are kept cool and damp by the mussels." Limited information on diet suggests they eat fishes, crabs, and fish eggs. Predators include cabezons, pigeon guillemots, and tufted puffins.

DIANE O'LEARY

GREGORY JENSEN

Hemitripterus bolini
(Myers, 1934)

Bigmouth Sculpin

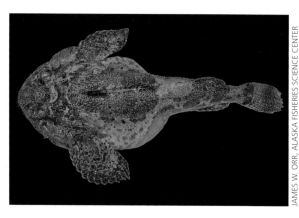

Bigmouths grow to 78 cm (31 in) TL, 12.4 kg (27.3 lb), and are found from the eastern Sea of Okhotsk and the northern Kuril Islands to the Commander–Aleutian chain, the Bering Sea to Cape Navarin, to the north side of the Alaska Peninsula, to Eureka (Northern California); commonly to at least southeastern Alaska. This sculpin lives on soft seafloors, in depths of 25–925 m (82–3,034 ft). In the eastern Bering Sea, they seem to be most abundant in perhaps 300–600 m (984–1,968 ft). They have been taken in waters between -0.2 and 8.5°C (32–47°F). Researchers have noted a northward distribution shift in the southeastern Bering Sea. Juveniles sometimes ascend into the water column at night. Bigmouth sculpin diets tend to lean toward fishes, squids, shrimps, hermit crabs, and clams. Length-weight parameters (TL, cm, gr): (sexes combined) $W = 0.0118L^{3.11}$ (Orlov and Binohlan 2009).

FAMILY PSYCHROLUTIDAE—Blob Sculpins or Fathead Sculpins

Fishes in the Psychrolutidae tend to be kind of flabby, benthic, and marine fishes, found in colder waters throughout the world. There are perhaps eight genera and 29 species, and nine species live within our range. Psychrolutids are oviparous and produce demersal eggs that are guarded by adults. Check out Mecklenburg (2002) for the descriptions of, and keys too, the North Pacific species.

Psychrolutes phrictus
Stein & Bond, 1978

Giant Blobsculpin

ETYMOLOGY AND COLLOQUIAL NAME: *Psychrolutes* means "one who bathes in cold water" in Greek and *phrictus* comes from a Greek word for "causing one to shudder," from the rather ungainly appearance of this species. In Japanese, these are called "nyudo-kajika."

THE BASICS: Maximum Length: About 70 cm (28 in) TL. Maximum Weight: 9.5 kg (21 lb). The Ranges: Okhotsk Sea and Pacific side of Honshu, to Commander Islands and western Bering Sea north to Cape Navarin, to eastern Bering Sea, to off San Diego. At depths of 366–2,800 m (1,200–9,186 ft). Larvae: flexion length = about 8 mm, transformation length = larger than 1.4 and smaller than 2.6 cm (0.6–1 in).

SALIENT CHARACTERS: Goodness, but they are blobby. You pick them up and they kind of melt in your hand, like some great, gray M&M that had gone horribly, horribly wrong. They have big heads, thick skin, an almost ovoid body, a spinous dorsal fin buried in flesh, and small cirri scattered over the whole.

LIFE HISTORY: Juveniles are caught thousands of meters off the bottom and probably settle to the bottom at about 3 cm (1 in) SL. Several benthic individuals were caught in waters of 3.4°C (38°F). Apparently females grow larger than males. Drazen et al. (2003) making observations in Monterey Bay, saw giant blobsculpin nests (containing an estimated 9,375–108,125 eggs) in August on flat exposed surfaces of boulders in cold seep areas. The eggs were pink and were guarded by adults (gender unknown) that sometimes lay on the eggs. The nests were often within 1–2 m (3–7 ft) of each other and were sometimes positioned in close association with the octopus *Graneledones* sp. Giant blobsculpins feed on a variety of benthic organisms including sea pens, crabs, snails, fishes, hermit crabs, sea cucumbers, and crinoids.

MBNMS

Dasycottus setiger

Bean, 1890

Spinyhead Sculpin

Spinyheads grow to at least 73 cm (29 in) TL and 1.6 kg (3.5 lb). They range from the seas of Japan and Okhotsk, and the Pacific coast of northern Honshu, to the Bering Sea at Navarin Canyon, and to Washington (commonly from the Sea of Japan to the eastern Bering Sea, and to at least Dixon Entrance, Alaska–British Columbia border). They live on the bottom at depths of 15–850 m (49–2,789 ft), most in less than 800 m (2,624 ft). Off southeastern Kamchatka and the northern Kuril Islands, young fish are found mainly in the deeper part of the species' depth range. Spinyheads live in waters of -0.6°C to at least 6.1°C (31–43°F) on sand, silt, and, at least occasionally, rocks. Larvae have been taken between April–July. Spinyhead sculpins simply dote on shrimps. Along with these crustaceans, they also consume crabs, mysid shrimps, gammarid and hyperiid amphipods, isopods, polychaetes, brittle stars, bivalves, and, fairly frequently, fishes. They are eaten by flathead soles, great sculpins, Greenland halibut, Kamchatka flounder, Pacific cod, and sablefish. Larvae: flexion length = about 10 mm. Length-weight parameters (TL, cm, gr): (sexes combined) $W = 0.0104L^{3.13}$ (Orlov and Binohlan 2009).

Malacocottus zonurus

Bean, 1890

Darkfin Sculpin

Darkfins grow to be 39 cm (15 in) TL and at least 1.2 kg (2.6 lb). They live from the seas of Japan and Okhotsk, to the Commander– Aleutian chain, and Bering Sea (to Cape Navarin) to Washington. They have also been reported from northern Oregon (45°03'N). They are common from the Sea of Japan to the eastern Bering Sea and to at least as far south as Dixon Entrance (Alaska-British Columbia border). Darkfins live at depths of 27–1,980 m (89–6,496 ft). Based on very limited visual observations, and from trawl studies, darkfins live over both soft and hard bottoms, at temperatures of

STAN KOTWICKI, ALASKA FISHERIES SCIENCE CENTER

less than 0 to 4.3°C (32–40°F). Off Kamchatka, younger fish are found mainly in the deepest part of the depth range. Here, in the spring and summer, most fish are on the lower shelf and upper slope (160–300 m, 525–984 ft). Beginning in September, they migrate into deeper waters, and by November and December, they tend to be in 300–470 m (984–1,542 ft). Females may grow larger than males. In general, polychaetes are the most important prey. Other frequently eaten animals include crustaceans (e.g., crabs, euphausiids, isopods, mysid shrimps, amphipods, hermit crabs, and shrimps), brittle stars, snails, sea cucumbers, squids, comb jellies, bivalves, and fishes. Predators include broadfin thornyheads, various flatfishes, Pacific cod, Pacific sleeper sharks, sablefish, shortraker rockfish, various skates, and walleye pollock.

GREGORY JENSEN

Psychrolutes paradoxus
Günther, 1861
Tadpole Sculpin

Tadpoles grow to 7 cm (3 in) TL. They range from the seas of Okhotsk and Japan to Norton Sound (Bering Sea) and to Puget Sound and commonly at least from the Sea of Japan and Sakhalin Island to the eastern Bering Sea. You find them at depths of 3–240 m (10–787 ft). Young-of-the-year settle into nearshore waters at about 1.3 cm (0.5 in) TL. Juveniles and adults are often found in eelgrass beds, sometimes on mud, and, on occasion, in kelp beds. Juveniles reportedly rise up in the water column at night. In deeper waters, adults have been seen on mud bottoms. Tadpoles are able to withstand at least slightly estuarine conditions. These are winter–spring spawners and their eggs are demersal. A study in the Puget Sound vicinity found that they ate mostly gammarid amphipods and mysid shrimps. They are eaten by black rockfish and tufted puffins. However, Jeff Marliave (2003) observed that at least some potential predators cough them up upon eating them. Larvae: hatching length = 6–7 mm, flexion length = about 1.1 cm, transformation length = about 1.3–1.4 cm.

Psychrolutes sigalutes
(Jordan & Starks, 1895)
Soft Sculpin

Soft sculpins grow to 8.3 cm (3 in) TL. They range from the Commander Islands and along the Aleutian Islands (off Adak Island), to southern Puget Sound. Larvae have also been taken in the eastern Bering Sea. This species lives from surface waters to depths of 281 m (922 ft), over rocks, on soft seafloors, and among various marine vegetation. While adults spend their days on the bottom, juveniles enter the water column to feed. Spawning occurs at least in July and August. Jeff Marliave (1975), reporting from Barkley Sound (British Columbia), found that: "A large male courts several females simultaneously, fending off ripe males which may approach by biting their heads." The pink eggs are laid on rocks in a monolayer. "The female parents tend the eggs until hatching (late October, early November). The females prevent fungal fouling by brushing their bodies over the eggs…The male patrols the nest from a distance of a few body lengths, signaling to prevent the approach of conspecifics. At hatching the females remove the larvae from the nest site and spit them toward the surface" (Marliave 1975). Eggs: 2.3 mm. Larvae: hatching length = 6–7 mm, flexion length = about 1.3–1.5 cm (0.5–0.6 in), transformation length = 1.8 cm.

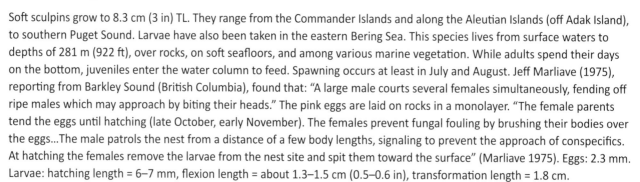

TOTALLY UNRELATED RIFF #6 — BECAUSE WE HAD SOME SPACE TO FILL

CUTEST FOREWORD IN A DOCTORAL DISSERTATION

"My daddy studies the mink….
Poor old mink" (Hatler 1976)

FAMILY AGONIDAE—Poachers

The poachers are benthic, marine fishes (I always see them sitting on the bottom looking like armored swizzle sticks) that are found in the North Pacific and Atlantic, and off southern South America. Some members of the family can be found from the intertidal to depths of about 1,300 m (4,264 ft), but most species live in 300 m (984 ft) or less. There are 46 species, in 21 genera, and 27 species live within our range. Poachers are oviparous (with planktonic larvae), and it is believed that all species lay demersal eggs in adhesive clusters. In at least some species, there is sexual dimorphism in some or all fin sizes (males tend to have larger fins per body size), males tend to be more brightly colored, and their various spots and bands are larger and more distinctly defined. Although poachers are eaten by a variety of predators, pigeon guillemot chicks reject them. If you use the information in Miller and Lea (1972), Mecklenburg et al. (2002), Nakabo (2002), and Lamb and Edgell (2010), you can identify most, if not all, of the poachers on the Pacific Coast.

Bothragonus swanii
(Steindachner, 1876)
Rockhead

BERNARD P. HANBY

ETYMOLOGY: *Bothragonus* is a combination of the Greek word for "pit" and "*Agonus*" and *swanii* honors James G. Swan (1818–1900). Swan was a keen observer of the Pacific Northwest and, along with being something of an ethnographer, was also a journalist, oysterman, customs inspector, judge, and somewhat failed promoter of Port Townsend, Washington. I have a friend whose kid went to Swan Elementary School in Port Townsend, so who says there is no justice? You might consider picking up a copy of his book *The Northwest Coast, or, Three Years' Residence in Washington Territory*, as it paints an evocative picture of a world long gone.

THE BASICS: Maximum Length: 8.9 cm (4 in) TL. The Ranges: Kodiak Island to Lion Rock, San Luis Obispo County (Central California). Common at least as far north as British Columbia. Intertidal to 18 m (60 ft).

SALIENT CHARACTERS: A very distinctive fish is our rockhead. They are stouter and deeper-bodied than most poachers, with a larger head, and a deep pit on the top of that head. Rockheads seem to be able to change colors, as their color often matches their surroundings. Popular colors are brown, scarlet, orange, and blue, with stripes and bars.

LIFE HISTORY: Rockheads live among boulders, gravel, and in kelp beds. They seem to like crevices and other hiding areas. A 5.3 cm (2 in) SL fish was 3 years old. Spawning appears to occur in winter and spring. Eggs are orange or brown, 2 mm in diameter at maturity, and demersal. Jeff Marliave (1975) notes that: "An egg mass…was found within the rhizomes of a *Macrocystis integrifolia* [giant kelp] holdfast." Rockheads feed on an assortment of small crustaceans and are known to be eaten by pigeon guillemots.

Hypsagonus quadricornis
(Valenciennes, 1829)
Fourhorn Poacher

CATHERINE W. MECKLENBURG

ETYMOLOGY AND COLLOQUIAL NAME: The word *Hypsagonus* is composed of "high" (Greek) and "*Agonus*" and *quadricornis* means "four" and "horn" in Latin. They are called "tsuno-shachi-uo" in Japanese.

THE BASICS: Maximum Length: 12 cm (5 in) TL. The Ranges: Sea of Okhotsk and northern Sea of Japan, to Aleutian chain and Bering Sea to northeastern Chukchi Sea (northwest of Cape Lisburne), and to Puget Sound. They are common from at least the northern Kuril

DIANE O'LEARY

Islands to the Gulf of Alaska (and apparently in the southern portions of the Bering Sea). At depths of 15–452 m (49–1,483 ft); mostly in 200 m (656 ft) or less. Busby (1998) states that this species may hatch from eggs directly into the flexion stage, which begins at a maximum of 6.4 mm and is complete at 9 mm. The juvenile stage begins at 1.4 cm (0.6 in).

SALIENT CHARACTERS: Another singular species from the mind of Gaia. Fourhorns have remarkably knobbly heads, liberally caked with protuberances and spines. There is a cirrus at the tip of the snout, a spine above the eye, and a first dorsal fin base that sort of humps way up. It is basically a brown fish, with assorted white, yellow, red, and black markings.

LIFE HISTORY: Fourhorns live amid rocks, sponges, and other structure-forming invertebrates, cobbles, and shell hash. Off Kamchatka, they appear to migrate into relatively shallow waters in the summer.

Most data on fourhorn life history come from the northwestern Pacific. Along the Northern Kuril Islands, fourhorns live to 7 years old. Males and females grow to the same maximum length and enjoy the same life span. Here the fish become mature by their third year of life, at 6.5–7.5 cm (3 in) TL. Spawning apparently occurs in the spring. Females spawn a single batch of eggs per season and fecundity ranges from 57–921. Polychaetes and amphipods are important foods. Larger fish (over 10 cm, 4 in, TL) also eat shrimps, limpets, and fishes. One study noted that males ate more polychaetes and females consumed more amphipods. Jensen (2005) found that by using the delicate, finger-like rays of their pectoral fins, fourhorn poachers lift up shells and rocks looking for prey and this appears to be one of the primary ways they find food (see the sequence to the right). They also walk about using their pectoral and caudal fins. Predators include Pacific cod and white-blotched skate.

REMARKS: Kitty Mecklenburg et al. (2002) report that hydroids and algae sometimes grow on the skins of fourhorns.

GREGORY JENSEN

GREGORY JENSEN

GREGORY JENSEN

Pallasina barbata

(Steindachner, 1876)

Tubenose Poacher

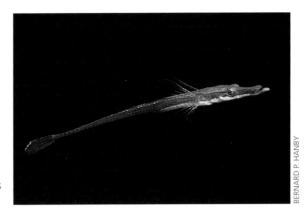

ETYMOLOGY AND COLLOQUIAL NAME: *Pallasina* honors
Petrus Simon Pallas (1741–1811), an early German naturalist (see
Clupea pallasii), and *barbata* means "provided with a barbel" in
Latin. The species is called "yagi-uo" in Japanese.

THE BASICS: Maximum Length: 20.8 cm (8 in) TL. The Ranges:
Japan Sea off Korea, Okhotsk Sea, and Pacific Ocean off Kuril Islands
to eastern Chukchi (as far north as 68°25'N, 166°40'W) and Bering
seas and Aleutian Islands to Bodega Bay (Central California). They
are abundant from the Sea of Japan to the eastern Bering Sea at Norton Sound and to at least Puget Sound. Intertidal zone,
including tide pools, to 128 m (420 ft); most often in perhaps 60 m (197 ft) or less. Larvae: flexion length = 7–12 mm.

SALIENT CHARACTERS: This is a skinny fish with a remarkably underslung jaw, gill membranes united at the throat, and a
lower jaw whisker that sticks forwards. They are brown or gray, with various darker spots, and sometimes a yellow belly.

LIFE HISTORY: Young-of-the-year settle to shallow waters at about 2.3 cm (1 in) SL. Both juveniles and adults are common
in shallow, often barely subtidal, waters, most often around eelgrass, but also among other aquatic vegetation, and over soft
seafloors. They are reputed to routinely swim in the water column. Andriyashev (1954) noted that tubenose poachers were
found in the shallowest waters during summer and then descended into deeper waters (how deep he did not say) in winter.
He also noted that they were "frequently encountered in strongly freshened lagoons, coastal brackish lakes, and even in river
estuaries." Off Kamchatka, they have been taken in water between about 0–12°C (32–54°F).

Off Kamchatka, this species lives to 5 years old. They seem to mature at about 9 cm (4 in) TL. Ripe adults moved into
Izembek Lagoon (Alaska Peninsula) in the summer to spawn. Marliave (1975) caught their larvae in April in Barkley Sound
(Vancouver Island). Tubenose poachers eat mostly small epibenthic crustaceans, such as mysid shrimps and euphausiids, but
polychaetes, caprellid amphipods, and copepods are also consumed. Predators include great sculpins.

Podothecus accipenserinus

(Tilesius, 1813)

Sturgeon Poacher

*With that chin full of whiskers and that underslung
mouth, this fish is stylin'.*

ETYMOLOGY AND COLLOQUIAL NAME: *Podothecus* comes
from "foot" and "box" (referring to a groove at the base of the
pelvic fin that appears in preserved fish) and *acipenserinus* means
"sturgeon-like." It's called "kitanotokubire" in Japanese.

THE BASICS: Maximum Length: 33 cm (13 in) TL. Maximum
Weight: At least 166 gr (6 oz). The Ranges: Northern Kuril Islands
and Okhotsk Sea off southwestern Kamchatka to Commander-Aleutian chain and northern Bering Sea, near Saint Lawrence
Island, to Point Reyes (Northern California). Common from Kamchatka to the eastern Bering Sea, and perhaps to Oregon.
2–300 m (7–984 ft), and perhaps to 500 m (1,640 ft), and mostly in 100 m (328 ft) or less. Larvae: flexion length 8–12.5 mm.
Juvenile stage begins at about 1.3 cm (0.5 in). An age-length table is provided in Smith and Gillispie (1988).

SALIENT CHARACTERS: True to their name, sturgeon poachers have a downward pointing mouth and a nest full of
whiskers around chin and snout. Large males have a black spot on the posterior margin of the anal fin. Sturgeons are brown to
gray, and white, yellow, or orange on belly.

LIFE HISTORY: Juveniles can be found in very shallow waters, commonly in eelgrass beds, but also in kelp beds and on
bare substrate. Adults are usually in somewhat deeper waters, on soft seafloors or shell hash. At least off Kamchatka, these

VALERIE LYTTLE

fish spend the summers in relatively shallow waters and winters somewhat deeper. As nearshore waters in the region are colder during the summer, the offshore movements in the winter are likely a response to chilly inshore conditions. Sturgeon poachers have been found in waters ranging from -2.1–12°C (28–54°F). They are able to withstand at least slightly estuarine conditions.

Sturgeon poachers live to at last 11 years old and they appear to spawn in the spring and summer. While diets vary with season, this species feeds mostly on benthic invertebrates, such as gammarid amphipods, cumaceans, harpacticoid copepods, polychaetes, and shrimps. Mysid shrimps, euphausiids, crabs, bivalves, fish eggs, and a few small fishes round off the diet. In some locations, fish move in to shallow waters to feed at night. Predators include arrowtooth flounder, great and plain sculpins, Pacific cod, Pacific halibut, yellowtail rockfish, common murres, Steller sea lions, and probably river otters.

Sarritor frenatus
(Gilbert, 1896)

Sawback Poacher

ETYMOLOGY AND COLLOQUIAL NAME: *Sarritor* means "one that scrapes" in Latin and *frenatus* means "bridled", also in Latin. They are called "yase-tengu-tokubire" in Japanese.

THE BASICS: Maximum Length: 32 cm (13 in) TL. Maximum Weight: At least 102 gr (4 oz). The Ranges: Pacific coast of Hokkaido to Norton Sound (Bering Sea), Commander-Aleutian chain, to Observatory Inlet (northern British Columbia). Very common from at least the northern Kuril Islands and southeastern Kamchatka to along the Aleutian Islands and in the eastern Bering Sea. Sawbacks start to become less abundant east of about Kodiak Island. At depths of 18–1,124 m (60–3,687 ft). Larvae: flexion length = 9–16 mm.

SALIENT CHARACTERS: Sawbacks have a snout that way overhangs the mouth, and a number of long barbels around the mouth, snout, and lower jaw. They look a lot like the longnose poacher and Mecklenburg et al. (2002) has all sorts of clever ways of telling the two species apart. Sawbacks are brown on back and white underneath, with various blotches.

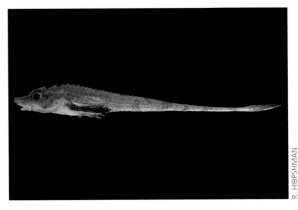
R. HIBPSHMAN

LIFE HISTORY: Young-of-the-year settle to the seafloor at around 2.4 cm (1 in) TL. A benthic species, it inhabits soft seafloors, mixed rock/mud, and boulder fields, in waters between -1.5–6.7°C (29–44°F).

Sawbacks live to at least 6 years old. In the northwestern Bering Sea, a few females mature at 24 cm (9 in) FL, 50% at 25 cm (10 in), and all at 30 cm (12 in). For males, the numbers are 21 cm (8 in), about 23 cm (9 in), and 30 cm (12 in), respectively. Again in the northwestern Bering Sea, spawning occurs in at least July and August, and females produce between 1,293–3,949 eggs per season. Sawbacks feed mostly on gammarid amphipods, but will not turn up their dorsal fins at euphausiids, isopods, polychaetes, crangonid shrimps, mysid shrimps, and cumaceans. Predators include Aleutian skate, great sculpins, Greenland and Pacific halibut, Kamchatka flounder, Okhotsk snailfish, and Pacific cod.

Xeneretmus latifrons
(Gilbert, 1890)
Blacktip Poacher

ETYMOLOGY: *Xeneretmus* is Greek for "strange" and "oar" and *latifrons* means "wide" and "forehead" in Latin.

THE BASICS: Maximum Length: 19 cm (8 in) TL. The Ranges: Near Queen Charlotte Islands (British Columbia) to Punta Colnett (northern Baja California), and in Gulf of California; typically southward to at least Southern California. The presence of larvae in the northern Gulf of Alaska indicates adults are likely present there. At depths of 2 m (7 ft) or less to 1,291 m (4,235 ft).

In Southern California, they are most abundant in 120 m (394 ft) and greater. Larvae: hatching length = less than 4.9 mm, flexion length = 9–11 mm, transformation length = about 1.5 cm (0.6 in). Length-weight parameters (TL, cm, gr): $W = 0.0031L^{3.03}$ (Love unpubl.).

SALIENT CHARACTERS: The black margin on each dorsal fin, the single, vertical spine on the snout, and the scales across the eyes, are good things to know. They have a brownish back and dark blotches on sides.

LIFE HISTORY: Benthic settlement appears to occur when fish are no more than 2.2–2.9 cm (1 in) SL. A 16.2 cm (6 in) TL fish I aged was about 3 years old. My kind of sketchy data implies that blacktips mature at 10–12 cm (4–5 in) TL. They appear to spawn throughout the year in Southern California and at least in the spring off British Columbia. Blacktip poachers feed mostly on gammarid amphipods, euphausiids, and polychaetes, as well as on other small crustaceans.

OTHER SPECIES

Agonopsis vulsa
(Jordan & Gilbert, 1880)
Northern Spearnose Poacher

They reach 20.3 cm (8 in) TL, are found from Kachemak Bay (northern Gulf of Alaska) to Point Loma (Southern California), and inhabit the intertidal (rarely) to depths of 393 m (1,289 ft). They appear to be spring spawners. Larvae: flexion length = 7.5–11.5 mm. The juvenile stage begins at about 2.5 cm (1 in) SL.

Anoplagonus inermis
(Günther, 1860)
Smooth Alligatorfish

Alligatorfish reach 15 cm (6 in) TL. They extend from the Aleutian Islands, at Petrel Bank, to Point Arena (Northern California), at depths of 2 m (7 ft) or less to at least 114 m (374 ft). Young-of-the-year settle out at around 1.7 cm (0.7 in) SL. In Puget Sound, nearshore smooths live among rocks. They are tolerant of slightly estuarine conditions. Predators include Pacific cod, Pacific halibut, and tufted puffins. Larvae: flexion length = 7.5–11 mm.

Bathyagonus nigripinnis
Gilbert, 1890
Blackfin Poacher

Blackfins grow to 29 cm (11 in) TL and are found from the Pacific coast of northern Japan, the northern Kuril Islands and southeastern Kamchatka, to the northern Bering Sea (near Cape Navarin), to Eureka (Northern California); typically southward to southeastern Alaska. They are found over soft seafloors, at depths of 18–1,248 m (59–4,094 ft), mostly at 50–800 m (164–2,625 ft), and in at least 0.4–3°C (33–37°F). They may move into shallower waters during warmer months. Blackfins live to 9 years old and feed primarily on gammarid amphipods, shrimps, and euphausiids.

Occella dodecaedron
(Tilesius, 1813)
Bering Poacher

Bering poachers reach 23 cm (9 in) TL. They are found from the northern Sea of Japan and Sea of Okhotsk to the southeastern Chukchi Sea (66°16'N, 161°21'W) and eastern Bering Sea to the western Gulf of Alaska, at depths of 5–92 m (17–302 ft) (mostly in less than 50 m, 164 ft). This is a soft bottom dweller, inhabiting water temperatures of about -1.5–12°C (29–54°F). One fish has been taken near the sea from a freshwater creek. Recent research in the southeastern Bering Sea shows that this species is tending to move northward as waters warm over time. These fish live to at least 9 years old and spawn in the spring. Females produce between 1,445–4,575 eggs. Small epibenthic crustaceans dominate their diets. Mysid shrimps are particularly important, but they also consume polychaetes, cumaceans, other small shrimps, and amphipods. Pacific cod and plain sculpins eat them.

Odontopyxis trispinosa
Lockington, 1880
Pygmy Poacher

Pygmies reach 13 cm (5 in) TL. They are found from Prince William Sound (northern Gulf of Alaska) to Isla Cedros (central Baja California), commonly to at least northern Baja California. They inhabit depths of 5–373 m (16–1,224 ft), perhaps typically in 70 m (230 ft) or less. Young-of-the-year settle at around 1.8 cm (0.7 in) SL. Based on my cursory studies, pygmies mature at around 7–8 cm (3 in) TL. In Southern California, they appear to spawn throughout the year. Small crustaceans (e.g., amphipods and copepods) dominate the diet, along with some polychaetes and hydroids. Predators include brown rockfish, pink salmon, vermilion rockfish, and pigeon guillemots. Hatching length = less than 4.3 mm, flexion length = about 7.1–11.7 mm, transformation length = about 1.5 cm (0.6 in). Length-weight parameters (TL, cm, gr): (sexes combined) W = 0.0223L$^{3.238}$ (Kinnetic Laboratories 1980).

Sarritor leptorhynchus
(Gilbert, 1896)
Longnose Poacher

This species grows to about 22.6 cm (9 in) TL. It lives from the Sea of Japan and Sea of Okhotsk to throughout much of the Bering Sea (as far north as the Pribilof Islands) to Prince William Sound (northern Gulf of Alaska), at depths of 15 to at least 460 m (48–1,509 ft). It is common from the Sea of Japan to the eastern Bering Sea, down to depths of about 200 m (656 ft). At least off Kamchatka, longnoses tend to live in somewhat shallower waters in the summer than in the winter. They inhabit temperatures of 0–12°C (32–54°F). Longnoses live to 6 years old. Females grow larger than males. Gammarid amphipods are the most important prey, but these fish also consume shrimps, euphausiids, polychaetes, and copepods. Predators include Pacific cod, great and plain sculpins, and Okhotsk snailfish. Length-weight parameters (FL, cm, gr): (sexes combined) W = $0.001025L^{3.3283}$ (Tokranov 1993).

FAMILY CYCLOPTERIDAE—Lumpfishes or Lumpsuckers

Marine fishes of cool or arctic waters, the cyclopterids are found only in the Northern Hemisphere. There are perhaps six genera and 28 species, of which 10 appear within our range, and most of those only as far south as Alaska. Cyclopterids are oviparous; apparently all lay eggs in nests and have planktonic larvae. Mecklenburg et al. (2002) present a description of, and keys to, North Pacific species.

Aptocyclus ventricosus
(Pallas, 1769)
Smooth Lumpsucker

R. HIBPSHMAN

ETYMOLOGY AND COLLOQUIAL NAME: *Aptocyclus* means "touching" and "circles" in Greek and *ventricosus* means "large-bellied" in Latin. They are called "hotei-uo" in Japanese.

THE BASICS: Maximum Length: 44 cm (17 in) TL. Maximum Weight: 4.2 kg (9.2 lb). The Ranges: Japan and Okhotsk seas to Providence Bay (Gulf of Anadyr), and northern Bering Sea; Alaska to North Pacific, south of Aleutian Islands, Gulf of Alaska to Mathieson Channel (British Columbia). Common from the Sea of Okhotsk to the eastern Bering Sea, and to about the Kodiak Island–Prince William Sound region. Usually found over deep waters, from near surface and tide pools (juveniles) to more than 500 m (1,650 ft). Eggs: 2.3–2.4 mm. Larvae: hatching length = 6.5–7 mm. Length-weight parameters (TL, cm, gr): (sexes combined) W = $0.7926L^{2.2068}$ (Orlov and Tokranov 2008b).

SALIENT CHARACTERS: A very globular species, with one dorsal fin set way back toward the tail (the first fin is covered with skin), smooth skin, and pelvic fins fused into a disc. They are gray or brownish, sometimes with small black spots.

LIFE HISTORY: Young-of-the-year are found in very shallow waters, often in tide pools. Over time, juveniles leave the nearshore and spend their adult lives (except for inshore spawning migrations) in deep waters (from midwater to the seafloor). They live in waters between -1–15°C (30–59°F).

Smooth lumpsuckers mature at about 20 cm (8 in) TL. They spawn from December–June. Females produce between 45,310–65,000 adhesive eggs and lay them in crevices of nearshore rocks. At least some females survive spawning and live to spawn again. Musienko (1970), musing about what goes on off Kamchatka, wrote: "Groups of up to 5 or 6 females spawn on a small area and die after the spawning. Male guards the eggs. The very low spring tides leave the eggs dry, and the males moisten them by ejecting a jet of water from their mouths from time to time. When disturbed, males become violently irritated, open their mouths, strike with their tail and roll the eyes." The eggs reportedly take about 1.5 months to hatch. Smooth lumpsuckers feed throughout the water column (perhaps mostly during the day), primarily on fishes, gammarid amphipods, shrimps, mysid shrimps, polychaetes, medusae, and ctenophores. A wide range of predators include fishes (e.g., Greenland and Pacific halibut, Pacific cod, sablefish, and salmon sharks), bald eagles, sea lions, seals, sperm whales, and sea otters.

FISHERY: In the past, native peoples on the Commander Islands ate them and used them as dog food. They are off minor commercial importance in Japan.

MISCELLANY: Andrew Malavansky, of the Saint George Island Traditional Council, notes that spring and early summer storms cast up large numbers (250-plus) on beaches. As they are only cast up during this period, it seems reasonable to assume they are not present at other times. A similar pattern was noted in the 19th century on the Commander Islands, where smoothies were cast up on beaches from March to May. Bean and Bean (1897) noted that "In the beginning [each year] the natives eat them with great gusto, but soon tire of them, and they are then only for food for the sledge dogs."

Eumicrotremus orbis
(Günther, 1861)

Pacific Spiny Lumpsucker

A fish that has quietly come to terms with looking idiotic.

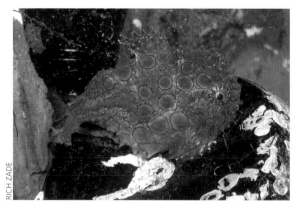

RICH ZADE

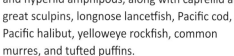

RICH ZADE

ETYMOLOGY AND COLLOQUIAL NAME: *Eumicrotremus* is Greek for "very," "small," and "aperture" and *orbis* is "orb" or "sphere" in Latin. The Japanese call them "ibo-dango," just one very cute-sounding name.

THE BASICS: Maximum Length: 12.7 cm (5 in) TL. Maximum Weight: At least 100 gr (4 oz). The Ranges: Pacific coast of Hokkaido to northern Bering Sea (Gulf of Anadyr) and to Puget Sound; common in the eastern Bering Sea and less common east of about Kodiak Island. 2 m (6.6 ft) or less, to 359 m (1,178 ft), mostly in 200 m (656 ft) or less. Eggs: 2.2 mm.

SALIENT CHARACTERS: They have oval bodies covered in cone-shaped protuberances and a ventral sucking disk. Lumpsuckers are sexually dimorphic. Adult females tend to be pale green and males dull orange to reddish-brown. Females have more and larger tubercles.

LIFE HISTORY: In April, off British Columbia, George Arita (1969) caught large numbers of 5 mm SL fish amid very shallow vegetation. A few juveniles have been taken in eelgrass beds off Juneau (Alaska). Larger fish tend to be found in deeper waters and, in the Bering Sea, Andriyashev (1954) described them as living over stony and pebbly bottoms. They have been found at temperatures as cold as -1.7°C (29°F).

George Arita (1969) found that the smallest ripe female was 3.4 cm (1 in) SL. The females in his study produced anywhere from 169–229 eggs and were perhaps batch spawners. Apparently, the eggs are laid in nearshore nests. At least one Russian biologist reported that males guard the eggs until they hatch, females die after spawning, and males die after the eggs hatch. Pacific spiny lumpsuckers feed on such small crustaceans as gammarid and hyperiid amphipods, along with caprellid amphipods, isopods, and cumaceans. Predators include arrowtooth flounder, great sculpins, longnose lancetfish, Pacific cod, Pacific halibut, yelloweye rockfish, common murres, and tufted puffins.

WILLIAM VAN ORDEN

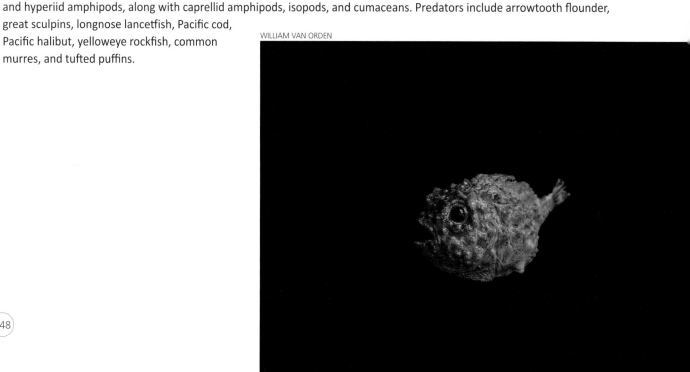

FAMILY LIPARIDAE—Snailfishes

The snailfishes are a pretty successful group of fishes, found in marine waters throughout the world. These are benthic animals that tend to inhabit cool to very cold conditions, often in quite deep waters. There are about 29 genera, and at least 342 species (although some of these species are debatable), of which 90 species live within our range. However, busy ichthyologists working in the North Pacific keep finding new ones, so stand by. Snailfishes are oviparous, with demersal eggs and planktonic larvae. Females of some genera lay eggs in the gill cavities of lithodid crabs, while others lay adhesive eggs on various other forms of substrata. Miller and Lea (1972) and Mecklenburg et al. (2002) provide keys to many of the species on the Pacific Coast, and Nakabo (2002) is also helpful.

Careproctus melanurus
Gilbert, 1892
Blacktail Snailfish

ETYMOLOGY AND COLLOQUIAL NAME: *Careproctus* is Greek for "head" and "anus" (one imagines a rather colorful allusion to the species' vent, which is located relatively near the head) and *melanurus* is Greek for "black" and "tail." At least one Japanese name for this species is "higashi-kon'nyaku-uo."
THE BASICS: Maximum Length: 54 cm (21 in) TL. Maximum Weight: 1.7 kg (3.7 lb). The Ranges: Western North Pacific, off Honshu, and southeastern Kamchatka to Bering Sea; Pacific south of Aleutian Islands to Baja California. Common southward to at least Southern California. 61–2,286 m (200–7,500 ft); mostly in 400 m (1,312 ft) or more. Eggs: 3.3–4.6 mm. Larvae: hatching length = about 8.5 mm. Length-weight parameters (TL, cm, gr): (sexes combined) $W = 0.00126L^{3.59}$ (Orlov and Binohlan 2009).
SALIENT CHARACTERS: Blacktails have a thick pink body, a very small pelvic disc, black-edged dorsal and anal fins, and a black caudal fin.

LIFE HISTORY: This is one of the more commonly seen snailfish for those of us who stare out submersible windows or at ROV monitors. Having said that, no one knows much about them. Stein et al. (2006), observing them in the Monterey Submarine Canyon, found that they mostly live on mud, with a few on rocks and walls, and that the species was "Usually observed hovering horizontally just above bottom or up to a meter above it, often with its head inclined slightly down-wards. When off the bottom, it swam very slowly (trunk and tail just rippling) holding its direction facing into the current, sometimes drifting slowly backwards...Occasionally it was observed directly on the bottom, when it was often curled in a 'U' shape." Off the West Coast, they have been caught in waters of 5.1–7.0°C (41–45°F). Based on just a bit of data, blacktails spawn from at least April–June and females produce at least as many as 534 eggs. Other *Careproctus* are batch spawners, so maybe blacktails are too. What is very cool indeed is that these fish lay their eggs in the gill cavities of box crabs. Neat, yes? You've got your flowing water; you've got your safety. Hey, it's like giving birth in an air conditioned Sherman tank. Blacktail snailfish feed on crustaceans (e.g., shrimps, hermit crabs, and gammarid amphipods), and larger snailfish add fishes to their diets. Steller sea lions eat them.

RELATIONSHIPS: Blacktails appear to be closely related to emarginated snailfish, *Careproctus furcellus*.

Liparis mucosus
Ayres, 1855
Slimy Snailfish

ETYMOLOGY: *Liparis* is Greek for "sleek-skinned" and *mucosus* is Latin for "slimy."

THE BASICS: Maximum Length: About 12.7 cm (5 in) TL. The Ranges: Samsing Cove (southeastern Alaska) to Bahia San Carlos (29°36'N, 115°12'W) (central Baja California). They are pretty common southward to at least northern Baja California. Intertidal to 15 m (50 ft). They seem to be relatively common down to depths of maybe 6 m (20 ft). Larvae: hatching length = about 2.2 mm, flexion length = about 5.9–8.5 mm, transformation length = about 1.1–less than 3.2 cm.

SALIENT CHARACTERS: The dorsal fin has a shallow lobe toward the front (it tends to be deeper in other *Liparis*) and the size of the pelvic disc is truly heroic. They are variously colored brown, pink, red, or purple, and may have striping or reticulations.

LIFE HISTORY: This is a common nearshore snailfish along much of the Pacific Coast. I often find them in tide pools and have pulled them out of kelp holdfasts. They are usually associated with relatively high-energy areas, mostly around boulders and algae, although I note that a couple were taken in Humboldt Bay, so maybe all bets are off. I have taken fish as small as 1.3 cm (0.5 in) TL from tide pools. Based on when larvae have been taken, slimies seem to spawn throughout the year. They prey on various crustaceans (e.g., isopods, ostracods, copepods, and gammarid and caprellid amphipods). Predators include giant kelpfish and kelp rockfish.

CLINTON BAUDER

Liparis florae
(Jordan & Starks, 1895)
Tidepool Snailfish

Tidepools grow to 18.3 cm (7 in) TL. They are found from Kodiak Island to King Harbor (Southern California), perhaps most commonly from British Columbia to Central California. They live mostly amid boulders, cobble, eelgrass, and algae (including holdfasts), in tide pools, and in the rocky subtidal, down to depths of 15 m (50 ft). Bruce Leaman (1980), diving off British Columbia, found them to live in: "Exposed environments…appears to be active nocturnally and could often be found attached by its ventral disc to blades of *Laminaria* spp. moving in the surge." He noted that at least some larvae settle on bull kelp (*Nereocystis*) blades near the surface. Tidepools may mature when about 3 cm (1 in) TL long. They feed primarily on such small crustaceans as gammarid amphipods, along with isopods, harpacticoid copepods, polychaetes, shrimps, and snails. Thus far, only sand soles and minks are known predators.

Liparis fucensis
Gilbert, 1896
Slipskin Snailfish

Slipskins grow to 17.8 cm (7 in) TL. They live from the southeastern Bering Sea and Unimak Pass (eastern Aleutian Islands) to near San Simeon (Central California), commonly southward to at least Point Arena (Northern California). This is a rock dweller. Juveniles often inhabit tide pools and adults tend to live a bit deeper (4–388 m, 13–1,272 ft, but likely mostly nearshore). Males as small as 6.7 cm (3 in) SL have been observed guarding eggs. Females lay eggs in nests, among such invertebrates as mussels and tubeworms. As an example, Ed DeMartini (1978), diving in September in Washington waters, observed a slipskin guarding a nest in a mussel shell. The nest contained four egg masses (containing tan, pink, and orange eggs) with 1,550–2,870 eggs in each clutch. Based either on collections of early stage larvae or on observations of males guarding nests, this species spawns at least from January–September. The eggs hatch in 2 weeks, at 11°C (52°F). Slipskins are eaten by copper rockfish. Eggs: about 1 mm. Larvae: hatching length = less than 2.8 mm, flexion length = about 7.3–9.7 mm, transformation length = about 2 to greater than 2.3 cm (0.8–0.9 in).

Liparis pulchellus
Ayres, 1855
Showy Snailfish

Growing to a mighty 25.4 cm (10 in) TL, this species ranges from the southeastern Bering Sea and Aleutian Islands to Monterey Bay and commonly from at least the Semidi Islands (Gulf of Alaska) to San Francisco. This is a benthic species that is occasionally found in the intertidal (sometimes in eelgrass beds), and down to 183 m (600 ft). The only large catch that I can find a record of was 220 taken in 13–26 m (42–84 ft) off Humboldt Bay. They also live in the Columbia River Estuary in salinities of perhaps 5 ppt. Gravid females have been found from December–July. The species matures

PHIL EDGELL

at between 7–9 cm (3–4 in) TL and the few females examined produced between 941–996 eggs. Showies eat a range of crustaceans (e.g., gammarid amphipods, isopods, mysid shrimps, cumaceans, shrimps, and crabs), and also polychaetes and fishes. Predators include arrowtooth flounder and Chinook salmon. Eggs: 1–1.5 mm. Larvae: hatching length = less than 3.4 mm, flexion length between 5–22 mm, transformation length = between 2.2–5.3 cm (0.8–2 in).

ORDER PERCIFORMES

FAMILY MORONIDAE—Temperate Basses

Moronids are among the more primitive of the Perciformes; that great and grand group of fishes comprised of more than 10,000 species. When most people think of "fishes," they tend to think of members of this order. There are three genera of moronids, six or more species, and they are found in fresh, brackish, and marine waters of North America, Europe, and North Africa. The temperate basses are not native to our area. These are oviparous fishes with planktonic eggs and larvae. Otoliths from what may be a moronid have been found in Cretaceous deposits (at least 71 million years old).

Morone saxatilis
(Walbaum, 1792)
Striped Bass

RENÉ REYES AND US BUREAU OF RECLAMATION

ETYMOLOGY: When Samuel Latham Mitchill (1764–1831) erected the genus *Morone*, way back in 1814, he did not see fit to explain what the hell the word meant, so here we are playing around in the dunghill of ignorance. On the other hand, *saxatilis* means "living among rocks" in Latin.

THE BASICS: Maximum Length: About 122 cm (4 ft) TL in eastern Pacific; 183 cm TL (6 ft) in Atlantic. Maximum Weight: 35.5 kg (78 lb). The Ranges: Native to Atlantic; Barkley Sound (British Columbia) to just south of the U.S.–Mexican border. Eggs: 3.2–4.6 mm. Larvae: hatching length = 2.5–4 mm. A table of mean sizes at age is given in Robinson (1960). Length-weight parameters (TL, mm, kg): (sexes combined) $W = 0.0000000107L^{2.907}$ (RecFin 2009).

SALIENT CHARACTERS: Stripers are usually greenish on back and silvery on sides, with 6–9 black stripes on flanks. On our coast, small stripers might possibly be confused with salemas, which have larger eyes and orange-brown stripes.

LIFE HISTORY: Peter Moyle (2002) goes into simply grotesque detail about the life history and fisheries for this species; so go peek at his words of wisdom.

These are anadromous fish. Born in freshwater, striper larvae are transported downstream to estuaries, where both larvae and juveniles rear. In San Francisco Bay, adult fish may leave for the ocean in the spring, but will return in the fall to spawn in freshwater. Spawning usually begins when water temperatures reach around 14°C (57°F) and peak around 18°C (64°F). Eggs have been found in 10–23.9°C (50–75°F). Regarding spawning, Miller and McKechnie (1968) note that in the Sacramento River: "Groups of three to six bass were observed splashing in the middle of the river. In addition to these splashing and spawning activities or 'rock fights' (this term originates on the Atlantic Coast, where striped bass are called 'rockfish'), there was an aggregation of large striped bass forming a 4- to 8-ft-wide band along the east bank of the river. This band, which was formed by several thousand fish, was about 1,000 yards long and was located 6 to 12 ft from the river bank. Some of these fish were in water as shallow as 1 ft and all were out of the main river current." Obviously, stripers are comfortable in a wide range of salinities and they will tolerate (for a short time) waters are warm as a wretched 34°C (93°F), but anything over 25°C (77°F) is mostly no bueno.

On the Pacific Coast, stripers probably live to at least 20 years old, perhaps to 30 years. Males mature at 1–3 years old (and around 25 cm, 10 in, FL) and females are 4–6 years (about 45 cm, 18 in). Most fish spawn between April–June, in the lower parts of the Sacramento and San Joaquin rivers. Females produce between maybe 200,000–5,000,000 eggs per season. Eggs hatch in about 48 hours in 19°C (66°F).

Striped bass eat a very wide range of prey. While smaller individuals feed more on invertebrates and larger ones eat more fishes, there is considerable overlap in food preferences. Important invertebrate prey include gammarid amphipods, crabs, shrimps, clams, sand crabs, mysid shrimps, copepods, insects, polychaetes, cladocerans, by-the-wind sailors (*Velella velella*), and isopods. In the Sacramento River, an occasional striper dies from getting a catfish caught in its throat. Predators include spiny dogfish, striped bass, white sturgeons, and harbor seals.

FISHERY: Commercial fishing has been banned since 1935. For recreational anglers who fish in San Francisco Bay and environs, this is one of the big target species, along with California halibut, white sturgeons, and king salmon. Stripers are an occasional catch in Southern California and sometimes surf and pier fishermen get little runs of them as far south as Santa Monica Bay (Southern California).

ORIGINS: *Morone* sp. lived at least as far back as the Late Miocene (5.3 million years ago).

MISCELLANY: Hermaphroditic striped bass, with both functional ovaries and testes, are found fairly often.

You know those sores you see on striped bass? Judy Sakanari and Mike Moser (Sakanari and Moser 1986) found that these open lesions are caused by the plerocercoids (larvae) of *Lacistorhynchus tenuis*, a tapeworm that, in its adult stage, lives in marine mammals. The tapeworm eggs are eaten by copepods, which are then consumed by striped bass. At least some of the parasites burrow out of the fish's intestine, die and are encapsulated by host tissue. This, in turn, causes an inflammation that results in the lesion. These do not appear, as a rule, to be fatal, and they tend to heal in a few months.

REMARKS: I know we all kind of accept the fact that striped bass are abundant in our waters. And some of us actually think it was a good idea to completely disrupt a perfectly good ecosystem by importing fish from the East Coast. But how is this any different from importing mongooses to Hawai'i, where they promptly set about eating up all of the eggs

"DO ANDROIDS DREAM OF ELECTRIC SHEEP?" OK, HOW ABOUT "DO STRIPED BASS GLOW IN THE DARK?"

And from the pen of C.E. Hubbock (1927) we have this story of passing strangeness: "Several curious experiences have convinced me that bass are able to cast a phosphorescent glow when feeding at night. I was camping by a brackish lagoon one very dark night when I heard a bass rush something in the weeds not more than ten feet from where I was sitting. Naturally, I watched the place from which the noise came, and was amazed to see a glow on the water, sufficient to enable me to see the outline of the weeds and grass clearly, and even the bubbles on the water three or four inches from the light. After the glow I heard the fish rush and make that popping or sucking sound. The entire performance was repeated six times. Another time, about the same thing happened to me on the Salinas River. I should be glad to hear from others on this subject as I was afraid of being doubted, so hesitated to tell of my experiences." Okay, C.E., if anyone verifies these observations I will whip out the ol' Ouija Board and give you a shout.

of the native birds? Okay, I will admit that it's probably easier to catch striped bass than mongoose on hook and line. On the other hand, how do we know this is true? Maybe tossing a line into the jungle on Kauai, using a number 1/0 Mammal Mangler™ circle hook baited with a chunk of Nukupu'u egg, would catch you a nice plump mongoose. And do they fight? Not only would one tear off your line, but when you brought it in, it would try to tear off your arm.

So, just who was it that for better or worse instigated bringing striped bass to California? Well, according to S.R. Throckmorton, Chairman of the California Fish Commission, it was him. In a letter written in 1880 to Spencer Baird, of the Smithsonian Institution, Throckmorton noted: "I have long had the impression, that the great bay of San Francisco, together with the bays of San Pablo and Suisun connecting with it...would be well adapted to the propagation and growth of the striped bass." He then contacted a biologist on the East Coast who collects some fingerlings from New Jersey and "deposited them at the head of the straits [sic] of Carquinez." And the rest is history.

And speaking of this, Lindley and Mohr (2003) have a nice statistical model that shows that different levels of striped bass population lead to different odds of almost complete extinction of winter-run Chinook salmon on the Sacramento River.

FAMILY POLYPRIONIDAE—Wreckfishes

The wreckfishes are a small group of tropical and warm-temperate marine fishes that live throughout the world. There are two genera and about five species. Wreckfishes are oviparous with pelagic eggs and larvae.

Stereolepis gigas
Ayres, 1859
Giant Sea Bass

Young juveniles look totally unlike the adults.

ETYMOLOGY AND COLLOQUIAL NAMES: *Stereolepis* means "firm" and "scale" in Greek, while *gigas* is both Latin and Greek for "giant." Giant sea bass, along with a number of other grouper or grouper-like fishes in the Northern Hemisphere, have been called "Jewfish" for hundreds of years. In our politically correct times, the term has been gradually eased out, like some kind of bumptious relative who always elicits a faint sense of embarrassment. The origin of the name is uncertain, with explanations going back to this one by Norman and Fraser (1949): "Concerning the name 'Jew-fish', Dampier writes in 1729: 'The Jew-fish is a very good Fish, and I judge so called by the English, because it hath scales and Fins, therfore a clean Fish, according to the Levitical law.'" It's still called "black sea bass" by many folks.

THE BASICS: Maximum Length: 226 cm (7.4 ft) TL. Maximum Weight: 256.1 kg (563.5 lb). Holder (1908) reports that a 363.6 kg (800 lb) fish was taken in the Gulf of California, but who knows? The Ranges: Northern Japan and Sea of Japan (*Note that these Asian records are likely just wrong. I present them only because no one has taken the trouble of formally discrediting them*); Humboldt Bay (Northern California) to Oaxaca (southern Mexico), including Gulf of California. Older records imply that giant sea bass were at least occasional as far north as the Farallon Islands (Northern California). Today, they are relatively abundant from the northern Channel Islands (Southern California) southward. Currently, they are known from depths of 5–46 m (18–150 ft), but I imagine that the maximum depth is considerably deeper. Eggs: 1.5–1.6 mm. Larvae: hatching length = 3–4.2 mm, flexion length = between 5.7–12.4 mm, transformation length = between 1.2–1.9 cm (0.5–0.7 in). Length-weight parameters (TL, mm, kg): (sexes combined) W = $0.00000002589L^{2.9616}$ (RecFin 2009).

SALIENT CHARACTERS: Very, very small and newly settled fish are perch-shaped and can be black with white caudal fins. Soon after, they are bright red or orange with black or dark brown spots (see image above). By the time they are maybe 20–30 cm (8–12 in) TL, giant sea bass have elongated and can be silvery, brown, or gray with black spots and blotches. Giant sea bass rapidly change colors and patterns.

LIFE HISTORY: From October–December, young ones recruit from the plankton (at as small as 4 cm, 2 in, TL) to the nearshore seafloor, often among drift algae, but also over soft sediments. While many settle right behind the surf line (in quieter waters), they will also recruit to depths of 18 m (60 ft) or so, in such places as the Redondo Submarine Canyon. Older fish tend to hang out over rocks and in kelp beds, but you can often see them out over nearby sand. And while larger juveniles

A juvenile sheephead is a dreamin' to start in a cleanin' of an adult giant sea bass.

and adults tend to remain kind of near the bottom, they do not disdain the kelp canopy. How much movement sea bass make is still unclear. However, Mike Domeier reports that one fish he tagged at Santa Catalina Island wound up a few days later at Anacapa Island, having quickly covered many miles, over very deep water (water too deep for moving along the bottom). At least in Southern California, giant sea bass tend to migrate into nearshore waters in the spring and depart in the fall. This was observed as far back as Holder (1910b), when discussing the species at Santa Catalina Island: "It appears in May in schools of six or seven...and spawns in August." Precisely where, and how deep, these fish go in the winter is still unclear. However, it does appear that there are favored shallow-water areas that fish come back to year after year. Fish along the Pacific Coast and in the Gulf of California form one large, genetically undifferentiated, population.

Giant sea bass live to at least 72–75 years (that was a 198 kg, 435 lb fish), but this is likely an underestimate of maximum age. These fish mature at perhaps 13–15 years old and 23–27 kg (50–60 lb) and spawning occurs from May–September. They feed on fishes, squids, crabs, and spiny lobsters.

FISHERY: Indigenous folks, like those living on Isla Cedros (central Baja California) caught giant sea bass. Giant sea bass were a popular and relatively high-priced food fish back in the 19th century, all the way up to San Francisco (where they were at least occasionally taken at the Farallon Islands) and down to San Diego. Almost all were sold fresh, although some were salted and dried. Catches remained moderate throughout much of the 20th century, although by 1933, due to overfishing off California, most of the commercial catch came from Mexican waters. Today, it is mostly illegal to catch and retain giant sea bass in U.S. commercial fisheries. There is a, perhaps unfortunate, loophole in the law as commercial fishermen are allowed to retain one giant sea bass per trip if taken accidentally (as bycatch). These loopholes always make me kind of uncomfortable because how do we know that a sea bass was taken by accident, rather than being targeted? Apparently also vastly overfished in Mexican waters, a few fish are still landed; you can see the occasional one in the Mercado Negro in Ensenada (northern Baja California).

Until made illegal toward the end of the 20th century, giant sea bass was a popular recreational species, taken by both hook-and-line and spear. I can remember watching folks hook them from partyboats off the Northern Channel Islands in the 1960s. It was kind of exciting, as a 300-pound fish could quickly strip all the line off a reel. A deckhand would then attach the original rod and reel to another line and throw the

JEWFISHING PROVES GOOD

The Point Loma area outside San Diego harbor was producing fair catches of giant black bass during December. The market boat "B-680", owned by Capt. George Tsikitas, delivered 5 jewfish scaling over 1,000 pounds, and caught 10 in three days' fishing, acording to John Odom, wharfmaster of the Associated marine service station on Fisherman's Wharf.

PACIFIC FISHERMAN 1943, 31(29): 1

first overboard. I once saw three rods and reels in sequence in the water, all with line completed stripped from reels. Eventually, all were recovered, although the fish was lost.

And this from Ray Cannon's absolutely fabulous *How to Fish the Pacific Coast* (Lane Publishing Company, 1953), the opening lines of his section on fishing for giant sea bass from piers: "The most patient man on any California pier." Jeez, I would think so. Even in 1910, catching a big one was unusual. Today, waiting to catch a honking giant sea bass off a pier elevates "patience" to a new level.

ORIGINS AND RELATIONSHIPS: The University of California, Berkeley, Paleontological Museum has a record of a *Stereolepis* sp. from the Miocene (at least 5.3 million years ago) of Northern California. However, I have been told that it is difficult to tell giant sea bass and grouper bones apart.

Ah, where to place this species? The giant sea bass started its metaphysical life safely ensconced in the Serranidae, along with the basses and groupers, and I imagine it was moderately content. And then some time in the 20th century, the species was promoted to the Percichthyidae, only to have that family fragged by some disgruntled systematists. And now? Well, now it sullenly lodges with the wreckfishes, Polyprionidae, acting like a dyspeptic boarder in an 1859 Kansas City lodging house.

MISCELLANY: Giant sea bass are cleaned by quite the coterie of species, including island kelpfish, juvenile sheephead (see image on previous page), giant kelpfish, bluebanded goby, and small kelp bass.

Brad Mongeau wrote me about a sound that, on several occasions, he heard giant sea bass make. "I was swimming on the surface above the edge of a bluff in about 35 ft of water...I look down and I see a big shadow below me so I grab a quick breath and bolt down there to get a picture of whatever it is...and much to my surprise it was a giant [sea bass] around 4 ft long. I had inadvertently placed him between myself and the bluff and he didn't like it one bit! He flared his gill plates and boomed at me a couple of times and that was THE weirdest sensation I have ever felt in the water. It literally shook my skeleton!"

RICHARD COLMAN

REMARKS: After being semi-wiped out of Southern California waters, giant sea bass have made something of a recovery, thanks, at least in part, to a ban on fishing for them. In addition, there has been at least one good year class, 1983, where large numbers of young-of-the-year successfully recruited. During that, El Niño, year I remember that we caught relatively large numbers of juveniles during research trawling operations in very shallow water in Long Beach Harbor (right next to the prison) and on the outer coast.

My associate, Frank Hurd, had a really large one suck a kelp bass from his pole spear, bending the tines into a clever shape, and then follow him around for the rest of the dive.

ON CHANGING FISH NAMES

In thinking about fish names like "Jewfish," I realize that I really like the Aussies.

I like them because they still like us. And the amazing thing is that they still like us even after our GIs went down there in World War II and married every available woman in the whole damn country. No, really, how would you like to come home after years of eating sand, dodging Stukas, and kicking Rommel's butt, only to find that the one eligible woman left in the whole town is 63 years old, the corresponding secretary of the Woman's Christian Temperance Union, and spends her nights practicing at the piano so she can pound out hymns at the Anglican Church on Sundays?

Oh, and I like the Aussies because they are unafraid of their fish names. In the politically correct U.S., great fish names like "squawfish" and "Jewfish" have been quietly laid to rest and replaced with "pikeminnow" and "goliath grouper." And by the way, I don't remember anyone taking a poll of us Jews and asking us how we felt about it.

The Australians, however, still have a sea filled with evocatively named fishes, like the "coffinfish," "Tasmanian numbfish," "swollenhead conger," "bastard red cod," "bigbelly seahorse," "old wife," "common stinkfish," and the "Chinaman leatherjacket." These names would find heavy sledding, indeed, in the United States. In fact, I assume that once the word got out, the following organizations would make their displeasure known. For the "coffinfish?" The American League of People Who are Cremated and Hence Do Not Use Coffins. The "Tasmanian numbfish?" The American League of People Who Cannot Feel Their Extremities Because They Have Hansen's Disease. The "swollenhead conger?" The American League of People who have Contracted, Through No Fault of their Own, Elephantiasis. The "bastard red cod?" The American League of Ichthyologists Who, Through No Fault of Their Own, Were Born Out-of-Wedlock. The "bigbelly seahorse?" The American League for the Metabolically Challenged. The "old wife?" The American League of Wives Who, Through No Fault of Their Own, are Old. The "common stinkfish?" The American League of People Who Only Bathe on Saints' Days Whose Names, the Saints that is and not the People, Begin with the Letter "Q." The "Chinaman leatherjacket?" The American League of People Who are Opposed to the Name Chinaman Leatherjacket.

There would be the requisite protests, the requisite letters to the editor, blog posts, and the requisite talk show outbursts. At a press conference, the President would be asked the Administration's policy on the common stinkfish controversy. The President would side step the issue by declaring war on Bhutan. And, inevitably, the "common stinkfish" would become the "spicily aromatic fish," the "bigbelly seahorse" would become the "giant economy-sized seahorse," and the "old wife" would become the "golden years significant other fish."

And the "Chinamen leatherjacket?" The President would suggest the species be overfished to extinction, thus neatly sidestepping the issue.

Bizarrely, in Australia none of this seems to have occurred.

That's it. No moral here.

Oh, and I still like the Aussies.

FAMILY SERRANIDAE—Sea Basses

First, it should be noted that, following the work of Matt Craig and a number of others (e.g., Craig and Hastings 2007 and Smith and Craig 2007), I have divided the basses and groupers into two families, the Serranidae and Epinephelidae, respectively. I hope these folks are right, because it was a pain in the butt to change everything at the last minute.

Serranids are marine tropical and temperate fishes that are found throughout the world. There are around 34 genera and 250 species, with 17 species found within our range, and seven of those entering Pacific U.S. waters. Serranids are oviparous, with planktonic eggs and larvae. Some species are sequential hermaphrodites, starting life as one sex and switching to the other. Otoliths of what might be a serranid have been found in the Paleocene (at least 56 million years ago) and other fossil remains are known from the Middle Eocene, about 50 million years ago. Members of the family, including the species *Protanthias fossilis*, lived during the Miocene in Southern California (at least 7.6–8.6 million years ago). The basses were important foods for Native Americans. Most of the serranids in the eastern Pacific are described in Fischer et al. (1995).

Paralabrax clathratus
(Girard, 1854)
Kelp Bass

Despite its name, does it really require kelp?

DAVID ANDREW

ETYMOLOGY: *Paralabrax* means "near" in Greek, and "*Labrax*," the name for a European bass (referring to its similarity to the European species). *Clathratus* means "latticed" in Latin (for the checkerboard patterns). Most folks call them "calico bass." In the 19th century, they were called "cabrilla" by Italian and Spanish fishermen in Southern California (and still are in Baja California) and "rock bass" by English speakers. The first record of "kelp bass" that I can find is from 1933. When I was a kid, big ones were called "bull bass."

THE BASICS: Maximum Length: 72.1 cm (28 in) TL. Maximum Weight: 6.6 kg (14.6 lb). The Ranges: Columbia River to Bahia Magdalena (southern Baja California); typically from about Point Conception (California) to, based on our fish surveys, at least Isla Asuncion (southern Baja California). Surface and surf zone to 61 m (200 ft); juveniles occasionally intertidal and adults mostly in 30 m (98 ft) and less. Eggs: 0.9–1 mm. Larvae: hatching length = about 2.2 mm, flexion length = about 5–6.5 mm, transformation length = about 1.1 cm. Von Bertalanffy parameters (TL, cm): (sexes combined) L_∞ = 69.8, k = 0.06, t_0 = -3.5 (Love et al. 1996). Length-weight parameters (TL, mm, kg): (sexes combined) W = 0.000000002716L$^{3.27}$ (RecFin 2009).

SALIENT CHARACTERS: These are handsome fish; brown, gray-brown, green, or olive on back and sides, alternating with pale blotches (hence the name "calico"). Kelp bass can alter their colors and patterns very quickly. For instance, a fish living among kelp or other algae tends to be brown or green, changing to pale green when it swims away from the weeds. There are also seasonal changes, linked to reproduction. For instance, most ripe males have orange snouts. Brad Erisman and Larry Allen (2005, 2006) have page after page after page of details about all kinds of patterns and colors.

LIFE HISTORY: Young-of-the-year settle out of the plankton at 0.9–1.4 cm (0.4–0.6 in) TL, 25–36 days following hatching. Kelp bass tend to settle out of the plankton just after the new and full moons, with a peak occurring about 5 days after the full moon. These little bass settle from barely subtidal waters to at least as deep as 18 m (60 ft), from April–December, but mostly from June–November. While there is lots of evidence that many kelp bass juveniles settle from the plankton to kelp beds, they also settle out on stuff like low algal and invertebrate turf, eelgrass. Kelp bass should more properly be called "structure" bass, as kelp is only one of the habitats they seem to enjoy. Juveniles are found around all kinds of aquatic vegetation (including drifting algal mats) and hard structure, and tend to be more abundant in somewhat quiet waters. Adults live around any kind of structure you can posit, including kelp beds, oil platforms (sometimes by the thousands), rock reefs, sewer pipes; hey, you name it. Honking big bass often frequent nearshore wash rocks. The biggest bass I ever caught (a 10-pounder, taken on a shiny sinker and a treble hook and released, mind you) was caught on a little bit of hard bottom a stone's throw from the Santa

Barbara Breakwater. When I was a kid in Santa Monica, the best spot, hands down, to catch really large kelp bass was The Pipe, which was…a pipe. Kelp bass can be active during both day and night and routinely swim throughout the water column, often leaping out of the water chasing prey. Similarly, whole schools will, on rare occasions, pick up and start to travel. Merit McCrea, in his days as a partyboat skipper, saw a school of kelp bass breezing many miles offshore Santa Barbara, headed for, well, who knows? Kelp bass frequently rub themselves on sand, although their motivations are unclear.

Just how much the average kelp bass moves is unclear. It appears that where habitat is primo, such as at Santa Catalina Island, bass may not move about much. For instance, when Chris Lowe and his minions (2003) tagged kelp bass at Santa Catalina, they found that the fish had home ranges of 33–11,224 m^2, averaging 3,349 m^2, and that some fish remained in a core area for up to 3 years. On the other hand, we did some bass tagging off Santa Barbara and had fish move all over the Santa Barbara Channel, from reefs to platforms, reefs to reefs, etc. And how do you explain the estimate of 400 kelp bass on Naples Reef that my associate Al Ebeling made, with the more than 5,000 bass taken off that same small outcrop, in that same year, by one partyboat? It seems likely that bass that find themselves in really nice habitat don't move much, while those in suboptimal situations, move about more. Similarly, Dan Pondella reports that the Horseshoe Kelp, a rocky feature located just off Long Beach Harbor, and fished by a few gobzillion boats every year, has some of the highest densities of kelp bass anywhere on the coast. The only way a heavily fished feature can retain high bass densities is if the fish are more or less continuously moving into the area.

How do kelp bass do it? For all the skinny, let's look in on Erisman and Allen (2006): "Adults formed aggregations of three to more than 200 individuals and spawning occurred in subgroups of three to 23 individuals with one female. Spawning occurred 32 minutes before sunset to two hours after sunset and both males and females were capable of spawning multiple times [males 3 times in 10 minutes] during a single evening…spawning occurred continuously throughout the summer months and showed no significant relationship to lunar cycle." Fish aggregated "under dense kelp canopies, around kelp fronds located on shelf edges or reef slopes, above rocky substrata and in the open water." They also formed around piers and harbor breakwaters. "Aggregations were most common at depth ranges of 8–18 m [26–59 ft] and were positioned on the reef from the bottom to more than 20 m [66 ft] above the bottom." They also noted kelp bass aggregations as much as 15 m (49 ft) off

Like a scene from The Anarchists' Convention *by John Sayles.*

the reef. Schooling begins as much as 2.5 hours before sunset and courtship starts 30–50 minutes before sunset. "The most common sequence of male courtship consisted of a male in checkered colour phase approaching a female, performing various display behaviours for several seconds, then swimming to the side of the female and hovering nearby for several minutes before approaching again." Sometimes several males at a time would display, while bumping and nudging a female, and male-male aggression was rarely noted. Erisman and Allen go into simply exquisite detail about all the various behaviors of males and females during this period and if you are ever in the mood (although one might suggest that this could be some intricate form of sublimation), one can go to their paper for the whole enchilada.

Kelp bass live to 33 years old. A few males and females mature at 18 cm (7 in) TL and 2 years old, 50% of males are mature at 22 cm (9 in), and 50% of females at 22.6 cm (9 in), both at 3 years. All males are mature at 26 cm (10 in) (4 years), and all females at 27 cm (11 in) (5 years). Spawning occurs from April–October, peaking June–August. Larger fish begin spawning earlier in the season and continue to spawn later than small ones. Kelp bass eat just a really, really, wide range of stuff. Smaller ones tend to concentrate on crustaceans (e.g., mostly gammarid and caprellid amphipods, shrimps, mysid shrimps, and crabs) and larger ones switch to fishes, squids, and octopuses. However, there are all kinds of exceptions and you get the impression that any kelp bass is willing to at least consider eating just about anything it sees. Other prey not previously mentioned include pelagic tunicates (one report noted that the fish preferred the gut portion), fish eggs, abalones, sea hares, mole crabs, hermit crabs, clam siphons, mussels, clams, sea urchins, and algae. A study at Santa Catalina Island found that juveniles, to about 6.5 cm (3 in) SL, ate zooplankton during the day and sheltered at night in vegetation. Those fish 6.5–16.5 cm (3–7 in) SL fed on crustaceans on or close to substrate during day and some fed in the water column at night. Larger fish became increasingly piscivorous and might be most active at dawn and dusk. Predators include angel sharks, giant sea bass, moray eels, Pacific electric rays, treefish, California sea lions, and bottlenose dolphins.

FISHERY: It is likely that kelp bass were important to Native American diets in Southern California, but because it is difficult to tell apart kelp bass and barred sand bass bones, the degree of importance is difficult to assess. Starting in the late 19th century, kelp bass, along with barred sand bass, formed a medium-size commercial fishery in Southern California. They were caught

mainly as a bycatch by fishermen targeting shallow waters for rockfishes, California sheepheads, and spiny lobsters. Until it was made illegal in 1953, recreational anglers could legally sell kelp, barred, and spotted sand basses, and this fishery formed perhaps 10% of the "commercial" bass catch. Kelp bass are still one of the most important fish in the artisanal commercial fisheries of northern Baja California; you see them just about every day in the Mercado Negro fish market of Ensenada (northern Baja California).

Kelp bass are hugely important in the party and private vessel sport fisheries of Southern California and parts of Baja California (particularly in the Ensenada area). Long-range partyboats catch large numbers of them all along the northern and central Baja California coast. Those shore fishermen fishing from rocks, jetties, and such accessible breakwaters as the Cabrillo breakwater in San Pedro also often take them. Selected piers (such as the Mole at Avalon, Santa Catalina Island) often hold fair numbers.

RELATIONSHIPS: A fossil *Paralabrax* is known from the Late Miocene (8.6–7.6 million years ago) in southern California.

MISCELLANY: Young kelp bass have been seen cleaning giant sea bass. And in the mutant files we have records of a snubnosed one taken from Alijos Rocks (Baja California) and another one equipped with strange, elongated fins.

SO CHUCK, TELL US HOW YOU REALLY FEEL.

Charles Holder, that great popularizer of Santa Catalina Island and its sport fisheries, minced few, if any words about his feelings on the "rock bass," as kelp bass were called in the 19th and early 20th centuries. Let's listen in at his study in Pasadena (Holder 1910c) and please wipe your feet and keep your hands off the antimacassar: "The rock bass requires a three-ounce rod and a three-thread line, as it is a poor fighter at best, though some of the larger ones afford good sport. I have seen them weigh eight or ten pounds and specimens I took at San Nicolás were larger than that. The vast numbers of rock bass at times are beyond belief. A good place for them is Ship Rock, off Cabrillo, Santa Catalina, where they may be taken literally by the hundred; also at San Clemente [Island], at Howland's at Anacapa, and Santa Cruz [Island], where they are of large size. But the pity of it is, that no one cares for the rock bass; as game he is considered a delusion and a snare. Some days at San Clemente [Island] when the professional [commercial] fishermen were in hard luck, and they had given us bait, we caught rock bass for them, and it was merely a question of baiting and hauling. We never could reduce the numbers of these pests; yet they are among the best of the market fishes."

Paralabrax maculatofasciatus
(Steindachner, 1868)
Spotted Sand Bass

KEVIN LEE

ETYMOLOGY AND COLLOQUIAL NAMES: *Paralabrax* means "near" in Greek, and "*Labrax*," the name for a European bass (referring to its similarity to the European species). *Maculatofasciatus* means "spotted" and "banded" in Latin. In the late 19th century, these were call "rock bass" or "cabrilla" by Southern California commercial fishermen. Biologists tried out "spotted bass" and "spotted rock bass," before "spotted sand bass" became the *nom de mare* in 1949. They are almost universally called "cabrilla" in Mexico.

THE BASICS: Maximum Length: 38.1 cm (15 in) TL. Maximum Weight: 3.1 kg (6.8 lb). The Ranges: Monterey to central Mexico, including the Gulf of California. Spotteds poop out north of about Marina del Rey (Southern California), are common from about Newport Bay (Southern California) southward, and really kick in from central Baja California to throughout much of the Gulf of California. They were reported from San Francisco Bay in the late 1800s. One survey estimated about 169,000 spotties in San Diego Bay. Surface to 61 m (200 ft), including intertidal, typically from the intertidal to 45–50 m (148–164 ft). Eggs: 0.8–0.9 mm. Larvae: hatching length = about 2.2 mm, flexion length = 4.3–5.8 mm, transformation length = about 1.1 cm (0.4 in). Von Bertalanffy parameters (mm, SL): (sexes combined) L_∞ = 351.3, k = 0.1077, t_0 = -6.99 (Allen et al. 1995). Length-weight parameters (SL, mm, gr): (sexes combined) W = $0.000026L^{3.0187}$ (Allen et al. 1995).

SALIENT CHARACTERS: Another handsome serranid, with a brown, green, olive, or white body, liberally covered with black spots and bars. With some exceptions, males tend to be white or light with black bars, white chins and jaws, and white spots on backs. Females tend to be less starkly patterned and be yellow-flushed with yellow chins and jaws. Young ones have several dark stripes running along their sides and a row of dots near their belly.

LIFE HISTORY: Young-of-the-year settle in the summer and fall to very shallow (sometimes intertidal) and quiet waters at 2.3 cm (0.9 in) SL or smaller. This translates to mangroves (in the tropics), lagoons, marshes, and bays. Juveniles (and the occasional adult) are found in tide pools, particularly in the Gulf of California, where spotteds can dominate the rocky intertidal. Otherwise, they are fishes of the nearshore and shallow channels. Spotteds are very partial to eelgrass and the interface between sand and hard structure. They are only occasionally found on the outer coast. While they spend most of their time more or less quiescent on the bottom, they are occasionally quite active in the water column. One tough fish, spotties can tolerate waters between 7.5–32°C (46–90°F). There is little gene flow between Pacific Coast and Gulf of California fish and Punta Eugenia (Baja California) may also form a barrier along the Pacific Coast. Water temperatures at the southern tip of Baja California may be too warm for this species and one study concluded that there has been little gene flow between Pacific Ocean and Gulf of California spotties for at least 120,000 years.

Do spotties change sex? I don't know. Tim Hovey and Larry Allen (2000) found some evidence that they do (with mature females sometimes changing to mature males). Sadovy and Domeier (2005) found that "fish pass through a juvenile (non-functional) morphologically bisexual phase…Bisexual juveniles then develop in either a male or female direction and elements of the [nonfunctional] early bisexual phase may be retained into adulthood [which means that, for instance, mature males may retain some of the nonfunctional female tissue of their childhoods]." They suggested that the potential for sex change of mature females into males was possible [was somehow latent]. As of now, the needed experiments (for instance putting mature females into a variety of densities and seeing if that leads to sex change) have not been conducted.

Observing captive fish, Miller and Allen (2006a, b) found that spotties engage in three types of spawning: pair spawning, group spawning, and spawning that includes a sneaker male. When densities are low, it is most often pair spawning with large males dominating females. As densities increase, group spawning increases. Spawning occurred in the afternoon and evening (from 5:45–7:45 p.m., and mostly after 7:00 p.m.) and spawning bouts lasted between 45 and 190 seconds. They also provide lots of details regarding courtship and color patterns.

Spotties live to at least 14 years old. In Southern California, about half of all females are mature before their first birthday and all are mature when one year old (at around 15.5 cm, 6 in, SL). Fifty percent of males are mature at about 1.5 years old (18 cm, 7 in) and all are mature at 2 years old (22.5 cm, 9 in). In aquaria, spawning has been noted from May–December, peaking in July. Eggs hatch within 24 hours at around 20°C (68°F). In another life, I examined the stomachs of 447 spotted sand bass and found they fed almost entirely on benthic organisms. Clams, particularly razor clams, and crabs made up most of their diets. While they usually eat razor clams, shell and all, they also nip off the siphons of other species. Fishes also can be important, and shrimps, gammarid amphipods, mysid shrimps, hermit crabs, brittle stars, snails, octopuses, and fish eggs are also occasionally eaten. Smaller fish tend to mostly eat crustaceans and mollusks; larger fish add fishes to their diets. Predators include California sea lions.

FISHERY: In the 19th century, the spotted sand bass was an important commercial species in San Diego Bay. Today, it is illegal to sell spotties in the U.S., but they are fairly common in the Mercado Negro fish market in Ensenada (northern Baja California). They are of major importance to artisanal fisheries in the Gulf of California. In the U.S., recreational anglers target them in inshore waters with San Diego, Mission, and Newport bays particular hotspots. They are also found on the back side of Santa Catalina Island in Twin Harbors. Spotted sand bass appear to be a reasonable candidate for aquaculture; there have been some attempts in Mexico to farm them.

RELATIONSHIPS: Spotties are most closely related to barred sand bass.

Paralabrax nebulifer
(Girard, 1854)
Barred Sand Bass

A recreational species designed for the lumpenproletariat (as defined by Marx in The Eighteenth Brumaire of Louis Napoleon).

ETYMOLOGY AND COLLOQUIAL NAMES: *Paralabrax* means "near" in Greek, and "*Labrax*," the name for a European bass (referring to its similarity to the European species). *Nebulifer* means "I bear" and "cloud" in Latin. Back in the 19th century, the usual name was "Johnny" (or "Juan") "Verde." Off Baja California, they are often called "cabrilla." Called "rock bass" (as were all three species of *Paralabrax*) by commercial fishermen in the 1930s, recreational anglers called them "sand bass," and that name was made official in 1949. Brad Erisman informs me that the rather evocative name "turd roller" is often heard aboard sport fishing vessels, because of the species' habit of kind of giving up and spinning around when brought to the surface.

THE BASICS: Maximum Length: Officially to 65 cm (26 in) TL. My associate, Merit McCrea, in the days when he ran a sportfishing vessel, saw sandies to about 76 cm (30 in). Maximum Weight: 6 kg (13.2 lb). Geographic Range: Santa Cruz (Central California) to Todos Santos (southern Baja California), and perhaps in southern Mexico around Acapulco. They are common from the Santa Barbara Channel southward to at least Isla San Roque (southern Baja California) and hyperabundant in Bahia de Sebastian Vizcaino and around Isla Cedros. Surf zone to 183 m (3–600 ft) ; mostly in 45 m (148 ft) or less, although Merit has mentioned to me that his passengers would occasionally catch a dozen or so on a drift in 91 m (300 ft) of water. Eggs: 0.9–1 mm. Larvae: flexion length = about 4.9–6.8 mm, transformation length = 1.1 cm (0.4 in). Von Bertalanffy parameters (TL, cm): (sexes combined) L_∞ = 66.2, k = 0.08, t_0 = 2.63 (Love et al. 1996). Length-weight parameters (TL, mm, kg): (sexes combined) W = $0.000000006844L^{3.1128}$ (RecFin 2009).

KEVIN LEE

SALIENT CHARACTERS: Typically, barred sand bass are greenish or gray, with dusky bars on sides. Most have freckles on their snouts. At night, they can be heavily blotched and spotted with brown, yellow, and silver.

LIFE HISTORY: Young-of-the-year settle out of the plankton mostly in the summer and fall, and mostly in shallow and relatively calm waters. Juveniles are particularly abundant in quiet bays, lagoons, and behind breakwaters, often among eelgrass and other vegetation. While some adults live in back bays, most older

SCOTT GIETLER

fish inhabit the open coast. They are particularly fond of the interfaces between rocks or other hard substrate and soft sea-floors. You can also find them over mud and sand, cobbles, shell mounds around oil platforms, and in kelp beds. Interestingly, off central Baja California, we found that they simply swarm over some pretty high-relief bottoms. While they tend to spend much of their time on or just above the bottom, folks like Dan Pondella have seen schools of hundreds well above the bottom in the midwater. I have seen them boiling at the surface on rare occasions. In the spring, they form large, and seemingly somewhat mobile, spawning aggregations in more-or-less predictable places. The northernmost of these large aggregations is off the Ventura area (in the Santa Barbara Channel) but some spawning occurs at least as far north as Santa Barbara. Other hotspots include (but are not limited to) areas in Santa Monica Bay, off Huntington Beach, and just below the U.S.-Mexican Border. It is unclear how mobile these fish are, but I would expect that some move about considerably. During the spawning season, at last some adults spend daytime hours in the midwaters of the spawning grounds, making occasional trips to the bottom. Around about dusk, these fish move to near the sea floor and may move inshore. Larry Allen and crew (2002) estimated that there were perhaps 133,000 barred sand bass in San Diego Bay.

Barred sand bass live to 24 years old. A few males mature at 19 cm (8 in) TL (2 years old), 50% at 21.9 cm (9 in) (3 years), and 100% at 26 cm (10 in) (4 years). For females, these values are 21 cm (8 in) (2 years), 23.9 cm (9 in) (3 years), and 27 cm (11 in) (5 years), respectively. Tim Hovey et al. (2002), working in Southern California waters, found that all barred sand bass, whether destined to become males or females, go through a "female-like juvenile stage." That is, all fish, including ones that are mature males, have female tissue present, even if it is non-functional. Apparently, and on very rare occasions, a barred sand bass will start life as a functional female and then change sex to a functional male. During the spawning season (mostly April–September, peaking in the early summer), females spawn, on average, every 2 days. Spawning occurs most often at midday, but may occur any time during daylight hours. Turner et al. (1969) observed spawning in 18–21 m (60–70 ft) and found that the fish were quite aggressive at the time. On the other hand, they also noted that, after breeding, barred sand bass would sit on substrate quite close together and they appeared listless for several weeks. Barreds feed on a wide variety of benthic prey. Crabs, clams, polychaetes, gammarid amphipods, brittle stars, shrimps, mysid shrimps, and octopuses are perhaps most important. However, you might also find caprellid amphipods, fat innkeepers, sea cucumbers, hermit crabs, nudibranchs, snails, and scallops. Smaller fish tend to focus on small crustaceans. Predators include giant sea bass, California sea lions, and Pacific white-sided dolphins.

FISHERY: As with kelp bass, until their sale was banned in 1953, barred sand bass were of some importance in the commercial fisheries of Southern California. And, combined with kelp bass, fish caught and sold by recreational anglers comprised about 10% of the "rock bass" sold in the California. It is still legal to sell barred sand bass in Mexico, and they are one of the most important species in the commercial artisanal fisheries of central and northern Baja California. On any day in the year, the Mercado Negro fish market in Ensenada (northern Baja California) is just loaded with them.

Barred sand bass are just really an important recreational species in Southern California and southward to at least Bahia San Quintin (northern Baja California). While party vessels and small boat anglers catch most of them, they are often taken from piers, jetties, and from shore. In 1969, Parke Young, a bass biologist for the California Department of Fish and Game, wrote these kind of sobering words: "At times in the last 20 years, particularly 1950 to 1957, sand bass have been scarce

in southern California...There is good reason to believe an extended cold water phase in southern California would drive sand bass south, out of range of all but a few partyboats." If this happened, those Southern California half-day partyboats that target barred sand bass spawning aggregations would have to start fishing for pipefishes. When I was a kid, I used to catch young-of-the-year sand bass from the Santa Monica Pier using embryonic shiner perch for bait.

RELATIONSHIPS: Barred sand bass are most closely related to spotted sand bass.

MISCELLANY: 1) Years ago, one or perhaps two albino fish were taken off San Onofre (Southern California). 2) Turner et al. (1969) observed a yellow rock crab cleaning a barred sand bass. 3) Ever notice that barred sand bass smell different from kelp bass when you clean them? Just an observation.

OTHER SPECIES

Paralabrax auroguttatus
Walford, 1936
Goldspotted Sand Bass

Goldspotteds reach 71 cm (28 in) TL and 4.7 kg (10.3 lb) They have been taken from just north of Punta Rosalia (28°40'N, 114°16'W) and Isla Cedros (central Baja California) to the Gulf of California. While they have been caught at depths of 2–183 m (5–600 ft) or more, they are typical from about 30–155 m (98–508 ft). We find them over rocks. They live to at least 24 years old, spawn from March to May, and feed on fishes, shrimps, crabs, octopuses, and squids. There is a fairly large artisanal fishery for them in the Gulf of California, where most are taken with gill nets and hook-and-line. Von Bertalanffy parameters (SL, mm): (females) L_∞ = 765.9, k = 0.036, t_0 = -6.519; (males) L_∞ = 438.9, k = 0.135, t_0 = -2.442 (Pondella et al. 2001). In the GOC, fishermen call them "extranjera."

OCTAVIO ABURTO-OROPEZA

FAMILY EPINEPHELIDAE—Groupers

Epinephelids are mostly marine (with the occasional rebel entering freshwater) fishes found in tropical and temperate waters throughout the world. There are about 30 genera and 225 species, with 17 species found in our range and eight of these entering U.S. waters. These are oviparous fishes with planktonic eggs and larvae. A number of species are sequential hermaphrodites. Most of the eastern Pacific species are described in Fischer et al. (1995).

Cephalopholis colonus
(Valenciennes, 1846)
Pacific Creolefish

This species reaches 43 cm (16.9 in) TL and has been found from San Diego to Islas Lobos de Afuera (Peru), including the Gulf of California. I saw at least a few as far north as Isla Cedros (central Baja California). They live from surface waters to depths of 100 m (328 ft). This is a schooling, water-column, reef-oriented fish; you can find aggregations of 1,000 or more on the upcurrent sides of reefs. While not territorial, creolefish do seem to have home ranges and likely stay in the same area for years at a time. They hole up in rocks at night. In the Gulf of California, creolefish were seen spawning in the afternoon, two days before and after the full moon. Spawning occurs at least May to September. Pacific creolefish feed on zooplankton. Now that the larger species have been overfished, this is an important commercial fish in the Gulf of California. Length-weight parameters (TL, cm, gr): (sexes combined) W = $0.01485L^{2.86333}$ (Balart et al. 2006). This species was previously called *Paranthias colonus*.

These are adult leather bass (see next page).

OCTAVIO ABURTO-OROPEZA

Dermatolepis dermatolepis
(Boulenger, 1895)
Leather Bass

Leather bass grow to 1 m (39 in) TL and 12.5 kg (27.5 lb). They range from El Segundo (Southern California) to northern Peru, mostly in tropical waters. These are reef dwellers, living at depths of 5–40 m (17–131 ft). They eat fishes and decapods and that feeding likely takes place during the day.

A juvenile does the zebra thing amid urchin spines.

Epinephelus analogus
Gill, 1863
Spotted Cabrilla

This cabrilla reaches 87 cm (34 in) TL, 22.4 kg (49.2 lb), and ranges from San Pedro (Southern California) to Pucusana (Peru), including the Gulf of California. Historically, even when there were lots of them, they did not appear to be abundant north of Punta Eugenia (Baja California). Found from less than 1 m to 107 m (3–353 ft), the young settle to tide pools, estuaries, and lagoons; older fish live among reefs. They feed on squids, fishes, mantis shrimps, and crabs. This is a species of great economic importance wherever it is found. It is normally eaten fresh. By the late 1920s, there was a considerable fishery for them by American fishermen, fishing off the west coast of Baja California. Spotted cabrilla were landed in several California ports under the name "golden bass" (kind of ironic as they were neither golden nor bass). By the end of the 1940s, the Mexican government, concerned with overfishing, placed a high tariff on fish caught by American commercial fishermen, making fishing for cabrilla unprofitable. Fossils of what might be an *Epinephelus* have been found in an Eocene formation (at least 34 million years ago). A fish living in the Miocene (at least 5.3 million years ago) of Southern California has been identified as a grouper, tentatively as *Epinephelus rhomalea*. It should be noted that it is pretty difficult to determine to genus a fossil grouper. Spotted cabrillas are likely most closely related to flag cabrillas (*Epinephelus labriformis*). Von Bertalanffy parameters (TL, cm): (sexes combined) L_∞ = 97.3, k = 0.12 (Morales-Nin 1994).

Hyporthodus acanthistius
(Gilbert, 1892)
Gulf Coney

Gulf coneys reach 1.3 m (51 in) TL and at least 5.8 kg (12.8 lb). They live from El Capitan (Southern California) to Isla Lobos de Tierra (Peru) (including the Gulf of California), at depths of 12–111 m (40–364 ft) (mostly in 46 m, 51 ft or more). Living over patch reefs or adjacent sand bottoms, gulf coneys feed on fishes, as well crustaceans (e.g., mantis shrimps and crabs), squids, snails, and pelagic tunicates. In tropical areas, they are of significant economic importance and have been heavily overfished in the Gulf of California. This species was formerly called *Epinephelus acanthistius*.

Mycteroperca xenarcha
Jordan, 1888
Broomtail Grouper

Broomtails reach a length of 150 cm (59 in) TL and a maximum weight of at least 53 kg (117.5 lb), but perhaps to as much as 91 kg (200 lb). At one time, they ranged as far north as San Francisco and they have also been taken as far south as Callao (Peru), including the Gulf of California. There are a few broomtails still left in Southern California, although clearly not many. They live all the way from the intertidal to 70 m (230 ft). Almost zippo is known about this species. Juveniles and young adults live in mangrove forests and other coastal embayments and adults live on rocky bottoms, often near caves and crevices (and commonly down to 60 m, 197 ft). There was at one time a little group of them near La Jolla (Southern California) and they tended to live in the kelp beds down to a depth of 18 m (60 ft). Broomtails live to perhaps 36 years old. In the Gulf of California, reproductive aggregations, over high relief, of as many as 100 fish have been observed during April on the full moon. Broomtails get hosed wherever they live. The small population that existed off Southern California was targeted by commercial fishermen and recreational divers. Into the 1940s, broomtails were caught along the Baja California coast and sold in California fish markets. By the early 21st century, most of the Gulf of California population was gone, the result of overfishing by artisanal commercial fishermen and recreational anglers. Length-weight parameters (TL, mm, kg): (sexes combined) W = 0.0000000259L[2.96] (RecFin 2009).

Pronotogrammus multifasciatus
Gill, 1863
Threadfin Bass

Threadfins reach 28.5 cm (11 in) TL and are found over rocky reefs from off the east end of Anacapa Island and south of Point Mugu (34°00'N, 119°00'W) (Southern California) to Talara (Peru), including the Gulf of California. In Southern California, we see them sheltering quite close to boulder fields and around rock ridges (in waters as cold as 9.9°C, 50°F). They live at depths of 14–300 m (45–984 ft). Their larvae have been collected mostly in the summer and fall. Length-weight parameters (SL, cm, gr): (sexes combined) W = 0.011L[3.316] (Rodriguez-Romero et al. 2009).

FAMILY PRIACANTHIDAE—Bigeyes

Bigeyes are marine, benthic, and generally tropical fishes that are found throughout the world. A few species creep, albeit unwillingly, into temperate waters. There are four genera, about 18 species, and four species live within our range, although only one lives as far north as Southern California. Priacanthids are oviparous, with planktonic eggs and larvae. The family may extend as far back as the Middle Eocene, maybe 40 million years ago. *Pristigenys spinosus* is a fossil species from the Late Oligocene-Early Miocene (around 23 million years ago) of the Caucasus.

Pristigenys serrula
(Gilbert, 1891)
Popeye Catalufa

STEVE DROGIN

ETYMOLOGY: *Pristigenys* is Greek for "saw" and "jaw" and *serrula* is Latin for "little saw," seemingly a reference to this species' rough scales.
THE BASICS: Maximum Length: 33 cm (13 in) TL. The Ranges: Newport (central Oregon) to Chile, including Gulf of California. They are occasional off Southern California and rare further north. Less than 3 to more than 200 m (10–656 ft).
SALIENT CHARCTERS: This is a compressed and oval species, with large eyes, a somewhat turned-up mouth, and red body. Underwater, we see them in crimson, often with white blotches on the back.
LIFE HISTORY: We see them over high-relief reefs, usually kind of tucked away in crevices. Subadults are caught as bycatch in commercial shrimp trawls in the Gulf of California, so I guess the younger ones also live over soft seafloors.

FAMILY APOGONIDAE—Cardinalfishes

Cardinalfishes are mostly tropical fish, found primarily in marine waters. Some species tolerate brackish conditions and a few live in freshwater. All are oviparous with planktonic larvae and many are mouth brooders with males sheltering fertilized eggs until hatching. Cardinalfishes are nocturnal and most live on shallow reefs. Worldwide, there are about 23 genera, maybe 275 species, and four species live within our range. The three species that currently are found off Southern California seem to have become established during warm-water periods and, when things cool down, they may not survive the experience. Fossil apogonids have been found in the Middle Eocene (about 50-million-year-old) formations at Monte Bolca (Italy).

Apogon pacificus
(Herre, 1935)
Pink Cardinalfish

GERALD ALLEN

ETYMOLOGY: *Apogon* means "without" and "beard" (these fish were at one time thought to be closely related to goatfishes which do have barbels) and *pacificus* relates to the Pacific Ocean.
THE BASICS: Maximum Length: 10 cm (4 in) TL. The Ranges: San Clemente Island and mainland off Arrecife Sacramento (29°40'N, 115°47'W) (central Baja California) to Cabo San Lucas (southern Baja California) to Pucusana (Peru), including Gulf of California. 1–96 m (3–315 ft). Length-weight parameters (TL, cm, gr): (sexes combined) $W = 0.01034L^{3.07492}$ (Balart et al. 2006).
SALIENT CHARACTERS: This small species is usually pink or reddish (sometime almost white), with a vertical black bar below the second dorsal fin, two very noticeable gold bars on each eye, and a black stripe on snout.
LIFE HISTORY: Pinks are nocturnally active reef dwellers that are usually found over high-relief rocky bottoms. They eat crustaceans and small fishes.

FAMILY MALACANTHIDAE—Tilefishes

Tilefishes are found in marine waters throughout the world. There are five genera and around 40 species. Within our range, there are two species (*Caulolatilus princeps*, which seems happy up our way, and *C. affinis*, a mostly tropical species), and a poorly documented record from Southern California of a third species, *C. hubbsi*. Tilefishes are oviparous, the eggs are likely planktonic, and the larvae are planktonic. Fossil malacanthids are known from the Middle and Late Eocene (maybe as much as 40 million years ago) of the Caucasus region.

Caulolatilus princeps
(Jenyns, 1840)
Ocean Whitefish

ETYMOLOGY AND COLLOQUIAL NAMES: *Caulolatilus* is Greek for "stem" and "*Latilus*" (a genus of Malacanthidae, now called *Branchiostegus*) and *princeps* means "a leader" in Latin. "Whitefish" and "blanquillo" were used in the 19th century. In Mexico, they are called "pez blanco" and "blanquillo."
THE BASICS: Maximum Length: 102 cm (40 in) TL. Maximum Weight: 6.3 kg (13.8 lb). The Ranges: Vancouver Island to Chile, including Gulf of California. They are occasional along the Central California coast, common in Southern California and northern Baja

A juvenile takes its ease in a sand dollar bed.

California, and are startlingly abundant starting in Bahia de Sebastian Vizcaino (central Baja California). At depths of 3–189 m (10–620 ft). Larvae: Hatching length = less than 2.6 mm, flexion length = about 5.5–7 mm, transformation length = 0.8–1.5 cm (0.3–0.6 in). Von Bertalanffy (TL, mm): (sexes combined) L_∞ = 778.74, k = 0.23, t_0 = 0.02 (Cooksey 1980). Length-weight (TL, mm, gr): (sexes combined) W = $0.00000304L^{3.22}$ (Cooksey 1980).
SALIENT CHARACTERS: These are very attractive, kind of fusiform, fish. They have long dorsal and anal fins and a small mouth. Whitefish are brown or tan on backs and sides and white below, with fins that are striped with light yellow and blue.
LIFE HISTORY: Young-of-the-year settle in nearshore waters at as small as at least 3.8 cm (2 in) SL. Juveniles seem to like low-lying structure or even sandy bottoms; you can often see young-of-the-year in sand dollar beds. It is not clear whether juveniles school; certainly solitary individuals are often observed. Juveniles are active during both day and night. Larger fish usually live over reefs and among eelgrass and the like, although they often root around in the surrounding sand flats. Adults form kind of loose aggregations, mostly near the bottom, but they occasionally are found in midwaters and, when in kelp beds, even in the canopy. Studies at Santa Catalina Island demonstrate that adults don't move about very much.

Ocean whitefish live to at least 13 years old. Off Southern California, females probably mature at 3–4 years of age (39–47 cm, 15–19 in, TL) and males at 4–5 years (47–56 cm, 19–22 in). At least off Southern California, something interesting seems to be happening, or rather not happening, with whitefish reproduction. Here, several studies have shown that females have large, and ripe, ovaries from about May–October. Despite this, no one has every captured a whitefish larvae off Southern California. On the other hand, a few larvae have been captured as far north as about Ensenada (northern Baja California) and they are plentiful from Bahia de Sebastian Vizcaino (central Baja California) southward. Most of these larvae occur in July and August, but a few have been taken in every month except December. What this implies is that, despite all these females with ripe eggs, whitefish fail to reproduce off Southern California. Thus, all of the whitefish in Southern California come northward from Mexico, as pelagic or benthic juveniles (and I suppose perhaps a few as adults). In the tropical waters off La Paz (Gulf of California), whitefish appear to be fall through spring spawners. Ocean whitefish feed on a very wide range of prey, including crabs, shrimps, octopuses, squids, polychaetes, copepods, clams, scallops, medusae, snails, bryozoans, and fishes. Whitefish feed in the water column and on and in the bottom, over both rocks and sand. They are eaten by giant sea bass.
FISHERY: Whitefish were an important species in the diets of the indigenous folks living on Isla Cedros (central Baja California). As far back as the 1890s, this was a commonly taken commercial species along the Southern California coast, where it was sold both fresh and salted. It remained of some importance to the fresh fish markets for many decades thereafter, but was often a bycatch of the rockfish hook-and-line fishery. Today, it is still taken in relatively small numbers by commercial

KEVIN LEE

rockfish fishermen. On the other hand, ocean whitefish are very important in the artisanal commercial fisheries on the outer coast of northern and central Baja California and one simply sees tonnage of them in the Mercado Negro fish market in Ensenada (northern Baja California). In addition, the massive overfishing of larger species in the Gulf of California has also shifted effort toward whitefish. Way back in 1892, Carl Eigenmann noted that ocean whitefish sometimes have a bitter flavor, and this observation has been repeated in various publications since that time. So far, I have yet to meet anyone who agrees with Carl, but maybe I have not yet spoken with the right foodistas? This is a very important species in the recreational catch in Southern California and northern Baja California (southward to at least Bahia San Quintin).

Here is a quote from Holder (1913) on catching 4.5 to 5.5 kg (10–12 lb) whitefish on a reef at San Clemente Island: "I took so many whitefishes that day on the side of that beautiful mountain of the sea, up whose sapphire sides Queen Gulnare [a royal underwater being in the *Arabian Nights*, don't you know] might have appeared at any moment, that I have never felt quite the same regarding a blanquillo since." *So, how many whitefish did Queen Gulnare catch?*

FAMILY ECHENEIDAE—Remoras

The remoras (here meant to include all of the four genera and eight species in this family) are found in all of the world's oceans, mostly in tropical and subtropical waters. Seven species live within our range and all have been taken as far north as Southern California. One expects they are most likely to reach our waters during warm-water periods. In all species, the spiny part of the dorsal fin has evolved (yes, I said evolved, don't get me started on that) into a disk with movable ridges that stick on to things. Depending on the species, hosts include sharks, rays, sea turtles, bony fishes, cetaceans, manatees, and ships. Some echenenids are fairly specific about what they attach to, while others are positively promiscuous. Remoras are oviparous and have planktonic eggs and larvae. Eggs of at least some species are 2.1–2.7 mm in diameter and newly hatched larvae are 7.5 mm (0.3 in) or less long. A fossil of an echeneid similar to *Echeneis* or *Remora* was found in 28 million-year-old strata (Oligocene) in Germany. None of the echeneids appear to be routinely caught or consumed. A key to the various eastern tropical Pacific species is in Fischer et al. (1995) and Eschmeyer and Herald (1983) have descriptions of most of the echeneids you are likely to encounter.

Early on, it was proposed that the remora-host relationship was symbiotic with both partners getting something out of the deal. Now, researchers wonder. Brunnschweiler (2006) (in spite of having a name that sounds like a particularly savory kind of sausage) makes the case that, at least for the sharksucker, *Echeneis naucrates*, the relationship is really a "subtle host-parasite" one, where the fish gets all the goodies and the host gets the shaft, albeit a small one. Given the kind of high-risk environment remoras find themselves in, what with hanging out with sharks, billfishes, and the like, remarkably few seem to get eaten by their hosts. It does happen, of course, as Stephanie Pancretz sent me a picture of one that a striped marlin had coughed up. Sea birds also eat small ones.

Pliny the Elder, a man who apparently believed every damn thing anyone ever told him, has this to say about remoras in his stylishly inaccurate *Natural History*. Referring to the adhesive power of remoras, he notes: "This little creature...prevents vessels from moving. How futile a creature is man, seeing that those rams, armed for striking with bronze and iron, can be checked and held fast by a little fish six inches long!...Within our memory the fish stayed the ship of the Emperor Gaius [Caligula] as he was sailing back from Astura to Antium. As it turned out, the little fish also proved ominous, because very soon after that Emperor's return to Rome on this occasion he was stabbed by his own men." *So, do I have this right? The Emperor Caligula was assassinated because his ship was delayed by a fish? I realize that Gibbons felt that the decline of the Roman Empire was caused in part by an inability to solve problems in emperor succession, but isn't this carrying things a bit too far?*

Again referring to remoras, and not content to associate them with the obviously opaque process dictating the Roman succession, Pliny also opines: "And for this reason it also has an evil reputation for supplying a love-charm and for acting as a spell to hinder litigation in the courts, which accusations it counter-balances only by its laudable property of stopping fluxes of the womb in pregnant women and holding back the offspring till the time of birth." *OK, if we properly understand this, not only can remoras cause someone to fall in love with you (perhaps a good thing), they also prevent premature births (clearly a better thing), and will also harass lawyers (certainly the best thing).*

William Dampier (1652–1715), pirate, explorer, mapmaker, and one of the first travel writers, noted that during his buccaneering days in the Caribbean those remoras associating with ships would dine on "such filth as is daily thrown over-board or on mere excrements" (Preston and Preston 2004). *Holy smokes, so if Dampier doesn't consider "mere excrements" as "filth," just what must "filth" have been like?*

Echeneis naucrates

Linnaeus, 1758

Sharksucker

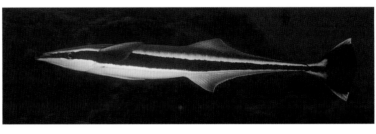

JOHN RANDALL

ETYMOLOGY AND COLLOQUIAL NAME: *Echeneis* is Greek for "holding back" and "a ship" and *naucrates* ultimately comes from the Greek for "ship" and "to guide." The Japanese call them "kobanzame."

THE BASICS: Maximum Length: 110 cm (43 in) TL. Maximum Weight: 5.4 kg (11.9 lb). The Ranges: Circumglobal; Sea of Japan, off northern Hokkaido, possibly as far north as southern Kuril Islands; Southern California to Chile, including the Gulf of California. Pelagic, surface to 35 m (116 ft), perhaps to 50 m (164 ft). Eggs: 2.5 mm. Length-weight parameters (FL, cm, gr): (sexes combined) $W = 0.0008L^{3.358}$ (Kulbicki et al. 2005).

SALIENT CHARACTERS: Sharksuckers are among the most distinctive of the remoras. They are very long and slim, have a projecting lower jaw, and are gray or brown with a black bar that runs the length of the body (lower jaw to caudal fin). Sharksuckers periodically have dark vertical bars.

LIFE HISTORY: Sharksuckers attach to a very wide range of hosts, including sharks, rays, bony fish, sea turtles, manatees, dolphins, and whales. Mostly found in shallow waters, they are one of the echeneids that are more loosely associated with their hosts and often separate from them. In an aquarium study, sharksuckers spawned at night. A female was driven to the surface by a male, a male stimulated the female's abdomen with his disk, and after egg release a number of males released sperm. A female spawned about 500 eggs per day and they hatched about 62 hours after fertilization at 28°C (82°F). In this study, juveniles would attach to aquarium sides after 35 days, at 5.5 cm (2 in) SL. Other studies have found that attachment to hosts starts at anywhere between 4–8 cm (2–3 in) SL. First hosts often include such bony fishes as boxfish and parrotfish. Brunnschweiler (2006) examined the position of sharksuckers on sharks and found that most were on the belly region or pectoral fins. There was evidence that these fish cause some discomfort to their shark hosts. Both blacktip sharks and bull sharks that have these fishes attached tend to swim faster and also go through various maneuvers, apparently attempting to shake loose their hitchhikers. It may be that the sharksuckers are increasing friction for the shark, thus increasing the amount of drag as the shark swims. The suckers may also just plain hurt. Shark suckers are known to eat zooplankton, parasitic copepods and isopods, and manatee feces. Hey, someone has to eat it.

ORIGINS AND RELATIONSHIPS: The oldest fossil sharksucker known is *Echeneis urupensis* from the Early Miocene-Late Oligocene (23 million years ago or older) of the Caucasus region. Sharksuckers are most closely related to *Echeneis neucratoides*.

AND THIS FROM THE FOLKS WHO GAVE US THE INQUISITION

Peter Martyr d'Anghera (1457–1526) was a scholar and political advisor in Spain, who worked both for the Church and nobility. His principal work, *De Orbe Novo*, first published in Venice in 1504 (a recent English edition is from Putnam, 1912), is a compilation of the travel accounts and official reports of Italian and Spanish explorers, beginning with Columbus. Martyr had access both to the explorers and to their letters and diaries. These undeniably colorful accounts, unsullied by any kind of logical filter, combine accurate portrayals and just weird stuff in equal proportion. One story, acquired from Columbus, details the use by Caribbean fishermen of remoras to catch turtles and fishes. Here is what P.M.A. wrote: "Everybody has assured me that they have seen fishermen use this fish just as commonly as we chase hares with French dogs…it is shaped like an eel and no larger. It attacks fish larger than itself, or turtles larger than a shield; it resembles a weasel seizing a pigeon or still larger animal by its throat, and never leaving go until it is dead. Fishermen tie this fish to the side of their barque, for it must not be exposed to the bright sun, from which it shrinks. The most extraordinary thing is that it has at the back of its head a sort of very tough pocket. As soon as the fisherman sees any fish swimming near the barque, he gives the signal for attack and lets go the little cord…The fish descends on its prey and turning its head throws the skin pouch over the neck of the victim, if it is a large fish. On the contrary, if it is a turtle, the fish attaches itself where the turtle protrudes from its shell, and never lets go till the fisherman pulls it with a little cord to the side of the barque…When the prey is in the barque, the hunting-fish returns to its place and never moves, save when they give it a piece of the animal, just as one gives a bit of quail to a falcon… The Spaniard calls this fish Reverso, meaning one who turns around, because it is when turning that it attacks and seizes the prey with its pocket-shaped skin." Interestingly, this form of fishing was practiced worldwide throughout the tropics and was still going strong in Cuba as late as the 1930s.

Remora remora
(Linnaeus, 1758)

Remora

ETYMOLOGY AND COLLOQUIAL NAME: *Remora* is an old name meaning "holding back." They are called "naga-koban" in Japan.

THE BASICS: Maximum Length: 86.4 cm (34 in) TL. Maximum Weight: An 80 cm (32 in) fish weighed 6.7 kg (14 lb). The Ranges: Circumglobal; in western Pacific as far north as southern Kuril Islands; in eastern Pacific from Washington to Chile, including the Gulf of California. Pelagic, surface to 100 m (330 ft) (perhaps to 200 m, 656 ft).

PETER WIRTZ

SALIENT CHARACTERS: Kind of the classic remora look about this species, what with the flattened head containing a relatively small sucking disc and the projecting lower jaw. They are dark.

LIFE HISTORY: Another of the fairly nonspecific suckerfish, remoras attach to a wide range of sharks, along with mantas, billfishes, yellowfin tuna, and sea turtles. Entire "families" ranging, from small juveniles to probably adults, are seen on the same fish. Remoras feed on zooplankton and parasitic copepods. They are eaten by marlins, sharks, tunas, and sea birds.

RELATIONSHIPS: This species is most closely related to *Remora brachyptera*.

REMARKS: The naturalist Frederick Debell Bennet wrote extensively (Bennet 1840) about the fish he called a "remora." This might or might not be this species, but, for the sake of argument, let's assume it is. Regarding what it attaches to, he notes: "Any convenient floating object is, however, also acceptable: we have seen them adhering to turtle, albacore [yellowfin tuna?], whales, and the bottom of ships. It is not true that the Remora receives any nutriment through its sucker, or that it in any way injures the animals to which it may adhere: its capacious and well-armed mouth, and the food contained in its stomach, denote that this fish is as capable of catering for itself as any other species, of more independent habits…The species is not altogether free from enemies, although it is evidently secure from the ferocity of the shark. I have already noticed, that two of these fish had been devoured by a Round-Diodon, and we took a third dead example from the maw of an albacore. Some perfectly white Remoras which we noticed, both adhering to a shark and swimming by its side, in company with others of the normal black hue, would sanction the belief that this species is liable to an albino variety…It often happened, after whales or sharks had been destroyed, that the Tuscan [the whaling ship] was attended by Sucking-fish for several successive weeks. Great numbers of them were taken by hook and line, baited with flesh. They take a 'still bait' readily: but some tact is required to draw them out of the water, as the instant they are hooked, they will sometimes fix themselves by their sucker to the keel of the ship, and defy every attempt to complete their capture."

FAMILY CORYPHAENIDAE—Dolphinfishes

The tropical marine family Coryphaenidae is comprised of one genus with two species. Both *Coryphaena hippurus* and *C. equiselis* are found within our range, although only *C. hippurus* reaches into California waters. Dolphinfishes are oviparous with pelagic eggs and larvae. A fossil of what might be a coryphaenid was found in 50-million-year-old Middle Eocene strata. A fossil dolphinfish was taken from 7.6–8.6-million-year-old strata in Southern California. Dolphinfishes are most closely related to cobia, family Rachycentridae.

Coryphaena hippurus
Linnaeus, 1758
Dolphinfish

Dolphinfish are mostly pelagic, albeit with one twist: they just love to hang around floating stuff.

ETYMOLOGY AND COLLOQUIAL NAMES: *Coryphaena* is the Greek word for this species that Aristotle used and it means "helmet" and "to show" and *hippurus* means "horse" and "tail" in Greek. Most people in both California and south of the border call them "dorado." The Japanese name is "shiira." Because they are found throughout the world, dolphinfish have acquired a nice variety of names, including the ever popular "bakhti bakhti" of Syria, the romantic "coriphene" of France, the mysterious "fei niau fu" of Taiwan, and the tongue twisting "dakaunomoutas" of Cyprus. In the past, Americanskis routinely referred to them as "dolphins," which caused some folks to think that people were fishing for Flipper. Some sporties call them "dodos."

THE BASICS: Maximum Length: 210 cm (83 in) TL. Maximum Weight: 46 kg (101.2 lb). The Ranges: Circumglobal; as far north as southern Kuril Islands; Grays Harbor (Washington) to Chile, including the Gulf of California. In the western Pacific, common as far north as the southern Kurils. In the eastern Pacific, dolphinfish are often relatively abundant as far north as Southern California. In the 1957 El Niño, there were numbers of them as far north as Grays Harbor. Surface to about 200 m (656 ft). Eggs: 1.2–1.7 mm. Larvae: hatching length = 3.9–5.1 mm, flexion length = about 7.5–9 mm, transformation length = about 1.4–2.4 cm. Von Bertalanffy parameters (FL, cm): (sexes combined, Eastern Tropical Pacific) L_∞ = 194,

This is pretty sad. Apparently, more than 3,600 years ago, Mediterranean dolphinfish fishermen made so little they couldn't afford to purchase skivvies.

THERA

©MASA USHIODA-COOLWATERPHOTO.COM

$k = 0.91$, $t_0 = 0.1049$ (PFMC 2003). Length-weight parameters (FL, mm, kg): (sexes combined) W = $0.0000000157L^{2.913}$ (RecFin 2009). Palko et al. (1982) has a bunch of other l-w relationships.

SALIENT CHARACTERS: These are truly gorgeous fish, compressed and sleek with very long single dorsal and anal fins. They tend to be gold or yellow-green, with flashes of metallic blue and green on backs and sides, and white or yellow on belly. Many fish have blue, green and/or black spots. Dark vertical bars cover the sides of small individuals (adults, too, at times display dark bars). At around 40 cm (16 in) FL, males develop a pronounced crest on their foreheads, giving them a very steep, blunt profile (think Charles Laughton in *The Bribe*). Small juveniles have a series of alternating dark and light bars.

LIFE HISTORY: Young-of-the-year (starting at least as small as 3.4 cm, 1 in, SL) recruit from the plankton to drifting stuff. Juveniles are mostly found in the open ocean, although occasionally they come into estuaries and harbors. Juveniles and adults stay in waters between 20–30°C (68–86°F), and mostly at 24°C (75°F) or greater. Although all life stages just love to hang out with drifting

material, small males and all sizes of females are most common around flotsam and jetsam. Schools enter Southern California when California Current flow decreases in intensity, causing low upwelling and relatively warm water. Fish in Southern California waters mostly stay inshore of the colder California Current (i.e., they are relatively close to shore). At least in Hawai'i, dolphinfish tend to be closer to the surface during the day. Studies imply that dolphinfish worldwide are part of a single, genetically similar, population. However, fish in the Mediterranean are the most divergent. Based on larval surveys, it appears that this species spawns mostly from about Punta Eugenia (Baja California) southward, although limited spawning occurs as far northward as Southern California.

Dolphinfish grow fast and die young. They live to about 4 years old, and grow to about 112–126 cm FL (44–50 in) in one year. Growth rates vary between areas. In the wild, they mature as early as 4 months old (around 40 cm, 16 in, FL) and at 3 months old in captivity. Females are batch spawners and release eggs throughout the year in waters of 24°C (75°F) or more, but only during the warm-water season in more temperate zones. Fertilized eggs hatch in 40–53 hours at 24–26°C (75–79°F). Over a year, a female may produce between 240,000 and almost 3 million eggs. Dolphinfish feed during the day, and mostly eat water-column fishes and invertebrates. In the eastern Pacific, a very wide range of fishes are consumed, along with euphausiids, hyperiid amphipods, pelagic red crabs, portunid crabs, squids, and octopuses. Hatchlings of olive ridley turtles were found in the stomachs of dolphinfish swimming just off a turtle nesting area near Sinoloa, Mexico. At least in the Caribbean Sea, males feed more on such fast-moving animals as flyingfishes and squids than do females. Dolphinfish also occasionally feed near the bottom, as a piece of coral was found in the stomach of one caught off Hawai'i. Predators include albacore, bigeye, skipjack, and yellowfin tunas, black, blue, and striped marlins, cookiecutter sharks, dolphinfish, scalloped hammerheads, swordfish, and wahoos. Young fish are eaten by a range of seabirds. One study hypothesized that rough-toothed dolphins *(Steno bredanensis)* may specialize in eating dolphinfish.

FISHERY: Historically, dolphinfish were occasionally landed by commercial fishermen in Southern California and it is likely that some of these were caught in Baja California waters. With the rise of the drift gill net fishery in the late 20th century, more dolphinfish were taken off California. Today, commercial fishermen catch fair numbers for sale fresh in retail markets. Early on off Japan, fishermen took advantage of the species' attraction to flotsam. They lashed bamboo poles together, forming a raft, and the dolphinfish huddled under these structures, the fishermen then encircling the fish with purse seines. From Southern

California southward, dolphinfish are often caught by recreational anglers, mostly when they fish under drifting kelp mats. About 85% of the fish taken in the Southern California fishery are less than 1 year old.

Here's a story from Ed Ries' lovely book *Tales of the Golden Years of California Ocean Fishing 1900-1950* (Monterey Publications, 2007). Ed notes that in the 1930s, when it was legal to catch and then sell fishes taken from sportfishing party vessels, he and a friend had taken a large number of dolphinfish while fishing off San Diego: "That evening we stowed the fish in the rumble seat of the Model A Ford and took off for L. A. to peddle our catch. To our dismay the small markets and restaurants on our route refused to buy. None had ever seen a dolphin or heard of the Hawai'ian taste treat, mahi-mahi...Noticing that the golden dorado tails protruding from the crushed ice in our fish box bore a close resemblance to the caudal fins of yellowtail, I had an inspiration...Chop, chop and back into the ice went the dolphins minus their funny-looking heads. They were quickly disposed of at yellowtail prices. One buyer remarked on the flat bodies, but I told him it was a result of the fish being well packed down in the ice."

MISCELLANY: For those of you who think about these things, a number of studies have shown that dolphinfish are low in mercury, likely the result of a short life span that does not give these fish much time to accumulate the stuff.

FAMILY CARANGIDAE—Jacks and Pompanos

Carangids are mostly marine fishes (although the young of some species inhabit estuarine waters), comprising around 32 genera and 140 species. There are 29 species within our range and 15 species have been found from Southern California northward. All are oviparous, with planktonic eggs and larvae. Fossil carangids, such as *Archaeus oblongus*, are known from as far back as the Late Paleocene/Early Eocene (about 55 million years ago) in southern Europe. Carangid fossils have been taken in Southern California Miocene strata that is 7.6–8.6 million years old. The many, many jack species living in the eastern tropical Pacific are presented in Fischer et al. (1995).

Naucrates ductor
(Linnaeus, 1758)
Pilotfish

MOBULAMOBULAR

ETYMOLOGY AND COLLOQUIAL NAME: *Naucrates* is derived from the Greek word meaning "ruler of ships" and *ductor* is Latin for "a leader." The colloquial name comes from the way these fish accompany sharks, rays, turtles, and ships. "Burimodoki" is the Japanese name.

THE BASICS: Maximum Length: 70 cm (28 in) TL. The Ranges: Circumglobal; in western Pacific as far north as southern Kuril Islands; Vancouver Island to Chile, including the Gulf of California. Only a few fish have been noted as far north as Southern California.

Surface to 150 m (495 ft). Eggs: 1.3 mm. Larvae: hatching length = <3 mm; flexion length = 4.1–6.4 mm; transformation length = 1.6–4.5 cm.

SALIENT CHARACTERS: It would be difficult to mistake this fusiform silver or bluish species, with 5–7 dark bars and a white-tipped caudal fin, for any other fish in the eastern Pacific.

LIFE HISTORY: Juveniles (at least as small as 2.9 cm, 1 in SL) often associate with drifting material (e.g., algae, medusae, and debris), which they leave for large, pelagic animals at around 6 months old and maybe 30 cm (12 in) TL. As noted above, pilotfish frequently accompany larger fish; they are often found at the base of the pectoral fins of sharks. Pilotfish have been known to accompany ships for as long as 80 days.

Females are batch spawners and, in the eastern tropical Pacific, larvae have been collected between February–October. Pilotfish feed on a wide range of zooplankton (e.g., pteropods, euphausiids, hyperiid amphipods, copepods, pelagic snails, fish larvae, and medusae), squids, and fishes. Predators include bigeye and yellowfin tunas, dolphinfish, sailfish, striped marlins, red-tailed tropicbirds, and various terns and noddies.

FISHERY: There doesn't seem to be much of a commercial fishery for these fish, although they are taken as a by-catch in the Mediterranean dolphinfish fishery.

REMARKS: The Greeks knew something about pilotfish, as Aristotle referred to them as the "Dolphin's Louse." And here is what the second-century Roman Empire poet Oppian (he was actually from Cilicia in what is now southern Turkey) wrote about them in *Halieutica*, his Greek hexameter poem about fish and fishing: "The pilot-fish which sailors revere exceedingly, and they have given him this name for his convoying of ships. For they delight exceedingly in ships that run over the wet seas...the pilot-fishes always attend swift-faring ships, so long as no fear of the earth diverts them away. But when they mark the dry land–and greatly do they abhor the solid earth–they all turn back gain in a body and rush away." Clearly, it's best to think of Oppian as a cross between Wordsworth and one of the pear-shaped guys who catch bass on cable television on Saturday mornings: "Woo doggies, didn' I tell you that marinated pork ear on one of these surface poppers is just dynamite, I mean dynamite, when fishin' the weeds in these-here sewer settlin' ponds?"

Bennett (1840), stuck on a whaling ship for 4 years and with a lot of time on his hands, wrote: "Pilot-fish are almost invariably found in attendance upon the shark...The reputation this has obtained of being the shark's pilot or provider...would appear to be groundless. A fact, however, which came under my notice during a voyage from India, in the year 1832, led me to believe that there is some just foundation for this popular opinion...A shark was seen close to the ship, and attended by two Pilot-fish, which generally swam one above and the other below him, and occasionally went off some distance, as if to explore the surrounding sea; although it was seldom long before they returned, and resumed their former positions. A baited hook was lowered from the bow of the ship; but the shark, when alone, passed it several times without notice, and apparently without seeing it. One of the foraging Pilot-fish then approached the bait, and immediately swam off to where the Shark was headed in a contrary direction; when the monster instantly turned, and followed his informant, which now swam ahead of him, in a direct line toward the suspended bait. He did not then hesitate a moment, but seized it, and was captured."

Seriola lalandi
Valenciennes, 1833
Yellowtail

ETYMOLOGY AND COLLOQUIAL
NAMES: *Seriola* is an Italian name for a related species in the Mediterranean and *lalandi* honors Pierre Antoine Delalande (1787–1823), a French explorer-naturalist who collected animals in Portugal, Brazil, and South Africa. The name "yellowtail" goes back at least to the late 19th century. In Mexico, they are called "jurel" and "hiramasa" in Japan.

In a misguided attempt to infantilize us, the American Fisheries Society wants to call this species "yellowtail jack" to avoid some presumed confusion with "yellowtail rockfish" and "yellowtail snapper." To the AFS, I say, "Pooey." To the AFS, I say, "May parasitic iso-

MARC CHAMBERLAIN

pods drink blood from your larynx." Because, oh AFS, this will not happen. For more than 125 years, Californians of All Races, Creeds, and Colors (well, not puce), Californians Tall and Californians Height-Challenged, Californians to the Manor Born and Californians Whose Parents Were in No Way Involved in Show Business, and Californians with Surfer's Knots and Californians Who Have Never Surfed Neither with Board nor Body, have called them "yellowtail." And we now go on record as stating, "Yellowtail Today, Yellowtail Tomorrow, Yellowtail Forever."

THE BASICS: Maximum Length: 250 cm (98 in) TL. Maximum Weight: The International Gamefish Association says the largest Pacific Coast fish weighed 41.8 kg (92.1 lb). In their records, the largest fish was from New Zealand and weighed 52 kg (114.6 lb). The Ranges: Circumglobal; in western North Pacific as far north as southern Kuril Islands; in eastern Pacific, from northern British Columbia (54°35'N, 31°00'W) to Chile, including the Gulf of California. While they are mostly found from about Santa Rosa Island southward, they are occasional at least as far north as about 482 km (260 nm) off the coast of southern Vancouver Island. Surface to 300 m (984 ft). Eggs: about 1.4 mm. Larvae: hatching length = about 3–4 mm, flexion length = about 6.6–8.6 mm, transformation length = about 2.2 cm. Von Bertalanffy parameters (FL, mm): (sexes combined) L_∞ = 1,291, k = 0.136, t_0 = -1.9 (Baxter 1960). Length-weight parameters (FL, mm, lb): (sexes combined) W = 0.00000007439L$^{2.85}$ (Baxter 1960).

SALIENT CHARACTERS: Kind of a classic pelagic species is the yellowtail. They are fusiform, with a yellow and deeply forked tail. Their backs are often metallic blue-green or olive-green, with a dusky or yellow stripe along each side, and a dark bar through each eye.

LIFE HISTORY: Juveniles as small as 5.6 cm (2 in) FL have been taken off Southern California. They commonly hang out among drifting kelp and other flotsam. These jacks frequently school (juveniles with similar-sized Pacific barracuda and Pacific bonito), although you will often see small groups or even single individuals. Yellows are most often found in association with some kind of structure, such as kelp, rock reefs, or oil platforms. In open water, all sizes are attracted to kelp mats and various other flotsam. Most yellows in Southern California migrate from central and northern Baja California, usually during the spring, but in some years they begin their northward migration as early as late winter. Tagging studies from the 1950s and 1960s show that many of the fish entering Southern California come from the Islas Cedros (central Baja California) region. Some fish, particularly larger ones, remain in Southern California year-round. Such areas as Anacapa Island and Cortes Bank were, in previous years, famous for their very large, apparently resident, fish. In the 19th century, they occasionally entered San Diego Bay. Along the Pacific Coast, yellows have been found in waters between 10.6–25°C (51–77°F), although mostly not on the lower end of that range.

Yellowtail live to at least 12 years old. Some females are mature when 20 months old and 50.6 cm (20 in) FL and all are mature by their third summer

(at 63.4 cm, 25 in). Along the Pacific Coast, spawning occurs from April–October, mostly from July–September. A few yellowtail spawn off Southern California, although larval studies imply that most spawning occurs from Bahia de Sebastian Vizcaino (central Baja California) southward to off Laguna San Ignacio (southern Baja California). Females are batch spawners and produce 450,000 to at least 3,914,000 eggs per year. David Starr Jordan, quoted in Goode (1884), noted: "It spawns about August 18." This is the kind of statement that comes from being one of only maybe five fish biologists at the time on the entire Pacific Coast. Unless, of course, the species does only spawn around August 18. In the Gulf of California, spawning was observed during April in 10–20 m (33–66 ft) of water, over rocky reefs and seamounts. Here, spawning started 3 days before the full moon, among aggregations of up to 80 fish. And here's an excerpt from a purse seine fisherman's diary recording spawning activity over the Uncle Sam Bank (southern Baja California) (Baxter 1960): "From 11:00 A.M to 4:00 P.M., hundreds of yellowtail were

ONE DAMN YELLOWTAIL STORY AFTER ANOTHER

Holder (1910c) wrote: "The yellowtail is the fish of the people. Boys, children, women, all fish for it, and few anglers can resist its game plays. In fact the Bay of Avalon will often be crowded in some place with rowboats, each containing two or three men, women, or children, all provided with light rods of various kinds, and all fishing for yellowtail. I have seen forty or nearly twice as many anchored together, and over two hundred anglers. Every time a fish was hooked the entire yellowtail village would raise a shout that echoed far back and up the canons of the Isle of Summer, and they would continue to shout until the fish was landed."

And then we have Holder (1913): "I have seen the bay [sic] of Avalon, ordinarily as smooth as glass, turned into a miniature maelstrom by seemingly ten thousand fishes, and all over twenty pounds. They came in like a raging band of wolves and tinted the waters of the beautiful crescent a golden hue. The roar of the waters quickly attracted the attention of the townspeople, and men, women and children ran for lines and rods, and then for the beach. I was one of the fortunates who secured a boat and drifted in the midst of the utterly frantic school that was driving a large shoal of anchovies in upon the shore, charging into the mass, glutting themselves, killing from mere blood lust and frenzy, utterly crazed with excitement and lost to all sense of security as they surged along the surface to catch the small fry that made loud splashes, the combined sound of which produced a roar as of the sea breaking on some distant beach, while the waters of the bay were converted into a silvery foam, as though a weird windless storm was tearing along the surface."

PIERRE ANTOINE DELALANDE

As noted above, between 1818 and 1820 Delalande collected animals in South Africa. The collections, made with the assistance of his 11-year-old nephew Jules Pierre Verreaux were, I suppose by the lights of today, appallingly successful. It included 131,405 items, of which over 120,000 were plants. However, there were also 288 non-human mammals, 2,205 birds, 322 reptiles, 265 fish, 3,875 shellfish, along with human skulls of various native peoples, and nearly two dozen skeletons of locals unearthed from a Cape Town cemetery and a South African battlefield. There's not much more to tell about Delalande, he died of fever in France in 1823. But his nephew, Jules Verreaux (1807–1873), deserves a bit more ink. Verreaux was the son of Jacques Verreaux, founder (in 1800) of the world famous French taxidermy emporium, Maison Verreaux. Jules showed an early talent for his father's trade and that was why he went to Africa with his uncle Pierre at such a young age. In 1825, soon after their return to France, Jules Verreaux went back to Africa and over the next 7 years, aided by his two brothers, collected thousands of specimens for the family taxidermy shop. The three Verreaux brothers exhibited what in hindsight was a rather single-minded pursuit of specimens, for among the lions, giraffes, cheetahs and other wildlife, they also shipped back the body of an African man. They prepared all of them to their usual high standards, arranged in a very lifelike way, and exhibited in their Paris shop. Time having passed, the dead-and-stuffed man was purchased by Francesc Darder, a Spanish naturalist, who, apparently stuck for something to present at the Barcelona World Exhibition of 1888, decided to use the gentleman for "Show and Tell." Precisely what a stuffed human being was meant to portray at the Barcelona World Exhibition of 1888, other than the grotesqueries of the colonial system, is unclear. Some time later the body, now termed "El Negro" because it had been inexplicably painted black (one supposes if it been painted red it would have been called "La Frambuesa" ["The Raspberry"]), wound up in the Franscesc Darder Museum of Natural History in Banyoles, Spain. Not until 2000, and apparently only after much resistance, was the body taken back to Africa and interred in Botswana.

milling about on the surface and a foot below, making short circles. Eggs and milt were streaming out of the fish so thick that the water was made white by them." Yellowtail feed primarily on small fishes and squids, but will not pass up a nice pelagic red crab, or large zooplankter (e.g., pteropods, isopods, and hyperiid amphipods). Off Baja California, I saw a few yellowtail with neat holes in their sides, so predators include cookiecutter sharks.

FISHERY: Yellowtail appear to have been caught in some numbers by Native Americans in Southern California (see a commentary by the British naturalist, A. Menzies, in the Pacific bonito section). Beginning in the late 19th century, the species was subject to a relatively small commercial fishery, centered between San Diego and Los Angeles. Historically, most commercially caught yellowtail were destined for the fresh or salted fish markets. Yellowtail were also occasionally canned. Even though the canned product was apparently acceptable table fodder, and despite spirited attempts at finding a niche market, canned yellowtail never acquired the cachet of canned tuna. Croker (1936) noted that even into the 1930s, yellowtail landed in San Diego were hard- or dry-salted and then shipped to San Francisco where Portuguese folks were the major buyers. In hard-salting, the fish were cleaned, beheaded and split open. Cuts were made in flesh and a great deal of salt rubbed into meat. "A layer of salt is then sprinkled on the floor of the saltery and fish place thereon. Then alternate layers of fish and salt are piled up. The fish are left that way until the moisture has ceased to run - a matter of 10 to 12 days. Then they are spread out on racks in the sun until quite dry." Croker goes on to note that during the same period many other species (including white croakers, various rockfishes, Pacific mackerel, and jack mackerel) were salted and dried. Today, yellows are caught in small numbers for the fresh fish trade. They are a fairly important species in the artisanal commercial fisheries of northern Baja California.

Early on, yellows were taken by handlines, trolling, and gill nets. However, purse seines were by far the most efficient way to capture this species; so efficient, in fact, that by the 1930s some biologists started getting kind of squirrelly about it. In 1933, seining for yellowtail in California waters was prohibited during certain months. This was followed, in 1941, with a law that banned all taking of yellowtail in California waters by purse seine. Of course, because much of the catch was taken in Mexican waters it is debatable how much effect this law had on retarding the catch.

This is one of the premier sport fish in both Southern California and northern Baja California. Particularly in Southern California, it is one of the "exotic" species that excites anglers. While the vast majority is taken from vessels, there are occasional runs near piers and jetties. During the 1983 El Niño, for instance, I saw a number of fish taken off the Goleta Pier, near Santa Barbara. To described the scene as utter chaos does not do justice to the event.

Yellowtail are cultured in New Zealand and Australia.

ORIGINS: An extinct *Seriola*, *S. prisca*, has been found in a Middle Eocene deposit (about 50 million years old) in Italy. *Seriola sanctae-barbarae* was a Miocene (at least 5.3-million-year-old) species living in what is now Southern California.

MISCELLANY: On at least several occasions, yellowtail have been seen rubbing themselves against sharks. In one sighting, 8–15 yellows rubbed themselves against the rear part of a blue shark, perhaps to dislodge parasites.

Here's another neat story. Yellowtail may act cooperatively. As an example, off Santa Catalina Island, divers observed seven yellowtail herding a large school of jack mackerel. After splitting off a small group and chasing them up against an underwater cliff, the yellows spread themselves out, 1–2 m (3–6 ft) apart, and faced the small fish. Suddenly, a single yellow chased into the prey, causing them to scatter outwards, toward the other waiting predators.

And one more. Richard Herrmann, ace underwater photographer, was once diving on a drifting kelp mat off San Diego. While gliding down the plant, he came across a large yellowtail whose rear end was sticking out of the foliage. Thinking the fish was dead, Richard pulled it out, only to have it promptly hurtle back in, this time at an angle that caused the tail to stick out of the water. A reasonable explanation came in the form of pilot whales circling the mat. Richard surveyed the area a bit more and found drifting bits of large fish, including gill covers and gills, implying that the yellowtail had a right to be a tad edgy.

Trachurus symmetricus

(Ayres, 1855)

Jack Mackerel

ETYMOLOGY AND COLLOQUIAL NAMES: *Trachurus* comes from two Greek words for "rough" and "tail" and *symmetricus* is Latin for "symmetrical." Say around 1880, jack mackerel were called "horse mackerel." Today, fishermen often call them "Spanish jack" or "Spanish mackerel."

THE BASICS: Maximum Length: 81.3 cm (32 in) TL. The Ranges: Pacific Ocean, south of Aleutian Islands, Gulf of Alaska to Gulf of California. Surf to 403 m (1,320 ft). Eggs: 0.9–1.1 mm. Larvae: hatching length = 1.9–2.4 mm, flexion length = about 7.5–11 mm, transformation length = about 1.6–2 cm. Von Bertalanffy parameters (FL, mm): (sexes combined) L_∞ = 602.9, k = 0.0935, t_0 = -3.252 (Wine and Knaggs 1975). Length-weight parameters (FL, mm, gr): (sexes combined) W = $0.00000331L^{3.223}$ (Wine and Knaggs 1975).

SALIENT CHARACTERS: Jack mackerel are streamlined fish, blue or green on back and silvery below. They have a dark spot on the upper gill cover and projecting scales (scutes) along a lateral line that dips sharply under the second dorsal fin.

LIFE HISTORY: Pelagic juveniles may associate with jellyfishes. They recruit from the plankton to nearshore waters, often in kelp beds and eelgrass. We saw a number of newly recruited ones in May schooling around a fish attracting device we set out in the Santa Barbara Channel. Juveniles form very large and dense schools that hang out in kelp beds, around oil platforms, over banks, around islands, and out in the middle of

CHRIS GROSSMAN

nowhere (but still mostly close to shore). These juveniles often school with Pacific sardine, Pacific mackerel, and blacksmiths. Both juveniles and adults also hang under drifting kelp. Juveniles have been seen rubbing themselves on a soupfin shark. The pelagic adults tend to be found further offshore, although large fish do move into inshore waters. Off Southern California, adults are perhaps most common more than 322 km (200 mi) from shore and have been found over 966 km (600 mi) from the coast. Eggs and larvae occur over 1,609 km (1,000 mi) from shore, so jack mackerel swim at least that far out. Jackmacks move northward as water temperatures rise and by August and September they wind up in the Gulf of Alaska. In particular, El Niños drive them up the coast. Most fish are found from surface waters to depths of perhaps 6 m (20 ft). Fish live in at least 9.7–19.5°C (50–67°F), perhaps mostly in 13–16°C (55–61°F), and in at least 22.8–33.6 ppt. They are tolerant of somewhat brackish waters. Jack mackerel spawn both in nearshore waters and well offshore (at least to the aforementioned 1,609 km, 1,000 mi), mostly 128–386 km (80–240 mi) offshore. Spawning takes place from Northern California to below Cabo San Lucas (primarily San Francisco–Punta Baja, central Baja California), and is usually earliest in southernmost-offshore locations. Interestingly (at least to me, but I'm easily impressed), most young-of-the-year are found in inshore waters between Southern California and central Baja California. This implies that even those fish that hatch hundreds of kilometers offshore, and way to the north, find their way to southern coastal waters. How do they do that?

Jack mackerel live to over 30 years old. A majority of females mature before their first birthday (at around 20 cm, 8 in, FL) and most are mature by the time they are a little more than a year old and maybe 23.5 cm (9 in). At least a few larvae have been found in every month, so it appears that there can be a little spawning throughout the year. However, most occurs between February–August, peaking about March–June. Larger fish tend to spawn earliest. These are batch spawners; females spawn on average every 5 days and 25 times per year, producing 800–437,000 eggs per batch. Most spawning occurs at water temperatures of 13.9–16.1°C (57–61°F) and the eggs hatch in 2–3 days. Jack mackerel feed primarily on such zooplankters as euphausiids, copepods, and pteropods (and occasionally crustacean larvae, isopods, and ostracods), as well as fishes and squids. They are eaten by lots of animals: a partial list includes fishes (e.g., blue, shortfin mako, and thresher sharks, California halibut, giant sea bass, kelp bass, Pacific bonito, striped marlins, swordfish, and various tunas), Brandt's and pelagic cormorants, seals, sea lions, Dall's porpoises, Pacific white-sided dolphin, and sei whales.

FISHERY: Jack mackerel were commonly caught by Native Americans. In the late 19th century, these fish were a pretty important commercial species, at least partly because they did not spoil quickly. For many decades thereafter, jack mackerel were a minor part of the fresh fish industry. Most were caught incidentally by those hook-and-line and purse seine vessels fishing for Pacific mackerel. And, in fact, jack macks tended to bring higher prices at these markets than did Pacific mackerel. Nevertheless, the overall demand for the species was small. It was not until the later 1940s, with the sardine population having bitten the big one, that the canning industry attempted to replace that venerable species with the still-abundant jack mackerel. As an example, catches rose from about 10 million pounds in 1946 to 130 million pounds in 1947. But before canners could take the big leap, they had to do something about the jack mackerel's name because at that time the species was called "horse mackerel," although the fish is related neither to the mackerel nor equine families. It was the perception of the fishing industry that the public, not being composed of Frenchmen, would not want to purchase something seemingly associated with horses (other than tickets to the Irish Sweepstakes). And thus, in the fateful summer of 1947, a petition was made to the California Division of Fish and Game to change the name to "jack mackerel," a move granted in May, 1948, by the United States Pure Food and Drug Administration. Thus fortified, the industry marched proudly out and did their best to push the now newly minted product. Unfortunately, this canned fish by any other name did not smell particularly sweet and jack mackerel did not become the new sardine. Currently, landings are low along much of the Pacific Coast, although they are caught as bycatch in the salmon and albacore troll fisheries, by the offshore Pacific hake trawl fishery, and by sardine seiners.

Juvenile jack mackerel are often taken from piers.

ORIGINS AND RELATIONSHIPS: It is likely that *Trachurus* first evolved in the Early Miocene (as much as 23 million years ago), in what is now southern European Russia. Regarding the jack mackerel, Cárdenas et al. (2005) note it is most closely related to *T. murphyi* (found off Peru and Chile) and to *T. picturatus*, a species found in the eastern Atlantic Ocean and Mediterranean Sea. They speculate: "One part of the ancestral stock of *T. picturatus*, the ancestor of the eastern Pacific species... extended its range westward across the Atlantic. This group then penetrated into the Pacific Ocean passing over the submerged Isthmus of Panama, spreading along the western coasts of North and South America. The northern part of this group originated into *T. symmetricus* and the southern part gave rise to *T. murphyi*."

MISCELLANY: One fish was found with a deformed lateral line. The lateral line as it extended along the back made a fish hook shape and turned back toward the head. There was a gap and then the lateral line began again.

OTHER SPECIES

Caranx caballus
Günther, 1868
Green Jack

Green jacks reach at least 70 cm (28 in) TL, 2.8 kg (6.2 lb), and live from Monterey Bay to Chile, including the Gulf of California and Hawai'i, but rarely in Southern California. A nearshore species, they inhabit the surf zone to a depth of 100 m (328 ft). Young greenies are often found in lagoons or around drifting material; older ones in shallow waters around sand and low rocks. Spawning reportedly occurs at least in June and October. They feed on fishes and crustaceans. This species is important in some artisanal fisheries (e.g., Gulf of California). Length-weight parameters (TL, cm, gr): (sexes combined) $W = 0.0166L^{2.87}$ (Rojo-Vázquez et al. 2009).

OCTAVIO ABURTO-OROPEZA

Caranx caninus
Günther, 1867
Pacific Crevalle Jack

This jack reaches 100 cm (39 in) TL, 17.7 kg (39 lb), and is found from Huntington Beach (Southern California) to Antofagasta (northern Chile), including the Gulf of California. It is not common off Southern California. Crevalle jacks are a mostly nearshore, usually shallow water species, that inhabits surface to (rarely) 350 m (1,148 ft). Schools of juveniles live in estuaries and lagoons and can tolerate low salinities. Adults are pelagic, but still mostly live inshore. Schools may contain 1,000 or more individuals and may stay within a relatively small area for weeks at a time. Crevalles live to 15 years old. Off Colima, southern Mexico, increased spawning has been noted in May and November. Males and females grow at the same rates. These are primarily crepuscular (dawn and dusk) fish-eaters, although they will also eat larger water column crustaceans. Juveniles eat zooplankton and insects. One study found mussels in the guts of a few fish. These jacks often hunt for food in small groups that may include black skipjack. This is a moderately important commercial species in the Gulf of California and points south. Von Bertalanffy parameters (SL, cm): (sexes combined) $L_\infty = 83.3$, $k = 0.202$, $t_0 = -0.283$ (Espino Barr et al. 2008). Length-weight parameters (TL, cm, gr): (sexes combined) $W = 0.013L^{2.97}$ (Rojo-Vázquez et al. 2009).

OCTAVIO ABURTO-OROPEZA

CHRIS GROSSMAN

Caranx sexfasciatus
Quoy & Gaimard, 1825
Bigeye Trevally

Trevallies grow to perhaps 120 cm (47 in) TL and 18 kg (39.6 lb), and live in both the Pacific and Indian oceans. In the eastern Pacific, they are found from San Diego Bay to Ecuador, including the lower Gulf of California, but are not common in Southern California. This is mostly a nearshore species, moving over reefs and sand, in 1–96 m (3–315 ft). They form widely roaming schools of thousands of individuals. Juveniles live mostly in lagoons and other shallow areas. In the Gulf of California, spawning occurs during daylight hours, from July–September, from the full moon to the waning crescent. Bigeyes feed on water column and benthic prey (e.g., shrimps, mantis shrimps, small fishes, and fish larvae). Inactive during the day, they feed at night. This is a commercially important species in tropical waters. Length-weight parameters (TL, cm, gr): (sexes combined) W = 0.0239L$^{2.78}$ (Rojo-Vázquez et al. 2009).

FAMILY BRAMIDAE—Pomfrets

Pomfrets are pelagic and marine fishes found around the world. There are seven genera, about 22 species, with five species found within our range. Pomfrets are oviparous with pelagic eggs and larvae. The earliest known bramid is *Paucaichthys neamtensis* from the Early Oligocene (at least 29 million year ago) of Romania.

Brama japonica
Hilgendorf, 1878
Pacific Pomfret

WILLIAM VAN ORDEN

ETYMOLOGY AND COLLOQUIAL NAMES: *Brama* comes from the Latin word "brama," referring to a European minnow, and *japonica* harkens to "Japan," the site of its first capture by researchers. "Small-scaled pomfret" is another name and they are called "shimagatsuo" in Japan.

THE BASICS: Maximum Length: 61.4 cm (24 in) FL, but reported to 122 cm (4 ft). Maximum Weight: At least 2.7 kg (5.9 lb). The Ranges: Southern Sea of Japan, off the southern coast of Korean Peninsula to Pacific Ocean (south of Aleutian Islands), and southern Bering Sea to Chile; apparently absent from the tropical eastern Pacific Ocean. In the western Pacific, they are abundant as far north as the southern Kuril Islands and, in the northern and eastern Pacific, from the Gulf of Alaska (seasonally) to at least well off California. Surface–620 m (2,034 ft). Eggs: 1.6–1.7 mm. Larvae: hatching length = about 4 mm, flexion length = about 6.5–8 mm, transformation length = about 1.5 cm (0.6 in). Von Bertalanffy parameters (FL, mm): (sexes combined) L$_\infty$ = 468, k = 0.76, t$_0$ = -0.52 (Pearcy et al. 1993). Length-weight parameters (FL, cm, kg): (sexes combined) W = 0.0001539L$^{2.641}$ (Manzer 1972).

SALIENT CHARACTERS: Another of the very distinctive, pelagic species, this pomfret is compressed, oval, fork tailed, and has a forehead that looks like the fish swam full-bore into something really hard. Generally, they have a dark back and silvery sides and belly; however, I have seen a few dead ones that are gray on back or just silvery all over.

LIFE HISTORY: This is a pelagic species that is usually found well offshore and pretty close to the surface. While albacore fishing off Oregon, Joe Rohleder saw them at the surface and says they were in small, fast-moving schools that reminded him of little sandpipers. In general, adults move northward to feed in subarctic waters in spring and migrate southward to mostly subtropical or (way off California) temperate waters to spawn in fall. Larger fish tend to move farthest northward; one study found that males tended to migrate further north than did females. Juveniles (to about 30 cm, 12 in, FL) remain in subtropical waters throughout the year. Pacific pomfrets have been found in waters between 7–26°C (45–79°F). In the North Pacific, small fish rarely inhabit waters less than 13°C (55°F), while larger fish are mostly in 8–13° (46–55°F). At least in the northwest Pacific, there is some evidence that only juveniles are found in near-surface waters during the day, with adults migrating upward at night.

Pacific pomfrets live to at least 9 years old. They probably mature at 30–40 cm (12–16 in) FL. In the California Current, at least a few larvae are taken throughout the year, although there appears to be a summer-fall peak. In the northwest Pacific, peak spawning occurs January–March. Females are batch spawners. Pacific pomfrets feed on whatever is in their water column environment. This translates to a wide variety of fishes, as well as squids, crustaceans (e.g., amphipods, euphausiids, and sergestid shrimps), pteropods, and heteropods. Predators include blue sharks, blue marlins, longnose lancetfish, and northern fur seals.

FISHERY: Off the west coast of North America, Pacific pomfrets are taken as bycatch by salmon and albacore trollers.

FAMILY LUTJANIDAE—Snappers

Snappers are mostly marine (but occasionally estuarine and freshwater), mostly tropical fishes that are found throughout the world. They comprise 17 genera, about 105 species, with nine in our range. Of these, four species have been found as far north as Southern California. Snappers are oviparous, with planktonic eggs and larvae. Many species are of economic importance. Fossil Lutjanidae have been reported from Miocene deposits (at least 5.3 million years old) in northern Baja California. Keys and illustrations of the many eastern Pacific snappers are found in Fischer et al. (1995).

Lutjanus argentiventris
(Peters, 1869)
Amarillo Snapper

ETYMOLOGY AND COLLOQUIAL NAMES: *Lutjanus* (originally spelled *Lutianus*) is derived from "ikan lutjang," the Malayan word for a local snapper. *Argentiventris* means "silver" and "belly" in Latin. Other names include "yellow snapper" and, in Mexico, "pargo amarillo."

THE BASICS: Maximum Length: 71 cm (28 in) TL. Maximum Weight: 11.4 kg (25 lb). The Ranges: Oceanside (Southern California) to Islas Lobos de Afuera (Peru), including the Gulf of California. While rare in California waters, it is the most common snapper in the Gulf of California. Intertidal zone (juveniles) to 94 m (308 ft). Larvae: hatching length = less than 3.6 mm, flexion length = 4.1–5 mm, transformation length = less than 1.4 through about 3.1 cm. Von Bertalanffy parameters (TL, mm): (sexes combined) L_∞ = 735, k = 0.097, t_0 = -2.05; (males) L_∞ = 455, k = 0.253, t_0 = 1.28 (Garcia-Contreras et al. 2009). Length-weight parameters (TL, mm, gr): (sexes combined) W = $0.0135L^{3.03}$ (Garcia-Contreras et al. 2009).

SALIENT CHARACTERS: Colors vary a bit, but, in general, they have some pink or rose on the head and anterior part of the body and pale yellow, golden, or greenish on the rest.

LIFE HISTORY: Aburto-Oropeza (2009) provides considerable information regarding the early life history of this species near La Paz (Baja California). Amarillo larvae drift in the plankton for about 3 weeks (at 1–2 cm, 0.4–0.8 in, TL) before settling

OCTAVIO ABURTO-OROPEZA

out over pebbly bottoms. This occurs mostly from September–November, but occasionally as early as August and as late as February. Most fish settle during the quarter moons. Fish remain among the pebbles for a few weeks before migrating to live among mangrove roots. After 6–8 months, juveniles move onto shallow rocky reefs, with adults inhabiting somewhat deeper ones. Throughout their range, schools of juveniles inhabit quiet nearshore waters including lagoons and tide pools. Juveniles were also abundant around fish attracting devices moored near the coast of Panama. Adults live over rocks, usually near caves and crevices, also mostly in nearshore waters. Adults can be solitary or form small schools of up to several hundred individuals. Amarillos are predominantly (although not exclusively) nocturnal predators and may move into shallower waters to feed. Juveniles, in particular, but even some adults, are tolerant of freshwater, as they are often found in the lower reaches of rivers with some tidal influence.

Sala et al. (2003) observed spawning behavior in the Gulf of California. Here fish spawned at a depth of 15 m (49 ft), over rocky reefs and boulders, in May and June at dusk on the last quarter of the moon. At this time, snappers darted upward in small groups, releasing gametes near the surface, then returned to shelter. Sala et al. write: "Snappers formed a sort of a living conveyor belt between the crevice and shallow waters: as some snappers swam toward the surface, some others swam back into the crevice." Fish exhibiting what appeared to be courtship behavior have also been observed during the winter in the GOC.

Amarillos live 17–20 years. A few females are mature at about 22.8 cm (9 in) TL, 50% at 32.4 cm (13 in) (3–4 years old), and all at about 50 cm (20 in). They spawn nearly year round in tropical waters and at least May to September where waters are a bit cooler. Juveniles feed on small crabs, hermit crabs, amphipods, and small fishes. Larger fish eat crabs, lobsters, shrimps, mantis shrimps, cephalopods, and fishes.

FISHERY: This is a big-time commercial species in the Gulf of California. When you visit the Mercado Negro fish market in Ensenada (northern Baja California), you can sometimes see amarillos that have been trucked in from the GOC.

OTHER SPECIES

Lutjanus novemfasciatus
Gill, 1862

Pacific Dog Snapper

Dog snapper are the largest of the snappers in the Gulf of California, reaching 1.7 m (67 in) TL and at least 35.7 kg (78.8 lb). They range from Morro Bay (Central California) to Puerto Pizarro (Peru), and throughout the Gulf of California, but are uncommon in California waters. A benthic and schooling species, juveniles live in such protected areas as mangrove forests, lagoons, tide pools, and sargassum fields. Some young fish ascend rivers. Adults live over reefs down to depths of 60 m (197 ft). On September afternoons in the Gulf of California, Sala et al. (2003) observed spawning in 20 m (66 ft) of water over offshore reefs. Find that paper and you can read more than you want to know about dog snapper courtship. This species reportedly spawns throughout the year off Costa Rica. Largely inactive and living in caves and around

OCTAVIO ABURTO-OROPEZA

boulders during the day, dog snapper are most active during twilight and night. Adults feed on fishes and crustaceans. This is a species of major commercial importance in the Gulf of California and points south. Larvae: hatching length = less than 3.1 mm, flexion length = about 4.2–5.9 mm, transformation length = from less than 1.6 cm to less than 2.8 cm. Length-weight parameters (TL, cm, gr): (sexes combined) $W = 0.0285L^{2.79}$ (Rojo-Vázquez et al. 2009).

Lutjanus peru
(Nichols & Murphy, 1922)
Pacific Red Snapper

Pacific red snapper reach 99.2 cm (39 in) TL and at least 7.9 kg (17.4 lb). They are found from La Jolla (Southern California) and Bahia Santa Maria (southern Baja California) to Huermey (Peru), and throughout the Gulf of California. They appear to be rare along most of the Pacific Coast, but abundant in the Gulf of California and southwards. Juveniles live in shallow, nearshore waters, apparently mostly over soft seafloors. They are found from surface waters to bottom depths of at least 80 m (262 ft). Adults tend to frequent reefs. A study in the Gulf of California demonstrated that this species moves off and on the El Baja Gorda Seamount. Red snapper live to at least 34 years old. Females may grow slightly faster than males. Off Guerrero (Mexico), females first mature at about 29.5 cm (12 in) FL. In the Gulf of California, these fish spawn at least May to September, while in more tropical waters they appear to spawn throughout the year. Fishes, various crustaceans (e.g., amphipods, stomatopods, shrimps, and crabs), and squids make up most of their diets. These are a big time commercial species. Unfortunately, the juveniles are a major bycatch in shrimp trawl fisheries. Larvae: hatching length = less than 2.7 mm, flexion length = 4.7–6.2 mm, transformation length = greater than 1.5 cm and less than 1.9 cm (0.6–0.7 in). Von Bertalanffy parameters (TL, cm): (sexes combined) L_∞ = 97.3, k = 0.111, t_0 = -0.316 (Rocha-Olivares 1998). Length-weight parameters (TL, cm, kg): (sexes combined) W = 0.00001816$L^{2.905}$ (Rocha-Olivares 1998).

OCTAVIO ABURTO-OROPEZA

FAMILY GERREIDAE—Mojarras

Mojarras are mostly small, mostly tropical and subtropical, and mostly marine fishes. A few species live only in freshwater and quite a number of them inhabit both freshwater and estuaries in their youths. There are eight genera, and 44 species; nine species live within our range, and two reach into Southern California waters. They are oviparous with planktonic eggs and larvae. All of the mojarras kind of look the same to me, but never fear, there are descriptions and keys of eastern Pacific species in Fischer et al. (1995).

Eucinostomus dowii
(Gill, 1863)
Pacific Spotfin Mojarra

ROSS ROBERTSON

ETYMOLOGY AND COLLOQUIAL NAMES: *Eucinostomus* means "well," "to move," and "mouth" in Greek and *dowii* commemorates John Melmoth Dow (1827–1892). A couple of names from Mexican waters include "mojarra aleta de bandera" and "mojarra cantileña."

THE BASICS: Maximum Length: 20 cm (8 in) TL. The Ranges: Camp Pendleton Harbor (Southern California) to Gulf of California and to Peru, fairly commonly from about Bahia de Sebastian Vizcaino (central Baja California) southward. Tide pools to 114 m (3–374 ft). Length-weight parameters (SL, cm, gr): (sexes combined) $W = 0.006L^{3.69}$ (Gonzalez-Acosta et al. 2004).

SALIENT CHARACTERS: In general, mojarras have a compressed body, forked tail, a somewhat elongated snout, and a single, elongated dorsal fin that will disappear into a groove if you press it down. There are some tedious technical ways to differentiate this species from other ones, so go look at Fischer et al. (1995).

LIFE HISTORY: Juveniles inhabit mangrove forests, tide pools, river mouths, and lagoons. Both juveniles and adults school over soft bottoms in protected nearshore areas. Adults tend to inhabit somewhat deeper waters than juveniles.

In Bahia Magdalena (southern Baja California), larvae are found from June–October. Pacific spotfin mojarras feed on small crustaceans, insects, mollusks, fishes, polychaetes, algae, and occasionally detritus. They are likely eaten by a wide range of such animals as brown boobies and California sea lions.

FISHERY: Mojarras are fairly important in some local artisanal fisheries.

CAPTAIN JOHN MELMOTH DOW

Dow was a captain of several shipping vessels, a shipping agent, and a naturalist. He worked extensively off Central and South America and collected marine organisms throughout the region. In 1885, he was briefly held hostage by the revolutionary Pedro Prestan and here is a headline in the *New York Times*, dated 4 September 1885: "Don Pedro Prestan Hanged. The Destroyer of Colon Slowly Strangled to Death."

The take-home message? Never, never, mess with a naturalist.

FAMILY HAEMULIDAE—Grunts

Grunts are found in all three of the world's oceans, in a fair number of estuaries and, occasionally, in freshwater. These are mostly tropical and subtropical fishes that are oviparous, with planktonic eggs and larvae. Grunts come in 17 genera and at least 145 species. Twenty-two species occur within our range and five make it as far north as Southern California. Otoliths of this family may have been found as early as the Paleocene (at least 56 million years ago) and other fossil remains may extend to the Middle Eocene (around 40 million years ago). There are many grunt species in the tropical eastern Pacific, see Fischer et al. (1995) for descriptions.

At beach front restaurants, in places like Puerto Vallarta (Mexico), where tourists sip rum drinks housed in green coconuts, you often see various species of haemulids barbecued on stakes—Grunts on Sticks.

Anisotremus davidsoni
(Steindachner, 1876)
Sargo

A schooling, reef-oriented fish with the kind of officious look one expects from a middle-level bureaucrat in pre-Anschluss Austria.

ETYMOLOGY AND COLLOQUIAL NAMES: *Anisotremus* means "unequal" and "aperture" in Greek (referring to the chin pores) and *davidsoni* honors Professor George Davidson (1825–1911), one of the best scientists in 19th-century California. While the name "sargo" goes back at least to the 1880s, this species was also called "Chinese croaker" or "Japanese croaker" at least into the 1950s.

THE BASICS: Maximum Length: 60 cm (24 in) TL. Maximum Weight: 1.9 kg (4.1 lb). The Ranges: Santa Cruz (Central California) to Bahia Magdalena (southern Baja California), with an isolated population in the Gulf of California. Abundant from about Santa Monica Bay (Southern California) to at least Punta Abreojos (southern Baja California). Surf and tide pools to 61 m (201 ft), mostly in less than perhaps 9 m (30 ft). Eggs: 0.8–0.9 mm. Larvae: hatching length = 1.7–2 mm, flexion length = 4.2–6.2 mm, transformation length = 1.4–2.2 cm (0.6–0.9 in). Length-weight parameters (TL, cm, gr): $W = 0.0152L^{3.056}$ (Love unpubl.).

SALIENT CHARACTERS: Sargos are deep bodied, perch-shaped fish. Juveniles have two dark stripes along their sides and closely resemble juvenile black croakers and salemas. Adults have a vertical dark bar on their sides, near midbody; they will also, on occasion, display the juvenile stripes. They are usually silvery or dusky gray on backs, although once in a while you can see golden, brassy, or even albino ones. I know, they look like pile or rubberlip perch, but here is how to tell the difference. Piles have a high, peaked soft dorsal fin and rubberlips have really thick lips.

LIFE HISTORY: Young-of-the-year (as small as 0.8 cm, 0.3 in, SL) settle out of the plankton in late summer and fall, mostly in 1–18 m (4–60 ft) of water, over low rocks and adjacent

sand. They are found both in backwaters and on the open coast. Juveniles school with salemas and black croakers. Both juveniles and adults live in eelgrass, surfgrass, and kelp (occasionally in the kelp canopy), and over rock and rock-sand seafloors. Adults tend to aggregate, sometimes in schools of 50 individuals or more. Sargos are diurnal (active during daylight hours) and may move about throughout the year. For instance, way back in 1892, Eigenmann noted that sargos were only common in San Diego Bay from April–November. Genetic studies imply that this species entered the Gulf of California from southern Mexico and swam over to the Pacific side of the peninsula, eventually winding up in California. Whether fish swam around Cabo San Lucas, or crossed the peninsula through one of the gaps in the peninsula that periodically opened up, is unknown. Currently, there is relatively little gene flow between fish from the outer coast and those in the Gulf of California.

Sargos probably live a long time, as a 42.1 cm (17 in) TL fish I aged was 27 years old. Sargo mature when about 18–25 cm (7–10 in) TL and 2–3 years old. Spawning takes place at least from June to about October and from southern California

GEORGE DAVIDSON—OUR KIND OF GUY

Dr. George Davidson was as close to a Renaissance man as California had during the 19th century. His diverse accomplishments are difficult to summarize in a brief sketch. Working for the United States Coast Survey, he helped map a good deal of the Pacific Coast and Alaska. From 1870 until his death, he served the University of California as Honorary Professor of Astronomy and Geodesy, Professor of Geography, and Regent and was President of the California Academy of Sciences. He was a world authority on irrigation problems and was instrumental in helping establish the Lick Observatory near San Jose (California). His 1889 edition of the "Coast Pilot of California, Oregon, and Washington" was the authoritative publication for those sailing the coast. Davidson also clearly thought that Theodore Gill (see longjaw mudsucker) was some sort of paranoid loon, and this alone puts him high up in my pantheon.

Davidson was refreshingly candid in many of his opinions and here are two examples. The first is a report titled *System of Sewerage for the City of San Francisco*, in which he notes that compared to other cities: "I fail to recall but one other where the sewerage is in such a deplorably low condition; that exception is the City of Mexico, which is simply in a horrible plight; but it is so unfavorably situated, and the finances of the country are so low, that there is the semblance of an excuse for its unfruitful efforts. In comparison, we have no excuse whatever…The character of the sewage during the last season has been shockingly bad…It has been shown… that the low-lying sewers had become so filled with human excrement and filthy products, that they afforded no proper outlets to the waters of the bay…This leads to deposits around our city fronts which, if not removed by dredging, will make the waters lethean as those of Venice or Amsterdam." "Lethean," by the way, is a very nice reference to the river Lethe, which, in ancient Greek mythology, flowed through the underworld. The dead, upon drinking its waters, forgot about their lives on earth. So the term kind of refers to death. In this document, Davidson later goes on to detail his "Great Low Level Sewer" project, but we will leave details of that for my next book, *From Wilde to Watercloset: The Art and Artistry of the Victorian Sewer*.

A second example comes from the *San Francisco Chronicle* of 20 November 1896. Headlined MORE OF A HOAX THAN AN AIR SHIP, the story details some Sacramento residents who clamed to have seen a brightly lit flying contraption, replete with passengers singing loudly. The *Chronicle* notes: "Professor George Davidson is righteously indignant. 'What do I think about it?' he said yesterday. 'I think it's the outcome of a sort of freemasonry of liars. Half a dozen fellows have got together, sent up a balloon with some electric light attachment, and imagination has done the rest. It is a pure fake. Why, if I were to get up on top of the Chronicle tower and sing 'Yankee Doodle' or the 'Marseillaise' [sic], do you think anyone down the street could hear me? I expect a couple of thousand fools will be craning their necks and wearying their eyeballs tonight, looking through every kind of telescope and binocular that they can lay their hands on. I can tell you one thing, I'm not going to be one of them.'"

southward. Sargos feed on such invertebrates as bryozoans, small crustaceans (e.g., shrimps, crabs, and gammarid amphipods), mollusks (e.g., snails, clams, and chitons), and polychaetes. Predators include spotted sand bass.

FISHERY: Starting in the late 19th century, sargos were of minor value as a commercial species. Today, they are rarely seen in U.S. fish markets, although I have seen them fairly frequently in the Mercado Negro fish market in Ensenada (northern Baja California). Fair numbers are taken by sport fishermen from piers, jetties, and boats, and occasionally by rocky shore anglers.

ORIGINS: Based on records of the University of California, Berkeley, Paleontological Museum, at least one species of the genus *Anisotremus* lived in Northern California in the Miocene (at least 5.3 million years ago). Sargo remains have been found in 100,000-year-old formations in California.

MISCELLANY: Both xanthic (yellow) and albino ones are occasionally taken.

This is a juvenile.

MILTON LOVE

Xenistius californiensis

(Steindachner, 1876)

Salema

ETYMOLOGY AND AN OLD COLLOQUIAL NAME: *Xenistius* means "strange" and "sail (or dorsal fin)" in Greek (an apparent reference to the difference in size between this species and members of the allied salema genus *Xenichthys*) and *californiensis* refers to the original fish's capture in San Diego Bay. Eigenmann and Eigenmann (1889) noted: "When they are pulled from the water they grate their pharyngeals together producing a noise like that of a rasp" and they called it a "rasper."

THE BASICS: Maximum Length: 30.3 cm (12 in) TL. The Ranges: Monterey Bay to northern Peru, including Gulf of California. Salemas are abundant from Santa Catalina Island and Santa Monica Bay southward at least to Bahia Magdalena (southern Baja California). At depths of 1–33 m (4–109 ft). Larvae: hatching length = less than 2.2 mm, flexion length = 4.3–6.2 mm, transformation length = about 1.6–2.1 cm (0.6–0.8 in).Length-weight parameters (TL, cm, gr): W = $0.00956L^{3.114}$ (Love unpubl.).

SALIENT CHARACTERS: This is a very distinctive, kind of elongated, little fish. Adults have 6–8 orange-brown stripes, big eyes, and a small mouth. Juveniles also have orange-brown stripes and kind of look like young black croakers and sargos.

DAVE RUDIE

LIFE HISTORY: Starting in late summer, young-of-the-year recruit from the plankton, at lengths as small as 1.6 cm (0.6 in) SL, to very shallow inshore waters (both in bays and on the open coast), down to depths of 18 m (60 ft). The young often school with juvenile sargos and black croakers, usually near the bottom along reef edges. Adults are common in eelgrass, surfgrass, and kelp beds (both near the bottom and in the midwaters), but also aggregate over sand. Schools of thousands of individuals will often move into just a few meters (8 ft or less) of water. Some studies imply that fish in southern California move into shallower waters in the summer and fall. While they swim in schools during the day, about a half hour before sunset salemas disperse and spend the night feeding in the water column.

Salemas live to at least 10 years old. Based on my data, a few mature at 9 cm (4 in) TL and all are mature by 14 cm (6 in). Spawning occurs at least from June–October, peaking during July and August. Salemas are nocturnal predators, feeding on gammarid and caprellid amphipods, cumaceans, mysid shrimps, and polychaetes, as well as the occasional brittle star, copepod, isopod, shrimp, and fish. They are eaten by kelp bass, yellowtail, and likely Brandt's and double-crested cormorants.

FISHERY: There has never been a commercial fishery for salemas. In the days of the hook-and-fishery for tunas, American vessels would purse seine them along the Baja California coast and use them as bait. Salemas are commonly taken from Southern California piers and are an occasional catch from jetties and calm surf areas.

ORIGINS: Salema parts have been found in 100,000-year-old formations in California.

MISCELLANY: Juveniles are cleaners, but apparently they have only been seen cleaning other salemas.

OTHER SPECIES

Anisotremus interruptus
(Gill, 1862)

Burrito Grunt

Burritos grow to 90 cm (35 in) TL. They are found from Isla Cedros and Lagunas Ojo de Liebre-Guerrero Negro (central Baja California) and throughout the Gulf of California, to Mancora (Peru). Young ones live in tide pools and we have seen them down to depths of 25 m (83 ft). All sizes live over rocks during the day (often sheltering in caves and crevices) and feed over sand and between those rocks at night (and occasionally during the day). Burritos live at least 9 years. Prey include anemones, soft corals, polychaetes, mollusks, crustaceans, and fishes. Spotted sand bass eat them. Length-weight parameters (TL, cm, gr): (sexes combined) W = 0.0235L$^{2.94}$ (Rojo-Vázquez et al. 2009).

CHRIS GROSSMAN

FAMILY SPARIDAE—Porgies

Sparids are found throughout the world, mostly in marine waters. Although there are 33 genera and around 115 species, only one occurs within our range. This is an oviparous group with planktonic eggs and larvae. Sparid otoliths are known from the Paleocene (at least 66 million years ago). David (1943) described three fossil species, *Plectrites classenim*, *Rhythmias starri*, and *R. gaviotae* from the Miocene (at least 5.3 million years ago) of Southern California.

Calamus brachysomus
(Lockington, 1880)
Pacific Porgy

A species that has the perpetual look of either preternatural wisdom or mild befuddlement.

ETYMOLOGY AND COLLOQUIAL NAMES: *Calamus* means "quill" in Latin (this refers to the shape of the second interhemal bone in fish of this genus) and *brachysomus* means "short" and "body" in Greek. They are called "mojarrón" or "mojarra" in Mexico.

THE BASICS: Maximum Length: About 61 cm (24 in) TL. Maximum Weight: 2.3 kg (5.1 lb). The Ranges: Oceanside (southern California) to Antofagasta (northern Chile), including the Gulf of California. They are relatively abundant at least are far north as Bahia Magdalena (southern Baja California). Surface and intertidal to 80 m (262 ft), common from very shallow waters to about 70 m (230 ft). Eggs: 1–1.1 mm. Larvae: hatching length = about 2 mm, flexion length = 3.1–4.5 mm, transformation length = about 8.5 mm.

SALIENT CHARACTERS: Porgies are deep-bodied, with a very steeply slanting forehead, and flattened molars in the rear of the jaw. Dead ones tend to be dusky, sometimes with darker barring, and often with a dark snout. Underwater, they are silvery, with little in the way of markings, except for a small black spot on the upper part of the pectoral fin base. You occasionally see one that has dark bars.

LIFE HISTORY: Schools of juvenile porgies live in the shallows of bahias and other quiet waters, usually over sand. Adults live over sand (mostly) and rocks (occasionally); they tend to forage in small groups, rooting about in the seafloor. They will move into the intertidal during high tides. You often see them following stingrays, waiting to pick off whatever the rays stir up. Porgies have home ranges; two adults tagged in the Gulf of California remained in the same area for 14 months.

One bit of research from Bahia Magdalena (southern Baja California) found larvae from February–October. Pacific porgies forage both day and night on snails, mollusks (like squids), crustaceans (such as shrimps), echinoderms, and algae. California sea lions eat them.

FISHERY: Of some interest are the findings by Ken Gobalet et al. (2004) that porgy remains are frequent in the Native American middens around San Diego Bay; perhaps implying that this species was more abundant in the bay in the past than today. In the Gulf of California and points south, this is a species of some commercial importance, usually sold fresh or frozen. They are found occasionally in the Mercado Negro (Ensenada, northern Baja California).

ORIGINS: *Calamus* sp. is known from the Oligocene (at least 23 million years ago). Fossil Pacific porgies have been recovered from 100,000-year-old deposits in Southern California.

FAMILY SCIAENIDAE—Drums and Croakers

Sciaenids are a very successful group of marine, estuarine, and freshwater fishes that are found throughout the world from temperate to tropical waters. Worldwide, there are about 70 genera and around 270 species. Thirty-five species inhabit our range, although only eight occur north of the U.S.-Mexico border. Sciaenids are oviparous batch spawners, with planktonic eggs and larvae. The earliest sciaenids lived in the Middle to Late Eocene (more than 34 million years ago) of, for instance, the Gulf Coast of North America. Sciaenids first appeared in West Coast fossil fauna in the Early Miocene (perhaps as much as 23 million years ago). Fischer et al. (1995) present keys and descriptions of the oh-so-many tropical eastern Pacific species.

Members of this family produce sounds, rather noisy ones in point of fact, and these sounds are used both as reproductive calls and when a fish is disturbed. Norman and Fraser (1949) explain it thusly: "The sounds are produced through the agency of a special muscle, which is attached either directly to the air-bladder or close to it. The rapid expansion and contraction of this muscle causes the walls of the bladder to vibrate and it acts after the manner of a resonator and amplifies the sound. An American investigator, experimenting with living Croakers, found that if the air-bladder was deflated or removed the sounds ceased altogether, but that if an artificial rubber bladder was then introduced the drumming started again." *Dang, what kind of freak thinks about sticking a rubber bladder into a fish?*

Of course, no discussion of croaker swimbladders would be complete without mention of the Chinese Soup Stock business. Um humm. Check out what Chute (1930) has to say about that. He notes that, at that time, there was a substantial fishery in the upper Gulf of California for totoaba (*Totoaba macdonaldi*), a croaker that attains a weight of over 91 kg (200 lb). While some of the flesh was marketed to southern California outlets (except in hot weather, when the unchilled fish were left to rot on beaches), the fishery really existed for the "big, glossy swimbladders, white and satiny as new taffy." These, when dried, were sold to local middlemen, and most were eventually forwarded to China as soup base. How much swimbladder are we talking about? Chute writes that "It is reported that the Chinese buyers at Quaymas [Guaymas], Mexico, bought more than eight tons of buche [dried swimbladder] from one Sonora Camp." The fishery for totoaba peaked in the early 1940s, then crashed and burned by the mid-1970s.

Atractoscion nobilis

(Ayres, 1860)

White Seabass

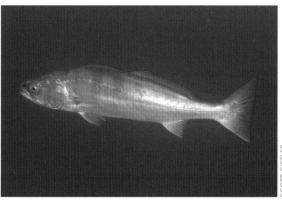

ETYMOLOGY AND COLLOQUIAL NAMES: *Atractoscion* is composed of the Greek word for "spindle" and the word "*Sciaena*" (an ancient Greek name for a European croaker) and *nobilis* means "noble" in Latin. "White seabass" and the now-disused "California sea bass" and "squeteague" are 19th-century names. And as with today, small ones were called "sea trout" back in the 19th century. For some reason, and I don't particularly care to know that reason, recreational anglers often refer to them as "biscuits." Jeez, is that a dumb name or what? In Mexico, they are often called "curvina" or "corvine."

THE BASICS: Maximum Length: 166 cm (65 in) TL. Maximum Weight: 42.3 kg (93 lb). For what it is worth, an old report (Lockington 1879a) reports them to 44.5 kg (98 lb). The Ranges: Juneau and the Boca de Quadra (southeastern Alaska) to Bahia Magdalena (southern Baja California) and Gulf of California. This is a mobile species that heads north as waters warm. As an example, during the 1957 El Niño, seabass were pretty common as far north as British Columbia and in the 1920s and 30s, they were abundant in Tomales and Bodega bays (Northern California). Currently, there are numbers of them as far north as Monterey Bay and as far south as perhaps 26°N (southern Baja California). Surf zone to 122 m (400 ft). Eggs: 1.2–1.3 mm. Larvae: hatching length = 2.8 mm, flexion length = 5.2–6.8 mm, transformation length = about 1.5 cm (0.6 in). Von Bertalanffy parameters (TL, mm): (sexes combined) L_∞ = 1,465, k = 0.128, t_0 = -.2805 (Thomas 1968). Length-weight parameters (TL, mm, kg): (sexes combined) W = $0.00001549L^{2.92167}$ (Thomas 1968).

SALIENT CHARACTERS: Very young seabass are silvery, brown, golden, or reddish, with darker bars. Adults are gray-blue, bronze, or almost yellow. Juveniles are often mistaken for white croakers. Hey, wise up out there. White croakers *don't* have bars on their sides and *do* have a tiny barbel on their chin.

LIFE HISTORY: From May–September, young-of-the-year (as small as 0.4 cm SL and 37 days old) settle out of the plankton, mostly onto bottom drift algae, from just behind the breakers down to depths of 10 m (33 ft). Juveniles in schools of 500 or more can be very abundant in bays, harbors, and along the shallow open coast, often among eelgrass, feather boa kelp, and other algae. Adults live over rocks and in kelp, from the bottom to way up in the canopy. Rocky headlands are good places to find both larger juveniles and

A newly settled juvenile, complete with racing stripes.

adults. In Southern California, they have been caught in surface waters of 11.4–23.8°C (53–75°F), with an average tempera-ture of 18.4°C (65°F). I've often seen them at night just below the surface and schools of seabass are sometimes seen in surface waters during the day. Seabass appear to move about a fair amount. There is no evidence for any population structure in Southern California.

Thus far Aalbers (2008), working at Santa Catalina Island, has conducted most of the research on seabass spawning. Spawning takes place from winter through early summer as "multiple males fertilize the eggs of a gravid female as gametes are broadcast into the water column." Most spawning occurs in a 2-hour period following sunset. Seabass spawn over the entire lunar period, but there is an increase in successive spawning events after each new moon and there is no relationship to tidal cycles. At Catalina, spawning takes place at 12.5–20.8°C (55–69°F), mostly from 15–18°C (59–64°F). During spawning days and at the peak spawning period of the year, seabass increase the amount of sounds they make. There are five types: "single pulse-trains," "multiple pulse trains," "drum rolls," "thuds," and "hydrodynamic booms." (I think that last one kind of reminds me of Ronnie Drew covering *The Rare Old Times*). Particu-larly during spawning periods there is an increase in drum-rolls and, as one might expect, thuds.

White sea bass live at least 13 years and probably longer. A few females are mature at 60 cm (24 in) TL and all are mature at 70 cm (28 in). A few males are mature at 50 cm (20 in), 50% at 60 cm (24 in), and 100% at about 70 cm (28 in). A 50 cm fish is about 3 years old, one 60 cm is 4 years old, and a 70 cm one is 5 years old. These fish spawn at least from January–October (and possibly a very few in November and December), but mostly from March–July. However, lest you think the last word has been written on the subject, Skogsberg (1939) wrote: "It is of interest to note that on one occasion, during an unusual freshet at San Diego in 1889, large numbers of ripe white seabass ascended the temporary fresh-water streams."

A STORY TOLD BY COMMERCIAL FISHERMAN CHRIS MILLER

"Well, you know I learned from a master fisherman, he always said you need to be versatile. At one point in his career he weathered a terrible series of southeasters [which prevented him from fishing at sea] by attaching a large pump to a Briggs and Stratton lawnmower engine and driving up to the Point Mugu Estuary in his Model-T. There he floated the contraption out into the slough at low tide and strip mined for clams. He was quite a genius at novel fishing methods. As you remember, he was one of the first marine reserve poachers in California. He often would repeat the story of it taking the Department of Fish and Game five boats with an unlimited fuel ration to get him out of the [Santa] Catalina [Island] reserve. One of his more interesting stories was of attaching a blasting cap to a harpoon attached to an electric switch. He would use a large oar to scull though the kelp bed until he found a school of sea bass. Throwing the harpoon into the fish he would detonate the charge and collect the fish as they floated to the surface stunned. He would always mention that he did this fishing out of Newport Harbor and chuckle a bit as he said: 'They would have flipped if they knew how much dynamite was in my boat.'"

Females are serial spawners and spawn at about 4-day intervals. Eggs hatch in about 2 days. Young-of-the-year eat mysid shrimps, along with copepods, gammarid amphipods, shrimps, and tiny fishes. Larger individuals target various fishes and have a real addiction to squids. Predators include angel, soupfin, and white sharks, and bottlenose dolphins.

FISHERY: Native Americans, often using spears, caught a lot of white seabass. Early commentators, as far back as Lockington (1879a), noted that white sea bass were very important in the commercial fisheries of California and they have remained so to this day. Lockington wrote that sea bass were "One of the most highly prized of the fishes of our markets, so much so that its name is given to the flesh of other species. Thus sturgeon is usually sold in the restaurants under the name of 'sea-basse'"[sic]. Up until 1940, most of the white seabass catch was made with gill nets or such roundhaul gear as purse seines and lampara nets. In 1940, roundhaul nets were banned as a tool for seabass, but some enterprising fishermen came up with a nice loophole, the so-called "hunting gill net." This involved spotting a seabass school and encircling the fish with a gill net and not, in theory at least, completing the circle. After almost completing the circle, the crew would scare the fish into the net's webbing through loud sounds. Today, there is a substantial commercial fishery for white seabass and most of the catch is made with set and drift gill nets. White seabass flesh tends to discolor within a few days of being frozen and there has usually been little demand for the frozen product.

How many white seabass were there back in the good old days? Here's something from Holder (1910a) describing a moment down at the Capitola (Central California) wharf in the early 20th century: "While I was waiting for my boatman…I amused myself by watching the Italians bring in 'sea trout' or white sea-bass, which they netted alongshore at night. The boats pulled up to the dock and the splendid fish, ranging from ten to fifty pounds, would be tossed into a big net and hoisted up to the pier, which was often fairly covered with white sea-bass—one of the finest game fishes of the coast, which I found interfered with the salmon fishing by getting on the line when they were not wanted."

White seabass are just terribly, terribly important to sport fishermen. I remember several trips I took on sportfishing boats out of San Diego in the 1960s. After a fruitless morning searching for seabass the skipper offered an afternoon of catching barred sand bass and ocean whitefish. The offers were, with the exception of one passenger, unanimously rejected. While most adult seabass are caught by boat anglers, surprisingly large ones are sometimes taken from piers. Off Baja California, there are a number

MATT LUM'S LIEDER OF THE PACK

Matt Lum is one of those talented freedivers who are just very good at hunting white seabass. And in that pursuit, he has learned to distinguish the various sounds they make. Let's listen in.

"The mystery and elusiveness of the California white seabass is often betrayed by the croaking sounds that it makes. Whether used for mating, locating other schooling seabass, or simply croaking up a good time, the seabass' distinctive croak undoubtedly alerts experienced freedivers to the presence of these fish. Unfortunately, simply hearing the fish doesn't mean that you'll actually see one. Sometimes the dynamics of the water column make the fish sound like they're right next to you when in fact they may be hundreds of feet/yards away in very deep water. There are several different sounds and croaks that a white seabass makes, and I have observed several of these sounds while lying quietly in a school of mating seabass. I think the most common croak sounds a bit like a frog "ribet," a slow, growling Raaaa-aa. Sometimes a "Raaaa-aa-aa." Other times it is a single, long, but repetitive MMMM, MMMM, MMMM. These two sounds are what I hear the most when the fish are unseen. On occasion, while attempting to chase down the croaking fish, a very noisy school would suddenly appear and swarm all around me, and I notice other sounds that the fish make. One is a quick repetitive thumping sound, not unlike that of a feisty Garibaldi. The other is a single resonating "Pop" that can range from a low thump to a sharper noise reminiscent of a champagne cork. Freedivers utilize several of these sounds and croaks to aid in hunting the wary seabass. Some divers slowly make their way in the direction from which the croaks are coming, to the degree it can be determined. Others try to mimic the croaking sounds to attract the fish. While I think I've been quite successful at croaking fish in, I'm not fully convinced that it is really my croaking or coincidence!"

of beaches where really big ones can be taken in the surf (and this also happens, on occasion, off California). In a surprising number of instances, fishing for white seabass is kind of like fishing for really large white croakers. Thus on partyboats it is often the tourist, fishing with a rental rod, right on the bottom, with a dead anchovy, that catches them.

Skogsberg (1939) wrote: "Two of the most exciting events of the sportfishing season in southern California are the brief runs of white sea bass at Newport Beach and Avalon, Santa Catalina Island. During the dark of the moon in May, the sea bass strike into the pier at Newport on nightly raids on the large sardine hanging around the pier. On those nights, from dusk until about 3 AM, the pier is literally thronged with fishermen. If there is any angler you want to locate, you will find him at Newport on some balmy May night." I remember a ferocious run of seabass off the Santa Monica Pier during the El Niño of 1957. Hundreds of anglers would snag sardine and transfer them to live bait rigs, then stand back and await developments. For a few weeks a number of big fish, some in the 30–40 lb class, were dragged off that pier. Large numbers of immature seabass, called "seatrout," are taken by pier anglers. People, throw these fish back.

ORIGINS: Remains of white seabass have been found in 100,000-year-old strata in California. White seabass may be most closely related to the striped weakfish, *Cynoscion guatucupa*, a southwest Atlantic species.

REMARKS: After a long period of relative scarcity, the white seabass population off Southern California appears to have rebounded. Dan Pondella and Larry Allen (2008) ascribe this to the ban on setting gill nets in inshore waters.

Buster Hyder was summoned to the bow of his sportfishing boat Sunday when anchored near Catalina island. Fishermen were yelling that a jewfish was chasing every fish in sight. Grabbing the gaff Buster hastened to the bow and found the big fish to be the largest white sea bass he had ever seen. It was nibbling at the tail of a barracuda which was being brought in by one of the anglers. The sea bass took Buster and the fisherman on the business end of the fishing rod around the boat five times, leisurely gnawing on the barracuda and keeping his distance at all times, just a few inches out of reach of the gaff. Hyder estimated the big fish to weigh 100 pounds. It is believed the monster fish put on a similar show for several other boats that day.

I don't know what paper this was from. Ed Ries sent me a copy of it. It is dated 18 July 1939.

Cheilotrema saturnum

(Girard, 1858)

Black Croaker

ETYMOLOGY AND COLLOQUIAL NAMES: *Cheilotrema* comes from the Greek words "lip" and "pore" and *saturnum* means "dusky" in Latin. In the 19th century, black croakers were often called "black roncador" or, rather mysteriously I might say, "red roncador." "Chinese croaker" was also heard.

THE BASICS: Maximum Length: 45 cm (18 in) TL. The Ranges: Point Conception (California) to southern Baja California (23°23'N, 110°12'W), and Gulf of California. Surf zone to 100 m (328 ft) or

These are juveniles.

more; mostly in 1–15 m (4–50 ft). Eggs: 0.8–0.9 mm. Larvae: hatching length = 1.5 mm, flexion length = 4.4–4.5 mm, transformation length = about 1.5 cm. Von Bertalanffy parameters (SL, mm): (sexes combined) L_∞ = 237.7, k = 0.31, t_0 = -1.78 (Miller et al. 2008b). Length-weight parameters (TL, cm, gr): (sexes combined) W = $0.0088L^{3.16}$ (Love unpubl.).

SALIENT CHARACTERS: Black croakers change their colors 1) as they mature, 2) from day to night, and 3) when stressed (like when you catch them). A detailed description is given in Limbaugh (1961), but basically these are perch-shaped fish with a dark brown, blackish, purplish, bluish, or coppery back and silvery belly. The rear part of the gill cover is black, there is a pale bar at midbody (particularly at night or when in caves), and light blotches on the back (also at night). Juveniles look sufficiently different that they were at one time thought to be a separate species, *Corvina jacobi*. They have a series of dark stripes and look unpleasantly similar to juvenile salemas and sargos. Adults can change both color and pattern and will sometimes switch to the juvenile striped pattern.

LIFE HISTORY: From August–October, young-of-the-year (as small as 1.4 cm, 0.6 in, SL) recruit to shallow waters (from barely subtidal to perhaps 5.5 m, 18 ft) in bays and on the open coast. The young form schools (often with sargos and sale-mas) in eelgrass, over low reefs, and along reef margins. Juveniles spend most of their time near the bottom and can remain in very small areas for months. By about 9 cm (4 in) TL, the fish have moved into caves and crevices and often live a solitary life, although aggregations (sometimes mixed with sargo) do occur. Older fish live primarily in nearshore rocky or algae-cov-

ered areas, but can also be found in the turbid waters of bays, away from structure. Writing in 1892, Eigenmann observed that black croaker males entered San Diego Bay in January and then left in September. So are they migratory? No one knows.

Black croakers have been known to live at least 21 years, but most fish live less than 14 years. Males and females grow at the same rates. My data implies that these fish mature at around 16–18 cm (6–7 in) TL and 1–2 years old. Spawning occurs from at least April–September, probably peaking in July. Black croakers eat mostly bottom-dwelling crustaceans (e.g., crabs, shrimps, amphipods, and isopods), polychaetes, and fishes.

SCOTT GIETLER

FISHERY: Black croakers were an important commercial species in San Diego Bay in the late 19th century. Since 1933, it has been illegal to sell them in California. They are an occasional catch in the artisanal commercial fisheries of northern Baja California. In Southern California, black croakers are taken fairly often from piers and nearshore vessels and by divers. Night fishermen catch many of them.

REMARKS: Want to know how quiet San Diego Bay was in the 19th century? Eigenmann (1892) notes that during evenings on the bay, while netting fertilized black croaker eggs from their breeding grounds: "Their frog-like croaking could be heard on all sides."

PETER BRYANT

Genyonemus lineatus
(Ayres, 1855)
White Croaker

A small schooling fish that inhabits nearshore and turbid waters and carries some sort of strange psychic burden.

ETYMOLOGY AND COLLOQUIAL NAMES: *Genyonemus* means "lower jaw" and "barbel" in Greek and *lineatus* means "striped" in Latin. This fish has been given about as many names, most of them uncomplimentary, as any species on the coast. On a more salutary note, in Southern California, from San Diego to perhaps Ventura, the most commonly heard is "tomcod," whereas in the Santa Barbara area, "ronkie" or "roncador" is usual. In Central California, and in most fish markets, "kingfish" is frequently used. Kirk Lombard reports that some folks fishing in San Francisco Bay call them "wongfa" and "chogy."

THE BASICS: Maximum Length: 41 cm (16 in) TL. The Ranges: Barkley Sound (British Columbia) to Bahia Magdalena (southern Baja California). They are reported to be common in Humboldt Bay (Northern California) and are abundant from about San Francisco southward to at least Bahia de Sebastian Vizcaino (central Baja California). They tend to be rare around offshore islands. Surf zone to 238 m (10–781 ft); most commonly from just behind the surf line to perhaps around 130 m (426 ft). Eggs: 0.8–0.9 mm. Larvae: hatching length = about 1.5–1.8 mm, flexion length = 5.3–6.6 mm, transformation length = about 1.7 cm (0.7 in). Von Bertalanffy parameters (TL, cm): (females) L_∞ = 60.72, k = 0.037, t_0 = -7.54; males: L_∞ = 59.17, k = 0.033, t_0 = -8.66 (Love et al. 1984). Length-weight parameters (TL, cm, gr): (females) W = $0.0109L^{3.0239}$; (males) $0.0111L^{3.0114}$ (Love et al. 1984).

SALIENT CHARACTERS: These are small, silvery fish, some with yellow-bronze backs. The fins are yellow or white and usually there is a small black spot where the pectoral fins meet the body. There is a very small barbel under the chin.

LIFE HISTORY: Young-of-the-year (as small as 1.5 cm, 0.6 in, SL) settle mostly in the spring to shallow sandy bottoms. A fish of turbid waters and soft seafloors, adults live mostly on the open coast or in large embayments. While white croakers are usually found in benthic or midwater schools, I have occasionally seen them chasing northern anchovy near the surface. They will live in estuarine conditions, such as in the Carquinez Straits or Tijuana Estuary. Schools may disperse a bit at night. Do white croakers move much? I wish I could tell you. It is likely that at least some fish move about a bit. Some of the trawling studies I was involved in demonstrated that these fish move into slightly deeper waters during the winter. During the 1983 El Niño, some white croakers moved into Oregon, well north of their usual haunts. White croaker numbers in Southern California appear to fluctuate greatly over time, likely in response to oceanographic conditions.

White croakers live to at least 12 years and likely longer. Females grow slightly faster than males and grow larger. A few fish are mature at less than 1 year old (at about 13 cm, 5 in, TL). Over 50% of both males and females are mature at 1 year old (about 14 cm, 6 in, for males and 15 cm, 6 in, for females). All fish are mature by 19 cm (8 in, 3–4 years old). As you read these words, regardless of whether you have just put that last dollop of suet in your Christmas figgy pudding or are trying to remove that Fourth of July firecracker from your 11-year-old's nose, some white croaker is spawning. On the other hand, spawning does seem to peak between about November–May. Larger females spawn earlier in the season than smaller ones. Small females may spawn for 3–4 months, larger ones for as long as 7 months. Batch fecundities range from 800–37,200 eggs. Most spawning occurs over seafloors less than about 30 m (99 ft) deep. White croakers feed primarily (but not exclusively) on bottom-oriented prey and polychaetes are hands down a very important part of their diet. Other commonly encountered foods include various crustaceans (e.g., gammarid amphipods, crabs, isopods, mysid shrimps, hermit crabs, and shrimps), fishes, arrow worms, larvaceans, ctenophores, brittle stars, and clam siphons. Predators include many fish species (e.g., angel, blue, leopard, soupfin, and thresher sharks, barred sand bass, California halibut, California lizardfish, gray smoothhounds, longnose skate, Pacific bluefin tuna, and spiny dogfish), Brandt's and double-crested cormorants, seals, sea lions, and dolphins.

FISHERY: White croakers were a major part of the fish diets of Southern California Native Americans. Its ease of capture made the species a popular commercial target back in the 19th century, as they were brought in to San Francisco and San Diego markets in very large numbers. At that time, white croakers were dried by Chinese fishermen and shipped to Asia. The 20th century brought with it a certain lack of interest in the species and catches remained relatively low until the 1970s, when immigrant Vietnamese fishermen found that: 1) they could catch large quantities using monofilament gill nets, and 2) their confreres really liked white croakers. The fishery boomed for a few years, only to sink back into stygian gloom as gill nets were banned from nearshore waters.

White croakers are easy to catch, and for this reason they are a mainstay of pier and small vessel fishermen. Without this species (along with topsmelt, shiner perch, and staghorn sculpins), young children on many piers would catch nothing. They are also common in the party vessel fishery. Catches tend to be highest during the summer. White croakers have always been popular among live bait fishermen as an excellent "brown bait" for California halibut and kelp bass.

ORIGINS: The genus *Genyonemus* evolved at least as far back as the Early to Middle Miocene (17.5–14.5 million years ago) in what is now Maryland. A Late Miocene species (a minimum of 5.3 million years ago) was *Genyonemus whistleri*, known from Southern California. White croaker otoliths were taken from formations as old as the Late Pliocene (1.8 million years ago) in Southern California.

REMARKS: There is no question that white croakers suffer from really bad press. Historically, many fishermen believed them to be inedible, worm-infested pests. While they are soft-fleshed (but how many of us also suffer from that condition?) white croakers are edible, and in fact, are eaten in large quantities by a number of ethnic groups. As for having parasitic worms (the ones to worry about are in the genera *Anisakis* and *Phocanema*), although some white croakers are infected, individuals of other, more popular, species (such as California halibut) actually contain more worms.

Menticirrhus undulatus

(Girard, 1854)

California Corbina

DAVID AND DORI DIRIG

ETYMOLOGY AND COLLOQUIAL NAMES: *Menticirrhus* means "chin" and "barbel" in Latin and *undulatus* means "waved" in Latin, referring to the wavy lines on the sides. Earlier names included "kingfish" and "California whiting." They are referred to as "berrugata" in northern Baja California.

THE BASICS: Maximum Length: 83.6 cm (33 in) TL. Maximum Weight: Holder (1913) noted that a 3.9 kg (8.5 lb) fish was "the largest registration on the records of the Southern California Rod and Reel Club." The Ranges: Point Conception (California) to the Gulf of California; also reported from Ecuador to Arica (northern Chile). They are abundant from Southern California to at least Bahia Magdalena (southern Baja California). Surf to 20 m (66 ft); relatively common from the surf down to about 12.1 m (40 ft). Egg diameter = 0.8 mm. Larvae: hatching length = about 1.4 mm, flexion length = about 4–5.2 mm, transformation length = about 1 cm (0.4 in). Joseph (1962) has a figure illustrating the age-length relationship. Length-weight parameters (TL, cm, gr): $W = 0.0167L^{2.838}$ (Love unpubl.).

SALIENT CHARACTERS: These are long, thin croakers with a short chin barbel. Corbinas are gray, brown, or blackish above, sometimes with distinct light and dark horizontal lines. Particularly underwater, they are often heavily marked with dark saddles and blotches.

LIFE HISTORY: Young-of-the-year, as small as 2.5 cm (1 in) SL, recruit as early as August to just outside the surf line. In the tropics, juveniles are found in coastal lagoons near mangroves. Adults are found on the open coast, in semi-enclosed bays, and in estuaries, where they tolerate salinities up to about 51 ppt. This is one of the major sandy-shore species, often seen in very, very shallow waters, with their tail or back sticking out of the water. While they are usually found either singly and in kind of loose aggregations, Limbaugh (1955) reported that he sometimes saw schools containing hundreds of individuals.

California corbinas live to as least 11 years old and I would imagine to somewhat older. Size and age at maturity are poorly known. It is said that most males mature at 2 years old (about 25.4 cm, 10 in, TL) and females at 3 years old (30.5–38.1 cm, 12–15 in) and 2–3 years. Spawning takes place at least from April to about October, most heavily from June–August. Spawning may occur a bit offshore, as ripe fish are rarely caught in shallow waters, but this is unclear. California corbinas eat whatever 1) lives in, on, or near the bottom, 2) is the right size, and 3) can't get away. In practice this includes sand crabs, gammarid amphipods, mysid shrimps, clams (particularly bean and razor) and their siphons, polychaetes, shrimps, fishes, and grunion eggs. Diets vary with area. They feed by taking in mouthfuls of sand, then blowing the inedible stuff out their gills. Some studies imply they feed both day and night. California halibut and bottlenose dolphins eat them.

FISHERY: Corbinas were a reasonably important commercial species in Southern California until 1915, when commercial fishing for them was declared illegal in California waters. On the other hand, they remain a common commercial catch off Baja California and you can often see them for sale in the Mercado Negro, the large fish market in Ensenada (northern Baja California).

Holder (1913) noted that this was a popular sport species: "It is a finny foeman worthy of any angler's skill." Today, surf and pier fishermen still avidly seek them out. They are, however, notoriously hard to hook, as you can often see them rooting about in the sand, while studiously ignoring every bait proffered. Off some piers, the species is sufficiently abundant that a few fishermen cast out large treble hooks and try to snag corbinas as they come into the surf. While legal, this method never fails to antagonize some of our more sportsmanlike anglers.

ORIGINS: Fish of this genus were present in the Caribbean Sea during the Late Miocene (at least 5.3 million years ago). California corbina remains have been found in 100,000-year-old formations in California.

Roncador stearnsii
(Steindachner, 1876)
Spotfin Croaker

ROY QI

ETYMOLOGY AND COLLOQUIAL NAMES: *Roncador* is Spanish for "grunter" or "snorer" and was the name widely given to a number of croakers off California and Mexico and *stearnsi* refers to Robert E.C. Stearns (1827–1909). Stearns was a clerk of the California Supreme Court, an assistant curator in the Department of Mollusks, Smithsonian Institution, and a paleontologist in the U.S. Geological Survey. For a time, he resided in San Francisco and was well known to the habitués of the California Academy of Sciences.

THE BASICS: Maximum Length: 68.6 cm (27 in) TL. Maximum Weight: 6.4 kg (14 lb). The Ranges: Point Conception (California) to tip of Baja California. One individual was reported from South San Francisco Bay, although documentation appears to be lacking. Spotfins are most common from about Los Angeles Harbor southward to at least Bahia de Sebastian Vizcaino (central Baja California). Surf to 22 m (73 ft); mostly in quite shallow water. Eggs: 0.6–0.8 mm. Larvae: hatching length = less than 1.9 mm, flexion length = about 5–6 mm, transformation length = about 1.3 cm (0.5 in). Von Bertalanffy parameters (SL, mm): (females) L_∞ = 468, k = 0.17, t_0 = -2.8; (males) L_∞ = 467, k = 0.1, t_0 = -6.3 (J. Williams, pers. comm.). Length-weight parameters (SL, mm, gr): (sexes combined) W = $0.000032095L^{2.94436}$ (Joseph 1962).

SALIENT CHARACTERS: Spotfins have very obvious black spots at the bases of their pectoral fins. They are bluish-gray or gray on back, brassy on flanks, with a white belly. Males may be a very impressive brassy or golden during the spawning season, while females develop blackish streaks on belly.

LIFE HISTORY: Young-of-the-year, at 2.9 cm (1 in) SL or smaller, settle in late summer and early fall to surf areas. This is a fish mostly of the sandy surf zone and quiet bays, although they will, on occasion, venture onto reefs. Adults are often found either singly or in small groups, but they can form very extensive schools of hundreds of individuals. Ed Ries (2007), thinking back to the Santa Monica of the 1930s, notes: "So vast was the school of [spotfin] croakers that on the back of each swell hundreds could be seen, their sides flashing and glinting in the glow from pier lamps." At least during some months the species appears to swim in single-sex schools. Do they move about much? No one knows, but a fish tagged in Los Angeles Harbor was recovered off Oceanside. One large study in Southern California found that few fish live in waters colder than 17°C (63°F).

Spotties live to at least 24 years. Females grow faster than males after about age 3. Spotfins spawn from at least April–September, mostly from June–August. Females are batch spawners and produce 35,169–640,703 eggs per batch. They target bottom organisms. Clams and their siphons are popular, as are polychaetes, gammarid amphipods, mysid shrimps,

DR. STEARNS AND THE BLACKGUARDS OF BODEGA BAY

This is an account written by Dr. Stearns of his shell-collecting trip with fellow conchologist Dr. Wesley Newcomb to Bodega Bay, just north of San Francisco: "I shall never forget a little trip to the coast made by Doctor Newcomb and myself about 1867. We were led to investigate the neighborhood of Bodega, and had a tiresome ride one day by stage to Bodega Corners where we had to stop over night before we could go on. We had an uncomfortable room together on the ground floor of the only public house there, so near the bar-room that we were kept awake long after we had gone to bed by the loud talk, wrangling, and profanity which surpassed in volume and unceasing flow anything I had ever before experienced. The next morning we were both glad to get away from such a 'hell-hole', and after paying our bill the doctor remarked to the landlord that he had never been in a place where such gross profanity prevailed, and he hoped never to have such an experience again. The landlord was so abashed by my friend's comments and rebuke, that not only he, but some of the rough looking loafers sitting near, really appeared to exhibit some shame" (Stearns 1888). *Sure.*

and crabs. Occasional prey include brittle stars, nemerteans, brachiopods, scaphopods, sand dollars, and scallops. Bottlenose dolphins eat them.

FISHERY: Spotfins were an important commercial species in Southern California (particularly in San Diego Bay) as far back as the late 19th century. In 1915, they were declared a sport species, and it is illegal to catch them for sale. On the other hand, you need only visit Baja California and, in particular, the Mercado Negro fish market in Ensenada (northern Baja California), to see numbers of them resting on ice. Today, they are important surf and pier fish and are also frequently taken by boat anglers plying nearshore waters.

ORIGINS: Remains of spotfin croakers have been found in Late Pliocene (at least 1.8-million-year-old) deposits in Southern California.

MISCELLANY: A fish tale from Norris and Prescott (1961): "Antonio Perisky, an American fisherman, who had lived at Estero de Punta Banda, [northern] Baja California, for thirty-six years at the time we met him in 1956, reported that many times he had seen bottlenose porpoises feeding during his netting operations in the lagoon. The porpoises were observed to come to the surface and repeatedly throw 2- or 3-pound fish into the air. Mr. Perisky thought these fish were probably spotfin croaker."

Seriphus politus

Ayres, 1860

Queenfish

Another hopelessly boring fish, the Wonder Bread of the Pacific Coast.

ETYMOLOGY AND COLLOQUIAL NAMES: Well, *Seriphus* can mean a number of things in Greek, including a species of insect, a kind of wormwood, and an island off Greece. Unfortunately, when Dr. Ayres described this species he did not tell us why he gave it this name and thus we are condemned to live in ignorance. On the other hand, *politus* is Latin for "polished" and one assumes that refers to the silvery coloration. They were called both "queenfish" and "kingfish" in the 19th century.

THE BASICS: Maximum Length: 30.5 cm (12 in) TL. The Ranges: Burrard Inlet (Vancouver Island) to southern Gulf of California. Currently, queenies are abundant from at least

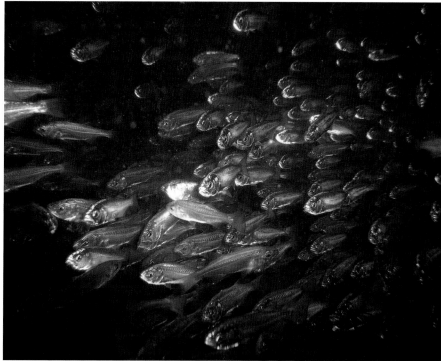

WALT CONKLIN

the Santa Barbara Channel (Southern California) to Bahia Tortugas (southern Baja California). Queenfish were reportedly quite common in San Francisco Bay in the late 19th century and in Monterey Bay during the 1930s. Surf to depth of 181 m (594 ft); mostly from very shallow waters to about 40 m (131 ft). Eggs: 0.7–0.8 mm. Larvae: hatching length = about 1.6 mm, flexion length = about 4–5.4 mm, transformation length = about 1.6 cm (0.6 in). Von Bertalanffy parameters (SL, mm): (females) L_∞ = 198.9, k = 0.2, t_0 = -3.1; (males) L_∞ = 179.9, k = 0.2, t_0 = -4.5 (Miller et al. 2009). Length-weight parameters (SL, mm, gr): (sexes combined) W = $0.00001L^{3.09}$ (Miller et al. 2009).

SALIENT CHARACTERS: This is a large-mouthed, very compressed croaker, sort of bluish, tan, or brownish on its back and silvery on sides and belly. The fins are yellow, sometimes with a sort of greenish tinge.

LIFE HISTORY: Most young-of-the-year settle from September–December to soft seafloors in shallow waters, at sizes as small as 1.4 cm (0.6 in) FL. This is a schooling species, found mostly over sandy or muddy seafloors (sometimes in eelgrass beds), on the open coast, and in bays and harbors. They do, on occasion, visit kelp beds, but only briefly, and only with much trepidation. Queenies tend to stay in relatively inactive and near-bottom schools during the day; they become more active and disperse just before sunset, in preparation for feeding in the midwaters at night. Schools may not move about much for weeks at a time. For instance, John Stephens (1983) noted, that a "huge school took up a diurnal position in five meters of water at the Point [in King Harbor, southern California] and remained in position for about 4 weeks."

Queenfish live to 12 years old. Females grow faster and larger than males. Fifty percent of both males and females mature at about 10 cm (4 in) SL and 1 year old. All are mature by 2 years old. Queenfish spawn in the late afternoon and evening and almost all spawning occurs between April–August, although a few fish appear to reproduce as early as February and as late as November. Most larvae are found within about 5 km of shore. Ed DeMartini (1991) reported that batch fecundity can vary between years; for instance it was low during the El Niño of 1984. Batches range from 5,000 to more than 90,000 eggs and annual egg production ranges from 60,000–2,300,000. Larger females start spawning earlier and finish spawning later in the year, females spawn on average every 7.4 days, and spawning for an individual female lasts anywhere from 3 months (for small fish) to 6 months (in the largest ones). Queenfish feed on a range of water column organisms, including mysid shrimps, gammarid amphipods, cumaceans, copepods, and fishes. Predators include fishes (e.g., angel sharks, California halibut, kelp bass, Pacific barracuda, Pacific bonito, Pacific hakes, and white seabass), seals, sea lions, and dolphins.

FISHERY: Queenfish remains are commonly found in Native American middens in Southern California. Beach seine commercial fishermen took enormous numbers of queenfish in the 19th century, although their small size meant that few were sold. In the 20th century, queenfish were taken by roundhaul nets, gill nets, and trawls, although, again, there was little market for them.

In Ray Cannon's *How to Fish the Pacific Coast* (Lane Publishing, 1953) (the book that taught me to read) he mentions catching: "Plump foot-long queenies." I don't know what there is about that phrase, but the term "plump foot-long queenies" is just so appealing to me. Personally, I don't care for queenies, plump, foot-long, or otherwise, but folks catch very large numbers of them off piers and jetties, both for food and for bait. They are often termed "brown bait" and are considered by many (including myself) to be just about the best bait for kelp bass and California halibut, second only to live squids, which are generally considered to be the gold standard.

ORIGINS: A fossil *Seriphus*, *S. lavenbergi*, was a Late Miocene (8.6-7.6 million years ago) species from Southern California. Queenfish remains have been found as early as the Late Pliocene (at least 1.8 million years ago) of Southern California. Queenies may be most closely related to croakers in the tropical genus *Nebris*.

REMARKS: Work by Miller et al. (2009a) has demonstrated that queenfish abundance in Southern California has declined markedly between about 1980 and the early 21st century.

Umbrina roncador

Jordan & Gilbert, 1882

Yellowfin Croaker

DAVID AND DORI DIRIG

ETYMOLOGY: *Umbrina* is Latin for "shade" and was apparently a name given to a European croaker species, while *roncador* is Spanish for "grunter" or "snorer" and was a common name for croakers in early California.

THE BASICS: Maximum Length: 55.6 cm (22 in) TL. Maximum Weight: 1.8 kg (3.9 lb). The Ranges: Point Conception (California) to Bahia Magdalena (southern Baja California), and in Gulf of California; old records to San Francisco. They are relatively common from Santa Barbara southward and, particularly, from Santa Monica Bay to Bahia Magdalena. While they are rare along most of the Southern California islands, a few of the more sandy and turbid areas at Santa Catalina and Santa Cruz islands have pretty good numbers. Surf to 46 m (150 ft); mostly near the shore, but occasionally to 12.1 m (40 ft). Eggs: 0.7–0.8 mm. Larvae: hatching length = about 1.5 mm, flexion length = about 3.2–5 mm, transformation length = about 1.3 cm (0.5 in). Von Bertalanffy parameters (SL, mm): (females) L_∞ = 313.2, k = 0.307, t_0 = -0.771; (males) L_∞ = 298.9, k = 0.269, t_0 = -1.072 (Pondella et al. 2008). Length-weight parameters (TL, cm, gr): W = $0.057L^{2.676}$ (Love unpubl.).

SALIENT CHARACTERS: Yellowfins have a gray, green, or bluish back, covered with a series of diagonal yellow-brown stripes. There is a pronounced barbel on the chin. All fins have some yellow, but pelvics, anal, and most of the caudal fin are all yellow.

LIFE HISTORY: Young-of-the-year settle in summer and fall to nearshore waters. Both juveniles and adults live over sand, usually in the shallows, in lagoons and other quiet waters, and also along the open coast. Although they often hang near the bottom, Ed Ries has seen yellowfins chasing little anchovies in the surface waters of San Diego Bay. In some areas, yellowfins tend to school during the day and disperse to feed at nightfall. Ripe fish do not appear to be common in the nearshore waters of Southern California and where they do spawn seems unclear.

Yellowfins live to 15 years old. Females grow faster and reach a larger size. The fish mature at about age 2 and around 21.9–23.1 cm (9 in) TL. Spawning occurs at least from May–August. Females are batch spawners and produce 99,259–405,967 eggs per batch. Yellowfins feed mostly on benthic and epibenthic organisms, although they also eat midwater stuff. Small invertebrates are most important. These include polychaetes, gammarid and caprellid amphipods, clams, brittle stars, and everyone's favorite phallic folk—the fat innkeeper. Fishes are also often consumed. Predators include California sea lions and bottlenose dolphins.

FISHERY: Back in the 19th century, these were important market fish; they were often split and salted. As with a number of other croakers, in 1915 the state of California made it illegal for commercial fishermen to catch them. On the other hand, on most days you can see dozens for sale in the Mercado Negro fish market in Ensenada (northern Baja California). This is one of the more important sport fish for pier and shore fishermen, and for anglers fishing from vessels in shallow waters. Having written that, it should be noted that in the summer of 1937 many were taken by sport boats and barges 3–8 km (2–5 mi) off the coast.

ORIGINS: Fossil *Umbrina* sp. have been found in Late Miocene formations (at least 5.3 million years ago). Yellowfin croaker pieces have been found in 100,000-year-old strata in California.

OTHER SPECIES

Cynoscion parvipinnis
Ayres, 1861
Shortfin Corvina

Shortfins grow to 60 cm (24 in) TL (and 4.7 kg, 10.4 lb) and are found from Huntington Beach (Southern California) to Mazatlán (Mexico), including the Gulf of California. They are reasonably common as far north as Mission Bay (Southern California). Found from the intertidal zone to 101 m (6–331 ft), they are mostly an inshore fish and usually live in 10 m (33 ft) or less. Juveniles live in lagoons, often around mangroves. Shortfin corvinas mostly eat shrimps, crabs, and fishes. It is a fairly important artisanal fishery species along the Baja California coast and in the Gulf of California.

ROXAS ACOSTA JR.

FAMILY CHAETODONTIDAE—Butterflyfishes

Butterflyfishes are mostly tropical, mostly marine (a few also are estuarine), and mostly shallow-water reef fishes that are found throughout the world. Worldwide, there are 11 genera and around 120 species. Four species are found within our range and two have been found (rarely) in Southern California waters. Butterflyfishes are oviparous and have planktonic eggs and larvae. Fossil chaetodonts have questionably been found from Middle Eocene deposits (about 50 million years old). A butterflyfish, perhaps in the genus *Chaetodon*, is known from the Late Oligocene (23 million years ago or more) of the Caucasus region.

Prognathodes falcifer
(Hubbs & Rechnitzer, 1958)
Scythe Butterflyfish

KEVIN LEE

ETYMOLOGY: *Prognathodes* is Greek for "before," "jaw," and "likeness." I have absolutely no idea what Gill meant by this, and his 1862 paper does not give any clue. What the hell was wrong with these people, did they think we were flaming mind readers? *Falcifer* is Latin for "scythe-bearer" and refers to the scythe-shaped mark on the body.

THE BASICS: Maximum Length: 17 cm (7 in) TL. The Ranges: Santa Cruz Island (Southern California) to Islas Galápagos, including the southern tip of Baja California and a number of islands off Mexico and central America. 3–270 m (10–896 ft).

SALIENT CHARACTERS: Scythes are compressed, mostly oval fishes with sharp snouts and little bitty mouths. The key character is the inverted dark "U" on side, often described as shaped like a scythe.

LIFE HISTORY: Not much is known about this species. It is a reef-dweller that likely is active during daylight hours. If similar to other butterflyfishes, scythes feed on algae and invertebrates. There is a small colony living on the shallow reefs of Santa Catalina Island.

FAMILY POMACANTHIDAE—Angelfishes

Angelfishes are shallow water, tropical marine reef fishes found throughout the world. There are eight genera and around 80 species. Three species occur within our range, with one in Southern California. Angelfishes are oviparous with planktonic eggs and larvae. The family arose at least as far back as the Middle Eocene (around 45 million years ago). Fischer et al. (1995) has keys to the tropical eastern Pacific species.

Pomacanthus zonipectus
(Gill, 1862)
Cortez Angelfish

ETYMOLOGY: *Pomacanthus* is "operculum" and "spine" in Greek and *zonipectus* is "zone" and "breast" in Greek.

THE BASICS: Maximum Length: 50 cm (20 in) TL. The Ranges: Redondo Beach (Southern California) to Máncora (Peru), including the Gulf of California, and typically as far northward as the Bahia Magdalena complex (southern Baja California). We have seen a few at Islas Cedros and San Benitos (central Baja California). Intertidal to 50 m (164 ft).

SALIENT CHARACTERS: Cortez angels are mostly oval, with kind of pointy snouts, and an obvious single spine on the lower cheek. Adults are tidily marked: Following a gray snoutish zone, there is a broad yellow band, followed by black, yellow, and black, a broad green-gray area, a dark zone, and a lighter tail. Juveniles look totally different from adults. They are black

with a series of narrow blue and yellow curved bars.

LIFE HISTORY: These are reef dwellers that are active during the day and shelter at night. You often see them over boulders or along rock walls; they tend to stay for extended periods within small home ranges. Spawning occurs from June–November. Juveniles are territorial, while adults often hang out in pairs or small groups. This species feeds during daylight hours on such reef-dwelling invertebrates as sponges, hydroids, bryozoans, and snails, as well as on

OCTAVIO ABURTO-OROPEZA

algae and fish eggs. Juveniles graze on algae and some also clean other fishes. This species apparently is most closely related to the Atlantic species *Pomacanthus paru* and *P. arcuatus*.

FAMILY PENTACEROTIDAE—Armorheads

The armorheads are an interesting group of fishes, comprising seven genera and about 12 species, with one species within our range, that mostly occupy colder waters of the Indian, Pacific, and southern Atlantic oceans. Armorheads are oviparous with planktonic eggs and larvae.

PHOTO FROM PISCES IV SUBMERISIBLE, HAWAII UNDERSEA RESEARCH LABORATORY

Pseudopentaceros wheeleri
Hardy, 1983
North Pacific Armorhead

ETYMOLOGY: *Pseudopentaceros* is Greek for "false," "five," and "horns/plates" and *wheeleri* refers to Alwyne Cooper Wheeler (1929–2005), a very talented ichthyologist and curator at the Natural History Museum in London. What I like most is that Mr. Wheeler did not have any university degrees and yet seemingly, by talent alone, wound up in that prominent position.

THE BASICS: Maximum Length: 53 cm (21 in) TL. The Ranges: Japan to Hawai'i, Gulf of Alaska to Central California. Surface to 1,060 m (3,478 ft).

SALIENT CHARACTERS: Well, they are not called bleeding armorheads for nothing. No, clearly some committee, perhaps the same committee that decided to call it part-skim mozzarella (and just what part is that?) was tasked with the job and came up with a perfectly reasonable and completely self-evident name. For make no mistake about it, North Pacific armorheads not only live in the North Pacific, they also have a head that is covered in bone, and that bone (and this is eventually what would have happened to your neighbors in *Night of the Living Dead*) is not covered in skin. Oh, and they (the armorheads, not your zombie neighbors) also have 2–5 anal fin spines, a long continuous dorsal fin, a long snout, and small mouth. They are reported to be bluish-brown or gray, with pink on heads, and orange on pelvic and anal fin spines.

LIFE HISTORY: Adults live near or on the bottom of the southern Emperor-northern Hawaiian Ridge, a series of seamounts and other rocky reefs extending thousands of kilometers north and west of the Hawaiian Islands. Juvenile armorheads, produced as larvae over the Ridge, are pelagic and drift northward. Most wind up in the Gulf of Alaska, although some fish head west to Asia and some east to the Pacific Coast of North America. In the northeast Pacific, pelagic juveniles live in waters between 8.6–15°C (48–59°F), averaging 12.1°C (54°F). At somewhere around 1.5–2.5 years, these juveniles have worked their way back to the sea mount-ridge habitat and take up a benthic existence, where they form dense schools.

A 33.8 cm (13 in) SL fish was judged to be 10 or 11 years old. A few males mature at 24–25 cm (9–10 in) TL, 50% at about 26 cm (10 in), and 100% at 32 cm (13 in). A few females are mature at 25 cm (10 in), 50% at 30 cm (12 in), and 100% at 34 cm (13 in). Spawning occurs between November–March. North Pacific armorheads feed on such zooplankters as copepods, tunicates, and euphausiids, as well as fishes. Predators include Bryde's and sei whales.

FAMILY KYPHOSIDAE—Sea Chubs

The kyphosids are nearshore, temperate or tropical marine fishes. Usually associating with complex habitat, sea chubs are found in the Atlantic, Pacific, and Indian oceans. Sixteen genera and about 45 species have been described, of which eight species live within our range, and five of these north of the U.S.-Mexican border. They are oviparous, with planktonic eggs and larvae.

Girella nigricans
(Ayres, 1860)

Opaleye

KEVIN LEE

ETYMOLOGY AND COLLOQUIAL NAME: *Girella* is derived from the French "girelle," which, in turn, comes from "julis," a European name for certain wrasses. *Nigricans* means "blackish" in Latin. *Nigricans* has always puzzled me, as opaleye are not blackish. However, in reading over Ayres' original description, he notes that the preserved specimens he used to describe the species (captured by Captain C.M. Scammon along lower Baja California) were "blackish brown." It might be that the specimens Ayres used (having stewed for months in alcohol) had changed color from their more usual dark green. Anglers sometimes call them "button bass."

THE BASICS: Maximum Length: 66 cm (26 in) TL. Maximum Length: One 64.5 cm (25 in) fish weighed 6.1 kg (13.5 lb). The Ranges: Otter Rock (Oregon) to Cabo San Lucas (southern Baja California); an isolated population in the Gulf of California. They are common from Central California to (in one of our fish surveys) at least Isla Asuncion (southern Baja California) and patchily abundant perhaps even to Punta El Conejo, southern Baja California. Intertidal to about 32 m (105 ft). Eggs: 0.9–1 mm. Larvae: hatching length = about 3 mm, flexion length = 5.8–8.4 mm, transformation length = 1.6–1.7 cm. Length-weight parameters (TL, mm, kg): (sexes combined) W = 0.00000001448L$^{3.0492}$ (RecFin 2009).

DESCRIPTON: Opaleyes are oval, perch-shaped fish. Pelagic juveniles are bright green on back and silvery along sides and belly. Older, benthic-dwelling individuals have a gray-green or olive-green body and really cute blue eyes. They have 1–3 white or yellow spots on their back.

LIFE HISTORY: Pelagic juveniles often associate with medusae, drifting kelp mats, and debris. One observer reported that they sometimes rest curled up (resembling wet feathers) just below the surface. In Southern California, young-of-the-year settle from the plankton to higher intertidal pools at about 2.3 cm (0.9 in) TL, generally starting in June, but sometimes as late as early winter. In the area between Bahia Tortugas and Bahia San Juanico (southern Baja California), substantial settlement has been observed as early as February. As soon as they hit the rock pools, opaleyes quickly trade in their pelagic silvery coloration for a more businesslike olive-drab with yellow or white back spots (it takes about 24 hours). Transforming and very small recruited fish live in the uppermost pools and are often found in waters as warm as 28°C (82°F) (up to a maximum of 31.2°C, 88°F). As the fish grow, they begin to move into the lower intertidal and eventually develop a "home" pool that they retreat to at low tide. With time (mostly 1–2 years), fish move out of the intertidal, school up (sometimes in the hundreds and sometimes with zebraperch), and you can find them 1) over rock reefs, 2) from the bottom through canopies of kelp beds, 3) around shallow water oil and gas platforms, 4) in eelgrass and surfgrass, and 5) often in lagoons, sloughs, and estuaries. They can tolerate, at least for short periods, salinities as low as 6.3–7.3 ppt and as high as 63 ppt. Interestingly, both juveniles and adults live under drifting kelp mats where they may school with halfmoons. While they are quite active during the day,

opaleyes tend to hide in crevices, or are at least inactive, at night. Several genetic studies demonstrate that there are at least two populations. There is agreement that fish in the Gulf of California form a distinct population from those on the outer coast, with little or no gene flow around Cabo San Lucas. Terry et al. (2000) held that the two populations should be considered cryptic species; physically identical but genetically distinct.

Opaleyes live to at least 10–11 years old. They mature at 20–22.5 cm (8–9 in) TL and perhaps 2–3 years old. Spawning occurs nearshore, often near kelp beds, at least from April–November, and mostly from May–August. Despite an abundance of older fish in Central California, no larvae have been taken north of about Point Arguello (in southernmost Central California) and no newly recruited tide pool young have been noted; so they probably do not successfully reproduce off that area. The inside of a typical opaleye gut looks like the Zen Special at that trendy restaurant, Let Us Eat Lettuce. Opaleyes eat algae, lots and lots of algae, along with a soupçon of polychaete worms, various crustaceans (e.g., gammarid amphipods, harpacticoid copepods, and shrimps), snails, and insects. Younger fish, those less than about 3 cm (1 in) TL, have a mixed animal-plant diet and juveniles will clean other species (e.g., topsmelt). Predators include soupfin sharks, treefish, Brandt's cormorants, and California sea lions.

FISHERY: In the 19th century, opaleyes were a fairly important commercial species in Southern California, as they were easily taken with gill nets in shallow waters. Their popularity waned in the 20th century and they have formed only a small part of the "perch" catch ever since. They are often seen in the Mercado Negro fish market in Ensenada (northern Baja California).

Opaleyes are commonly caught by rocky shore and pier fishermen and by spearfishermen. They are notoriously hard to hook and, although mussels and other baits will work, moss and green peas are often superior. My friend, Hunter McCrea, has caught them on live euphausiids in Santa Barbara Harbor. And then there is this from the typing machine of Charles Holder (1910c): "I can wish you no better luck than to go up to White Rock, just this side of Long Point [Santa Catalina Island], with some old and experienced boatman, and spend a morning fishing for blue-eyed perch. You must anchor and 'chum' the fish up with abalone or crayfish [spiny lobster] bait. They are hard to lure, and you may have to jerk your bait away from the omnipresent rock bass to catch the dignified fish with a small mouth...I think I am not over stating it, when I say that unless you have the right bait you will angle in vain all day for these fish. When they are hooked the fight is on, and the rushing, plunging, and tricks that are played, put to shame many a fish of twice their size."

MISCELLANY: 1) Several studies has looked at variability in spot number in this species. Frankly, after reading them, I am confused. Basically, fish in Southern California usually have two spots, one on each side. However, fish with up to six spots have been noted. At least one study implies that the further south you go, the more fish you find with more than two spots. 2) Chris Okamoto reports a yellow opaleye with scattered black spots and Scott Gietler sent me an image of a green one with yellow blotches. 3) Juvenile opaleyes can aerially respire. Karen Martin wrote me that, at low tide in sheltered areas, they can be found out of the water.

Hermosilla azurea

Jenkins & Evermann, 1889

Zebraperch

ETYMOLOGY: *Hermosilla* comes from Hermosillo, the name of the capitol city of Sonora Province in Mexico, near the site where the type specimen was collected. *Azurea* means "sky-blue" in Latin.

THE BASICS: Maximum Length: 45 cm (18 in) TL. Maximum Weight: A 40 cm (16 in) TL fish weighed 1.4 kg (3.1 lb). The Ranges: Klamath River estuary (Northern California) to Gulf of California. On the Pacific side, commonly from Southern California to at least Punta Abreojos (southern Baja California). A report from the 1970s noted that they were common in the hot water discharge at the Morro Bay (Central California) Power Plant. Tide pools to 15 m (49 ft). Hatching length = less than 2.5 mm. Larvae: flexion length = 4.1–6.3 mm, transformation length = larger than 11 and smaller than 14 cm (4–6 in). Length-weight parameters (TL, mm, kg: (sexes combined) W = $0.0000000107L^{3.1025}$ (RecFin 2009).

SALIENT CHARACTERS: Zebraperch are oval and may have a blue blotch on the gill cover. The body color is green, silvery, or brown on the back and there are a number of dark bars on the sides.

LIFE HISTORY: Small juveniles are usually found in tide pools and older fish live in subtidal waters. You usually see them singly or in small schools, on the open coast around rocks, surfgrass, and kelp (and very occasionally in backwaters). Zebraperch will school with opaleye. They tend to spend nights in crevices. There is apparently lots of gene flow between Pacific Coast fish and those living in the Gulf of California.

Zebraperch mature at 20–22.5 cm (8–9 in) and 2–3 years old. Spawning takes place from at least July–October. They eat green and red algae, gammarid amphipods, isopods, and a few mollusks.

FISHERY: Zebraperch is not an important commercial species in either the United States or Mexico. However, I have on occasion seen them for sale in the Mercado Negro fish market in Ensenada (northern Baja California). They are taken in small numbers by pier, jetty, and rock fishermen.

MISCELLANY: Juveniles, particularly those less than about 5 cm (2 in) SL, clean other fish (e.g., opaleye and shiner perch) and often focus on eating the scales.

Medialuna californiensis
(Steindachner, 1876)

Halfmoon

They have that compact and buff look of a middle-distance runner on selective androgen receptor modulators.

KEVIN LEE

ETYMOLOGY AND COLLOQUIAL NAME: *Medialuna* means "half moon" in Spanish (referring to the shape of the tail), a name given to this species by California colonists. *Californiensis* was coined because the type specimen was caught off San Diego, and because Dr. Steindachner was having a day filled with a lack of imagination. The name "halfmoon" goes back at least to the 1880s. They are often called "blue perch."

THE BASICS: Maximum Length: 48.3 cm (19 in) TL. Maximum Weight: 2.2 kg (4.8 lb). The Ranges: Vancouver Island to southwestern corner of Gulf of California. We saw pretty good numbers as far southward as Isla Asuncion (southern Baja California). A number of fish wound up off Washington during the 1983 and 1997–1998 El Niños. Surface to 44 m (144 ft), including intertidal areas, mostly from near the surface to perhaps 18 m (60 ft). Larvae: hatching length = about 2.6 mm, flexion length = 5.8–8.4 mm, transformation length = about 1.2–1.4 cm (0.5–0.6 in). Length-weight parameters (TL, cm, gr): $W = 0.0196L^{2.963}$ (Love unpubl.).

SALIENT CHARACTERS: These are elongated and oval. That graceful half-moon shape to the tail is a good character. Pelagic juveniles are blue above and silvery below. The offshore mature ones are dark blue on their back and silver below; inshore fish are often an overall gray-blue. Follett et al. (1960) note that they are capable of changing color and pattern. As an example, when frightened by a sea lion, halfmoons developed a "dark-gray longitudinal band along the middle third of the side, and above it a narrower, whitish band."

LIFE HISTORY: Halfmoons are highly mobile, one might almost say quasi-pelagic, schooling and structure-oriented fish. Young-of-the-year (as small as 2.5 cm, 1 in, SL) recruit to nearshore waters, including kelp beds, and schools of 10–50 individuals are common over rocks, throughout kelp beds, around eelgrass and surfgrass, inside oil platforms, and underneath drifting kelp mats and other flotsam. How pelagic are they? Well, adult halfmoons routinely are taken many miles offshore, apparently in the absence of drift material. A few have been found in gill nets as much as 482 km (260 n. mi) off the coast of southern Vancouver Island. Juveniles will, on occasion, school with sauries.

A 41.3 cm (16 in) TL one was aged at 8 years and they mature when as small as 18.8 cm (7 in) long. Halfmoons spawn at least from May–November, peaking perhaps from June–August or September. They feed primarily during daylight hours and are largely, although by no means completely, herbivorous. Along with algae, common prey are bryozoans, sea anemones, sponges, hydrozoans, gammarid and caprellid amphipods, polychaetes, brittle stars, and the occasional fish. In some locations, halfmoons feed extensively on blacksmith poo. Some fish enter the intertidal at high tide to feed. Predators include lingcod, soupfin sharks, striped marlins, treefish, yellowtail, Brandt's cormorants, northern fur seals, and California sea lions.

FISHERY: In the late 19th century, the halfmoon was a very important commercial species and was taken in large numbers with gill nets off Santa Catalina Island and sold in Los Angeles. At that time, they were second only to Pacific barracuda in importance in the LA markets and were also of some importance in San Diego. Catches declined in the 20th century and today they are only rarely part of the commercial take. They are often sold in the Mercado Negro fish market in Ensenada (northern Baja California). Halfmoons are commonly taken by recreational anglers from vessels, a few piers (such as in Avalon, Santa Catalina Island), and from rocky shores.

MISCELLANY: Both juveniles and adults will sometimes clean other fishes. Follett et al. (1960) noted that on a number of occasions, halfmoons were seen in a "floating leaf" posture, lying on their sides near the surface, motionless, with head and tail flexed downwards. Why they do this is anyone's guess.

FAMILY EMBIOTOCIDAE – Perch, Seaperch, Surfperch, Whatever

First, what is it with this "surfperch," "seaperch," and "perch" business? Early on, most of these species were called "surf-fish," which we all agree was a little vague. Jordan (1892), a "surf-fish" proponent, wrote that the group "are commonly and wrongly known as perch." By the early 20th century, almost all of these species were called "perch," prefaced with some qualifier like "rubberlip" or "rainbow," and all seemed well. Really, nomenclature-wise, all *was* well. There were no poison pen letters demanding perchy clarifications. There was not an enraged citizenry petitioning the government for a redress of embiotocinic grievances. But in 1953 (yes, right in the heart of the McCarthy Period and oft we have wondered about that confluence), there was published *Official Common Names of Certain Marine Fishes of California* (P.M. Roedel, California Fish and Game, volume 39, p. 251–262), a document that will live in infamy. For in that paper we find this cure for a disease that did not exist: "Heretofore each species has been termed simply 'perch' preceded by the appropriate attributive. The typical surf dwellers are now identified by the name 'surfperch,' those associated with the ocean but not primarily with the surf are 'seaperch,' while those of varying habitat remain 'perch.'" Well, I put to you that we don't call grass rockfish, "grass barelysubtidalrockfish," rock blennies are not, "rock intertidalblennies," and we don't call Pacific barracuda, "Pacific quasipelagicbutstillsubstrateorientedbarracuda."

The perch are temperate-water, mostly nearshore, and primarily marine (except for the freshwater *Hysterocarpus traski*). With the exception of a few species in Japan and Korea, all live in the northeastern Pacific. Worldwide, there are 13 genera and 23 species, 18 of which live within our range. Based on genetic evidence, Bernardi and Bucciarelli (1999) believe that the separation of Japanese and eastern Pacific forms occurred perhaps 5 million years ago. A fossil perch from North America is *Eriquius plectrodes* from the Miocene (at least 5.3 million years ago) of Southern California. Are perch good to eat? I suppose they are okay. Lots of people eat them and many seem to like them. But we should always remember that lots of people also like lite beer. So what do we really know about what resides in the human soul?

Perhaps the most distinctive feature of the embiotocids is their viviparity. After a bit of courtship, males (using that swollen area of their anal fins to help in mating) inseminate females and the females store the sperm for a few months until their eggs are ready for fertilization (often in the winter). Then, while the young are in-utero, the female provides them with nutrition. By the bye, for those of you who are laid up with the ague or gout, a fruitful afternoon may be had by reading all about the development and physiology of young embiotocids in Webb and Brett (1972a,b) and Wiebe (1968a).

The discovery that perch give birth to live young probably took place maybe 10,000 years ago when some newly arrived immigrant from Asia caught one, cut it open, and thought, "Now, this is cool." The discovery of this phenomenon by white guys occurred almost simultaneously among a number of visitors to the West Coast in the early 1850s. The first person to write down a description of sea perch viviparity seems to have been John LeConte (1825–1883), later a well-known butterfly expert, who noted it in his diary. Dr. George Davidson (1825–1911) later claimed that "he had noted their [perch] viviparity long before any published notices of the fact appeared." *Kids, here's a fact of life. If you keep it to yourself, it don't count.*

So, proving again that life is just so unfair, Dr. A.C. Jackson was the one who, in 1852, first sent word of the peculiar reproductive habits of perch to the great ichthyologist Louis Agassiz (1807–1873) of Harvard; thus Jackson gets the credit for the discovery. Jackson was hired by the U.S. Navy to examine potential port facilities in San Francisco Bay and, while fishing near Sausalito, he caught an unknown (to him) fish and cut it open. And then, quoting the good Jackson: "I was vastly astonished to find next to the back of the fish and slightly attached to it, a long very light violet bag, so clear and so transparent, that I could already distinguish through it the shape, color and formation of a multitude of small fish (all facsimiles of each other) with which it was filled...The young which I took from her [the female] were in shape, save as to rotundity, perfect miniatures of the mother."

Now, Dr. Agassiz was, well, conservative, and plainly thought that Jackson (who had not supplied any specimens of this marvelous fish along with his initial letter) was just possibly some sort of yahoo [in the Swiftian, rather than world-widewebbian, sense]. To put this in perspective, Agassiz was a Swiss guy, it was 1852, and he never, ever, accepted the theory of evolution[1]. So perhaps we can cut the guy some slack. But on the off chance that Jackson was not the issue of first cousins who had married up there in Possum Rump, Kentucky, Agassiz asked Jackson for more information and, hopefully, a specimen or two preserved in alcohol. Meanwhile, Agassiz also contacted his brother-in-law, Thomas Cary. Cary, a San Francisco businessman, was an ardent student of natural history and came from New England, where marrying one's first cousin was an only occasional indulgence. By 1853, Jackson had written a letter containing more details of his find and Cary had sent specimens to Agassiz. A number of fish were transported around Cape Horn and three specimens, as Agassiz noted, were shipped via "express." In this context "express" can only mean either a transcontinental ride back from California via covered wagon or the west-to-east crossing of the Panamanian Isthmus, at that time simply redolent of yellow fever and malaria.

Ultimately, Dr. Agassiz had to admit that the perch were indeed livebearers. In his seminal (no pun intended, I think) paper on the topic, Agassiz wrote: "The perseverance and attention with which Messrs. Jackson and Cary have for a considerable length of time been watching every opportunity to obtain the necessary materials for a scientific examination of these wonderful fishes, has induced me to commemorate the service they have thus rendered to zoology by inscribing with their names the two species now in my hands...labeled *Emb.* [iotoca] *Jacksoni* and *Emb.* [now *Hypsurus*] *Caryi*" (Agassiz 1853).

[1]In 1867, referring to Darwin's theory, Agassiz wrote "I trust to outlive this mania." *He didn't.*

Amphistichus argenteus

Agassiz, 1854

Barred Surfperch

ETYMOLOGY: *Amphistichus* means "double" and "series" in Greek (referring to the double series of teeth in each jaw) and *argenteus* means "silvery" in Latin.

THE BASICS: Maximum Length: 43.2 cm (17 in) TL. Maximum Weight: 2.1 kg (4.5 lb). The Ranges: Bodega Bay (Northern California) to Bahia Santa Rosalia (28°35'N, 114°10'W) (central Baja California); most commonly from about San Francisco to at least Punta Blanca (central Baja California). Surf to 73 m (240 ft). Von Bertalanffy relationships are figured in Carlisle et al. (1960). Length-weight parameters (SL, mm, gr): (females) $W = 0.0000386L^{2.9914}$; (males) $W = 0.0000214L^{3.1025}$ (Carlisle et al. 1960).

SALIENT CHARACTERS: Barreds are silvery or brassy fish, usually with 8–10 yellow or rust-colored bars on their sides. Often there are spots between the bars. Confusingly, Follett (1936, 1942) observed that a number of barred perch (at least in Northern California) have no or only faint barring. In a survey Kirk Lombard conducted along Stinson Beach (Northern California), about 60% of the fish caught by fishermen had either no or only faint barring. Kirk notes that local anglers call these fish "California perch" and the puckish Lombard has coined the name "freeperch," because they are unbarred. Kirk also has observed that many fish in the spring have a reddish flush, particularly about the head, and purplish chins. Carlisle et al. (1960), citing an observation by Limbaugh of mating fish in an aquarium, state that during mating: "The male was especially dark below and on the head."

LIFE HISTORY: Newly born barred perch are 4.2–5.3 cm (2 in) SL long and are found in shallow waters, mostly over sand (although not exclusively as they also live among eelgrass, surfgrass, and low structures). Barred perch are a schooling species (sometimes found with walleyes) that are most common from right in the surf zone out to depths of 12 m (39 ft) or so.

Bars: now you see them...

ROY QI

Now you don't.

MARK WON

Although mostly found in seawater, they can regulate down to 20% of the salinity of seawater and are occasionally found in estuaries. Older tagging studies imply that these are not heavily migratory fish, the greatest distance traveled in one study (from Long Beach to Santa Monica in 48 days) was 50 km (31 mi).

Barreds live to at least 9 years old. Females live longer and grow larger than males. Males mature before their first winter and females when about 2 years old and about 13 cm (5 in) SL long. There is considerable stuff about courtship behavior in Carlisle et al. (1960). Mating occurs in November and December and the young are born from February–July. Females carry between 4–113 embryos and larger females give birth earlier in the season. Barred surfperch feed mostly on sand crabs, but you also find clams and clam siphons, gammarid amphipods, mysid shrimps, sand dollars, polychaetes, fish eggs, and very occasionally limpets, gooseneck barnacles, and bits of sea urchins. Predators include California corbinas, California halibut, California scorpionfish, kelp bass, lingcod, elegant terns, and bottlenose dolphins.

FISHERY: Barred perch were commonly eaten by Native Americans. Although mainly reserved as a sports fish, it is legal to catch and sell those barred perch caught along a short strip of Central California coastline: some hardy surf fishermen catch modest numbers in this fishery. I have seen many barred perch for sale in the small pesquerias in such northern Baja California towns as San Quintin and you can see fair numbers in the large Mercado Negro fish market in Ensenada.

This is one of the most important recreational species for shore, jetty, and pier fishermen in Southern and Central California. It is also taken in great numbers off northern Baja California. Boat fishermen fishing in shallow waters also take it with some frequency.

Amphistichus koelzi
(Hubbs, 1933)
Calico Surfperch

ETYMOLOGY AND COLLOQUIAL NAME: *Amphistichus* means "double" and "series" in Greek (referring to the double series of teeth in each jaw) and *koelzi* honors Walter Koelz (1895–1989), a well-known zoologist (he was a whitefish specialist) and botanist at the University of Michigan. Dr. Koelz held an appointment there for a mind-blowing 74 years. They are called "strawberries" by some.

THE BASICS: Maximum Length: 32.5 cm (13 in) TL. Maximum Weight: 0.9 kg (2 lb). The Ranges: Cape Flattery (Washington) to off Los Ojitos (central Baja California); most commonly from about southern Oregon to perhaps Santa Barbara and perhaps off northern Baja California. Surf zone to 9.1 m (30 ft). Length-weight parameters (TL, mm, kg): (sexes combined) $W = 0.000000004699L^{3.227}$ (RecFin 2009).

SALIENT CHARACTERS: I'll be the first to admit it, this one looks a lot like its two close relatives, redtail and barred surfperch. I asked ace fish sampler Kirk Lombard how to tell calicos apart from these other species and he mentioned the calico's "Pronounced notch between dorsal soft rays and hard rays" and "the longest dorsal hard rays and longest dorsal soft rays nearly equal in length", along with its "broken bars and spots on sides and it is the most oval of the three *Amphistichus*."

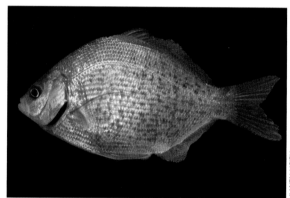

This is the way they usually look.

Note the barred perch-like vertical bars on this one.

LIFE HISTORY: There is not much to say about this species. Calicos inhabit the sandy surf, particularly on the open coast, but I have frequently taken them among eelgrass in more protected coastal waters. They live for about 6 years and are known to eat gammarid amphipods, sand crabs, and shrimps. Harbor seals eat them.

FISHERY: This is a major sport fish, particularly in Central California. They are mostly taken from sandy shores and off piers and jetties.

ORIGINS: An otolith of one has been reported from a 100,000-year-old deposit in Southern California.

SECRET AGENT MAN?

Walter Koelz was not only a zoologist, he also worked in Tibet during the 1930s, where he developed an interest in, and collection of, Tibetan textiles (now on exhibit at the University of Michigan Museum of Anthropology). All of this is well and good, and certainly this is reason enough for Carl Hubbs to honor Dr. Koelz. But wait, for in the Political and Secret Department of the now-defunct British India Office we come across a perhaps problematic file (Fiche 373 (74), L/P and S/12/4312 Pol Ext. Coll 37 File 79). Listed under "Travelers and Entry Control 1905–1950," is a file labeled "Dr. Walter Koelz, American Scientist." Now at the time Tibet was nominally controlled by the British and one wonders what reason the British might have had in keeping a secret file on Dr. Koelz. Was this merely a case of the British keeping tabs on any visitor to Tibet? Or, and this is of course purely speculation, was Dr. Koelz debriefed by British Intelligence on his observations in an area of great interest to that colonial power? In fact, what if Dr. Koelz was a British Intelligence officer, and had used his job as a scientist as cover for his spying activities on behalf of the British? And what if he had continued his intelligence activities for that great, dying power in the twilight of its years, when he returned to Ann Arbor? Indeed, what if all the British knew about southeastern Michigan (there being another agent up around Mackinaw) came from Dr. Koelz's meticulous reports, carefully copied on microfilm, placed in a Marmite jar, and shipped to MI6 in London? All speculation, of course, and, except for the British India Office file, almost certainly untrue. However, if this were the case, I think it is possible that the calico surfperch is one of the few fishes on the Pacific Coast named in honor of a secret agent.

Amphistichus rhodoterus

(Agassiz, 1854)

Redtail Surfperch

KIRK LOMBARD

ETYMOLOGY: *Amphistichus* means "double" and "series" in Greek (referring to the double series of teeth in each jaw) and *rhodoterus* is Greek for "rosy."

THE BASICS: Maximum Length: 40.6 cm (16 in) TL. Maximum Weight: 1.8 kg (4.1 lb). The Ranges: Kyuquot Channel (northwest Vancouver Island) to Avila Beach (Central California) and between Punta Colnett to off Bahia San Quintin (both in northern Baja California). They are at least locally common from Vancouver Island to Northern California. Surf anglers (complete with photographic proof) tell me that they are caught with some regularity in northern Baja California. While one fish was reported from the ocean off San Diego (Eigenmann 1892), redtails appear to be really rare in Southern California waters. Surf zone to 7.3 m (24 ft). Von Bertalanffy parameters (FL, mm): (females) L_∞ = 450, k = 0.2, t_0 = 0; (males) L_∞ = 330, k = 0.3, t_0 = 0.1 (Ngoile 1978). Length-weight parameters (TL, mm, gr): (sexes combined) W = 0.00000912L^{3.12} (Bennett and Wydoski 1977).

SALIENT CHARACTERS: Redtails are silvery or occasionally brassy fish, with 8–11 red or brown bars on their sides. All fins are reddish. Kirk Lombard, who identifies nearshore fishes for a living, reminds us that there generally are only bars (no spots) and the longest dorsal spines of redtails are much longer than the soft rays.

LIFE HISTORY: This is a sandy surf species. Having said that, I should note that they are also found over low-lying rocks and that at least some females enter bays and estuaries to give birth (which also occurs on the open coast).

Redtails live to at least 13 years old; mature females are larger at age than males. A few females are mature at 3 years and 24 cm (9 in) TL and all are mature at 27 cm (11 in) and 6 years. Males are somewhat younger and smaller at maturity; a few mature at 20 cm (8 in) and 2 years and all at 26.9 cm (11 in) and 3 years old. The fish mate in the winter and females release young at least from June–September. Females produce 1–51 young, young that are as small as 6.6 cm (3 in) SL at birth. Redtail surfperch simply dote on gammarid amphipods. Other prey include clams, crabs, sand crabs, shrimps, mysid shrimps, caprellid amphipods, isopods, polychaetes, barnacles, bryozoans, and fishes. Harbor seals eat them.

FISHERY: Historically, there has been a modest commercial fishery for redtails in California. They are an important sport fish, particularly from Northern California northward.

ORIGINS: An otolith of a redtail was found in 100,000-year-old strata in California.

Brachyistius frenatus

Gill, 1862

Kelp Perch

ETYMOLOGY: *Brachyistius* means "short" and "sail" [dorsal fin] in Greek and *frenatus* is Latin for "bridled."

THE BASICS: Maximum Length: 21.6 cm (9 in) TL. Maximum Weight: 130 gr (0.3 lb). The Ranges: Near Sitka (southeastern Alaska) to Bahia Tortugas (central Baja California), including Isla Guadalupe; commonly from southeastern Alaska to at least Punta Banda (northern Baja California) (and probably further southward), and at Islas San Benito and Isla Guadalupe (previously regarded as *B. aletes*). Intertidal to 76 m (249 ft). While seldom found in tide pools, they are common from just barely subtidal waters to perhaps 15 m (49 ft). Length-weight parameters (SL, mm, gr): (sexes combined, fish over 65 mm) W = 0.00001184L^{3.1686} (Quast 1968).

SALIENT CHARACTERS: These perch are small, brassy or golden-brown, with a sharply upturned snout and mouth. Underwater, a silver bridle runs through the eye, is broken along the middle of the body, and then continues in splotches.

LIFE HISTORY: The diminutive kelp perch, true to their name, are very abundant in giant kelp and other large algae. However, they are also common among eelgrass, surfgrass, and other plants, over boulders, and occasionally in sand channels. In kelp beds, younger fish tend to be found in the canopy, while older ones live along much of the kelp plant, right down to the holdfast. You can find them as solitary individuals, in small groups, and in large schools. Larger individuals seem to wander a

bit more from cover at night. Juvenile fish do not usually move from their natal reefs. An aquarium study found that these fish died when temperatures got down to 8°C (46°F).

Both sexes mature at one year (about 8.5 cm, 3 in, SL) and seem to live only 2–3 years. Females produce between 3–50 young per year and these are about 3.3 cm (1 in) SL at birth. Kelp surfperch mate as early as September (perhaps through December) and females release their young from spring to as late as August. While most females release their young amid heavy plant cover, John Stephens (1983) reported that they gave birth along the plant-less boulders of the Redondo Beach (Southern California) Breakwater. Ed DeMartini (1988) noted that "large male kelp perch courted large females much more frequently than expected...small male kelp perch also preferentially courted large females." Kelp perch feed mostly during the day, but larger individuals may also feed at night. Smaller fish tend to feed on zooplankton (e.g., copepods, ostracods, cladocerans, larval crustaceans, and fish eggs) and larger ones concentrate on picking prey off algae. Benthic prey include bryozoans, gammarid and caprellid amphipods, small snails, isopods, mysid shrimps, shrimps, polychaetes, hydroids, and ectoparasites. Among other predators, kelp perch are eaten by copper rockfish, giant kelpfish, Pacific bonito, Brandt's and double-crested cormorants, common murres, and harbor seals.

FISHERY: Kelp perch were occasionally eaten by Native Americans. While of little commercial value, a few were brought into the San Pedro markets in the early 20th century. They are occasionally caught from piers.

RELATIONSHIPS: Based on genetic analyses, kelp perch are most closely related to pink seaperch. Tarp (1952) described a kelp perch from Isla Guadalupe (central Baja California) as the species *Brachyistius aletes*. This designation has generally been discounted, although as far as I know no one has compared the genetics of the Guadalupe fish with those of mainland individuals.

MISCELLANY: Kelp perch clean other fishes, including blacksmiths, garibaldis, halfmoons, kelp bass, opaleyes, and walleye surfperch. Because they feed on a variety of kelp eaters (e.g., amphipods, isopods, and snails), kelp perch may reduce predation on kelp fronds.

Cymatogaster aggregata
Gibbons, 1854

Shiner Perch

ETYMOLOGY: *Cymatogaster* means "foetus" and "belly" in Greek and *aggregata* is Latin for "crowded together." "Shiner" is a name that goes back to the 19th century as was "sparada." When I was a kid we called them "7-11s." Why "7-11?" I dunno. Maybe because it was fancied that the three bars looked like "7" and "11."

THE BASICS: Maximum Length: 20.3 cm (8 in) TL. The Ranges: Saint John Baptist Bay (57°17.46'N, 135°34.44'W) (southeastern Alaska) to Bahia San Quintin (northern Baja California). They appear to be abundant all along their geographic range. Surf and tide pools to 146 m (480 ft), reported to 303 m (1,000 ft); most commonly from barely subtidal waters to about 90 m (295 ft). Von Bertalanffy parameters (SL, mm): (sexes combined) L_∞ = 128.7, k = 0.063, t_0 = -0.45 (Eckmayer 1979). Length-weight parameters (SL, mm, gr): (females) W = $0.000009697L^{3.212}$; (males) W = $0.0000158L^{3.111}$ (Eckmayer 1979).

SALIENT CHARACTERS: These are small, silvery fish, very often with three vertical bars on the sides. Males have dark edges on the scales and during mating season the scales darken considerably, sometimes becoming almost completely black. At night, shiners can also darken up and the vertical bars become brighter.

LIFE HISTORY: Shiners can form schools of many thousands that occur over a wide range of habitats. These include kelp, eelgrass, surfgrass, rocky reefs, sandy bottoms, and oil platforms, in both quiet waters and along the open coast. While they mostly school up, at times you can find them as solitary individuals, particularly at night. They are common in both marine and estuarine systems, and for extensive periods will tolerate everything from freshwater to high salinities of perhaps 53 ppt. Arguably, this species has the widest salinity tolerance of the sea perch. They are at times extremely abundant in nearshore waters. As an example, Larry Allen and crew (2002) estimated that there were 2 million of them in San Diego Bay. Matt Wilson lives on Hood Canal (Washington). Matt spends many hours snorkeling over the shallow eelgrass beds just in front of his house. He has noted that individual shiner perch appear to set up temporary territories among the algae beds, territories that disappear when the beds are exposed at low tide. Pretty neat stuff, yes?

During spring and summer, shiners tend to move into shallow, quiet waters (often less 1 m, 3 ft) to release their young and copulate among algae and other plants. A number of studies have found that, post-mating, adults move into somewhat deeper waters, in some instances down to at least 91 m (300 ft). On the other hand, Byerly (2001) reporting on a study from Sitka (Alaska) found that shiners were abundant throughout the year in nearshore eelgrass beds, so you just never know, do you? Wiebe (1968b) described in detail the elaborate courtship by males of females. He notes that in males: "In the winter months the [anal] fin shows no fleshy modifications. By mid-may swellings have appeared on each side of the anterior anal rays." He then divides courtship and mating into 6 phases: "(1) the female is chased by the male(s), (2) one male heads off the female and isolates her from other males, (3) the male keeps his new mate isolated by applying aggressive charges at intruders, (4) the male, with the dorsal fin raised, performs a dance in front of the female in the form of an undulating figure eight interspersed with wide circular sweeps; this may continue for many minutes but may be interrupted repeatedly by aggressive charges at intruders, (5) the body of the courting male becomes limp and quivers near the female; the quivers are accompanied by rapid jaw movements and undulations of the dorsal fin, (6) the male attempts to copulate by briefly turning on his side and applying the anal fin appendages to the urogenital region of the female." John Stephens (1983), soaking his head in King Harbor (Southern California), noted that males defend territories in the spring and summer along shallow rocky areas and females remain in schools until attracted into a male's territory. Both males and females leave the harbor in separate schools in the fall.

Shiners live to 6 years old. Females live longer and grow larger. Males are variously reported to be either mature at birth or at least in the summer after birth. Females may be mature shortly after birth or (in at least one study) in their second year (in general, this seems to be in the range of 4–6 cm, 2 in, TL). Mating occurs in spring and summer and females may have offspring by more than one male (as many as eight). Ed DeMartini (1988) found that: "Small male shiner perch only courted small females, large males never courted small females…Large females are preferentially courted by small and large" males. Females release young at least from April–August, smaller, younger females give birth later in the season than do larger ones, and fish in more northerly areas tend to parturate a bit later than those to the south (likely because embryos develop faster in warmer waters). The young emerge tail-first and the birth of a young fish can take several hours. Fecundity ranges from 2–20 young and the young are released at 1.7–3.6 cm (0.7–2 in) SL. Larger females tend to produce larger offspring. Shiner perch eat more-or-less whatever small thing is in their environment, both in the water column and on substrate. Smaller individuals tend to feed mostly in the water column; bottom feeding (pecking away at the sand or other substrata) becomes more important as the fish grow. Prey include polychaetes, calanoid and harpacticoid copepods, gammarid and caprellid amphipods, algae and other plant material, isopods, arrow worms, barnacles, mussels, brittle stars, clams, insects, larval fishes, and fish eggs. While much of their feeding occurs during the day, some (perhaps mostly the larger individuals) also feed at night. Shiners can have a profound effect on prey populations. As an example, in Puget Sound, caprellid amphipods have very high densities in eelgrass beds in the early spring. In May, when the shiners come in, they just whomp on these amphipods (almost to the exclusion of other prey), driving the population down to near extinction. As you might expect, a wide variety of animals eat shiners. A partial list includes bat rays, brown smoothhounds, California halibut, Chinook salmon, kelp bass, kelp rockfish, leopard sharks, lingcod, shovelnose guitarfish, spiny dogfish, staghorn sculpins, Arctic and common loons, Brandt's and double-crested cormorants, elegant terns, California sea lions, harbor seals, and bottlenose dolphins.

FISHERY: Shiners were commonly eaten by various native peoples. Although not usually of much commercial importance, in previous years British Columbia trawler fishermen sold shiners to the animal food industry.

On the other hand, this is one of the most important species for pier fishermen. I caught about 5 million of them before I was 8 years old. My friend, Lynne Yamanaka, remembers that her mom would split, brine, dry, and then fry them. Pier fishermen also target them as a baitfish and many of the bait shops in the San Francisco area carry live shiners as bait for such species as California halibut.

ORIGINS AND RELATIONSHIPS: Shiner otoliths have been found in Pliocene (at least 1.8 million year old) deposits in Oregon and California. Based on genetic studies, shiners are most closely related to tule perch, *Hysterocarpus traski*, and to the two species of the genus *Micrometrus*. The putative species, *Cymatogaster gracilis*, once believed to live around islands, does not exist. However, there may be relatively little gene exchange between island and mainland groups and between groups along the mainland.

Embiotoca jacksoni

Agassiz, 1853

Black Perch

ETYMOLOGY AND COLLOQUIAL NAMES: *Embiotoca* means "living within" and "offspring" in Greek and *jacksoni* refers to Dr. A.C. Jackson, who, while fishing in Sausalito, caught several black perch, noted the female was filled with young, and wrote of this to Professor Agassiz. To find out what happened next, read the introduction to the sea perch found above. I grew up calling them, rather charmingly, I think, "buttermouths" and a lot of anglers still do. "Pogie" remains another commonly used moniker.

THE BASICS: Maximum Length: 39 cm (15 in) TL. The Ranges: Fort Bragg (Northern California) to Punta Abreojos (southern Baja California), including Isla Guadalupe (central Baja California); most commonly from at least Bolinas (Northern California) to about Punta Abreojos. Surface to 46 m (150 ft), occasionally in tide pools; mostly from just subtidal depths to perhaps 24 m (80 ft). Von Bertalanffy parameters (SL, cm): (sexes combined) L_∞ = 217.9, k = 0.35, t_0 = 1.648 (Froeschke et al. 2007). Length-weight parameters (SL, cm, gr): W = $0.000085L^{2.8636}$ (Froeschke et al. 2007).

SALIENT CHARACTERS: These are variably colored fish (they can rapidly change color), rarely black, most often various shades of brown, red, orange, gray, and green. Sometimes they have a very tasteful blue flecking on scales and blue and gold markings on anal fins. Lips run from orange or yellow to reddish-brown, and there is a patch of large scales between the pectoral and pelvic fins. Kirk Lombard has noted a dark "mustache" on the upper lip and a bluish-white line at the base of the anal fin. Dark barring may or may not be present.

LIFE HISTORY: Females release their young among nearshore algae, down to depths of about 15 m (49 ft). Immediately after they are born, the young-of-the-year from a single female form groups and, apparently, remain together for some time. These groups are often found around giant kelp holdfasts and other vegetation, and over rock reefs. Older fish are found over many types of embayment and open coast habitats including kelp and other algae (where they occasionally swim in midwaters), eelgrass, surfgrass, rocky ridges, cobble, and out over sand. They are found singly or in schools containing up to several

hundred individuals. In certain locations, large males may be territorial (defending a shelter site and some turf algae where they feed), however this is not a universal behavior. Black perch are particularly fond of the benthic turf community and the more turf there is, the more fish you will find. On the other hand, on reefs in Southern California, striped seaperch will exclude black perch from the best reef spots, driving them to suboptimal habitats in deeper areas. Black perch are pretty residential, although in at least some areas, such as Elkhorn Slough, numbers seem to decline in the winter. They are most active in the early morning and early evening; alert, but inactive, near the bottom at night. In laboratory experiments, black perch prefer 12–19°C (54–66°F). Genetic studies imply that there are several isolated or semi-isolated groups. On the mainland, one group is found from at least Tomales Bay (Northern California) on the north to Santa Monica Bay (Southern California); the other one ranged from Palos Verdes (Southern California) to south of Punta Eugenia (Baja California). There is also evidence that gene flow across Punta Eugenia is restricted. Among the offshore islands of Southern California, the Northern Channel Islands (San Miguel to Anacapa) form a unit, as do Santa Catalina, San Clemente, and San Nicolas. Fish at all of these islands were more closely related to the northern tier (with the southern boundary at Santa Monica Bay).

Mating occurs from at least July–November in shallow waters along the edges of reefs. Males only court females that are either similar-sized or larger than themselves. Courtship behavior, involving a great deal of male fin raising and fluttering, is nicely illustrated in Froeschke et al. (2007). Regarding courting aggregations, Froeschke et al. (2007) state: "Black perch tended to aggregate around one central point (e.g., a boulder) in large groups of up to 20 individuals. The aggregations consisted of males and females swimming around the central point, with males performing courtship rituals at a short distance from the group of females...After the female appeared receptive, the male would lead her to a nearby cave." Females successfully mate with 2–6 males per season. A black perch female may store sperm for as much as 6 months before fertilizing her eggs.

Black perch live to at least 9 years (that one was 31.7 cm, 13 in, TL). At least in King Harbor (Southern California), males and females grow at the same rates. Most fish appear to mature at around 12–15 cm (5–6 in) SL and perhaps 1–2 years old. Fish in the more northern part of the range tend to grow larger than do those in Southern California. Females release between 2–31 young (as small as 4.7 cm, 2 in, SL), from as early as March to at least November, apparently depending on geographic area. Black perch feed on a wide range of benthic organisms, including crustaceans (e.g., gammarid and caprellid amphipods, isopods, and mysid shrimps), polychaetes, clams, scallops, sipunculids, brittle stars, brachiopods, hydroids, sea urchins, chitons, snails, algae, bryozoans, and very occasionally, fishes. While most feeding takes place on hard surfaces, they will occasionally venture out over sand to feed. These fish take up a mouthful of sediment, winnow and swallow food organisms, and pass debris out their gill openings and mouths. Predators include kelp bass, leopard sharks, moray eels, Pacific electric rays, Brandt's and double-crested cormorants, elegant terns, bottlenose dolphins, harbor seals, and California sea lions.

FISHERY: Black perch were commonly caught by Native Americans. By the 1880s, the species was an important commercial fish in Southern California and the most important perch in San Francisco markets. Its popularity in the U.S. commercial fishery dropped in the 20th century and today it is a very small player, although you will still find them both alive and dead in San Francisco fish markets. It is, however, fairly commonly sold at the Mercado Negro fish market in Ensenada (northern Baja California). Black perch are a major species in the rocky shore, jetty, and pier sport fisheries of California and northern Baja California and are also quite commonly taken by small boat fishermen.

ORIGINS: Otoliths of black perch have been found in 100,000-year-old strata in Southern California.

RELATIONSHIPS: Black perch are very closely related to both rainbow and striped seaperch.

MISCELLANY: Young black perch will sometimes clean other fishes.

Embiotoca lateralis

Agassiz, 1854

Striped Seaperch

ETYMOLOGY AND COLLOQUIAL NAMES: *Embiotoca* means "living within" and "offspring" in Greek and *lateralis* means "lateral" in Latin (a reference to the stripes). Folks, at least in the San Francisco area, call these "rainbows" which, true to form, is the official name of *Hypsurus caryi*, thus adding more confusion to the lives of creel census biologists. "Blue perch" is another name for this species and the English speakers of Puget Sound called them "sapphire perch" during the 1850s.

THE BASICS: Maximum Length: 39.6 cm (16 in) TL. Maximum Weight: 1 kg (2.1 lb). The Ranges: Southeastern Alaska at Klakas Inlet, perhaps as far north as Wrangell (Alaska) to Punta Cabras (northern Baja California). Stripes (although basically a colder-water species) are at least occasional throughout southern California. Eigenmann (1891), for instance, noted this fish from San Diego Bay. Currently, the species is common northward from Santa Cruz Island, around Cortes Bank, and San Nicolas Island (Southern California), and in northern Baja California as far southward as about Punta Colnett. Surface to 50 m (165 ft), including intertidal, and perhaps to 96 m (312 ft); probably mostly in 30 m (98 ft) and less. Length-weight parameters (TL, mm, kg): (sexes combined) W = 0.0000000154L$^{3.01}$ (RecFin 2009).

SALIENT CHARACTERS: I could give you the usual coloration, but it would be wrong. Rather, let us go back to Lord's (1866) rather more poetic description: "Eighteen

exquisitely beautiful mazarine-blue lines or stripes mark its entire length from head to tail; and above and below this line are a number of spots of most dazzling blue, arranged in a crescent shape, about the eyes and gill-covers. Between these spots the colour changes, as it does in the dolphin [the fish not the mammal], throwing off a kind of phosphorescent light of varying shades of gold, purple, and green--the back bright-blue, but darker than the stripes; the belly white, marked by golden-yellow streaks."

LIFE HISTORY: While juveniles are common in rocky tide pools, it is not known if females actually give birth there. It is clear that newly extruded stripes are found in understory kelps and eelgrass. One study found that, in general, the higher the density of foliose algae, the higher the density of stripes. This is a species of rock reefs, kelp beds, eelgrass, surfgrass and other plant life, piers, sand channels, and (improbably) mud flats. You can find them both near the bottom and, when there is some vertical stuff about (like giant kelp), in the midwaters. It is found both along the open coast and in bays and estuaries and commonly enters brackish waters. While at least some individuals are territorial, at high tide others move inshore to feed in the rocky intertidal and over mud flats. A study in Yaquina Bay (Oregon) found that these fish kept to waters 16°C (61°F) or lower. They are inactive at night, mostly hovering near the bottom. Giacomo Bernardi (2005) found that there are two populations: one from Central California to the northern Channel Islands and San Nicolas Island (he did not look further north), and the other off northern Baja California. Edwards (1970) observing what he took to be mating behavior in October off Monterey in 8 m (25 ft) of water noted: "The most striking feature of each [male and female] was the bright yellow snout. While one specimen assumed the normal vertical or slightly oblique swimming position, the other swam parallel to it in an almost horizontal plane."

Stripes live to at least 9 years old. Most fish mature at 2–3 years of age and around 19–22 cm (8–9 in) SL. Females release young (2.6–5.8 cm, 1–2 in) from March–September (with older females giving birth earlier in the season). A typical brood has 2–9 fathers. While broods between 18–92 young have been reported, anything over about 45 embryos appears to be unusual. Striped seaperch feed on many species of benthic and epibenthic organisms. Commonly found prey include various crustaceans (e.g., gammarid and caprellid amphipods, harpacticoid copepods, isopods, barnacles, crabs, and shrimps), polychaetes, mussels, snails, limpets, fish eggs, bryozoans, brittle stars, sea urchins, sipunculids, colonial tunicates, insects, hydrozoans, bryozoans, and algae. Predators include cabezons, copper rockfish, lingcod, staghorn sculpins, Brandt's and double-crested cormorants, common murres, and harbor seals.

FISHERY: In the 19th century, stripes were an important commercial species in San Francisco fish markets. By the mid-20th century, they were of only moderate importance in the "perch" catch and today they are patchily (like in the San Francisco area) landed and sold fresh, both dead and alive. Stripes are a very important part of the recreational catch, particularly from Central California northward. They are taken primarily by shore, pier, and jetty fishermen, but also by boat anglers fishing near structure.

RELATIONSHIPS: All kinds of genetic evidence shows that striped seaperch are closely related to both black perch and rainbow seaperch.

MISCELLANY: Young stripes will, on occasion, clean other fishes.

Hyperprosopon anale
Agassiz, 1861

Spotfin Surfperch

ETYMOLOGY: *Hyperprosopon* is Greek for "above" and "face" (referring to the slanting forehead) and *anale* is Latin for "anal" and likely refers to the dark blotch on the anal fin.

THE BASICS: Maximum Length: 20 cm (8 in) TL. The Ranges: Seal Rock (Oregon) to Bahia Blanca (central Baja California). They are reasonably abundant down to the Santa Barbara Channel. Surface to 101 m (331 ft), including surf. Common from the surf and tide pools down to about 35 m (115 ft). An age-length table is given in Baltz and Knight (1983). Length-weight parameters (TL, mm, kg): (sexes combined) W = 0.0000000003558L$^{3.717}$ (RecFin 2009).

KIRK LOMBARD

SALIENT CHARACTERS: They are small, sort of silvery or dusky on back, with a pinkish tail, pelvic fins without black tips, and with a dark patch at the base of the anal fin, and on the dorsal fin. Sometimes, like in the fish in the photo above, that dorsal patch is just a little dab.

LIFE HISTORY: Spotfins are kind of an interesting species, under appreciated because they are small and of little economic value. It appears that for some of the year much or most of the population lives over soft seafloors in offshore waters (commonly down to 35 m, 115 ft). In the summer months, female-dominated schools enter shallow waters (often, but not always, in the most turbulent parts of the surf zone) and release their young. While they mostly live over soft bottoms, you can occasionally see some in kelp beds.

Spotfins live to at least 4 years old; however, relatively little research has been conducted on them. Females may grow somewhat faster and live a bit longer than males. The fish mature at least as early as one year old and 8.1 cm (3 in) SL. Females (who produce 4–20 embryos per season) release their young between June–August, with older females releasing their young earlier in the season. Spotfins feed on planktonic microcrustaceans (e.g., crab larvae, mysid shrimps, and copepods) as well as sand dollars, macruran shrimps, and fishes. California sea lions eat them.

FISHERY: Spotfins are often caught by recreational anglers from shore and piers, particularly in Central California.

ORIGINS: Otoliths from this species have been found in strata at least 100,000 years old.

Hyperprosopon argenteum
Gibbons, 1854

Walleye Surfperch

ETYMOLOGY AND COLLOQUIAL NAMES: *Hyperprosopon* is Greek for "above" and "face" (referring to the slanting forehead) and *argenteum* is Latin for "silvery." "Walleye" (also "walleyed") are names that go back to the 19th century. Historically, they were called "pogies" in San Francisco Bay.

THE BASICS: Maximum Length: 30.5 cm (12 in) TL. The Ranges: Vancouver Island to Punta San Rosarito (central Baja California), including Isla Guadalupe. The northernmost area of abundance is not known, but to the south they are common to at least Bahia Playa Maria (28°52'N) (central Baja California). Surface to 182 m (597 ft), including surf; rarely in tide pools and commonly from the surf to depths of about 20 m (66 ft). One was taken inside the mouth of a stream (24.6 ppt) during tidal inflow. Von Bertalanffy parameters (SL, mm): (sexes combined) L_∞ = 173.7, k = 0.538, t_0 = -0.257 (Eckmayer 1979). Length-weight parameters (SL, mm, gr): (females) W = $0.00001714L^{3.114}$; (males) W = $0.00009448L^{3.238}$ (Eckmayer 1979).

SALIENT CHARACTERS: Walleyes are distinguished by just what their common implies—a pair of very large eyes. Otherwise, they are silvery fish, with purple or bluish backs and a large, upturned mouth. Scales near the pectoral fins have yellow spots and the pelvic fins of males are bright yellow. During breeding season both sexes will have 5–6 dark bars on their sides (these are faint or absent at other times). Occasionally there is a reddish blush to the sides of the head.

LIFE HISTORY: Walleyes are schooling fishes that are found on the open coast, in quiet bays, and in estuaries, in salinities down to at least 25 ppt. By day, walleyes aggregate in dense schools (often comprising several thousand individuals) along sandy beaches and sand-structure margins. At night, they move onto reefs and into kelp beds, eelgrass, and surfgrass, and disperse to the midwaters to feed. This is one of the relatively few species on our coast that is active at night, and during this period they can be the most abundant midwater fish in kelp beds. In Southern California, mating has been seen from October–December, over shallow reefs and in algae. During these periods, these normally schooling fish form little groups of 4–10 individuals, composed of one male and the rest females. Rechnitzer and Limbaugh (1952) discuss courtship behavior.

Walleyes live to at least 7 years old. A variety of life history parameters, such as growth rates, maximum sizes, and size and age at maturity, vary with geographic

SCOTT GIETLER

location. Check Ed DeMartini et al. (1983) for some comparisons. As an example, Ed found that for fish near San Diego almost all males (at 6.5–9.5 cm, 3–4 in, SL) and a majority of females (at about 9–11 cm, 4 in) mature before their first birthday. He notes that fish living in Arcata Bay (Northern California) did not mature until they were 1 year old. Over their geographic range, females give birth from April–June (larger females giving birth earliest), producing between 1–29 young that average 3 cm (1 in) SL. Larger females tend to produce larger offspring. Walleye surfperch feed on both planktonic and epibenthic prey. Mysid shrimps, gammarid amphipods, and polychaetes are all important, as, on occasion, are various other crustaceans, snails, small clams, insects, and fishes. Predators include California halibut, Brandt's and double-crested cormorants, elegant terns, bottlenose dolphins, and harbor seals.

FISHERY: Walleyes were an important part of the diets of Native Americans. They have always been of only minor commercial importance. Pier fisherman catch simply huge numbers and they are also an important catch by those fishing off jetties and rocks, from sandy surf, and from boats working shallow waters. People take them home to eat, but they are also used for bait for halibut and other species.

Hyperprosopon ellipticum
(Gibbons, 1854)
Silver Surfperch

ETYMOLOGY: *Hyperprosopon* is Greek for "above" and "face" (referring to the slanting forehead) and *ellipticum* is Latin for the elliptical body shape.

THE BASICS: Maximum Length: 26.7 cm (11 in) TL. The Ranges: Brooks Peninsula (British Columbia) to Rio San Vicente (northern Baja California). Apparently common from Vancouver Island to about Point Conception (California). Intertidal to 110 m (360 ft). They are most abundant in waters perhaps 1–4 m (3–13 ft) deep. A table giving calculated lengths at age for males and females is given in Wydoski and Bennett (1973). Length-weight parameters (TL, mm, gr): (sexes combined) $W = 0.000004699L^{3.227}$ (Wydoski and Bennett 1973).

SALIENT CHARACTERS: A silver surfperch is oval, the back is silvery-gray or sort of olive, with silvery sides and belly. The sides may have darker pinkish bars. It has fairly large eyes (though not as large as the walleye), a pinkish caudal fin, and a dark spot on the anal fin.

LIFE HISTORY: Silvers live in large schools, in shallow waters, both along exposed beaches in high surge areas (in kelp beds, eelgrass, and over reefs) and in quiet bays. They can tolerate nearly freshwater conditions for at least moderate periods of time. Young-of-the-year are found in very shallow waters, including in tide pools. Most of the time you can spot them a few meters above the seafloor.

Male silvers live to at least 7 years old and females to at least 5 years. A few males mature at 14–15 cm (6 in) TL (1 year old), 50% at about 16–17 cm (6–7 in) (2 years old), and 100% at 18–19 cm (7–8 in) (3 years old). A few females mature at 17–18 cm (7 in) (2 years old) and all are mature by 19 cm (8 in) (3 years old). Silvers mate in the fall and give birth to young from June–August. Fecundity ranges from 4–30 embryos and the young are born at 2–4 cm (2 in) TL. They prey on various crustaceans (e.g., gammarid amphipods, shrimps, and sand crabs), as well as small clams and fishes. Harbor seals eat them.

FISHERY: Silvers are a very common catch of pier, jetty, and shore sport fishermen.

ORIGINS: Otoliths from this species have been found in 100,000-year-old strata from California.

Hypsurus caryi
(Agassiz, 1853)
Rainbow Seaperch

ETYMOLOGY: *Hypsurus* is Greek for "high" and "tail" and *caryi* was named by Louis Agassiz for Thomas G. Cary (1824–1888), brother of Agassiz's wife, Elizabeth Cary Agassiz (who, parenthetically, was a founder of Radcliffe College in Massachusetts).

THE BASICS: Maximum Length: 30.5 cm (12 in) TL. The Ranges: Cape Mendocino (Northern California) to Punta Santo Tomas (31°33'N, 116°24'W) (northern Baja California) and abundant northward to at least San Francisco Bay. Surf and tide pools to at least 50 m (165 ft). They are most common from depths of perhaps 2 to about 45 m (148 ft). Length-weight parameters (TL, mm, kg): (sexes combined) W = 0.00000001535L$^{3.007}$ (RecFin 2009).

SALIENT CHARACTERS: Very lovely fish are the rainbows. This is one of the more elongated perch (with a particularly long belly). They have blue and orange stripes along their bodies with orange bars on their back. There are also a number of blue spots, streaks, and blotches on the head. Look, too, for the dark blotches on the anal and soft dorsal fins.

LIFE HISTORY: Young rainbows are born among understory kelps in nearshore waters, down to depths of 15 m (49 ft). There is some evidence that, at least in some areas, females move into shallow waters in the spring or summer, release their young, then retreat into somewhat deeper depths. Both juveniles and adults are usually found near the bottom (adults occasionally swim in the kelp canopy), mostly either singly or in small groups, although they do form quite large schools (of at least 100 individuals) on occasion. John Stephens noted dense aggregations in winter and spring in King Harbor (Southern California). This species is common over quite a wide range of habitats, including many kinds of algae, eelgrass, and surfgrass, over high-relief rocky reefs, cobbles, and in sand channels. This is a cool-water species, with adults usually found in waters below 16°C (61°F) and preferring 11°C (52°F). They are inactive at night, when they stay close to the bottom.

The life history of this species has not been well investigated. In one study, the smallest mature female was 13.1 cm (5 in) SL. Females give birth in shallow waters during at least August and September, producing between 6–22 young, that are released when about 5.5 cm (2 in) SL. Rainbow seaperch eat mostly benthic and epibenthic prey, including gammarid amphipods, polychaetes, isopods, crabs, snails, bivalves, brittle stars, hydroids, bryozoans, and occasionally algae. Brandt's and double-crested cormorants eat them.

FISHERY: Rainbows were commonly caught by Native Americans. Historically, this was a fairly important part of the "perch" commercial catch in California, particularly for the Monterey and San Francisco markets. Rainbows are often taken by sport fishermen plying rocky shores, jetties, piers, and by small boaters who fish in nearshore waters. Catches are larger in the central and northern part of California than in Southern California.

RELATIONSHIPS: Giacamo Bernardi (2009) makes a good case that rainbow surfperch are quite closely related to both black and striped seaperch and thus should be placed in the genus *Embiotoca*.

MISCELLANY: Small rainbows have been seen cleaning other fishes.

THOMAS G. CARY

In the early 1850s, Cary was a principle in the San Francisco shipping firm of Macondray and Company. While living on the West Coast, he collected and shipped this species to his brother-in-law (see the introductory remarks under Embiotocidae). He was described by an acquaintance of the time as "a merchant, a scholar, an ichthyologist; an accomplished master in self-defense, a gentlemen and a rare good fellow." He later wrote an article for the *Atlantic Monthly* about the San Francisco Vigilance Committee and I wonder if he might have had something to do with the organization famed for scragging several miscreants in Baghdad by the Bay (see W.O. Ayres, Frontier Ichthyologist, in the river lamprey section for more on those Vigilance folks).

Micrometrus aurora
(Jordan & Gilbert, 1880)
Reef Perch

MILTON LOVE

ETYMOLOGY: *Micrometrus* means "small" and "measure" in Greek (referring to the species' small size) and *aurora* means "sunrise" in Latin, for the orangish glow on the sides.

THE BASICS: Maximum Length: 18 cm (7 in) TL. The Ranges: Tomales Bay (Northern California) to Punta Baja (central Baja California). Reef perch are abundant from at least Moss Beach (Central California) to Punta Baja. Intertidal to 6.1 m (20 ft), mostly in the intertidal and just barely subtidal. Hubbs (1921) provides data on length-at-age for females. Length-weight parameters (TL, cm, gr): (sexes combined) W = 0.0104L$^{3.2074}$ (Love unpubl.).

SALIENT CHARACTERS: A very pert fish, reefs have a black triangular patch at the base of their pectoral fins and, the big tipoff, a bunch of black-tipped scales between the pectoral and anal fins. There is also a yellow or yellow-orange stripe on the lower sides.

LIFE HISTORY: Females release their young in lower intertidal pools and these newly born fish move into the higher intertidal soon after. Schools of adult reef perch are found in the lower intertidal, and in the shallow subtidal, among surfgrass and algae, in surge channels, and over shallow reefs. I have occasionally seen them leaping out of the water.

Females live to at least 6 years and males to 4 years. Females are larger at age than males. Males are mature at birth. Females release 5–30 young (of 2.9–3.6 cm, 1 in, SL) from June through perhaps August and then mate soon after. Smaller and younger females give birth later in the season than larger ones. Reef perch eat mostly algae and gammarid amphipods, along with isopods and copepods.

FISHERY: They are only rarely taken by recreational anglers.

RELATIONSHIPS: Reef perch are most closely related to dwarf perch. The two species in this genus are likely most closely related to shiner perch and to the freshwater tule perch, *Hysterocarpus traski.*

Micrometrus minimus
(Gibbons, 1854)
Dwarf Perch

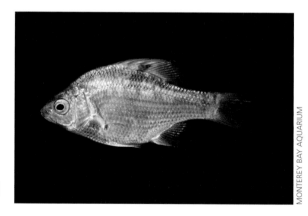

MONTEREY BAY AQUARIUM

ETYMOLOGY: *Micrometrus* means "small" and "measure" in Greek (referring to the species' small size) and *minimus* means smallest in Latin, because the species is just itsy bitsy.

THE BASICS: Maximum Length: 16.1 cm (6 in) TL. Maximum Weight: 76 grams (3 oz). The Ranges: Salt Point (Northern California) to Isla Cedros (central Baja California); common from Sonoma County (Northern California) to at least Bahia Playa Maria (28°52'N) (central Baja California). Intertidal to 9.1 m (30 ft); mostly in tide pools and in the subtidal down to 3–4 m (9–13 ft). Warner and Harlan (1982) provide data on length and age for males and females. Length-weight parameters (TL, cm, gr): W = 0.01L$^{3.207}$ (Love unpubl.).

SALIENT CHARACTERS: Dwarfs are blue or green on the back, with a black triangle, like reef perch, at the base of the pectoral fins. Unlike reefs, dwarfs are more oval and their bodies are covered in dark blotches. Males have a half-moon shaped depression at the base of their anal fins and a large gland on the anal fin itself.

LIFE HISTORY: This is a reef fish of high surge and wave-swept habitats, usually found in areas of surfgrass and eelgrass, mostly in less than 3–4 m (10–13 ft) of water. Juveniles are only (and adults are often) found in tide pools. While they often live on the open coast, they can be surprisingly abundant in bays and estuaries, where they are able to regulate down to salinities that are 20% of seawater. One individual was collected from the mouth of a creek at a salinity of 1.1 ppt. You mostly see them in small schools of up to about 25 individuals.

Dwarf perch live to at least 4 years old. Females grow faster than males and live longer. Males are mature at birth and females soon after. Males that are born early in the season tend to grow more slowly than those born later. This is because early-born males have more opportunity to mate (and hence shift more energy into sperm production) than later-born ones (these scope out the dating scene, are not impressed, and use that energy for growth instead). Some females mate with more than one male during the breeding season. Females release their young from at least April–July (perhaps into August) and fish mate soon after. Smaller and younger females give birth later in the season than larger ones. Mating occurs soon after a female gives birth, sometimes within five minutes. Females produce between 2–25 young. Warner and Harlan (1982) note: "Courtship consists of a male swimming toward a female from the rear at about a 45° horizontal angle, terminating with a bite to the area just posterior of the operculum. This is followed by the male positioning himself in front of and at a right angle to the female, head slightly downward. His median fins are erected, and he rapidly lowers and raises his pectoral fins...A reciprocating female will tip toward the male. Both will shudder, not swimming, with their heads slightly down and at right angles and their genital areas in contact for less than 2 sec." Dwarf perch primarily target such small crustaceans as caprellid and gammarid amphipods, cumaceans, isopods, crabs, and ostracods, but they also eat insects, calcareous sponges, polychaetes, snails, bivalves, and algae. Thus far, only Chinook salmon have been reported to eat them, but doubtless the list of predators is long.

FISHERY: Ken Jones, the Doyen of the Docks, the Prince of Pier Fishing, notes that pier fishermen, particularly those fishing in San Francisco Bay, catch fair numbers.

RELATIONSHIPS: Dwarf perch are most closely related to reef perch. The genus *Micrometrus* is most closely related to the genera *Cymatogaster* and *Hysterocarpus*.

REMARKS: Eric Schultz (2008) has found that juveniles born early in the parturition season are more often males. He hypothesizes that sex determination in this species may, at least in part, be linked to the temperature of the water where the mother finds herself. He then goes on to give a quite thorough exposition on the theoretical underpinnings as to why this should occur and, at some point, I kind of vagued out and went and made myself a cup of tea.

Phanerodon atripes
(Jordan & Gilbert, 1880)
Sharpnose Seaperch

ETYMOLOGY: *Phanerodon* is Greek for "evident" and "tooth" (an obscure reference, as this species does not have particularly large teeth) and *atripes* means "black" and "foot" (for the black-tipped pelvic fins).

THE BASICS: Maximum Length: 29 cm (11 in) TL. Maximum Weight: 271 gr (10 oz). The Ranges: Yaquina Bay (Oregon) to Islas San Benito (central Baja California). Surface to 229 m (750 ft), mostly shallower than 80 m (262 ft). Length-weight parameters (TL, mm, kg): (sexes combined) $W = 0.0000000137L^{2.98}$ (RecFin 2009).

DAVID ANDREW

SALIENT CHARACTERS: These are sort of silvery or reddish fish, with a relatively sharp snout, and black or dusky-tipped pelvic fins.

LIFE HISTORY: Sharpnoses are structure-oriented fish, found in kelp beds, in eelgrass (particularly the young ones), oil platforms, over rocky reefs, and only rarely over soft seafloors. There is some evidence that they make inshore-offshore migrations, certainly many or most pregnant females migrate into shallow waters to give birth. You can often find them in schools, sometimes with black perch, pile perch, and white seaperch. A study off La Jolla found that these fish were usually present in waters less than around 13°C (55°F). In Southern California, we see them in 10.8–17.8°C (51–64°F), but mostly in 11.2–13.9°C (52–57°F).

Not much work has been done on this species. They live to at least 7 years old. They spawn from spring–early summer and females produce a maximum of 11 embryos. Sharpnoses feed on such benthic organisms as bryozoans, gammarid and caprellid amphipods, isopods, limpets, chitons, bivalves, and sponges. They are eaten by Brandt's cormorants.

FISHERY: Sharpnoses are taken in moderate numbers by shore, pier, and boat anglers.

MISCELLANY: Juveniles are cleaners.

Phanerodon furcatus

Girard, 1854

White Seaperch

A remarkably unremarkable fish whose lack of ornamentation gives it a Bauhaus sensibility.

DAVID ANDREW

ETYMOLOGY AND COLLOQUIAL NAME: *Phanerodon* is Greek for "evident" and "tooth" (an obscure reference, as this species does not have particularly large teeth) and *furcatus* means "forked" in Latin. A number of folks call them "split-tails."

THE BASICS: Maximum Length: 37.5 cm (15 in) TL. The Ranges: Vancouver Island to Bahia San Carlos (29°36'N, 115°12'W) (central Baja California), commonly to at least Bahia San Quintin (northern Baja California). Surf zone to 70 m (230 ft), mostly from the surf zone to 50 m (164 ft). Von Bertalanffy parameters (SL, mm): (sexes combined) L_∞ = 202, k = 0.425, t_0 = -0.782 (Eckmayer 1979). Length-weight parameters (SL, mm, gr): (females) W = $0.00002254L^{3.013}$; (males) W = $0.00002655L^{2.978}$ (Eckmayer 1979).

SALIENT CHARACTERS: After capture, these fish are silvery, with one or more black spots near or on the corner of the mouth, yellow at the base of the pelvic and anal fins, a dark stripe at the base of dorsal fin, and (compared to pile perch) no dark bar below the dorsal fin.

LIFE HISTORY: White seaperch are schooling fish found over a wide range of habitats including various types of structures (e.g., rocks, kelp beds—both near the bottom and in the canopy, eelgrass, surfgrass, piers, and oil platforms) and also often over sand. They inhabit open coasts and, quite often, relatively quiet waters, including bays and estuaries. Females give birth from quite shallow waters to at least 15 m (49 ft). There is fragmentary evidence that the species is migratory. For instance, one study in Tomales Bay (Northern California) noted that males were rarely present until the fall mating season. In Southern California, we see them in 10.5–17.6°C (51–64°F), mostly in 11–13.1°C (52–56°F).

White seaperch live to at least 10 years old. Females may grow a bit larger and live slightly longer than males. In one study, the smallest female carrying young was 11.8 cm (5 in) SL. Gravid females, some time before they release their young, reportedly school together. Females release young from April–August and larger females release young earlier in the season. Reportedly, some embryos emerge head first and some tail first. Females produce between 3–34 young and are born at between 3.5–5.2 cm (1–2 in) SL. White seaperch generally feed on substrate-oriented prey. This includes gammarid and caprellid amphipods, isopods, polychaetes, crabs, shrimps, cumaceans, snails, bivalves, bryozoans, brittle stars, and fish eggs. White seaperch feed primarily during daylight hours. Turner et al. (1969) reported that white seaperch in Southern California ate the striped wentletap, *Epitonium bellastriatum*. This snail contains a purple substance that is absorbed by fish tissue, giving this species a rather striking purple tone to their snouts (in deeper waters this appears bluish). Predators include angel sharks, barred sand bass, broadnose sevengill sharks, cabezons, California halibut, grass rockfish, gray smoothhounds, Pacific bluefin tuna, striped bass, Brandt's and double-crested cormorants, mew gulls, California sea lions, harbor seals, and bottlenose and common dolphins.

FISHERY: White seaperch were commonly caught by Native Americans. In 19th century San Diego, this was a popular food fish, when flounder, bass, and croakers were scarce. However, Jordan (1884) wrote: "It is always present in the markets and is held in low esteem." Throughout much of the 20th century, whites were a fairly important part of the commercial "perch" catch. Today, they are a very important part of the recreational pier and jetty fishery and are often taken by shore fishermen.

ORIGINS AND RELATIONSHIPS: Folks have found white seaperch remains in Pleistocene (about 100,000 years ago) deposits. In what seems to me to be an eminently obvious result, a genetic study implies that *Phanerodon* are perhaps most closely related to pile perch. Hey, they just look really similar. In fact, a lot of fishermen call both species "split-tails" and can't seem to tell them apart.

Rhacochilus toxotes
Agassiz, 1854
Rubberlip Seaperch

A large seaperch with pouty bee-stung lips; think of Mae Murray in The Merry Widow.

ETYMOLOGY: *Rhacochilus* is Greek for "rag" and "lip" [kind of a nice allusion here] and *toxotes* refers to an archer fish that lives in southeast Asia and apparently reminded Agassiz of the rubberlip.

THE BASICS: Maximum Length: 47 cm (19 in) TL. Maximum Weight: 1.9 kg (4.3 lb). The Ranges: Mendocino County (Northern California) to Cabo Thurloe (southern Baja California), including Isla Guadalupe (central Baja California). They are reasonably common from at least the San Francisco area to at least as far south as Bahia San Carlos (central Baja California), and at Isla Guadalupe. Surf to 90 m (295 ft), mostly from very shallow waters to about 50 m (164 ft). Length-weight parameters (TL, cm, gr): $W = 0.064L^{2.549}$ (Love unpubl.).

SALIENT CHARACTERS: These are the only perch with very thick white or pale pink lips. Their body colors range from silvery-green to brassy and they occasionally come in black. Underwater, these fish are sometimes quite difficult to tell apart from pile perch as their coloration can be similar, and they can have a pile perch-like dark midbody band.

LIFE HISTORY: This is a schooling species, found around all kinds of structures, including kelp beds, reefs, cobble, eelgrass, surfgrass, piers, and rarely over sand. While found mostly on the open coast, they also live in quiet bays, and occasionally in somewhat estuarine waters. The fish school (sometimes in groups of 50 or more) mostly in the midwater or near the bottom; only occasionally will you see a few fish in the kelp canopy. Rubberlips commonly school with pile perch. The young are released in shallow waters, down to at least 15 m (49 ft), often among understory kelps. Shane Anderson reports collecting a bunch and finding that they were all females, implying that at least some of the time the sexes may be separated. Rubberlips are active at night, when they do a considerable amount of feeding.

There is just not much information about this species. I aged a 42 cm (17 in) TL fish to 10 years old. Based on my admittedly limited data, they mature at around 25 cm (10 in) TL and females produce between 5–21 young that are released during spring and early summer. Rubberlips eat a wide variety of hard-substrate organisms, but crabs, polychaetes, bivalves, snails, isopods, brittle stars, and gammarid amphipods tend to be most important. Caprellid amphipods, shrimps, barnacles, hydroids, mysid shrimps, mantis shrimps, cephalopods, and hermit crabs are also consumed. Occasionally you can find an individual packed with algae. Predators include grass rockfish, Brandt's cormorants, bottlenose dolphins, and harbor seals.

FISHERY: Rubberlips were a locally important species to Native Americans. Jordan (1884) sniffed: "As a food-fish it is considered the best of this very indifferent group." They remained reasonably important in the commercial fishery through much of the 20th century, although they are rarely sold today. I have often seen them for sale in the Mercado Negro fish market in Ensenada (northern Baja California). They are commonly taken by vessel, pier, and jetty fishermen and anglers fishing off rocky shorelines. However, their habit of slowly gliding around pier pilings, blithely ignoring all baits, has driven any number of 10-year-old anglers (including yours truly) into frenzies of frustration.

MISCELLANY: Little ones are cleaners.

REMARKS: Rubberlips use their large, flexible lips as suction devices when feeding; clamping them onto invertebrate-covered rocks and pulling their food into their mouths. What is really cool about this is their ability to separate small invertebrates from all the mung they suck in, without having help from a tongue. (Surprise! Fish don't have tongues. The structure that looks like one is actually a support for their gill arches.) This trick is equivalent to your putting a bunch of miniature marshmallows, broken glass, lawn clippings, and cubic zirconia in your mouth, then separating and swallowing only the marshmallows, all without using your tongue or fingernails. Good trick, yes?

Rhacochilus vacca

(Girard, 1855)

Pile Perch

PHIL COLLA

ETYMOLOGY AND COLLOQUIAL NAME: *Rhacochilus* is Greek for "rag" and "lip" and *vacca* is Latin for "cow" (referring to the species giving birth to live young). You hear them called "splittails" on the docks.

THE BASICS: Maximum Length: 44.2 cm (17 in) TL. Maximum Weight: about 1.8 kg (4 lb). The Ranges: Southern British Columbia to Isla Guadalupe (central Baja California). Individuals were observed at Bahia Playa Maria (28°52'N, 114°30'W), but specimens were not saved. They are common from at least as far north as Barkley Sound (Vancouver Island) to at least as far south as Bahia San Carlos (central Baja California), and Isla Guadalupe. Intertidal to 90 m (295 ft), reported to 210 m (690 ft), and common from barely subtidal waters to perhaps 55 m (180 ft). Wares (1971) provides data on length and age for males and females. Length-weight parameters (TL, cm, gr): $W = 0.0156L^{2.998}$ (Love unpubl.).

SALIENT CHARACTERS: Pilers are gray, occasionally brown or dusky, with a dark midbody bar on the sides. They have a deeply forked caudal fin and the soft rays of the second dorsal fin are long. When breeding, the pelvic and anal fins are bright yellow and males have dark black spots (they look like freckles) on snout.

LIFE HISTORY: Pilers are mostly found around structures, such as rock, oil and gas platforms, piers, kelp beds (from the canopy to the bottom), in eelgrass (where the young are particularly abundant), and also sometimes over sand. They are abundant on the open coast, in sheltered bays, and, on occasion, in brackish waters. Based on my observations, females release their young from just barely subtidal waters (often in understory kelps and eelgrass) to depths of at least 70 m (230 ft). In British Columbia, only gravid females releasing young and the young themselves are found in nearshore eelgrass beds. While isolated individuals can often be seen, pilers will school up (often with rubberlips) in aggregations of 200 or more. Studies in Southern California backwaters have found that schools disappear during the warmest water periods and return several months later. They tend to be inactive at night, usually hanging out near the bottom, and they appear to prefer waters cooler than about 16°C (61°F). In some areas, for instance off British Columbia, large numbers invade the rocky intertidal at high tide and simply waste on intertidal snails. And while it is clear that pilers move about a bit, it is unclear how migratory they are. For instance, in Siletz Bay (Oregon), one study demonstrated that mature fish enter the bay in spring and leave in fall, after the females have released their young. In that bay, the sexes are partially segregated, with mostly males nearest mouth and mostly females at the head of estuary. After the young are born in the upper estuary, the young leave the bay and do not return until they mature.

I aged a 40.4 cm (16 in) TL fish to 13 years old. Some males are mature at 2 years old (around 20 cm, 8 in, TL); when all males are mature is unknown. Some females are mature at age 2 (20 cm) and almost 90 percent at about 3 years (about 27 cm, 11 in); although some 5-year-old fish are not mature. Pilers mate in October–December and the young are born from April–October, with larger females giving birth, on average, earlier than small ones. Females produce between 7–80 young. Howard Feder et al. (1974), writing during a period when both articles and some verbs were severely rationed, noted: "Male displays himself to female and then rotates to his side or even turns upside down. Both then press ventral surfaces together and swim slowly on their sides (or raise heads toward surface). Entire procedure, taking approximately 10 second, repeated many times."

Pile perch love to eat things with shells. Smaller fish eat mainly gammarid and caprellid amphipods, polychaetes, and other small prey. Larger ones add mussels, barnacles, crabs, shrimps, snails, bivalves, hermit crabs, brittle stars, sand dollars, octopuses, fish eggs, and fishes. Most feeding occurs during daylight hours. As do white seaperch, some pile perch eat the striped wentletrap snail, *Epitonium bellastriatum*, which stains their flesh violet. Off Isla Guadalupe (central Baja California), adults have been seen to carry flattened pebbles in their mouths, perhaps to help crush shellfish. Pile perch have a single row of short and blunt teeth on their lips that are handy for grasping little mussels from rocks and pilings. The pharyngeal teeth (located in the throat) are thick, blunt, and flattened, perfect for grinding hard-shelled prey. While feeding, pile perch extend their lips and grasp a mussel. If successful, they then crush the prey within 20–30 seconds. Brett (1979), who did a lot of the work on how pile perch manage to eat whole mussels, noted that when he dropped an unopened mussel into an aquarium filled with hungry pile perch: "The sound of the crunch was quite audible in a quiet room…The sound was not unlike the cracking of a hen's egg." He also pointed out that despite the broken up shell having very sharp edges, mussels manage to go all the way through and out of the perch without damaging it. Brett found that the crushed mussels were "encapsulated in a mucous coating, and passed along the gut in small cocoonlike bundles." He showed that it took about 3 days for most of a mussel dinner to pass through the fish. Predators include copper rockfish, kelp bass, river lampreys, striped bass, Brandt's and double-crested cormorants, harbor seals, California sea lions, northern elephant seals, and bottlenose dolphins.

FISHERY: Pile perch remains are very commonly found in Native American middens in Central and Southern California. In the 20th century, they were a fairly important commercial species, particularly in San Francisco and Monterey fish markets. Today, California commercial landings are very small, although you can occasionally see them for sale in the large Mercado Negro fish market in Ensenada (northern Baja California).

They are a very important species in the recreational fishery, taken from rocky shorelines, piers, and small boats. The habit of pilers feeding on barnacles and small mussels often makes them difficult to hook. I can remember precariously perching on a 4 x 4 beam underneath the Santa Monica Pier (Southern California), perhaps 2 feet above the waterline, watching pile perch swim around pilings, ignoring all of my offerings. At some point, an elderly woman took pity on me and taught me how to catch them. She would bind a mussel clump in wire, attach leaders with hooks to the wire mesh, and insert whole small mussels onto each hook. The entire unit was then hung by a rope off the pier with the rope draped over a sturdy coat hanger. When a pile perch ate one of the hooked mussels, the coat hanger would bounce up and down.

MISCELLANY: 1) Small ones are cleaners. 2) In a likely humiliating experience, I have seen several overly adventurous pile perch tossed onto rocks by waves. 3) And speaking of humiliating experiences, dig this from Limbaugh (1955): "A half-grown specimen was observed being forced into eating external fish parasites by a group of blacksmiths. The blacksmiths would crowd in front and around the pile perch until it was unable to proceed. It would pick at a parasite and then move on until blocked by another blacksmith."

ORIGINS AND RELATIONSHIPS: A fossil *Damalichthys* [another name for the pile perch genus] has been found in a Miocene deposit (at least 5.3 million years old) of Northern California. Remains of pile perch are known from 100,000-year-old strata in California. Based on several genetic studies, pile perch are likely most closely related to the white seaperch, not the rubberlip seaperch. Thus an argument can be made that this species does not belong in the genus *Rhacochilus*.

Zalembius rosaceus
(Jordan & Gilbert, 1880)
Pink Seaperch

KEVIN LEE

ETYMOLOGY: *Zalembius* means "surges of the sea" and "life within" [an unusually romantic moment for Jordan and Gilbert] and *rosaceus* is Latin for "rosy."

THE BASICS: Maximum Length: 20.3 cm (8 in) TL. The Ranges: Point Delgada (Northern California) to Bahia de San Cristobal (central Baja California); isolated population in Gulf of California. Common at least between San Francisco and Southern California. They are probably abundant along much of the Baja California coast, but no one seems to have data from that area. Surf to 229 m (750 ft), reported to 238 m (784 ft), mostly between maybe 50–150 m (164–492 ft). Length-weight parameters (TL, cm, gr): (females) $0.0153L^{2.928}$ (Love unpubl.).

SALIENT CHARACTERS: This one's easy. Really quite an elegant species, it's the only embiotocid that is pink (sometime pink-brown underwater) and has two chocolate spots below the dorsal fin. The upper lobe of the male's caudal fin trails off in a merry little streamer.

LIFE HISTORY: I have seen young-of-the-year in waters anywhere from 40–210 m (131–689 ft) deep. Pinks are found over a wide range of habitats, commonly over sand, mud, mud-cobble, along sand-rock interfaces, over cobble and even, although rarely, on high relief. I usually see young-of-the-year in small groups of maybe 5–10 fish and adults either as solitary individuals or in groups of up to 20 fish. Most of their time is spent hovering or slowly swimming just over the bottom, although I have observed them as much as 3 m (10 ft) above the seafloor, and also sitting in little sand divots. Young-of-the-year sometimes school with adults and both occasionally school with halfbanded rockfish. Pinks retreat from the shallowest part of their depth range during El Niños. Over the years, we have seen over 1,300 of them in our submersible surveys in Southern California and while they live in 8.7–13.5°C (48–56°F), we see most of them in 9.8–11.9°C (50–53°F).

An 18.5 cm (7 in) TL fish I aged was about 8 years old. A few females are mature at about 4 cm (2 in) TL, most can reproduce at about 7 cm (3 in), and all fish 10 cm (4 in) long are mature. Mating occurs in the spring and females release young from November to at least March. Larger females may release young earlier in the season than smaller ones. Near-term young are about 3.4 cm (1 in) SL. Females produce between 1–12 young and larger females produce larger embryos. Pink seaperch feed on both planktonic and epibenthic organisms. Ostracods, gammarid amphipods, and cumaceans are often some of the more important prey, but calanoid copepods, polychaetes, shrimps, brittle stars, and caprellid amphipods are also consumed, along with the occasional fish. Predators include California halibut, lingcod, longnose skate, Pacific bonito, Pacific hakes, Brandt's and double-crested cormorants, glaucous-winged gulls, California sea lions, and harbor seals.

FISHERY: Not much going on here. A boat angler catches one on occasion.

RELATIONSHIPS: Pinks are most closely related to kelp perch.

FAMILY POMACENTRIDAE—Damselfishes

The damselfishes are mostly tropical and almost entirely marine fishes that are found throughout much of the world. There are about 28 genera and 350 species. Thirteen species live within our range and five have made it as far north as Southern California. Damselfishes are oviparous with attached, demersal eggs and planktonic larvae. Depending on the species, either males or both parents guard the fertilized eggs. Some species, although thankfully not any living off California, change sex. The earliest member of the family is found in the famous Monte Bolca formation in Italy (Middle Eocene from about 50 million years ago). The oldest North American pomacentrid appears to be *Priscacara serrata* from the Eocene of Wyoming. There are a lot of damselfishes in the eastern Pacific, see Fischer et al. (1995) for keys and descriptions. One older name for these fishes is "Demoiselle," a very romantic *nom* that we should reinstate although it is, I admit, French. And even though France is "Old Europe," and even though the French are kind of surly at times regarding U.S. foreign policy, and even though we once changed "French Fries" to "Freedom Fries," and came to our senses and changed it back again, and even though they insist on eating ground up goose liver from geese that have been force-fed, I still think there is room in our lives for a little romance. Don't you?

Chromis punctipinnis
(Cooper, 1863)

Blacksmith

ETYMOLOGY: *Chromis* is the ancient Greek word for some sort of fish in the Mediterranean (type unknown) and *punctipinnis* is Latin for "spot" and "fin."

THE BASICS: Maximum Length: 30.5 cm (12 in) TL. The Ranges: Monterey Bay to Punta San Pablo (central Baja California). They are most common from Southern California to (based on our fish surveys) at least Isla Asuncion (southern Baja California) and, based on larval abundance, maybe to Punta Abreojos (southern Baja California). 2–62 m (7–203 ft); common from shallow nearshore waters to at least 49 m (160 ft) and abundant down to 40 m (131 ft). Eggs: 1.1–1.3 x 0.6–0.7 mm. Larvae: hatching length = about 2.7–3.1 mm, flexion length = about 5–7 mm, transformation length = about 7–13 mm. Length-weight parameters (TL, cm, gr): W = $0.0082L^{3.255}$ (Love unpubl.).

SALIENT CHARACTERS: These are perch-shaped fish, gray-blue or gray on sides with black spots on the rear of their bodies. Young ones are bicolored; they have blue-gray fronts and brassy-orange rears. At night, when hunkered down in some cave, these fish have a distinctly blotchy appearance.

LIFE HISTORY: Young-of-the-year settle from June–December (mostly in the late summer–early fall) to nearshore waters and down to depths of 49 m (160 ft), at lengths as small as 1.2 cm (0.5 in) SL. This is a structure-loving species, found over rocks, throughout kelp beds, eelgrass, surfgrass, and oil platforms. Fish will often swim out over sandy bottoms, but quickly return to structure. Juveniles are also often found around drifting kelp mats. Both juveniles and adults often form large schools (with fish often numbering in the hundreds or even thousands), sometimes mixed with señoritas, jack mackerel, and topsmelt. Blacksmiths are active only during the day and retreat to crevices with the night. As Ted Hobson et al. (1981) observed: "Evening migrations began up to 30 minutes or more before sunset, while at other times they were not evident until about sunset. Generally, however, the migrations peaked from shortly before sunset until about 15 minutes after...When there are too many fish for available crevices...excess individuals sometimes cluster after dark in dense numbers on the sand next to the reef." In the eternal quest for bigger and better plankton, larger blacksmiths (greater than about 15 cm, 6 in, TL) will generally gather at the

Young-of-the-year.

upcurrent side of structure, attempting to get the first crack at whatever the currents bring in. Smaller fish, there having been selection for the more wary, tend to stay closer to shelter. Blacksmiths have at least some ability to home, as fish transported 0.5 km (0.3 mi) away homed to their original reef. If you see a group of blacksmiths churning around in a tight ball, there is a señorita in their midst, busily cleaning away. Turner and Ebert (1962), who knew more than is healthy about blacksmith reproduction, wrote that blacksmiths nest in waters between 4 and at least 24 m (12–80 ft) with nests located under ledges or in caves. And then: "A male would first clean an area well back under the cave roof and then force a gravid female into the site by nudging and biting her...the eggs were attached by adhesive filaments to the previously cleaned area of the cave roof...

the male would position himself in the nest opening, fanning the eggs with his tail and keeping out predators by his pugnacious behavior...The nest guarding males undergo a very conspicuous color change. From their normal bluish-gray with black flecks along the sides, they transform into a very pale, almost white, mottled gray. Two pronounced dark bands, each about one-quarter inch wide, show up dorsal and slightly anterior to the eyes." When larvae hatch "blacksmith and other fish then ganged-up on the nesting male...freshly spawned eggs were salmon pink...oblong...had up to seven filament at one end." They found up to 615,000 eggs per nest, probably laid by up to perhaps four females. They live in waters at least as cold as 10.1°C (50°F).

A 28.8 cm TL (11 in) fish was 7 years old. Blacksmiths mature at 14 cm (6 in) TL and maybe 2 years old. There is some spawning from April possibly to November, and mostly from July–September. Blacksmiths feed on zooplankton and apparently whatever zooplankton of the right size happens to be in their environment. In practice, this usually turns out to be larvaceans, calanoid copepods, gammarid amphipods, polychaetes, arrow worms, crustacean larvae, mysid shrimps, and euphausiids. On several occasions, I have seen a group of blacksmiths pecking away at a large salp. Predators include angel, blue and horn sharks, black-and-yellow rockfish, California scorpionfish, kelp bass, lingcod, moray eels, treefish, Brandt's cormorants, California sea lions, harbor seals, and Pacific white-sided dolphins. Pete Haaker et al. (1984) saw a harbor seal poke its snout into crevices at night and then eat the startled blacksmiths as they scooted out.

FISHERY: Blacksmiths were a fairly common food of Native Americans and later they made up a small part of the commercial "perch" catch in California. Today, they are only occasionally landed by commercial fishermen, but are commonly caught by recreational anglers fishing from boats, on a few piers (such as the Avalon Mole, Santa Catalina Island), and occasionally from rocks.

ORIGINS: *Chromis* sp. lived in the Late Miocene (at least 5.3 million years ago).

MISCELLANY: 1) For What It's Worth—Dick Bray and colleagues (1981) found that, as noted above, a blacksmith "Regularly forages on zooplankton during the day and shelters in rocky reefs at night." And that "This behavioral pattern results in the importation of 8 grams of carbon per square meter per year, deposited as feces in the nocturnal shelter." 2) Blacksmiths have been observed removing ectoparasites from mola. 3) A bicolor adult (dark blue-black posteriorly and light blue-gray anteriorly) was observed at Santa Catalina Island.

REMARKS: Watching blacksmiths delicately inhale zooplankton reminds one of the naturalist Gerald Durrell's poignant request while traveling through France: "Can we stop somewhere and press to our lips, like a nosegay, a pungent little pastis," he is reputed to have said, referring to the anise-flavored liqueur that is so beloved in Provence [David Hughes, *Himself and Other Animals*, 1998, Vintage/Ebury].

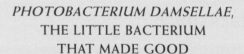

PHOTOBACTERIUM DAMSELLAE, THE LITTLE BACTERIUM THAT MADE GOOD

If you dive at Santa Catalina or Anacapa islands during late spring or early summer, you may see hundreds of dead blacksmiths on the bottom, all with sores on their sides. The sores and subsequent deaths are caused by *Photobacterium damsellae*, a bacterium my friends and I discovered (and named) in 1980. Since its discovery, *P. damsellae* has been implicated in fish die-offs around the world, particularly in marine aquaculture facilities, and has even been responsible for the deaths of the occasional human. Whenever I read about some problem "my" germ causes I get the same kind of feeling that Mrs. Hun (Attila's mom) must have felt watching her son terrorize much of the Roman Empire.

Hypsypops rubicundus
(Girard, 1854)

Garibaldi

ETYMOLOGY AND COLLOQUIAL NAMES: *Hypsypops* is Greek for "high," "below," and "eye" (referring to the large forehead) and *rubicundus* is "red" in Latin. The name "Garibaldi" goes back to Italian fishermen of the 19th century. They were also called "gold-fish" and "red perch" back then.

THE BASICS: Maximum Length: 35.6 cm (14 in) TL. The Ranges: Monterey Bay to southwest corner of Gulf of California (southern Baja California); common San Miguel Island to the Bahia Magdalena complex (southern Baja California). Intertidal to 39 m (128 ft), mostly from barely subtidal to 25 m (82 ft). Eggs: 1.2–1.3 x 0.7–0.8 mm. Larvae: hatching length = 2.9–3.5 mm,

A blue-spotted juvenile hovers in front of an orange-lipped rock scallop. JIM LYLE

flexion length = 3.9–4.7-less than 6.2 mm, transformation length = about 7–9 mm.

SALIENT CHARACTERS: Garibaldis are ovalish and bright orange; the juveniles have intense blue markings. That's it.

LIFE HISTORY: Young-of-the-year, 1.8–2.6 cm (0.7–1 in) TL, begin recruiting to shallow reefs (from tide pools to depths of 12 m, 40 ft) from July–November. You can find them darting around in little schools until they are 4–6 cm TL, when each individual goes its own way. Once in a while a few older juveniles will kind of vaguely associate with each other, but this is an uncommon occurrence. For whatever it is worth, juveniles reportedly hang with red sea urchins (*Strongylocentrotus franciscanus*). Almost all of the intertidal

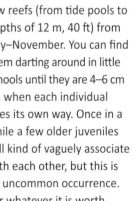

juveniles eventually move into somewhat deeper waters, although once in a while an adult will visit a tide pool. Juveniles and adults are definitely structure-oriented; they rarely travel even a few meters (maybe 6 ft) away from hard stuff. Among other hard things, you can find them on rock reefs, among kelp beds (often in the midwater and occasionally in the canopy), around oil platforms, and in eelgrass and surfgrass. While they are mostly solitary, these fish occasionally aggregate in midwater. Ted Hobson et al. (1981) describe adult garibaldis as being relatively quiet, although alert, at night and capable of moving about their territories.

A never-ending source of interest and, one perceives, amusement, the territorial and reproductive behavior of garibaldis has been intensively studied (e.g., Clarke 1970, 1971; Sikkel 1994a,b, 1995, 1998) and here are some of the highlights: Both sexes maintain and defend territories although, interestingly, on some reefs there appear to be a few adults that are not territorial at all. These territories contain a crevice to hide in, places to graze on, and, for males, a nesting site. Adult males, particularly during spawning season, are *über*-territorial. Adults will defend their territories against fishes that are a number of times larger than themselves, swimming up to an intruder and grinding together their pharyngeal (throat) teeth, producing a thumping sound. This is enough to cause most fishes to retreat. However, a garibaldi will hide in a crevice when a harbor seal comes by, likely because these mammals view the thumping as before-dinner entertainment. Adults occupying adjacent territories will fight only on occasion; they lock jaws for up to 15 seconds or so. Planktivorous fishes (that neither compete with garibaldis for food nor eat garibaldi eggs) are often ignored. In addition, juvenile garibaldi, coated with those lovely blue spots and blue edging to the fins, are also tolerated. The blue coloration on the juveniles appears to tell the adults: "Hey, I'm just a kid and not competition for you." Once juveniles mature, they lose the blues and are fair game for other adults.

Beginning in about March, males prepare nest sites by pulling out everything that is not red algae. These sites may be used for many years, likely by the same individuals. A nest at Santa Rosa Island (Southern California) was used continuously for at least 10 years. Ultimately, nests consist of a mat of red algae (usually 2–4 cm, 0.8–1.6 in, high) that range in area between 300 and 3,000 cm^2. Spawning begins when water temperatures reach about 15°C (59°F). When a female is ready to spawn, she leaves her territory, erects her fins, and heads toward the nesting males. Males respond by dipping their bodies and making thumping sounds. Spawning occurs during the day, from dawn to late afternoon. Once a female has selected a male, she may lay her eggs all in one go, or in several batches, returning to her territory between bouts. Females preferentially spawn with males that are already guarding eggs, particularly eggs in an early stage of development. When there is more than one clutch already in the nest, a female will always lay her eggs near the youngest eggs (the theory is that males will guard newly spawned eggs more rigorously than those that have been in the nest for a while). Newly spawned eggs are bright yellow, become gray as they mature, and are stuck onto the red algae by short filaments. The male fans and guards the eggs, warding off potential predators (e.g., sea perch, wrasses, and sea stars). Alcalay and Sikkel (1994) found that after receiving an initial egg clutch the male "Continues to receive eggs from multiple females for about 5–10 days (up to 20 days on rare occasions) and then does not receive additional eggs until all the previous eggs have hatched [it takes 2–3 weeks for an egg to hatch]...

Garibaldis chilling on a medusa.

Hatching within a brood began no earlier than 6 minutes and no later than 66 minutes after sunset...Newly hatched larvae appeared to be positively phototactic" [they head toward the moonlight]. A male defends a nest containing a large number of clutches more aggressively than when there are few eggs. Occasionally, a male will receive only one clutch of eggs. When this happens, perhaps in a fit of pique, he almost always eats them. Once all the larvae have left, the male starts a new brood cycle, with up to four brood cycles in a season.

Garibaldis have been aged to 13 years old. However, a fish thought to have been tagged at Santa Cruz Island in 1985 was sighted in 2003, so they likely live to at least 18 years old. In one study, the smallest mature female was 21.8 cm (9 in) TL and the smallest male with a nest (and hence assumed mature) was 21.7 cm (9 in);

Lots of eyes on lots of garibaldi embryos.

these fish were 5–6 years old. Males may grow somewhat larger than females. Females spawn from April–September (and perhaps occasionally into October). In most years, spawning peaks in June. Based on the number of eggs laid in a clutch, females produce between 34,000–190,000 eggs at a time. Young-of-the-year eat mostly crustaceans (e.g., copepods, gammarid amphipods, isopods, and crustacean larvae). Larger garibaldis eat a variety of benthic organisms, including the aforementioned prey, as well as sponges, brittle stars, sea anemones, bryozoans, tunicates, gorgonian tips, polychaetes, nudibranchs, crabs, snails, and shrimps. Garibaldi stomachs are often packed with algae, although it is unclear whether they actually digest the plants or are feeding on them to get at the various invertebrates living there. They also seemingly go nuts for any wayward medusae that drift over the reef. Male garibaldis sometimes eat the eggs they are guarding and females will eat the eggs of other females, when entering the nests of courting males. Soupfin sharks eat the adults.

FISHERY: Garibaldis were a minor commercial species in the 19th century. Jordan (1887) noted that they were commonly taken at Santa Catalina Island with gill nets and were destined for Los Angeles markets. Way back in 1912, Metz wrote: "The 'Sunday fishermen' catch numbers of goldfish from the rocky points and coves along the coast." Today, garibaldis are taken fairly frequently by jetty and rock fishermen. Note, however, that California state law makes it illegal to retain any garibaldi. While Californians appear to be just hung up on this species, folks in Mexico have no such misconceptions. They are commonly sold in the Mercado Negro, the Ensenada (northern Baja California) fish market. My friend, Jorge Rosales Casián, says they are just yummy.

REMARKS: For reasons that escape me, the garibaldi is the California state marine fish. Other than a gold color, grumpy and territorial garibaldis have absolutely nothing going for them that would make them emblematic of California. On the other hand, garibaldis do remind me of what John Adams wrote about Benjamin Franklin when both were American representatives to the French Court in 1778. Adams, sent to deal with the French government during the Revolutionary War, was both jealous and appalled by Franklin, who had conducted a brilliant diplomatic and personal campaign before Adams' arrival. Notoriously upright and strait-laced, Adams wrote that Franklin had "a monopoly of reputation here and an indecency in displaying it" (W. Isaacson. *Benjamin Franklin: An American Life*. Simon and Schuster, 2003).

FAMILY LABRIDAE—Wrasses

Wrasses are very successful, circumglobal, marine fishes found from temperate to tropical waters. About 68 genera and at least 450 species grace the planet. Sixteen species are found within our range, although only three reach as far north as Southern California. They are oviparous, with planktonic eggs and larvae. Fossil members of this family are known from the Middle Eocene, about 50 million years ago, in the justly famous Monte Bolca deposit of Italy. Genetic studies imply that labrids may have first evolved about 63 million years ago, in the Early Paleocene. Fischer et al. (1995) has keys and descriptions of the eastern tropical Pacific species.

Halichoeres semicinctus
(Ayres, 1859)

Rock Wrasse

ETYMOLOGY: I don't know what *Halichoeres* means. I kind of waded through Wilhelm Peter Eduard Simon Rüppell's *Neue Wirbelthiere zu der Fauna von Abyssinien Gehörig* and couldn't figure out if Ruppell actually gave the meaning of that word. *Semicinctus* is Latin for "half-banded."

THE BASICS: Maximum Length: 38 cm (15 in) TL. The Ranges: Diablo Cove (Central California) to southern Baja California (perhaps to Cabo San Lucas), also Gulf of California and Isla Guadalupe (central Baja California). They are common as far northward as Southern California. Tide pools and surface to 79 m (259 ft), mostly at 2–15 m (7–50 ft). Larvae: hatching length = about 1.5–2 mm, flexion length = about 5–6 mm, transformation length = mostly larger than 1.3 and smaller than 2.1 cm (0.5–0.8 in). Von Bertalanffy parameters (SL, mm): (sexes combined) L$_\infty$ = 213.1, k = 0.52, t$_0$ = -2.09 (Adreani 2003).

> **ON MALE WRASSES MATING NUMEROUS TIMES PER DAY**
>
> A wrasse once said, in a daze,
> Priapism is not just a craze,
> For if we can't mate,
> We'll self stimulate,
> And get warts on our pelvic fin rays."

Juvenile.

KEVIN LEE

Initial phase.

KEVIN LEE

Mid-phase.

PETE HAAKER

That night-time look.

KEVIN LEE

SALIENT CHARACTERS: Juveniles are orange-yellow with a broad cream-white horizontal midline, a second light line that extends from the snout over the eye and along the dorsal fin base, and a black spot mid-dorsal. At night, they get lighter and blotchier. Initial phase fish (females and immature males) are browny, yellowy, and orangey, with a series of dark scales on the back. Mid-phase individuals (males with female coloration) have a dark bar behind the pectoral fin. Terminal phasers (all males) have the dark bar, along with a yellow pectoral fin, pink eyes, and green or orangish bodies. Length-weight parameters (TL, mm, kg): (sexes combined) W = 0.0000000045L$^{3.16}$ (RecFin 2009).

LIFE HISTORY: Young-of-the-year settle (at as small as 1.2 cm, 0.5 in, SL) from September–November to rocky areas interspersed with sand patches. These young ones are often found in small groups. In the Gulf of California, juveniles are common in tide pools, but that does not seem to be the case in Southern California. Adults live over boulders, cobble, in kelp beds, eelgrass, and surfgrass, and will often wander more than 10 m (33 ft) onto the sand. While they mostly stay near the bottom, one will occasionally move into kelp bed midwaters. Often found as solitary individuals, small groups of maybe a dozen individuals are not unheard of. You frequently see them kind of rooting about in soft sediment. Rock wrasses both bury in the sand and lie among rocks and algae at night, taking shelter about 20 minutes before sunset and arising to meet the day around 20 minutes before sunrise. A laboratory study found that this species preferred temperatures around 25°C (77°F). There is apparently extensive gene flow between Pacific Coast fish and those living in the Gulf of California.

And reproduction? There is simply a ton of information in Diener (1976) and Adreani (2003). Adreani has a drawing of the various stages and a mating schematic. To summarize: Adults come in three flavors, 1) females, 2) males that did not start out as females (primaries), and 3) males that were once females and became males (secondaries). In Adreani's study, about 40% of all adult males had at one time been females. If females do change sex, it seems to occur after their first year. Most individuals engage in group spawning, with an average of 10 males and one female spawning together as they rush toward the surface. However, where rock wrasse densities are high, some large males hold territories and spawn with one female at a time. Spawning occurs primarily in the morning over rocky reefs.

Rock wrasses live to at least 14 years old. While some males mature at about 11.5 cm (5 in) and perhaps 1 year old, most fish of both sexes mature at 12.5–16 cm (5–6 in) and 2–3 years old. Fish that change sex transition at between about 13–14.5 cm (5–6 in) and, again, 2–3 years old. Fish spawn between June–October, mostly in June and July, and females are likely batch spawners. Rock wrasses primarily feed by plucking prey (mostly benthic invertebrates) from the substrate. Prey organisms include crustaceans (e.g., gammarid and caprellid amphipods, crabs, cumaceans, and ostracods), polychaetes, snails, brittle stars, ascidians, bivalves, bryozoans, and algae. Kelp bass eat them.

FISHERY: Eigenmann, writing in 1892, noted that this species was occasionally sold in the fish markets of San Diego. There is virtually no commercial fishery for them today. As far back as 1912, Metz observed that rock wrasses were commonly caught by pier anglers in Southern California and today they are still caught in some numbers by vessel, pier, and rock recreational fishermen.

MISCELLANY: Rock wrasses occasionally clean other fishes.

Oxyjulis californica
(Günther, 1861)
Señorita

ETYMOLOGY AND COLLOQUIAL NAMES: *Oxyjulis* is Greek for "sharp" and *Julis* is an ancient name for a Mediterranean species and *californica* for the location of the type species. "Pescerey" and "Chinese smelt" are older, and now abandoned, names.

THE BASICS: Maximum Length: 25.4 cm (10 in) TL. The Ranges: Salt Point (Northern California) to Bahia Magdalena (southern Baja California), and perhaps in the Gulf of California. Larvae have been taken south of Bahia Magdalena at about 23°30'N. They are common from Monterey to at least central Baja California, and

occasional to at least Bahia Ballenas (southern Baja California). Intertidal to 101 m (331 ft), mostly from 5–50 m (164 ft). Eggs: 0.7–0.8 mm. Larvae: hatching length = about 2 mm, flexion length = about 6.4–7.7 mm, transformation length = about 1.9–2.2 cm. Length-weight parameters (TL, mm, kg): (sexes combined) W = 0.0000000045L$^{3.16}$ (RecFin 2009).

KEVIN LEE

SALIENT CHARACTERS: Little cigar-shaped fish, señoritas have large scales and cute little buck teeth that stick out of their mouths and simply cry out for a competent orthodontist. Most señoritas are orangish or brownish; a few are sort of pink, yellow, or green. All have a large black blotch at the base of their caudal fin. The sexes share similar colors and patterns.

LIFE HISTORY: Young-of-the-year (at as small as 1.9 cm, 0.8 in, SL) drop out of the plankton from June–November, from very shallow waters to depths of (rarely) 58 m (190 ft). These juveniles settle to bays and the outer coast, around eelgrass, kelp, rocks, oil platforms, and other hard structures. Schools of juveniles and adults are abundant around all of the aforementioned structures and throughout the water column. On several occasions, Mike Moss has seen them rub themselves on gorgonians. Around 15 minutes after sunset, señoritas bury themselves in the seafloor and stay there throughout the night. They mostly bury in sand, but Shane Anderson notes that some fish may bury in pebbles. He also has seen them remain buried until as late as 10 a.m. So, how do they breathe down there? Scott Gietler saw one lying on sand at night, apparently fast asleep. Laboratory studies imply that they prefer water temperatures of 12–17°C (54–63°F). Señoritas may increase the density of giant kelp fronds by feeding on such kelp grazers as amphipods, isopods, and snails.

Señoritas live to perhaps 7 years old. A few individuals of both sexes mature at about 5 cm (2 in) SL and all are mature at 11 cm (4 in) SL. Unlike their more adventurous wrasse confreres, señoritas do not appear to change sex. Based on larval and egg surveys, there is some spawning in every month, with a likely late spring–early fall peak, and females are probably batch spawners. Here is what Brock Bernstein wrote about señoritas in his 1977 doctoral thesis: "Forages constantly, usually swimming alone, but sometimes forming loose aggregations that break up after 20 to 30 seconds…[in waters 15 m or less deep] foraged vertically from the surface to the bottom and back again in a matter of minutes. Their horizontal range, however, appeared to have a limit of approximately 30 m. Fish spend most of their time associated with a [algae or rock] surface…fish appeared to be intensely interested in unusual items. These were inspected, picked at or taken into the mouth, and then spat out if undesirable." In the kelp bed that Brock investigated, señoritas ate giant kelp covered with the bryozoan *Membranipora*, the worm *Spirorbis*, or various hydroids. In small kelp beds, where all of the blades were covered in *Membranipora*, an entire bed could be leveled as the señoritas chomped away at the encrusted blades. Other prey noted in various studies include such substrate-oriented organisms as gammarid and caprellid amphipods, mysid shrimps, and snails, as well as some zooplankton (e.g., copepods, ostracods, and larval crustaceans), and the feces of other fishes. Ted Hobson and Tony Chess (2001) found that fish smaller than 10 cm (4 in) SL fed mostly in the water column by plucking zooplankton out of the water. Fish larger than this tended to both take prey from substrates and feed in the water column. Predators include cabezons, giant kelpfish, kelp bass, Pacific barracuda, Brandt's cormorants, common murres, bottlenose and Pacific white-sided dolphins, and California sea lions.

FISHERY: Señoritas were often eaten by Native Americans. Yearly commercial landings tend to top out in the low two digits (like 27 pounds in 2006). Very occasionally, you can see them for sale in the Mercado Negro fish market of Ensenada (northern Baja California). They are taken fairly commonly by boat, pier, and occasionally rocky shore fishermen, usually by folks using pretty small hooks. When my son was a kid he liked to eat them and suffered no ill effects.

REMARKS: Señoritas are cleaners, picking external parasites and dead tissues from the bodies of such fishes as bat rays, giant sea bass, garibaldis, mola, blacksmiths, and topsmelt. However, while some tropical cleaners are full-timers, señoritas are kind of dilettantes, cleaning only when really in the mood; a mood that strikes only an occasional fish, only once in a while. However, when the "cleaning thing" happens, it causes quite a commotion. For instance, a señorita might begin by casually inspecting a blacksmith's skin. When the blacksmith notices this, it often stops swimming, holds its fins erect and motionless, and drifts (frequently in a head down position). Other fish see what is going on and quickly move in, forming a ball of activity around the cleaner. The señorita soon moves away, perhaps to inspect and pick at other fishes, which are busily throwing themselves in its path. After a relatively short time, the cleaner loses interest and swims off, leaving in its wake a trail of disappointment, despair, and the heartbreak of psoriasis.

Semicossyphus pulcher
(Ayres, 1854)
California Sheephead

A species that plays both sides of the street.

ETYMOLOGY AND COLLOQUIAL NAMES: *Semicossyphus* was coined by A. Günther and I can't access the paper where he coined the name, so I don't know precisely what he had in mind. However, *Cossyphus* was erected by Cuvier and Valenciennes for a group of large wrasses, so if you add *semi* ("half" in Latin) to *cossyphus*, you kind of get the picture. *Pulcher* is Latin for "beautiful." In the 19th century, sheepheads were almost universally called "redfish" or "fat-head." The name "sheephead," although occasionally used early on, did not come into vogue until the early 20th century. Recreational anglers sometimes refer to them as "goats" and they are "vieja" in Mexico.

THE BASICS: Maximum Length: 91.4 cm (36 in) TL. Maximum Weight: 18.4 kg (40.4 lb), but we have all heard of ones that were bigger, so who knows? The Ranges: Monterey Bay to the Gulf of California, and at Isla Guadalupe (central Baja California). Occasional in Central California, much more abundant in Southern California, crazy abundant along parts of central Baja California, and reasonably common down to about Bahia Ballenas (southern Baja California). Intertidal–90 m (295 ft). Most fish are found from the barely subtidal to 55 m (180 ft), although an adult male was taken from a tide pool at Palos Verdes (Southern California). They are often taken in relatively deep waters (60 m, 197 ft) at Cabo San Lucas (tip of Baja California). Eggs: 0.8–1 mm. Larvae: hatching length = about 2.5 mm, flexion length = 5.4–6.6 mm, transformation length = 8.3–15.6 mm.

Night pattern.

Newly settled juvenile.

Throughout their range, sheepheads exhibit oh so many growth patterns (Warner 1975, Hamilton et al. 2007). Here is one (courtesy of Scott Hamilton) that is kind of the average of a number of von Berts from up and down the coast (TL, mm): (sexes combined) L_∞ = 467.7, k = 0.182, with t_0 held at 0. Length-weight parameters (TL, mm, kg): (sexes combined) W = $0.00000002952L^{2.9066}$ (RecFin 2009).

SALIENT CHARACTERS: Young ones are red-orange, gold, salmon, or lemon-yellow, with at least one white stripe along the side, two black spots on the dorsal fin, one each on the anal and dorsal fins, and one on the caudal peduncle. They start to dull up when they reach around 10 cm (4 in) TL. Mature females are pink all over, with a white chin; an occasional fish will be brown or almost black. Males are a bit more imposing, with black heads (and white chins) and tail regions, and a red or pink midriff. Males have a prominent bump on their forehead. Both sexes also have large, thick canine teeth.

LIFE HISTORY: Young-of-the-year (as small as 1.3 cm, 0.5 in, SL and between 35–78 days old) settle from the plankton from late May through late December to reefs in waters from the barely subtidal to as deep as 70 m (230 ft). Settlement in Southern California is sporadic, perhaps reflecting greater or lesser transport of larvae from the south. While these youngest fish can be found around rocks and algae, they often hang out amid gorgonians. Andres and Anderson (2004) found that young ones tend to settle out in areas with a "protective rock ledge leading to open habitat, not in holes between rocks or under ledges of rocks." Near the end of their first year, at between 15–25 cm (6–10 in) TL, the fish begin to join the adults. Older juveniles and adults are common around various structures, including rocks, cobbles, kelp beds (where they are found from the bottom to the canopy) and other algae, oil platforms, and occasionally eelgrass. On the other hand, older sheepheads are commonly found 20–30 m (66–98 ft) away from structure, often busily digging away in the soft sediment. We see them in waters between 10.1 and 20.7°C (50–69°F), mostly between 11 and 18°C (52–64°F). While you won't see herds of sheepheads these days, John Stephens,

REPRODUCTIO AD ABSURDUM

There are fishes, we scarcely dare mention,
With behavior that merits attention.
　　At ages quite tender,
　　They blithely change gender,
Disdaining the normal convention.

There's *Labroides*, a wrasse quite compact,
Where polygamy, in harems, is fact.
　　If the male succumbs,
　　A female becomes,
The male in appearance and act.

Some basses now fight for their rights,
After lifetimes of onerous slights.
　　When all's said and done,
　　They're both sexes in one,
Power to oppressed hermaphrodites!

These fishes go others one more:
"To us, one sex is a bore.
　　It may not be great,
　　But if we can't find a date,
On ourselves we surely can score."

These are, all you fathers and mothers,
The wrasses and basses and others.
　　If we followed their lead,
　　Henceforth, then, our creed:
"All humans are sisters *and* brothers."

440

When sheephead collide.   TODD WINNER

who is quite old, remembers seeing schools of dozens of big males on the reefs around Palos Verdes (Southern California). Sheepheads become quiescent at night (in caves and crevices); usually all are tucked in one way or another by about 30 minutes after sunset. At least some fish use the same resting area night after night. At this time their body colors become blotchy and the fish may produce a mucus coating. In the mornings, just after first light, fish leave their rest area and move as much as 1,000 m (3,280 ft) away to feed. During warmer water periods, sheepheads tend to make their longest excursions. It's a little unclear how much movement the average sheephead might make over time. Fish at Santa Catalina Island seem to have a core area, and while they might move away from it on occasion, they seem to stay in the general vicinity for months or years at a time. Contrary to what has been observed (or not observed) in Southern California, sheepheads in the northern Gulf of California move into shallow waters in winter and then appear to migrate into cooler, deeper depths as waters warm. There apparently is extensive gene flow between Pacific Coast fish and those in the Gulf of California.

Adreani et al. (2004) watched lots of sheepheads spawning at Santa Catalina Island and here is what they found. First, all spawning occurred at or after sunset and "did not appear to be correlated with tides or lunar cycles." They went on to note: "Females appear to congregate at spawning sites in the evenings but are more widely dispersed while feeding throughout the day, indicating that they are not part of a strict harem and may spawn with multiple males. Large males, however, appear faithful to specific sites throughout the day during the spawning season...Courting began when the male approached a female with pelvic fins down, circled above her and made contact with her laterally. He then positioned himself slightly above her and led her in a slow circular pattern with his pelvic fins down, maintaining constant pressure on the top of her head with his chin. After 3–4 downward circles and a series of head jerk motions, the female made a quick upward motion with her head and the two rushed to the surface, side by side. At 3–4 m [10–13 ft] below the surface, the pair tilted to touch vents while releasing gametes, swam apart and slowly spiraled back down toward the base of the kelp. The male immediately began courting another female upon returning to the kelp stipes." They also noticed smaller males trying to enter the larger males' territories, where they were chased off although they occasionally succeeded when the larger males weren't looking. While it was unclear whether females spawned more than once per day, they do spawn more than once per season. Male spawning territories were about 20 m (66 ft) long along a rocky shelf. Adjacent territory holders "would frequently face each other [see the pic above], opening their mouths wide, gaping and occasionally making contact, or even locking jaws." As a caveat to this nice story, it should be mentioned that territoriality of large males, during spawning season, was not observed in fish at Anacapa Island (just up the road from Catalina). This may be yet another example of the plasticity of behavior in this, and other, fish species.

Sheepheads live to at least 53 years. As noted previously, growth rates are highly variable between areas (see Warner 1976 and Hamilton et al. 2007 for the details). For instance, fish grow much faster at San Nicolas Island (Southern California) than at Bahia Tortugas (southern Baja California). Sheepheads are protogynous hermaphrodites; they always start out life as females and, if they live long enough, eventually turn into males. The extent of social (as opposed to genetic) control of sheephead sex change is

Juvenile.

DAVID AND DORI DIRIG

A female.

unknown and it is also not known how long it takes to change sex. It is known that a fish cannot reproduce while changing sex. Scott Hamilton et al. (2007) also showed that sheephead size and age at first maturity (as a female) and size and age at sex change are all variable between areas. This is probably due both to variable levels of overfishing and to differences in habitat quality. In particular, they found that overfishing leads to females maturing earlier and changing sex when smaller and younger. In general, fish first mature at between 3–6 years old and 13.8 to at least 29.1 cm (5–12 in) SL. In the past, fish changed sex at between 13 and 14 years old at San Nicolas Island, 8 years old at Santa Catalina Island, and 6–7 years old at Bahia Tortugas. With overfishing, San Nicolas Island fish now mature at 7–8 years old and at 6 years at Catalina. Size at sex change seems to vary between 21–51.5 cm (9–20 in) SL, although a 12.6 cm (5 in) mature male has been documented. Spawning takes place from April–September (and, at least in aquariums, into October), but mostly from June–September. Total annual fecundity is about 1,942,000 eggs/kg of female body weight. The eggs hatch in about 48 hours at 18–19°C (64–66°F). California sheepheads tend to focus on benthic invertebrates and while much of their feeding occurs on hard structure, they do spend a fair amount of time digging about in the sand. Among the quite broad range of prey are crabs, hermit crabs, sea urchins, shrimps, barnacles, many kinds of mollusks (e.g., snails, abalones, rock scallops, mussels, octopuses, and squids), tube-dwelling polychaetes, bryozoans, brittle stars, sea cucumbers, and the occasional fish. And this from Limbaugh's (1955) kelp bed work: "On several occasions large adults were observed above water hanging onto mussels after a wave had retreated." Predators include giant sea bass, soupfin sharks, Brandt's cormorants, and California sea lions.

FISHERY: Sheepheads were a major food source for Native Americans, at least as far southward as Isla Cedros (central Baja California). Not unlike the theory of Trickle Down Economics within the Republican Party, sheepheads have had their ups and downs in the hearts and minds of the fish-buying public. Jordan (1887) found it to be the major commercial species off San Diego and a commonly taken commercial species at both Santa Catalina and off Santa Barbara. Goode (1884) noted that, in the 18th century, they were "taken chiefly by the Chinese, who salt and dry it. The fat forehead is said to make excellent chowder," thus evoking the homey image of Mom, Dad, towheaded Henry, and that little hellion Myrtle, sitting down to a sheephead dinner. "Henry, would you please pass that vat of forehead chowder to your sister?" Eigenmann (1892) reiterated that at San Diego the Chinese dried large quantities, but "It is a rather coarse fish and on account of its uncouth appearance it is not in general favor" with Caucasians.

Indeed, the esteem with which sheephead were held by some of our paler citizens of the day can best be understood from two passages in Margaret Eton's marvelous book *Diary of a Sea Captain's Wife* (McNally & Loftin, 1980). Ms. Eton lived

AN APPRECIATION OF THE LATE FRANK AND TONY HAMPTON

In the mid-1970s, part of my doctoral research involved describing the partyboat recreational fishery off Santa Barbara. Once a week for 3 years I rode aboard the 50-foot *Hornet* and identified and measured all of the fishes caught by the passengers. For a while, Frank Hampton ran the boat and his brother Tony was the deckhand. My goodness, but they were a roguish pair of scamps, of the sort one finds in the works of Boccaccio and Chaucer. On their first day of work, I was up in the wheelhouse as we left the harbor with the dawn, Frank at the helm and Tony sitting next to me on a bench. Tony reached into his jacket pocket, pulled out some illegal herbs wrapped in paper, lit it, took a toke, and handed it to me. I was, of course, in a quandary, concerned, I suppose, for the Scientific Method. Could I, I mused, accurately measure fish later in the day if I were ripped out of my mind? The answer was yes, although the passengers seemed to wonder what was so funny.

The boys spent a seemingly inordinate amount of time trying to figure out how to separate passengers from their funds. At the time this was, of course, an almost obsessive pastime for the chronically underpaid crews of almost all sportfishing boats. Very often, these plans revolved around the "jackpot." The jackpot is a pool of money gathered at the beginning of the trip. All anglers who wish to participate put in a sum, at that time one dollar, and whomever of the entrants catches the largest fish wins all the money. My favorite Hampton scam involved a very old, one might say positively moldering, sheephead. The two tricksters ran that game like this. One day, one of their friends was on the *Hornet* and caught a large sheephead, one perhaps weighing 10–12 pounds. It was not a terribly large fish, but larger than normally taken. And, indeed, on this day it won the jackpot. Rather than filleting the fish, Tony asked their friend if he might donate it to the cause; he readily agreed to the request. For the next week, friends of Frank and Tony were invited to come aboard the *Hornet* for a free day's fishing and, quite unaccountably, they all won the jackpot with a 10–12-pound sheephead.

on Santa Cruz Island (Southern California) in the early 20th century; here is an entry from 1908: "The water in the bay was so blue and so transparent that I could see the rocks on the sandy ocean bottom. Under the boat a school of fish swam lazily back and forth; they had large, strange-looking heads and thick bodies with a 3-inch-wide red stripe around the middle. They were sheephead, said the Captain, and not good to eat." Here is another from 1909, "Then Mr. Rogers asked me if we were going to camp on the island for the winter, and I told him that we expected to move to Scorpion Anchorage. 'When the crawfish [spiny lobster] season opens,' he said, 'I'll come over sometime and bring my tent and blankets. I can sit in the skiff all day and catch enough sheephead to keep all Ira's traps baited.'"

For most of the 20th century, the commercial sheephead catch was relatively low and the species was primarily taken as a bycatch in other fisheries. The rehabilitation of sheepheads as a food fish came about with the dawning of the live fish commercial industry in Southern California. Sheepheads are relatively easy to keep alive and their red color makes them popular with Asian consumers of live fish. This has made them a major target of the live fish fishermen. Sheepheads are also one of the most important species in the artisanal commercial fisheries of northern Baja California. On almost any day, you can see a bunch of them at the big Mercado Negro fish market in Ensenada (northern Baja California).

Regarding the sheephead's contribution to the recreational fishing industry, we need only turn to Metz (1912) noting that this species was "One of the commonest species taken by anglers fishing from the rocks along the shore." As true today as it was then, sheephead are a major recreational species, taken mostly from boats, but also from rocky shores, jetties, and piers.

ORIGINS: The University of California, Berkeley, Paleontological Museum lists pharyngeal teeth, perhaps of this species or at least of a *Semicossyphus* sp., from Miocene (at least 5.3-million-year-old) deposits of Central California. An otolith of a California sheephead was found in 100,000-year-old strata in Southern California.

MISCELLANY: And this from Phleger et al. (1976) who noted that sheephead store between 79% and 93% of their body lipids in their bones: "The bones contain the majority of the organism's reserve energy." Juveniles sometimes clean other fishes.

Terminal phase.

Initial phase.

OTHER SPECIES

Bodianus diplotaenia
(Gill, 1862)

Mexican Hogfish

Mexican hogfish grow to 76 cm (30 in) TL and are found from Islas Guadalupe and Cedros (central Baja California) and, on the mainland, from Bahia Magdalena (southern Baja California) to Peru or perhaps Chile, including the Gulf of California. They are nearshore, rocky reef dwellers, living at 3–76 m (10–250 ft), and mostly in 18 m (59 ft) and less. Hogfish are solitary or form small aggregations. They feed on various invertebrates and small fishes. Juveniles clean other fishes. These fish are active during the day and lie among rocks at night. Hogfish change sex from female to male; females mature at about 14 cm (6 in) SL and change sex at about 27–30 cm (11–12 in).

FAMILY SCARIDAE—Parrotfishes

Closely related to the wrasses are the parrotfishes, a group of mostly tropical marine fishes that are found throughout the world. There are 10 genera and around 90 species, three species make it to the outer coast of Baja California, and one is found as far north as Southern California. Parrotfishes are oviparous, with pelagic eggs and larvae. Many, if not all, species change sex, starting as females and changing to males. At night, some parrotfishes find a hole or overhanging rock ledge and bed down until morning, first wrapping themselves in a mucus cocoon. The family Scaridae evolved sometime before the mid-Miocene (maybe 15 million years ago) and may go back to the Eocene (perhaps 42 million years ago). Fischer et al. (1995) has keys and descriptions for the eastern Pacific species.

Nicholsina denticulata
(Evermann & Radcliffe, 1917)
Loosetooth Parrotfish

ETYMOLOGY: *Nicholsina* honors John Treadwell Nichols (1883–1958), a curator of fishes at the American Museum of Natural History and the founder of *Copeia*, the ichthyology and herpetology journal. *Denticulatus* means "toothed" in Latin. The teeth are not completely fused together and hence are "loose."

THE BASICS: Maximum
Length: 30 cm (12 in) TL. The
Ranges: Santa Catalina Island;
also Islas San Benito and Cedros
and (mainland) Rocas Chester
(central Baja California) to
Islas Chincha (Peru), including
the Gulf of California. 1–10 m
(4–33 ft). Larvae: flexion length =
<4.8 mm, transformation length
= about 12 mm through <19 mm.

SALIENT CHARACTERS:
Loosetooths have that typical
loosey-goosey parrotfish look,
with the long dorsal fin, heavy
scales, and orthodontically challenged mouth. Most individuals
are red, brown, or gray. Terminal
males have a red lower jaw and
caudal fin edge.

LIFE HISTORY: Loosetooths
are nearshore reef fish. Juveniles
live in the intertidal or shallow
subtidal and adults live mostly in
the shallow subtidal among reefs
and sea grass.

DAN RICHARDS

FAMILY BATHYMASTERIDAE—Ronquils

The ronquils are a group of colder-water fish found only in the western and eastern North Pacific and Bering Sea. There are three genera and seven species, six of which are found within our range. The group is oviparous with demersal eggs that are guarded by a parent. Stevenson and Matarese (2005) have a key and lots of descriptions for all the species.

Bathymaster signatus
Cope, 1873
Searcher

R. HIBPSHMAN

ETYMOLOGY AND COLLOQUIAL NAMES: *Bathymaster* is Greek for "deep" and "searcher" and *signatus* is Latin for "marked" (referring to the black blotch on the anterior part of the dorsal fin). The Japanese name is "soko-medamauo" and the Russians call them "blue-eyed searchers."

THE BASICS: Maximum Length: 38 cm (15 in) TL. Maximum Weight: At least 368 gr (0.8 lb). The Ranges: Pacific coast of Hokkaido, Sea of Okhotsk to Bering Sea, about as far north as Saint Matthew Island (61°N, 178°31'W), and throughout Aleutian Islands to perhaps Washington; common to at least Dixon Entrance (between Alaska and British Columbia). Adults at depths of 25–380 m (82–1,247 ft), perhaps to 825 m (2,707 ft), mostly in maybe 180 m (590 ft) or less. Eggs: 1.4 mm. Length-weight parameters (FL, cm, gr): (sexes combined) W = 0.0028L$^{3.3288}$ (Glubokov 2009).

SALIENT CHARACTERS: A typical ronquil, with that elongated body, long dorsal and anal fins, large pectoral fin, and truncate caudal fin. They have that blotch on the anterior part of the dorsal fin and orange or yellow pores behind the eye and on the preopercle.

LIFE HISTORY: Searchers are found over a wide range of habitats, but they seem to really like sandy areas amid rock and cobble, mostly on the mid-shelf, in waters down to 0°C (32°F). You generally see them either sitting on the seafloor or just over it. Chris Rooper suspects they withdraw into shelter at night. Work in the Bering Sea implies that the population is moving northward likely in response to warming ocean waters.

Searchers live to at least 9 years old (that was a 36 cm, 14 in, TL fish). Females may grow slightly larger than males. Females and males mature at about 27 cm (11 in) FL. In the Western Pacific, spawning occurs from May–July. Females produce an average of about 90,000 eggs per season. Searchers feed on a wide variety of mostly benthic prey. Depending on the fish's size and location, the laundry list includes polychaetes, crabs, shrimps, larvaceans, gammarid amphipods, isopods, fishes, sea anemones, euphausiids, hermit crabs, snail eggs, echiuroids, priapulids, ostracods, bivalves, and octopuses. Predators include Alaska skate, arrowtooth flounder, Pacific cod, Pacific halibut, threespine sticklebacks, harbor and northern fur seals, and Pacific octopuses.

FISHERY: The species was listed as a food fish at Sitka by Bean (1887b) and has been important as bait in the Shumagin Islands (Aleutian Islands).

KEVIN LEE

This is a female.

Rathbunella hypoplecta
(Gilbert, 1890)
Bluebanded Ronquil

ETYMOLOGY: *Rathbunella* honors Richard Rathbun (1852–1918) and *hypoplecta* means "beneath" and "braid" in Greek, a reference to that checkerboard pattern. Rathbun worked for, among other organizations, the United States Fish Commission and the United States National Museum. The current common name is relatively new, it was previously "smooth ronquil." Although "stripefin ronquil" was a name in general use for this species, *R. alleni* is the stripefin form. It reaches 16.1 cm (6.3 in) SL and is found from Marin County (north of San Francisco) to Bahia

This is a male. CHRIS GROSSMAN

San Carlos (northern Baja California), at depths of about 2–40 m (6–131 ft).

THE BASICS: Maximum Length: 23 cm (9 in) TL. The Ranges: Point Conception (California) to Santo Tomás anchorage (31°33'N, 116°24'W) (northern Baja California). Previous reports from San Francisco and farther north are probably due to confusion with *R. alleni* and perhaps *Ronquilus jordani*. At depths of 2.7–91.4 m (9–300 ft), and perhaps to 136 m (446 ft).

SALIENT CHARACTERS: Male bluebands have several rows of alternating lighter and darker rectangular blotches. Females are variously colored and marked, often relatively pale or brownish, with darker splotches and spots dorsally and kind of light barring on the lower sides. Females, in particular, may have a bright blue spot on the anterior part of the dorsal fin. Males are reputed to have these, also, but the males I have seen didn't seem to. The anal fin has a blue band parallel to each ray. I am not confident that most folks, including myself, can differentiate this species from the stripefin ronquil, *R. alleni*, when we see them underwater. On the other hand, Stevenson and Matarese (2005) provide all kinds of ways to tell them apart when you have a dead one in hand.

LIFE HISTORY: Despite being a fairly common species in Southern California, perilously little is known about our little checkerboard friends. We see them lying on the bottom, often in a U-shape, on low rocks and rock/sand interfaces. They might be territorial, 'cause certainly they are solitary. They often hang out in the same habitat as deepwater blennies. Although little is known about their food habitats, I found bryozoans, polychaetes, crustacean pieces, and a nudibranch (and thanks to Leslie Harris for that identification) in the stomachs of fish housed in the Natural History Museum of Los Angeles County. Predators include California sea lions.

RICHARD RATHBUN

Here is a surprisingly modern view expressed by Rathbun in 1884 regarding overfishing of lobsters in New England: "Past legislation has certainly not been very effective, nor can any laws avail much until the true character and extent of the evil has been determined; neither, are laws beneficial unless they can be enforced; an exceedingly difficult task in the case of any fishery." Right on, Richard.

MARC CHAMBERLAIN

Ronquilus jordani
(Gilbert, 1889)
Northern Ronquil

ETYMOLOGY: *Ronquilus* comes from a Spanish word for a similar species and *jordani* refers to David Starr Jordan (1851–1931), the all-around heroic ichthyologist. See petrale sole, *Eopsetta jordani*, for more on DSJ.

THE BASICS: Maximum Length: 20 cm (8 in) TL. The Ranges: Southeastern Bering Sea and Amchitka Island (Aleutian Islands) to La Jolla (Southern California), perhaps most abundant as far southward as Washington. At depths of 3–275 m (10–908 ft), usually shallower than 150 m (492 ft). Larvae: hatching length = 5.5–6 mm. Length-weight parameters (TL, mm, gr): (sexes combined) W = $0.000006L^{3.177}$ (Litzow et al. 2002).

SALIENT CHARACTERS: Adult males are orange on back and olive below; females are olive on back and lighter below. There is a dark area between the eyes and in front of the dorsal fin. Stevenson and Matarese (2005) give other distinguishing characters, most of them involving such arcana as the anterior lateral canaliculus of the nasal cephalic sensory canal.

LIFE HISTORY: Northern ronquils are territorial, benthic fish that inhabit both rocky reefs and surrounding sand. They can tolerate slightly estuarine conditions. This species may be most active during the day. The eggs laid under rocks and are reportedly "spawned in a nonadhesive mass that the male incubates" (Matarese et al. 2003). Based on larval surveys, northern ronquils appear to spawn mostly in the late winter and early spring and perhaps early summer. The eggs are amber. Little is known about their food habits, although the few that have been examined had eaten polychaetes and gammarid amphipods. Predators include black rockfish, coho salmon, jack mackerel, steelhead, pelagic cormorants, tufted puffins, and probably river otters.

OTHER SPECIES

Bathymaster caeruleofasciatus
Gilbert & Burke, 1912
Alaskan Ronquil

Alaska ronquils grow to 30 cm (12 in) TL. They are found from the Commander Islands (Russia) and Aleutian Islands to Prince Rupert (northern British Columbia) and are common as far south as southeastern Alaska. They live at depths of 5–225 m (16–738 ft), often in nearshore waters. This is a fish mostly of rock outcrops and boulder fields (often in thick algae) and less often in low rocky relief and sand. They usually rest on the bottom, but on occasion will ascend a few meters. Alaskan ronquils are territorial and they will engage in mouth fighting with intruding ronquils. They feed on a variety of small benthic prey such as crustaceans (e.g., gammarid and caprellid amphipods, crabs, and shrimps), bivalves, snails, brittle stars, and polychaetes.

PAULINE RIDINGS

FAMILY ZOARCIDAE—Eelpouts

Eelpouts are marine and mostly benthic (although there are midwater species) fishes that range throughout the Atlantic and Pacific. They are usually found in relatively cold waters, meaning that tropical species are found in deep water. Most eelpouts are oviparous, although members of the genus *Zoarces* give birth to live young. In many or most species, eggs are laid on or in the bottom (some species of *Lycodapus* are pelagic spawners) and at least one parent guards them. There are about 46 genera, 240ish species, and 62 species within our range, although new species are seemingly described every year. At least some currently described species are likely synonyms of other described species. Kitty Mecklenburg and colleagues (2002) present a fairly exhaustive description, including keys, of a majority of the eelpouts of the northeastern Pacific. Add Eric Anderson et al. (2009) and almost all the species are covered.

Lycodes pacificus
Collett, 1879
Blackbelly Eelpout

ETYMOLOGY: *Lycodes* is Greek for "wolffish" and *pacificus* means "Pacific."

THE BASICS: Maximum Length: 46 cm (18 in) TL. The Ranges: Aleutian Islands and Gulf of Alaska to Ensenada (northern Baja California). They are common at least as far south as Southern California. 7–1,036 m (23–3,399 ft); in Southern California, mostly in 50 m (164 ft) or deeper. Eggs: about 5 mm. Length-weight parameters (TL, cm, gr): W = $0.00013L^{4.211}$ (Love unpubl.).

SALIENT CHARACTERS: These are very elongated fish with long dorsal and anal fins that merge into the caudal fin. Blackbellies have a blackish spot on the front of their dorsal fins and blackish bellies. Males have larger mouths than females.

LIFE HISTORY: In Southern California, young-of-the-year recruit to mud bottoms from March–May. Blackbellies live on soft sediment and we usually see them curled in a flat, tight coil.

All of what we know about the biology of this species comes from work conducted off British Columbia (Levings 1969). Blackbellies live to at least 5 years old and probably longer. Males grow faster than females and seem to grow larger. Males first mature at 14–14.9 cm (6 in) TL (2 years old), 50% at 16–16.9 cm (6–7 in) (3 years old), and 100% at 20–20.9 cm (8 in) (4–5 years old). Close to 50% of females are mature at 14–14.9 cm (6 in) (2 years). The size at which 100% of the females are mature is not known. At least off British Columbia, they spawn from late August–January and females produce between 7–52 yellow-orange eggs. Blackbellies are likely oviparous. Divers in Southern California observed male and female pairs and thus the eggs may be guarded by the adults. Blackbelly eelpouts feed on such benthic prey as gammarid amphipods, cumaceans, clams, and polychaetes. They also consume lesser numbers of crabs, shrimps, euphausiids, brittle stars, mysid shrimps, and copepods. Predators include sablefish, sand soles, spiny dogfish, starry flounder, pigeon guillemots, California and Steller sea lions, and harbor seals.

FISHERY: Well, at least on the Pacific Coast, eelpouts have never been particularly feted in the halls of the gastronomes. However, Lockington (1879c), a habitué of the San Francisco in the 1870s, did note that this species found its way into the fish markets from March–May. He goes on to state that it was "But seldom in sufficient abundance to make it of any account as an article of food, a circumstance which is to be regretted, as it is of excellent flavor, superior, in my opinion at least, to many of the flat fishes."

ORIGINS AND RELATIONSHIPS: Møller and Gravlund (2003) found that fishes of the genus *Lycodes* probably originated in the Pacific Ocean and traveled to the Arctic and Atlantic when the Bering Strait opened 3–3.5 million years ago. Blackbellies are most closely related to bigfin eelpouts.

Bothrocara brunneum

(Bean, 1890)

Twoline Eelpout

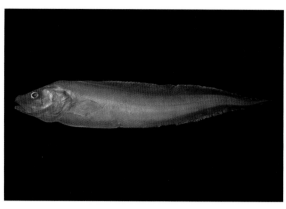

Twolines grow to 74 cm (29 in) TL and 3.1 kg (6.8 lb) and are found from the Sea of Okhotsk to the Commander–Aleutian islands and from the Bering Sea to the Islas Coronados off Bahia Descanso (32°04'N, 117°12'W) (northern Baja California), perhaps commonly as far southward as Central California. They are also known from the Gulf of California. This benthic species lives at depths of 129–1,829 m (423–5,999 ft), but mostly deeper than about 400–1,000 m (1,312–3,280 ft). They have been caught in waters of 2.4–7°C (36–45°F). Fecundity ranges from 1,003–1,960 eggs. Twolines feed on benthic and epibenthic crustaceans (e.g., euphausiids, gammarid amphipods, shrimps, and mysid shrimps), fishes, and squids. Length-weight parameters (TL, cm, kg): (sexes combined) $W = 0.000988L^{3.46}$ (Orlov and Binohlan 2009).

Gymnelus viridis

(Fabricius, 1780)

Fish Doctor

Fish doctors grow to 30 cm (12 in) TL. They are circumpolar in the Arctic Ocean, and off North America they live from the Beaufort Sea to the Islands of Four Mountains (eastern Bering Sea). Found from rocky intertidal kelp beds and boulder fields to mud seafloors, they live out to a depth of 318 m (1,043 ft) (although mostly in less than 50 m, 164 ft). This species lives to about 12 years and males grow larger than females. Spawning occurs in late summer–early fall and females may not spawn every year. The smallest mature female on record was 9.7 cm (4 in) TL. Eggs are laid in nests and fecundity is between 20–106 eggs. Fish doctors mostly feed on benthic and epibenthic crustaceans (e.g., gammarid amphipods, copepods, and mysid shrimps), polychaetes, and bivalve siphons. Eggs = 1.8–5.2 mm. Von Bertalanffy parameters (TL, cm): (sexes combined) $L_\infty = 22$, $k = 0.13$ (Green and Mitchell 1997). Length-weight parameters (TL, cm, gr): (females) $W = 0.001905L^{3.34}$; (males) $W = 0.0009772L^{3.65}$ (Green and Mitchell 1997).

Lycodapus mandibularis

Gilbert, 1915

Pallid Eelpout

Pallids grow to 19.8 cm (8 in) SL and range from Prince William Sound (northern Gulf of Alaska) to La Jolla Canyon (Southern California), commonly between perhaps Clarence Strait (southeastern Alaska) and Central California. This is a midwater, mesopelagic species found in 96–1,237 m (315–4,058 ft). Some individuals migrate vertically into shallower waters at night. Pallids live to at least 5 years old. Males and females appear to grow at the same rates and mature at the same size and age: 3–4 years old, 14–16 cm (6 in) SL. Spawning likely occurs year round and a female may produce more than one batch of eggs per year. The two females that have been checked contained 23 and 46 eggs. Anderson (1980) noted that mature males have "enlarged recurved teeth which may play a role in initiating spawning." And, no, I don't want to know what that might mean. In the laboratory, pallids had adhesive and negatively buoyant eggs and females laid the eggs in burrows they dug in the aquarium floor. Pallids eat a range of water column prey, including crustaceans (e.g., euphausiids, copepods, amphipods, and various shrimps), fishes, and squids. Growth relationships for males and females are figured in Anderson (1980).

Lycodes brevipes
Bean, 1890
Shortfin Eelpout

Shortfins grow to 32.8 cm (13 in) TL. They live from the Bering Sea, and eastern Aleutian Islands, to Central California (34°34'N). Bottom-dwellers, living over soft sediment, they are found at depths of 2 m or less to 973 m (6–3,192 ft). Shortfins have been taken in waters as cold as -1.4 (29°F) and work in the Bering Sea implies that the population is moving northward probably in response to warming waters. They feed on benthic and epibenthic prey. Important foods include brittle stars, polychaetes, crustaceans (e.g. shrimps, crabs, euphausiids, and gammarid amphipods), clams, and fishes. In turn, they are eaten by such predators as Alaska skate, flatfishes, Pacific cod, and walleye pollock.

Lycodes cortezianus
(Gilbert, 1890)
Bigfin Eelpout

Bigfins grow to 49.3 cm (19 in) TL (or perhaps 58 cm, 23 in) and at least 346 gr (0.8 lb). They are found from Prince of Wales Island (southeastern Alaska) to San Diego. Like so many other eelpouts, bigfin live on the bottom, usually on mud or in mud-low rock habitat, at temperatures of at least 5.1–9.9°C (41–50°F). While they have been found at depths of 61–1,190 m (200–3,903 ft), most live in maybe 70–400 m (230–1,312 ft). I aged several, and one 38 cm (12 in) TL was 7–8 years old. In an aquarium study, females laid adhesive and negatively buoyant eggs (0.6 cm, 0.2 in, in diameter) in August and the young (at about 2 cm, 0.8 in, TL) hatched in late March and early April. I looked at a few specimens at the Natural History Museum of Los Angeles County and found some copepods and euphausiids in the guts. Predators include arrowtooth flounder, longnose skate, and California sea lions. While there has not been a directed fishery for bigfins, they were caught in the California trawl fisheries and sold as mink food during the 1950s and 1960s. Bigfins are closely related to blackbelly eelpouts. Length-weight parameters (TL, cm, gr): W = 0.0015L$^{3.309}$ (Love unpubl.).

Lycodes diapterus
Gilbert, 1892
Black Eelpout also called Blackfin Eelpout

Black eelpouts reach 39 cm (15 in) TL. They range from the Pacific side of Vancouver Island to the northern Channel Islands (Southern California), and perhaps to San Diego. This benthic species lives at depths of 13–1,300 m (42–4,265 ft), mostly in 146–844 m (479–2,768 ft), and to temperatures at least as cold as 4°C (39°F). The stomach of one fish contained euphausiids and shrimps. Predators include arrowtooth flounder, longnose skate, Pacific halibut, harbor and northern elephant seals.

Lycodes palearis
Gilbert, 1896
Wattled Eelpout

Wattleds grow to 62 cm (24 in) TL and at least 488 gr (1.1 lb). They live from the Okhotsk Sea to Beaufort Sea (71°22'N, 156°19'W) and to Oregon at depths of 2–925 m (7–3,035 ft), mostly in less than 200 m (656 ft). They are common at least off eastern Kamchatka, in the northeastern Chukchi Sea, Bering Sea, and in the Gulf of Alaska. They live on muddy bottoms, at -2.1–7.9°C (28–46°F), most commonly at temperatures of 0–3°C (32–37°F). Wattleds feed on benthic invertebrates such clams, crustaceans (e.g., shrimps, gammarid amphipods, and crabs), polychaetes, brittle stars, and fishes. Predators include arrowtooth flounder, great sculpins, Greenland and Pacific halibut, and Pacific cod.

Melanostigma pammelas
Gilbert, 1896
Midwater Eelpout

This dwarf species reaches 13.3 cm (5 in) TL. They are found from the Queen Charlotte Islands (British Columbia) to the Gulf of Tehuantepec (Mexico). As their name implies, midwater eelpouts live above the bottom, mostly in the mesopelagic, from 97–2,012 m (318–6,601 ft). Unlike a number of other midwater fishes, this species does not migrate vertically over the course of 24 hours. They live to at least 8 years old and there is no difference in growth rates between the sexes. Males generally became sexually mature at a younger age (3–5.5 years, 8.8–12.3 cm, 4–5 in, SL) than females (5.5–7 years, 8.9–13.3 cm, 4–5 in). Females have one ovary and produce between 1–34 yellow or golden-colored eggs (that are 2 mm or larger when mature). Spawning appears to occur throughout the year. Most females probably reproduce once, or rarely, twice in a lifetime and, not to be outdone, it is possible that males, too, only mate once. Midwaters eat pelagic crustaceans, such as calanoid copepods, ostracods, euphausiids, and gammarid amphipods. Predators include Chinook salmon.

FAMILY STICHAEIDAE—Pricklebacks

Pricklebacks are cool- or cold-water marine fishes. Most are found in the North Pacific, with a few species hanging out in the North Atlantic. As far as is known, all pricklebacks are oviparous and have adhesive eggs that are guarded by at least one parent. There are perhaps 37 genera, 76 species, and 32 species within our range. The family goes back to the Miocene (at least 5.3 million years ago) as a number of fossil forms, in the genera *Ascoldia*, *Ernogrammus*, *Stichaeus*, *Stichaeopsis*, and *Nivchia*, have been recovered from deposits in Sakhalin and Japan. Pricklebacks are not widely commercially fished. Mecklenburg et al. (2002) has a nice key to most of the Pacific Coast species.

Anoplarchus purpurescens
Gill, 1861

High Cockscomb

RICH ZADE

ETYMOLOGY: *Anoplarchus* is Greek for "unarmed" and "anus" (not only a great name for a rock group, but also referring to the anal fin not having spines) and *purpurescens* is Latin for "purple."
THE BASICS: Maximum Length: 20 cm (8 in) TL. The Ranges: Attu Island (Aleutian Islands) and Pribilof Islands (Bering Sea) to Santa Rosa Island. They are abundant from at least Amchitka Island (Aleutian Islands) to about Diablo Cove (Central California). Intertidal to 30 m (100 ft), including tide pools. Eggs: unfertilized = 0.8–1.4 mm, fertilized = 1.3–1.5 mm. Larvae: hatching length = 7.5–9 mm. Mean lengths at age for males and females are given in Peppar (1965). Length-weight parameters (TL, cm, gr): (females) W = $0.0058L^{2.93}$; (males) W = $0.004L^{3.14}$ (Coleman 1992).
SALIENT CHARACTERS: These are long and snake-like, with a fleshy crest (cockscomb) on top of the head. Males have larger, and more prominent, cockscombs than females, particularly during breeding season. And colors? Oh, so many colors. Let's look over Jeff Cross's shoulder (1981) as he notes that colors: "Varied from light olive-green to dark brown and sometimes black; it was solid or subtly reticulated with olive-green or brown. Some individuals had a light gray, pinkish, or olive-green band extending from the lips to the tail on the dorsal fin and upper back; occasionally the band was orange or reddish-orange…Recently transformed individuals (1.5–3 cm [0.6–1 in] TL) bore a striking resemblance to fir needles that often occurred in the pools." Seasonally, males have red-orange on dorsal, pectoral, and anal fins.
LIFE HISTORY: Young-of-the-year settle out of the plankton at 1.7 cm (0.7 in) SL or less. High cockscombs live in the rocky intertidal (mostly in the mid- and low zone), in both tide pools and on cobble beaches. In some areas they are also quite abundant in the shallow subtidal. Bruce Leaman (1980), for instance, found them to be very common (to 1.3/ m²) in the kelp beds of British Columbia, often in the holdfasts of bull kelp and understory plants. There is some evidence that this species is more abundant in relatively protected waters than in areas swept by high waves. They do not live around rocks that are embedded in sand or mud. They also frequent some estuaries (e.g., Yaquina Bay, Oregon) and occasionally live amid eelgrass. Cockscombs have a home range and, at least during breeding season, are often territorial.

High cockscombs live to at least 5 years old. Females grow slightly faster than males. This species matures at mostly 8–9 cm (3–4 in) SL (occasionally slightly smaller) and 2–3 years old. Spawning occurs from January–March, when females produce anywhere between 828–3,183 eggs; these are lime green to white when first laid and later turn silvery-gray or greenish. Spawning takes place under boulders or in shells under rocks in the intertidal, where they are lightly stuck to the substrata and tightly stuck to each other. The eggs are tended by the female (she coils around the egg mass), and a male may also be present. Although you often see one nest per rock, territoriality sometimes breaks down, and there will be a number of nests under the same rock. During the spawning season, males compete for mates by displaying to each other and Coleman (1992) was there to record the action: "During a spasm display the fish oriented either directly at an opponent or, more typically, laterally to an opponent and the whole body jerked in a single spasm…During male-male agonistic encounters, the fins of the males became deep red/orange and the spot at the anterior of the dorsal fin became outlined in gold." Males may spawn with more than one female and females spawn all their eggs at one time. The embryos hatch out in 28–29 days and the larvae immediately swim toward the surface. Just about wherever you go, high cockscombs love those polychaetes. In particular, the high cockscomb is one of the few fish species that eats *Cirriformia luxuriosa,* an apparently nasty-tasting intertidal worm. They also go in a big way for a number of other small benthic and epibenthic organisms, including gammarid amphipods, crabs, isopods, copepods, pycnogonids, snails, clam siphons, tunicates, nemerteans, insects, and algae. Cockscombs appear to feed during daylight hours. Predators include rock and masked greenlings, garter snakes, Steller sea lions, and likely both river otters and minks.

MISCELLANY: 1) They aerially respire and can live as long as 20 hours out of water. 2) For what it's worth, based on meristic characters, Sribhibhadh (1959) believed there are a number of populations in Puget Sound.

Cebidichthys violaceus
(Girard, 1854)
Monkeyface Prickleback

ETYMOLOGY: *Cebidichthys* comes from the Greek words "sapajou" (the monkey often called "capuchin") and "fish" and *violaceus* is Latin for "violet."

THE BASICS: Maximum Length: 76.2 cm (30 in) TL. Maximum Weight: 2.3 kg (6.1 lb) for a California fish, but Kirk Lombard (who holds the record) notes that heavier fish have been unofficially reported. The Ranges: Southern Oregon to Bahia San Quintin (northern Baja California). They are common in Northern and Central California and along the eastern-most northern Channel Islands. Intertidal to 24 m (80 ft), reported but not confirmed to 91 m (300 ft); typically intertidal to perhaps 3 m (10 ft). Von Bertalanffy parameters (SL, cm): (females) $L_\infty = 62$, $k = 0.14$, $t_0 = -1.95$; (males) $L_\infty = 70$, $k = 0.12$, $t_0 = -1.91$ (Marshall and Wyllie Echeverria 1992). Length-weight parameters (SL, cm, gr): (sexes combined) $W = 0.00965L^{2.971}$ (Marshall and Wyllie Echeverria 1992).

SALIENT CHARACTERS: There are simply slugs of eel-shaped fishes along our coast, and here is how to tell a monkeyface from the others. First, these fish are a uniform black, gray, or olive, and have black lines radiating from their eyes. A few monkeyfaces have orange spots on their sides and orange-tipped fins. Adults have a lumpy ridge on top of their heads, one lateral line, and (this is important, so stop playing with your oatmeal) the first half of their dorsal fin is composed of spines and the second half of soft rays. Most other pricklebacks have dorsal fins composed entirely of rays and/or have more than one lateral line. Helm (1990) notes that monkeyfaces have the "ability to change their body color from a very light, almost transparent gray, to dark black in 1–2 minutes."

LIFE HISTORY: Monkeyfaces recruit to the rocky intertidal, mostly in the late winter–spring, at lengths as small as 1.2 cm (0.5 in) SL. The species is most abundant in the rocky intertidal (with smaller fish in shallower waters). However a fair number of fish, and particularly the larger ones, live in the shallow subtidal, particularly near kelp holdfasts. The fish seek crevices when disturbed or (for the intertidal ones) when the tide is out. The species is tolerant of a wide range of temperatures, from 8.9–24.2°C (48–76°F). Helm (1990) provided evidence that some monkeyfaces are capable of homing to the same under-rock site day after day. During at least part of the year this species is pretty social, at least you can find multiple individuals under the same rock. Nesting takes place under rocks and one sex—apparently ain't no one knows which one—guards them.

Both sexes live to at least 18 years old. Growth rates seem to be about the same for both sexes. A few females are mature at 36 cm (14 in) SL (4 years), 50% are mature at 39 cm (15 in) (5 years), and all are mature at 45 cm (18 in) (7 years). Based on larval collections, these pricklebacks spawn at least from January–August. Older fish spawn earlier in the season than young ones. The only two monkeyface females checked for eggs contained 17,000 and 40,000. As the latter fish was 61 cm (24 in) SL long, it is probable that even larger females produce more eggs. Small monkeyfaces, less than maybe 8 cm (3 in) long, eat various invertebrates, such as polychaetes, gammarid amphipods, calanoid and harpacticoid copepods, mysid shrimps, crabs, and hydroids. Larger fish have a diet composed almost entirely of plant material. One study found that they ate 60 species of algae, mostly reds and greens, but also colonial diatoms, and surfgrass. Monkeyfaces may feed mostly on ebbing tides and their diets can change with season. Juveniles are heavily predated upon by birds, such as eared grebes, great egrets, and red-breasted mergansers.

The Haiku Corner

year after year
on a monkey's face
a monkey face

Basho (Matsuo Munefusa, 1644–1694), haiku's first great practitioner.

FISHERY: Monkeyface pricklebacks were an important part of Native American diets. Small numbers are landed by commercial fishermen; Kirk Lombard reports there is one guy in the harbor at Princeton (Central California) who claims to be the only person who has caught them commercially for the last several decades. They are very commonly taken from rocky shores and jetties by recreational fishermen using conventional hook-and-line gear or by poke poling. Poke poling is the perfect activity for someone who has a bamboo pole or broomstick, a short piece of wire, a hook, some squid, and the driving need to use all of them at the same time on a rocky beach. (You would be surprised at the number of people who seem to have this compulsion.) Well, what these good folks do is attach the wire to the pole and connect a hook to the wire. They bait the hook with squid (mussels are good, too) and clamber onto a rocky promontory at low tide. Now, you might think that most folks would be content to just stand there, poke pole in hand, and savor a job well done. But some people (and just isn't that the way?) go even further; they insert the baited hook into various crevices and holes in tide pools and surge channels. Along with monkeyfaces and other pricklebacks, this is a good way to catch cabezons, grass and brown rockfishes, and even the occasional lingcod.

And here's the skinny on the yumminess of the monkeyface prickleback from Pat Shelton, hard on the Oregon coast: "This fish is one Denizen of the Creep. When it comes out of the water on the end of a fishing line, it looks like a snake. A big, fat brown snake. It doesn't flap like a fish, it undulates like a snake. When you hit it over the head with the fish conker, it doesn't die. So you have to keep on hitting it and still it won't die. Once you think you've finally subdued the beast, you put it in the bucket, turn your back on it, and it humps its way out of the bucket and starts out across the beach. But if you manage to persevere and get the thing filleted and under a broiler, it's delicious. The texture is lobster-like and the flavor is delicate. But as always, nature bats last - in this case, human nature. JUST TRY to enjoy this delicacy when you sit down to the table and think you're eating snake for dinner tonight. Just try." Thank you, Pat. Clearly, the spirit of foodie James Beard, who was another notable Oregon resident, resides within you.

MISCELLANY: Monkeyfaces aerially respire. They can live as long as 37 hours out of water.

SOMETHING OF AN APOLOGY

In earlier editions of this book I made the modest proposal that, far from looking like a monkey (really a rather far-fetched idea that), *Cebidichthys* really resembles Stalin.

Well, not to put too fine a point on it, this was met with less than universal approbation. And, in fact, several of the Trotskyites in our lab actually responded rather harshly. In reality, with the well-appreciated exception of the few surviving Spanish followers of Delores Ibarruri (La Pasionaria), there was a singular lack of enthusiasm for the analogy. And, having considered the matter very carefully, I think that the problem is that most readers, not without reason, conjured up the image of the Stalin of 1938, the time-worn malevolent figure of the last of the great Purge trials, when Yagoda and Bukharin got what was coming to them. Whereas I, perhaps in my naiveté, was envisioning the Stalin of 1905, the kinder, gentler Stalin, the Stalin that had fooled even Lenin's wife, Krupskaya. So, does that help?

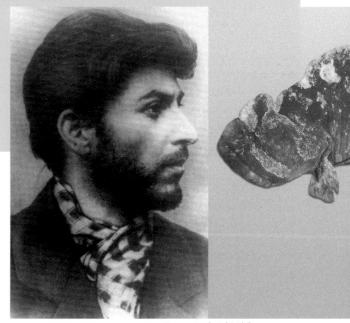

Separated at birth?

IS THIS A
NEW CAREER FOR YOU?

Kirk Lombard binds books in monkeyface eel skins. Here's how he treats the skins: "I skin the eels and soak them in dish soap for three 2-day periods. Each second day I pour out the snotty water, rinse the skins, and then soak again. Finally, at the end of that period (six days), I pin out the reasonably de-greased skins and salt the hell out of the meat side, leaving these stretched out skins sitting on my roof (to the horror of my neighbors) in the sun for two or three days (longer if it's not sunny). Then I rinse off the salt, soak them in clean water for a day and repeat the whole pinning out and salting process. Finally at the end I rinse them one last time, work the wretched pelts with my hands until they are pliable enough to use as the bindings for my books. Then, using a book press (or C clamps) and glue I press them onto binding cloth. I actually prefer cabezon skin to MF because it retains the mottled patterning, is very smooth and easy to work with and looks exotic when dried."

KIRK LOMBARD

456

Chirolophis nugator
(Jordan & Williams, 1895)
Mosshead Warbonnet

ETYMOLOGY: *Chirolophis* is Greek for "hand" and "crest" and *nugator* means "elegant appearance" in Latin.

THE BASICS: Maximum Length: More than 14.6 cm (6 in) TL, for here is a coy statement from Peden and Wilson (1976): "At 146 mm total length, our largest specimen is larger than that reported... and we know of a considerably larger specimen." Okay, don't tell us, 'cause we really don't want to know. No, we are not just being petulant. Hell, if you do try to tell us, we will stick our fingers in our ears and run around humming loudly. The Ranges: Western Aleutian Islands to San Miguel Island (Southern California); abundant as far southward as Central California. Intertidal–80 m (264 ft), mostly in subtidal waters. Length-weight parameters (TL, mm, gr): (sexes combined) W = $0.00001003L^{2.952}$ (Burge and Schultz 1973).

SALIENT CHARACTERS: A shaggy mat of equal-length cirri on the top of its head gives the mosshead its name. Look also

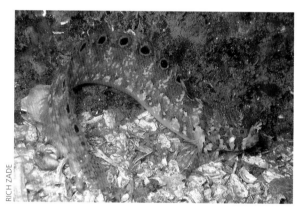

for the 12–13 dark ocelli or bars that run all along the dorsal fin. There is a dark or red streak under each eye and a series of white markings along the lower flank.

LIFE HISTORY: Mossheads live in high relief rocky areas (mostly in the subtidal), both inside and outside kelp beds, in kelp holdfasts, shells, along with bottles and other debris. In some areas, there can be as many as 0.8 fish per m^2. Clinton Bauder has noted several individuals living in crevices for at least three straight years.

These fish live at least to 5 years old and probably mature in their second year at 8 cm (3 in) TL or larger. One study in British Columbia found that mossheads ate mostly polychaetes, nemerteans, and shrimps. Predators include pigeon guillemots and likely pelagic cormorants.

Lumpenus sagitta
Wilimovsky, 1956
Snake Prickleback

ETYMOLOGY AND COLLOQUIAL NAME: *Lumpenus* harkens back to the Danish word "lumpen," an old name for the European fish *Zoarces viviparous* (once thought to be related) and *sagitta* is Latin for "arrow." In Japanese, it is "unagi-gaji."

THE BASICS: Maximum Length: 51 cm (20 in) TL. The Ranges: Seas of Japan and Okhotsk to Bering Sea (to at least Saint Lawrence Island and Norton Sound) and eastern Aleutian Islands to Humboldt Bay (Northern California). Possibly as far northward as Cape Lisburne, Chukchi Sea. They are common from the Sea of Japan and the Unalaska Island region of the Bering Sea to at least northern Oregon. Intertidal to unconfirmed depth of 425 m (1,394 ft), mostly from the intertidal to about 200 m (656 ft).

SALIENT CHARACTERS: A very long, indeed snake-like, body, along with large pelvic fins, scale-less cheeks, and a small snout sum up this interesting fish. They come with a tan or green back, lighter sides and belly, and a variety of brown saddles, large spots, and well-organized blotches on back and sides.

LIFE HISTORY: Juveniles recruit to the seafloor at around 3.4 cm (1 in) SL. Juveniles and adults are found from nearly fresh to marine waters, over sand, mud, cobbles, and often in eelgrass. Once in a while you will find one in a kelp bed. Although they likely spend most of their time on or near the bottom, both juveniles and adults do swim in the water column, particularly at night. They can reach fairly high densities of more than 3,625 per hectare. Snakes reportedly migrate into shallow waters during summer and early fall.

Snake pricklebacks are kind of an unknown quantity, as apparently no one has considered getting a masters thesis looking at their life history. They probably have demersal and adhesive eggs and likely spawn from about January to perhaps June. Their larvae are pelagic. Benthic and epibenthic organisms are what snake pricklebacks crave. Benthic juveniles target small crustaceans, like gammarid amphipods and harpacticoid copepods; older fish add polychaetes, clams, snails, and fish eggs to the mix. Predators include flathead soles, Pacific cod, Pacific halibut, sculpins, cormorants, pigeon guillemots, and harbor seals.

FISHERY: On occasion, anglers catch one.

Stichaeus punctatus
(Fabricius, 1780)
Arctic Shanny

CATHERINE W. MECKLENBURG

ETYMOLOGY: *Stichaeus* is Greek for "to set in rows" and *punctatus* is Latin for "spotted."

THE BASICS: Maximum Length: 22 cm (9 in) TL. The Ranges: Canadian Arctic east to Greenland and Gulf of Maine, west to Beaufort (west side of Point Barrow, 71°34'N, 156°22'W), Chukchi and East Siberia seas and south to Seas of Okhotsk and Japan, and to Skidegate Inlet (British Columbia). In our part of the world, relatively common at least from the northern Sea of Okhotsk to the southern and southeastern Chukchi Sea and down to Prince William Sound (Gulf of Alaska). Deeper intertidal–100 m (328 ft), mostly in 55 m (180 ft) or less. Length-weight parameters (FL, dm, gr): (sexes combined) W = 4.89L$^{3.12}$ (Elliott and Gaston 2008).

SALIENT CHARACTERS: Useful things to look for are a dorsal fin that has 4–7 dark spots (sometimes fringed with yellow) and a single lateral line that ends (somewhat forlornly methinks) around midbody. Arctics reportedly range from brownish to scarlet on back with darker blotches and other markings.

LIFE HISTORY: Arctic shannies are benthic fish that mostly live in nearshore waters. Young-of-the-year settle to the bottom at perhaps around 2.5 cm (1 in) SL. Both juveniles and adults can be found in very shallow, often really intertidal, waters. While they often hang around attached algae and eelgrass, you can also find them over small rocks, shell hash, and mud. Young fish are territorial; older individuals may not be. Off Newfoundland, adults move into shallow waters in summer and migrate back offshore in the fall. Tolerant of somewhat brackish conditions, they can withstand water temperatures at least as cold as 3°C (37°F).

Spawning likely occurs in the spring. A 15.7 cm (6 in) female caught off western Greenland contained 2,475 eggs. Off Newfoundland, Arctic shanny eat various small crustaceans (e.g., copepods and amphipods) and polychaetes. In the Arctic, they are eaten by black guillemots and thick-billed murres.

Xiphister atropurpureus
(Kittlitz, 1858)
Black Prickleback

ETYMOLOGY: *Xiphister* is Greek for "swordbelt" and *atropurpureus* means "black" and "purple" in Greek.

THE BASICS: Maximum Length: 32.3 cm (13 in) TL. The Ranges: Kodiak Island to Rio Santo Tomas (northern Baja California). Fairly common between at least northern British Columbia and Central California, occasional along the Northern Channel Islands, and abundant again in the Punta Clara area of northern Baja California. They don't appear to live along the Southern California mainland. Intertidal to 12 m (39 ft), including tide pools. Eggs: 2 mm. Larvae: hatching length = 7–10 mm. Mean lengths at age are given in Wingert (1975). Length-weight parameters (TL, mm, gr): (sexes combined) W = 0.000003266L$^{3.0387}$ (Burge and Schultz 1973).

SALIENT CHARACTERS: Check the characters for the rock prickleback and you will get most of the picture. The big difference is that this species has dark bars, edged with white, radiating backward from the eyes, and often a light-colored vertical

PHIL EDGELL

bar down the base of the caudal fin. Their bodies are often solid black.

LIFE HISTORY: Black pricklebacks recruit to the rocky intertidal at lengths as small as 1.1 cm (0.4 in) SL. The species lives throughout the rocky intertidal (along the open coast and in bays and inlets), mostly in boulder fields, occasionally on cobble beaches, and often with rock pricklebacks. They can also be fairly abundant in rocky areas of the shallow subtidal and occasionally around kelp holdfasts and can withstand waters as brackish as 6 ppt (about 20% of seawater). Genetic studies imply that the Strait of Georgia population is considerably different from others. During at least one ice age, black pricklebacks probably found multiple refugia to the north and south ends of their geographic range.

A 26.2 cm (10 in) TL fish was aged to 12 or 13 years old; so some black pricklebacks likely live longer than that. These fish mature at 12–12.5 cm (5 in) TL and 2–3 years old. Females spawn from December–May, producing between about 500–8,000 eggs per season. It is likely a female spawns all her eggs at one time. The white or yellow eggs are laid under those lower intertidal boulders that are sitting on small stones or shells. The egg masses are 20–50 cm (8–20 in) in diameter and males guard the eggs (up to three masses, likely representing three females) until they hatch. You can find more than one male guarding nests under a single boulder, so they don't appear to be territorial. Jeff Marliave (1975) reporting from Barkley Sound (Vancouver Island) notes: "Larvae start schooling inshore around kelp beds or rocky prominences." Diets of black pricklebacks appear to center around crustaceans (e.g., gammarid amphipods, harpacticoid copepods, isopods, shrimps, and crabs), polychaetes, snails, red and green algae, and surfgrass. Predators include whitespotted greenlings, Steller sea lions, minks, and probably river otters and, really, garter snakes. Amphipods eat prickleback eggs.

FISHERY: Black pricklebacks are only occasionally taken by shore anglers.

MISCELLANY: Black pricklebacks aerially respire (at least partly through their skins).

Xiphister mucosus
(Girard, 1858)
Rock Prickleback

ETYMOLOGY: *Xiphister* is Greek for "swordbelt" and *mucosus* is Latin for "slimy."

THE BASICS: Maximum Length: 58.6 cm (23 in) TL. The Ranges: Kodiak Island to Santa Cruz Island (Southern California). Intertidal to 18 m (60 ft). Eggs: About 2.4 mm. Larvae: hatching length = 11 mm.

SALIENT CHARACTERS: Let's see here. They are eel-shaped, have no anal spines, no pelvic fins, and little bitty pectorals. The color is basically greenish-black (less frequently black) and the small ones have white blotches on their rear end. The big giveaway is the light bars radiating backward from the eyes; they are bordered in black. Mean lengths at age are given in Wingert (1975). Length-weight parameters (TL, mm, gr): (sexes combined) W = 0.00000144L$^{3.2224}$ (Burge and Schultz 1973).

BERNARD P. HANBY

LIFE HISTORY: Young-of-the-year (at around 1.7 cm, 0.7 in, TL) recruit over a broad range of the rocky intertidal. Both juveniles and adults associate with boulders, cobbles, and various algae, mostly on the open coast. Adults also live in the shallow subtidal in the same kind of habitats. Rock and black pricklebacks often hang out together. Like the black prickleback, this species can withstand brackish conditions. These fish spawn in the lower intertidal (and perhaps subtidal), under boulders, and the males guard the eggs (donated by multiple females) until they hatch. Genetic studies imply this species retreated southward during one or more of the ice ages of the last few million years. One study found that rock pricklebacks were unashamedly incapable of homing back to their home tide pool.

Rock pricklebacks live to at least 11 years old (that one was 52 cm, 20 in, TL). They mature at perhaps 28–30 cm (11–12 in) TL and 4–5 years old. Spawning occurs from at least December (and perhaps as early as October) through May, with females spawning once per season, and producing 2,000–15,000 white eggs. Small rock pricklebacks (less than maybe 5 cm, 2 in) eat mostly small crustaceans (e.g., calanoid and harpacticoid copepods, gammarid amphipods, and mysid shrimps) and polychaetes. Larger fish appear to concentrate on red and green algae, and sometimes surfgrass. Adult fish occasionally eat the small invertebrates of their youth. Predators include cabezons, grass rockfish, kelp and whitespotted greenlings, minks, and river otters.

FISHERY: Native Americans ate a lot of these. They are occasionally taken from piers and rocky shores, perhaps most often by poke polers.

MISCELLANY: Rock pricklebacks aerially respire and can live as long as 20 hours out of water.

OTHER SPECIES

Anisarchus medius
(Reinhardt, 1837)
Stout Eelblenny

Stouts reach 18 cm (7.1 in) TL. They are nearly circumpolar in the Arctic Ocean and live in the Arctic (to north of Wrangell Island) and Beaufort seas to the Sea of Japan, and to southeastern Alaska (at Auke Bay and Coco Harbor, 55°03'N, 133°02'W). They are common throughout the Chukchi Sea and perhaps in the eastern Bering Sea, over muddy bottoms and occasionally in brackish waters. They live from the intertidal to 265 m (869 ft), perhaps mostly in 100 m (328 ft) or less. Found between -1.8–7.9°C (29–46°F), they may prefer temperatures around 0°C (32°F). Larvae drift off Kamchatka in June. Stouts feed on benthic invertebrates (e.g., polychaetes, bivalves, and crustaceans).

Chirolophis decoratus
(Jordan & Snyder, 1902)
Decorated Warbonnet

Decorateds grow to 42 cm (17 in) TL. They live from the eastern Bering Sea and Aleutian Islands to Humboldt Bay (Northern California), from the shallow subtidal to depths of 232 m (761 ft). They are found mostly in complex habitats, such as rocks and sponges, often with their heads sticking out of holes. Little is known regarding their life histories, although Lamb and Edgell (2010) report that they eat crustaceans.

MARC CHAMBERLAIN

Leptoclinus maculatus
(Fries, 1837)
Daubed Shanny

Daubed shannies grow to 22 cm (9 in) TL and live throughout most of the Arctic. In our area, they are found from the Beaufort Sea to the seas of Okhotsk and Japan to Puget Sound, commonly in the eastern Bering Sea. They range from depths of 2–491 m (7–1,610 ft), and possibly to 607 m (1,991 ft), but mostly in less than 170 m (558 ft). These benthic fish live on soft and low-relief seafloors, in marine and slightly brackish waters. Spawning may take place in the winter. They eat copepods and, one expects, other small zooplankton. Predators include arrowtooth flounder, Greenland halibut, Pacific cod, walleye pollock, flathead soles, tufted puffins, and probably river otters.

Lumpenella longirostris
(Evermann & Goldsborough, 1907)
Longsnout Prickleback

Longsnouts grow to 43 cm (17 in) TL. They are found in the western North Atlantic and North Pacific. In the North Pacific, they live from the seas of Japan and Okhotsk to the Bering Sea and Aleutian Islands to Burrard Inlet (southern British Columbia). Longsnouts are common over soft seafloors from at least eastern Sakhalin westward to about the Alaska Peninsula. The species lives in 25–1,195 m (82–3,921 ft), with adults usually dwelling in 140 m (459 ft) and more. Longsnouts live at least 4 years and all fish are mature by 27 cm (11 in) TL. They probably spawn in the spring and the eggs are probably demersal. Longsnout diets vary greatly among locations. Polychaetes tend to be quite important, as do small crustaceans (e.g., euphausiids, hyperiid amphipods, and mysid shrimps), bivalves, snails, and squids. Predators include Alaska and Okhotsk skates, arrowtooth and Kamchatka flounder, Greenland halibut, Pacific cod, twoline eelpouts, Steller sea lions, and bearded seals.

PHIL EDGELL

Phytichthys chirus
(Jordan & Gilbert, 1880)
Ribbon Prickleback

This little species reaches 21.1 cm (8 in) TL. It ranges from the Aleutian Islands and Gulf of Alaska to Southern California, but by Central California it is starting to peter out. A nearshore species, you find them in the intertidal and down to depths of 12 m (39 ft). Young-of-the-year recruit to complex habitat at lengths at least as small as 2.4 cm (1 in) SL. Juveniles and adults tend to live in areas of high relief, often around kelp and other algae, surfgrass, mussels, and the like. Ribbons feed mostly on gammarid amphipods, along with caprellid amphipods, isopods, crabs, mollusks, polychaetes, and algae.

BERNARD P. HANBY

FAMILY CRYPTACANTHODIDAE—Wrymouths

The aptly named wrymouths form a small group of benthic marine fishes that are found only in the North Pacific and northwest Atlantic. There is one genus and four species, and two of these live within our range. Wrymouths are oviparous, with demersal eggs, and pelagic larvae.

Cryptacanthodes aleutensis
(Gilbert, 1896)
Dwarf Wrymouth

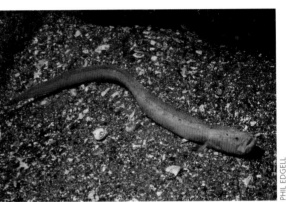

PHIL EDGELL

ETYMOLOGY AND COLLOQUIAL NAME: *Cryptacanthodes* is Greek for "hidden" and "spined" (referring to the dorsal spines hidden in the skin) and *aleutensis* refers to its capture in the Aleutian Islands. The Japanese name is "hadakaookamiuo-rui."

THE BASICS: Maximum Length: 31 cm (12 in) TL. The Ranges: Southeastern Bering Sea and eastern Aleutian Islands (Unalaska Island) to Eureka (Northern California). Relatively high densities of larvae have been collected as far southward as Oregon. 21–750 m (70–2,460 ft).

SALIENT CHARACTERS: They are eel-like, red or pink, and have that funky, almost vertically oriented, lower jaw, no pelvic fins, and no scales. Eggs: 1.8 mm.

LIFE HISTORY: There is just not a lot to work with here. Apparently, young-of-the-year settle to the bottom at around 3.2 cm (1 in) SL. It is thought that they live in burrows in soft sediments. Based on larval collections, they spawn at least from winter–summer, probably mostly in the spring. OK, that's about it. Predators include flathead soles, longnose skate, Pacific cod, and walleye pollock.

ORIGINS: The University of California, Berkeley, Paleontological Museum has a record of otoliths of this species from the Pliocene (at least 1.8 million years ago) of Oregon.

FAMILY PHOLIDAE—Gunnels

Gunnels are small, nearshore marine fishes that mainly inhabit the rocky intertidal and shallow seafloor of the North Pacific and North Atlantic. There are three genera and about 15 species. Nine species live within our range. Gunnels are oviparous with adhesive eggs (that are guarded by parents) and planktonic larvae. Fossil pholids (*Agnevichthys gretchinae* and *Palaeopholis laevis*) have been taken in Miocene deposits (at least 5.3 million years ago) of the Sakhalin Islands. Kitty Mecklenburg et al. (2002) have a key to many of the species.

JANNA NICHOLS

Apodichthys flavidus
Girard, 1854
Penpoint Gunnel

ETYMOLOGY: *Apodichthys* rather cleverly means "without feet" and "fish" in Greek (referring to the lack of pelvic fins) and *flavidus* is Latin for "yellowish."

THE BASICS: Maximum Length: 46 cm (18 in) TL. The Ranges: Kodiak Island to Santa Barbara Island and Gaviota (Southern California). They are abundant from at least Prince William Sound (northern Gulf of Alaska) to Central California. Intertidal to 8 m (25 ft), including tide pools. Most fish live in the intertidal or barely subtidal. Eggs: 3 mm. Larvae: hatching length = 13 mm average flexion length = about 1.4–2 mm, transformation length = 2.3–3 cm. Length-weight parameters (TL, mm, gr): (sexes combined) $W = 0.0000007612L^{3.296}$ (Burge and Schultz 1973).

VALERIE LYTTLE

SALIENT CHARACTERS: Penpoints are long, thin, and eel-like, distinguished by a deeply grooved spine on the front of the anal fin (hence the name "penpoint"), a line extending downward through the eyes, and no pelvic fins. The body color is highly variable: orange, red, and magenta, bright green, olive, or bronze. While usually a solid color, the body can be highly mottled, with a row of dark or light spots along the midline.

LIFE HISTORY: Young-of-the-year (at about 1.5 cm, 0.6 in, TL) settle into tide pools in the spring at as small as 2.3 cm (0.9 in) SL. This species is very widely distributed in the intertidal (and in the shallow subtidal) in boulder fields, pebble and cobble beaches, mud, sand, and among various algae, surfgrass, and eelgrass. While it is mostly a species of marine waters, it can tolerate estuarine conditions.

As a 30.5 cm (12 in) TL fish was 6 years old, they likely live longer. The fish spawn at least from January–April. Females lay whitish-colored eggs in the rocky intertidal and it has variously been reported that either the male or both parents guard the eggs. Incubation lasts for 2.5 months and the larvae settle out of the plankton after 50 days. Penpoints feed almost entirely on small crustaceans. Gammarid amphipods are often among the most important prey, but harpacticoid copepods, mysid shrimps, isopods, shrimps, hermit crabs, along with polychaetes and nemerteans, are also eaten. Predators include cabezons, flathead soles, lingcod, double-crested and pelagic cormorants, Steller sea lions, minks, and probably river otters.

FISHERY: Penpoints are very rarely taken by recreational anglers.

Apodichthys fucorum
Jordan & Gilbert, 1880
Rockweed Gunnel

VALERIE LYTTLE

ETYMOLOGY: *Apodichthys* means "without feet" and "fish" in Greek (referring to the lack of pelvic fins) and *fucorum* comes from the seaweed genus "*Fucus*" (and stop smirking, that is pronounced "few cuss.")

THE BASICS: Maximum Length: 22.9 cm (9 in) TL. The Ranges: Banks Island (British Columbia) to Punta Escarpada (north-central Baja California), abundant southward to northern Baja California. Intertidal to 9 m (30 ft), mostly in the intertidal, but also fairly commonly to 6.1 (20 ft). Eggs: 2 mm. Larvae: hatching length = 1.3 cm, early flexion length = about 1.4 cm, postflexion length = 2 cm.

SALIENT CHARACTERS: Another of the patented eel-shaped gunnels, this one has tiny pectoral fins (about the same diameter as the eyes), an anal spine that is not grooved, and no pelvic fins. The species comes in yellow-brown, red, and green and fish tend to be found in background colors matching their own. Red fish can change color gradually (within 2–12 days) and most green fish cannot change their color.

LIFE HISTORY: In the spring, young-of-the-year settle (at around 2.2 cm, 0.9 in, SL) in the nearshore, probably mostly to tide pools. Both young and adults live around such vegetation as red algae and surfgrass, usually among rocks. There is some evidence that at low tide, intertidal fish move under rocks, occupying algae as the tide rises. They often entwine in vegetation.

Rockweeds spawn at least during the winter and perhaps into the early spring. Females lay eggs under rocks in the lower intertidal and these are guarded by males. Rockweed gunnels really like small crustaceans (e.g., harpacticoid copepods, isopods, gammarid amphipods, hermit crabs, shrimps, and ostracods), and snails. Predators include shorebirds such as great blue herons.

MISCELLANY: 1) This species aerially respires and can live as long as 12 hours out of the water. 2) Kirk Lombard, who has an eye for such things, relates that on a number of occasions he has seen both rockweed and penpoint gunnels living amid the seaweed and tunicates that foul ship bottoms. When the boats are hauled out and the bottoms cleaned, lots of these fish can be found in the stuff spilling on to the ground.

W—E N S

BERNARD P. HANBY

Pholis laeta
(Cope, 1873)
Crescent Gunnel

ETYMOLOGY: *Pholis* is a Greek word for "one who lies in wait" and *laeta* is Latin for "joyful."

THE BASICS: Maximum Length: 25.4 cm (10 in) TL. Geographic Range: Southeastern Kamchatka to the Aleutian Islands, east to Port Heiden (southeastern Bering Sea) and Gulf of Alaska to Crescent City (Northern California). Apparently common along the Aleutian Islands and in the southeastern Bering Sea to at least Puget Sound. Tide pools to 73 m (240 ft), reported to 99 m (324 ft).

They are very abundant in the intertidal and shallow subtidal. Larvae: hatching length = about 9 mm. Mean lengths at age in Hughes (1985).

SALIENT CHARACTERS: Crescents are eel-shaped with very small pelvic fins. Jeff Cross (1981) noted: "Varied from red to yellowish- and greenish-brown to gray. Solid or mottled, it possessed 13–15 paired concentric markings (parentheses) along the dorsal fin that frequently extended onto the back." During winter, "mature males exhibited an orange or reddish coloration along the cheeks, throat, pectoral fins and ventral region anterior to the vent. Immature males and females had creamy or green coloration in the same regions."

LIFE HISTORY: Young-of-the-year (as small as 1.5 cm, 0.6 in, SL) recruit to the intertidal and shallow subtidal. Both juveniles and adults live in a wide range of habitats, including rocks, cobbles, eelgrass, surfgrass, kelp, but also over smooth seafloors. They are able to tolerate at least mildly estuarine conditions. Although they usually live on the bottom, or at least closely associated with substrate, at night crescents sometimes rise into the water column. They have been taken in waters as cold as 1.4°C (35°F). While it is unlikely they move about much, in Izembek Lagoon (eastern Bering Sea) these fish move out of shallow waters in the winter.

JANNA NICHOLS

Crescents live to at least 6 years old. Some fish mature at as small as 10 cm (3.9 in) SL. Females lay eggs in nests under rocks, from the intertidal down to depths of 5 m (16 ft) or more. Females spawn at least during January and February. The eggs are usually, although apparently not always, guarded by both parents, who coil themselves around the egg masses. Generally, there is one nest per rock underside. Females produce at least between 621–1,598 eggs, these hatch in about two months, and the larvae are planktonic. Eggs are white when laid and turn cream-colored with age. Crescent gunnels feed on caprellid and gammarid amphipods, isopods, shrimps, and harpacticoid copepods, along with polychaetes, bivalves, insects, and the occasional fish. They are eaten by rock greenlings, yellowfin soles, walleye pollock, various birds (e.g., common goldeneyes, double-crested cormorants, and pigeon guillemots), minks, and probably river otters.

OTHER SPECIES

Apodichthys sanctaerosae
(Gilbert & Starks, 1897)

Kelp Gunnel

Kelp gunnels reach 28.6 cm (11 in) TL. They range from Pacific Grove (Central California) to Bahia Papalote (northern Baja California), and at Isla Guadalupe (central Baja California), from the intertidal to 12 m (40 ft). This is a little-known species that mostly lives in the kelp canopy, where it entwines around stipes. They appear to spawn in the winter and spring, with females laying demersal eggs. The few that have been examined had eaten mysid shrimps and amphipods. One was found in the gut of a black-and-yellow rockfish. Larvae: hatching length = perhaps near 9 mm, flexion length = about 9.3–15.1 mm, transformation length = larger than 2.4 and less than 7.1 cm (1–2.8 in). I present this species just because of the creamy-good photograph by Kawika Chetron.

KAWIKA CHETRON

RICH ZADE

Pholis clemensi

Rosenblatt, 1964

Longfin Gunnel

BERNARD P. HANBY

Longfins grow to 13.4 cm (5 in) TL. They live from Fillmore Island (southeastern Alaska) to Arena Cove (Northern California), at depths of 7.3–64 m (24–210 ft), typically perhaps in 6–18 m (20–60 ft). Longfins are found among rocks, (often mixed with sand) and around hydroids and bryozoans. They occasionally come to the surface at night. Lamb and Edgell (2010) suggest that this species cleans other fishes.

Pholis ornata

(Girard, 1854)

Saddleback Gunnel

Saddlebacks reach a length of 30.5 cm (12 in) TL. They range from Vancouver Island to Point Loma (Southern California) and are abundant at least as far southward as Northern California. You definitely can find them from the intertidal to 37 m (120 ft), and perhaps to 60 m (198 ft). Young-of-the-year (as small as 1.8–2 cm, 0.7–0.8 in, SL) recruit to very shallow waters from spring to early fall. This is a benthic species of bays, estuaries, and other quiet waters, inhabiting eelgrass and other plant life, over (and under) rocks, or on mud. An occasional fish associates with drifting algae. They are very tolerant of brackish, almost fresh, waters. Their maximum age is unknown. An 11.7 cm (5 in) SL fish was 2 years old. Saddlebacks spawn during the winter. Presumably, females lay eggs in nests

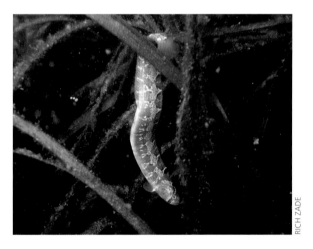

RICH ZADE

under structures. They eat a relatively wide variety of organisms, mostly comprised of epibenthic prey. Gammarid amphipods are often quite important, as are polychaetes, harpacticoid copepods, mysid shrimps, isopods, crabs, shrimps, and clam siphons. Fish are occasionally consumed. Predators include copper rockfish, Pacific cod, and harbor seals. Hughes (1985) gives mean lengths at age for the first few years.

Pholis schultzi

Schultz, 1931

Red Gunnel

Red gunnels grow to 12.7 cm (5 in) TL. They are found from the Queen Charlotte Islands (British Columbia) to Diablo Cove (Central California), and they are pretty common down to about the Mendocino area (Northern California). This is a rock and kelp dweller that lives in the intertidal and down to at least 25 m (82 ft), and perhaps to 29 m (95 ft). They appear to be most common down to about 7.6 m (25 ft). A 9.1 cm (4 in) SL fish was 2 years old. These fish eat isopods and gammarid and caprellid amphipods. They are eaten by pigeon guillemots.

RICH ZADE

FAMILY ANARHICHADIDAE—Wolffishes

Wolffishes are cold-water marine fishes found in the North Pacific and North Atlantic. Worldwide, there are two genera, five species, and two species within our range. These are oviparous fishes and it is likely that all have adhesive, demersal eggs that are brooded by parents. They have planktonic larvae and juveniles.

Anarrhichthys ocellatus

Ayres, 1855

Wolf-eel

Adults look like the Pillsbury Doughboy channeling Frederick North, 2ⁿᵈ Earl of Guilford.

ETYMOLOGY AND COLLOQUIAL NAMES: *Anarrhichthys* is derived from *"Anarhichas"* (referring to the related wolf-fishes) and the Greek word for "fish" and *ocellatus* is Latin for "eye-like" (referring to the spots). "Wolf eel" was used in the 19ᵗʰ century, as was "azia" and "morina."

THE BASICS: Maximum Length: 240 cm (7.9 ft) TL. The Ranges: Southeastern Bering Sea, east to Cape Menshikof, along Aleutian Islands, and Gulf of Alaska to northern Baja California (31°41'N, 116°42'W) and perhaps to Isla Guadalupe (central Baja California). They are abundant from Central California northward and are at least occasional throughout Southern California. Intertidal to 309 m (1,013ft), reported but not confirmed to 416 m (1,365 ft). In Southern California, wolf-eels are generally absent from shallow water. Eggs: 5.2–5.5 mm. Larvae: hatching length = 1.9–4.5 cm (0.7–1.8 in), flexion length = about 2–3.7 cm (0.8–1.5 in), transformation length = about 15–61 cm (6–24 in). Length-weight parameters (TL, mm, gr): W = 0.00002234L^{2.604} (W. VanBuskirk, pers. comm.).

VALERIE LYTTLE

SALIENT CHARACTERS: Wolf-eels are marvelous eel-shaped fishes with extremely long bodies, large canines and molars, and dorsal and anal fins that taper together to form a point. Adults are blue-gray, gray, red-brown, or sometime almost white, and darkly spotted (sometimes heavily, sometimes not). Females are sometimes brownish. At maturity, males develop fleshy mandibles and a head crest. Juveniles tend to be brownish and have large dark spots.

A young one.

LIFE HISTORY: Juveniles can be pelagic (often near the surface) for as long as 2 years before settling out on nearshore reefs, often around kelp and other algae. A pelagic juvenile tagged in Port Hardy (British Columbia) was recovered at Willapa Bay (Washington) 2 years later. Juveniles recruit to the bottom, probably mostly at around 20–55 cm (8–22 in) TL, although pelagic juveniles to 60.1 cm (24 in) TL have been caught. Adults live over reefs or around large hunks of human-made material (e.g., piers and oil platforms). You mostly see the adults with just their heads sticking out of crevices and caves, although they will go out for undulating sojourns on occasion. Although these are often solitary animals, they do form male-female pairs that sometimes last for months or even years. Wolf-eels may share their homes with Pacific giant octopuses, ling-cod, sailfin sculpins, and sundry rockfishes. The octopuses may kick out the wolf-eels. They can be active at night. Spawning occurs in the dens and both parents guard the eggs. Wolf-eel dens occur to depths of at least 20 m (66 ft). Parra et al. (2001) found: "The effects of habituating wolf-eels to feeding is likely to include a decrease in the frequency and extent of foraging excursions, which in turn may allow them to remain in the same den and with the same mate for extended periods. Wolf-eels at popular recreational dive sites in British Columbia have been reported to remain in the same den for up to 25 years."

Wolf-eels live to at least 28 years. In aquaria, fish first reproduce at 7 years old. Spawning occurs from at least October–January and eggs take 13–16 weeks to hatch. Waldo Wakefield writes to me that pelagic juveniles ate the late pelagic stage of sand soles and other flatfishes: "The large flatfish larvae were rolled up like crepes suzettes (blintzes) in the stomachs." He also found they were eating larval decapods and hyperiid amphipods. Larger and bottom-associated individuals mostly eat sea urchins, crabs and sand dollars, and also some octopuses, brittle stars, snails, barnacles, clams, and fishes. Predators include rockfishes, sablefish, river otters, and harbor seals.

Another young one.

FISHERY: Native Americans often ate wolf-eels. Lockington (1879a) reported that wolf-eels were commonly brought into the San Francisco market in the summer. He wrote: "Some of the dealers and fisher-men...have given it the name of 'wolf-eel'. A specimen sent to the California Academy of Sciences, by Capt. Lawson of the Coast Survey, and unfortunately lost through the lack of means to preserve it, measured eight feet in length; and one seven feet in length was noticed in the daily papers about three years since as an 'infant sea-serpent.' One large individual that lay upon the stall recently, showed the effects of a battle in the want of all that portion of the body situated posterior to the anus." Into the 20th century, wolf-eel fillets were occasionally sold in the fish markets of Washington and they remain a fairly common by-catch in crab traps. A handful of fish are landed each year. They are occasionally taken by pier and boat anglers.

ORIGINS: The University of California, Berkeley, Paleontological Museum has a record of *A. ocellatus* from a Miocene formation (at least 5.3 million-year-old) in Northern California.

MISCELLANY: Here's some random stuff. 1) "An adult wolf-eel salmon-orange in over-all colour, instead of gray or dark green, was taken off Ucluelet on August 29, 1959, by G.R. Grosmith...Mr. G.R. Grosmith, a commercial fisherman of Victoria, bears scars of a wolf-eel bite on the ankle. The teeth penetrated hip-waders and broke the skin on both sides of the ankle joint" (Carl 1964). 2) "A fish of the Anarrhichthys tribe is frequently killed during the summer months at low tide among the rocks. This is called the "doctor fish" by the Indians [Makah], and is never eaten except by some medicine-man who wishes to increase his skill in pharmacy" (Swan 1868).

CONFESSIONS OF A NORTH AMERICAN ECHINODERM-EATER

I just came back from the city, city, to wear that ball and chain.

It ain't because you're pretty, pretty, that I came back again.

It's how you eat those urchins, urchins, the way you chew your food.

I just don't need that urgin, urgin, to get into the mood.

FAMILY PTILICHTHYIDAE—Quillfish

There is only one species of quillfish. It is oviparous and has pelagic larvae.

Ptilichthys goodei

Bean, 1881

Quillfish

BERNARD P. HANBY

ETYMOLOGY AND COLLOQUIAL NAME: *Ptilichthys* means "quill" and "fish" in Greek and *goodei* refers to George Brown Goode (1851–1896) (see chilipepper). They are called "hane-gaji" in Japan.

THE BASICS: Maximum Length: 39 cm (15 in) SL. The Ranges: Seas of Japan and Okhotsk to Commander, Aleutian, and Pribilof islands (southern Bering Sea) to central Oregon. Surface to 360 m (1,181 ft). Larvae: transformation = about 11–12 mm.

SALIENT CHARACTERS: Quillfish have hyperskinny bodies, a projecting lower jaw that has a fleshy tip, and the end of the caudal fin is thread-like and sad. They are yellow, green, or orange, sometimes with several maroon stripes.

LIFE HISTORY: Quillfish are believed to burrow in soft substrates. They may mature at about 27 cm (11 in) TL. Based on larval surveys, quillfish probably spawn in the spring. Predators include black rockfish, coho and Chinook salmon, great and plain sculpins, Pacific cod, Pacific halibut, and tufted and horned puffins.

FAMILY ZAPRORIDAE—Prowfish

Like the quillfish, there is only one species of prowfish.

CLEO BRYLINSKY

Zaprora silenus

Jordan, 1896

Prowfish

ETYMOLOGY AND COLLOQUIAL NAME: *Zaprora* is formed from two Greek words, the first a prefix that intensifies the rest of the word and that word means "prow." *Silenus* was a Greek god, a drunken follower of Dionysus, whom in one story fell into a swamp and was covered in slime; a kind of clever reference to this species' mucous pores. The Japanese name is "Bozu-ginpo."

THE BASICS: Maximum Length: At least 1 m (39 in) TL. Maximum Weight: At least 9.3 kg (20.5 lb). The Ranges: Hokkaido and Sea of Okhotsk to southeastern Chukchi Sea (west of Kivalina, 67°32'N, 165°54'W), Bering Sea and Aleutian Islands to San Miguel Island (Southern California). They seem to be most abundant from the Kuril Islands to the Bering Sea about as far west as Navarin Canyon, as far north as about Saint Matthew Island, and southward down to about 50°N (off Vancouver Island). 10–801 m (33–2,628 ft), mostly in 100–250 m (328–820 ft). Larvae: about 3 cm (1 in). Von Bertalanffy parameters (TL, cm): (sexes combined) L_∞ = 89.3, k = 0.18, t_0 = -0.55 (Smith et al. 2004). Length-weight parameters (TL, cm, gr): (females) W = 0.017$L^{2.922}$; (males) W = 0.0164$L^{2.922}$ (Smith et al. 2004).

SALIENT CHARACTERS: Prowfish are compressed, kind of stocky fish, with a blunt head, long dorsal and anal fins that are separate from the caudal fin, and no pelvic fins. Young fish are a bit more oval and they have more expansive dorsal and anal fins. Young ones are various shades of brown and may have dark bars on dorsal and anal fins and sometimes lighter spots on sides. Adults range from cobalt blue to greenish, may have dark or light spotting or yellow blotches on sides, and their head is often profusely spotted with blue, silvery, or yellow.

A quite small juvenile.

LIFE HISTORY: Pelagic juveniles may be obligate commensals of medusae, as they are commonly found around jellyfish. They usually hang out near the top and sides of the bell, but when frightened they shelter inside it or around the tentacles. As many nine individuals have been seen around a single medusa. At perhaps 18 cm (7 in) TL or more, the fish settle to the bottom and take up a benthic existence, mostly living in high-relief areas of caves and crevices, sometimes sharing holes with lingcod. Some fish have been observed over cobbles and mud. Off the northern Kurils and southeastern Kamchatka, prowfish may make seasonal migrations from the deep shelf to shallow slope in late fall and early winter. They are found at as cold as 0.2°C (32°F). Fish in Alaska occasionally live in waters at least as warm as 8.5°C (47°F).

Prowfish live to at least 20 years old. Males and females grow at the same rate and perhaps to the same size. Fifty percent of females are mature at about 57 cm (22 in) and about 5 years old. Females are slightly heavier than males at any given length. It's a little unclear when this species spawns; however most newly hatched larvae are taken in the winter and spring, but the season may extend into the summer. Prowfish eat mostly water column animals. Medusae are often very important, as are pelagic tunicates and comb jellies. Euphausiids, hyperiid amphipods, mysid shrimps, fish larvae, larvaceans, and polychaetes are also consumed. Juveniles are eaten by Chinook and coho salmon, other prowfish, and tufted puffins. Larger fish have been found in black rockfish, Pacific cod, and whiteblotched skate.

FISHERY: There is no targeted fishery for this species. Alexi Orlov notes that Japanese fishermen use this species in surimi, but that there is no market for it.

ORIGINS: *Araeosteus rothi*, a species definitely in this family, and perhaps in this genus, lived in what is now California during the Miocene, at least 5.3 million years ago.

FAMILY SCYTALINIDAE—Graveldiver

One species graces the family Scytalinidae and here it is.

Scytalina cerdale
Jordan & Gilbert, 1880
Graveldiver

ETYMOLOGY: *Scytalina* is Greek for "small viper" and *cerdale* is Greek for "wary one." Sometimes the scientific names are a bit of a stretch, but these are spot on.

THE BASICS: Maximum Length: 15.2 cm (6 in) TL. The Ranges: Western Aleutian Islands to Diablo Cove (Central California). There is a small colony at Diablo Cove. Intertidal to 7.6 m (25 ft).

SALIENT CHARACTERS: They really do kind of look like snakes, particularly around that swollen, fangy head. Graveldivers are eel-like, lack scales and pelvic fins, have dorsal and anal fins that

begin way back on the body, and have canine teeth. Reportedly, they range from pinks and purples to brownish and yellowish, sometimes with darker mottling and a red or orange caudal fin margin.

LIFE HISTORY: Graveldivers spend at least part of their days buried in intertidal and subtidal gravel and shells. Aaron Setran has also found them lying exposed under rocks. Burge and Schultz (1973) found that graveldivers living in the intertidal were young-of-the-year, while subtidal dwellers were older. A 6.9 cm (3 in) SL fish was 3 years old. While their diets are poorly known, they do eat gammarid amphipods.

FAMILY TRICHODONTIDAE—Sandfish

Sandfishes are limited to the North Pacific. There are two genera and two species (*Arctoscopus japonicus*, the sailfin sandfish, is the other), and both are found within our range.

Trichodon trichodon
(Tilesius, 1813)
Pacific Sandfish

ETYMOLOGY AND COLLOQUIAL NAMES: *Trichodon* means "hair" and "tooth" in Greek. An Aleut name from the 19th century was (and perhaps still is) "anamlukh." The Russians call them "Japanese sandfish" and the Japanese name is "ezohatahata."

THE BASICS: Maximum Length: 30.5 cm (12 in) TL. Maximum Weight: 350 gr (12 oz). The Ranges: Japan to southeastern Kamchatka and southeastern Bering Sea (to Pribilof Islands) to San Francisco; commonly from eastern Kamchatka to the eastern Bering Sea and at least Puget Sound. There are also poorly documented reports of catches from eastern Canada at James Bay, Hudson Bay, and Hudson Strait. Intertidal to 375 m (1,230 ft), but usually shallower than 150 m (492 ft). Eggs: 3.3–3.4 mm. An age-length relationship is figured in Paul et al. (1997). Length-weight parameters (FL, mm, gr): (sexes combined) $W = 0.0000012L^{3.452}$ (Paul et al. 1997).

SALIENT CHARACTERS: Sandfish have a very characteristic upturned mouth, fringed lip, and scaleless body. They have a dark back laced with darker spots, silvery sides, and belly.

LIFE HISTORY: Schools of juveniles tend to be found in nearshore waters, often in the intertidal, mostly over cobble, sand, bedrock, and other low relief (and occasionally in eelgrass), frequently near the surface or in midwaters. Here they sometimes school with juvenile pink salmon. Adults are generally in slightly deeper waters, mostly no deeper than 100 m (328 ft) or so. Throughout much of their range, Pacific sandfish live primarily in 4–12°C (39–53°F), although they have been found in waters as cold as -0.6°C (31°F). This species can tolerate at least slightly estuarine conditions. As their name implies, these fish bury themselves in the sand with only their eyes, lip fringe, and a bit of tail exposed. Although it has been assumed that Pacific sandfish stay under the sand during the day and swim about at night, large schools of juveniles will feed in surface waters during the day.

Pacific sandfish live to 9 years old and females grow larger than males. Females produce between 1,000–15,000 eggs per season and the species appears to be a batch spawner. Spawning occurs at least during February and March and perhaps into June, but the exact months are unknown. Jeff Marliave (1981b) found an egg mass in a rocky surge channel in 0.6–1 m (2–3 ft). The egg mass contained about 1,000 amber-colored eggs that "adhered firmly to the rock surface." He assumes that it takes a year for the eggs to hatch. In the lab, "*Trichodon* first burrowed into sand as metamorphosed juveniles at 5–6 cm SL…The eyes and nostrils usually remained exposed above the sand, although the entire body could be buried. Burrowing did not occur until fleshy fringes had developed on the jaws. The fringed lips may permit water to be inhaled without allowing sand to enter the buccal cavity." Pacific sandfish feed mostly on water-column fishes and invertebrates. Depending on location, the most important invertebrates are likely to be euphausiids, calanoid and harpacticoid copepods, mysid shrimps, hyperiid amphipods, and crustacean larvae. Predators include Chinook and coho salmon, great sculpins, Pacific cod, Pacific halibut, yellow Irish lords, black-legged kittiwakes, common murres, horned and tufted puffins, pigeon guillemots, rhinoceros auklets, sooty shearwaters, several tern species, harbor and northern fur seals, Steller sea lions, minks, and river otters.

FISHERY: Sandfish are very occasionally taken by recreational anglers.

FAMILY AMMODYTIDAE—Sand Lances

Sand lances are marine fishes that are found throughout the world. There are eight genera and about 23 species, apparently two (see below) within our range. Sand lances are oviparous and have planktonic larvae.

Ammodytes hexapterus
Pallas, 1814

Pacific Sand Lance

ETYMOLOGY AND COLLOQUIAL NAMES: *Ammodytes* comes from the Greek for "sand" and "to dive" and *hexapterus* means "six" and "fins" in Greek (this last an allusion that is so subtle it is positively opaque). Also called "needlefish," "kitaikanago" in Japan, and "panmaksraq" by the Inupiats. An older spelling is "launce" and I kind of like that because the pronunciation is so much more refined. It would be the "a" in "law," rather than the harsher "a" as in "banana" that we are stuck with today. Really, saying the word "lance" makes you appear to be the guy who polishes the grain elevator in Dismal Seepage, North Dakota. "Launce," on the other hand, implies that you fairly reek of Old Money, and spend part of at least each winter at your casually rundown villa, one that was casually rundown under the *ancien régime*, in the better part of Provence.

THE BASICS: Maximum Length: 28 cm (11 in) TL. The Ranges: Well, this turns out to be a kind of tricky proposition, as recent genetic studies have shown that there are apparently two species of *Ammodytes* within our range, rather than just *A. hexapterus* (which would have made things easier). The second species may well be *A. personatus* Girard, 1856, which has, until now, been thought to be restricted to the western Pacific (this species was recently discovered in the western Gulf of Alaska). If there are, indeed, two species along our coast, their geographic ranges are not known. Thus, what I present below may be the ranges of the two species combined. Sea of Japan to Aleutian Islands, Bering Sea, and western Canadian Arctic, eastward to at least Franklin Bay (Northwest Territories) and to Balboa Island (Southern California). Records from the Hudson Bay area are likely in error. They are abundant from the seas of Japan and Okhotsk, eastward into the Bering Sea, and to Northern California. Intertidal to at least 100 m (330 ft) and perhaps to 272 m (892 ft). Most common from the intertidal to about 80 m (262 ft). Eggs: 0.7–1.2 mm. Larvae: hatching length = 4–7 mm, flexion length = 1.1–1.3 cm (0.4–0.5 in), transformation length = 1.6–about 5.5 cm (0.6–2.2 in). Both growth rate and length-weight relationships vary greatly between even nearby sites, see Robards et al. (2002). Here's a length-weight relationship from Litzow et al. (2002): (TL, mm, gr): (sexes combined) $W = 0.000002L^{3.1224}$.

SALIENT CHARACTERS: It's long, with a projecting lower jaw, very long dorsal fin, forked caudal fin, and a curious fold of skin along each side of the belly. Add to that a blue or green back and silvery belly and, *voila.*

LIFE HISTORY: Young-of-the-year settle in shallow waters at lengths of at least as small as 4 cm (2 in) FL. Both juveniles and adults occupy shallow eelgrass and algae beds and also live over sand, cobble, and bedrock. While it had long been assumed that juveniles were limited to shallow waters, a great wad of them (tens of millions of fish) has been discovered living in sand waves in 60–80 m (197–262 ft) in Puget Sound. Adults are also found along the shallower parts of the continental shelf. This species lives in waters at least as cold as -1.6°C (29°F). Sand lances have two very distinct behaviors that change daily and over time:, a water-column-schooling phase that mostly (but not exclusively) occurs during the day and a burying-in-the-sand (or fine gravel) phase, that mostly (but not exclusively) occurs at night. Both juveniles and adults are found in very shallow waters. These fish school (sometimes with Pacific herring) from right under the surface to near the bottom and burrow into the

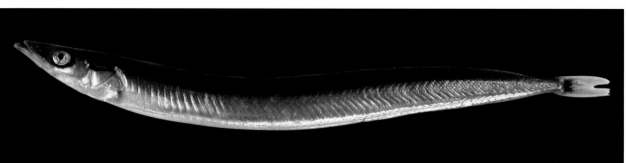

MANDY LINDEBERG

MICHAEL JOHNSTONE II

seafloor in the intertidal and subtidal. There is considerable evidence that most sand lance spend both days and nights under the sand throughout the winter, although individuals are occasionally taken in the water column during this time. They can tolerate fresh or nearly freshwater conditions. On occasion, tens of thousands of fish will swim too close to shore and become inadvertently stranded. Robards and Piatt (1999) note: "Sand lance can survive at least 5.5 hours in damp exposed sand... Interstitial water may be pumped over gills as well as held within the gill cavity, aiding oxygen transfer while the sand lance is buried in damp sand...on hot days...surfacing ensues...[and they] emerge spontaneously from Alaska nearshore substrates in extremely cold [air] conditions (-13°C) [9°F]. As sand lance emerged, they spontaneously froze at the surface." Pacific sand lances do not appear to be highly migratory. In the Gulf of Alaska, fish populations living within 100 km (62 mi) or less of each other exhibit significantly different growth rates.

Sand lances spawn mostly in the intertidal (occasionally in the shallow subtidal) over fine gravel and sandy beaches. Spawning can occur year after year on the same beaches. Robards et al. (1999) observed: "Initially, the laterally compressed schools (about 1–8 m in length and up to 1 m across) of adult sand lance were observed at high tide moving back and forth along the length of the beach, within 5 m of shore, and in less than 1 m of water. Spawning was preceded immediately by sand lance moving back and forth along a 20-m [66 ft] stretch of beach...then the school moved to the tide line and com-pressed into a tight spherical formation just above the bottom...Milt was observed in the water soon after the school adopted this formation. Apparently at this time, females create shallow (less than 50 mm deep) pits in the beach from about 2–5 m [7–16 ft] above the low tide line and lay their eggs in them. Spawning seems to occur throughout the day or night without much regard to tidal cycle, although there is some evidence that it may be more frequent at high tide."

In the Gulf of Alaska, Pacific sand lances live to at least 6 years old, while in Asian waters this species is believed to live to about 11 years old. Males and females grow at the same rates and growth rates are highly variable and are controlled by both productivity and water temperatures. In the Gulf of Alaska, most fish mature at slightly less than 2 years old (a few at as old as 4 years) and the smallest ripe male can be 8.8 cm (3.5 in) FL and the smallest ripe female 11.3 cm (4 in). Females (who produce between 1,468–16,081 translucent eggs) lay all of their demersal and slightly adhesive eggs in a single batch. Based on a range of both direct observations and captures of small larvae, sand lances may spawn at different times of the year in different locations. Between the Gulf of Alaska and Monterey, these fish spawn some time between about August–April. In Alaska, where most of the direct observations seem to have taken place, spawning occurs during the fall. The eggs hatch in 62 days at 2°C (36°F) and as little as 13 days at 15.7°C (60°F), but up to 67 days on occasion.

Pacific sand lances feed primarily on small, pelagic organisms, although occasionally a benthic invertebrate appears in a stomach. Depending on location and season, various copepods, gammarid and hyperiid amphipods, cladocerans, crustacean and polychaete larvae, and copepod eggs may be most important. Infrequently, small fishes are also consumed. Anything that is anything eats sand lances. Based on the scientific literature, at least 60 species of fishes, 31 species of birds, seven pinni-peds (seals and sea lions), six whales, a couple of porpoises, and river otters, all partake. And I'm sure this is an underestimate.

Tales of Predation: Sand lances are, *bien sur*, eaten as they swim about in the water. But they are also preyed upon when buried in the sand, particularly when they first enter the seafloor and are still moving about. Here are several reports. Willson and Armstrong (1998), from near Juneau, Alaska: "Bald eagles...rapidly patted the loose sand with their feet, shifting their weight from side to side. This activity disturbed buried sand-lance, which emerged from the sand and were seized by the eagles. Up to 85 eagles sometimes 'danced' together in a tight cluster on the sands, especially at minus tides." And, in an example of art imitating life, or life imitating art or...well, something imitating something, my colleague Nancy Elder's beagle, Kramer, does the same thing. He walks along Washington mudflats and gobbles up sand lances as they pop to the surface.

Here's something from Willson et al. (1999): "Ravens, crows and bald eagles forage on intertidal sand lance. Corvids [ravens and crows] and gulls often dig for sand lance with their bills...In addition, humpback whales may scuff the seafloor with their jaws to disturb subtidally buried sand lance and flush them from their hiding places."

FISHERY: Pacific sand lances are not particularly important commercially, although I do see them fairly frequently in California Asian markets. They were used for food by Alaskan indigenous peoples and have been used for bait for various larger species. Recreational anglers occasionally take them.

ORIGINS: A fossil species, *Ammodytes antipai*, lived in what is now the Caucasus Region of Asia in the Early Miocene-Late Oligocene (around 23 million years ago). Fossils of what appear to be this species have been found in Pliocene deposits (at least 1.8 million years old).

REMARKS: Sand lances are really, really important fishes. They are the quintessential forage fish, with a high energy content that makes them a preferred food item for young birds as well as all kinds of marine birds, mammals, and fishes. Arguably, some marine birds, in particular, may be mostly dependent on sand lances.

FAMILY URANOSCOPIDAE—Stargazers

Those silly stargazers, with those piquant upturned eyes, are found circumglobally mostly in the ocean but sometimes in estuaries. There are eight genera, about 50 species, and two species come as far north as Southern California. Stargazers are oviparous, probably have planktonic eggs, and do have planktonic larvae.

Kathetostoma averruncus

Jordan & Bollman, 1890

Smooth Stargazer

MILTON LOVE

ETYMOLOGY: *Kathetostoma* is Greek for "vertical" and "mouth" and *averruncus*, according to Jordan and Evermann (1898) is "a deity which wards off; from the mailed head." "Pez sapo" is a Spanish name.

THE BASICS: Maximum Length: 32 cm (13 in) TL. The Ranges: Piedras Blancas Point (Central California) to Isla Lobos de Tierra (Peru), including the mouth of Gulf of California. They are mostly occasional in Southern California, but during El Niños we seem to see more of them there. 13–600 m (42–1,968 ft). Larvae: flexion length = about 5.8–6.8 mm, transformation length = about 2–less than 6 cm (0.8–2.4 in). Length-weight parameters (SL, cm, gr): (sexes combined) $W = 0.025L^{3.076}$ (Rodriguez-Romero et al. 2009).

SALIENT CHARACTERS: Stargazers are just great, great fish. They have that really thick and flat head, the eyes that sit way up on that flat head, the upturned mouth ready to receive whatever those eyes spot, and a substantial spine (that may be venomous) above the base of the pectoral fin. Smooths are blackish or gray and have light spots and blotches.

LIFE HISTORY: Not much is known about them. They live on soft seafloors, probably spending some of their time buried or semi-buried in the sand. There is a 3.2 cm (1 in) SL fish in the collection of the Los Angeles County Museum of Natural History so maybe young-of-the-year settle at around that size. The smallest mature female I have examined was 26.5 cm (10 in) TL, but I have not seen many fish that were smaller than that. In the eastern Pacific, larvae have been taken from January–August. I have found ripe females in September, November, and February and fishes in the guts of the smooths I examined. As far as I can tell, folks do not consume this species.

FAMILY LABRISOMIDAE—Labrisomid Blennies

The labrisomids are small, nearshore, marine and mostly tropical fishes found in the Pacific and Atlantic oceans. These fishes are oviparous with planktonic young. There are 14 genera, 110 species, mostly in the tropical eastern Pacific. Seventeen species live within our range and three species reach to Southern California. Various authors in Patzner et al. (2009) cover some stuff about this group.

Alloclinus holderi
(Lauderbach, 1907)
Island Kelpfish

ETYMOLOGY: *Alloclinus* was erected by Carl Hubbs and means "another + *Clinus*," probably because he had moved it from *Starksia*, where it had originally been assigned. *Holderi* refers to Charles Frederick Holder (1851–1915). Originally from Massachusetts, Dr. Holder came to Southern California in 1885 and clearly was swept away by its pristine qualities. An author, angler, and naturalist, he was the editor of a Los Angeles newspaper, co-founder of the Tournament of Roses, and was a tireless promoter of Southern California. He was a major force for the idea that fishermen should give fishes an even break.

THE BASICS: Maximum Length: 11.5 cm (5 in) TL. Maximum Weight: 16 gr (1 oz). The Ranges: San Miguel Island to Punta San Pablo (27°12'N, 114°29'W) (southern Baja California). They are abundant from Santa Cruz Island to, from our surveys, at

DAVID AND DORI DIRIG

least Isla Asuncion (southern Baja California). Intertidal to 91 m (298 ft). Larvae: hatching length = less than 4.4 mm, flexion length = about 7.8–9 mm, transformation length = mostly about 2–2.3 cm (1 in). Length-weight parameters (TL, cm, gr): W = $0.0083L^{3.089}$ (Love unpubl.).

SALIENT CHARACTERS: These are elongated, with long dorsal and anal fins, a cirrus (3-pronged) above each eye, and a short snout. They change color to match their backgrounds; so expect red, purple, or brown, along with a series of dark back saddles, blotches (that may merge with each other) along the center of the flank, and a lighter patch on each cheek. They may have very thin striping of various colors, spots of red, white, or blue, and bright orange fins.

LIFE HISTORY: Young-of-the-year settle when at least as small as 1.8 cm (0.7 in) SL to nearshore waters. Island kelpfish are usually solitary (and perhaps somewhat territorial) and are found on rocks, in shells, and occasionally in eelgrass. You can find them both fully exposed or in crevices during the day and more sheltered at night. Densities have been reported as high as 2.5/m².

From my data it looks like females mature at a minimum length of 6.8 cm (3 in) TL and fecundity ranges from 212 eggs (in a 6.8 cm, 2.7 in, fish) to 1,386 eggs in one 9 cm (4 in) TL. I found ripe females from April–September; however, I collected no females in other months, so the spawning season may be longer. It is likely that females lay eggs in nests on rocks, although this has not been established. They feed on substrate-oriented prey (e.g., gammarid and caprellid amphipods, isopods, shrimps, mysid shrimps, snails, and polychaetes).

MISCELLANY: Island kelpfish clean other fish, including giant sea bass.

BOYZ CLUBHOWSE, GRILS GO AWAY

It might truly be said that sophisticated recreational marine fishing as we know it today, graced with a sense that the hooked fish should have some sort of chance to escape, was started by Charles Frederick Holder in 1898, when he founded the Avalon Tuna Club at Santa Catalina Island. Here we have Holder in 1913 describing the founding of the Club: "Thousands of men visit the islands and nearly all fish. It is fair to say that fifty per cent have never heard of the ethics or high standards of sport, or even dreamed that a fish should be given a fighting chance for life. If such men were not attended to, and taught, they would go out with four or five hand-lines or small ropes and their definition of sport would be to see *how many* fish they could bring in. In 1886 this was the every-day disgrace of the most beautiful sea angling region in the world. Boats went out with a number of hand-lines and tons of yellowtail were brought in, many to be hung up and photographed, then thrown into the channel. It was to stop this gross over-fishing, and to inculcate an idea of sport as it is understood by civilized people, by gentlemen, that the Tuna Club is organized for gentlemen, and it is a matter of gratification to the distinguished men who joined the Club and lent to it their moral support, that a complete and utter change has been brought about at this greatest of the world's angling centres."

Indeed, within a few years of its founding, the Club had a nifty little clubhouse on the water at Avalon. It was a place where white gentlemen from around the world could come and fish with other white gentlemen (except for the Club fishing guides, some of whom were non-white, and all of whom were non-gentlemen), and drink and converse with similarly minded gentlemen while being served by "Japanese boys." And, even better, the gentlemen could do all this in an environment that was free—except between the hours of 10 a.m. and 4 p.m.—of women. And that was because women were not allowed to be members of the Tuna Club. And because women were barred from the Club's scaly bosom, one can only assume that it was because it was deemed impossible to "inculcate an idea of sport as it is understood by civilized people, by gentlemen" in the fairer sex.

Cryptotrema corallinum
Gilbert, 1890
Deepwater Blenny

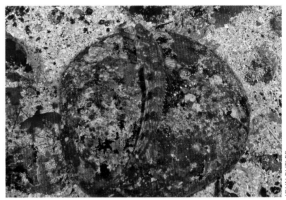

ETYMOLOGY AND COLLOQUIAL NAME: *Cryptotrema* means "concealed" and "pore" in Greek (referring to the hidden lateral line pores on the anterior part of the body) and *corallinum*, to a calcareous alga. This species is also called "deepwater kelpfish."

THE BASICS: Maximum Length: 12.7 cm (5 in) TL. The Ranges: Off Cook Point, San Miguel Island to Bahia San Quintin (northern Baja California). They are common as far north as San Miguel Island. 24–195 m (78–639 ft) and, in Southern California, mostly in 55–95 m (180–312 ft). Larvae: hatching length = less than 3.9 mm, flexion length = 8.5–9.5 mm, transformation length = greater than 1.2 cm (0.5 in).

SALIENT CHARACTERS: These are elongated fish with very long dorsal and anal fins and thin red, orange, and yellow stripes against a white, gray, or brownish background. There are usually a number of small and dark blotches on the mid-side.

LIFE HISTORY: Not much is known about this species. They seem to live mostly around the rock-sand interfaces of reefs (often on the sand within sight of the rocks), frequently in the same general habitat as blackeye goby. These are solitary animals and, judging from the fact that they occasionally lock jaws, probably territorial. Deepwater blennies appear to spawn from about August–February. Presumably, the females lay eggs in nests, but this is just speculation.

FAMILY CLINIDAE—Kelp Blennies

The kelp blennies, in our area usually called kelpfishes, are nearshore, marine, and mostly temperate fishes, found circumglobally. Some clinids are oviparous (the females lay eggs in nests that are guarded by males), other species are viviparous, and larvae are planktonic. There are about 26 genera, 85 species, and four live within our range.

I'm not completely convinced that anyone can tell apart all of the Gibbonsia *with 100% accuracy. So here are four nice photographs of one or more species.*

Gibbonsia elegans
(Cooper, 1864)
Spotted Kelpfish

ETYMOLOGY: *Gibbonsia* is named for William Peters Gibbons (1812–1897), one of the early naturalist members of the California Academy of Sciences and *elegans* is Latin for "elegant."

THE BASICS: Maximum Length: 16 cm (6 in) SL. Maximum Weight: 40 gr (2 oz). The Ranges: Piedras Blancas Point (Central California) to Bahia Magdalena (southern Baja California), including Isla Guadalupe (central Baja California); abundant from at least Piedras Blancas (central California) to about Punta Abreojos (southern Baja California). Intertidal to 56 m (185 ft), mostly from the lower intertidal to 30 m (98 ft). Larvae: hatching length = about 4.5 mm, flexion length = about 6.5–8 mm, transformation length = about 2.1–2.2 cm (0.8–0.9 in). Length-weight parameters (SL, mm, gr): (sexes combined) W = $0.000006L^{3.171}$ (Miller et al. 2008a).

CAPTAIN FISH BLOOD

What happens when a naughty, naughty actor and a respected ichthyologist team up on a research cruise to Mexico? About what you'd expect.

It all happened like this. Once upon a time in Tinseltown, Errol Flynn, he of *Captain Blood*, *The Adventures of Robin Hood*, and *I Hope My Trusted Lawyer Jerry Geisler Can Get Me Out of this Statutory Rape Charge*, contacted Dr. Carl Hubbs, he of *Let's Count the Gill Rakers of Another 1,500 Specimens Just to Make Sure*. The actor had an interesting proposition. How would Hubbs like to accompany Flynn, his wife Nora, and his father, the marine biologist Theodore Thomson Flynn, on a collecting cruise to Mexico aboard Erroll's 118-foot schooner *Zaca*? The ship would be

sailing in 3 weeks. The offer was too good to refuse and Hubbs spent that time gathering up all of the collecting and surveying paraphernalia so dear to a marine scientist's heart. However, while Hubbs was busily boxing up formaldehyde, spears, and netting, distressing events were afoot. Most crucially, virtually all of the *Zaca*'s crew quit and Flynn hired what appears to have been quite the grotesquery to replace them. Once at sea, what transpired was, I suppose, a matter of some contention, but here are a few of the events that are said to have occurred. There was much drunkenness and a considerable amount of recreational drug use; a pregnant Nora may have been punched by Errol; the body odor of one of the party members was so offensive he was thrown overboard and dragged behind the vessel; and one of the crew shot himself in the foot with a harpoon, necessitating immediate surgery by Errol and associates. That was just in the first few weeks. At that point, things started heading south, what with the crew mutinying, Errol perhaps threatening to commit suicide, the *Zaca* developing engine trouble, and Hubbs and some of the other party members having to take it upon themselves to navigate to Acapulco.

Ultimately, Hubbs got some interesting observations on flyingfishes and collected a fair number of fishes, but the results were likely less than he might have wished. Three fishes were named for Flynn and Company: *Gibbonsia erroli* (now considered to be *Gibbonsia elegans*), *Gibbonsia norae* (now *G. montereyensis*), and the putative subspecies *Paraclinus integripinnis zacae*.

When it was all said and done, the *Daily Variety* headline might well have read: "Flynn, Gin, and Sin = Min. Fins."

SALIENT CHARACTERS: On dead ones, look for scales on the caudal fin. Spotteds have 1–3 dark eyespots on the back. Carol Stepien et al. (1988) did an exhaustive study on coloration of this species. Basically, all fish can come in red, green, and brown and fish usually match their backgrounds. Females tend to have a yellow or tan belly (ripe females have a yellow belly) and males and immature females have white ones. Spotteds will slowly change color to match their backgrounds. For a trip down memory lane, find a copy of Metz (1912) for another extensive description of colors and patterns.

LIFE HISTORY: Young-of-the-year (as small as 1.1 cm, 0.4 in, SL) settle out in very shallow waters amid algae. Spotted kelpfish live in rocks and heavy plant cover (e.g., surfgrass, eelgrass, and red and brown algae), along the open coast and in bays. They spend most of their time motionless and hunkered down. This is neat—females tend to be found in shallower waters than males. Off Palos Verdes (Southern California), Williams (1954) found that fish living in the intertidal and down to 2.4 m (8 ft) were almost all females, but by 16–30 m (53–98 ft), the ratio was about 50-50. Along with the reef finspot, this is the dominant cryptic species on a number of very shallow reefs in Southern California. Spotted kelpfish are extremely territorial and fish seem to have a home pool that they retreat to at low tide. Spotteds are active during the day.

Females grow larger than males. Based on larval surveys, spotteds spawn throughout the year, with a spring peak. Mean fecundity is 2,250 eggs. Females lay their eggs among short seaweeds and Limbaugh (1955) [not Rush, mind you, so we can probably believe this] notes: "The female lays her eggs periodically, getting astride the egg mass and undulating her body stiffly as she adds to the egg mass. Occasionally she gets off the egg mass and pushes seaweed into it with her head. The male brings his vent as close to the female as possible without pushing her…The egg mass is white and the total mass less than 1 inch in diameter. The male remains and guards the nest." Spotted kelpfish feed on a wide range of small and benthic prey. Gammarid amphipods and isopods are often most important, but snails, crabs, caprellid amphipods, polychaetes, shrimps, algae, and the occasional fish are all preyed upon.

RELATIONSHIPS: Spotted kelpfish may be most closely related to crevice kelpfish.

FISHERY: All *Gibbonsia* are on occasion caught by pier fishermen.

WILLIAM PETERS GIBBONS

Along with his seemingly fanatical devotion to the subject of the live-bearing perch, William P. Gibbons was also interested in a wide range of other topics, including redwoods, insects, weather patterns, and how East Coast scientists were ripping off California researchers. Gibbons must have been one feisty dude, as he seemed to have been constantly upset by one thing or another. He resigned from the California Academy of Sciences at least twice and once was asked to resign as corresponding secretary of that body. He refused.

At a CAS meeting on 30 January 1854, he made a motion that "A committee of three be appointed to prepare a memorial [request] to the Board of Supervisors of San Francisco, the object of which shall be to encourage the cultivation of shade trees within the city limits by offering a premium for every tree, which shall be planted and found to be in flourishing condition within a specified time," which seems a very reasonable request indeed. He then went on to add a strange caveat: "The *Ailanthus* to be excluded from the list as being unworthy of cultivation." So what is the *Ailanthus*, and why is it unworthy of cultivation? According to *A California Flora* (P. A. Munz and D. D. Keck, University of California Press, 1968), *Ailanthus*, also called "tree of heaven," is a 15- to 60-foot tree with large leaves that is native to Asia and has naturalized in California. At first reading, there is nothing particularly disturbing, dangerous, or grotesque about it and it's kind of hard to see why Gibbons was having ants in his pants about a tree. But wait, Munz and Keck also note that the tree was "Introduced in early mining days by Chinese."

Good grief, yet another example of the anti-Chinese feeling that was rampant in California at the time. Hey, not only don't we want *you* here, we don't want *your trees* here either. And we're not very fond of your intense work ethic, your cuisine is weird, and your habit of keeping clean all the time makes us nervous. So when you go back to China take all that stuff with you. Well, except if you do that, who's going to grow the crops and do the grunt work we don't want to do? And we've kind of grown fond of cashew chicken and green tea. So, okay, you can stay, but we won't let you bring in any Chinese women, because, well, you know. *And no Ailanthus trees in San Francisco.*

Gibbonsia montereyensis

Hubbs, 1927

Crevice Kelpfish

ETYMOLOGY: *Gibbonsia* is named for William Peters Gibbons (1812–1897), one of the early naturalist members of the California Academy of Sciences, and the species was named *montereyensis* 'cause that is where Carl Hubbs captured it.

THE BASICS: Maximum Length: 13.9 cm (6 in) SL. The Ranges: British Columbia to Bahia San Carlos (central Baja California), including Isla Guadalupe. They are fairly common at least from Barkley Sound (Vancouver Island) to Central California, around many of the Southern California islands, Isla Guadalupe, and northern and central Baja California to maybe Punta Cabras (around 30°26'N). Intertidal to 37 m (121 ft), mostly in 7.6 m (25 ft) and less. Larvae: hatching length = 6 mm.

SALIENT CHARACTERS: When you have a dead one in hand, this species' best diagnostic characters are 1) a lack of scales at the base of, or on, the caudal fin and 2) the dorsal fin rays, toward the posterior end of the fin, are more widely spaced than other rays. Crevices are reddish or purplish, with spots, stripes, or plain. Maybe it is just a lack of experience, but I am not a big believer that you can tell the different *Gibbonsia* species apart underwater, so *bonne chance*, you are just on your own.

LIFE HISTORY: This, like other *Gibbonsia*, is an algae, eelgrass, and rocky reef dweller, spending its days being very, very cryptic. In Southern California, young-of-the-year settle from the plankton to nearshore waters at 1.6 cm (0.6 in) SL or less, from April–October (mostly from May–July).

Crevice kelpfish live at least 3 years and spawn from March–May. Jeff Marliave (1975), with his head underwater in Barkley Sound (Vancouver Island), reported seeing egg masses in April. He notes they were located on "The top of a boulder on a moderately exposed shore. The masses (about 100 eggs each) were together in coralline algae, with *Polyneura latissima* [a red alga] blades matted over them and stuck together with adhesive threads." Crevice kelpfish feed heavily on gammarid amphipods, polychaetes and sipunculids, along with crabs, shrimps, isopods, snails, chitons, pycnogonids, and some algae. Pigeon guillemots eat them.

RELATIONSHIPS: This species is likely most closely related to spotted kelpfish.

Heterostichus rostratus

Girard, 1854

Giant Kelpfish

ETYMOLOGY: *Heterostichus* means "different" and "rank" (alluding to the first five dorsal spines being wider apart and separated from the rest) and *rostratus* is "long-nosed" in Latin.

THE BASICS: Maximum Length: 61 cm (24 in) TL. The Ranges: British Columbia to Cabo San Lucas (southern Baja California), including Isla Guadalupe (central Baja California). They are common from Point Conception (California) to at least Bahia Magdalena (southern Baja California). Intertidal to 40 m (132 ft). While they occasionally live in tide pools, they are most abundant from the shallow subtidal to perhaps 25 m (82 ft). Eggs: 1.2–1.4 mm. Larvae: hatching length = 5.1–6.2 mm, flexion length = about 7.5–10 mm, transformation length = about 3–4.5 cm (1–2 in). Age-length relationships are figured in Stepien (1986). Length-weight parameters (TL, cm, gr): (sexes combined) $W = 0.0031L^{3.243}$ (Stepien 1986).

A young one just fresh from the plankton.

KEVIN LEE

SALIENT CHARACTERS: Giant kelpfish have long bodies, pointy snouts, and forked tails. They come in three colors: green, red, and brown and an individual's color usually matches its background. Males tend to be brown and occasionally olive-green, females can be any of the three colors. Juveniles are either green or brown. While most colors are confined to the skin, green fish often have green muscle. Along with variations in color, these fish come in four patterns: plain, barred, striped, and mottled. Females are most often plain or barred; males are more often striped or mottled. Both sexes can change pattern within a few seconds during courtship or territorial displays. Fish living in wide-bladed algae, such as giant kelp, are most often plain or somewhat striped, while those dwelling in finer algae, such as red algae and sargassum, are often mottled or barred. Some fish, particularly females, have a white bar that runs from tip of snout along the head and between the eyes. Both a red spot and white patches may occur on the sides of fish, particularly females.

LIFE HISTORY: Young-of-the-year recruit to nearshore plants at as small as 2.5 cm (1 in) TL and sometimes form aggregations of hundreds of individuals. Once they take up a benthic existence, giant kelpfish are virtually always found amid plants (e.g., brown, green, and red algae, eelgrass, and surfgrass). They are common in both bays (where they tend to live in eelgrass) and on the outer coast. Carol Stepien (1987) found that these fish are quite territorial and will defend plants against other giant kelpfish. She also noted: "Females are more common in shallow waters (0 to 8 m) [26 ft] as well as in deeper waters (13 to 25 m) [43–82 ft]...males more common in ...9–12 m [30–39 ft]" and "Females are more numerous among green and red plants...males were more often than females only in the brown algae *Sargassum*, *Cystoseira*, and *Zonaria*, which are located in the mid-depth range. This mid-depth range was the most frequent location of kelpfish nests, which the male guard." You will often see them hanging vertically in the kelp canopy or in mid-depths, often with their heads down, waving rhythmically with the surge.

Giant kelpfish live to about 5 years old and females may live somewhat longer than males. Both sexes mature at about 18.6 cm (7 in) TL and 1–1.5 years old. They spawn throughout the year, perhaps peaking in the spring. A female will spawn all of her eggs at one time (it takes 40–60 minutes) and will spawn more than once per year. Brown females most often produce brown eggs, but sometimes lay red ones. Red females produce either brown or red eggs. The eggs are adhesive and are

KAWIKA CHETRON

attached to red or brown algae. Stepien (1986) wrote: "The male parent hid in the overlying clump of brown algae, emerging to chase away intruding fishes. Male kelpfish were observed to defend their nests against other kelpfish, sheephead, and rock wrasse. Each nest contains the eggs of a single female...the male kelpfish chases away the female [after she lays the eggs]... all eggs in a given nest were either red or brown and remained that color throughout development. Nest and egg color did not always match. Eggs hatched in 12 to 17 days at 18°C (64°F), the largest number hatching in 13 days. Nests contained 400 to 1,200 eggs, for an average of 700. Two week old larvae began swimming in schools." Schooling generally ceases at about 2 months as the fish begin to associate more and more closely with algae. Mysid shrimps, isopods, gammarid amphipods, and other small shrimps are often most important, but they also eat caprellid amphipods, polychaetes, copepods, crabs, snails, and the occasional fish. These fish are mostly daytime feeders, often darting out from among algal cover to capture prey. Predators include cabezons, kelp bass, olive rockfish, soupfin sharks, Brandt's cormorants, and California sea lions.

FISHERY: Native Americans occasionally ate this species. Historically, giant kelpfish were only rarely landed in commercial catches. Rocky shore and boat anglers commonly catch them.

RELATIONSHIPS: Giants are most closely related to the various species of *Gibbonsia*.

MISCELLANY: Giant kelpfish will, on occasion, clean other species, such as giant sea bass.

REMARKS: Giant kelpfish can change color. For instance, when placed in a red setting in an aquarium, green and brown adult females go red in 2–3 weeks. On the other hand, under similar conditions, males and juveniles do not change color. Given time and background motivation, most adult females will rotate among all three colors. In contrast, a few males will grudgingly switch from brown to olive-green, while juveniles can alternate between green and brown.

OTHER SPECIES

Gibbonsia metzi
Hubbs, 1927

Striped Kelpfish

Striped kelpfish grow to 23.5 cm (9 in) TL. They live from Vancouver Island to Punta Rompiente (central Baja California) and from the intertidal down to 9 m (30 ft). Striped kelpfish live among algae and eelgrass in the nearshore, occasionally in tide pools, but more commonly in shallow subtidal waters. Young-of-the-year (as small as 1.2 cm, 0.5 in, SL) recruit to algae. Williams (1957), poking about the intertidal at San Simeon (Central California), found that striped kelpfish were capable of homing to specific tide pools. Striped kelpfish live to 8 years old and females grow larger than males. Females reportedly spawn at least between October–May, peaking in February and March. As with other *Gibbonsia*, striped kelpfish dine on a range of small benthic animals. Isopods, gammarid amphipods, and crabs are often consumed, and copepods, shrimps, limpets, slipper shells, fish eggs, hermit crabs, mysid shrimps, and polychaetes round out the diet. Predators include Chinook salmon. As one might expect, this species is most closely related to spotted and crevice kelpfishes. Length-weight parameters (SL, mm, gr): (sexes combined) $W = 0.000109L^{2.5704}$ (Burge and Schultz 1973).

Paraclinus integripinnis
(Smith, 1880)

Reef Finspot

Reef finspots grow to 7 cm (3 in) TL. They are found from Santa Cruz Island and Naples, Santa Barbara County (Southern California), to Bahia Almejas (southern Baja California), typically from about Santa Monica Bay (Southern California) to the Bahia Magdalena complex (southern Baja California). While they have been captured from the intertidal to 15 m (50 ft), most live in the lower intertidal and down to at least 10 m (33 ft). This is a reclusive fish that usually hides away amid coralline algae and small invertebrates, in rocky crevices and eelgrass. They can be quite common in backwaters (e.g., Alamitos and San Diego bays, and Bahia San Quintin) as well as on the outer coast. Young-of-the-year recruit to very shallow waters during summer months at sizes at least as small as 1.5 cm (0.6 in) SL. They are active during the day and quiescent at night. Reef finspots live about 2 years. In my studies, the smallest mature female was 3.7 cm (2 in) TL and I have found ripe females from May–October. Fecundity ranges from 76 eggs in a 3.7 cm (1.5 in) fish to 701 eggs in one that was 6.1 cm (2 in) TL. Females reportedly attach their eggs to bottom algae and males guard them until they hatch. Reef finspots focus much of their attention on gammarid amphipods and isopods, however polychaetes and algae are also occasionally consumed. Copper rockfish and, one imagines, other relatively large fish eaters, eat them. Fish of the genus *Paraclinus* are likely most closely related to the sargassum blenny, *Exerpes asper*. Eggs: 0.9–1 mm. Larvae: hatching length = 3.8–4 mm, flexion length = 6–about 6.9 mm, transformation length = between 9 and less than 14 mm (0.5 in). Length-weight parameters (TL, cm, gr): $W = 0.0067L^{3.387}$ (Love unpubl.).

FAMILY CHAENOPSIDAE—Tube Blennies

The tube blennies are mostly tropical and marine benthic fishes that live in the eastern Pacific. There are 14 genera and about 91 species. Ten species live within our range and four of these are found as far north as Southern California. They are oviparous with eggs in nests and planktonic larvae.

Chaenopsis alepidota
(Gilbert, 1890)

Orangethroat Pikeblenny

ETYMOLOGY: *Chaenopsis* means "to yawn" and "face" in Greek and *alepidota* is Greek for "scaleless."

THE BASICS: Maximum Length: 15.2 cm (6 in) TL. The Ranges: Point Sur (Central California) to Gulf of California. Orangethroats are rare in Central California and only patch-ily found in Southern California; here they seem to be most abundant along some of the islands (to at least as far west as Anacapa Island). The only known mainland population in Southern California is in King Harbor (Redondo Beach). 1–23 m (3–75 ft).

SALIENT CHARACTERS: With an elongated body and

A clearly grumpy male makes known its displeasure.

pointed snout, orangethroats are a distinctive species. Basic colors lean to browns and greens, peppered with numerous white spots. Males have an expanded dorsal fin and those in breeding condition have a bright orange or orange-red slash running backwards from the mouth.

LIFE HISTORY: This poorly known species lives in tubeworm beds and (less often) in burrows in coarse sand. In the Gulf of California, young-of-the-year (at as small as 1.5 cm, 0.6 in, TL) settle to shallow waters in the spring. In Southern California, we see all size classes primarily among worm tubes. These are pugnacious fish, and males will lock jaws over possession of shel-tering sites. When sufficiently upset, orangethroats rear up and open their cavernous mouths and flare their branchiostegals, giving the fish a kind of freaky cobra/lizard quality. One study found that fish in the Gulf of California are most active in the morning, when they come out of their sheltering holes and search for food. There are two populations of these animals, one found on the Pacific Coast and the other in the Gulf of California; there appears to be little gene flow between them.

The lifespan of this pikeblenny is unknown, although it likely lives just a few years. A study in Bahia Magdalena (southern Baja California) found high densities of larvae throughout the year, with perhaps a spring–summer peak. On the other hand, fish living in more temperate waters may have a more discrete spawning season. Orangethroats feed on small crustaceans (e.g., mysid shrimps and amphipods), polychaetes, and fishes.

FISHERY: They are occasionally caught by anglers.

KEVIN LEE

Neoclinus blanchardi

Girard, 1858

Sarcastic Fringehead

A singularly bad-tempered fish.

ETYMOLOGY: *Neoclinus* is a combination of "new" (in Greek) and "*Clinus*" and *blanchardi* honors Dr. S.B. Blanchard, who collected this species in San Diego Bay in 1849. There is an "SB Blanchard" listed as leaving for San Francisco on the Brig *Taranto*, from Boston, Massachusetts, on 30 March 1849. Beyond that, and the fact that the fish was caught by Blanchard at San Diego, that's all I can find about the good doctor.

A young one amid sand dollars.

Sarcastic fringehead, sarcastic fringehead...I love that name so much. Sarcastic fringehead. A good name for a rock group, a good name for a video game company, heck, a good name for a massage parlor.

THE BASICS: Maximum Length: 30.5 cm (12 in) TL. The Ranges: Bodega Bay (Northern California) to Isla Cedros (central Baja California). It's probably uncommon north of Point Conception (California), common in Southern California, and its abundance off Baja California is unknown. 3–73 m (10–239 ft). Eggs: 0.9–1 mm. Larvae: flexion length = about 7.5–8.5 mm, transformation length = between 2.9 and less than 5.5 cm (1–2 in). Length-weight parameters (TL, cm, gr): W = 0.009L$^{3.003}$ (Love unpubl.).

SALIENT CHARACTERS: Goodness, what a great fish. Sarcastics are elongated with a great big head, huge mouth and jaws (hugest in males), often yellow at the rear of the jaw (males), and two blue, brown, or dark spots on the anterior end of the dorsal fin. They come in almost black, browns, grays, purples, greens, and reds with assorted blobs and blotches of reds, greens, lights, and darks. Metz (1912) reported an entirely blue one.

LIFE HISTORY: Sarcastics are solitary, and extremely territorial, benthic fish that live in stuff. They appear to be singularly cavalier about what that stuff is, as they have been found in (among other things) shells, rock crevices, holes in the muddy sides of submarine canyons, worm tubes, and beer bottles. Most fish live on the open coast, but an occasional one frequents quiet backwaters. They must move around at least a bit, because my associate Shane Anderson put some empty wavy top-shells out on sand in 24 m (80 ft) of water, way away from any hard structure, and within a few days each shell was occupied by an adult fringehead. David Andrew reports that they come out of their shelters at night.

Based on larval surveys, sarcastics spawn throughout the year, although heaviest spawning may be in the spring and summer. In a study I conducted, the smallest mature female was 12 cm (5 in) TL and they carried between 712–9,732 eggs. Females lay eggs (described either as orange or almost colorless) in shells, holes in rocks, and other hard stuff, and males guard them. Walter Marti, observing males guarding nests underneath the Newport Pier (Southern California) saw lots of fights. In one instance, a male drove another one off a nest and the victor moved in and ate the loser's eggs. Typical behavior? Who knows? Almost no one has thought to check out what sarcastic fringeheads eat. One small study found crabs and shrimps in their guts.

KEVIN LEE

FISHERIES: Anglers catch them with some frequency.

REMARKS: Here is what Jordan and Evermann (1898) say about sarcastic fringeheads: "A remarkable fish." Okay, it's not Shelley or Wilde, but remember, J. and E. were a couple of pretty uptight guys. "A remarkable fish" was florid prose for a scientific paper in 1898.

These are just the most aggressive fish around. If they grew any larger than 12 inches no one would go in the water. There are legions of divers who, when incautiously swimming by a fringehead ranchero, have been lunged out or even nipped.

Neoclinus stephensae

Hubbs, 1953

Yellowfin Fringehead

Clearly the Punk Species of the Pacific Coast and recently nominated as the Marine Fish Most Likely to have Its Genitals Pierced.

ETYMOLOGY: *Neoclinus* is a combination of "new" (in Greek) and "*Clinus*" and *stephensae* refers to Katherine "Kate" Stephens (1851 or 1853–1954) who first collected this species.

THE BASICS: Maximum Length: 10 cm (4 in) TL. The Ranges: San Francisco (Northern California) to Punta San Hipolito (central Baja California). A very abundant fish in Southern California and pretty common from at least Monterey Bay to northern Baja California. Intertidal to 27 m (90 ft). Larvae: hatching length = less than 4.3 mm, flexion length = about 7–9 mm, transformation length = about 2.1 to less than 4.8 cm (0.8–2 in). Length-weight parameters (TL, cm, gr): $W = 0.0095L^{2.824}$ (Love unpubl.).

SALIENT CHARACTERS: A head filled with three pairs of multi-branch cirri is the key character. They come in all kinds of colors, from scarlet, orange, and brown to olive, with all kinds of body spots and fin striping. Unlike sarcastics and onespots, yellowfins do not have eyespots on the dorsal fin.

LIFE HISTORY: Yellowfins live in empty shells and holes in mud or rocks and you can usually see them with just their little frilly heads exposed. Data from a little study that I did implied that females mature at about 4.9 cm (2 in) TL and produce between 94–421 eggs. I found ripe females in every month and others have collected larvae in every month. It is likely that this fringehead lays eggs in nests, with males guarding the eggs until they hatch.

KATHERINE STEPHENS

Born in England, Ms. Stephens had an early interest in natural history and when she moved to the San Diego area in 1890 she quickly became a leading local (and later national) malacologist and paleontologist. Ms. Stephens was for many decades intimately involved with the San Diego Society of Natural History and the San Diego Natural History Museum. Of particular importance to the yellowfin fringehead story, Ms. Stephens taught natural history to many students in the San Diego area, students that included budding ichthyologist Carl Hubbs, the father of Clark Hubbs, who was the guy who described this species, don't you know.

JOHN YASAKI

JESSIE ALSTATT

OTHER SPECIES

Neoclinus uninotatus
Hubbs, 1953
Onespot Fringehead

Onespots grow to be 25 cm (10 in) TL. They range from Bodega Bay (Northern California) to northern Baja California, and are reasonably common at least from Monterey Bay to Southern California. They are found from the surf zone to 55 m (180 ft). This is a very territorial species (both sexes) that live in all kinds of burrows, shells, crevices, and in hollows under structures. At least in Southern California, spawning may occur throughout the year. The smallest mature female that I have found was 11 cm (4 in) TL. Females produce between 598–6,472 eggs at a time. The orange eggs are cemented to the upper inside surfaces of nests and then guarded by males. I see them caught off piers fairly often. Length-weight parameters (TL, cm, gr): $W = 0.0044L^{3.216}$ (Love unpubl.).

FAMILY BLENNIIDAE—Combtooth Blennies

Combtooth blennies are a large group of mostly marine, and primarily warm-water, benthic fishes, found throughout the world. There are about 390 species, in 57 genera, with seven species within our range, four of which have found their way into Southern California. They are oviparous, lay eggs in nests and, depending on the species either the male or both parents tend the eggs. The larvae are planktonic. Combtooths go back at least to the Middle Eocene (50 million years ago or more) of Italy. Many of the tropical eastern Pacific species are illustrated with keys in Fischer et al. (1995) and the figures of the three California *Hypsoblennius* in Miller and Lea (1972) are particularly useful. Check out Patzner et al. (2009) for tonnage about this group.

Here is what Losey (1968) has to say about the three species of *Hypsoblennius* on the West Coast: "All males possess a pigmented urogenital papilla [a tube extending from the urogenital opening], and adult males have pads on the first two anal spines...The adult males are usually somewhat larger than the adult female...Both sexes...are territorial and, except during their sexual phase, defend the territory against all intruders, including other species...males guard nests."

MAYBE IT'S BECAUSE WE FLUORIDATE THE WATER

Look, I know that, as I write these words, we are just coming out of a time of "Don't Ask, Don't Tell," and I know you haven't asked, but I think I should probably tell.

Back in 1969, George Losey showed that, when mating with females, males of at least two California *Hypsoblennius* species [*H. jenkinsi* and *H. gentilis*] produce a pheromone that attracts other ripe males. That's right, we are not talking about guys attracting other females, here we have guys attracting guys. And never mind that the hypothesis is that these other guys are coming around hoping to find females in the vicinity; the point is that we can't have guys attracting other guys. I would, of course, ask that you keep all this under your metaphorical hat, because if it becomes widely known, it is likely that both species will be asked to leave California waters. Because, we can't have fishes that have chosen this kind of lifestyle living in the same waters where our children swim. After all, this is not Canada or Argentina.

Hypsoblennius gentilis

(Girard, 1854)

Bay Blenny

ETYMOLOGY: *Hypsoblennius* is a combination of "high" in Greek and "*Blennius*" and *gentilis* means "related" in Latin.

THE BASICS: Maximum Length: 14.7 cm (6 in) TL. The Ranges: Monterey Bay to Gulf of California, mostly from the Santa Barbara Channel southward. Intertidal to 25 m (82 ft), commonly down to about 10 m (33 ft). In warmer areas, such as around Cabo San Lucas, they tend to stay in deeper and colder waters (down to about 25 m, 82 ft). Eggs: 0.6 mm. Larvae: hatching length = 2.3–2.6 mm, flexion length = 5.2–5.9 mm, transformation length = about 1.6–2.1 cm (0.6–0.8 in). Von Bertalanffy parameters (SL, mm): (sexes combined) L_∞ = 170.7, k = 0.0685, t_0 = -3.68 (Stephens et al. 1970). Length-weight parameters (TL, cm, gr): (sexes combined) W = $0.01122L^{2.97916}$ (Balart et al. 2006).

SALIENT CHARACTERS: The key feature here is the shape of the cirrus over the eye. In bay blennies, the cirrus is a single flap and the back edge is serrated. Losey (1968) notes: "The males have a higher profile and a very much longer supraorbital cirrus, that of the female is reduced to a mere stud. Females have a more or less conspicuous metallic black spot on the second dorsal spine, followed by a red streak." Colors are variable, as this species can quickly change color to match background.

LIFE HISTORY: In Southern California, bay blennies recruit from the plankton to substrate from about August–October at lengths of 1.2–1.4 cm (0.5 in) SL. True to its name, off the Pacific Coast, bay blennies mostly live in bays and other sheltered areas. In these waters, it is particularly common in eelgrass and other plants, mussel beds, floats, and other structures. In the Gulf of California, this species lives not only in bays (often in mangroves), but also in rocky tide pools, sheltered cobble beaches, or even rocky subtidal areas. This is a territorial and cryptic fish that is active only during the day. Losey (1968) has lots and lots about its behavior.

Bay blennies live at least 5 years and probably somewhat longer. Larval surveys imply they spawn throughout the year, although the vast majority of spawning activity (at least in Southern California) takes place in the summer and early fall. Females lay eggs in nests on hard substrate and males guard the fertilized eggs until they hatch. Bay blennies are omnivorous grazers, feeding on such benthic invertebrates as crustaceans, burrowing anemones, tunicates, hydroids, and polychaetes, as well as algae.

Hypsoblennius gilberti

(Jordan, 1882)

Rockpool Blenny

A pugnacious fish, living the swaggering, but ultimately doomed, life of Studs Lonigan.

ETYMOLOGY: *Hypsoblennius* is a combination of "high" in Greek and "*Blennius*" and *gilberti* honors Charles Henry Gilbert (1859–1928), who, along with David Starr Jordan, was the greatest describer of Pacific Coast fishes.

THE BASICS: Maximum Length: 17 cm (7 in) TL. The Ranges: Morro Bay (Central California) to Bahia Magdalena (southern Baja California). They are abundant between about Point Conception (California) and southern Baja California. Usually intertidal and subtidal to 18 m (60 ft), mostly in the mid-intertidal and down to depths of 5 m (16 ft). Larvae: hatching length = about 3 mm, flexion length = about 6–7.5 mm, transformation length = about 2.1–2.2 cm (0.8-0.9 in). Von Bertalanffy parameters (SL, mm): (sexes combined) L_∞ = 154.5, k = 0.1381, t_0 = -3.3029 (Stephens et al. 1970). Length-weight parameters (SL, mm, gr): (sexes combined) W = $0.000019L^{3.044}$ (Dayneko 1975).

CHARLES HENRY GILBERT

Gilbert, trained by David Starr Jordan in the Midwest, eventually was brought by him to Stanford University. Over the course of 145 papers, Gilbert was the author or co-author of descriptions of about 117 new genera and 620 new fish species. Early on, most of the papers Gilbert wrote were listed as written by "Jordan and Gilbert," although it is likely that Gilbert did the legwork and Jordan got the credit (not an unusual occurrence in those days). For instance, by the age of 24, Gilbert was the author of over 80 papers, and in almost all of them he was the second author. At some point, Gilbert appears to have said the hell with it, broke off the "co-authorship" relationship, and proceeded to publish most papers under his name alone. Gilbert was the ichthyologist in charge of a number of collecting expeditions, to such places as Alaska, Mexico, Central America, Japan, and Hawai'i. During these cruises, it is clear that he was, at times, simply maniacal about getting the work done. The Hawaiian expedition of 1902, aboard the United States government research vessel *Albatross*, provides a clear example of this. During the course of that cruise, Gilbert seems to have had a mini-meltdown, preserved in letters to David Starr Jordan, in which he charges that the ship's captain, Commander Chauncy Thomas, Jr., was not getting the job done. For his part, Thomas, in letters to the Office of the Commissioner of Fisheries, strikes a clearly frustrated tone writing: "Now the Angel Gabriel could not satisfy Dr. Gilbert. He is insatiable."

Gilbert was, by all accounts, a man simply stewing in high standards. His descriptions of fishes were meticulous, his teaching style was rigorous, and he was clearly not a man to be crossed. Regarding Gilbert, David Starr Jordan wrote: "Tobacco and alcoholics he did not use, and apparently he never felt the slightest temptation to any form of dissipation." In 1913, regarding the possibility of San Francisco as the site of a biological congress, Gilbert wrote Jordan: "I doubt the advisability of trying to coax the Congress to San Francisco. They [the city fathers] haven't the decency enough to clean up the city, preferring to share the profits of vice. I consider San Francisco the shame of the state and the Nation, and have no desire to spread its fame" (Dunn 1997). As might be expected, this stick-up-where-the-sun-don't-shine attitude carried over to his family. When Carl, his only son, became a lawyer against his wishes, Gilbert did not speak to the man for six years.

Clearly, here is man who could have used just a smidge of dissipation.

SALIENT CHARACTERS: A round-headed little fish is our rockpool blenny. Rockpools can rapidly change colors to match their backgrounds. They are gray or olive-brown and have multistranded cirri (each strand reaching almost to the base of the cirrus) above each eye. If you look at them from the side, you will see a little notch behind the eye. During spawning season, females turn golden and males become a sort of velvety-black.

LIFE HISTORY: Rockpool blennies are small, cryptic, and benthic fish that live primarily in tide pools and secondarily in the shallow intertidal. They settle at 1.8–2.1 cm (0.7–0.8 in) SL in late summer and early fall, apparently entirely to the rocky intertidal. Adults are most frequently associated with crevices and holes in rocks, on open wave-exposed areas, along semi-protected shores (perhaps most commonly), and occasionally in sloughs and other embayments. One study found that the average population in a Southern California tide pool was 1.6 fish/m². Rockpools have home pools that they return to when displaced up to about 12 m (40 ft) away. Intertidal fish appear to move shoreward at high tide, retreating to these home pools at low tide. At the commencement of the spawning season, the males create under-rock nests by cleaning rocky areas of debris. Then, as noted by Losey (1968): "After a series of courtship behavior patterns, the female will enter the nest and deposit her eggs on the prepared rock surface while the male undergoes a strong mating action that suggests ejaculation. The females are then driven from the nest. The males may spawn with several females, and will guard the nest until the eggs are hatched... The eggs of *Hypsoblennius* and most other blenniids are fastened to the substrate by a fibrous, adhesive pad on the egg." Nelson (1970) goes on to state that females lay eggs to "the wall of the shelter and depositing the eggs a few at a time. The first eggs are deposited at the top of the shelter. After oviposition the female is driven from the nest...The male remains in the

KEVIN LEE

nest for most of the day...Courtship may continue throughout this period as long as there is room in the shelter for new eggs."

Tidepools live to at least 9 years old. Females mature at as small as 5.1 cm (2 in) SL, at the end of their first year. Spawning occurs between March–October, perhaps with a peak in July and August. Larval surveys imply there may be a very low level of spawning throughout the year. Females are batch spawners (producing 685–3,209 eggs at a time) and spawn perhaps three times in a season. The fertilized eggs are purplish-pink and the larvae hatch in 5–18 days. Rockpools eat a wide variety of benthic prey (e.g., limpets, chitons, algae, polychaetes, gammarid amphipods, sponges, and barnacles). More adventurous individuals also dine on the spines and tube feet of sea urchins. Feeding occurs during day. Predators include kelp bass and woolly sculpins.

MISCELLANY: While rockpools do not voluntarily leave the water, they can aerially respire.

Hypsoblennius jenkinsi
(Jordan & Evermann, 1896)
Mussel Blenny

ETYMOLOGY: *Hypsoblennius* is a combination of "high" in Greek and "*Blennius*" and *jenkinsi* refers to Oliver Peebles Jenkins (1850 or 51–1935). Jenkins was a student of David Starr Jordan at Indiana University and wound up as a professor of physiology at Stanford.

THE BASICS: Maximum Length: 13 cm (5 in) TL. The Ranges: Morro Bay (Central California) to Punta Marquez (southern Baja California), including Gulf of California. On the Pacific Coast, commonly from at least Santa Monica Bay (Southern California) to the Bahia Magdalena complex (southern Baja California). Intertidal to 21 m (70 ft), typically to at least 10 m (33 ft). Eggs: 0.7–0.8 mm. Larvae: hatching length = about 2.5 mm, flexion length = about 4–5.7 mm, transformation length = 1–1.8 cm (0.4–0.7 in). Von Bertalanffy parameters (SL, mm): (sexes combined) L_∞ = 100.8, k = 0.1621, t_0 = -1.8085 (Stephens et al. 1970).

SALIENT CHARACTERS: Look for the cirrus above the eye to have only short strands at the tip, with a substantial part of the stalk undivided. Losey (1968) reports that the eye cirri are much longer in males. There is often a dark crescent behind each eye. The body color is variable, although often brownish or gray. Nelson (1970) found that females were usually gray.

WALTER HEIM

LIFE HISTORY: Mussel blennies are cryptic fish that usually live in the shallow subtidal, most often in or near shelled organisms (e.g., worm tubes, mussels, barnacles, or in boring clam burrows), pier pilings, floats, and eelgrass. They settle from the plankton at 1.2–1.4 cm (0.5 in) SL, mostly from August–October. They are most abundant in relatively sheltered waters; harbors and embayments are particularly favored. In Southern California, they live mostly in the subtidal, although in the northern Gulf of California they are often found in the intertidal. Gulf of

California fish can tolerate a very wide range of temperatures
(i.e., 13–35°C, 55–95°F). These are sedentary and high territorial fish; each individual defends a burrow or home shell. As with
other *Hypsoblennius*, the males guard egg nests (with eggs from
more than one female) even against female mussel blennies. Losey
(1968) discusses their territorial behavior in what can only be
referred to as remarkable detail. A number of studies have shown
that there is relatively little genetic flow between fishes living in
the Gulf of California and those found on the Pacific Coast.

Mussel blennies live for at least 6 years. There is some
spawning throughout the year, but in Southern California it
mostly happens from May–October. Larval studies in Bahia Magdalena (southern Baja California) found that there was considerable spawning in January and February, as well as from May–July.
Females spawn 3–4 times per season, producing about 532–
1,540 eggs per batch. The eggs hatch in 14–21 days at 15–18°C
(59–64°F) and 6–8 days at 24–27°C (75–81°F). Mussel blennies
feed on benthic and planktonic crustaceans. They are eaten by
cabezons, giant kelpfish, kelp bass, and spotted sand bass.

OTHER SPECIES

Ophioblennius steindachneri
Jordan & Evermann, 1898
Panamic Fanged Blenny

This species grows to 18 cm (7 in) TL and lives from Isla Guadalupe and (mainland) Arricefe Sacramento (29°40'N, 115°47'W)
(central Baja California) into the northern Gulf of California and to Islas Lobos de Afuera (Peru). They are found from tide
pools to 12 m (40 ft), and perhaps to 20 m (66 ft); you can find these territorial fish on boulders and along rock walls. Fanged
blennies may spawn throughout the year. Males guard nests of eggs. Active during the day, fanged blennies feed on algae and
small invertebrates. Eggs: 0.5–0.6 mm. Larvae: hatching length = about 2.5 mm, flexion length = about 4.5–6.1 mm, transformation length = 3.6–6.6 cm. Length-weight parameters (TL, cm, gr): (sexes combined) W = $0.01147L^{2.93324}$ (Balart et al. 2006).

Oh so pensive is the blenny, of its problems it has many.

OCTAVIO ABURTO-OROPEZA

FAMILY ICOSTEIDAE—Ragfish

Ragfish inhabit their own, kind of idiosyncratic, family. They are oviparous and have planktonic eggs and larvae.

Icosteus aenigmaticus

Lockington, 1880

Ragfish

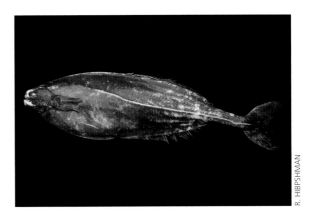

ETYMOLOGY AND COLLOQUIAL NAME: *Icosteus* means "to yield" and "bone" in Greek, referring to the limp body and *aenigmaticus* means "puzzling" in Greek. "Ragfish" comes from its *über*-limpness. The Japanese name is "irequmikonnyakuaji."

THE BASICS: Maximum Length: At least 213 cm (7 ft) TL. The Ranges: Okhotsk Sea and Pacific Coast of Honshu to Bering Sea and Gulf of Alaska to Point Loma (Southern California). Larvae have been taken further southwards, off northernmost Baja California. Surf to 1,420 m (4,092 ft). While their optimal depth range is not known, off the Kuril Islands most fish are taken by bottom trawls in 800–1,200 m. Eggs: 2.5–3.1 mm. Larvae: hatching length = 6.5 mm, flexion length = about 1.1–1.7 cm (0.4–0.7 in), transformation length = greater than 2.9 cm (1 in). Lengths and weights of a few small fish are given in Allen (2001).

SALIENT CHARACTERS: Oh so flabby is the ragfish; that's the character you do wish; but if, by chance, you're satisfied—not; we'll tell you other things they have got. The juvies: spotted, scaled, and rounded; have pelvic fins to keep them grounded; adults lack pelvics, spots, and scales; are brown and purple, both fems and males.

LIFE HISTORY: Ragfish under about 30 cm (12 in) TL live in shallow water or offshore near the surface. Scott Gietler saw a pelagic juvenile associating with salps (check out the photograph below). Adults inhabit deeper waters, at least some near the bottom. Adults are occasionally found in the surf zone and these are likely disoriented individuals. This is a relatively cold-water species; they have been taken in 2.5 to at least 10°C (50°F) and probably also live in somewhat warmer waters.

Based on egg and larval surveys, ragfish spawn mainly during winter–spring, although a few eggs have been taken in late autumn. Females likely spawn once per year and produce anywhere between 144,000–552,000 eggs (and probably more). Females may spawn at depths deeper than 220 m (722 ft). Larger ragfish eat fishes, squids, and octopuses. One juvenile had eaten a medusae. Predators include Steller sea lions, fin and sperm whales. Young ones have been found in tuna stomachs.

FISHERY: On occasion taken by both commercial fishermen and recreational anglers.

A pelagic juvenile.

FAMILY GOBIESOCIDAE—Clingfishes

The clingfishes are nearshore, marine (OK, a few are freshwater), and mostly reef fishes found throughout the world in tropical to cold-temperate waters. There are around 35 genera and 140 species, 12 of which live within our range. Clingfishes are oviparous with eggs laid in nests and at least many (if not all) have planktonic larvae. They have an adhesive disc on the belly, formed from modified pelvic fins. This disc has a number of small papillae that help the fish hold on to substrata in high currents. See Eschmeyer and Herald (1983) for a number of tips on telling at least some of the species apart.

Gobiesox maeandricus
(Girard, 1858)
Northern Clingfish

ETYMOLOGY: *Gobiesox* is a combination of "*Gobius*" (a genus of goby) and "*Esox*" (the pike), although why a clingfish was thought to look like either fish is unclear. *Maeandricus* means "meandering" in Latin.

THE BASICS: Maximum Length: 16 cm (6 in) TL. The Ranges: Noyes Island (southeastern Alaska) to central Baja California (between Isla Guadalupe and mainland on drifting kelp), apparently most commonly from Vancouver Island to Central California. Intertidal to 140 m (459 ft), including tide pools. Eggs: 1–2 mm. Larvae: hatching length = 5.8 mm.

SALIENT CHARACTERS: Northern clingfish have a very large depressed head and a very large adhesive disk. They come in a variety of algae- or earth-tones and one imagines (although one has never experimentally shown) that they can change color to match their surroundings, unless they find themselves at a gathering of Clan Cameron in Lochaber and are trying to blend in with one of its four tartans. Northerns tend to have a webwork of darker colors and sometimes have a light bar between the eyes that may extend onto the gill cover. Not satisfied? Well none of us are; it's the human condition.

LIFE HISTORY: Northern clingfish are small, cryptic fish that live underneath rocks and on the blades of algae and eelgrass. Larval northern clingfish appear to live within a few meters of rocky shorelines. A study in Puget Sound found that young-of-the-year settled out of the plankton on to nearshore algae and then at least some individuals migrated into the intertidal. Young ones settle out of the plankton at 0.9 cm (0.4 in) SL or less. This species is particularly abundant in rocky tide pools, but is also common on cobble beaches, and in some shallow subtidal areas. Except when they are swimming about, northerns cling tightly to the substrate. They are occasionally found in the dens of giant Pacific octopuses. Fish along the Pacific Coast form semi-genetically isolated populations; Strait of Georgia fish are isolated from those on the open coast.

Females are mature at as small as 6.4 cm (3 in) TL. Spawning occurs from November–May. Jeff Marliave (1975), observing intertidal spawning, found that males tend the fertilized eggs and eat the dead ones. He comments: "The egg mass is a monolayer of eggs. The eggs are attached to the underside of a boulder on a rocky substrate. The eggs are 2 mm diameter and bright yellow, becoming golden brown toward hatching. Concentric rings of eggs are laid, the most recently developing

Is this cute, or what?

mode being outermost (200–500 eggs per mode)...Late-stage larvae accumulate in large schools around kelp beds from the last week in May until late June in Barkley Sound [Vancouver Island]." He later discovered (Marliave 1986), that larval schools are found in shallow waters, and appear to "descend toward the substrate (into low beds of *Alaria nana* [a brown algae]) at dusk." Epibenthic and benthic crustacea and benthic mollusks tend to be the most important part of the diet. Gammarid amphipods, harpacticoid copepods, isopods, and limpets loom large. However, snails, crabs, polychaetes, nudibranchs, bivalves, barnacles, hermit crabs, algae and the occasional fish are also consumed. Larger fish tend to eat more limpets than smaller individuals. The larger ones develop large chisel-like teeth to help pry the limpets off rocks. One does this, as noted by Stadler (1988), by "inserting its lower teeth under the shell and, using its adhesive disk as an anchor, levers the limpet from the substrate." The fish secrete a mucus cocoon around the shells as they travel down the digestive tract. Predators include black and China rockfishes, pelagic cormorants, minks, and garter snakes (these often come into the intertidal zone to search for food).

FISHERY: Incredibly, on a very few occasions they are taken by shore anglers.

MISCELLANY: This species is capable of breathing air.

OTHER SPECIES

Rimicola muscarum
(Meek & Pierson, 1895)
Kelp Clingfish

Kelp clingfish grow to 7 cm (3 in) TL. They live from Glacier Bay (southeastern Alaska) to Punta Baja (northern Baja California), and perhaps to Kachemak Bay (northern Gulf of Alaska). They are common from at least the Queen Charlotte Islands (British Columbia) to Southern California. Kelp clingfish live in the intertidal zone and shallow nearshore, while clinging to kelp, other algae, and eelgrass. A few have also been seen on drifting kelp mats. In kelp bed forests, you can find this species hanging on from the canopy to the holdfasts. Fish reportedly live for about one year. Females spawn from at least April–June—although Limbaugh (1955) reported seeing their eggs throughout the year—laying eggs on aquatic plants. The eggs are yellow

JOHN YASAKI

and laid in concentric rings containing several dozen ova. Kelp clingfish eat small invertebrates (e.g., harpacticoid copepods, mysid shrimps, gammarid amphipods, isopods, ostracods, flatworms, crustacean larvae, and insects). Predators include black, kelp, and olive rockfishes, giant kelpfish, kelp bass, and shiner perch. Eggs: 1.3 mm. Larvae: hatching length = 4 mm.

Jeez, is it me or do we all need a break from this seemingly endless onslaught of information? Yep, I thought so. Thus, in the interest of keeping what is left of our sense of proportion, I present

PEACEFUL INTERLUDE.

SO YOU WANT TO BE A MARINE BIOLOGIST?

So you want to be a marine biologist? Well sonny, or sonnette, as the case may be, why don't you just sit down and let a real marine biologist give you some damn good advice. And wipe that smirk off your face, sit up straight, and for goodness sakes stop fidgeting! You'd think you had lice the way you are carrying on. You do? Oh well, never mind.

First of all there are two really, really bad reasons to want to be a marine biologist. If you have even an inkling that these are yours, please run away as fast as possible, 'cause neither you nor we will be happy.

TWO REALLY, REALLY BAD REASONS TO WANT TO BE A MARINE BIOLOGIST

Bad Reason Number One: "I want to be a marine biologist so that I can talk to dolphins."

Believing this is simply the Kiss of Death. This is the verbal equivalent of reaching down your throat, pulling out your intestines, wrapping them around your neck and choking yourself. When we hear this our impulse is to thwack you a good one on your keester with the frozen haddock we keep within arm's reach just for this occasion.

And why is that? It is because, and please listen carefully, while you may want to talk to dolphins, dolphins do not want to talk to you. That's right. Mostly, dolphins want to eat fishes and have sex with other dolphins. And that pretty much cuts you out of the loop, doesn't it? Oh, I know that there are the occasional dolphins that hang around beaches, swim with humans and seem to be chummy, but these are the exceptions. You don't judge the whole human race by the people who attend monster car rallies, do you?

Just be honest with yourself. If you want to talk to dolphins you don't want to be a biologist. What you really want to do is explore your past lives, get in touch with the Cosmic Oneness, and conduct similar-minded individuals on tours to Central America looking for evidence that We Are Not Alone. Our experience is that people who feel this way last about 6.5 minutes in any biology program.

Bad Reason Number Two: "I want to be a marine biologist because I want to make big bucks."

Okay, here's the bottom line. By federal law, marine biologists have to take a vow of poverty and chastity. Poverty, because you are not going to make squat-j-doodly in this job. Just how squat is the doodly we are talking about? Well, five years after finishing my PhD I was making slightly less than a beginning manager at McDonalds. Ooh, a 36 year old guy with 13 years of college and 5 years of post-doctoral experience making just about as much as a semi-literate 19 year old with pimples the size of Bolivia, who can speak perhaps 3 words at a time before the term "you know" enters the conversation.

And chastity because, well, who's going to date a marine biologist? The smell alone tends to dissuade a large proportion of the opposite sex.

TWO REALLY, REALLY GOOD REASONS TO WANT TO BE A MARINE BIOLOGIST

Good Reason Number One: "You can dress and act almost any way you want."

This is true. Marine biologists are almost entirely free of any of those silly restrictions that blight the professional landscape of our fellow proletarians. This is because no one really cares about what we do or what we say. You want to come to work dressed in scabrous khaki shorts and a torn black Sandman shirt? Fine. You want to grow a scruffy beard, get a tattoo of a gooseneck barnacle on your arm, or burp at inopportune moments? No problem, just do good work.

Good Reason Number Two: "If you like it, just do it."

Look, the reality is that you only go around once in life and if, by chance, you do come back, knowing how you have behaved in this life, you will undoubtedly come back as a slime mold. And most slime molds cannot be marine biologists. So just go out there and do what you enjoy. Marine biology is a wonderful profession. You want to find cancer cures by grinding up sponges? How about figuring out why hammerhead sharks always come back to the same seamount? Or where is the missing carbon dioxide that industries are producing; could the ocean be soaking it up? All neat projects. But pay attention here. None of this involves drinking copious quantities of fermented grape juice, while intoning "The ocean, she is strange and wondrous, filled with animals that disturb even a Frenchman."

The ocean is an exciting, never-dull place that is perfect for piddling away your existence. And just think, you actually get paid to think cool thoughts and do cool things.

And so what if you will never have sex again?

FAMILY GOBIIDAE—Gobies

Gobies are benthic, generally small, and mostly nearshore fishes that are almost ubiquitous in marine, estuarine, and freshwaters throughout the world. There are a staggering 210 genera and at least 1,951 species, and 29 species live within our range. Sixteen species reach as far north as California and four of these are introduced species that originated in Asia. Gobies are oviparous and in many (if not all) species, parents take care of eggs in nests. Their larvae are plank-tonic, although the larvae of species that inhabit semi-enclosed estuaries may rarely leave. Fossil gobies have been taken from the fabulous Monte Bolca site in Italy, a Middle Eocene deposit about 50 million years old. Miller and Lea (1972) has keys to many eastern Pacific temperate species and Fischer et al. (1995) has keys to the many genera of the eastern tropical Pacific.

Clevelandia ios
(Jordan & Gilbert, 1882)
Arrow Goby

ETYMOLOGY: Clevelandia is named for Daniel Cleveland (1838–1929), patron of science in San Diego and ios is Greek for "arrow."
THE BASICS: Maximum Length: 5.7 cm (2 in) TL. The Ranges: Rivers Inlet (British Columbia) to Bahia San Bartolome (southern Baja California), and in the Gulf of California; commonly from at least the outer coast of Vancouver Island to about Punta Abreojos (southern Baja California). 2 m (7 ft) or less to 45 m (148 ft), typically from the high intertidal to at least 10 m (33 ft). Like other gobies, eggs are club-shaped with attachment threads at one pole. Eggs: 1.3–2.6 x 0.7–0.8 mm. Larvae: hatching length = 2–3 mm, flexion length = 5–6.1 mm, transformation length = about 1.4–1.7 cm (0.6–0.7 in). Von Bertalanffy parameters (SL, mm): (sexes combined) L_∞ = 36, k = 0.96, t_0 = -0.527 (Brothers 1975). Length-weight parameters (SL, mm, mg): (sexes combined) W = $0.014L^{2.918}$ (Brothers 1975).
SALIENT CHARACTERS: Arrows have a relatively large mouth, with jaws that extend beyond the eye. They are olive or gray with black or white speckling. Confusion reigns supreme when it comes to a black stripe on the anal fin. Prasad (1948) states that many mature females and all males ready to spawn have this streak. Ed Brothers (1975) mentions only that the stripe occurs on the anal fin of breeding males.
LIFE HISTORY: Arrow goby are small fishes that live on soft sediment and in eelgrass, mostly in quiet bays, coastal lagoons, estuaries, and occasionally in freshwater. Young-of-the-year settle in very shallow waters at 1–1.6 cm (0.4–0.6 in) SL and burrowing behavior starts at about 1.2 cm (0.5 in) SL. They often live in burrows, particularly those built by fat innkeepers and various shrimps or through the retraction of clam siphons. As many as 15 goby will occupy one burrow and, in many instances, they share burrows with the original occupants. One study demonstrated that at least ghost shrimps may not like to share, as some were observed chasing the goby out of the burrows. If no burrows are available, they apparently live in shallow pools, partially burying themselves (with only eyes and back exposed) if frightened. Unlike some other gobies, they are not territorial, and you can occasionally find very large numbers of them in a small pool (how about over 400 in a pool 1 m wide by 2.1 m long, 3 ft x 7 ft). At low tide, arrows either retreat to burrows (if the seafloor starts to dry out) or remain in shallow pools. At night, these fish are often exposed and relatively inactive. Kent and Marliave (1997) noted: "Larvae drifting offshore appear to rise toward the surface layer where they may be transported back to shallow water...Thus early larval drift dispersal tends not to remove this species from the region of soft-bottom water." Arrow goby tolerate a wide range of salinities, 0–55 ppt, but prefer 15–35 ppt.

Arrow goby live to at least 3 years old. Note that there are geographic differences in growth rates, mortality, and fecundity. For instance, fish in Elkhorn Slough (Central California) tend to grow somewhat larger and live a bit longer than those in Mission Bay (Southern California). As a generality, a few fish are mature at as small as 2.3 cm (0.9 in) SL (1 year old) and all are mature by 3.4 cm (1 in) (2 years old). Females are larger at age than males, grow faster, tend to be bigger than males at any locality, and live somewhat longer. Females likely spawn multiple times a year, producing between about 300 (and perhaps

DANIEL CLEVELAND

Born in New York State, Cleveland practiced law in both New York and Texas and, in 1865, was appointed to run the city of San Antonio, Texas, when it was under martial law after the Civil War. In 1867, he immigrated to San Francisco, only to move to San Diego in 1869 upon learning that his brother was ill. Here, along with making simply scads of money as a lawyer and investor, he quickly established himself as a general do-gooder and major Pillar of Society. There was scarcely a civic activity that Cleveland did not become involved in, including helping to found the San Diego Society of Natural History. One imagines it was in that capacity that the Eigenmanns named a new genus of goby honoring this early science supporter. In an astounding cosmic confluence, Mr. Cleveland's goddaughter was named Beatrice L. Fish.

as little as 50) and 1,100 eggs per spawning event. Different studies give differing pictures of when arrow goby spawn and I can't figure out if there is some sort of geographic variation going on or if every year is a crapshoot. Suffice it to say that, apparently, some spawning goes on throughout the year and that, on average, winter–spring is the peak period, but don't hold me to that. In addition, there is a controversy about where females lay their eggs. Brothers (1975) says it happens inside burrows that are likely constructed by the males, who then guard them until the eggs hatch. On the other hand, Prasad (1948) and Carter (1965) hold out for egg-laying outside of burrows and Prasad saw no evidence of parental guarding of eggs. So, like what is going on? The eggs incubate for 10–12 days before hatching. Arrow goby eat a variety of small organisms including harpacticoid copepods, gammarid and caprellid amphipods, and polychaetes, as well as the occasional isopod, clam siphon, crustacean larva, and fish egg. Algae and diatoms are sometimes important in their diets. Not highly specialized, a fish usually takes a bite of substrate and ejects it out of its opercles. A fairly long list of animals eats them. These include, but are not limited to, bat rays, California halibut, diamond turbot, round stingrays, shovelnose guitarfish, staghorn sculpins, walleye surfperch, white croakers, dowitchers, greater yellowlegs, kingfishers, terns, and harbor seals.

ORIGINS AND RELATIONSHIPS: Arrow goby are most closely related to tidewater goby (the two species occasionally occupy the same area) and these two species probably diverged 5–10 million years ago; both diverged from the bay goby lineage 6–12 million years ago. The bay goby type probably emerged 10–20 million years ago.

REMARKS: 1) For what it's worth, a study that looked at various morphometric and meristic characters found significant differences between fish living in Gray's Harbor (outer coast of Washington) and those living at two sites within Puget Sound (Carter 1965). 2) Want to win a bar bet? Larry Allen et al. (2002) estimated that there are about 3 million arrow goby in San Diego Bay. 3) For those who want to know more, Ed Brothers' doctoral thesis (1975) has lots of stuff about this species' complex behaviors.

Eucyclogobius newberryi
(Girard, 1856)
Tidewater Goby

ETYMOLOGY: *Eucyclogobius* comes from "well" and "circle" in Greek (referring to the cycloid scales) and "*Gobius*" and *newberryi* honors the geologist, physician, and explorer John Strong Newberry (1822–1892).

THE BASICS: Maximum Length: 5.7 cm (2 in) TL. The Ranges: Mouth of Smith River (Northern California) to Agua Hedionda Lagoon (San Diego County). Shallow waters to at least 5 m (15 ft). Eggs: 0.5–1.2 mm. Larvae: hatching length = 5–6 mm, transformation length = about 1.3–1.6 cm.

SALIENT CHARACTERS: The upper part of the pectoral ray is located above the gill opening, there are two pores on the top of the head between the eyes (although these are hard to see in the field), and the edge of the first dorsal fin is clear. The spacing between the dorsal fins is very narrow. Non-breeding fish tend to be brown or gray, with darker dorsal mottling. Breeding individuals are fish of a different color. Females are tan or reddish-brown with gold-brown or dark brown sides. Females change color when fighting, becoming blue-black on their sides. Breeding males are blackish, with small white spots on back and sides.

LIFE HISTORY: As their name implies, tidewater goby live in various coastal lagoons, the lower parts of coastal streams, and other estuarine situations. There is at least one record of a fish living in a shallow coastal marine environment. In general,

GREG GOLDSMITH

a tidewater goby spends its entire life inside one water system, usually in the estuarine part, but occasionally swimming as much as 8 km (5 mi) upstream. Young-of-the-year settle out at about 1.6–1.8 mm (0.6–0.7 in) TL. Most fish live in shallow, quiet water in both vegetated and unvegetated areas, and usually hunkered down on the soft bottom, where they use their fused pectoral fins to hold on. Because tidewater larvae rarely leave their birth waters, there are a number of semi-isolated populations. One study suggested that there were barriers to gene flow in the vicinities of Los Angeles, Seacliff (Ventura County), Point Buchon, Big Sur, and Point Arena. Densities at least as high as 198 fish/m² have been noted. Population sizes range from perhaps less than 100 fish in a small lagoon to a few million in Lake Earl (Del Norte County). In the wild, they have been found from freshwater to salinities of 65 ppt and have experimentally survived even higher salinities. They likely prefer brackish waters, but salinity does not seem to be a limiting factor.

Okay, it's spawning time and the ready-to-mate females become very aggressive, frequently attacking each other over a male. This involves a lot of posturing, with fin erection, tail-slapping, and some biting (reminiscent of some military reunions). A female finds males by selecting a sandy area and either settling on the bottom with her lower jaw on the sand or hopping about in a circle. Usually, this causes a male to create an opening in his burrow and stick his head out of the sand. Once a male comes into sight, the female kicks into high gear, erecting her dorsal and anal fins and really putting the hurt to a whole repertoire of hops and short dashes. She will often bump the male's head with her caudal fin or anal vent area or lay her vent over the burrow opening. Amazingly enough, despite what we all would call a very direct approach, a large number of these female come-ons are unsuccessful. One study found that of 23 courtships, only one led to a female entering a male's burrow. Hey, its no wonder these fish may soon be considered endangered. Fellas, fellas, it's time to get a life. If you guys don't get your acts together, some studly male mosquitofish is going to take over your responsibilities. I mean, this is just one more indication of the decline in the American Spirit, a decline I attribute to the invention of Jockey shorts. More details about reproductive behavior are in Swift et al. (1989).

JOHN STRONG NEWBERRY

Among his other accomplishments, Newberry was the secretary to the Sanitary Commission of the Mississippi Valley during the Civil War (after having first paid his dues, one suspects, in the Unsanitary Commission). He was also a member of the briefly lived Megatherium Club, at the Smithsonian Institution. By all accounts, the scientist club members were a rowdy lot, who drank and ate to excess and who greeted each other with a hearty "How, how!" Really, I am not making that up.

Most tidewaters live for one year, although in captivity they have survived for 3 years. Males mature at about 2.4 cm (0.9 in) SL and females at 2.7 cm (1 in). While spawning has been observed in every month, it peaks in early spring (mostly from about February–April) and again in late summer and fall (mostly August–October). Females are batch spawners and produce between 179–1,010 pale yellow eggs at a time. Prior to spawning, males dig and defend small burrows in the sediment and the eggs are laid about 2.5 cm (1 in) below the entrance. The male guards the eggs until they hatch and males rarely guard eggs from more than one female. Males feed little during this time. Both sexes spawn repeatedly in a season, often 4–6 times; one female was observed spawning 12 times. Females spawn every 13 days on average. In nature, spawning occurs over salinities of 2–27 ppt and water temperatures of 9–25°C (48–77°F). The eggs hatch in 9–11 days at 18–25°C (64–77°F). Tidewaters feed by sifting sand through their mouths, plucking prey from the lagoon floor, and by grabbing stuff from the midwaters. Small prey, such as crustaceans (e.g., gammarid amphipods, isopods, copepods, and mysid shrimps), insects, snails, and various worms are eaten. Steelhead and introduced centrarchids eat them.

ORIGINS AND RELATIONSHIPS: This species is most closely related to the arrow goby. The lineage probably diverged 5–10 million years ago and both species diverged from the bay goby lineage 6–12 million years ago.

Gillichthys mirabilis

Cooper, 1864

Longjaw Mudsucker

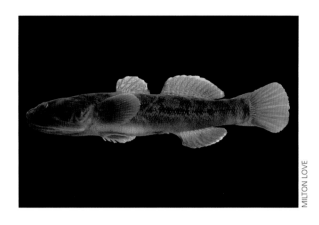

MILTON LOVE

ETYMOLOGY: *Gillichthys* refers to Theodore Nicholas Gill (1837–1914), a well known, if somewhat controversial, ichthyologist and professor of zoology at George Washington University and the Smithsonian Institution. *Mirabilis* is Latin for "wonderful."

THE BASICS: Maximum Length: 21 cm (8 in) TL. The Ranges: Tomales Bay (Northern California) to Gulf of California. Along the Pacific Coast, they are pretty common from San Francisco Bay to southern Baja California. Shallow waters to at least 4 m (13 ft). Eggs: 2.8–3.4 x 1.1 mm. One end has adhesive threads. Larvae: hatching length = about 3–4 mm, flexion length = about 5.5–6.5 mm, transformation length = about 10.5–15 mm. Length-weight parameters (SL, mm, gr): (sexes combined) W = $0.0001L^{2.4415}$ (Miller et al. 2008).

SALIENT CHARACTERS: Mudsuckers are thick little fishes, with a round, depressed head, and little beady eyes kind of perched on top. Adult males and females have very long upper jaws, those of males are longer (almost extending to the gill opening). Adults are brown, black, or olive on back, lighter or yellowish on belly, with some mottling and faint vertical bars on back and sides. Juveniles are small-mouthed and large-eyed and have about eight vertical bars on their sides and a dark blotch on the posterior portion of the first dorsal fin.

LIFE HISTORY: Longjaws are benthic fish that live in salt marshes, estuaries, and mangrove forests, in both vegetated and unvegetated areas. Young-of-the-year recruit to these habitats at lengths at least as small as 0.8 cm SL. All sizes live in burrows.

THEODORE NICOLAS GILL

Gill was born in New York City, where his father pushed him to become a clergyman. Instead, Gill went into law, but soon migrated into science, specifically into the taxonomy and systematics of fishes and other animals. Undoubtedly, in some ways Gill was an excellent ichthyologist. He clearly, as David Starr Jordan noted: "Had an unprecedented mastery over the literature of science and a keener appreciation of the meaning of structure in classification and in evolution than that shown by any other naturalist." Jordan later went on to call him a "Master of Taxonomy" and Gill eventually produced more than 500 papers, most of them on fishes.

He was also clearly something of an eccentric. He never married and for many years lived at the Cosmos Club in Washington, D.C., spending most of his days in a small room at the Smithsonian. With the exception of clean and dry skeletons, or occasionally dried specimens, he did not like to touch the bodies of fishes. Therefore, much of what he knew about them was based on the writings of others. He had difficulty completing large research projects. One researcher became so disgusted that he told Jordan: "I wouldn't do another stroke of work with Gill to save his immortal soul!" Even worse, when it came to the work of West Coast ichthyologists, Gill was clearly an Eastern Establishment punk. To be most charitable, Gill may have felt that the self-taught biologists in San Francisco, who were describing many of the new species of fishes, were just a bunch of rubes. To be less charitable, Gill somehow thought he owned the West Coast fishes, even though he never deigned to come out here and look at one. For whatever reason, on several occasions Gill wrote crass papers criticizing the work of such West Coast biologists as William O. Ayres and William N. Lockington. Even more ironic is that on at least one major issue, that regarding the relationships of the rockfishes with each other, Gill has turned out to be just flat wrong. So intense, not to say wrong-headed, were Gill's criticisms of Ayres, that that mild-mannered physician just stopped describing new fishes.

It is a bit unclear who actually digs these burrows, but the excavators could include the mudsuckers, mud and ghost shrimps, or fat innkeepers. In many instances, the burrows, and their fish inhabitants, are exposed at low tide and the fish breathe air. You can also find mudsuckers wriggling over mudflats at low tide, apparently searching for some place to hide out. While they can tolerate fairly brackish waters (and can survive 3–7 days in freshwater), they are simply champs in the High Salinity Follies, seemingly comfortable at levels (82.5 ppt) almost three times that of seawater. Gee, 82.5 ppt is about the salinity of Lot's wife. Although they tolerate temperatures between at least 9–35°C (48–95°F), mudsuckers begin to get uncomfortable at above about 23°C (73°F). Not much is known about their reproductive habits. In aquaria, males create and defend territories (and later eggs) and the eggs are glommed on to surfaces with adhesive threads. During territorial battles, the combatants raise their dorsal and anal fins and their anal and pelvic fins turn black. Soon after, the dorsal fin darkens and, finally, the entire body turns sooty. The mouth then billows out to those cavernous openings and the fish go orifice to orifice. There appears to be little gene flow between fish north and south of Punta Eugenia (Baja California).

Mudsuckers live to at least 2 years old. They are mature within maybe 6 months of hatching and at 6–8 cm (2–3 in) SL. While there appears to be some low level of spawning throughout the year, much of it likely occurs in winter–spring. Females (producing at least 4,000–27,000 yellow eggs per season) are batch spawners and may spawn 2–3 times a season. Larvae hatch in 10–12 days. Longjaws simply dote on gammarid amphipods and polychaetes, but they won't pass up shrimps, crabs, fishes, isopods, bivalve siphons, and algae. Predators include, but are not limited to, bat rays, brown smoothhounds, leopard sharks, shovelnose guitarfish, double-crested cormorants, elegant terns, and garter snakes. Watching a ton of elegant terns, Schaffner (1982) notes that mudsuckers are "commonly used by courting males, who fed them to females."

FISHERY: Native Americans living near San Francisco Bay occasionally ate mudsuckers. Today, commercial fishermen catch a few for sale in bait shops. They are taken fairly often by anglers fishing from California piers and along the shores of such waterways as San Francisco Bay. In SFB, they are used as bait for stripers and other species.

In an essay published in 1877, Lockington noted that the Chinese living around San Francisco Bay dug them out of mud banks and ate them. Then, perhaps because it was widely stated that the Chinese would eat any fish, he also noted that a "gentleman" [read white person] had acquired some from a Chinese fisherman "and that he had had about eleven specimens cooked, and found them good tasting, he thought, something like eels."

MISCELLANY: If the oxygen content of the water drops too low, or if they find themselves out of the water, mudsuckers can breathe air. The air is taken into the mouth, held in the throat, which contains lots of blood vessels and acts like a lung, transferring the oxygen to the blood. After the oxygen is used up, the fish releases the gas and takes another breath. Even if held underwater, mudsuckers will live between 6.5 and 12.5 hours in deoxygenated conditions.

Lepidogobius lepidus

(Girard, 1858)

Bay Goby

ETYMOLOGY: *Lepidogobius* means "scale" in Greek and "*Gobius*" and *lepidus* is "pretty" in Latin.

THE BASICS: Maximum Length: 15.5 cm (6 in) TL. The Ranges: Kegan Cove (southeastern Alaska) to Isla Cedros and Bahia de Sebastian Vizcaino (central Baja California). They are common from at least the west coast of Vancouver Island to Bahia de Sebastian Vizcaino. Intertidal to 305 m (1,000 ft), typically in 70 m (230 ft) or less. Eggs: unfertilized = 1.2–1.8 x 0.8–1 mm. Larvae: hatching length = about 3–3.2 mm, flexion length = 6.2–7.5 mm, transformation length = about 2.4–2.9 cm (0.9–1.1 in). Length-weight parameters (TL, mm, kg): (sexes combined) W = 0.0000000032L$^{3.15}$ (RecFin 2009).

KEVIN LEE

SALIENT CHARACTERS: Bay goby have a black margin on the first dorsal fin and a wide space between the dorsal fins. They are brown, olive, or reddish-brown on sides, sometimes with small blotches or saddles.

LIFE HISTORY: These are small benthic fish that are found on a wide variety of soft bottom habitats, including eelgrass beds, from coastal estuaries (down to at least 14 ppt) and quiet bays to sandy bottoms of the open coast. They are usually found in burrows, either by themselves or occupied by the shrimps, clams, and fat innkeepers that dug them. Under experimental conditions, shrimps try to grab the goby, so this is not some airy-fairy commensal relationship. In fact, bay goby seem to prefer living in unoccupied burrows.

Bay goby probably spawn throughout the year. I looked in the stomachs of a few individuals and they had eaten small crustaceans. They are eaten by brown smoothhounds, spiny dogfish, staghorn sculpins, various cormorants, and harbor seals.

FISHERY: Improbable as it sounds, bay goby were apparently sold as "whitebait" in San Francisco markets at least in the 1930s. Pier fishermen occasionally take them.

RELATIONSHIPS: Bay goby appear to be most closely related to arrow and tidewater goby and likely diverged from these two species 6–12 million years ago. The bay goby "type" probably emerged 10–20 million years ago. Otoliths of what are believed to be bay goby have been found in Late Pliocene (at least 1.8-million-year-old) deposits in Southern California.

Lythrypnus dalli
(Gilbert, 1890)
Bluebanded Goby

Changing sex only when it's damn good and ready, this is a species for the 21ˢᵗ century.

ETYMOLOGY: What does *Lythrypnus* mean? I don't know. You would think that Jordan and Evermann (1896), would have had the grace to tell us what it meant when they coined the name, but no. The first part of the word means "gore" in Greek and that's as far as I can get. What gore could possibly have to do with this fish is beyond me. *Dalli* refers to William Healey Dall. See *Sebastes dalli* for an exposition on this gentleman.

THE BASICS: Maximum Length: 6.4 cm (3 in) TL. The Ranges: Morro Bay (Central California) to Islas Lobos de Afuera (Peru), including the Gulf of California. Bluebandeds are common from Southern California southward. Intertidal to 76 m (250 ft), typically deeper than 3 m (10 ft) or so. Larvae: hatching length = about 2–2.2 mm, flexion length = about 4–4.4 mm, transformation length = about 9.5–13 mm. Length-weight parameters (TL, cm, gr): (sexes combined) $W = 0.00992L^{2.97336}$ (Balart et al. 2006).

SALIENT CHARACTERS: Bluebanded are crimson with 2–9 iridescent blue bands.

LIFE HISTORY: Young-of-the-year (at 0.9–1.1 cm, 0.4 in, SL) settle on reefs from June–January, mainly in the late summer or early fall. During the day, you can often find them quite exposed, perching on rocks, shells, worm tubes or, alternatively, huddled under the protective spines of sea urchins, particularly the long-spined urchin (*Centrostephanus coronatus*), but also both red (*Strongylocentrus franciscanus*) and purple (*S. purpuratus*) ones. As many as 16 fish have been seen under one *C. coronatus*. Young-of-the-year will often settle out of the plankton right to these urchins. Behrents (1983) noted that *C. coronatus* may be important shelter for both bluebanded and zebra goby, particularly bluebandeds. When she removed the urchin from a good goby site, or even when she clipped the urchins' spines down a bit, the number of goby in the area decreased significantly. During the day, bluebandeds dart into the water column to catch prey and will actually stay up there for a while if the dining is good. At night, they retreat into crevices. An individual bluebanded may use the same crevice night after night. You can sometimes see two fish facing each other with mouths agape and dorsal and pectoral fins erect. Bluebandeds reportedly can tolerate water temperatures up to 31.3°C (88°F), although breathing become erratic at 23°C (73°F). There is relatively little gene flow between Pacific Coast fish and those in the Gulf of California.

Bluebandeds are usually found in small groups with a large male bossing

DAN RICHARDS

Bluebanded sheltering under sea urchin.

females around. If the male is removed, the largest female will change sex. Behrents (1983) described the courtship behavior, as seen in the laboratory, thusly: "The male would initiate courtship with females…by displaying lateral body quivers toward one. He would then rush at that female and nip gently at her caudal fin presumably in an effort to direct her to the nest. As soon as this encounter was made he would immediately plunge into the nest and quickly reappear. He would again approach her, perform several more lateral body quivers, nips, and then swim swiftly back into the nest. This procedure was repeated several times often without nipping but rather many swimming maneuvers in and out of the nest were substantiated until the female either left the area or was chased into the tube in front of the male. Once the female was inside the nest she would remain there for up to two hours…Although no more than one female was allowed entrance to the nest at a time, the simultaneous presence of eggs at various stages of development indicated that several females deposit eggs over a series of days within the same nest…Eggs are attached in a single layer by adhesive filaments to the inner surface of the nest."

Bluebandeds are short-lived; a few survive to 20 months old and fish mature about 1 month (and maybe 1.7 cm, 0.7 in, SL) after they settle out of the plankton. Without putting too fine a point on it, bluebandeds have a very complex set of reproductive patterns. First, they can change sex in both directions and sometimes be both sexes simultaneously. As Rodgers et al. (2007) explained, the "decision" about whether to change sex can be summarized as: "If [you are] subordinate [to other bluebandeds] express female, if dominant or not subordinate express male." In addition, males can be either "bourgeois" (these are territorial and dominate the females) or parasitic (mini-males that maybe sneak around and fertilize eggs behind the bourgeois male's back and do all kinds of other antisocial things). If you are interested in this kind of thing—and it takes a very special person to be interested in this kind of thing—you should read St. Mary (1996), Drilling and Grober (2005), and Rodgers et al. (2007). Spawning may occur throughout the year, but in Southern California it seems to be mainly from February–September. Females produce between 64–2,194 eggs. Larvae drift in the plankton for 2–3 months before settling out. Bluebandeds feed mostly on water column zooplankton, although some fish prey on small benthic creatures. This translates to dining on various crustaceans (e.g., copepods, caprellid and gammarid amphipods, isopods, and crustacean larvae), along with gastropods, bivalves, and polychaetes. Most of the feeding takes place at dawn and dusk. They are eaten by black-and-yellow rockfish and kelp bass and, one imagines, other reef-based predators.

MISCELLANY: Bluebandeds have been caught red-handed (red-finned, one wonders?) cleaning giant sea bass.

REMARKS: Annual bluebanded recruitment is highly variable; some years there are simply tons of them and in others they are scarce indeed. In fact, even between nearby reefs their densities can be quite different.

Lythrypnus zebra

(Gilbert, 1890)

Zebra Goby

ETYMOLOGY: I don't know what *Lythrypnus* means, see *L. dalli*. *Zebra* comes from the Latin for, well, "zebra."

THE BASICS: Maximum Length: 5.7 cm (2 in) TL. The Ranges: Carmel Bay (Central California) to Cabo San Lucas (southern Baja California), mostly from Southern California southward. Intertidal to 97 m (318 ft). Larvae: flexion length = about 4–5 mm, transformation length = about 1–1.2 cm (0.4–0.5 in).

SALIENT CHARACTERS: Dull red with numerous fine blue bars or bands is the zebra goby.

LIFE HISTORY: Zebras are reclusive, benthic fish that live on reefs, among rocks, and empty shells. They often hang vertically, or even upside down, in crevices and under ledges. Densities are highly variable among reefs, even relatively nearby ones, and certainly between years. This species seems to need algal turf because it feeds mostly on crustaceans living in that

KEVIN LEE

stuff. When this turf is not available (for instance where sea urchins have stripped the area more-or-less bare) this goby is not abundant. They are inactive at night. Like bluebanded goby, zebras will hide amid the spines of the sea urchin, *Centrostephanus coronatus*. In Southern California, young-of-the-year settle from the plankton (at lengths as small as 0.9 cm SL) to reefs from August–February.

Zebra goby are short-lived, although some make it to 23 months old. The fish mature in their first year and the smallest mature female in one study was 1.9 cm (0.7 in) SL. I have found females with ripe eggs from April–December. Females produce between 161–800 eggs. The eggs are attached in a single layer by adhesive filaments to the inner surface of the nest and males guard the eggs. A very nice summary of their courtship behavior is to be found in Behrents (1983). Like their cousins the bluebanded goby, the reproductive habits of zebras are kind of interesting. What with female-biased

hermaphrodites (mostly female tissue with a soupçon of male), male-biased hermaphrodites (you can figure that out), and a small number of pure females (that one's straightforward), and no pure males, it's kind of a rococo world down there. You might consider checking out St. Mary (1996) for just lots more stuff regarding reproduction. Zebras feed mostly on benthic prey, the kind of stuff they can eat while staying hidden away in crevices. This translates to gammarid amphipods, harpacticoid copepods, isopods, ostracods, and the like, along with smaller numbers of such zooplankters as euphausiids.

Rhinogobiops nicholsii

(Bean, 1882)

Blackeye Goby

ETYMOLOGY: *Rhinogobiops* means "like *Rhinogobius*" and *nicholsi* honors Captain Henry E. Nichols, United States Navy, the discoverer of this species.

THE BASICS: Maximum Length: 15 cm (6 in) TL. The Ranges: Near Sitka (southeastern Alaska) to south of Punta Rompiente and Isla Guadalupe and Isla Cedros (central Baja California). While fairly common in northern British Columbia, the species really kicks into gear from southern British Columbia to northern Baja California.

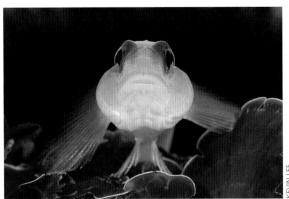

KEVIN LEE

Intertidal to more than 640 m (2,100 ft), and mostly down to 80 m (262 ft). Eggs: 2.1–2.2 x 0.5 mm. Larvae: hatching length: 2.8–3 mm, flexion length: 5.8–6.8 mm, transformation length: about 1.6–2.5 cm (0.6–1 mm). Length-weight parameters (TL, cm, gr): $W = 0.0115L^{2.984}$ (Love unpubl.).

SALIENT CHARACTERS: This is a small fish with a large black eye and a black tip at the top of the first dorsal fin. Their colors and body patterns are really, really variable. They range from plain gray-white and tan through greenish and lemon yellow (particularly the ones in deeper waters) and from no markings to heavily blotched, banded, and saddled. Reportedly, pelvic fins of males are black during the breeding season.

LIFE HISTORY: Blackeyes are small benthic fish that live on or near structure. Young-of-the-year recruit to shallow sea-floors at 1.5–2.5 cm (0.6–1 in) SL, settling in June and July in Southern California. We have seen very small, and perhaps newly settled fish, as deep as 91 m (300 ft). These fish tend to settle inside reefs, although you will also find them on the margins. During the day, juveniles and adults tend to lie on the sand, usually near rocks, worm tubes, kelp, eelgrass, or other material. At night, the fish take shelter in crevices and caves. In general, you will not see these animals on homogeneous soft sediments well away from hard habitat. Both larger males and females are territorial and both sexes defend their territories (of 0.01–1.2 m²) throughout the year. They defend their territories through, as described in Cole (1984): "Displays...of dorsal, anal, caudal and sometime pectoral fin erection, branchiostegal membrane extension and mouth gaping, and tailbeating...often followed by biting." Every territory has at its heart a sheltering spot where the fish can go when disturbed. Often this spot is a little refuge the fish excavates under a rock. Densities of these goby can be pretty high, up to 8.8 fish/m², depending on how many of these sheltering spots are crammed into an area. While they are most often seen resting on the bottom, at times hundreds will hover a meter or so above the seafloor. Blackeyes are able to withstand pretty brackish waters (down to at least 13 ppt) and have been found down to at least 9.5°C (49.1°F) off Alaska (they died in an aquarium when the water reached 3.8°C, 39°F). Both field and laboratory observations in Southern California imply that temperatures around 15°C (59°F) are preferred by blackeyes down that way.

KEVIN LEE

Preparatory to accepting eggs, as observed by Ebert and Turner (1962): "Males hollow out a small depression beneath rock, then clean its underside; later the female would attach her eggs to this cleaned undersurface...During courtship, the male would rise straight off the bottom a few inches and settle back again, attracting the female's attention by spreading his dorsal and blackened pelvic fins which are quite striking at this time...the male remains on guard and fans the nest...nests average 4 inches [10 cm] in diameter, are roughly circular and are made up of a single layer of eggs...do not have adhesive threads...eggs are faded pink...mature eggs are grayish." The entire spawning behavior takes 10–30 minutes. Small males, probably "sneakers," have been observed darting into the nest at this time and trying to fertilize the eggs. (For lots more on this, see Wiley 1973 and Cole 1983). Males guard egg clutches containing eggs from 1–6 females.

Most blackeyes probably do not live longer than about 3 years, but some have lived to the age of 5. The fish mature about 2.5 months after they settle to the bottom, and Mark Steele says that is at about 4.5 cm (2 in) SL. At least in Southern California, they spawn throughout the year. Off British Columbia, the season may be more restricted, perhaps from March– August. Blackeyes are sequential hermaphrodites; they start out life as females and then become males. There is evidence that some fish change from immature females to mature males, while others become mature females first. Females produce anywhere from 990–11,327 eggs per batch and they spawn 3–4 times a season. Blackeye goby feed mainly during daylight hours on a wide variety of prey, including gammarid amphipods, ostracods, brittle stars, polychaetes, snails, and bivalves, as well as copepods. They exhibit three feeding behaviors, 1) in the water column, 2) picking at stuff on the bottom, and 3) grabbing mouthful of sand, spitting it out, and then selecting loosened food material. Known predators are angel sharks, barred sand bass, black croakers, copper rockfish, kelp bass, kelp and painted greenlings, ronquils, pelagic cormorants, harbor seals, and California sea lions.

FISHERY: Blackeyes are caught fairly often from piers.

MISCELLANY: Blackeyes occasionally duke it out for shelter areas with such species as plainfin midshipman.

MILTON LOVE

Typhlogobius californiensis
Steindachner, 1879
Blind Goby

ETYMOLOGY: *Typhlogobius* means "blind" in Greek and "*Gobius.*" *Californiensis* reflects the species having been first recognized in San Diego Bay.

THE BASICS: Maximum Length: 8.3 cm (3 in) TL. The Ranges: San Simeon Point (Central California) to Bahia Magdalena (southern Baja California). Intertidal to 15 m (50 ft). Eggs: 2.7–2.9 x 0.7 mm. Larvae: hatching length = 3–3.3 mm, flexion length = 5–6 mm, transformation length = 1.2–2.7 cm (0.5–1.1 in).

DESCRIPTON: Like a creature out of one of those early 1950s movies, where radiation from a secret test facility has gotten into the water (e.g., *The Thing With Pale Pink Skin, Small or Absent Eyes, and Loose Skin*), blind goby have very small or absent eyes, loose skin, and are pale pink.

LIFE HISTORY: A most interesting fish, the blind goby usually lives in ghost shrimp burrows (and thus mostly in quite shallow waters), often in the sand patches near rocks. While young fish may have some sight, the adults are completely blind and apparently sense much of their world through smell. Male-female pairs are usually the rule in these burrows. These fish are very territorial and invading blind goby are in for a fight, with fish locking jaws for as long as 3 hours.

MacGinitie (1939) claims this species lives 10–15 years, but provides no evidence for this. He goes on to state that the fish mature at about 1 year old. Based on larval surveys, there is at least a little spawning all through the year; however direct observations of fish and nests imply that most of it occurs from about March–July. At least in captivity, females spawn 3–4 times a season, producing 2,500–15,000 eggs at a time. Both males and females guard the eggs and they hatch after 10–12 days at 17–20°C (63–68°F), Apparently, blind goby are able to discriminate sexes by chemicals signatures. Their predators include moray eels and pistol shrimps.

MISCELLANY: 1) There are a lot of blood vessels in the skins of these goby and much of their respiration occurs here. If they are moist, they can live out of water for at least a week. 2) MacGinitie (1939) claims that, in aquaria, he saw blind goby bring large pieces of food to their hosts shrimps, said shrimps then ripped up the food, and both ate the resulting pieces. I don't know, I just don't know.

OTHER SPECIES

Acanthogobius flavimanus
(Temminck & Schlegel, 1845)
Yellowfin Goby

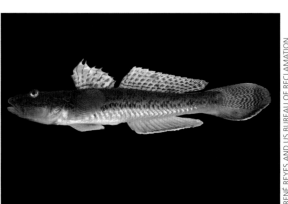
RENÉ REYES AND US BUREAU OF RECLAMATION

Yellowfins reach a length of 25 cm (10 in) TL in the eastern Pacific and 30 cm (12 in) in Japan. They are native to the northwestern Pacific. In North America, they live from Tomales and San Francisco bays, and other central and Southern California bays and estuaries, to Ensenada (northern Baja California), from the intertidal to at least 6.5 m (21 ft). This is a benthic species that is usually found in mud and eelgrass. Young-of-the-year settle out in shallow waters at as small as 1.2 cm (0.5 in) SL. Yellowfins can tolerate anything from basically freshwater to salinities greater than that of seawater (at least to 40 ppt) and a wide range of temperatures (at least 4–31.6°C, 39–89°F). However, these fish require waters of at least 5 ppt to breed. So, for instance, fish living in the Mokelumne River (California) have to move into at least slightly more saline waters when it is time to spawn. Adults are territorial. Females attach eggs to the roof of burrows dug by males. Genetic studies show that the fish on our coast likely came from Japan and probably from Tokyo Bay. Yellowfins live to at least 3 years old. In Japan, males mature at the end of their first year and females at end of their second year. In Central California, spawning has been reported variously as "January to May" or "fall and late winter." Females produce between 6,000–32,000 eggs that hatch in about one month. Yellowfin goby eat a variety of small planktonic and epibenthic invertebrates, such as gammarid amphipods, crabs, shrimps, various copepods, mysid shrimps, insects, polychaetes, as well as plant material. Predators include leopard sharks, Brandt's cormorants, and harbor seals. In Japan, this species is of some commercial importance. It is taken fairly frequently in San Francisco Bay by recreational anglers fishing from piers and shore. Eggs: 0.5–1 mm. Larvae: hatching length = 4.5–4.6 mm, flexion length = about 6.7–less than 8.6 mm, transformation length = about 1.6–1.8 cm (0.6–0.7 in). Length-weight parameters (TL, mm, kg): (sexes combined) W = $0.0000000136L^{2.89}$ (RecFin 2009).

Ctenogobius sagittula
(Günther, 1861)
Longtail Goby

Longtail goby grow to 20.3 cm (8 in) TL and have been found from Marina de Rey (Southern California) to Puerto Pizarro (Peru), commonly northward to about Mission Bay (Southern California). They live on mud and sand flats in lagoons, mangrove forests, and other quiet waters, from the intertidal to 5 m (17 ft). Longtails eat diatoms, filamentous and other algae, snails, nematodes, and other small prey. When feeding, they reportedly crawl or flip out of the water onto mud flats, grab a mouthful of mud, then flip back into water to flush the mud away. Length-weight parameters (SL, cm, gr): (sexes combined) W = $0.015L^{2.6}$ (Gonzalez-Acosta et al. 2004).

GERALD ALLEN

Ilypnus gilberti
(Eigenmann & Eigenmann, 1889)
Cheekspot Goby

Cheekspots reach 6.4 cm (3 in) TL and range from Tomales Bay (Northern California) to Bahia Magdalena (southern Baja California), and Gulf of California. On the outer coast, they are abundant from Tomales Bay to the Bahia Magdalena complex (southern Baja California). They live from the intertidal zone to depths of at least 10 m (33 ft). Cheekspots are estuarine and bay dwellers, usually found in quiet, shallow waters. Young-of-the-year settle onto soft substrate in backwaters, starting at about 1.1–1.6 cm (0.4–0.6 in) SL. Both juveniles and adults are particularly abundant on sand or mud flats containing little vegetation, although they do not despise eelgrass. One fish was also collected in a remnant, freshwater, pool upstream from the mouth of a stream in Baja California. Adults of this very feisty fish live in burrows and Ed Brothers (1975) notes: "Burrows… are typically 20–26 cm [17–10 in] long and 8–11 mm in diameter…Burrowing is initiated by the fish rapidly pushing its head into the sand until the anterior body up to the origin of the dorsal fin is buried. The head is held in the sand for as long as 20 seconds. The action is repeated until a permanent depression about 1 cm deep results. The fish then begins to take mouthfuls of sand out of the depression, expelling them around the burrow."

Most fish smaller than 2.5 cm (1 in) SL do not have burrows and rather dive into the sand when disturbed. These fish are highly territorial, each adult driving off intruders that stray within their sphere of influence; an area that, on average, encompasses about 600 cm². Cheeks have a complex set of behavioral interactions toward one another that includes all kinds of ritual displays and intense color changes. Check out Ed's 1975 thesis for more than is healthy to know about this stuff. Cheekspots are inactive at night.

Cheekspots live to 5 years old. Females may grow slightly faster and larger than males. Fish in California may grow larger than those in the Gulf of California and those north of Point Conception

ED BROTHERS

may be the largest of all. Most females are mature at 2.6–3 cm (1 in) SL (2 years old) and all are mature at 3.6–4 cm (1–2 in) SL (3 years old). In Southern California, they probably spawn throughout the year; it is unclear if there is a peak season. Females spawn more than once per year and fecundity ranges from about 350–2,000 eggs. The only time this psychotic, territorial thing breaks down is during spawning season, when the males allow females into their burrows to lay eggs. After that (to the male) unpleasantness is over, the female is escorted out and the male guards the eggs until they hatch. A female lays as many as 350 eggs at a go. Cheekspots are relatively unspecialized predators; they feed either by taking bites out of the substrate (then ejecting the inedible portions out of their opercles) or dining on water column creatures. Gammarid and caprellid amphipods, harpacticoid copepods, ostracods, and polychaetes are important. They also eat snails, clam siphons, and mysid shrimps. Predators include barred sand bass, California corbinas, spotted sand bass, staghorn sculpins, and herons. They are most closely related to shadow goby. Eggs are club-shape with attachment threads at one end. Eggs: 0.6–0.6 mm. Larvae: hatching length = 3.1 mm, flexion length = 5–6 mm, transformation length at perhaps 1.1–2 mm (0.4–0.8 in). Von Bertalanffy parameters (SL, mm): (sexes combined) L_∞ = 60, k = 0.18, t_0 = -1.41 (Brothers 1975). Length-weight parameters (SL, mm, mg): (sexes combined) W = $0.004L^{3.253}$ (Brothers 1975).

Quietula y-cauda
(Jenkins & Evermann, 1889)
Shadow Goby

Shadows grow to a mighty 7 cm (3 in) TL. They live from Morro Bay (Central California) to the Gulf of California and from the intertidal zone to depths of 6 m (20 ft). They dwell in bays and estuaries, mud and mangroves. Most settlement of young-of-the-year occurs from spring to early fall and at as small as 0.7 cm (0.3 in) SL. Adults mostly live in burrows (25 cm, 10 in, deep or more), often within eelgrass and green algae beds. The males tend to be restricted to their burrows and surrounding territory and tend to be pretty aggressive. Females are perhaps less site restricted and more likely to be out in the open and moving about more. Most fish hold territories, particularly the males during the breeding season, and there is a lot of kind of complex interpersonal stuff going on. One of the more unusual behaviors is "mouth-fighting" where two fish grab each other's jaws and twist around for a while. Ed Brothers (1975) wrote: "Several conflicts were observed that lasted up to 30 minutes. In these situations fighting was very intense, with prolonged mouth fights that took the combatants as much as 50 cm [20 in] off the bottom. Only males were collected with healed-over jaw injuries." Ed gives lots and lots of details about all kinds of behaviors of this species. Interestingly, genetic studies show little in the way of discrete populations along the California coast, implying that there is considerable gene flow.

Shadow goby live to at least 5 years old. A few fish are mature at 2.1–2.4 cm (0.8–1 in) SL (1 year old), most at 2.5–2.9 cm (1 in) (2 years old), and all are mature at 3.6–4.1 cm (1–2 in) (3 years old). They likely spawn throughout the year, perhaps peaking in summer, and females spawn more than once per year. Fecundity ranges from about 400 to over 2,000 eggs. The eggs are deposited in the male's burrow and then guarded by the male until hatching. Shadow goby are not highly specialized predators. They either feed by taking a bite out of the substrate and ejecting the nonedible parts out their opercles or by biting off chunks of plant material, likely removing crustaceans and other animals. Feeding occurs primarily at night, or at least at dusk and in the early morning. Among their most important prey are gammarid amphipods, along with harpacticoid copepods, caprellid amphipods, ostracods, polychaetes, and clam siphons. They also eat fertilized goby eggs, so watch out, it's a jungle out there. Predators include barred sand bass, California halibut, California needlefish, California scorpionfish, giant kelpfish, staghorn sculpins, and octopuses. They are most closely related to cheekspot goby. Ripe ovarian eggs are 0.6–0.7 mm in diameter, are club-shaped, and have threads attached to one end. Larvae: hatching length = about 2.8–3 mm, flexion length = 5–5.8 mm, transformation length = as large as 1.2 cm (0.5 in). Von Bertalanffy parameters (SL, mm): (sexes combined) L_∞ = 70, k = 0.16, t_0 = -0.931 (Brothers 1975). Length-weight parameters (SL, mm, mg): (sexes combined) W = $0.0138L^{2.963}$ (Brothers 1975).

Tridentiger trigonocephalus
(Gill, 1859)
Chameleon Goby

This species grows to 12.5 cm (5 in) TL and is found in salt, brackish, and freshwater, from the surf to more than 15 m (49 ft). A native of China, Japan, and Siberia, it has been found in San Francisco Bay, Los Angeles Harbor, and San Diego Bay. In San Diego Bay, chameleons recruit from the plankton to eelgrass beds during the summer.

DAN HEILPRIN

FAMILY LUVARIDAE—Louvars
Louvars sit neatly in their own family. They are oviparous, with planktonic larvae.

Luvarus imperialis
Rafinesque, 1810
Louvar

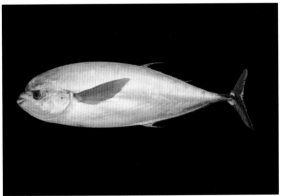

OSCAR SOSA-NISHIZAKI

ETYMOLOGY: I could not get a hold of Rafinesque's 1810 work, which by the way is in Latin, so I don't know what *Luvarus* means. On the other hand, *imperialis* means "imperial" in Latin.

THE BASICS: Maximum Length: 2 m (79 in) TL. Maximum Weight: The largest fish reported off California weighed 139 kg (305 lb). The Ranges: Circumglobal; Washington to Chile, mostly between 40°N and 40°S.

SALIENT CHARACTERS: How do these fish compete? Major things to look for are the very blunt head, the little piggy eyes set too far down that head, the too-small mouth, and the lovely lunate caudal fin. Freshly dead ones are pinkish or silvery, sometimes with a darkish back, red fins, and (occasionally) dark spots. Fish that have been dead for a while tend to lose the spots and the red fins fade.

LIFE HISTORY: Louvars are pelagic fish that live at least part of the time in surface waters. Folks don't know much about them. Based on the handful of larvae that have been taken, louvars may spawn in temperate waters north and south of the Equator. Most larvae have been captured in summer months; however, off southwest Africa one was taken in winter and one in spring. A fish caught off California in May had ripe or nearly ripe ovaries. One fish had an estimated total fecundity of 47.5 million eggs. Louvers feed on such gelatinous fare as medusae and ctenophores. Predators include thresher sharks, tunas, and wahoos.

FISHERY: Although the catch is small, louvars are caught with some predictability off the West Coast (including well down into Baja California) by those commercial fishermen targeting swordfish and other pelagic fishes. Recreational fisherman only rarely hook one. They are fairly yummy.

ORIGINS: The oldest fossil louvar is *Luvarus necopinatus* from the Late Paleocene or Early Eocene (perhaps 55 million years ago) of southern European Russia.

FAMILY SPHYRAENIDAE—Barracudas

Barracudas are circumglobal, mostly tropical and temperate fishes. There is one genus, and 21 species; four species live within our range and two (*S. argentea* and *S. ensis*) are found as far north as Southern California. They are oviparous with pelagic eggs and larvae. Barracudas are known from as far back as the Middle Eocene (perhaps 50 million years ago). The four eastern Pacific species are illustrated in Fischer et al. (1995).

Sphyraena argentea
Girard, 1854
Pacific Barracuda

"Long, slender, silvery cylinders of animated protein" (Pinkas 1966).

ETYMOLOGY AND COLLOQUIAL NAMES: *Sphyraena* comes from the ancient Greek and means "hammer fish" and *argentea* means "silvery" in Latin. They have been called "slime sticks," "snakes," and "Catalina stovepipes."

THE BASICS: Maximum Length: 122 cm (48 in) TL, reported to 152 cm (60 in) TL. Maximum Weight: 7.2 kg (15.9 lb). The International Game Fish Association world record is 12 kg (26.5 lb), but that fish was taken off Costa Rica, well southward of the reported geographic range of the species, so one is perhaps hesitant to accept it. The Ranges: Kodiak Island to Cabo San Lucas (southern Baja California), southwestern Gulf of California, and Islas Revillagigedo. They are routinely abundant as far north as Point Conception (California) and Santa Rosa Island, and, in many years, are pretty common into Central California, up to maybe off Morro Bay. Surface to 38 m (125 ft), including surf zone. Eggs: 1–1.6 mm. Larvae: hatching length = about 2.3–2.5 mm, flexion length = about 5.5–7.2 mm, transformation length = about 2.6 to less than 4.7 mm. Von Bertalanffy parameters (SL, mm): (females) L_∞ = 777, k = 0.2618, t_0 = -2.711; (males) L_∞ = 763.5, k = 0.2373, t_0 = -3.042 (Bottinelli and Allen 2007). Length-weight parameters (TL, mm, gr): (sexes combined) W = $0.007856L^{2.818}$ (Bottinelli and Allen 2007).

SALIENT CHARACTERS: It would be difficult to confuse Pacific barracuda with anything else. These puppies are long, skinny, have bluish or brownish backs, silvery sides, and mouths full of pointy teeth.

LIFE HISTORY: Pacific barracuda are what we might call nearshore, quasi-pelagic, schooling fishes. While they often swim well away from structure, albeit usually fairly near the coast, they also foray into kelp and eelgrass beds and over reefs, even entering surf, harbors, and backwaters at times. Small ones are usually found in quite shallow waters, both in bays and on the open coast. Larger ones will school with yellowtail and Pacific bonito. I have seen schools as large as maybe 500 fish. In a study off Southern California, they were found in 10.6–23.3°C (51–74°F), at an average temperature of 18°C (64°F). This is a highly migratory species; they can travel up to 16 km (10 mi) per day, although average speeds seem to be 2–3 km (1–2 mi) per day. Tagging studies show that some fish tagged off San Pedro (Southern California) may travel as far north as Point Sur (Central California). Fish off northern Baja California and Southern California likely form one population. In general, fish move northward in the spring and summer and southward in the fall. However, some fish overwinter off California. As far back as the 19th century, Collins (1892) noted that Pacific barracuda were commonly caught by commercial fishermen during the winter off Avila (Central California). Barracuda appear to be very responsive to ocean temperatures, as El Niños can bring up simply zillions of these fish into Southern California. The first time I saw this

RICHARD HERRMANN

MEA CULPA

Fishing columnist extraordinaire Bill Beebe remembers the 1930s through 1950s as the heyday for barracuda in Southern California. Partyboats found them in abundance and restaurants listed them on the menu. In the early days, it was quite legal for folks to catch them on partyboats and sell them. Lots of kids paid for lots of fishing trips that way. By the 1950s, this was clearly illegal, but the statute of limitations having run out, I should note that in the late 1950s and early 1960s, I rode the partyboats of Santa Monica and caught quantities of barracuda, yellowtail, and rockfishes and sold them to eager customers waiting on the Santa Monica Pier. In the early 1960s, I would get 2 dollars per fish for yellowtail and 25¢ per rockfish. At one time or another I have been asked how I now feel about engaging in such illegal activities. Repentant? Defiant? Embarrassed? Shoot, I feel great. I was maybe 14 years old, couldn't get a job, and liked to go fishing on sportfishing boats. And, oh, I forgot to mention that I also captured sand crabs in the surf and, without a commercial fishing license, sold them to the Santa Monica Pier bait shop. If Sherlock Holmes described Professor James Moriarty as the "Napoleon of Crime," I was the "Napoleon of Slime."

was during the 1957–1958 El Niño, when they were so abundant these fish became a burden to anglers in Santa Monica. I saw lots of large ones caught in the surf during that period. Barracuda spawn in nearshore waters.

Pacific barracuda live for at least 18 years and females are larger than males at every year. Females mature at 2–3 years old (at as small as 44 cm, 17 in, TL), 50% at perhaps 49 cm (19 in), and all at 55 cm (22 in). Males mature at 1–2 years (33–45 cm, 13–18 in). Almost all spawning occurs from April–October (but the errant larvae has been picked up in the winter and early spring), mostly from May–August, depending on area and year. Based on larval captures, spawning occurs between Point Conception and Punta Eugenia (Baja California). The eggs are yellow before maturing and then turn grayish. Females are batch spawners and produce 42,000–512,987 eggs per batch. They eat fishes and squids. Predators include giant sea bass, soupfin sharks, thresher sharks, sailfish, California sea lions, and bottlenose dolphins.

FISHERY: Pacific barracuda were commonly eaten by Native Americans in Southern and, to a certain extent, Central California, and as far southward as at least Isla Cedros (central Baja California). In the 19th century, they were a very important commercial species as far north as San Francisco. Lockington (1879b) wrote: "It is usually obtained south of the bay [San Francisco] and at the Farallones, but occurs at least as far north as Tomales." Fishermen of the time caught them by trolling (from sailing vessels) and with gill nets. In those days before refrigeration, much of the catch was dried and salted. Well into the 20th century, barracuda remained a very popular species with California fish-eaters. Most were sold fresh, but Japanese processors used barracuda to make canned fish cakes, there was a small smoked trade, and the roe

was also highly desirable. In an attempt to limit the catch, in the 1920s California banned their take with the efficient purse seine and lampara nets, leaving the fishery to gillnetters, live bait fishermen, and trollers. The fish was sufficiently valuable that during the 1920s, American vessels would travel to southern Baja California to catch them. Well, times change, and the popularity of Pacific barracuda, at least in the commercial fishery, began to decline in the mid-20th century. As of this writing, Pacific barracuda are of only limited importance in the California commercial fishery and, in fact, in some instances the roe is worth more than the fish it came from. Off Baja California, this species still forms a fairly important artisanal fishery and you can commonly see them in the Mercado Negro in Ensenada (northern Baja California).

J.C. Van Hook, writing in the 31 October 1889 edition of *Forest and Stream* (and quoted in Collins 1892), has these words for us regarding accompanying a commercial fisherman trolling for barracuda off Point Loma (San Diego) in the days of sail: "At daybreak we were drifting past Ballast Point. After floating a mile out into the ocean…we concluded to tie up to the kelp and wait for the wind…About 9 o'clock a light breeze sprung up, and, cutting loose from the kelp, we began to move slowly over the water, but not fast enough, as Bob said, to put out our lines. In my anxiety to begin the sport I cast out two lines, and very soon we hooked two so-called Spanish mackerel [bonito] of 10 and 12 pounds…Presently the breeze came along, and within half an hour we were sailing at a lively rate, so we adjusted outriggers, one on either side, about in the waist of the boat, with two lines each. We also trolled one from the stern, making five in all…Now the fun commenced in earnest; first one, then two, four, five, are hooked at a time, and rare sport it was to haul them in…Occasionally, in attempting to land the

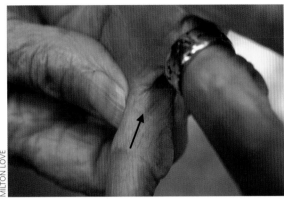

MILTON LOVE

Disfiguring scar, the remnants of a Pacific barracuda's wrath. Be afraid, be very afraid.

fish in the box, we missed it, and they fell down into the bottom of the boat, or our footing would be lost and we were bunched in a slippery mass—fish and all. The sloop was pitching heavily, as half a gale of wind was blowing...We caught 68 barracuda and 2 Spanish mackerel—about 425 pounds of fish—filling our box...The fish were selling at the time for 10 cents each." He goes on to say that most of the fish were salted and dried, sent to San Francisco, and thence to China.

While barracuda have declined in importance as a commercial species, they remain very popular with recreational anglers. Most are taken from boats, but they are also caught with some regularity from piers and jetties and there is even the occasional flurry in the surf. As far as barracuda as a recreational fish is concerned, Charles Holder (1910c) wrote: "The California barracuda is taken here by the thousands and is caught when fishing for yellowtail...but it requires a long and elastic imagination to consider it a game fish, for some barracudas of twelve pounds will come in so readily as to almost jump into the boat. They grow to weigh fifteen pounds, and once in a while one will imitate a game fish." Holder was clearly an upper class toff and if you had asked the average Joe or Jane on the Redondo Pier they would have said that Holder could stick his jodhpurs where the sun don't shine and they would be pleased, thank you very much, to catch a barracuda or two.

ORIGINS AND RELATIONSHIPS: A Miocene (at least 5.3-million-year-old) *Sphyraena*, collected in northern Baja California, is listed in the collections of the University of California, Berkeley, Paleontological Museum. Remains of Pacific barracuda are known from 100,000-year-old strata in California. Pacific barracuda may be most closely related to the eastern Pacific species *Sphyraena lucasana* and *S. idiastes*.

REMARKS: Conventional wisdom holds that only great barracuda (*S. barracuda*) are linked to barracuda attacks. But wait. Way back in 1933, my wife's aunt Dorothy Albee was bitten while removing a hook from a Pacific barracuda, leaving a scar still visible after many decades (see horrifying image above). The stress of this deformity later led Ms. Albee to dance with Harry Bridges, the arguably communist head of the International Longshore and Warehouse Union on the West Coast.

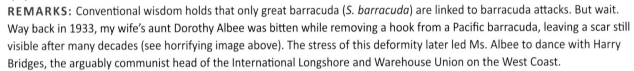

CALLING ALL VENTURE CAPITALISTS

And for those of you with an entrepreneurial bent, and perhaps for those of you who are bent in various other ways, you must order today (assuming you can go back in time) *Kippering Barracuda, with Especial Reference to Canning*, published in about 1918, by the U.S. Board of Chemistry and written by E.D. Clark and H.D. Davi. The publication notes that during the Great War (as opposed to some of our other wars which were Not-So-Great) about 3 million pounds of barracuda were caught and sold in California, most of it was in a fresh state. But wait! When large catches were made the fresh fish market was glutted and what could fish purveyors do? Well, in stepped Messrs. Clark and Davi, with the good news about kippering barracuda. Yes, it's all here in *Kippering Barracuda*. From cleaning the fish, to smokehouse requirements, to cooling, packing, and canning your smoked barracuda in peach-kernel oil, you can have the lifestyle you have always dreamed of in the booming barracuda kippering industry.

FAMILY GEMPYLIDAE—Snake Mackerels

The gempylids are circumglobal pelagic relatives of the tunas and mackerels that live in tropical and subtropical marine waters. There are 16 genera, about 24 species, and five within our range. Snake mackerel are oviparous with planktonic eggs and larvae. Otoliths from what might have been gempylids are known from the Cretaceous (about 71 million years ago) and likely these fish lived during the Late Paleocene/Basal Eocene (around 55 million years ago). On the West Coast, three species, *Thyrsocles kriegeri*, *Trossulus exoletus*, and *Zaphleges longurio*, lived in Southern California during the Miocene (at least 5.3 million years ago) and an unidentified taxa (maybe one of the former species) is known from a Southern California Miocene formation of 7.6–8.6 million years ago. The eastern Pacific gempylids are figured and described in Fischer et al. (1995).

Both escolar and oilfish are widely caught and sold, sometimes as "escolar" and, in a number of countries, as "codfish," "butterfish," and other pseudonyms. And for a certain percentage of you diners out there, escolar and oilfish are not your friends. Halibuts are your friends, salmon (wild, of course) are your friends, even white croakers are your friends. But escolar and oilfish, well, they are just not your friends. Unless you are interested in uncontrollable anal leakage, in which case, yes, escolar and oilfish are your friends. Various medical journals around the world have documented the "purgative" effects on some of us of consuming the meat of either species. The substances that seem to be doing the damage are wax esters and both *L. flavobrunneum* and *R. pretiosus* seem to have these in spades.

Lepidocybium flavobrunneum
(Smith, 1843)
Escolar

ETYMOLOGY AND COLLOQUIAL NAME: *Lepidocybium* means "scale" (in Greek) and "cybium" (a now-disused name for Spanish mackerel) and *flavobrunneum* is Latin for "yellow" and "brown." The Japanese name is "abura-sokomutsu." "Escolar" may be derived from the Spanish "assacolar" meaning to "scour or burnish."

THE BASICS: Maximum Length: 220 cm (87 in) TL. Maximum Weight: 68.4 kg (150.4 lb). The Ranges: Circumglobal; in western Pacific as far north as southern Kuril Islands; Washington to Cabo Blanco (Peru), and Gulf of California. 25–200 m (82–656 ft) and more, usually caught at 100–300 m (328–984 ft). Larvae: hatching length = less than 3 mm, flexion length = about 5–6 mm, transformation length = about 1.6 cm (0.6 in).

SALIENT CHARACTERS: Escolar are fusiform, with a wavy lateral line, low anterior dorsal fin, large scales surrounded by small ones forming a mosaic, and three keels on the caudal peduncle. They are black or dark brown.

LIFE HISTORY: Another species that, despite its modest economic importance, is poorly understood. Escolar are pelagic fish that are believed to migrate upward at night. A 145 cm (57 in) FL fish was 13–14 years old. In the eastern equatorial Atlantic, they appear to mature at perhaps 30–35 cm (12–14 in) TL and spawn in July and August. They feed on fishes, squids, and crustaceans and are eaten by billfishes, other escolar, and various tunas.

FISHERY: As noted above, escolar are often taken by commercial fishermen and you can find it, as a fairly expensive product, in upscale fresh fish markets in the U.S.

RELATIONSHIPS: Escolar are most closely related to oilfish and, a little more distantly, to wahoos.

Ruvettus pretiosus
Cocco, 1833
Oilfish

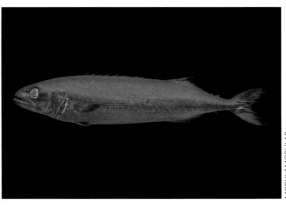

Oilfish are documented to reach 203 cm (80 in) TL and at least 45 kg (99 lb), but have been reported to 305 cm (10 ft) and 63.5 kg (139.9 lb). They are circumglobal in temperate and tropical waters. In our part of the world, they live as far northward as the southern Kuril Islands, and from Encinitas (Southern California) to southern Baja California, and Guatemala to Chile. Based on catches by sportfishing boats, oilfish are probably reasonably common off central Baja California. They live in 60 m (197 ft), and probably shallower, to 1,160 m (3,806 ft). These are benthic or near-benthic fish, usually found in relatively deep waters. Work off the eastern coast of South America and in the southeastern Atlantic and Indian oceans has established that oilfish spend at least part of the day either lying on the seafloor or swimming just above it. This research also noted some fish swimming 300 m (984 ft) above the bottom, leading researchers to speculate that they migrate vertically to feed in shallower waters at night. A 156 cm (61 in) TL fish was 8 years old. Oilfish eat fishes, squids, and crustaceans, and are eaten by billfishes and, one assumes, other larger fishes. Cookiecutter sharks take plugs out of them. Norman and Fraser (1949) warn: "The fish is heavily charged with oil, which has a strongly purgative action - a circumstance that has given it the name of 'Castor-oil Fish'. Being aware of this fact, the natives of some parts of the world boil the flesh and decant the oil, after which it can be eaten with impunity." Oilfish are most closely related to escolar and, a little more distantly, wahoos. They keep themselves buoyant by storing oil in their skull bones and skin. Larvae: hatching length = less than 3 mm, flexion length = about 4–6 mm.

FAMILY SCOMBRIDAE—Mackerels and Tunas

Worldwide, there are 16 genera and about 51 species of tunas, mackerels, bonito, and Spanish mackerels, all inhabiting marine waters. Fifteen species live within our range and although almost all of them are found as far north as Southern California, most are more abundant to the south in warmer waters. All species are pelagic or semi-pelagic and all live at least part of the time at or near the surface. All scombrids are oviparous, are broadcast spawners, and have planktonic eggs and larvae. Fishes in the family Scombridae appear to have first appeared in the Late Paleocene or Early Eocene, around 55 million years ago. Fossil scombrids are known from a Southern California Miocene formation of 7.6–8.6 million years ago.

Canning tuna, the way most of us plain folks were introduced to these fishes, began in Southern California in 1907, when A.P. Halfhill packed some. Have you noticed how some folks speak of "tunafish" sandwiches or "tunafish" salad? Why is that? The tunas *are* fishes, so the term "tunafish" is redundant. Why not speak of "salmonfish" or "sardinefish" sandwiches? Maybe it's a class issue, like the difference between those who say "couch" and those who say "sofa." Of course, this kind of thing has been going on for some time. For instance "pork" is a Norman word for swine, while "pig" is the Saxon term. Both terms entered our language, one from the oppressors and one from the oppressed. So perhaps those in the "tunafish" crowd are bourgeois exploiters of the workers, while just plain folks like us say "tuna." Maybe Big Bill Hayward and Joe Hill (may he rest in peace) called for a "tuna" sandwich, while the Astors and Rockefellers requested "tunafish," with the crusts trimmed off, thank you very much.

The California tuna canning industry, that stinky, kinky, but never dinky business that fueled the economies of San Pedro and San Diego is, alas, no more. Globalization spelled the end of California tuna canning, as the industry, comprising almost 2,000 fishermen, as well as 6,000 cannery and associated crafts workers, disappeared in the early 1980s, when entire canneries were boxed up and shipped to Asia, Puerto Rico, and the South Pacific. However, not to worry, you can relive the sociological implications of the glory days, in some detail, in M. Orbach's *Hunters, Seamen, and Entrepreneurs* (University of California Press, 1977).

THERE'LL BE A HOT TIME IN THE OLD TOWN TONIGHT

Tunas, particularly members of the genera *Thunnus* and their close relatives, the skipjacks, genera *Euthynnus* and *Katsuwonus*, have extensive adaptations for pelagic living. For instance, many species have very large hearts and gill surfaces that have up to 10 times the surface area of most other fishes. Of perhaps most importance, these fishes have versions of a heat exchange system that keeps various parts of their bodies 1–20°C warmer than the surrounding water. The elevated muscle temperatures increase the capacity of muscles to conduct work. The remarkable Dr. John Davy (1790–1868), writing in the *Edinburgh New Philosophy Journal* of 1835, was the first person to write about this phenomenon. Davy, the brother of the equally remarkable Sir Humphrey Davy, was for many years a member of the Medical Department of the British Army. In that capacity, he served in Ceylon (now Sri Lanka) and Malta (during this stint he proscribed putting leeches on the head of a stroke-ridden Sir Walter Scott) and was ultimately the family doctor to Wordsworth and his family up there in the Lake District (where he probably proscribed leeches for just about everything the daffodil-lover contracted). Wherever he was stationed Davy wrote prodigiously about the natural history, geology, agriculture, and peoples of the locale.

It was while serving in Ceylon, doing his bit to keep the Empire's happy subjects relatively free of disease, that he noted that, while such piscine luminaries as Linnaeus and Baron Cuvier held that fish maintained body temperatures equal to that of the surrounding water: "It was...on a voyage to Ceylon, that I first met with an exception to this universally received opinion: it was in the instance of the Bonito (Thynnus palamys [sic], Cuv. and Valen.) [now *Katsuwonus pelamis*], whose temperature was 99 degrees of Fahr. in the deep-seated muscles in the thickest part of the fish a little below the gills, when the surface of the sea, from which it had just before been taken, was 80.5, the difference being the remarkable one of eighteen degrees and a half." He then goes on to say that he noted the same phenomenon in bluefin tuna taken off the Sicilian coast. And while he did not have his trusty thermometer at hand: "It immediately occurred to me, that its temperature also might be high, and the result of careful inquiry among the fishermen of most experience in the tunny fishery confirmed the conjecture. All who were asked, declared that the tunny is warm-blooded, and one of the most intelligent of them [the fishermen, one assumes, and not the tunny], when questioned as to the degree of heat, said it was much the same, or little less than that of the blood of a pig, when flowing from the divided vessels of the neck in being killed." And on that evocative note, we leave Dr. Davy.

This really quite interesting observation was followed up by, well, really nothing for the better part of a century, at which time it was brought back to light by Dr. Kamakichi Kishinouye, a gentleman acknowledged to be one of the fathers of tuna biology. In his scarily exhaustive work "Contributions to the Comparative Study of the So-called Scombroid Fishes" (Kishinouye 1923), which encompassed simply every aspect of a tuna's life short of how it feels to be fated to end up in a can, he went into some detail about the possible relationship between a pelagic existence and the tuna's anatomy and physiology. For those wishing to be slapped upside the head on the subject, the anatomy and physiology of heat exchange mechanisms, aspects of metabolisms, energetics of tunas and their relatives, and the rationale for the evolution of these systems can be found in distressing detail in Altringham and Shadwick (2001), Brill and Bushnell (2001), Graham and Dickson (2001), and Korsmeyer and Dewar (2001).

Schaefer (2001) points out that little real data exists on the size and age at which most of the tunas and skipjacks mature. This, however, will not stop me from presenting whatever information comes at hand. For I am, if nothing else, the Loki of fish biologists; but a mischievous force spreading a farrago of information for those who find themselves data-poor.

Acanthocybium solandri
(Cuvier, 1832)
Wahoo

ETYMOLOGY AND COLLOQUIAL NAMES: *Acanthocybium* means "spine" and "*Cybium*" (a now-disused genus name for Spanish mackerel) and *solandri* honors Daniel Carlsson Solander (1733–1782). "Ono" is the name you often see in fish markets. I've seen "peto" and "guajo" used in Mexico and the Japanese name is "kamasu-sawara."

THE BASICS: Maximum Length: 2.5 m (8 ft) TL. Maximum Weight: 83.6 kg (183.9 lb). The Ranges: Circumglobal; in western Pacific as far north as southern Kuril Islands; about 130 km (80 mi) south of the U.S.-Mexican border to Paita (Peru). There are a few (and unconfirmed) reports of small commercial catches from California waters. Common from about Isla Cedros (central Baja California) southward. Surface to 253 m (830 ft). McBride et al. (2008) present a number of von Bertalanffy growth parameters from the Atlantic and Caribbean and here are a couple: (FL, mm): (females) L_∞ = 1,797, k = 0.317, t_0 = -1.911; (males) L_∞ = 1.555, k = 0.44, t_0 = -1.64. Length-weight parameters (FL, cm, kg): (sexes combined) W = $0.0000001415710693L^{3.3034}$ (Uchiyama and Boggs 2006).

SALIENT CHARACTERS: Wahoos are very elongated, with a long (for a scombrid) first dorsal fin, and large, triangular teeth. They have a blue or green back with a silvery blush, and dozens of blue bars on each side. These bars are very striking in newly caught fish; they may not be intensely pigmented in fish seen underwater.

LIFE HISTORY: Wahoos are surface or near-surface dwellers that are found around the world in tropical and subtropical waters. At least in the eastern tropical Pacific, they often hang around floating debris. When chasing stuff, wahoos will leap

out of the water as much as 3 m (10 ft). There is substantial evidence that there is a single population distributed throughout the world. In the eastern North Pacific, they inhabit waters between at least 11.1–27.9°C (52–82°F°), but mostly in the zone around 25°C (77°F).

Wahoos live to 10 years or more and females grow larger than males. Growth rates of fish in the eastern Pacific are unknown, but fish around Florida and the Bahamas grow extremely quickly, reaching around 100 cm (40 in) in one year. Males mature at less than 93.5 cm (37 in) FL and one year old or less. Females occasionally mature at as small as at least 87.5 cm (34 in), 50% are mature at about 102 cm (40 in), and all are mature when larger than 105 cm (41 in). In tropical waters, such as those around Hawai'i, wahoos spawn throughout the year, while in somewhat more temperate climes, as in the northern Gulf of Mexico, spawning likely occurs from May–August. Females are multiple spawners, releasing eggs every 2–6 days. Batch fecundity ranges from around 400,000 to, apparently, over 6 million eggs per spawning. Multiplying it all out, it appears that a 5-year-old fish may spawn 30 million–92.8 million eggs per season. Wahoos feed on many species of pelagic fishes, as well as squids and octopuses, and a few crustaceans. They are eaten by dolphinfish, brown boobies, and sailfish, and chunks of them are removed by cookiecutter sharks.

FISHERY: Everyone loves to eat them wahoos. They are a major commercial species in many parts of the world (and caught in small numbers by pelagic gill netters off Baja California) and recreational anglers avidly seek them. The species is a major target of the long-range sportfishing

DANIEL SOLANDER

Daniel Solander was born in Pitea, Sweden, about 80 miles south of the Arctic Circle. Carolus Linnaeus passed through the town about one year before Solander was born and, after viewing two beheaded Finns and one quartered Lapp, on public display after being executed for murder, described the village thusly: "Never can the priest describe Hell, this is much worse; never can the poet describe Styx, as this is much uglier." Nevertheless, Solander managed to escape this Grand Guignol with Reindeer and wound up as one of Linnaeus's most adept botany students at dear old Uppsala U. Linnaeus, the father both of modern taxonomy and four daughters, appears to have thought of Solander as the son he never had and was apparently grooming the young botanist to replace him. However, Solander, despite what might very well have turned into a cushy future complete with an academic sinecure and Swedish message, was lured to England by several wealthy naturalists eager to introduce modern taxonomic practices to Great Britain.

Once in England, Solander more-or-less turned his back on Sweden. He became estranged from Linnaeus and even stopped writing his widowed mother. Perhaps this was because, upon arriving in England in 1760, Solander was an immediate hit. Fluent in at least four languages and armed with an extremely agreeable personality and a head full of the Linnaean Way, Solander made friends, influenced people, and rather quickly made himself indispensable to Sir Joseph Banks. The latter was clearly an excellent career move as the wealthy Banks was the botanical mover and shaker of England in the late 18th century. Within a few years, Solander was Banks' good friend, librarian, and curator of his massive collections, as well as a major figure at the nascent British Museum. Perhaps the crowning achievement in Solander's career was his accompanying the redoubtable Banks and the hyper-redoubtable Captain James Cook on Cook's first voyage to the Pacific and, ultimately, around the world. On this cruise, Banks and Solander collected plants and animals with a zeal bordering on the maniacal and, upon their return to England, set about formally describing hundreds of species. On more than one occasion, Banks stated that this magnum opus was only months away from publication. But ultimately, and for reasons that remain obscure, nothing was published. Solander died of what was probably a stroke in 1782 and while Banks, who lived for many more decades, could certainly have finished the monograph, he never did. After Solander's death, other researchers used Solander's descriptions and put their names to his work and within a few years this very good naturalist was semi-forgotten. The reality of his time was that if you did not get your stuff printed before you died, you often could kiss your sweet, sweet reputation goodbye.

vessels that work Baja California and points south. The most effective jigs for this species are of a singular construction (basically as elongated sinker, with lots of decoration and a single hook) and are usually referred to as "wahoo bombs." This is in keeping with the kind of martial spirit of the sport and is the reason one rarely hears of lures named "marlin nipple rings" or "yellowfin knickers."

ORIGINS AND RELATIONSHIPS: A fossil that may be an *Acanthocybium* was found in the Early Eocene (as much as 55 million years ago) of England. The related fossil genera, *Palaeocybium*, is found in the Early Eocene of Europe. A fossil *Acanthocybium* sp. from the Miocene (at least 5.3 million years ago) of northern Baja California is in the collection of the University of California, Berkeley, Paleontological Museum. Although kind of by themselves evolutionarily speaking, wahoos appear to be most closely related to the Spanish mackerels.

©MASA USHIODA-COOLWATERPHOTO.COM

Katsuwonus pelamis
(Linnaeus, 1758)
Skipjack Tuna

ETYMOLOGY AND COLLOQUIAL NAMES: *Katsuwonus* comes from the word "katsuwo," the Japanese word for this species, and *pelamis* is Greek for "tuna." Confusingly, back in the late 19th and early 20th centuries off California, this species was called "oceanic bonito" or "bonito," while *Sarda chiliensis* (now called Pacific bonito) was called "skipjack." "Striped tuna" was also used in the early 20th century. Barnhart (1936) placed this species in its own family, Katsuwonidae, the Victor Fishes. So, who was Victor and why did Barnhart name a fish family after him? They are called "Barrilete" by Baja California fishermen.

THE BASICS: Maximum Length: 120 cm (47 in) TL. Maximum Weight: 34 kg (75 lb). The Ranges: Circumglobal in tropical and subtropical waters; in western Pacific as far north as southern Kuril Islands; Yakutat Bay (southeastern Alaska) to Chile, including the southern Gulf of California. They are common as far north as the southern Kurils in the western Pacific and Southern California in the eastern Pacific. During El Niños, they may be abundant as far northward as Oregon. Surface to 596 m (1,955 ft). Eggs: 0.8–1.2 mm. Larvae: hatching length = about 2.3–3 mm, flexion length = about 5–7 mm, transformation length = about 1.8 cm (0.7 in). Length-weight parameters (FL, cm, kg): (females) W = $0.000010693L^{2.9337}$; (males) W = $0.0000080856L^{3.0157}$ (Uchiyama and Boggs 2006).

SALIENT CHARACTERS: Skipjack are readily identified by the four to six stripes on the lower sides of their bodies. A typical fish is colored blue or blue-purple on back with a silvery belly. Stressed fish, like ones that are courting, have dark bars or have reddish and purple hues.

LIFE HISTORY: Skipjack are highly motile, schooling, and pelagic fish. Like a number of other pelagics, they are terribly fond of drifting stuff. In the eastern Pacific, this might include trees that have been carried down Central and South American rivers, living and dead marine mammals, whale sharks, and sea turtles. And like yellowfin tuna (with whom they often hang out), eastern Pacific skippies commonly associate with a number of small cetaceans, spotted dolphins are probably the most important. In some years, skipjack never make it as far north as Southern California, but when they do it tends to be in the summer or early fall, and the fish may stay into November or even longer. Skippies appear to be most abundant south of 10°N and east of 135°W. While they tolerate waters of at least 7.7–30°C (46–86°F), they rarely are found in less than 18°C (64°F), and may be most abundant in 20–29°C (68–84°F). In the eastern tropical Pacific, young fish tend to live relatively nearshore with older ones offshore. Schaefer and Fuller (2007) note: "When not associated with floating objects, skipjack tuna displayed bounce-diving behavior to depths between 50 and 300 m [164–984 ft] during the day." In the eastern Pacific, skipjack spawn when temperatures are at or exceed 24°C (75°F). In the western and central Pacific, spawning occurs between 1500 and 2100 hours. Spawning is widespread from nearshore waters of Central America to well offshore, at about 15°N–10°S.

WHEN GOOD TUNAS GO BAD

Scombroid poisoning is an allergic reaction that is occasionally fatal. It occurs when fishes are eaten after being poorly chilled after capture. As noted in Thomas and Scott's *All Stings Considered* (University of Hawai'i Press, 1997): "When the fish becomes warm, bacteria on the skin begin to break down the fishes' flesh, normally laden with the amino acid histidine. During the breakdown process, histidine turns into histamine and saurine, a salt of histamine. Histamine is a major chemical messenger for allergic reactions." And while the condition is called "scombroid" poisoning, implying that the problem occurs only in the tunas, mackerels, and skipjacks, any fish that is poorly preserved can be problematic. Along with the tunas, fishes that often cause problems are dolphinfish and various jacks. Damaged fish may taste "peppery" but this is often not the case. Symptoms, which usually occur within a few minutes after eating the fish, include a very wide range of allergic reactions occasionally leading to death.

Think this was figured out recently? Maybe not, for here is what Frederick Debell Bennett observed in 1834 (*Narrative of a Whale Voyage Round the Globe from the Year 1833 to 1836*, 1840, Richard Bentley). A pretty good scientist, Bennett was aboard a British whaler in the central Pacific and for several months the crew had been catching and preserving in brine large quantities of "albacore" [perhaps yellowfin tuna]: "For more than the two previous months, albacore had constantly attended the ship in incredible numbers, and our crew, in anticipation of a traffic with the Sandwich Islanders, had preserved a large quantity of them in cases of brine. When thus preserved they appeared so excellent that, on one occasion, the sailors were tempted to eat them; but all who partook suffered for their imprudence. A few hours after their repast they complained of head-ache and fever, their skin was covered with a scarlet rash, and they exhibited all the other symptoms usually attendant upon eating poisonous fish. As we had sufficient and daily proofs that albacore were always wholesome in their fresh state, the ill effects they now produced could only be attributed to some decomposition, not perceptible to the senses, which they had undergone in the process of salting. It is an opinion common amongst sailors, that fish acquire a poisonous quality by being exposed for a night to the rays of the moon. A knowledge, however, of the early period at which fish becomes tainted in a tropical climate should lead us to admit, that a few hours, much more a night's keeping [at a warm temperature], is sufficient to produce that effect, independent of planetary influence."

It should be noted that other compounds produced by bacteria may also be involved in the symptoms of scombroid poisoning. These, according to Thomas and Scott, include "cadaverine or putrescine." Good grief, these sound like the names of those large-busted actresses who dress in black and host horror movies at 11 p.m. on cable television channels.

Tagging studies (Yuen 1970) off the Hawaiian Islands demonstrate that these fish: "Made nightly journeys of 25–106 km [15–65 mi] away from the bank and, with one exception, returned to the bank every morning to remain there for the day." In the eastern Pacific, there may be two groups of fish. One is found off the Islas Revillagigedo and migrates northward along Baja California and California before moving to the central Pacific; the other lives off Panama and migrates both northward to Central America and southward to the Gulf of Guayaquil. However, there is some movement between these populations. Fish tagged off southern and central Baja California have been recaught in the central Pacific and off southern Mexico and Central America. There is probably one world population, but the Pacific population does display some genetic heterogeneity.

Skipjack may live to 12 years old, however data on age and growth are not too good. There appears to be considerable geographic variability in size at maturity and spawning season. Size at first maturity seems to be from 40–50 cm (16–20 in) FL and one year or less. In some tropical waters, the fish may spawn throughout the year, while in more temperate areas the season is limited to warm-water months. Females spawn, on average, every 1–2 days and fecundity ranges from 87,600–2,000,000 eggs. Fertilized eggs hatch in about 21–32 hours at 25–29°C (77–90°F). Off Southern California, skipjack eat lots of euphausiids, along with some fishes, cephalopods, hyperiid amphipods, and pelagic red crabs. Feeding may peak in early morning and late afternoon. Predators include various marlins and tunas, cookiecutter, oceanic whitetip, and thresher sharks, wahoos, various boobies, red-tailed tropicbirds, shearwaters, great frigatebirds, and sooty terns.

FISHERY: Skipjack were at least occasionally caught by Native Americans in Southern California. Throughout much of their range, skipjack are a very important commercial species. In the eastern Pacific, much of the catch is made by purse seines wrapping drifting stuff, either that which nature and chance provides or material intentionally placed in the water to attract skippies. Off California, they are taken commercially in relatively small numbers in most years and most is shipped frozen to canneries out of the country. Fishermen off Senegal developed a novel and effective way to catch skipjack, yellowfin, and big-eye tunas with hook and line. The fishermen took advantage of these tunas' tendency to hang around drifting material. A fishing vessel will find a tuna school and associate itself with it. Gradually, more and more tuna are drawn to the vessel, which then begins hook and line operations. The vessel stays with the tuna day and night, until its hold is full, and then trades position with a second vessel, which assumes the duties of the first.

Party vessel and small boat fishermen fishing in Southern California nail these guys pretty good in the late summer and fall, primarily in warm-water years. They are usually taken with albacore or yellowfin tuna, but also occur in their own schools. Their relatively small size makes them a less-prized catch than the larger tunas. In fact, when you have a boatload of anglers who have paid $150 to catch yellowfins but catch skipjack instead, you do not have a lot of happy campers.

RELATIONSHIPS: Various studies (Block et al. 1993, Collette et al. 2001, Graham and Dickson 2001) have shown that skipjack are closely related to the tunas (*Thunnus* spp.). No wait, they are really most closely to *Auxis*, no wait... Well, there still appears to be some discussion.

MISCELLANY: We have quite a random selection for your enjoyment. 1) First, it has been reported that schools being chased by billfishes were seen hiding next to whale sharks and basking sharks and possibly whales. 2) The temperatures of skipjack muscles, eyes, and brains are elevated above those of the surrounding seawater. 3) In other news, there are magnetic particles in skipjack heads; these likely aid in navigation. 4) One skipjack was caught that lacked stripes. 5) Hermaphrodite skipjack have been caught.

REMARKS: Bestor (*Tsukiji*, University of California Press, 2004) writes of the importance of skipjack to many Japanese: "For the citizens of Edo [the former name of Tokyo], *hatsugatsuo* (the season's first *katsuo* [skipjack]) was almost emblematic of their civic identity; one famous verse exults, 'To be a man, born in Edo and eat the first katsuo of the season.' Another is by the famous poet Yamaguchi Sodo (1642–1716): 'Fresh green leaves to see; the cuckoo's song to hear; and the first katsuo taste.'"

Sarda chiliensis

(Cuvier, 1832)

Pacific Bonito

ETYMOLOGY: *Sarda* is derived from Sardinia (where one of the bonito species was taken in abundance) and *chiliensis* refers to the first description of this fish, based on one taken off Valparaiso, Chile.

THE BASICS: Maximum Length: 122 cm (48 in) TL. Maximum Weight: 11.3 kg (24.9 lb). The Ranges: Gulf of Alaska to southern Baja California, and just into Gulf of California; Máncora (Peru) to Talcahuano (Chile). Surface to 110 m (361 ft). Eggs: 1.5–1.7 mm. Larvae: hatching length = about 3.8 mm, flexion length = about 7.5–9 mm, transformation length = about 2–3.2 cm (0.8–1.3 in). Kuo (1970) and Campbell and Collins (1975), both working with Pacific bonito from the northeastern Pacific, arrived at growth rate estimates that are painfully different. Here you go. Kuo (FL, mm): (sexes combined) $L_\infty = 2,661$, $k = 0.038$, $t_0 = -0.60$; Campbell and Collins (FL, cm): (sexes combined) $L_\infty = 76.87$, $k = 0.6215$, $t_0 = -0.41$. Length-weight parameters (FL, cm, kg): (sexes combined) $W = 0.00000762728L^{3.0892}$ (Campbell and Collins 1975).

SALIENT CHARACTERS: Bonito are typical tuna-shaped fish and are easily identified by the dark, slanting stripes on their greenish-blue backs. Just to confuse you, a rare individual will not develop striping. Magnuson and Prescott (1966) could identify 18 of 22 bonito in an aquarium based on unique patterns of the diagonal stripes. During both feeding and spawning, bonito develop dark vertical bars. Holder (1913) sums them up thusly: "I should call it the humming-bird of the sea, so radiant is it, so bathed in myriads of color and tints...its silvery skin blazing and flashing with ten thousand tints and coruscations." Coruscations, eh? Nice, going, Chuck.

LIFE HISTORY: Pacific bonito are pelagic and schooling fishes, most commonly found in nearshore waters. Young ones enter such protected areas as San Diego Bay and small ones will also charge right into the surf line. You commonly encounter both juveniles and adults on the margins of kelp beds (or even in the canopies), over reefs, as well as in the open ocean away from structure. This is a highly migratory species and schools tend to be constantly on the move. While they usually are most abundant from Southern California southward, during warm-water episodes they move into Central California, and when it is really toasty (like during the 1957 and 1983 El Niños), they can be quite common off Northern California and Oregon. Off Southern California, they have been caught in surface waters of 10.6–22.8°C (51–73°F), with largest catches in temperatures above 18.2°C (65°F). They often school with Pacific yellowtail and Pacific barracuda. These fish go through real boom and bust cycles. For instance, they were very abundant in the California Current system from the late 1950s through the 1970s, then suffered a generalized decline and were quite low until at least the early 2000s.

Observing courtship and spawning in an aquarium, Magnuson and Prescott (1966) report: "Courtship included temporary pairing [and] aggressive defense of females by males...A wobbling swimming motion by a female released a following by males, and likewise, if a male swam immediately behind a female, she began a wobbling type of swimming...If more than one male was in the following position, agonistic behavior occurred which included the transient vertically barred coloration observed in both sexes at feeding time. During courtship, only males assumed the coloration."

Pacific bonito live to at least 6–8 years old. A few males are mature at 42 cm (17 in) FL and 1 year old and all are mature at 51 cm (20 in) (2 years old). Females mature at around 56 cm (22 in) and 2 years old. Based on larval surveys, bonito occasionally spawn as far north as Southern California, although more spawning occurs off Baja California. Depending on year, the spawning season extends from at least February–August. Females are batch spawners and produce between 104,900–420,800 eggs per season. Larger fish begin to spawn earlier in the season than do small ones. Off Southern and Baja California, Pacific bonito feed mostly on fishes and squids. Euphausiids, pelagic red crabs, and amphipods are also consumed. Predators include striped marlins, California sea lions, and common dolphins.

FISHERY: Pacific bonito were commonly caught by Native Americans in Southern California and indigenous peoples southward at least as far as Isla Cedros (central Baja California). Archibald Menzies (1754–1842) was a naturalist and surgeon aboard George Vancouver's HMS *Discovery*, during its around-the-world voyage. In November 1792, the *Discovery* anchored off Santa Barbara (Southern California) and Menzies' reported: "There was a Village of Indians close to the place where we daily landed from the Vessels to whose industrious inhabitants we were greatly indebted for a regular supply of fish...particularly Boneto & a kind of Herring with a yellow tail [yellowtail] & in the forenoon they always came along side of the Vessels & for a few beads supplied each with whatever quantity was wanted for all hands" (Menzies 1924).

In the 19th century, bonito was a fairly important commercial catch. The fish were taken by trolling, mostly in Southern California (although catches are far north as Monterey were reported). Most of the catch was salted and dried and, in reading these old reports, there is a sense that it was considered somewhat inferior to, for instance, yellowtail or barracuda. During the late teens of the 20th century, a medium-sized and rather sporadic bonito canning industry developed. This was a kind of modest endeavor as canned fish buyers were never too enthusiastic. There was also a small market for fresh bonito. Most fish were taken in Southern California and (in the winter) off northern Baja California. Since then, California catches have waxed and waned, to a certain extent reflective of the cycles of abundance. Today, you mostly see them sold fresh in California and they are also fairly important in the Mercado Negro in Ensenada (northern Baja California).

Pacific bonito can be extremely important in the recreational catch. While many are taken from boats, pier, jetty, and even surf fishermen catch considerable numbers. Bonito are about the most exciting fish normally caught from piers, and a decent run can fill up a pier in a hurry. I have seen pre-dawn arrivers unable to get a spot on a pier when the word gets out.

RICHARD HERRMANN

ORIGINS: The oldest known member of the genus is *Sarda palaeocenica* from the Early Paleocene (perhaps 60 million years ago or more). The oldest bonito on the Pacific Coast was named *Sarda stockeri*; it is from the Miocene (at least 5.3 million years ago) of Southern California. At one time, it was thought this species might be *S. chiliensis*, however, additional specimens have allowed it to be recognized as an extinct species. There are two subspecies of *Sarda chiliensis*, *lineolata* (found in the Northern Hemisphere) and *chiliensis* (in the Southern Hemisphere), separated by *Sarda orientalis*.

MISCELLANY: 1) Occasionally you will find individuals that lack stripes. 2) Bonito have a very characteristic swimming style. After swimming upright for a while, they often roll over a bit and swim partly on their sides.

REMARKS: There is no pleasing some people. From the late 1930s until 1957, bonito were relatively scarce in Southern California, and everyone got excited at the thought of catching one. The 1957–1958 El Niño brought gobs of these fish to the area. They were everywhere, with folks catching them on virtually every bait, even in the surf. Well, everyone was happy, for about 2 months. And then the grumbling began. People started complaining that they were catching bonito while fishing for bass, yellowtail, or even halibut. Suddenly, these fish were trash. Aren't you folks every satisfied?

By the way, bonito are really excellent food fish, but only if bled soon after capture and kept really damp and cool. If you let them warm up, sitting in the sun in a dry bag, you will get what you deserve.

Scomber japonicus
Houttuyn, 1782

Pacific Chub Mackerel

The most arabesque species on the Pacific Coast.

ETYMOLOGY AND COMMON NAMES: *Scomber* is the ancient Greek word for "mackerel" and *japonicus* comes from "Japan," the site from which it was collected and described. On the West Coast, these fish are often called "Pacific mackerel" (that's what I use), "blue mackerel," "green mackerel," or, quite often, "greenies." There is not a fisherman on this coast who says "chub" mackerel. Russian biologists call them "big-eyed mackerel" and off northern Baja California "macarela" is used. "Ma-saba" is a Japanese name.

THE BASICS: Maximum Length: About 63.5 cm (25 in) TL. Maximum Weight: The heaviest Pacific mackerel on record weighed 2.9 kg (6.4 lb). It was taken on 8 June 1938 in Santa Monica Bay. And, lest you think that fish was the only one taking steroids during the Depression, a fish taken in Monterey Bay in August 1937 weighed 2.7 kg (6 lb). The Ranges: Pacific and Indian oceans; in western Pacific as far north as southeastern Kamchatka; western Gulf of Alaska to Gulf of California; Panama to Chile. Collette et al. (2001) list it as world wide in temperate seas, although they note that some consider it an Indo-Pacific species replaced by *Scomber colias* in the Atlantic. In the western Pacific, they are common as far north as the southern Kuril Islands. In the eastern Pacific, during warm-water periods, they are abundant to at least off Vancouver Island. In other times, their range contracts to where they are relatively rare even as far north as Southern California; at these times most of the Pacific Coast fish are off central Baja California. Surface to depths of about 300 m (984 ft). Eggs: 0.8–1.4 mm. Larvae: hatching length = about 2–3 mm, flexion length = about 6–8 mm, transformation length = about 1.2–1.9 cm (0.5–0.7 in). Von Bertalanffy parameters (FL, mm): (sexes combined) L_∞ = 436.1, k = 0.244, t_0 = -3.02 (Knaggs and Parrish 1973). Length-weight parameters (FL, mm, gr): (sexes combined) $W = 0.0000001366L^{3.39358}$ (Knaggs and Parrish 1973).

SALIENT CHARACTERS: Pacifics are sleek little fish, easily identified by the series of slightly wavy, dark bars on their green or blue backs.

Mostly Pacific mackerel with a few jack mackerel thrown in. KEVIN LEE

LIFE HISTORY: Pacific mackerel are schooling and pelagic fish. Off California, they are common from the shoreline out to at least 370 km (200 nautical mi). Most larvae reside in a band from the surface to 23 m (75 ft) and begin to school when at about 3 cm (1 in) FL. Young fish live in inshore waters and sometimes wade right into the surf. While they are most often found in open waters, they commonly enter kelp forests and, in the Gulf of California, the young live among mangroves. These fish are highly migratory and in most years are most common off California during summer and fall. They often school with similar-sized Pacific sardine and jack mackerel. Like other pelagics, Pac mac populations definitely go through boom and bust periods. For instance, it has been estimated that for some intervals between 1928–1968 there was as much as 965 million pounds of mackerel in the California Current region, while at other times the population crashed to as low as only 3.3 million pounds. Various studies show that the spawning stock runs from British Columbia to Punta Abreojos (southern Baja California). However, the fish are not completely mixed within this area. As an example, when the mackerel population crashed off Southern California in the 1950s, it remained large in Bahia de Sebastian Vizcaino (central Baja California), implying that not all the fish from down there migrated northwards. Pacific mackerel have been caught in waters between 9–27°C (48–81°F). At one time or another a case has been made for there being at least two populations in our area, one along the Pacific Coast and the other swimming in the Gulf of California.

Pacific mackerel can live as long as 12 years, but 9 years seems to be the usual maximum. Now, usually this is the place where I would give you the age and size at maturity. But, in scouring the literature, these estimates are so different and so confusing that, well, the reality is that I have a life, I have things to do and people to see, so here are some numbers that seem kind of okay. It looks like fish less than a year old are not mature. Whether 1-year-olds mature or not depends on the size of the population; the more fish there are, the fewer 1-year-old fish spawn. At anywhere between 1–3 years old, 50% of the fish are mature, and almost all fish 6 years and older reproduce. Fish off central and southern Baja California may grow more slowly and be smaller at any given age than those off Southern California. If you want more information try Fry (1936), Knaggs and Parrish (1973), Parrish and MacCall (1978), and Gluyas-Millán and Quiñonez-Veláquez (1997). Larger females begin to spawn earlier in the season than smaller ones. Off California and northern Baja California, most spawning occurs from March–October, with a peak in April–August. Further south, the season is earlier, and by Bahia Magdalena (southern Baja California) spawning occurs from December–June. In the Gulf of California, it's from November–April. Larvae hatch in around 3 days, depending on temperature. Spawning takes place between 14–21.9°C (57–71°F), but much of it seems to take place between about 16.7–20.6°C (62–69°F). Planktonic crustaceans (e.g., calanoid copepods, euphausiids, amphipods, and crustacean larvae) are very important to their diets, as are small fishes, arrow worms, squids, ctenophores, and sea butterfly snails (*Limacina helicina*). In addition to these more traditional foods, mackerel have also been found with buttons, spools, stones, and a lamb spare rib in their guts. On our coast, lots of animals eat Pacifics. A random list includes fishes (e.g., albacore, bocaccio, California halibut, giant sea bass, lingcod, longnose lancetfish, shortspine thornyheads, striped marlins, swordfish, white seabass, thresher

IT KIND OF MAKES YOU THINK

"I got my best training for the law from a study of the mackerel tribe." So said Minnesota Judge Bert Fesler, who studied ichthyology with David Starr Jordan at Stanford University in the 1890s. Is that because mackerel are slimy and difficult to hold? Is it because mackerel are voracious predators gobbling everything in their path? Is it because mackerel charge exorbitant rates...or chase ambulances?

sharks, and yellowtail), birds (e.g., brown pelicans, elegant terns, Heermann gulls, and sooty shearwaters), seals, sea lions, dolphins, fin and sei whales, and Humboldt squids.

FISHERY: Native Americans in both Southern and Central California caught considerable numbers. Pac macs have had a long and kind of mixed career as a commercial species. The earliest mention I can find comes from the diaries of William Dane Phelps, an American sea captain who plied California from 1840 to 1842, trading in hides and tallow. Dane meticulously recorded his daily doings including listing each time he or his men went fishing. Thus we have the following entry for 23 October 1841, while the trader was anchored off what is now Long Beach (Southern California): "Went to fish for mackerel with the pinnace [a small boat kept aboard the trading vessel]; caught about 60. They are just making their appearance, and are quite fat." And here is one from 2 days later: "At noon the cutter returned with about 2 barrals [sic] large fat mackerel and a halibut." Parenthetically, Dane also has a rather colorful entry about a sturgeon and some Native Americans, but it is so pathetically racist that I felt it was kind of out of tune with the high moral tone that clearly permeates the volume you are currently holding in your well-manicured hands. Of course, if you wish to wallow in that kind of excess, the book is *Alta California, 1840-1842. The Journal and Observations of William Dane Phelps Master of the Ship "Alert,"* (see page 260).

(see page 260).

In 1859, an East Coast fisherman named J.L. McDonald started fishing the Pacific Coast and, with only a few exceptions, did not like what he found. "The coast extending from San Diego on the south, to Cape Flattery on the north, is very destitute of fish," he wrote, and, lest we fail to understand his message, he continues that: "The warm stream bathing the shores of Santa Barbara afford genial resort to various species of fish, which like all fish found in warm water are lean and poor and of little value to the practical fisherman" (*Hidden Treasures; or Fisheries Around the North-West Coast.* Procter Brothers, 1871). McDonald goes on to inform us that his explorations of the mackerel resources off Southern California left him with the sort of despair that only Kierkegaard ("Despair is an expression of the total personality") could comprehend, should that Dane have been into slickers, hooks, and members of the family Scombridae: "In the summer season mackerel are found in the channel; they congregate in considerable numbers, and range from ten to twelve inches in length, lean, poor and slimy; they bear some resemblance to the 'Dollar mackerel' on the eastern coast, and when salted are hard and tough. In the season of 1859 the writer caught 246 barrels of poor mackerel in Prisoner's Cove, on the north-east side of Santa Cruz island [sic]. Opposite the old mission of Santa Barbara we encountered large bodies at times. They are annually taken along the coast of California, but not in sufficient numbers to justify any great preparation. The scarcity of fat mackerel along the north-west coast is a *fatal drawback* [italics added] to our commercial development." So let me get this straight. Because the mackerel aren't plump enough out here, that is going to jeopardize the economy of the Pacific Coast? What about mining, logging, agriculture, and the world of dotcoms? Gee, isn't the porno industry in the San Fernando Valley alone large enough to overcome this mackerel plumpness issue?

Well, times change, and by the late 19th century, the mackerel was well established as a commercial species. Not a first-rate species, mind you, but a species that you could catch, sell, and make enough money to pay the rent. By that time, mackerel were caught all up and down the coast, mostly in Southern California to be sure, but also, on occasion off San Francisco, where it sold for a remarkable 30 to 50 cents a pound in the 1870s. Over the years, a consistent, albeit modest, demand existed for fresh mackerel; but only with the advent of a canned product did it become the target of a fairly good-sized fishery. Canning was attempted in San Diego as far back as 1892, but apparently without much success. Indeed, for a number of years canners, flushed with victory in canning sardine, continued to experiment with canned mackerel. It was not until 1927 that a product that someone other than unneutered male cats was willing to consume was produced. Canners first tried marketing mackerel in the Philippines, which at the time was a major buyer of both sardine and pink salmon. As the aptly named Fish and Game biologist Phil Croker noted in 1933, to get the Filipinos to try canned mackerel: "a ruse was resorted to in order to get the mackerel [demand] started...Nearly all [cans] bore a picture of a salmon-like fish and the words 'salmon brand,' 'salmon style pack' were placed in a prominent position. Naturally the buyers thought they were getting a new kind of salmon at a real low price, so sales mounted rapidly." In a few years, a dual mackerel fishery evolved. Fish that were destined for the fresh fish markets were taken by hook and line and most were marketed in the Los Angeles, San Francisco, and San Diego regions. Purse seines and other round haul nets brought in most of the to-be-canned mackerel and much of that industry occurred in the canneries of Long Beach-San Pedro. Small numbers of mackerel destined for canneries were also taken by dipnet and by "striker" boats. Striker boats used barbless feather lures to catch mackerel. The mackerel schools were brought to the boat by chumming with ground fish or live bait, and the lure, mounted on a short line connected to a bamboo pole, was wiggled in the water. When the fish struck the fishermen flipped the pole and fish through the air, the mackerel came unhooked, and flew onto the deck. As noted in Bureau of Commercial Fisheries (1937): "When this method is working properly, it simply rains fish." It should also be noted that there was a small, but steady, niche market in Southern California for salted and smoked mackerel. In fact, a number of sportfishing landings (I remember that Ocean Park sportfishing did this in the 1950s) would take mackerel left by anglers on sportfishing boats, then smoke and sell them, a lovely and egregious flaunting of fish and

Just a whole lot of Pacific mackerel caught in a purse seine.

game laws. Japanese processors also used mackerel for canned fish cakes, when Pacific barracuda were not available. This remained a major fishery throughout the first half of the 20th century, ultimately crashing in the 1950s and 1960s. Clearly, both mackerel numbers and catches vary greatly. Today, when fishing is good, most catches are made from Southern California and northern Baja California (though large catches are occasionally made further north to at least Oregon) and much of the catch is exported to southeast Asia, China, Egypt, and the like. The demand for fresh Pacific mackerel is not helped by the occasional domoic acid health advisory that leads to bans on human consumption.

As far back as 1892, Eigenmann noted that mackerel (he called them "tinkers," an East Coast term) "afford sport to many idlers on the wharves" in San Diego Bay. *Hey, I spent most of my childhood as an idler on a pier; don't knock it until you have tried it.* Some things don't change, as Pacific mackerel have always been a popular sport fish. People catch them in large numbers from boats, piers, and, in places like San Diego and Mission bays, from the beach. In the 1950s, when my dad took me fishing on the barge anchored off Santa Monica (Southern California), mackerel was the target for most of us. Folks would lug sacks of them home. Phillips (1932b) wrote about an unusually large mackerel run in Monterey Bay, during the El Niño year of 1931: "The fall season of 1931 furnished what is probably the best mackerel fishing that dock fishermen have ever experienced in Monterey...Oldtimers, who have spent their entire lives at Monterey, have pronounced this season's 'run' as exceptional....During the last three weeks of August and the first three weeks of September, great numbers of fishermen lined the Municipal Pier...Strong, graceful, fighting mackerel, weighing one-half to three pounds, broke many a window on the Municipal Pier, when over-anxious fishermen swung their catch out of the water." Mackerel runs can still lead to crowded piers, although not all of the fish are taken home to eat. A fair number are retained to bait lobster nets, or as bait for sharks, rays, and other larger species.

ORIGINS AND RELATIONSHIPS: The genus *Scomber* goes back at least to the Eocene (34 million years plus). In 1943, David described *Scomber sanctae-monicae* from Miocene deposits (at least 5 million years old) of Southern California. She also noted fossils of the same age from the Lompoc area of what she referred to as *Pneumatophorus* cf. *grex*, that showed "practically no differences from the living chub mackerel." Mackerel systematics remain in some minor disarray. At one time there were thought to be at least six different species worldwide, this has now dropped down a bit, but questions still remain. *Scomber japonicus* on the Pacific Coast are more closely related to *S. japonicus* off Taiwan than to those in the Atlantic or Mediterranean. On the other hand, some folks think that the Atlantic form is a different species.

MISCELLANY: 1) Occasionally someone catches an hermaphroditic one. 2) Pac macs from both Monterey and Cabo San Lucas (southern Baja California) sometimes contain domoic acid; be careful, it's a jungle out there.

Thunnus alalunga
(Bonnaterre, 1788)

Albacore

I thought about using the last lines from Rimbaud's A Dream of Winter *here, but for some reason decided not to.*

ETYMOLOGY AND COLLOQUIAL NAMES: *Thunnus* is ancient Greek for "tuna" and *alalunga* comes from Sardinia and means "wing" and "long." "Albacore" is said to be derived from two Arabic words meaning 'a little pig.' They are called "long-finned tuna" by the Russians and "bin'naga" by the Japanese.

THE BASICS: Maximum Length: 152 cm (5 ft) TL. Maximum Weight: 40.9 kg (90 lb). The Ranges: Circumglobal in tropical to temperate waters; in western Pacific, north to southern Kuril Islands; northern and eastern Gulf of Alaska to Chile, including the entrance to the Gulf of California. In the western Pacific, they are most common are far north as Japan and in the eastern

Pacific from about Vancouver Island to central Baja California. However, Scofield (1914) reported that albacore were plentiful in that year off Cabo San Lucas (southern Baja California) in January and again in August. Surface to 600 m (1,968 ft), commonly from the surface waters to 200 m (656 ft) and more. Eggs: 1 mm. Von Bertalanffy parameters (FL, cm): (sexes combined) L_∞ = 135.6, k = 0.17, t_0 = -0.87 (PFMC 2003). Length-weight parameters (TL, mm, kg): (sexes combined) W = $0.0000000226L^{2.988}$ (RecFin 2009).

SALIENT CHARACTERS: Albacore are readily identified by their very long pectoral fins, which (except in very small fish) reach beyond the front of the anal fin. These elegant, streamlined fish have a dark blue, almost black, back and silvery belly.

RICHARD HERRMANN

LIFE HISTORY: Albacore are highly migratory, schooling, and pelagic fish that tend to be found in off-shore waters. In some years, off Southern California, you can catch a few just off the mainland. Orin Winfield, a lovely man who operated a sport-fishing boat out of Santa Monica when I was a kid, remembered anchoring a partyboat near a kelp bed off Palos Verdes in the 1930s. Soon after, a school of albacore came through, hurtling right along the kelp line and Orin's passengers made out

A rather evocative painting by Ed Ries of tuna trollers and bait boats.

like bandits. Irv Leask reports catching a handful in a gill net set for salmon just a short distance off the coast in southeastern Alaska. So, you never know, do you? These fish tend to move about in smaller schools (usually of similar-sized individuals) than do other tunas (e.g., skipjack and yellowfins).

There are likely two populations in the Pacific, one north and one south of the Equator. It s likely that almost all of the fish of the North Pacific population are born in the Western and Central Pacific. However, there is tantalizing evidence that albacore do, on occasion, spawn in the eastern Pacific. This includes records by Japanese fishery biologists who caught 20 fish in spawning condition off Bahia Magdalena (southern Baja California) during March of 1912 and limited numbers of albacore larvae that have been taken in the eastern Pacific. In addition, the capture of a small and very young fish (38.1 cm, 15 in, FL, and weighing 0.9 kg, 2 lb) off Isla Guadalupe (central Baja California), implies that this fish might have been spawned somewhere in that vicinity. After maybe a year, young fish may migrate to waters south and east of Japan and, after maybe a year or so, begin their migrations to the eastern Pacific. Most of these fish arrive in the summer and fall, and most return to the western Pacific late in the year. Commonly (although subject to change without notice), albacore hit the Southern California coast in July and are off Vancouver in August or September. There is an intriguing hypothesis that there are also two stocks in the North Pacific. One migrates between the western and eastern Pacific Ocean north of about 40°N (the latitude of Northern California) and the other, southern, one hits the West Coast south of 40°N and only rarely travels back to western Pacific Ocean waters, preferring to return to the Central Pacific. Regardless of putative stock, during some years, some fish remain in the eastern Pacific into the early winter. The first fish in a season to hit the Baja California-Southern California area tend to be small; larger ones come along later in the year. Most of the fish living off the West Coast of the U.S. are 3–4-year-old juveniles, although older adults are occasionally taken. At 2–6 years old, albacore begin to enter subtropical waters west of Hawai'i and south of about 30°N. Genetic studies from fish taken off Japan, Australia, Chile/Peru, and the Biscay Bay (off Spain, don't you know) showed that, in general, fish in each area were at least somewhat different genetically.

These tuna have been found in waters between 9.5–25.2°C (49–77°F) and they appear to prefer waters perhaps between 14–19.5°C (57–67°F). Although you can, on occasion, find them in most any water mass off North America, their normal preference is to patrol the warm, clear, and "albacore-blue" waters (of maybe 33–35 ppt salinity) that form on one side of frontal zones. These zones, with their sharp temperature breaks and high productivity, often house large amounts of prey. In contradiction to a number of other tunas, albacore stay mainly in near-surface waters, at or in the thermocline. In surface waters, albacore may school with bluefin, skipjack, and yellowfin tunas. During a routine 24 hours, an albacore swims at about 1.6 knots and swims slightly faster during the day.

Albacore live to 12 years of age. A few males mature at 78 cm (31 cm) FL and some not until about 93 cm (37 in). Values for females are 83 cm (33 in) and 94 cm (37 in), respectively. On average, albacore mature at perhaps 4–5 years old. Those albacore spawning off eastern Taiwan and the Philippines do so from March–September, peaking in April and May. Females in these waters (in April) spawn on average every 1.7 days. One study found that the right ovary or testes tended to be heavier and larger than the left one. Females produce 170,000–2,600,000 eggs at a time and larvae hatch from eggs 2–4 days after fertilization. Along the Pacific Coast, albacore feed mostly on fishes, as well as some euphausiids, pelagic red crabs, hyperiid amphipods, sergestid shrimps, heteropods, and squids. Predators include other albacore, black and blue marlins, cookiecutter and Pacific sleeper sharks, brown and black noddies, and great frigatebirds.

FISHERY: This species was apparently caught in pretty fair numbers by Native Americans in Southern California. Until the early 20th century, they were not of commercial importance. About that time, folks found that when you put them in cans, they are really good with a little mayonnaise, celery, and pickle relish. And the rest is history. Early catches were made by fishermen trolling or "jack poling" (my own personal favorite way to fish). In jack poling, the vessel drifts and live bait is thrown into the water. This attracts the fish and they will snatch anything that moves, including a barbless feathered hook attached to a strong leader, bamboo pole, and awesome biceps. A quick pull of the arms and the fish comes flying past onto the deck. Ooh, I've only done that a few times, but it is so cool. Historically, albacore were rarely taken in large numbers by purse seines, although the occasional catch was made, particularly when the fish were schooling with bluefin tuna. Beginning in the early 1950s, the development of better and lighter nets and the use of the power block (making net retrieval faster and more efficient) led a number of seiners to try more energetically. However, while some substantial catches were made (perhaps several hundred tons in 1960), it became clear that purse seines were not a particularly effective way to catch these highly mobile fish. However, large catches were made in the mid-Pacific by pelagic squid gill netters. On our coast, commercial albacore fishing has mostly remained the province of less efficient technologies, such as trolling and various hook-and-line techniques, with lesser numbers taken with gill nets and purse seines. Most fish taken in West Coast waters are exported and canned and some are sold fresh in domestic markets.

What is it like to be a commercial troller for albacore? Well, as we have on several other occasions, we turn to Marie De Santis's really fine autobiography, *Neptune's Apprentice* (Presidio Press, 1984), for a rather lyrical answer: "I could see the fleet on the horizon when every line on the boat pulled tight with fish. What a rush! I put the boat in a circle and hardly touched the wheel for the next three hours. I was all by myself in a fisherman's dream, pulling fish after fish after fish, as if they were being propagated by an infinite wellspring below that fed right into my lap. It was all magic and transcendence; I no longer thought about bills, fuel, people, docks, or tomorrow. I even stopped counting the fish. It was just the moments of fish splashing on the water and pulling them arm over arm into the boat. The light blue wake of my boat circled a world more perfect than I have ever imagined. Each time around I was drawn deeper into its vortex." Nice, eh?

Albacore are in the major leagues of sport fisheries of the Pacific Coast, particularly off California, but also occasionally off Oregon and Washington. While the species was traditionally taken by partyboats, the rise of small recreational vessels with good electronics and access to satellite sea surface temperature images has made everyone their own sportfishing skipper. So, on a typical Saturday in August off southern California, the radio waves are filled with: "I'm off the 403, I got a good temperature break here, and two fish on the jig sticks." Usually followed by "I'm out of fuel, anyone got some to spare?"

RELATIONSHIPS: Several studies have shown that albacore and Pacific bluefins are very closely related. While this may show that the two species are closely related, it may also imply that albacore and bluefins interbreed with some frequency.

MISCELLANY: 1) The temperatures of muscles, eye/brain, and viscera are elevated as much as 15.3°C above ambient. 2) Albacore can swim at speeds of over 80 km (50 mi) per hour for short periods of time. 3) The first commercial catch of albacore off Oregon was on 11 August 1936, when the F/V *Pilchard* took a ton off Coos Bay.

REMARKS: Several albacore caught in Monterey Bay contained domoic acid; that stuff makes you coo-coo before you die.

Thunnus albacares

(Bonnaterre, 1788)

Yellowfin Tuna

A fish that seems to have invented sprezzatura long before Castiglione defined it.

ETYMOLOGY AND COLLOQUIAL NAMES: *Thunnus* is from the ancient Greek and was a name given to the tunas. Bonnaterre (1788) called this fish an "albacore" and gave it the species name "*albacares.*" It is "ahi" in sushi joints, they are "kihada" in Japanese, and "aleta amarilla" in Spanish.

THE BASICS: Maximum Length: 220 cm (87 in) TL. Maximum Weight: Apparently, there have been several fish taken in the 172–182 kg (380–400 lb) range and they may grow to 200 kg (440 lb). The Ranges: Circumglobal in tropical and subtropical waters; in western Pacific, north to southern Kuril Islands; eastern North Pacific, at 50°00'N, 150°02'W, and Morro Bay (Central California) to Chile. In some years, they are common as far north as Southern California. Surface to 1,022 m (3,352 ft). Eggs: 0.9–1 mm. Larvae: hatching length = about 2.7 mm, flexion length = about 4.5–6.1 mm, transformation length = about 1.8 cm (0.7 in). Length-weight parameters (FL, cm, kg): (sexes combined) W = 0.00001387L$^{3.086}$ (Wild 1986).

Terry used a number of images to create this lovely piece.

SALIENT CHARACTERS: True to their name, yellowfins have, well, yellow fins. The finlets are light yellow, edged in black. Their pectoral fins are long but do not extend back to the anal fin. These beautiful fish have a blue back and silvery belly. Schaefer (1999) writes that yellowfins have "prominent lateral markings on the body, consisting of narrow, closely-spaced, vertical, white stripes, usually alternating continuous lines and dotted lines, extending from below the origin of the pectoral fin to the caudal peduncle region." Yellowfins periodically have dark vertical bars. In contrast to bigeye and Pacific bluefin tunas, the livers of yellowfins are not striated.

LIFE HISTORY: Yellowfins are schooling and pelagic animals that have a profound penchant for associating with all kinds of floating objects. These include logs, living and dead marine mammals, whale sharks, and sea turtles. Note that this behavior is mostly limited to small- and medium-sized fish, larger ones are less common around drifting stuff. In the eastern tropical Pacific, but not, curiously, in some other parts of the world, yellowfins also associate with schools of dolphins. Spotted dolphins are probably the ones they associate with the most, but they are also commonly found with spinner and common dolphins. My associate Merit McCrea has noted that yellowfins are sometimes caught under dolphins off Southern California as well. Generally, 2- and 3-year-old fish (about 55–125 cm, 22–49 in, FL) are the ones that interact with these small cetaceans. Why do they do it? A number of theories have been put forth, including: (1) The tuna perceive the dolphin schools as surface "stuff," not unlike the surface flotsam and jetsam that they orient to, or (2) that tuna are somewhat protected from sharks by associating with dolphins. Another kind of elegant theory (that is not mutually exclusive of the other two) is that in many cases it is energetically advantageous for tuna to hang out with dolphins. The idea is that both small yellowfins and dolphins eat about the same things, these prey (mostly fishes) are patchily distributed, a typical dolphin has to eat more of them then a typical tuna (and thus has a higher incentive to find these foods), and that dolphins are better at finding the prey than are the tunas. If this is true, the tuna follow the dolphins in an effort to have a more efficient way of finding lunch.

In general, adults are found at temperatures between 18–31°C (64–88°F), most often in 20°C (68°F) or greater. In their search for both food and optimal water temperatures, yellowfins move about quite a bit, even on a daily basis. Several studies show that some groups of fish will establish a strong 24-hour rhythm, moving about from place to place, but always returning to the same locales day after day. There is lots of evidence that these fish are expert underwater navigators, somehow able to use underwater features as signposts on their travels. Although yellowfins tend to stay a bit offshore of Southern California, Merit McCrea caught a bunch just a few hundred meters offshore in the western Santa Barbara Channel. He thinks they came in during a warm water event and got trapped there when upwelling created a cold water barrier just offshore.

Along with horizontal movements, yellowfins also make substantial vertical ones, roving from the surface to depths of about 1,160 m (3,805 ft) and in a single dive experiencing temperatures from 28.4–4.5°C (83–40°F). Schaefer et al. (2007) state: "Yellowfin, in contrast to bigeye, do not have the thermoregulatory physiological capacity to remain for prolonged periods below the mixed layer." They found that yellowfins exhibited two types of dives. In Type-1 (which was most of the time), fish remained at less than 50 m (164 ft) at night and did not dive to greater than about 100 m (328 ft) during the day. Type-2 dives (these were occasional) were characterized by 10 or more dives in excess of 150 m (492 ft) during the day and were apparently related to following deep scattering layer prey back downwards. During their descents, it has been theorized that yellowfins glide downward to save energy and then swim back upwards. Yellowfin schools are positively clubby, as individuals may stay together for many months. Juveniles school with skipjack and juvenile bigeye tunas, and tend remain in surface waters. Adult yellowfins are also sometimes found with adult bigeyes.

Most of the yellowfins that arrive off California are juveniles. These fish move into Southern California waters only during some years. In fact, there seem to be extended periods, maybe decades, when yellowfins do not make it that far north. This was noted as far back as 1908, when Charles Holder wrote that yellowfins had not been seen in Southern California before 1904, at least by the commercial fishermen who plied those waters. When the fish are there, however, they can stay off Southern California into November.

Is there more than one yellowfin population out there? Well, probably, but it depends on what research you buy into. Work on yellowfin proteins implies that there are four stocks: Atlantic Ocean, Indian Ocean, west-central Pacific Ocean, and eastern Pacific Ocean. A genetic study found three stocks: Atlantic Ocean, Indian Ocean, and Pacific Ocean. In the eastern Pacific, there is some evidence for some sort of population differences between fish in northern equatorial and southern equatorial waters. Fish living in the Gulf of California may be partially isolated from other fish. Tagging studies summarized by Schaefer et al. (2007) also demonstrate that yellowfins are far less given to wanderlust than, for instance, northern bluefins or albacore.

THERE'S NO SUCH THING AS A FREE LUNCH, BLAH, BLAH, BLAH

Ultimately, we pay some price for every action.

Dr. Martin Hall, who appears to live and work deep inside the Land of Moral Ambiguity, can certainly speak to this truism. Dr. Hall, who at this writing works for the Inter-American Tropical Tuna Commission, has produced compelling evidence that, by encouraging changes in tuna fishermen's behavior to reduce dolphin mortality, society has caused a vast increase in the deaths of a variety of fishes and sea turtles.

Here is the problem. At one time, much of the yellowfin tuna headed for our cans came from fish that were caught by purse seine off Mexico, Central and South America. And much of that catch was made by deploying purse seines around mixed groups of large tuna and dolphins. This resulted in large catches of tunas and considerable dolphin mortality. Over the years, through a series of technological and fishing changes, dolphin mortalities decreased. However, the drive for a nearly "dolphin-safe" tuna fishery forced fishermen to focus on setting their nets on drifting objects, such as tree limbs and other debris, that attract tunas. This has led to very low dolphin mortalities but very large increases in deaths of all of the other animals that associate with drifting material, including undersized (unusable) tunas, sharks, sea turtles, etc. So, at least at the present time, we are presented with this moral dilemma. What is one dolphin worth? Early on, large numbers of dolphins died in the eastern Pacific purse seine tuna fishery, but the bycatch of other animals was relatively low. Now, many fewer dolphins die, but many other animals are killed. Is it more important to save dolphins but have more sea turtles, sharks, small tunas etc. die? Is it better to allow some increase in dolphin mortality to protect these other species? Are there ways to better protect all species when fishing for yellowfin tuna?

Toward the end of his career Robert Heinlein may have come perilously close to self-satire, but his character Manny in *The Moon is a Harsh Mistress* just may have been the first one to neatly package the now well-worn dictum: "There Ain't No Such Thing As A Free Lunch" (often abbreviated TANSTAAFL by the cognoscenti). And, although Milton Friedman later used the more grammatically correct: "There's no such thing as a free lunch" for the title of a book, TANSTAAFL has the more common touch needed in discussing the "Dolphin Safe" tuna issue.

For a more complete look at a really complex issue, see: Norris, S. et al. 2002. Thinking Like an Ocean. *Conservation in Practice* 3(4):10-19.]

In the eastern Pacific, yellowfins spawn from southern Baja California (at least as far north as 26°11'N, 113°09'W) southward to about 2°S (off Ecuador). Spawning occurs at water temperatures between 21.5–30.5°C (71–87°F), mostly between 26–30°C (79–86°F). Observing fish in captivity, one study found that spawning ceased when water temperatures decreased to below 24°C (75°F). Courtship behavior usually began in the afternoon, and spawning occurred most often in the late afternoon or evening.

The maximum life span of yellowfins is not known, although it might be 6–7 years. On average, females may have a shorter life span (usually 3.5 years) than males (usually 5 years). Females grow faster than males early on and then by about 2.5 years males grow faster and are larger. A few females are mature at 59 cm (23 in) FL, 50% are mature at 92.1 cm (36 in), and 100% at about 148 cm (59 in). Males mature at smaller lengths. A few spawn at less than 50 cm (20 in), 50% at 69 cm (27 in), and 100% at about 132 cm (52 in). In captivity, most females mature at about 1.6 years old (but some at as young as 1.3 years old). In tropical waters (say from 0–20°N), these fish spawn throughout the year, while further north it takes place in the summer. Females spawn about once per day and produce between 162,918–8,026,026 eggs per batch. Smaller females spawn less often than larger ones. Larvae hatch in 18 hours at 29°C (84°F) and 28 hours at 24°C (75°F). Yellowfins eat substantial amounts of various crustaceans (primarily pelagic red crabs, portunid crabs, euphausiids, and crustacean larvae), along with lots of fishes and some squids. The fishes eaten encompass almost every species from the surface to mesopelagic waters. In the eastern Pacific, predators are all the likely suspects, such as black and blue marlins, dolphinfish, cookiecutter and other sharks, wahoos, yellowfin tuna, sperm whales, orcas, and (on juveniles) sea snakes.

FISHERY: Well, yellowfins are one of the big commercial species in the tropical eastern Pacific and they are taken mainly by purse seiners. In some years, pretty good commercial catches are made as far north as off Southern California, but the really heavy-duty fishery begins at around 10°N, off Panama. Their value to the canning industry was recognized as far back as the early 1930s, when American purse seiners began to work off Mexico. As these vessels became larger, the boats hunted further afield and often fished off Central or even South America. At some point it was observed that, as noted above, many yellowfins school with dolphins and fishermen began targeting and setting their nets around these mammals, killing large numbers of them in the process. This led to a number of innovations that drastically decreased dolphin mortality, but has raised a whole new set of issues (see *There's No Such Thing as a Free Lunch*, on the previous page). Off California, most fish are taken with purse seines and a bit by hook-and-line and gill nets. Most are frozen and sent to places like Mexico where they are canned. Besides being a favorite fish for canning, sushi parlors simply dote on fresh ahi. Tony restaurants serve the fish seared on the outside and raw on the inside, something this good ol' boy just cannot abide.

Yellowfins are eagerly sought after by recreational anglers. In particular, a number of anglers, forming what must be as much of a cult as those loony steelhead fishermen, board long-range party vessels operating out of San Diego and head into tropical waters to target this species. Yes, with their arcane discussions of two-speed reels, fluorocarbon leaders, and chunk bait, and with their fingers calloused and bruised from tying endless Bimini knots, these monastic folk seek the Holy Grail, the 300-pound yellowfin.

RELATIONSHIPS: The folks that have looked at tuna genetics say that yellowfins are perhaps most closely related to blackfin (*Thunnus atlanticus*), or perhaps bluefin, tunas.

MISCELLANY: 1) Yellowfins have magnetic particles, likely used in orienting the fish during migrations, within the anterior parts of their skulls. 2) Like a number of other pelagic fishes, the temperatures of the muscles and eye/brains are elevated above that of the surrounding waters.

Thunnus obesus
(Lowe, 1839)

Bigeye Tuna

KURT M. SCHAEFER (INTER-AMERICAN TROPICAL TUNA COMMISSION)

ETYMOLOGY AND COLLOQUIAL NAMES: *Thunnus* is from the ancient Greek and was a name given to the tunas and *obesus* is Latin for "fat." The Japanese call them "mebachi" and in Spanish it's "patudo."

THE BASICS: Maximum Length: 250 cm (8 ft) TL. Maximum Weight: 210 kg (462 lb). The Ranges: Circumglobal in tropical and subtropical waters; in western Pacific, north to southern Kuril Islands; Iron Springs (central Washington) to Chile; apparently not in Gulf of California. In the eastern Pacific, they are sometimes taken in Southern California, but are more abundant off Baja California and points south. Surface to 1,695 m (5,560 ft). Eggs: 1–1.1 mm. Zhu et al. (2009) present von Bertalanffy growth parameters from a bunch of studies. I have no idea which (if any) is the most valid. Length-weight parameters (FL, cm, kg): (females) W = $0.00003L^{2.9278}$ (Sun et al. 2001).

SALIENT CHARACTERS: These fish look a lot like yellowfins. A sure-fire difference is the striated liver in bigeyes and the nonstriated ones in yellowfins. To separate the two species when they are less than 125 cm (49 in) FL, Schaefer (1999) reports: "The lateral markings of the body consist of [compared to yellowfins] wider, relatively widely-spaced, vertical, white continuous stripes [alternating continuous lines and dotted lines in yellowfins] restricted primarily to the posterior half of the body [they start at the base of the pectoral fin in yellowfins]. Yellowfins longer than 70 cm (28 in) FL have longer second dorsal and anal fins.

LIFE HISTORY: Bigeyes are schooling (at least when small) and pelagic fish with the remarkable ability to withstand both rapid changes in water temperature and low oxygen levels. Bigeyes routinely make extensive vertical movements (apparently swimming deep to reach prey) during the day; in the tropics this means encountering waters that range from the tropical (say 25°C, 77°F) at the surface to an arctic less than 3°C (37.4°F) deep down. Small fish tend to stay in 15°C (59°F) or more, while adults just seem to ignore the temperature changes. Smaller bigeyes (and to a lesser extent adults) often hang around drifting stuff. Fish less than about 100 cm (39 in) FL often school with skipjack and yellowfin tunas, and kawakawas (*Euthynnus affinis*).

Larger fish are apparently solitary or swim in loose aggregations composed of a few fish. Research on fish in the Hawaiian Islands demonstrated that fish moved among set locations over a 24-hour period, repeatedly returning to the same areas day after day. Conventional wisdom is that there is no genetic structure within the Indo-Pacific population; these fish do somewhat differ genetically from those in the Atlantic Ocean.

I can't describe their behavior any better than did Schaefer and Fuller (2002). They found that the fish in the equatorial eastern Pacific moved at a "mean velocity [of] 117 km/day (73 mi). The fish exhibited occasional deep-diving behavior, and some dives exceeded 1,000 m [3,280 ft] where temperatures were less than 3°C [37°F]...The mean residence time at floating objects was 3.1 days." During the diel vertical migrations: "They were mostly at depths of less than 50 m [164 ft] (within the mixed layer) through the night, and during the day between 200 and 300 m [656–984 ft] and 13°–14°C [55–57°F]." The fish also tended to occupy deeper waters at night around the time of the full moon. In some instances, it looks like fish associated with drifting stuff did not make the deep-water excursions.

Bigeyes live to 10 years old. At least in the eastern and central Pacific, males may grow larger than females. Estimates of size at first maturity vary with area, but a decent estimate appears to be 90–110 cm (35–43 in) FL and about 3 years old. In tropical waters, these fish spawn throughout the year, while in higher latitudes spawning occurs during the warmer-water months. Spawning occurs near or at the surface at water temperatures greater than about 23° or 24°C (73–75°F) and individuals appear to spawn every day. In the eastern Pacific, bigeyes spawn between southern Mexico and northern South America. Females will produce between 400,000–5,900,000 eggs per day. In a study off Java, bigeyes spawned from about 1900–2400 hours. Eggs hatch in about 21 hours. In the eastern tropical Pacific, bigeyes often target mesopelagic fishes as well as more surface-oriented species. Some invertebrates, like portunid crabs and squids, are also taken. One study found that bigeyes feed both during the night and day. Bigeyes are eaten by black and blue marlins, swordfish, various sharks (like cookiecutters), and orcas.

FISHERY: Bigeyes form a substantial fishery in the tropical Pacific. Longliners catch the greatest share of the fish, but purse seiners and bait boats also bring in substantial numbers. As reported by Schaefer and Fuller (2002): "They are captured by longliners operating in the eastern Pacific Ocean from about 40°N to 40°S and by purse seiners from about 5°N to 10°S...The longline fishery targets medium to large bigeye tuna. There is a growing purse-seine fishery that catches primarily small to medium bigeye tuna, most of which are associated with drifting fish-aggregating devices." What that last means is that fishermen are putting out drifting stuff in order to attract bigeyes, yellowfins, and skipjack. Along with its significance as a canned product, bigeyes are also important in the Japanese sashimi trade. For raw-fish lovers, longliners freeze their catches at temperatures below -60°C (-76°F). There is some evidence that as much as 9% of the fish landed as yellowfin tuna by U.S. purse seiners in the central and western Pacific are actually bigeyes, so be careful out there. Bigeyes have been hit really hard, and in 2006 the Pacific Fisheries Management Council declared them overfished throughout the eastern Pacific.

Bigeyes are occasionally taken by anglers in Southern California, usually in years with good yellowfin tuna runs. They form a larger part of the recreational catch as one goes south along the Baja California coast.

RELATIONSHIPS: Two studies have shown that bigeyes are most closely related to 1) either yellowfin tuna, blackfin (*T. atlanticus*), or longtail (*T. tonggol*) tunas or 2) perhaps to bluefins. So what are we to make of that?

MISCELLANY: The temperatures of the muscles, eye/brain, and perhaps viscera are elevated above the temperature of the surrounding waters.

Thunnus orientalis
(Temminck & Schlegel, 1844)
Pacific Bluefin Tuna

ETYMOLOGY AND COLLOQUIAL NAMES: *Thunnus* is from the ancient Greek and was a name given to the tunas and *orientalis* refers to it being first described from off Japan. "Kuro-maguro" is the Japanese name and "aleta azul del norte" is Spanish. Until recently, Pacific bluefins were lumped with *Thunnus thynnus*, the bluefin tuna of the Atlantic and Mediterranean.

Charles Frederick Holder, the 19th-century founder of the Tuna Club at Santa Catalina, and really the originator of much that we would call light tackle fishing for large game fish, called bluefins "leaping tuna." In *The History of the Tuna Club 1898–1998*, Michael L. Farrior states that Jose Felice Presiado, also known as "Mexican Joe," a well-known Santa Catalina fishing guide of the 19th century, was the first one to change the usual name "tunny" to "tuna." And speaking of names, one might ask why Holder, who originally hailed from the East Coast, was not called "Massachusetts Chuck" or "East Coast Fred"?

THE BASICS: Maximum Length: About 3 m (10 ft) TL. Maximum Weight: Largest fish on record in Pacific was 555 kg (1,221 lb), caught April 1986 about 483 km (300 mi) south of Kyushu Island (Japan). The largest *T. orientalis* taken off California was 271.2 cm (106.8 in) FL and weighed 457.7 kg (1,007 lb). The Ranges: Japan to southern Kuril Islands and southern Okhotsk Sea; Shelikof Strait (Gulf of Alaska) to tip of Baja California. In the western Pacific, they are common as far north as the southern Kurils and in the eastern Pacific to about Washington. Surface to 450–550 m (1,476–1,804 ft). Eggs: about 1 mm. Length-weight parameters (TL, mm, kg): (sexes combined) $W = 0.0000000922L^{2.7901}$ (RecFin 2009).

SALIENT CHARACTERS: Bluefins are dark blue or black on back and silvery below, with short pectoral fins. The first dorsal is yellowish or bluish, the second sort of red-brown. Bluefin livers are striated.

LIFE HISTORY: Pacific bluefin tuna are pelagic and schooling fish and, of the great tunas, this is the species that routinely comes closest to shore. Small ones, up to maybe 18.2 kg (40 lb), are often found just outside kelp beds and other shallow waters. Here purse seiners can catch them if they are very, very skilled. I remember sitting in a rowboat just off the Santa Monica Pier as a kid and seeing a frothing school breeze past, just a few feet away from the breakwater. Smaller ones (40–80 kg, 88–176 lb) tend to swim in very large, surface-oriented schools. How large are the schools? Well, catches of more than 100 tons have been taken from

© MONTEREY BAY AQUARIUM, PHOTO BY RANDY WILDER

a single aggregation, so we are talking serious numbers here. Smaller bluefins school with a number of similar-sized species, including with albacore, bigeye, skipjack, and yellowfin tunas, yellowtail, and Pacific bonito.

Itoh et al. (2003) state: "The majority of bluefin tuna spawn in the northwest Pacific Ocean in an area from the Philippines past Taiwan to Okinawa from April to June, and small numbers spawn off southern Honshu in the Pacific Ocean in July and in the Sea of Japan in August…Carried by the Kuroshio Current, juveniles arrive near the coast of Japan, move northward during summer and early autumn, and then most turn around and move back southward during late autumn and winter along the Japanese coast. During the first few years of their lives, the majority of young repeats a similar north-south seasonal migration. However a small fraction, increasing each year, moves away from the Japanese coast and often reaches the eastern side of the Pacific Ocean, off the United States and Mexico. These fish stay in the eastern Pacific Ocean for 1–3 years." At least some of the immature fish travel north from the western Pacific (like in the East China Sea) to the Subarctic Frontal Zone (up there at about 45°N in maybe 14.5°C, 58°F) before heading west to North America. One juvenile fish tagged in the East China Sea crossed the Pacific in about 2 months.

In summarizing eastern Pacific research, bluefins tend to spend the winter and spring off northern and central Baja California, although in some years you can find them in Southern California waters. In summer and fall, they move northward to

TSUKIJI

Tsukiji, that remarkable Tokyo fish market, is the great piscine black hole, where fishes from around the world swirl in and are lost forever. And, as noted by Theodore Bestor (*Tsukiji*, University of California Press, 2004), Tsukiji dominates the global market for bluefin tuna "in part because its high fat content and the delicately marbled quality of its flesh are both highly prized by consumers in the Tokyo area. But these same features make the tuna less attractive to Osaka consumers and in Osaka and other major Kansai [central Honshu Island] markets, yellowfin tuna, much leaner than bluefin, is the reigning fish."

At Tsukiji, the symbolic value of bluefins can't be overstated. Bestor notes: "The hatsumaguro [auction of the first tuna of the season] is a harbinger of the New Year and an opportunity for spectacular displays of entrepreneurial derring-do…On January 5, 2001, a Tsukiji trader made global news for his purchase of a 202-kilogram bluefin tuna (caught off northern Japan) for 100,000 yen per kilogram, roughly doubling the previous auction record…Using the exchange rate of the time, the hatsumaguro of the millennium sold for $174,138—a wholesale price of $392 per pound, skin and bones included. This auction price was widely misinterpreted in the foreign press as a benchmark, but market insiders recognized it as a publicity stunt, though perhaps one gone awry; even the buyer, interviewed by Japanese media, commented that he had gotten carried away with bidding." Here even cleaning a bluefin is fraught with meaning: "Ando's assistants must learn what he calls *maguro no kaiwa*—'the conversation of the tuna'—that is, to listen to the fish as they are cutting it; to gauge the pressure of forearm and wrist on the hilt of the knife and on the back of the blade from the smooth sound of a blade sliding through a block of red meat; to be alert for the small, sharp crunch when the blade reaches the bottom, outer layer of skin; to respond to that crunch—almost before they hear it—with a short concentrated push to put the blade cleanly through to the cutting board."

Central California (or even further poleward), as they follow such prey species as Pacific sardine. During these times, bluefins tend to home in on oceanographic fronts, features that aggregate both plankton and prey fishes. Unlike, say, bigeye tuna, bluefins mostly stay close to the surface, spending a majority of their time in perhaps 50 m (164 ft) or less. And unlike yellowfins, bluefins like that relatively cool water; they are found mostly in perhaps 14–20°C (57–68°F) (although they will enter waters as warm as 29°C, 84°F). Adults prefer warmer waters than do juveniles. Spawning does not occur on our side of the Pacific. As they mature, the fish migrate to the northwest Pacific Ocean to spawn. Fish tagged off San Diego and Isla Guadalupe wound up off both the eastern and western coasts of Japan.

It is unclear how long wild fish live. Those in captivity live to 16 years old. In Japanese ocean pens, bluefins as small as 107 cm (42 in) TL were mature. In the wild, bluefins tend to mature at 3–5 years old and around 150 cm (59 in) FL. Regarding maturation, size may be a more important determinate than age. They spawn from April–August (or perhaps as early as March), with fish in the southern part of the spawning area spawning first. In Japanese holding pens, bluefins spawned at temperatures between 21.6–29.2°C (71–85°F) and from 6:30–8:00 p.m. Females are batch spawners, releasing eggs every 2–4.5 days. Fish of 270–300 kg (594–660 lb) have about 10 million eggs. Off Southern and Baja California, bluefins eat large amounts of fishes (from surface- to bottom-dwellers), along with smaller quantities of crustaceans (pelagic red crabs, euphausiids, mysid shrimps, hyperiid and gammarid amphipods, copepods, and isopods), the pelagic snail *Atlanta* sp., and squids. Bluefins appear to feed less at night. I was only able to find one reference to bluefin predators; Bayliff (1980), citing a Japanese study, regarding some bluefins response to orcas: "They fear killers [orcas] so greatly that they are frightened several miles away from the spots where these ferocious enemies are found…sometimes tunas leap recklessly on to beaches to escape their enemies."

FISHERY: Native Americans in Southern California caught the occasional bluefin. There is substantial evidence that at least 5,000 years ago peoples of the Pacific Northwest (from northern Washington to the southern Queen Charlotte Islands) hunted very large bluefins (some a minimum of 1.7 m (68 in) TL long). It is likely that this was a summer fishery targeting fish that had migrated up with warm waters. It is reported that tuna were harpooned at night as they fed in surface waters nearshore. Giant bluefin tuna hunting seems to have continued there at least until around 1890. What is particularly interesting, aside from the "wow" factor of thinking about people harpooning humongous tuna from small water craft, is that large bluefin tuna do not seem to migrate into these waters today. So, is it changes in water conditions or no more large tuna to make the swim?

Interestingly, although bluefins are caught in considerable numbers by baitboats and trollers in the western Pacific, they are taken mainly by purse seiners in the eastern Pacific (with smaller number taken by drift gill nets, particularly off California). Most eastern Pacific fish are caught between Cabo San Lucas (southern Baja California) and Point Conception (California). However, bluefins are taken both north and south of these lines on occasion. For instance during September of 1960, a purse seiner caught 50 metric tons about 80 km (50 mi) west of Cape Mendocino (Northern California).

This is just a really valuable fish, the premier species for those who like their pisces raw. Pacific bluefins are commercially pen-reared in various places in the world. In general, juvenile fish are caught in the wild (Japanese fishermen catch 300,000–400,000 per year) then raised for 3–6 months on massive amounts of sardine, mackerel, and other fishes, whence they are air shipped to sashimi-eaters around the world. The conversion rate, the number of pounds of food fed to a tuna to the number of added pounds of tuna, is truly sucky, at 12:1 you have to feed 12 pounds of sardine to get one pound of tuna. People, this is not sustainable and I'm not even sure it is moral. Japanese aquaculturists have managed to raise bluefins to marketable size from eggs that came from other bluefins bred in captivity and reportedly they are working on a vegetarian diet for their livestock.

While the massive tuna caught by the early members of the Santa Catalina Tuna Club are rarely taken today, bluefins are caught with some regularity off Southern California by recreational anglers. They are notoriously hook-shy, however, and many are the disgruntled anglers who have thrown everything in their tackle boxes at a school of breaking bluefins, to no avail.

RELATIONSHIPS: Until recently the Pacific bluefin tuna was considered to be identical with the bluefin tuna of the southern Pacific, Indian, and Atlantic Oceans. Tuna systematists are much wiser today and have decided that bluefin tuna comprise three species, Pacific bluefin, southern bluefin (*T. maccoyii*) and, well, just plain bluefin (*T. thynnus*). Several genetic analyses have implied that Pacific bluefins are reasonably closely related to albacore or bigeye tuna.

MISCELLANY: Temperatures of muscles, eye/brain, and viscera are elevated and can be at least 10°C above ambient water temperatures. One hermaphroditic individual was taken off Japan.

REMARKS: Holder (1908), writing of his observations at Santa Catalina Island: "Few fishes leap for the pleasure of it; the tuna is one, and this school covering acres and made up of fishes of large size, of from seventy-five to three hundred or more pounds, seemed to be in the air most of the time." Turn you head about 0.5 inches to the right and check out the figure that attended these words.

DODGING FLYING FISHES.

Sushi-in-the-round being off-loaded in Santa Barbara Harbor.

THE YEAR OF REALLY BIG FISH

Off California, mondo-sized bluefins are rare, although an 8-foot-long fish was recorded from Monterey in the late 19th century and Holder (1913) talks of 800-pounders seen off Santa Catalina Island. Thus, the 1988 run of very large male fish in Southern California attracted a lot of attention. The run occurred from 28 October 1988 to 4 January 1989 and fish were spotted, if not caught, all the way from the 60 Mile Bank to Rodriguez Seamount. How big were these fish? Many were over 227 kg (500 lb) and the largest was 457.7 kg (1,007 lb) and 271.2 cm (8.9 ft) long. Purse seiners working the area of Santa Rosa Island make huge scores. It is said that one vessel grossed $1 million in one night with each crewman scoring $20,000 apiece. And it was a time when skippers docking with a load of bluefins could play it safe or go for a bucket of brass rings. If you played it safe you could sell your catch to a buyer at the dock for $15.40–$26.40 per kg ($7–$12 per lb), which was pretty good scratch indeed, and within 48 hours it would be gracing a plate in a sushi parlor in Japan. Ah, but if you were of the gambling persuasion, you could air freight your fish to Japan and gamble on the feelings of a hard-eyed buyer with a little knife in the remarkable Tsukiji fish market in Tokyo. If a tiny slice from your fish found favor, you would get from $35.20–$77 per kg ($16–$35 per lb).

Auxis rochei

(Risso, 1810)

Bullet Mackerel

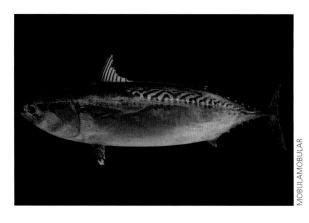

Bullet mackerel reach a length of 55 cm (22 in) TL. They are circumglobal in warm waters and have been taken from Redondo Beach (Southern California) to northern Chile, including the Gulf of California. They are rare in California waters. Off the west coast of Panama, bullets likely spawn throughout the year. Bullet mackerel feed primarily on small fishes, amphipods, crustacean larvae, arrow worms, and squids. Predators include a variety of pelagic fishes, including skipjack and yellowfin tunas, blue and striped marlins, pelagic threshers, and white sharks. Length-weight parameters (FL, cm, gr): (sexes combined) $W = 0.077L^{2.509}$ (Uchida 1981).

Auxis thazard

(Lacepède, 1800)

Frigate Mackerel

Frigate mackerel grow to 61 cm (24 in) TL and 1.7 kg (3.8 lb). They live worldwide, mostly in tropical waters. In the eastern Pacific, they range from Santa Catalina Island to Chile, including the southern Gulf of California, but are very rare off Southern California. This is a pelagic, near-surface, and nearshore species, often found associated with drifting material. Similar to bullet mackerel, frigates living off the west coast of Panama appear to spawn year round. Frigate mackerel feed primarily on small fishes, euphausiids, sergestid shrimps, crustacean larvae, and squids. Predators include the usual suspects found under bullet mackerel. The genus *Auxis* is known from the Eocene (48 million years ago or more). Length-weight parameters (FL, cm, gr): (sexes combined) $W = 0.00464L^{3.362}$ (Uchida 1981).

Euthynnus lineatus

Kishinouye, 1920

Black Skipjack

Black skipjack reach a length of 92 cm (36 in) TL and a weight of 9.1 kg (20 lb). They have been taken from San Simeon (Central California) to northern Peru, including the Gulf of California, and off the Hawaiian Islands. They are relatively common south of Punta Eugenia (Baja California). This is both a nearshore and oceanic species, found from surface waters to a depth of perhaps 40 m (131 ft). While they usually live within a few hundred miles of shore, they have been recorded as much as 3,200 km (2,000 mi) from the beach. They are rarely found in waters colder than about 23°C (73°F); they frequently school with similar-sized skipjack and yellowfin tunas, often around floating debris. In the eastern Pacific, spawning occurs at least from 29°45'N to about 04°00'N; most larvae have been collected within about 240 km (150 mi) of the mainland. Spawning occurs during the summer on the outer coast of Baja California, peaks October–December in the Gulf of California, and occurs throughout the year in more tropical waters (i.e., off the west coast of Panama). Black skipjack feed mostly on fishes, squids, and pelagic red crabs. These fish often work cooperatively in small groups, sometimes with Pacific crevalle jacks, herding schools of prey fishes. Historically, there has been no targeted fishery for this species; it was taken as a bycatch in other fisheries. The genus Euthynnus may have evolved in the Late Miocene (at least 5.3 million years ago). Length-weight parameters (TL, mm, lb): (sexes combined) W = 0.0000000242L2.0817 (Klawe and Calkins 1965).

Scomberomorus sierra
Jordan & Starks, 1895
Pacific Sierra

Pacific sierras grow to 112 cm (44 in) TL and 8.2 kg (18 lb). This basically tropical species has been found from Santa Monica Bay (Southern California) to central Chile, including the Gulf of California. They are most abundant from southern Baja California southward. However, in 1931, a number were taken in Southern California by San Diego and San Pedro commercial fishermen. Pacific sierras are schooling, pelagic and nearshore fish. Juveniles live in coastal lagoons, mangroves, and other quiet spots. Adults enter lagoons and estuaries to feed. Not much is known about their biology. One study found that sierras may live to 11 years old. Spawning occurs from July–November. In the southern Gulf of California, a few females mature at 31.8 cm (13 in) FL, 50% at 44.3 cm (17 in), 100% at 56 cm (22 in). However, size at first maturity appears to vary with area. There are very few studies on their food habits. The one that I could locate found that they feed on fishes and crustaceans. Predators include black skipjack and scalloped hammerheads. Pacific sierras have been sold commercially in California, at least in a small way, for many years. Way back in 1912, C.W. Metz reported that Pacific sierras were "often found in the market [of Newport Beach, Southern California], but not valued as food." Despite this less than sterling endorsement, I think this is a truly yummy fish. You can often see them in the Mercado Negro fish market in Ensenada (northern Baja California). In the Gulf of California and points south, Pacific sierras are a very important part of the artisanal fisheries. Here they are marketed fresh, frozen, salted, smoked, and occasionally canned. Small ones are also often taken as bycatch in the Gulf of California shrimp fishery. Fishes in the genus *Scomberomorus* swam at least as far back as the Paleocene (56 million years ago or more). As you might expect, genetic analyses shows that Pacific sierras are most closely related to the gulf sierra, *S. concolor*. Larvae: hatching length = about 2–2.5 mm, flexion length = about 4.5–7.5 mm, transformation length = about 1.8 cm (0.7 in). Length-weight parameters (FL, mm, gr): (females) W = 0.0000162L2.81; (males) W = 0.0000142L2.83 (Aguirre-Villaseñor et al. 2006).

BILLFISHES – The oldest billfish family is the Hemingwayidae from at least the Late Paleocene (maybe 56 million years ago).

Okay, here is something that, at first glance, appears improbable, but at second glance…still appears improbable. According to Little et al. (2010), their work on genetics implies that the billfishes are more closely related to the flatfishes (Pleuronectiformes) and jacks (Carangidae) than to the mackerels and tunas (Scombridae), thus pushing back against the kind of accepted wisdom of close to a zillion years. Will a third glance cause the skies to open?

FAMILY XIPHIIDAE—Swordfish

One species graces this marine family. It is characterized by a long, flat bill, in contrast to the smooth, rounded bill of marlins. Swordfish are elongate, round bodied, and, as adults, lack teeth and scales.

Xiphias gladius
Linnaeus, 1758

Swordfish

TONY ORTON WWW.TOSF.CO.NZ

ETYMOLOGY AND COLLOQUIAL NAMES: *Xiphias* is the ancient name for this species and means "sword" in Greek and *gladius* means "sword" in Latin. Broadbills are sometimes called "albacora" in Spanish. On the other hand, albacore are not called "swordfish" in Spanish, so go figure. "Pez espada" is what I hear from Baja California fishermen. The Japanese call them "mekajiki."

THE BASICS: Maximum Length: 457 cm (15 ft) TL. Maximum Weight: Over 650 kg (1,430 lb). The Ranges: Circumglobal in tropical, subtropical, and temperate waters; in western Pacific as far north as southern Kuril Islands; south of Vancouver Island to Valdivia (Chile), including the southernmost part of the Gulf of California and mostly from Northern California southward. Surface to 2,878 m (9,442 ft). Eggs: 0.8–1.7 mm. Larvae: hatching lengths = 4–4.5 mm.

Generalized Von Bertalanffy parameters (eye to fork length, cm): (females) L_∞ = 227.2, k = 0.524, t_0 = -2.41; (males) L_∞ = 221, k = 0.07, t_0 = -0.15 (DeMartini et al. 2007). DeMartini et al. give growth curves from a number of Pacific Ocean studies. Length-weight parameters (EFL, cm, kg): (sexes combined) W = 0.00001299L$^{3.079}$ (DeMartini et al. 2000).

SALIENT CHARACTERS: Dead swordfish are black or brown-black; live ones are purple. Swordfish do not have pelvic fins. The sword is a flattened extension of the upper jaw. Other billfishes, such as the sailfish and various marlins, have rounded bills and do have pelvic fins.

LIFE HISTORY: When most folks think of swordfish, assuming they think of swordfish at all, they imagine a fish basking at the surface, usually just barely making headway, with dorsal and upper lobe of caudal fin sticking out of the water. Interestingly, while swordfish commonly bask in temperate waters, they do so only rarely in the tropics. Despite our seeing them at the surface in the daylight, many swordfish tend to rise to shallow waters at night and descend deeper, even to near the seafloor (upon which they are speculated to rest), during the day. During these ascents and descents, a fish can go from waters as warm as 27°C to as cold as 3°C (81–37°F). Carey and Robison (1981) tagged 2 fish that moved offshore about 20 km a night, but returned to the same bank every day. Three other fish moved about considerably over the course of the study and did not exhibit fidelity to a particular feature. Females tolerate colder waters than males. Based on larval fish collections, swordfish do not spawn off either California or Baja California, although mature-sized fish are often caught there. However, one ripe female was taken off Santa Catalina Island in 1958. Swordfish seem to spawn most often when surface waters are above maybe 22–24°C (72–75°F) and most larvae are found in waters between 24–29°C (75–84°F).

Off California, most swordfish hang a bit offshore, but I have seen them perhaps 8 km (5 mi) off the Palos Verdes Peninsula. In a letter written to his superiors in 1822, Father José Señán, missionary at the Mission San Buenaventura (in what is now Ventura, Southern California) wrote that swordfish were commonly taken "3, 4, or 5 leagues" from

IS THAT AN ÉPÉE IN YOUR PANTS OR ARE YOU JUST HAPPY TO SEE ME?

Swordfish, along with marlins, seem to believe that their protuberances are not just the result of some fancy makeover. There are lots of reports of swordfish spears found in whales, drifting bales of rubber, and even the research submarine *Alvin*.

the Mission. As a league was about 2.6 miles, 3–5 leagues off Ventura would be fairly nearshore, perhaps over the Hueneme Submarine Canyon. Not a lot is known regarding movements, but some fish from Hawai'i do migrate to North America. Folks have repeatedly conducted genetic population studies on swordfish and, in general, have found a bit of differentiation between far-flung groups (like fish in the Mediterranean compared to those in the Pacific Ocean). However, once you look at the fish living in the Pacific, there is perhaps only a hint of population structure. Look at Grijalva-Chon et al. (1994), Alvarado-Bremer et al. (1998), Chow (1998), Reeb et al. (2000), Hinton (2003), and Alvarado Bremer et al. (2006) and decide for yourself.

Age and growth of swordfish remain confused and contradictory. It is likely that fish in different parts of the world grow and mature at different rates. Suffice it to say, females live to at least 15 years old and males to 9 years. At least one study implied that females may live to 32 years and males to 14 years. Females grow both larger and faster than males. Out Hawai'i way, Ed DeMartini et al. (2000) found that a few males are mature at 95 cm (37 in) EFL (eye to fork length), 50% are mature at about 102 cm (40 in), and more than 95% are mature at 123 cm (48 in). For females, similar values were 105 cm (42 in), 144 cm (58 in), and 173 cm (69 in). Females are believed to mature at 4–5 years and males at 3–4 years old. In the tropical eastern Pacific, spawning occurs throughout the year and from March–August in cooler waters. Females are batch spawners. An estimate of fecundity of a 68 kg (150 lb) fish gave 16,130,400 eggs. The eggs hatch in 2.5 days. Fishes and squids dominate the diet and octopuses

are occasionally eaten. Young swordfish are eaten by bigeye and yellowfin tunas, black and blue marlins, blue sharks, dorado, sailfish, and such seabirds as sooty terns, blue-gray noddies, and great frigatebirds. Good-sized swordfish are eaten by shortfin mako sharks and carry holes punched by cookiecutter sharks.

FISHERY: The swordfish appears to have had a very special place in the culture of the Chumash, the Native Americans who occupied parts of the coast of Central and Southern California. The Chumash began to hunt swordfish, apparently with harpoons, about 2,000 years ago. Much of the skeletal material that has been found had been worked into various utilitarian articles, such as cups made from vertebrae and fin-ray awls, needles, or pins. A Chumash found buried on the Channel Islands wore a shell-inlayed swordfish skull on its head.

Off the Pacific Coast, the commercial swordfish fishery got off to a kind of slow start. By about 1920, fishermen working out of San Diego had started harpooning them, but the demand was small. Mick Kronman (unpublished) quotes Santa Barbara fisherman Sonny Castognola as saying: "My dad Salvatore told me that in the old days you could tell who the swordfishermen were. They had patches on their pants. They were too poor to buy new clothes." Around 1927, an East Coast market developed, quickly followed by a local one, and the fishery took off. For decades, all swordfish were taken by harpoon as the fish swam with their backs out of the water. Fishermen stood on platforms (which was sometimes nothing more than part of a telephone pole shaved down to allow sure footing) attached to the bow of the vessel. The harpooner thrust the spear into the fish; the harpoon was attached to numerous hundreds of feet of line and thence to a buoy. After the fish was struck the buoy was tossed overboard and the fish dragged the line and buoy around until worn out. After about 1–3 hours the fish was hauled in. During this time, vessels would usually look

JOAQUIN PEDRO, who learned his business from the old master, Dominick Nunes, pioneer swordfisherman of the Pacific coast, broke all records for four days of broadbill fishing last month when he unloaded at San Diego 42 large fish in one day and returned the following day with 23 more.

PACIFIC FISHERMAN 1937, 33(31):13

around for other fish to stick. In some cases, fishermen retrieved the fish from small boats, while the main vessels sought other fish. This was always a kind of risky venture as the fish might or might not be dead and pulling an extremely angry swordfish into a little boat was then, and still remains, an adventure. Although harpooning might not be the most efficient way to capture swordfish, the guys who did it for a living could really put the hurt to it on occasion. As an example, after an 11-day trip in August of 1942, the F/V *Bernard Pedro* landed 58 swordfish. The catch weighed over 9,500 pounds and sold to wholesale dealers for 25 cents a pound, dressed.

By the early 1970s, fishermen began to hire spotter planes. Planes were extremely efficient at finding fish and this engendered an "arms race," as more and more fishermen had to hire the planes to compete—but at much higher cost. And then it kind of all fell apart, as in the late 1970s drift gill-netters targeting mako and thresher sharks began to catch swordfish. This marked increase in efficiency (needing no spotter planes, for instance) almost spelled the demise of the harpooner. The gill nets were deployed at sundown and retrieved in the early light. The swordfish drift gill net fishery rapidly expanded and extended as far north as Washington. Today, gill nets take most of the California catch, although some retro folks are harpooning a few and getting paid more per pound for their trouble. Drift gill nets are also the major means of catching these fish on the Pacific side of Baja California. Folks with longline take many fish in other parts of the world ('cause they are currently illegal along the west coast of the U.S.).

COURTESY OF MICK KRONMAN

Holder (1908) on the chances of sportfishing for swordfish ever catching on: "That such sport would become popular if cultivated in Southern California waters is doubtful, as there is an element of danger in it to be considered—that of being rammed by the fish; and as many of the tuna boats [sportfishing] now have from two to four horsepower engines, they would undoubtedly go to the bottom if injured by a revengeful swordfish." The swordfish has turned out to be a popular recreational species, although it is notoriously hard to get the attention of a basking one. Off California, most recreational fish are taken from July–September.

ORIGINS AND RELATIONSHIPS: *Xiphias* sp. have been around since at least the Middle Miocene (maybe 15 million years ago). *Xiphias gladius* lived at least as far back as the Pliocene (at least 1.8 million years ago). There has been some concern among People Who Think About These Things that swordfish evolved separately and are not closely related to the other fishes that have pointy things coming out of their foreheads. Thus you will be relieved to know that at least one genetic study found swordfishes to be most closely related to the marlins, spearfishes, and the sailfish, just like you always figured.

MISCELLANY: 1) Highly modified and heat-retaining eye muscles serve to heat swordfish brains and eyes. 2) One of the smallest reported fish off Southern California was 183 cm (74 in) long and weighed 17.3 kg (38 lb).

FAMILY ISTIOPHORIDAE—Billfishes

Billfishes are pelagic and marine fishes, almost always found in tropical to warm temperate waters. There are three genera containing about 11 species. Five species are found within our range and all have been taken at least as far north as Southern California. Arguably, only the striped marlin is common in the northeastern Pacific U.S. Billfishes are oviparous with pelagic eggs and larvae. Fierstine (2006) notes: "Extinct billfishes inhabited the Tethys and Parathethys Seas and the Atlantic and Pacific Oceans from the Paleocene [at least 66 million years ago] to the Oligocene...whereas the extant billfishes inhabited all temperate and tropical seas from the Miocene [at least 23 million years ago] to the recent." In general, female billfishes are capable of growing larger than males. Both billfishes and swordfish are characterized by elongate bills (or rostrums) and occasionally you will see one without a bill. The difference is that marlins/spearfishes have rounded bills and broadbills have flattened ones. Istiophorids warm their brains and eyes through highly modified and heat-retaining eye muscles.

C. Thomas and S. Scott, in their cleverly titled book *All Stings Considered* (University of Hawai'i Press, 1997), report that hooked billfishes fairly routinely wound fishermen while being landed or after being boated. In addition, they note: "In the early 1980s, researchers on Hawai'i's remote Kure Atoll found a Boston Whaler washed ashore with a marlin spike through the hull and into one of the seats. The operator was not found." Yep. If I was sitting in a boat and a marlin stuck its spear through the boat, through the seat, and into my tush, I probably wouldn't be found either. In fact, marlins seem to spend much of their free time jabbing things with their spears. This was nicely exposited by the famous South African ichthyologist J.L.B. Smith, who, in 1956, wrote of a most curious observation. He noted that during World War II, a number of allied vessels carrying bales of rubber from Southeast Asia to Britain were sunk by German submarines off southern Africa. The bales, now released from the ships, drifted about the area, showing up on south and east Africa beaches for years afterward. And: "It was soon noticed that many bales contained the tips of spears of marlins...as many as four. Marlin must deliberately charge floating or submerged objects, intending to impale them, possibly to secure food, but possibly also from plain aggressiveness." Smith then notes that the spear on one marlin was 2 feet long and must have come from a fish at least 11 feet long. How the massively thick spear broke off was soon clear when Smith found sharks' teeth in the same bale. "This marlin paid dearly for its pugnacity. Its struggles must soon have attracted sharks... that in increasing numbers would rapidly have torn it to pieces and become blood crazed in the process. In the mêlée one of them must have seized the bale of rubber and it was doubtless this that provided the extra force needed to fracture the stout spear."

It's easy to see how pelagic and charismatic species, such as the blue marlin, are important to the economies of resort towns such as Cabo San Lucas (southern Baja California). When last I visited the town I wandered down to the end of Marlin Street, between the "Apostardero Naval Militar de los Cabos BCS" and a mercado selling tee shirts demonstrating the 26 different types of women's bosoms. Here resides the weighing station for fishes caught by sport fishermen. On my visit, five large guys from Visalia were weighing a 500-pound blue marlin. There was the usual hubbub as the fish was pulled up a ramp and hung on a scale. There were the obligatory pictures taken next to the fish as a nice crowd gathered around. Clearly, if a local taxidermist was not going to be retained, the fish was destined for the smokehouse and local restaurants.

Tetrapturus audax
(Philippi, 1887)

Striped Marlin

ETYMOLOGY AND COLLOQUIAL NAMES: *Tetrapturus* is Greek for "four," "wing," and "tail" (referring to the wide keels on the caudal area) and *audax* is Latin for "bold." "Makajiki" is Japanese and "marlin rayado" is Spanish. Collette et al. (2006) calls it *Kajikia audax*, so I guess there will be decades of argument here. "Marlin" is probably a condensation of "marlin-spike," referring to that long schnozz.

THE BASICS: Maximum Length: 4.2 m (13.8 ft) TL. Maximum Weight: 440 kg (968 lb). The Ranges: Pacific and Indian oceans; in western Pacific, as far north as Kuril Islands; near Westport (Washington) to Chile (35°S), including the Gulf of California. Mostly from Southern California southward, but during El Niños fairly frequent as far northward as off San Francisco. Near surface to 289 m (948 ft). Von Bertalanffy parameters (mandibular length, cm): (females) $L_\infty = 221$, $k = 0.23$, $t_0 = -1.6$ (Melo-Barrera et al. 2003). Length-weight parameters (mandibular length, cm, kg): (sexes combined) $W = 0.00008L^{2.523}$ (Melo-Barrera et al. 2003).

SALIENT CHARACTERS: Striped marlins are large fish with a long, round bill, small teeth, and a very tall anterior dorsal fin that decreases rapidly in height. The fish are dark

DOUG PERRINE-SEAPICS.COM

blue on back and silvery on belly, with 15–25 light blue bars or vertical rows of spots on sides. These fish will also develop dark vertical bars, when feeding or otherwise emotionally engaged.

LIFE HISTORY: Striped marlins are pelagic and highly migratory fish, that live either singly or in small groups. Off Southern California (which forms the usual northern limit of their range), fish begin arriving in June and, in some years, remain until at least late November. The number of fish and the extent of their northward migration are linked to water temperatures and Southern California catches are greatest with sea surface temperatures are greater than 20°C (68°F) and particularly when they are over 22°C (72°F). During El Niño years, for instance, marlins can often be found as far north as near San Francisco. Worldwide, striped marlins are found in 16–29°C (61–84°F), but mostly in maybe 20°C (68°F) and warmer. This species moves around a lot. Fish tagged off Southern California have traveled to Baja California, Hawai'i, and the South Pacific. The longest movement known was 6,713 km (4,171 mi), from Southern California to Peru. However, on the basis of his tagging study, Domeier (2006) postulated that there was little mixing of individuals between far-flung parts of the Pacific Ocean. It is unclear if striped marlins in the Pacific form a single population or if there are several stocks in play. One study found that Southern California fish were genetically most like those living off Japan and, to a certain extent, Hawai'i. Unlike a number of other pelagic species (the tunas come to mind), striped marlins spend most of their time in the mixed layer of water as opposed to deeper depths. This translates to surface to maybe 40–90 m (131–295 ft) down, depending on where you are in the Pacific. In general, striped marlins tend to occupy the warmest waters available. Holts and Bedford (1990) found no single day-night behavior that was engaged in by all striped marlin in Southern California waters. They did find that fish were often most active in the late afternoon. They observed that fish tended to rapidly swim at the surface (termed "breezing") down-wind and down-swell when it was windy. In the same study, fish were least active during the late night and early morning and would occasionally aggregate in number up to 10 individuals. Some spawning occurs in the eastern tropical Pacific (and also in tropical waters west of 150°W), although it is unknown if all eastern Pacific fish spawn there. Fish in Southern California are not reproductively active.

Striped marlins live to at least 11 years old and, off Cabo San Lucas (southern Baja California), males and females grow at the same rate. Stripes mature at 3–4 years of age (around 27–40 kg, 59–88 lb). Off Cabo, females mature at as small as 157 cm (62 in) EFL (eye-fork length). In this area, and in the southern Gulf of California, spawning occurs mainly in the summer and fall and larvae have been taken in waters between at least 27.5–31.5°C (82–88°F) (elsewhere, spawning occurs in waters as cold as 24°C, 75°F). Larvae live in the top 50 m (164 ft) of the water column and may move upward at night. Striped marlins feed primarily on surface-dwelling to mesopelagic fishes, as well as pelagic red crabs, and squids. Cookiecutter sharks take chunks out of them.

FISHERY: In 1937, selling marlin meat in California was banned. However, even in the days when it was legal, there never was much of a commercial demand in California, particularly compared to that for broadbill swordfish, as the dark flesh just did not lend itself to the fresh fish trade. Some fish were smoked, however, and there were at least some sales of that product. In Mexico, smoked marlin is a staple in many markets and restaurants and it is really, really yummy. Currently there are commercial fisheries in the central and eastern Pacific and in the Indian Ocean. Although much of the catch comes as bycatch in tuna longline fisheries, Mexican fishermen target this species.

This is an important sport fish in Southern California as well in such other selected locations as Cabo San Lucas. Here's a great quote from Holder (1913) of what happened while trolling for marlin off Santa Catalina Island. The fish referred to is probably a striped marlin or possibly a blue marlin, but not a swordfish as he calls it: "We were trolling...sitting comfortably in the chairs of Mexican Joe's launch, side by side, and facing the stern. It was a hot day in September, and there was scarcely a ripple on the deep-blue ocean...Thinking my bait might be foul with weed, I rose, and stepping onto the little deck, reeled in. As the one-pound flying fish came up out of the clear and scintillant depths, directly at me came the biggest swordfish I had ever seen, of so splendid a blue that I could compare it only to a great tourmaline, melting into the ineffable labradorite hue of the water. I was fascinated, hypnotized, and he came up until I could have jumped onto his back or impaled myself on his sharp rapier and dagger, as the upper jaw in this species of *Tetrapturus* bears the sword, while the lower is a dagger which carries much as the Italians carried them, in the left hand, in the time of Cellini. The moment it saw me it turned, and for a second I saw the entire length of this tiger of the sea--a twelve-foot, or over, sapphire, striped with at least sixteen whitish bars which gave it a rakish and tiger-like appearance. Its large, black, hypnotic ichthyosaurian eyes were magnified until they appeared like saucers."

Is that cool, or what? Oh, and Cellini? Benvenuto Cellini (1500–1571) was the egotistical and picaresque brawler, consummate sculptor, and goldsmith, who so enlivened Renaissance Florence and Rome.

AND THE AWARD FOR THE BEST BOOK FOR LOOKING AT LARGE DEAD BILLFISH HANGING FROM VARIOUS STRUCTURES GOES TO...

Well, probably that would be a tome by Zane Gray or Charles Holder? No, clearly the winner is Selwyn Kip Farrington Jr's *Fishing the Pacific* (Coward-McCann, 1953). S. Kip Farrington Jr. was a big-time, big-fish guy, who held a lot of world records for catching big billfish. He was also a pretty good writer, in that sort of faintly snooty, 1930s, East Hampton kind of way. He wrote for a number of magazines, such as *Field and Stream*, and published 21 books on everything from, as one might expect, big-game fishing to railroads. Oh, and he wrote two childrens' books, *Bill, the Broadbill Swordfish* and *Tony the Tuna*. And I am not making up that last part. *Fishing the Pacific* is a virtual Grand Goignol of dead black marlins, dead blue marlins, dead striped marlins, dead swordfish, occasionally leavened with a dash of dead bigeye tuna and dead mako sharks. Many of the pictures were taken at Cabo Blanco (Peru), apparently the place to go if you wanted to catch a large billfish, hang it from its tail, and then stand next to it looking either really happy, kind of pensive, faintly concerned, or in the case of the fish, mildly bemused.

ORIGINS AND RELATIONSHIPS: The genus *Tetrapturus* goes back to something less than 5 million years. Based on genetic analyses striped marlins are most closely related to white marlins (*T. albidus*) of the Atlantic Ocean.

MISCELLANY: 1) One study looking at sport-caught fish found that marlins that were bleeding from gill cavities when brought to the boat always died and most that were deeply hooked also croaked. 2) There is one report of a striped marlin with a perky upturned bill. 3) This species warms its brain and eyes through highly modified and heat-retaining eye muscles.

FOR THOSE OF YOU WHO JUST CAN'T SEEM TO GET ENOUGH OF THESE FINE, FINE FISHES

Get yourself a copy of Peter Davie's *Pacific Marlins: Anatomy and Physiology* (Massey University Press, 1990). Along with drawings and photographs of every single part of a marlin, you will be treated to a veritable cascade of facts, such as: "There are over 400 bones in a marlin and most are in the fins or fin supports. About 120 or so are in the head while the rest make up the backbone and ribs." "Black marlin, unlike other marlins, are unable to bring the pectoral fin to lie close to the body." "Stomach throwing [eversion of the stomach] is commonly seen in marlins and other teleosts. The absence of mesenteric attachments and blood vessels other than those at the esophagus allow stomach eversion with no obvious damage…Stomach throwing may be a normal activity to help marlin get rid of indigestible items such as squid beaks."

OTHER SPECIES

Istiophorus platypterus
(Shaw, 1792)

Sailfish

Sailfish grow to 360 cm (12 ft) TL and 100.2 kg (220 lb). Circumglobal; in the western Pacific, as far north as the southern Kuril Islands; in the eastern Pacific, Dana Point (Southern California) to Chile, including the Gulf of California. Sailfish move northward as waters warm, predictably as far north as the southern tip of Baja California in summer and fall. This is a semi-coastal, near-surface species found down to at least 80 m (262 ft) (but usually in the upper 25 m, 82 ft). Sailfish are capable of making fairly long movements; the longest known one was from the northeast coast of the U.S. to off Brazil, a total of 3,861 km (2,399 mi). They have been found in 14–32°C (57–90°F), but mostly in 28–30°C (82–86°F). Schools of up to 75 fish have been observed. They live to at least 17 years old and females grow

BRANDON COLE

faster and reach a larger size than males. Fifty percent are mature at about 175 cm (69 in) EFL (eye-fork length) and the smallest mature female is about 121–130 cm (48–51 in) long. In tropical waters, they probably spawn throughout the year (but perhaps July–October in the southern Gulf of California, where occasional spawning occurs) and females may spawn every 3.6 days on average. In the eastern Pacific, spawning occurs from the southern Gulf of California to northern South America, usually near land and most often in waters of at least 27° (81°F). Batch fecundity is about 420,000–2,520,000 eggs per spawning event. Sailfish feed mostly on near-surface fish species, as well as squids, and pelagic octopuses. Cookiecutter sharks prey on them. *Istiophorus* spp. are known from at least the Middle Miocene (about 11 million years ago). Von Bertalanffy parameters (lower jaw-fork length, cm): (sexes combined) L_∞ = 203.6, k = 0.8, t_0 = 0.0015 (Alvarado-Castillo and Félix-Araga 1998). Additional information is in Chiang et al. (2004). (Length-weight parameters (LJFL, cm, kg): (females) W = $0.000004592L^{2.97}$; (males) W = $0.000004159L^{2.985}$ (Chiang et al. 2004). Some splitters (and you know who you are), consider the Atlantic form to be a separate species, *I. albicans* (Latreille, 1804). I have gone with the lumpers, for the self-serving reason that I can, with a clear conscience, present Brandon Cole's very nice image of fish taken in the Atlantic.

Makaira indica

(Cuvier, 1832)

Black Marlin

Black marlins grow to 5 m (16 ft) TL and 750 kg (1,650 lb). This species is circumglobal. In the western Pacific they live as far north as the southern Kuril Islands, while in the eastern Pacific, they are found from Southern California to northern Chile, including the Gulf of California (and mostly southern Mexico–Ecuador in eastern Pacific). They are not common in temperate waters. While a pelagic species, and found from surface waters to 140 m (459 ft), usually within 10 m (33 ft) of the surface, black marlins tend to hang out relatively close to shore. There is likely one Pacific-wide stock with a major spawning ground in the Coral Sea (and spawning when waters warm to 27°C, 81°C, in October—November). The longest movement known was 14,556 km (9,044 mi), from northern Australia to Central America. One fish tagged off Baja California was recaptured northwest of northern New Zealand. Black marlins feed heavily on fishes as well as the occasional crustacean and octopus. Length-weight parameters (lower jaw-fork length, mm, kg): (sexes combined) W = $0.000000000661L^{3.361}$ (Speare 2003).

Makaira nigricans

Lacepède, 1802

Blue Marlin

Blue marlins grow to 5 m (16 ft) TL and at least 624 kg (1,376 lb) in the Pacific and 636 kg (1,402 lb) in the Atlantic. They are circumglobal, mainly in tropical seas. In the western Pacific, they are found as far northward as the southern Kuril Islands and, in the eastern Pacific, from Southern California to Mejillones (Chile). They are occasional off Southern California and are abundant off the southern tip of Baja California (from June–November). A pelagic species, they live in surface waters to depths of 600 m (1,968 ft) and prefer waters over 26°C (79°F). This is a well-traveled species, with some fish making trans-oceanic and trans-equatorial movements; one swam 14,893 km (9,256 mi) from the east coast of the U.S. to Madagascar. Fish tagged off southern Baja California were recovered in the north-central Pacific. Graves and McDowell (1995) found some differences between Atlantic and Indo-Pacific fish, but also "a high degree of genetic similarity." Males live to at least 18 years and females to at least 27 years. Females grow larger than males. Off Cabo San Lucas, one study found mature females at as small as 219 cm (86 in) EFL (eye-fork length). The smallest mature female in one survey weighed 61.3 kg (135 lb) and the smallest mature male weighed 30.9 kg (68 lb). In Hawai'i, spawning apparently occurs from May–September and it is assumed that near the Equator spawning occurs throughout the year. In the Pacific, spawning occurs around Hawai'i and from southern Japan to Australia and eastwards into the South Pacific. Blue marlins feed on fishes and cephalopods. Interestingly, cookiecutter sharks, known to take plugs out of lots of pelagic species, apparently are unable to break through the thick scales of this species. A fossil blue marlin from the Late Miocene (at least 5.3 million years ago) was found in Orange County (Southern California). A *Makaira* sp., maybe a blue marlin, who knows, has been found from 15 million-year-old Miocene deposits. An Atlantic speciman had bills from two billfish embedded in its head. Analyses of growth rates are found in Skillman and Young (1976) and Hill et al. (1989). Length-weight parameters (EFL, cm, kg): (females) W = $0.0000767L^{2.678}$ (Ortega-Garcia et al. 2006). Some folks call them *Makaira mazara*.

FAMILY CENTROLOPHIDAE—Medusafishe

Medusafishes are pelagic marine fishes found from temperate to tropical waters throughout much of the world. There are about seven genera and about 28 species, only one of which occurs within our range. Medusaefishes are oviparous with planktonic eggs and larvae. The oldest centrolophid fossils are from the Late Paleocene (around 56 million years ago) of Turkmenistan.

Icichthys lockingtoni
Jordan & Gilbert, 1880
Medusafish

ETYMOLOGY: *Icichthys* means "to yield" in Greek (referring to the flexible skeleton) and *lockingtoni* honors William N. Lockington (ca. 1840–1902).

THE BASICS: Maximum Length: About 46 cm (18 in) TL. The Ranges: Japan and Kuril Islands to Pacific side of Aleutian Islands to about Punta Eugenia (central Baja California). Larvae have been taken further southwards, to off Punta Abreojos (southern Baja California). In the western Pacific, they are common at least as far north as the southern Kurils. In the eastern Pacific, they are abundant as far north as off Washington (during some El Niños) to about northern Baja California. Juveniles near surface, adults to 1,010 m (3,314 ft) and perhaps to 1,257 m (4,124 ft); also reported as intertidal (but this is rare). Eggs: 1.5–1.8 mm. Larvae: hatching length = about 4 mm, flexion length = about 9–13.5 mm, transformation length = about 1.9–2 cm (0.7–0.8 in).

SALIENT CHARACTERS: Medusafish are limp, elongate and compressed, with long dorsal and anal fins, and a rounded caudal fin. Adults are blue, gray, or brown and juveniles can be silvery or tan.

LIFE HISTORY: Not much is known about this interesting species. Medusafish are pelagic fish whose juveniles associate with jellyfishes in surface waters. Russian studies off California imply that adults may migrate into deeper waters during the

MICHAEL HALLACK

day and into relatively shallow waters at night. This species has been taken in waters of about 11–22°C (52–72°F), but mostly in perhaps 15–20°C (59–68°F). It appears that most spawning occurs well off shore, as many young ones are found more than 321 km (200 mi) from the California coast.

Medusafish likely spawn throughout the year, mostly from spring–summer. They eat a variety of zooplankton, including medusae, ctenophores, pelagic tunicates, larvaceans, hyperiid amphipods, and an occasional fish larvae. Predators include coho salmon, Pacific hakes, Arctic loons, Brandt's cormorants, common murres, California sea lions, Pacific white-sided dolphins, and northern right whales.

RELATIONSHIPS: Medusafish are perhaps most closely related to the western Pacific centrolophid, *Hyperoglyphe japonica*.

WILLIAM N. LOCKINGTON

Of all the ichthyologists who have worked on the Pacific Coast, William N. Lockington is perhaps the least known. But, if for nothing else than his wildly diversified interests, this polymath is the one most worthy of knowing and I thank Jeff Cohen, of Bryn Mawr College, for helping me understand more about this remarkable man.

Lockington, born in England in about 1840, appears to have been trained as an architect and to have worked in that trade in London in the late 1860s. The early 1870s finds him in San Francisco, where he described a number of fish species. He moved to Philadelphia in the 1880s, designed buildings there, then moved back to England in the 1890s and died near Brighton in 1902. Along the way, he published papers on fishes, buildings, invertebrates, botany, kind of poetic musings about San Francisco, essays on the Order of the Universe (*The American Naturalist*, 1882, vol. 16(6), p. 484–487) (which after at least nine readings I still don't understand), and Man's Place in Nature. This last work (*The American Naturalist*, 1883, vol. 17(10), p. 1003–1007) starts off okay with a discussion of specialization of body parts in the animal kingdom, but gets a little shaky by declaring that humans are about as evolved in all ways as animals can get. It then takes a sharp stick and pokes itself in the eye by declaring that: "The Chinese and the Ethiopian" are as distinct species from the 'Aryan', as the wolf and jackal are from the dog."

He was also the creator of rather florid poetry. And from his book *Day-Dreams*, published by Lockington in 1880 (Pacific Press, San Francisco), I have taken a verse from his work entitled "San Francisco." To set the stage, after going on at some length about how San Francisco is like a maiden who has not yet reached full growth, Lockington goes on to write:

"Thou art a problem. Form and face are fair,
Yet heterogeneous parts compose they frame;
Diversities of blood course in thy veins,
And mingle in the offspring thou dost bear.
By some strange chance thou hast a saintly name,
Yet are not saintly. Fed with wrongful gains
Is thy proud stomach; and the guilty stains
Of vice are hidden by thy silken skirts.
Passion in thee unchecked her power asserts;
Strong-limbed, full-chested, ample-waisted, strong,
Cruel as thou are fair, and wanton as thou'rt young."

My goodness. "Guilty stains of vice," "full-chested," "wanton." Well, clearly some things have not changed in Baghdad by the Bay.

Hang on to your socks before you turn the page. This outstanding photo is by Kevin Lee.

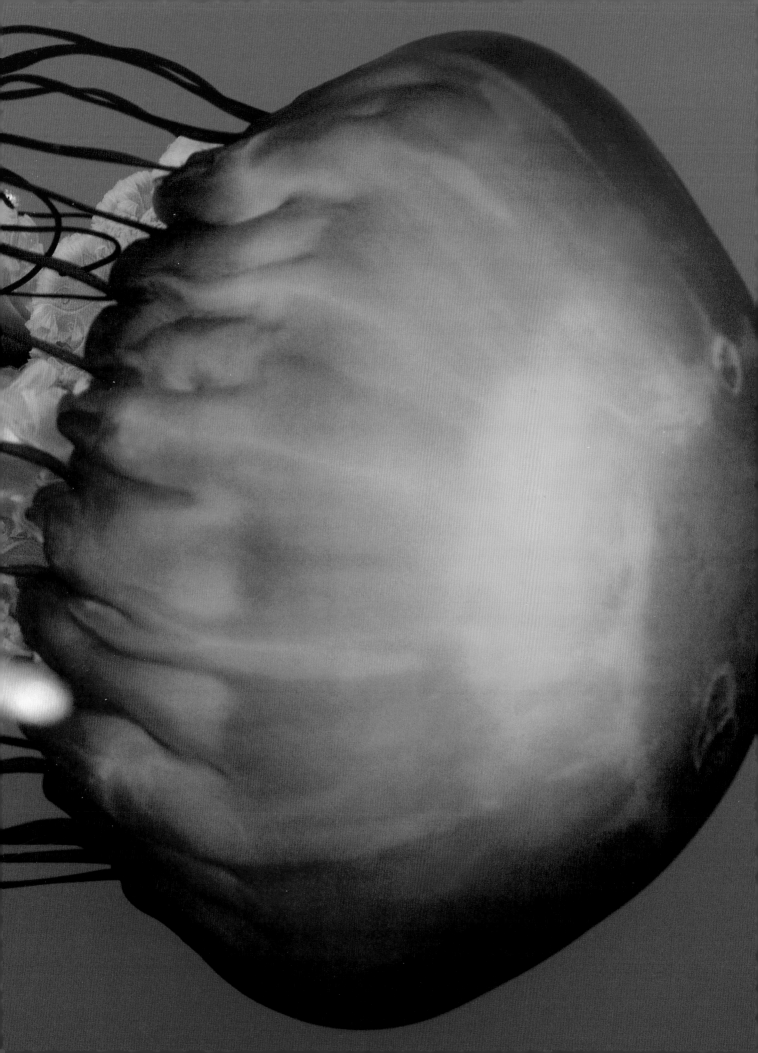

FAMILY TETRAGONURIDAE—Squaretails

Squaretails form a small family of marine fishes (with one genera and three species) that are found from relatively cold waters to the tropics. Two species live within our range, and one enters Pacific U.S. waters. Squaretails are oviparous with pelagic eggs and larvae.

Tetragonurus cuvieri
Risso, 1810
Smalleye Squaretail

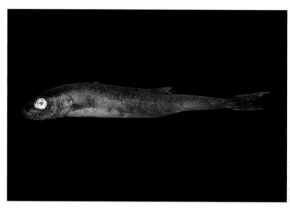

ERIC MILLER

ETYMOLOGY AND COLLOQUIAL NAME: *Tetragonurus* means "square" and "tail" in Greek and *cuvieri* honors Georges Chrétien Leopold Dagoert Cuvier (1769–1832), comparative anatomist, ichthyologist, and superb survivor of the nastiness that convulsed France during his lifetime. See *Galeocerdo cuvieri* for more details. The Japanese name is "doku-uroko-ibodai."

THE BASICS: Maximum Length: 70 cm (28 in) SL. The Ranges: Circumglobal; Japan to south of Aleutian Islands to Chile. In the eastern Pacific, most larvae occur from well off Monterey Bay to off Bahia Magdalena (southern Baja California). However, in the 1950s, 146 fish were caught in surface gill nets south of the Aleutian Islands. Young fish near surface, adults to about 700 m (2,296 ft). Eggs: 1.1–1.3 mm. Larvae: hatching length = about 3.3–3.4 mm, flexion length = about 7.6–10.1 mm, transformation length = about 1.8–greater than 2.1 cm (0.7–0.8 in).

SALIENT CHARACTERS: Smalleyes are cylindrical, have two spiny keels at the base of the caudal fin, a scoop-shaped mouth, and scales placed in curved rows. They are brown or gray.

LIFE HISTORY: Smalleyes are another poorly known pelagic species. The young are found under jellyfishes and also associated with other gelatinous zooplankton. Kevin Lee took a picture of a juvenile living inside a pelagic tunicate off Southern California. A Russian study found that adults are more common 321 km (200 mi) or more offshore of Central and Southern California than nearer the coast. This same study found that the adults appeared to vertically migrate, moving into surface waters at night.

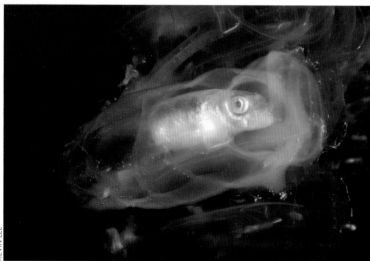

KEVIN LEE

A pelagic juvenile sits inside a pelagic tunicate.

Smalleyes may spawn throughout the year, perhaps peaking in the fall. Most spawning occurs well off shore, off the continental shelf. They feed on a variety of medusae, various other gelatinous zooplankton, and small crustaceans. Predators include California sea lions, northern fur seals, and sperm whales.

MISCELLANY: Fitch (1952) noted that Risso (the guy who described this species) twice ate this fish and was terribly sick both times. Fitch had four California samples tested and "Analysis of this material yielded less than one mouse unit of poison per gram of meat. A mouse unit is the amount of poison that will kill a 20 gram mouse in 15 minutes when administered intraperitoneally in a one cubic centimeter dose." So these fish were not toxic. OK, so then what made Risso sick? Conspiracy or coincidence? We wonder.

FAMILY STROMATEIDAE—Butterfishes

Three genera and 15 species live in various nearshore marine waters in a number of spots around the world. Three species live within our range. They are oviparous with planktonic eggs and larvae. The family Stromateidae likely goes back to the Paleocene (55.8 million years ago).

Peprilus simillimus
(Ayres, 1860)
Pacific Pompano

ETYMOLOGY AND COLLOQUIAL NAMES: *Peprilus* comes from a Greek word for an unknown fish and *simillimus* means "similar to," referring to the genus *Rhombus*. Back in the 19th century (and even today) most everyone called them just plain "pompano." "Pacific butterfish" was tried out as the official name by the Powers That Be, but that foundered on the metaphorical rocks. So, what goes around comes around, and even though *P. simillimus* is not a true pompano, we get the name back.

THE BASICS: Maximum Length: About 28 cm (11 in) TL. The Ranges: Queen Charlotte Sound (British Columbia) to southern Baja California, and Gulf of California. During some years, pompano are common at least as far north as Washington and British Columbia, and they are abundant in Southern California. Their abundance of Baja California is unknown. Surf to about 91 m (300 ft), reported to 311 m (1,026 ft), typically from maybe 3–70 m (10–230 ft). Eggs: 1.2–1.3 mm. Larvae: hatching length = 1.8–2 mm, flexion length = 4.8–6.2 mm, transformation length = 1.9 to about 2.8 cm. Length-weight parameters (TL, cm, gr): W = 0.0097L$^{3.23}$ (Love unpubl.).

ROY QI

SALIENT CHARACTERS: Pacific pompano have a round, compressed body, no pelvic fins, silvery-green or blue back, and are silvery below. They have a small mouth, blunt head, and forked tail.

LIFE HISTORY: Young-of-the-year recruit from the plankton at between about 3–4.7 cm (1–2 in) SL. I have seen fish about 4.5 cm (2 in) TL living among the tentacles of jellyfish. A study in Southern California found that nearshore fish school in shallow waters (5–11 m, 16–36 ft) during the day, and then disperse slightly offshore at night. Pompano can tolerate somewhat brackish waters (down to 19 ppt in San Francisco Bay) and temperatures down to at least 11°C (52°C).

My data imply that pompano mature at 12–14 cm (5–6 in) TL. Females are batch spawners and while some spawning goes on throughout the year most takes place from about spring–fall. There has been no comprehensive food habits study of this species, although Larry Allen, thinking back 28 years to his gut-checking days, remembers that they fed on pelagic crustaceans and likely gelatinous zooplankton. This species seems to feed both day and night. Pacific pompano are eaten by albacore, California halibut, kelp bass, Pacific bluefin tuna, Pacific barracuda, Pacific bonito, sablefish, thresher sharks, Brandt's cormorants, common murres, tufted puffins, harbor seals, California sea lions, common dolphins, and Dall's porpoises.

THE FISH WITH TWO MOUTHS

Yes, straight from W.N. Lockington's Crypt of Horrors (*American Naturalist*, 1879, vol. 13, p. 684–687) comes this terrifying tale of Nature Gone Horribly Wrong: "In the market of San Francisco there was recently a specimen of *Poronotus simillimus* (the pompino [sic] of this coast) that had *two mouths* [emphasis added for dramatic effect], one below the other, both furnished with teeth, and in size and external appearance the exact counterparts of each other. The lower mouth was situated somewhat behind the upper or normal mouth, directly beneath the eye…I much regret that I was unable to obtain possession of the fish, which is now, I believe, preserved in alcohol by the watchman of the market." *If this thing ever comes up on e-Bay, I am all over it.*

FISHERY: Pompano were very popular in the fresh fish markets of San Francisco and San Diego way back in the late 19th century. When supplies were tight, they went for as much as $1.50 a pound, which was real money at the time. Lockington (1879b), strolling around the San Francisco markets, wrote that the Italian fishermen called them "pompino" and that they were mostly caught in Monterey Bay: "Our 'pompino' is also highly prized as a delicate morsel, and is one of the dearest [most expensive] fishes in the market." Pompano remained popular well into the 20th century, always caught in relatively small numbers as bycatch in lampara and purse seine fisheries. In the 1960s, I was the crew on a two-person lampara boat that supplied anchovies to the partyboats in Santa Barbara Harbor. Once in a while we would get a load of pompano and my boss, Ed Kennedy, would jump for joy. After celebrating with a 4 a.m. beer, we would ice the fish down and drive them down to San Pedro, where the wholesale markets, having a virtual monopoly on the fish business, would give us a pittance, but a lot more than the anchovies brought in. Today, you often see them in various Asian fish markets. Pompano are commonly caught by sport fishermen off piers and, occasionally, from the surf.

ORDER PLEURONECTIFORMES

And now we come to the flatfishes. All flatfishes start out life swimming about in the plankton, looking like normal fishes, with one eye on each side of the head. Then, before settling to the bottom, one eye migrates over the top of the head and comes to rest next to the other. At about the time this is completed, the fish flops over on its side and starts swimming with the eyed side up. Somewhat after this (often shortly, but sometimes months, later) the fish settles to the bottom, blind side down. In almost all species (Greenland halibut are an exception), the blind side is white or maybe gray (unless there are developmental problems) and the eyed side is heavily pigmented. Many or perhaps all flatfishes are capable of changing patterns (and, to a certain extent, colors) to match their surroundings.

If the left eye migrates to the right side of the head, the fish is called *dextral*. If the right eye moves to the left side, the fish is *sinistral*. The ability of one eye to move rather than the other is genetically fixed. This is not a case where a flatfish, trying to break out of the sinistral mold of its parents, can operate on the principle of "Visualize Dextrality."

You want to know what effect legalizing the growing of hemp can have? Okay, researchers at Queen's University, Ontario, Canada state that they have genetic evidence that flatfishes are relatively closely related to…yep, the billfishes. Hey, don't blame me, check out Little et al. (2010).

A DAB BY ANY OTHER NAME?

If you were, like some nomenclatural Fred Astaire, to trip nimbly back over the last 150 years of Pacific Coast flatfish names, you would quickly become enmeshed in a veritable briar patch of "soles," "flounders," "turbot," "halibuts," "plaices," and even the errant "dab" and "brill." And, as you were busy picking metaphorical thorns out of your rhetorical nether regions, you might wonder if there was any biological rhyme or reason to it all. And the answer would be…no. There is no scientific basis, for instance, for naming one flatfish "Pacific halibut" and another species, from the same family, "Dover sole." As Weaver (1892) wrote after hanging out in the commercial San Francisco fish markets: "The flounders and soles are abundant throughout the year. In general the name flounder is applied to most of the flat fish brought in except the best of the flounders, which is called a sole. This confusion in names indicates how impossible it is to give an accurate account of the fish product without the scientific names."

HALIBUT BLUES

You know I had a roving eye, but it didn't last too long.

You know I had a roving eye honey, but it just did not last too long.

Cause if my eye had kept on roving, you know that would have been so very wrong.

    [refrain]

    I got blindsided by you baby, but what was I supposed to do?

    I got blindsided by you baby, yeah but what was I supposed to do?

    Cause when you sneak on my blind side, you know I just can't see through you.

You got a light and dark side baby, you know you hide it oh so well,

Yeah, you got a light and dark side baby, but you know you hide it oh so well,

But when I see your dark side, don't you know I like it, truth to tell.

    [refrain]

Oh baby you once were pelagic and then you really hit the bottom

Oh, darlin, you really were pelagic, and then you really hit the bottom

And when you hit the bottom, you know the blues you really gottem.

    [refrain]

I was a bottom feeder honey, till I hooked up with you,

I was a seafloor crawler darling, till I hooked up with you

But now my seafloor days are numbered, I am pelagic through and through.

FAMILY PARALICHTHYIDAE—Sand Flounders

Sand flounders are circumglobal, mostly marine flatfishes. There are about 16 genera and maybe 105 species, of which 21 species live within our range. Only seven species reach as far north as Southern California. Fishes in this family are oviparous with planktonic eggs and larvae. Although most sand flounders are sinistral (right eye migrates), in some species, such as California halibut and fantail sole, the left eyes of many individuals make the move. You can tell the sexes apart by holding a fish up to the light and looking at their gonads. Females have long ovaries that extend well back toward the tail and males, well, their testes don't. Fossil paralichthyids have been found in 7.6–8.6 million-year-old Southern California Miocene formations. Paralichthyids change color and pattern as easily as you change your underwear (maybe more easily, who knows?). When looking for ways to tell one species apart from another, along with the many other fish guides you might read to gain further insights, you should also acquire Kramer et al. (1995), Fischer et al. (1995), and Mecklenburg et al. (2002).

Most Metaphysical Chapter Subheading in a PhD Thesis on Sanddabs, One Worthy of Proust on a Very Good Day
   "The Indifferent Gonad" (Chamberlain 1979).

Citharichthys sordidus
(Girard, 1854)
Pacific Sanddab

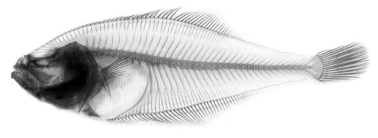

MATT SOAVE AND COREY SHEREDY

ETYMOLOGY AND COLLOQUIAL NAME:
Citharichthys comes from "*Citharus*" (a genus of Atlantic flounder) and "fish" and *sordidus* is Latin for "sordid" (having dull coloration). The old name "Bellingham Bay sole" is still used by some Puget Sound fishermen.

THE BASICS: Maximum Length: 41 cm (16 in) TL, reported to 48 cm (19 in) FL. Maximum Weight: Rarely over 0.9 kg (2 lb). The Ranges: Kodiak Island to Cabo San Lucas (southern Baja California). Also reported off Peru. Pacific sanddabs are locally common at least to Cook Inlet (Alaska), but really kick into gear at about Vancouver Island, and there are lots of them to at least Bahia de Sebastian Vizcaino (central Baja California). Intertidal to 549 m (1,800 ft), but mostly in 150 m (492 ft) and less. Eggs: 0.8 mm. Larvae: hatching length = <2.6 mm, flexion length = 9.3–11.2 mm, transformation length = about 2.5–4 cm (1–1.6 in). Age-growth patterns for both sexes are figured in Arora (1951). Length-weight parameters (TL, cm, gr): (sexes combined) $W = 0.0052L^{3.2325}$ (Love unpublished data).

SALIENT CHARACTERS: Pacifics are more-or-less oval, have large scales, and a very slightly rounded caudal fin. The ridge between the eyes is concave and when you pull the pectoral fin forward it reaches to the middle of the eye. When dead, Pacifics are brown or tan, often with yellow, orange, or reddish-brown mottling. Underwater, Pacifics can be all sorts of colors, often with lots of white and black.

LIFE HISTORY: The pelagic stage is relatively long; the little ones may stay out there for as long as 271 days. Young-of-the-year settle on soft sediments at 2.3–5+ cm (0.9–2 in) TL. In northern waters, they may recruit to eelgrass or filamentous algae beds. Pacific sanddabs live on soft seafloors, commonly in areas of sand waves and shell hash,

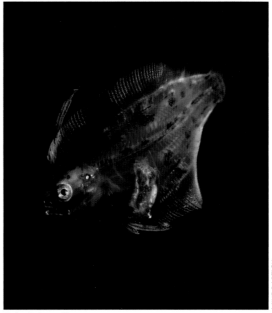

Pelagic juvenile.

MIKE BARTICK

but also over featureless bottoms. We see a lot of them on those parts of the shell mounds that surround oil platforms where shells are sparse. This is one of the few flatfish that routinely swims well above the bottom; I often seen them aggregating 5 m (16 ft) or more in the water column. Young fish are common in estuaries; in Yaquina Bay (Oregon), juvenile densities reach as high as 6,578 per hectare. While relatively uncommon in shallow waters in Southern California (mostly in 30 m, 99 ft, and deeper), adults are often found in shallower waters to the north (as shallow as 9–18 m, 30–60 ft). A study in Southern California found that Pacifics don't like waters warmer than about 13°C (55°F). In these waters, they tend to move into deeper waters during extended warm-water periods. At least a few fish have been taken in waters as cool as 5.3°C (42°C) off Alaska.

Pacific sanddabs live to about 13 years old. Females grow larger and may live slightly longer. Off San Francisco, a few females are mature at 17.5 cm (7 in, 3 years) TL, more than 50% at 19.5 cm (8 in, 3–4 years), and all at about 24 cm (9 in, 5 years). Females are batch spawners. Based on studies of eggs and larvae, they appear to spawn, at least at a low level, throughout much of the year. However, spawning is likely heaviest from the late spring–fall. Pacifics feed on a wide range of water column and benthic organisms. Commonly eaten prey include euphausiids, mysid shrimps, polychaetes, shrimps, gammarid and hyperiid amphipods, ostracods, crabs, hermit crabs, brittle stars, copepods, clams, pelagic tunicates, squids, and fishes. At least some fish feed at night. Predators include fishes (e.g., cabezons, Chinook salmon, various flatfishes, rockfishes, sharks, and skates), birds (e.g., cormorants, Heerman's gulls, common murres, and pigeon guillemots), seals, sea lions, dolphins, porpoises, and Humboldt squids. One study found that despite the hopes of their parents, pigeon guillemot chicks refused to eat sanddabs.

FISHERY: In the 19th century, Pacific sanddabs were taken in great numbers by Chinese fishermen in San Francisco Bay and then dried, usually for export to China. They were also fairly common in the fish markets of both the Bay and at Monterey. Historically, many of the sanddabs taken in the trawl fisheries were also sold for mink food. Over the years, there has developed a small, but consistent, demand for this species as a fresh product and a small commercial trawl fishery still exists.

Today, a surprising number of sanddabs are taken, and in fact targeted by, pier, jetty, and (in quiet, more northern, waters) shore recreational fishermen. When the rockfish season is over, this species is now a major fish in the partyboat fishery of Southern California.

ORIGINS: A *Citharichthys* sp. lived in the Late Miocene (at least 5.3 million years ago). *Citharichthys sordidus* fossils have been found in Late Pliocene deposits (at least 1.8 million years old) in Southern California.

MISCELLANY: 1) Once in a while the left eye of an individual will migrate. 2) Have you ever seen something peculiar sticking out of the eye of a Pacific sanddab? Well, that is the blood-feeding parasitic copepod, *Phrixocephalus cincinnatus*. See Remarks under arrowtooth halibut for more eye-popping details. 3) Lefebvfre et al. (2002) found domoic acid in sanddabs caught during a toxic dinoflagellate bloom in Monterey Bay. Given their penchant for feeding off the bottom (the sanddabs, not the researchers) on fishes and other planktivores, this kind of makes sense.

MARCOS PERREAU GUIMARAES

Citharichthys stigmaeus
Jordan & Gilbert, 1882
Speckled Sanddab

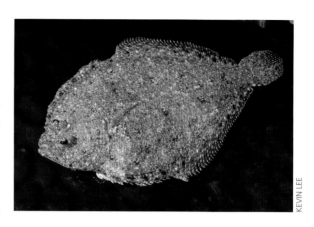

ETYMOLOGY: *Citharichthys* comes from "*Citharus*" (a genus of Atlantic flounder) and "fish" and *stigmaeus* means "speckled" in Greek.
THE BASICS: Maximum Length: 19.2 cm (8 in) TL. The Ranges:
Prince William Sound (northern Gulf of Alaska) to Bahia Magdalena
(southern Baja California), and in Bahia Concepcion (Gulf of California). Larvae have been collected as far west in the Gulf of Alaska as
around Kodiak Island. Also reported from Ecuador to Puerto Pizarro
(Peru). Based on larval surveys, they are reasonably common
from somewhere in the Gulf of Alaska to at least Punta Abreojos (southern Baja California). Intertidal to 366 m (1,200 ft), but
mostly from very shallow waters to maybe 60 m (197 ft). Eggs: 0.6–0.7 mm. Larvae: hatching length = about 1.3 mm, flexion
length = about 9.3–10.5 mm, transformation length = about 2.4–3.8 cm (0.9–1.5 in). Length-weight parameters (SL, mm, gr):
(sexes combined) $W = 0.00002L^{3.0021}$ (Miller et al. 2008a).
SALIENT CHARACTERS: The ridge between the eyes is flat or concave and the pectoral fin, pulled toward the head, falls
short of the lower eye. The eyed sides of dead ones are brown or tan with black speckling. Underwater, they can change colors and patterns, but are often heavily speckled with brown, black, or white.
LIFE HISTORY: Speckled sanddab larvae can remain in the plankton for as long as 324 days. Metamorphosis from the
planktonic to benthic stage takes place at between 2–4 cm (0.8–1 in) SL and juveniles settle out onto shallow mud and sand
flats, and in tide pools. Peak settlement in Southern California occurs mostly on the open coast, but you will find new recruits
in backwaters. And while it can occur throughout the year, the peak period is spring through early fall. On the other hand, one
study in San Francisco Bay found settlement from November–May. Speckleds are small flatfish that live over a wide range of
substrata, both on the open coast and, perhaps a bit less commonly, in bays and estuaries. They live almost anywhere there is
a bit of sand to lie on. You can often find them in kelp and eelgrass beds, next to rocks and piers, and over featureless soft bottom. Scott Gietler reports as many as 100 fish in a 7.6 x 7.6 m (25 ft x 25 ft) area at Santa Catalina Island. They tolerate nearly
freshwater conditions and temperatures down to at least 8.2°C (47°F).

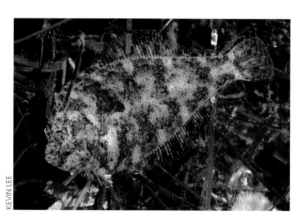

While diving on an August evening, in about 4 m (12 ft) of
water off La Jolla (Southern California), Kathryn Bouic observed a
mating pair of what were likely speckleds. The smaller, and whitish
or opaque, fish was about 6 cm (2–3 in) long and the larger, darker
one 13 cm (4–6 in) in length. She writes: "They started off flat on
the bottom nose to nose if you will. Both seemed to be moving
quite fast without going anywhere. That is their fins were moving
rapidly, but they stayed in one spot, somehow undulating their
bodies so they didn't actually move. They began to come slightly off
the bottom, an inch or two, still nose to nose. The smaller one at a
slight angle down at the tail end, the larger one staying horizontal.
They rose slightly more and more until maybe a foot off the bottom
when POOF! they darted up and apart and were gone in different
directions. Total time I witnessed was maybe 30 seconds. It looked to me like the smaller one was trying to get the larger one
to rise by nosing under it slightly. It appeared to me that the smaller dab was doing more of the pushing into the larger one as
though it may have been the male trying to stimulate the larger female."

Speckleds live to 4 years old. Females grow faster and reach a larger size. A few females mature at as small as 5.9 cm (2 in) SL
and all are mature by about 9 cm (4 in) (2 years old). In Southern California, speckleds spawn throughout the year. Females,
spawning perhaps 3 times a season, produce 4,100–30,800 eggs in that time. Speckled sanddabs feed in the midwater, on
the seafloor surface, and also appear to dig about in the bottom. These fish feed during the day. They often hang out with bat
rays and round stingrays and as these fishes dig about in the seafloor the speckleds pick off small crustaceans disturbed by the
ruckus. Crustaceans (particularly gammarid and caprellid amphipods, isopods, mysid shrimps, cumaceans, shrimps, crabs, and

copepods), polychaetes, and clams, form most of their diet. Larger individuals also eat fishes. Predators include fishes (e.g., various flatfishes, barred sand bass, cabezons, California corbinas, California lizardfish, leopard sharks, longspine combfish, lingcod, Pacific hakes, several rockfishes, skates, spiny dogfish, spotted ratfish, striped bass, and thornback rays), cormorants, common murres, seals, sea lions, and porpoises.

FISHERY: Historically, speckleds were caught in modest numbers for restaurants in Southern California. Most were taken by hook-and-line and, as noted in Bureau Marine Fisheries (1949): "One type of gear used in southern waters is unique. It consists of an iron hoop about 6 feet in diameter to which short gangions are fastened around the rim. The hooks attached to the gangions are baited, and the entire device is lowered by a rope to sandy bottoms around Santa Catalina Island. After a short 'soak' the hoop is lifted, the dabs removed, the gear rebaited and then reset." Today, although speckleds are rarely sold commercially, on occasion you can see them for sale in the Mercado Negro in Ensenada (northern Baja California). They are frequently taken by sport fishermen from boats, piers, and sometimes along the shore.

ORIGINS: *Evesthes jordani*, from the Miocene (at least 5.3 million years ago) of Southern California, closely resembles *Citharichthys* and a *Citharichthys* has been reported from the Miocene of Santa Cruz County (California). Fossil remains of speckleds exist in Late Pliocene (at least 1.8 million-year-old) deposits in California.

MISCELLANY: An ambicolored one was taken in Southern California.

MILTON LOVE

Hippoglossina stomata
Eigenmann & Eigenmann, 1890
Bigmouth Sole

ETYMOLOGY AND COLLOQUIAL NAME: *Hippoglossina* comes from the diminutive of "*Hippoglossus*," the genus of halibut, and *stomata* is "large-mouthed" in Greek. It's also called "bigmouth flounder."

THE BASICS: Maximum Length: 39.9 cm (16 in) TL. The Ranges: Monterey Bay to Gulf of California, including Isla Guadalupe (central Baja California). They are abundant from Southern California to at least Isla Creciente (about 24°N) (southern Baja California). 10–237 m (33–777 ft), but one individual was taken in a remnant pool in Arroyo San Miguel (northern Baja California). They are abundant in maybe 20–140 m (66–459 ft) off Southern California; they are apparently pretty common down to at least 200 m (656 ft) off the southern Baja California coast. Eggs: 1.2–1.4 mm. Larvae: hatching length = less than 2.8 mm, flexion length = about 4.5–5.2 mm, transformation length = about 9–11 mm. Length-weight parameters (TL, cm, gr): W = $0.005L^{3.188}$ (Love unpubl.).

SALIENT CHARACTERS: The things to look for are an elongated body, large mouth, and a highly arched lateral line. When dead, the eyed side is brown, with a profusion of blue spots and dark blotches.

LIFE HISTORY: Bigmouths live on soft sediments of the continental shelf. In Southern California, young-of-the-year settle (at lengths at least as small as 2.5 cm, 1 in, SL) mostly from November to early February.

I looked at a bunch of bigmouths and they mature from 17–20 cm (7–8 in) TL. While at least a few larval bigmouths are found in every month off Southern California, larval data and my observations of the presence of ripe eggs imply there may be a summer–fall peak. Females are batch spawners. They prey on fishes, crabs, shrimps, gammarid amphipods, mysid shrimps, pelagic red crabs, and mantis shrimps and are eaten by California sea lions.

FISHERY: Historically, way back in the early 20th century, they were a fairly important part of the "small flatfish" catch in Southern California. They are occasionally taken by pier and vessel anglers.

MISCELLANY: Ambicolored ones are occasionally noted.

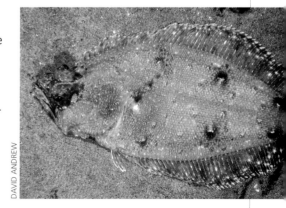

DAVID ANDREW

Paralichthys californicus
(Ayres, 1859)
California Halibut

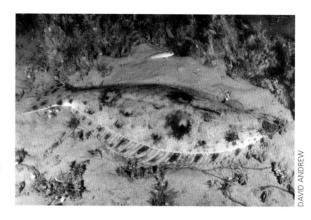

DAVID ANDREW

ETYMOLOGY AND COLLOQUIAL NAME: *Paralichthys* means "parallel" and "fish" in Greek and *californicus* refers to the first collection of the species in San Diego. In the 19th century, both David Starr Jordan and William N. Lockington commented that this species was called the "bastard" halibut in San Francisco. While the derivation of this name is a bit obscure, it is likely not an aspersion on the marital status of the fish's parents. Lockington, writing in 1879, does propose a reasonable rationale. Apparently using the definition of bastard meaning "unusual" or "irregular," he notes that this species was relatively rare in the San Francisco catch, was a relatively large species among the San Francisco market flatfishes, and was more elongated than other flatfishes.

THE BASICS: Maximum Length: 152 cm (5 ft) TL. Maximum Weight: 33 kg (72.5 lb). The Ranges: Quillayute River (northern Washington) to Cabo Falsa (22°50'N) (southern Baja California), and upper Gulf of California. They are common from about Tomales Bay (Northern California) to perhaps Isla Creciente (about 24°N) (southern Baja California), with the bulk of the population apparently from Southern California to Bahia de Sebastian Vizcaino (central Baja California). Surf to 281 m (922 ft), commonly from the surf line to about 60 m (197 ft). Eggs: 0.7–0.8 mm. Larvae: hatching length = about 1.6–2.1 mm, flexion length = about 5–7 mm, transformation length = about 7.5–9.4 mm. Von Bertalanffy parameters (TL, mm): (females, Central California) L_∞ = 1,477, k = 0.1, t_0 = -0.2; (females, Southern California) L_∞ = 1,367, k = 0.08, t_0 = -1.2; (males, Central California) L_∞ = 956.7, k = 0.0.1, t_0 = -2.1; (males, Southern California) L_∞ = 925.3, k = 0.08, t_0 = -2.2 (MacNair et al. 2001). Length-weight parameters (TL, mm, kg): (sexes combined) $W = 0.00000000849L^{3.033}$ (RecFin 2009).

SALIENT CHARACTERS: While these are in the family of right-eyed flounder, a reported 40% are left-eyed. They are elongated, with a highly arched lateral line, nice big teeth, and a caudal fin that is notched near the upper and lower tips. Dead ones tend to be greenish or brownish, often with lighter or darker eyespots and mottlings. Live ones can quickly change color and pattern to match their surroundings. You can also find them with orange-brown or brown patches.

LIFE HISTORY: California halibut live on soft substrata along the shallow parts of the continental shelf. Halibut larvae swim in surface waters at night and closer to the bottom during the day. Young-of-the-year (0.7–1.2 cm, 0.3 in, SL, and as young as 20 days old) recruit from the plankton to the shallow waters of lagoons, bays, estuaries, and the open coast. Many fish that settle on the open coast migrate into more sheltered waters and stay there for half a year or more. However, as noted by Larry Allen et al. (1990): "Even though open coast YOY [young-of-the-year] halibut densities are low, these areas may represent important nursery habitat...based simply on the large size of this habitat in southern California." Once they are a bit bigger, larger juveniles and subadults often live on the open coast, sometimes right behind the surf line. Most, but not all, larger adults leave the very shallowest areas for somewhat deeper waters. While lying on sand and mud, adult fish are common near structure, and almost any structure (e.g., rocks, kelp, piers, and the like) will do. Halibut are also justly famous for hanging out in sand dollar beds. They are able to tolerate estuarine conditions down to at least 1.7 ppt (but mostly

ON AMBICOLORATION

As noted above, California halibut are sometimes partially or completely ambicolored, with dark pigment on the normally white blind side. Completely ambicolored fish always have a "hook" (a large depression) behind the eye, near the dorsal fin. What seems to have caused this anomaly is botched-up eye migration. As a larva begins to settle out of the water column, one of the eyes begins to migrate from one side of the fish to the other. The fish then flops over on its side, eyes upwards, and lives from then on as a "flatfish." Only the up (eyed) side develops pigment; the downside, which is against the seafloor, is white. If the eye does not migrate properly (that hook is a symptom), the fish's brain seems to get confused and does not turn off pigment production to one side and both sides are colored.

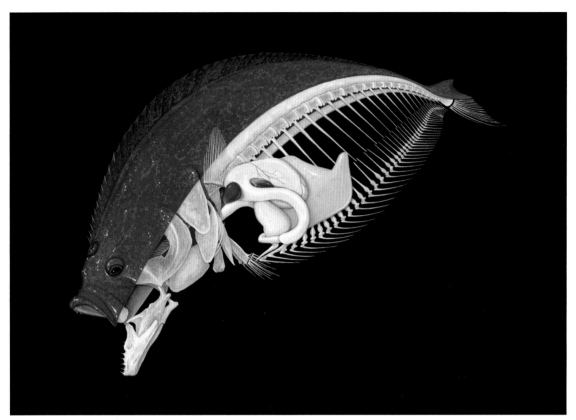

Illustration by Tim Gunther.

favor 20 ppt or higher), as well as salinities as high as 53 ppt and temperatures to at least 26°C (79°F). Juveniles and small adults can be very abundant in some bays with an estimated 80,000 in San Diego Bay.

Do halibut move much? Well, I guess that depends on how you define "much." There have been a number of tagging studies and some tagged fish traveled considerable distances. Two of the longest moves were of 319 and 313 km (198 and 194 mi), of fish that swam from Santa Monica Bay to Morro Bay, and one of 291 km (181 mi) of a fish that went the other direction. Two of the fish I tagged in Santa Monica Bay wound up at Santa Cruz Island, having crossed pretty deep water to get there. Having nodded our metaphorical heads at these wanderlust-struck individuals, we have to note that most fish are recaptured near or short distances away from where they were tagged. Moreover, what movements they do make do not show any particular pattern. On the other hand, individual halibut often follow schools of anchovy, sardine, or other prey species and likely can cover a bit of territory in the process. In the pursuit of a square meal, halibut will, on occasion, jump out of the water or, when chasing grunions, run up on beaches after the little sex maniacs.

Females live to at least 30 years and males to 23 years. Beginning at 3–4 years of age, females are larger than males; the largest male in one study was 108.5 cm (43 in) TL. Fish in Central California tend to be larger at a given age than those in Southern California. In a study I did in Southern California, a few males matured at 19 cm (8 in) TL, 50% at 22.7 cm (9 in), and 100% at 32 cm (13 in). Females were larger when they matured. Their lengths were 36 cm (14 in), 47.1 cm (19 in), and 59 cm (23 in) respectively. A few males mature at one year old and all are mature at 3 years. A few females mature at 2 years old, 50% at 4.3 years, and all at 7 years old.

Based on surveys of their eggs and larvae, California halibut spawn throughout the year, at least at a low level. Off Southern California and northern Baja California, spawning may, on average, be heaviest from about January–April, with perhaps a second peak in the summer and early fall. Further south, the spawning peak apparently shifts to June–August, with another, and smaller, one in February and March. There is likely considerable between-year variation in peak spawning intensity. Based on the presence of newly spawned eggs, halibut spawn from afternoon into the evening. In a laboratory study (Gadomski and Caddell 1991): "Eggs hatched successfully at 12, 16, and 20°C [54–68°F]. Larval survival was relatively good at 16, 20, and 24°C [61–75°F]. Survival of 3-month-olds was greater at 20, 24, and 28°C [68–82°F]." Eggs hatch in 50 hours at 16°C (61°F) and in 34 hours at 20°C (68°F). There is general agreement that small halibut feed mostly on crustaceans (particularly mysid shrimps,

small shrimps, cumaceans, and gammarid amphipods), along with fishes. As halibut grow, they tend to feed more and more heavily on fishes. Other organisms eaten include clam siphons, squids, isopods, crabs, polychaetes, and copepods. Predators include angel sharks, California halibut, Pacific electric rays, soupfin sharks, elegant terns, California sea lions, and bottlenose dolphins.

FISHERY: California halibut were a fairly important species for Native Americans. By the late 19th century, commercial fishermen targeted them all up and down the California coast. Way back in 1884, David Starr Jordan reported: "It is said that large individuals are much less plentiful than they formerly were" as even at that time the average size brought in weighed less than 3 pounds (Jordan 1884a). In 1880, Jordan and Charles Gilbert traveled along the Pacific Coast from San Diego to British Columbia, assessing the fish and fisheries of a largely unpopulated seacoast. Jordan made the point that, while he was not sure what the San Diego Bay halibut fisheries had been like before he got there, he had a sense that intensive beach seining had "greatly reduced" the halibut population in the bay, particularly in light of the very large numbers of "2 to 6 inch long" fish that were being caught and retained (Jordan 1887). Gee, if Jordan thought things were bad in 1880, what would he think today?

Well, since that time, California halibut have remained an extremely popular species with both commercial and sport fishermen. Probably the glory days for the commercial fishery ended in the 1920s, when overfishing put the hurt to populations near large ports. During much of the 20th century, the fish were taken by trawls, trammel and gill nets, and by hook-and-line. Halibut are still taken by these methods, although some commercial guys troll for them. Some troll-caught fish are kept in tanks and sold alive to buyers from Asian restaurants. Here is one commercial technique that drives sport fishermen crazy. Guys will go out on piers and, having spotted a legal-sized fish (they sometimes have people do the looking for them), they toss a line full of hooks at it, snag the flattie, and bring it in. Although legal (at least as of now), this never fails to induce a great deal of tension in neighboring anglers. Halibut are also one of the more important fish in the artisanal commercial fisheries of northern Baja California.

As noted above, California halibut are very popular with sport fishermen. Most are taken by people on boats, but there is a cadre of true believers who target them from piers and even in the surf. Most of these folks assiduously first catch smelts, perch, and other small fishes for bait, then go after their primary quarry. I think attitudes toward halibut fishing aboard partyboats have changed over the years. For instance, in the 1950s and 1960s, skippers of many Southern California partyboats would think nothing of spending most of the day drifting for halibut just behind the surf line, even if the final take was maybe a fish per passenger or less. I can even remember a number of occasions when passengers requested a halibut drift or two, even during a hot kelp bass bite. Today, I don't think most partyboat operators could get away with that, as anglers seem to require a little more in the way of stimulation.

While overfishing was a part of the problem, undoubtedly a contributing factor to the general decline in numbers of this flatfish has been the demolishment of most of the coastal wetlands that once served as nursery grounds for this species. Major backwaters, such as Mission Bay, have been filled in and dredged out, in the seemingly endless search for more prime real estate to put yet another upscale restaurant ("Come to Scurvy and Relive the True Nautical Experience"), marinas ("Come to Snug Harbor, and Park Your Overbuilt Vessel Well Away from Human Beings Still Dependent on Salaries to Make Ends Meet"), and housing ("Come to Botany Bay, Where the Only Lowlifes are the Folks Who do Your Laundry and Make Your Beds"). In a universe that seems to positively delight in the ironic, it is ironic that some of the only remaining coastal wetlands in Southern California are in the safekeeping of the military. The naval base at Pt. Mugu, for instance, harbors a rather nice little coastal wetland.

ORIGINS: A fossil halibut, *Paralichthys antiquus*, has been described from the Miocene (at least 5.3 million years ago) of Southern California. California halibut remains have been found in Late Pliocene (1.8-million-years-old) deposits in Southern California.

MISCELLANY: Ambicolored ones (partially or completely colored on the blind sides) are fairly common. An albino halibut was caught off Southern California, and a hermaphrodite was taken off Morro Bay.

REMARKS: In a previous edition of this book, I stated that one way to tell this species apart from a sanddab was to stick your finger in its mouth. If the finger came out bloody, it was a halibut. My friend Ken Jones, in his lovely book *Pier Fishing in California* (Publishers Design Group, 2004), takes issue with this advice. Hey Ken, America wasn't built by people afraid to stick their fingers in the mouths of fishes, for crying out loud. America was built by people who would stick their tongues into light sockets if it meant getting more stock options.

Xystreurys liolepis
Jordan & Gilbert, 1880
Fantail Sole

ETYMOLOGY AND COLLOQUIAL NAMES: *Xystreurys* means "raker" and "wide" in Greek and *liolepis* is "smooth" and "scale" in Greek. Bureau Marine Fisheries (1949) notes that they were "Sometimes called long fin sole or true petrale." Ironically, of course, fantails are not "true" petrale (that would be *Eopsetta jordani*), clearly a case of some commercial guys trying to scam the buying public.

THE BASICS: Maximum Length: 53 cm (21 in) TL. Maximum Weight: 3.9 kg (8.5 lb). The Ranges: Monterey Bay to Gulf of California. Although common off Southern California, larval surveys and trawl studies imply they really kick into high gear from Bahia de Sebastian Vizcaino (central Baja California) to at least Isla Creciente (about 24°N) (southern Baja California). Surf to 136 m (446 ft). In Southern California, they are mostly at 6 to about 50 m (20–164 ft), while off southern Baja California, fantails apparently like it down to perhaps 100 m (328 ft). In Southern California, they tend to move a bit deeper during El Niños. Eggs: 0.8–0.9 mm. Larvae: hatching length = about 1.8–2.3 mm, flexion length = about 5.5–7 mm, transformation length = about 7.5 to greater than 9 mm. Length-weight parameters (TL, cm, gr): W = $0.012L^{3.05}$ (Love unpubl.).

SALIENT CHARACTERS: These are fairly oval fish, with a highly arched lateral line. The mouth is small and the pectoral fin is longer than the head. Dead ones are brown on the eyed side, with some blue in there somewhere, and often with whitish spots. Often you will find a couple of dark spots, one near the pectoral fin, the other further back. Live ones are often tannish,

SCOTT GIETLER

with lots of blue spots and, again, two dark large spots fore and aft. Like the California halibut, some individuals are right-eyed.

LIFE HISTORY: Fantail soles are small flatfish that live along open coasts. Young-of-the-year settle out of the plankton (at maybe 1.8 cm, 0.7 in, SL) to soft seafloors in relatively deep waters, say 20–45 m (66–148 ft). After that, some of them move inshore, but rarely shallower than maybe 6 m (20 ft), and rarely into bays. Along with resting on featureless seafloors, you can often find this species in sandy patches among eelgrass beds, rocks, and kelp.

A 47.5 cm (19 in) TL fish was 8 years old, so they probably live a bit longer than that. Males grow to a smaller maximum size than females. Based on my data, these fish mature at about 18 cm (7 in) TL. Fantails spawn throughout the year, but mostly from August–December. They eat lots of crabs, gammarid amphipods, and various shrimps, along with cumaceans, mysid shrimps, polychaetes, mantis shrimps, brachiopods, and fishes. Brandt's cormorants eat them.

FISHERY: Historically, fantails were sold with some regularity in Southern California fish markets; I see them occasionally in fresh fish markets today. In at least one artisanal fishery in Baja California (Laguna Manuela, Bahia de Sebastian Vizcaino), they are reportedly an important and valuable fish. They are caught fairly often in the sport fishery, particularly by boat anglers.

MISCELLANY: I found one partially ambicolored one.

OTHER SPECIES

Citharichthys fragilis
Gilbert, 1890
Gulf Sanddab

Gulf sanddabs grow to 22 cm (9 in) TL and have been taken from Manhattan Beach (Southern California) to the Gulf of California. They are fairly common in Southern California and more so along the Baja California coast, to about Isla Creciente (about 24°N) (southern Baja California). While they have been taken at depths of 18–347 m (60–1,138 ft), in Southern California, they seem to be most common in 100 m (328 ft) or more. Length-weight parameters (SL, cm, gr): (sexes combined) W = $0.004L^{3.455}$ (Rodriguez-Romero et al. 2009).

Citharichthys xanthostigma
Gilbert, 1890
Longfin Sanddab

Longfins grow to 29 cm (11 in) TL and about 150 gr (5 oz). They occur from Monterey Bay to Costa Rica, including the Gulf of California, most abundantly from northern Baja California southward. During warm-water periods, you see more of them off Southern California. Longfins live on soft sediments in depths of 2.4–250 m (8–820 ft). They are most abundant in perhaps 20–150 m (66–492 ft). Longfins live to at least 10 years old. Females grow a bit larger than males. All males are mature by 12.2 cm (5 in, 2 years) TL. A few females mature at 12.2 cm (5 in, 2 years), 50% at 14.6 cm (6

MILTON LOVE

in, 3 years), and all are mature at 17 cm (7 in, 4 years). Females are batch spawners and larval studies imply that there may be at least low levels of spawning throughout the year. However, most takes place from late fall–winter. Longfins feed on a variety of bottom and near-bottom invertebrates, including polychaetes, mysid shrimps, copepods, gammarid amphipods, shrimps, nemerteans, isopods, mussels, clams, sea cucumbers, brachiopods, medusae, and the occasional fish. Way back in 1927, Villadolid wrote that longfins were an excellent food fish, probably superior to Pacific sanddabs, but were too scarce to form a major fishery. Nonetheless, longfins were fairly important in the San Pedro and San Diego flatfish fisheries of the time. In the U.S., there is not much going on with them today, however. They are taken commercially in some numbers along the central and southern Baja California coast. This species is occasionally taken by anglers, although in nowhere the numbers of Pacific sanddabs. One partially ambicolored one has been taken. Based on a genetic study, longfins are most closely related to flounder of the genera *Etropus* and *Syacium* (however, no other *Citharichthys* was examined). Larvae: hatching length = less than 2.3 mm, flexion length = 7.8–10 mm, transformation length = about 2.3–3.1 cm. Von Bertalanffy parameters (SL, mm): (females) L_∞ = 264, k = 0.116, t_0 = -1.939; (males) L_∞ = 169, k = 0.257, t_0 = -1,144 (Groce 2002). Length-weight parameters (SL, mm, gr): (sexes combined) W = $0.0000007L^{3.232}$ (Groce 2002).

FAMILY PLEURONECTIDAE—Righteye Flounders

Righteye flounders are mostly marine flatfishes (some are found in brackish waters, but they only rarely enter freshwater) that are found throughout the world. Some species are notable for being able to withstand extremely cold-water conditions, sometimes a degree or so below freezing. There are 23 genera and about 60 species, of which 30 are found within our range. Many North Pacific pleuronectids are found in cold temperate waters. In the northeastern Pacific, righteye flounders are oviparous and have planktonic eggs and larvae, with the exception of the northern and southern rock soles. The rock soles have demersal, adhesive eggs. As their name implies, fishes in this family almost always have the left eye migrate and then individuals swim with the right side upwards. Pleuronectid fossil fishes (*Evesthes jordani, E. hooveri, Zororhombus veliger*, and *Diatomoeca zatima*) are known from the Miocene diatomite beds (at least 5.3 million years old) of California. At least one species of fossil righteye flounder lived 7.6–8.6 million years ago during the Southern California Miocene.

A note about body coloration. Many or all of the flatfishes are masters at changing colors and patterns to match their surroundings. So, given our relatively brief time here in this Veil of Tears, trying to list all of the possible color and pattern variants that a species might assume is, well, it's a poor use of that flickering spark, isn't it? Thus, under Salient Characters, body coloration and pattern is mostly that seen on dead ones, unless otherwise stated. See Kramer et al. (1995) and Mecklenburg et al. (2002) for many more descriptive details.

Atheresthes stomias

(Jordan & Gilbert, 1880)

Arrowtooth Flounder

ETYMOLOGY AND COLLOQUIAL NAMES: Personally, I find the etymology of *Atheresthes* to be particularly obscure. Jordan and Evermann (1898) report that *Atheresthes* comes from the Greek words for "the beard or spike of an ear of corn" and "to eat" and they go on to note that this refers to the "arrow-shaped teeth." *Hmm, what? Stomias* is Greek for "large-mouthed." They were called "long-jaw flounder" and "arrow-toothed halibut" early on, the Russians call them "American arrow-toothed halibut," and the Japanese name is "arasukaaburagarei."

THE BASICS: Maximum Length: 86 cm (34 in) TL. Maximum Weight: 8.7 kg (19.1 lb). The Ranges: East coast of Kamchatka to Bering Sea at Cape Navarin and south of Saint Lawrence Island (62°08'N, 170°18'W), and Gulf of Alaska to Santa Barbara (Southern California). They are abundant along the Aleutian Islands, southern and eastern Bering Sea, and southward to about Oregon or Northern California. 9–1,145 m (29–3,756 ft). Adults are found primarily in about 100–500 m (328–1,640 ft), although one survey (Hoff and Britt 2005) found them to be abundant in 1,000 m (3,280 ft) or more in the Bering Sea. Eggs: fertilized, about 1.6–2 mm. Larvae: hatching length = 3.9–4.8 mm, transformation length = 2.6–4.4 cm (1–1.7 in). Von Bertalanffy parameters (FL, cm): (females) L_∞ = 85, k = 0.161, t_0 = 0.812; (males) L_∞ = 57.9, k = 0.172, t_0 = -2.172 (Zimmerman and Goddard 1996). Additional von Berts are found in Demory et al. (1976) and Bakkala et al. (1985). Length-weight parameters (TL, cm, gr): (sexes combined) W = $0.00271L^{3.32}$ (Orlov and Binohlan 2009).

SALIENT CHARACTERS: Arrowtooths have elongated and diamond-shaped bodies, scales with dark edges, lots of sharp and widely spaced teeth, an upper jaw that reaches beyond the eyes, and the upper eye sits on the dorsal ridge and is visible from the blind side. The eyed side is gray-brown to olive-brown and the blind side is white to light gray.

ON FLATFISHES

[Most flatfishes, such as halibuts, soles, and flounders, are dark on their topsides and white on the underside.]

It's a thing that's scaring the nation,
It's a cause for investigation,
　　When flatfish come to town,
　　They're both white and brown,
It's the ultimate miscegenation.

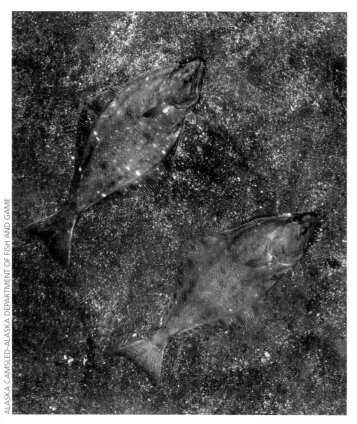

LIFE HISTORY: Young-of-the-year settle in shallow bays (sometimes slightly estuarine ones) over mud, sand, or occasionally gravel, at between about 4–6 cm (2 in) TL in depths to at least 75 m (246 ft). After about a year, these fish begin migrating into deeper waters; fish of 40 cm (16 in) FL or so live on the deeper parts of the continental shelf and on the continental slope. Fish have been seen both on soft sediments and low-relief rocks. On average, females may live at somewhat deeper depths than males. Females are synchronous spawners and spawning mostly occurs over the continental slope. As an example, off Kodiak Island most fish reproduce in 400–500 m (1,312–1,640 ft). Arrowtooths have been found from -1.5 to at least 12°C (29–54°F), perhaps mostly in 1–5°C (34–41°F), and young fish may be most cold tolerant. Adults move into somewhat shallower waters in the summer. It is unclear how much along-shore movements, if any, this species makes.

Arrowtooths live to at least 56 years old. Females grow larger than males (males larger than maybe 68 cm, 27 in, FL, appear to be rare). Females are larger at a given age and males reach maximum size more quickly. Okay, I've read most of the recent papers regarding size and age at first maturity (Rickey 1995, Zimmerman 1997, Kaplan and Helser 2007, and Stark 2008) and, frankly, these numbers are just all over the map. Generally, at any given location males mature when smaller than females. It appears that fish off Alaska are larger at maturity than those off, say, Oregon or maybe Washington. Fifty percent maturity for males can range from 28–42.2 cm (11–17 in) FL and females from 36.8–47 cm (14–19 in). Estimates of ages at 50% maturity seem to range from 4–7 years for males and 7–10 years for females. Spawning has been reported in every month of the year and one supposes that the season varies with year and perhaps between areas. Spawning in the Gulf of Alaska occurs at least from January–August, perhaps with a spring peak, while fish off Washington were noted spawning from September to at least December, and those off Oregon from December–March. Females are batch spawners, produce between 103,000–2,339,000 eggs per season, and, reportedly, the eyed-side ovary lobe is heavier than the blind-side one. The eggs are pelagic and are mostly in deeper than 200 m (656 ft) until they hatch. Eggs hatch in 3.1°C (38°F) at between 21–31 days, while those in 6°C (43°F) hatch in 12–15 days. The larvae drift about for 4–5 months before settling out. Smaller arrowtooths lean toward crustacean eating (e.g., euphausiids, pandalid shrimps, and hermit crabs), although they do eat fishes, while the larger ones tend to focus on fishes (lots and lots of fishes) and often crabs. Squids, octopuses, gammarid amphipods, and mysid shrimps fill out the diet. As you might expect, arrowtooth diets vary between years and there is some evidence that there are decadal differences as water masses change properties. These fish appear to feed less in the winter than in the summer. Predators include arrowtooth flounder, bigmouth and great sculpins, Pacific cod, Pacific hakes, Pacific halibut, Pacific lampreys, Pacific sleeper sharks, sablefish, shortspine thornyheads, spiny dogfish, walleye pollock, bald eagles, seals, sea lions, and probably river otters.

FISHERY: Native peoples, for instance those living on Kodiak and the Shumagin islands, ate arrowtooths in considerable numbers. And white folks? Well not so much. As Smith (1936) noted regarding commercial fishing off Washington: "Numbers of arrowtooth halibut are taken in this area, but are not marketed. Experimental attempts to market this fish were unfavorable, owing to the softness of the meat when it was kept for several days after capture." In fact, arrowtooth muscle contains an enzyme that softens tissue; untreated, this protease makes the meat a poor candidate for most fresh fish applications or for surimi-making. And so, before the 1950s, the commercial fishery for arrowtooths just kind of limped along, with the occasional catches being filleted and, one hopes, sold. And then, like a knight in furry raiment, the burgeoning mink-raising industry of the 1950s came to the rescue. For it was the hardy mink farmer, looking for a cheap way to feed their coats-in-training, that caused catches of arrowtooths to escalate. And it was not until the collapse of the mink industry in the late 1970s that

A fish and its eye parasite.

the commercial fishery returned to its semi-somnolent ways. Today, there are relatively small arrowtooth landings made by trawlers in the Pacific Northwest and most of that product goes into the fresh fish markets. One assumes that someone will come up with some way of making something out of arrowtooths that people like and then the species will be overfished. Many arrowtooths are caught as bycatch in other trawl fisheries and discarded at sea. Recreational anglers occasionally take them.

ORIGINS AND RELATIONSHIPS: Remains of this species from Pliocene deposits (at least 1.8 million years old) have been found in California. Several genetic studies have found that arrowtooths and Kamchatka flounder are closely related.

MISCELLANY: The eyes of arrowtooths are often infected with the parasitic copepod, *Phrixocephalus cincinnatus*. In one study, 82.8% of all fish examined were infected, most in the right eye, but some in the left, and 28.3% in both eyes. Most of the fish that have both eyes infected die from the infection. This copepod initially lives in an unknown intermediate host. Here adult males and preadult females mate and only the postmated female infects the final fish host. The female copepod swims about and enters the arrowtooth eye by breaking through the cornea. She then burrows her head into the retina and drinks the host's blood. The posterior of the growing parasite eventually break through the cornea again and what you usually see are the string of eggs that hang off. *Phrixocephalus* can live up to 1.5 years, the animal dying when all the eggs are shed. Interestingly, the damage to the eye at this point is minimal and it is only when the copepod dies and disintegrates, leaving the hole in the cornea, that the eye is blinded.

Eopsetta jordani
(Lockington, 1879)
Petrale Sole

ETYMOLOGY AND COLLOQUIAL NAMES: *Eopsetta* means "morning" and "flounder" in Greek and *jordani* honors David Starr Jordan (1851–1931), eminent ichthyologist, first president of Stanford University, and tireless advocate for world peace. And the dark side? Well, see below. Early on, the species was referred to merely

as "sole," although "round-nosed sole" and "round-nosed flounder" were early favorites. In the 1940s, the Canadians floated "brill" as the official name, but in yet another example of cultural imperialism, the U.S.-derived "petrale" won out.

THE BASICS: Maximum Length: 70 cm (28 in) TL. Maximum Weight: about 3.6 kg (8 lb). The Ranges: Unalaska Island (Aleutian Islands) and Gulf of Alaska to Islas Coronados (northern Baja California), typically from Icy Bay–Yakutat (Gulf of Alaska) to Southern California. 0–550 m (0–1,800 ft). When their deeper-water winter grounds are included, they are found mostly from perhaps 55–457 m (180–1,500 ft). Eggs: 1.2–1.3 mm. Larvae: hatching length = about 2.8–3 mm, flexion length = about 10.9 mm, transformation length = 1.6–1.8 cm (0.6–0.7 in). Von Bertalanffy parameters (TL, cm): (females) L_∞ = 57.37, k = 0.1450, t_0 = 0.05; males: L_∞ = 44.89, k = 0.176, t_0 = 0.45 (Lai et al. 2005). Length-weight parameters (TL, cm, gr): (females) W = $0.003416L^{3.3462}$; (males) W = $0.007168L^{3.1337}$ (Lai et al. 2005).

SALIENT CHARACTERS: This is a large-mouthed, fairly oval species. Its jaws reach to the middle of the eye, the upper jaw has two rows of teeth, the caudal fin is pointed in the center, and the lateral line is only mildly curved. Dead ones are brown with some darker mottling.

LIFE HISTORY: Young-of-the-year settle out of the plankton at 6 cm (2 in) TL, or smaller, in about 18–90 m (59–295 ft), in spring to fall. Juveniles tend to move into deeper waters as they mature. Petrales make quite distinct seasonal migrations, moving inshore (often migrating at least several hundred miles) in the spring and back offshore in fall to spawn. Forrester (1969) noted that off British Columbia the fish exhibited: "Extensive geographic migrations...fish which feed in shallow waters [73–128 m, 240–420 ft] in summer in the Hecate Strait area...accumulate for spawning in winter in deep water [311–457 m, 1,020–1,500 ft] off the west coast of Vancouver Island." Generally, fish spawn in discrete areas (10 have been described between British Columbia and California) and then spread out along the coast in shallower waters to feed. While most fish return to the same spawning grounds year after year, there is some intermingling during summer. It is unclear how much coastal movement the average fish makes, although some fish are afflicted with wanderlust, as individuals tagged off Fort Bragg (Northern California) were recaptured off Oregon, Washington, and Vancouver Island. Petrales live mostly on soft seafloors, but I have seen fair numbers lying near or on small cobbles. They have been found in waters between at least 4.1–12.2°C (39–54°F).

Petrales may live to perhaps as much as 40 years old, but few fish live more than 25 years. Females grow slightly larger than males and are larger at age. Size and age at maturity probably vary slightly with location and, perhaps, with year. Here is an estimate that should hold up reasonably well wherever you travel. For males, a few mature at about 26 cm (10 in, 3 years) TL, 50% at about 32 cm (13 in, 4 years), and 100% at about 39 cm (15 in, 8 years). For females, the numbers are 28 cm (11 in, 4 years), 36 cm (14 in, 5 years), and 44 cm (17 in, 8 years), respectively. At one time or another, researchers have found fish as old as 10 years that were still immature. Most spawning occurs from November–March, but ripe fish have been reported as late as May or even in mid-summer, so what the hey, there is probably a little spawning throughout the year. Females produce at least 400,000–1,200,000 eggs per season and spawn them all at one time. The eggs hatch in about 8.5 days at 7°C (45°F) and the egg/larva pelagic stage may last about 6 months. Larvae are often found in the upper 50 m (164 ft) of the water column. Juveniles feed on small invertebrates (e.g., gammarid amphipods, caridean shrimps, and cumaceans), while adults feed mostly on fishes, along with octopuses, squids, snails, gammarid amphipods, euphausiids, shrimps, and hermit crabs. Predators include bocaccio, other petrale soles, ratfish, steelhead, and harbor seals.

DAVID STARR JORDAN

Jordan was a complex man and, in many ways, quite admirable. And yes, he did have some kind of funky and troubling views on eugenics. And yes, he might have thought that Europeans were somewhat more advanced than everyone else on the planet. But you know, compared to a simply astounding number of his contemporaries, Jordan seems pretty progressive.

Of course, on the flip side of the coin, he was quite possibly the major conspirator in the cover-up of the murder of Mrs. Leland Stanford. Really, I'm not making that up. For all the details take a look at *The Mysterious Death of Jane Stanford* (Stanford University Press, 2003). In this rather meticulously researched book, Dr. Robert W.P. Cutler, a professor emeritus of neurology at Stanford University, makes the compelling case that while on a trip to Hawai'i in 1905, Mrs. Stanford was poisoned and died from ingesting strychnine. Following her death, Jordan immediately hopped a boat for the islands and, despite an abundance of evidence pointing to death by poison, upon his arrival in Hawai'i he quickly smeared the reputations of the physicians in charge of the investigation. Jordan soon thereafter hired a doctor of dubious credentials who, having never examined the deceased, brought in a verdict of death by heart disease. Soon after, a statement issued by Jordan and Stanford Board Trustee Timothy Hopkins [of *Sebastes hopkinsi* fame] stated that Mrs. Stanford's death was from natural causes. It seems telling that William Henry, Honolulu High Sheriff at the time, stated that he had told Jordan and Hopkins that: "The real purpose they were working for was to make it believed that Mrs. Stanford died from natural causes and was not murdered." As Dr. Cutler notes in his summary: "It seems remarkable today that the considered opinions of the attending and autopsy physicians, the toxicologists, the Honolulu police department, and the coroner's jury could be so easily dismissed on the basis of a brief declaration by President Jordan and Trustee [Timothy] Hopkins that Mrs. Stanford died of natural causes…[Jordan and Hopkins] claim was not supported by any new clue, medical or forensic evidence, or expert testimony that the poisoning diagnosis was 'without foundation'…No other evidence [by Jordan and Hopkins regarding their assertion of death by heart attack] was ever presented to the public, or, in all likelihood, to law enforcement officials."

Why would Jordan and Hopkins help block a murder investigation and thus by all odds help the murderer escape both identification and punishment? Read the book and see what Dr. Cutler says.

FISHERY: Petrales have been a popular fish market species at least as far back as when Lockington checked out the San Francisco fish markets in the late 1870s. Jordan (1884a) noted: "Great numbers are dried yearly by the Chinese, who suspend them by strings on a frame placed on the roofs of the houses, as they are too fleshy to dry well on tables. Here they rustle in the wind, and, striking together produce a sound like the wind among the leaves." They remained a very important flatfish all along the Pacific Coast (from British Columbia to about Santa Barbara, Southern California) for many years and still are caught in some numbers by the trawl fleet. On a per-pound basis, petrales are the most valuable flatfish (other the Pacific halibut) landed in the northeastern Pacific. During the "vitamin A rush" of the 1930s and 1940s, when everyone busily tested fish livers for that nutrient, it was found that petrales had high levels, comparable to those gold standards, spiny dogfish and Pacific cod. Petrales are commonly taken by anglers from boats; small ones are taken from piers.

ORIGINS AND RELATIONSHIPS: Petrales have been found in 100,000-year-old formations. They are perhaps most closely related to, among other species, Pacific halibut and slender soles.

LINDA SNOOK

Glyptocephalus zachirus
Lockington, 1879
Rex Sole

ETYMOLOGY AND COLLOQUIAL NAMES: *Glyptocephalus* means "sculptured" and "head" in Greek and *zachirus* is Greek for "long hand," referring to the long pectoral fin. In the 19th century, just "sole" or "long-fin sole" was used in the U.S. and "witch flounder" was a Canadian donation. The Japanese name is "hirenaganameta."

THE BASICS: Maximum Length: 61 cm (24 in) TL. Maximum Weight: 2.5 kg (5.5 lb). The Ranges: Northern Kuril Islands to western Bering Sea at Navarin Canyon, and Aleutian Islands, eastern Bering Sea, and Gulf of Alaska to Isla Cedros (central Baja California). They are most abundant along the Aleutian Islands, the eastern Bering Sea as far northward as about Saint Matthew Island, and to Southern California. Their abundance off Baja California is unknown. 0–1,145 m (0–3,756 ft), most adults in perhaps 100–500 m (320–1,640 ft). They tend to be found deeper in the more southerly part of their range. Eggs: 1.8–2.3 mm. Larvae: hatching length = about 5 mm, flexion length = 1.5–2.6 cm, transformation length = 4.7–7 cm. Growth rates may be considerably different between fish living off Oregon and those in the Gulf of Alaska. Von Bertalanffy parameters (TL, cm) (Oregon, otolith surfaces read): (females) L_∞ = 37.2, k = 0.1749, t_0 = 0.5667; (males) L_∞ = 33.4, k = 0.1778, t_0 = 0.8551 (Hosie and Horton 1977). Von Bertalanffy parameters (TL, mm) (Gulf of Alaska, break-and-burn otoliths read): (females) L_∞ = 41.9, k = 0.388, t_0 = -0.22 (Abookire 2006). Length-weight parameters (TL, cm, gr): (females) W = $0.000762L^{3.6127}$ (Abookire 2006). Length-weight parameters for Oregon fish in Hosie and Horton (1977).

SALIENT CHARACTERS: Rex soles are brown or gray, elongated, small-mouthed, round-snouted, have a caudal fin that is pointed in the center, and have a long, dark pectoral fin.

LIFE HISTORY: During the winter, young-of-the-year recruit (at as small as about 4 cm, 2 in, SL) to soft seafloors, from relatively nearshore waters to the edge of the continental shelf. This fish's pelagic life can last for one year or more, and the occasional rogue pelagic larva can stay aloft to as long as 8.9 cm (4 in). Most rex soles are found on the open coast, particularly on the lower continental shelf and upper continental slope, but you can also find them in such embayments as Cook Inlet (Gulf of Alaska), where they can withstand slightly brackish waters. Juveniles tend to occupy shallower waters than adults. This is a benthic species, living mostly over mud or mixed mud-rock seafloors, but occasionally I see them on cobble bottoms. They move inshore during the spring and summer and migrate offshore as waters cool. During the spawning season, these fish aggregate along the deep parts of the shelf and down the slope. Rex soles can be found at temperatures as low as -0.5°C (31°F), but more often stay at higher temperatures (occasionally to at least 12.2°C, 54°F).

Rex soles live to 29 years old. Females live longer and grow larger than males. The sexes appear to grow at the same rates. Fish in the Gulf of Alaska are larger at all ages (at least to 15 years old) than those from off Oregon. Size and age at maturity also vary greatly with location. Off Oregon and California, fish are smaller at maturity than those living in the Gulf of Alaska. In the GOA, a few females are mature at 28.7 cm (11 in) TL, 50% at 35.2 cm (14 in), and all at 42 cm (17 in). Off Oregon, comparable lengths are 19 cm (8 in), 24 cm (10 in), and 30 cm (12 in), respectively. Off Oregon, males mature at 13–21 cm (5–8 in) and 3–5 years old. In both locations, fish mature at between about 3–9 years old. Some level of spawning probably occurs throughout the year, most takes place from late winter–early summer, and in many areas it peaks in the spring. Fish in the Gulf of Alaska spawn earlier (starting in October) and for a longer duration (ending in May) than do those living off Oregon (January to June). Females are batch spawners and produce between 3,900–238,100 eggs. Most eggs tend to remain from near-surface waters down to about 120 m (394 ft) and the larvae occupy the top 40 m (131 ft) or so. Polychaetes and gammarid amphipods head the list of the stuff rex soles eat. Also consumed are various crabs, euphausiids, cumaceans, fishes, snails, sea urchins, copepods, sipunculids, and the occasional clam. Overall, you get the sense of a fish that mostly feeds on or perhaps in the seafloor. A study in Puget Sound found that these soles fed both day and night. Get this, Waldo Wakefield (1984) noting that rex soles eat heart urchins, wondered if the flatfish might be able to hear the urchins as they walk around under the mud. For some reason, I love that thought. The usual suspects eat rex soles. These include fishes (e.g., flatfishes, rockfishes, salmon, sharks, and skates), sea birds (Brandt's and pelagic cormorants), seals, and sea lions.

FISHERY: Rex soles, taken simply in the gobzillions by the paranzella trawls of the late 19th and early 20th centuries, and by otter trawls from the mid-20th century on, have been a reasonably popular commercial species. There was a fair demand for them as a fresh fish and, in the mid-20th century, they also made up a large part of the mink food fishery. Today, there remains a fairly large commercial harvest and Ken Gordon reports that rex soles have found a niche market as whole fish in some Asian restaurants. Anglers only rarely take them.

ORIGINS AND RELATIONSHIPS: Otoliths attributed to this species have been found in Pliocene (at least 1.8 million-year-old) Oregon deposits. Based on morphological characters, rex soles appear to be most closely related to *Glyptocephalus cynoglossus* of the Atlantic, and to the Western Pacific species, *G. stelleri*. Genetic studies imply that they are related to deep-sea and Dover soles.

MISCELLANY: 1) Both ambicolored fish and ones with diffuse pigmentation (a dark gray blind side) have been caught. 2) Two sinistral fish, with eyes on the left side of the body, were taken off Northern California.

Hippoglossoides elassodon
Jordan & Gilbert, 1880

Flathead Sole

ETYMOLOGY AND COLLOQUIAL
NAMES: *Hippoglossoides* combines "*Hippoglossus*" (the genus of halibut) and "resemblance" in Greek and *elassodon* is Greek for "to diminish" and "tooth." Other names have included "cigarette paper," "paper sole," and "Pacific plaice." The Japanese name is "uma-garei."

THE BASICS: Maximum Length: 56 cm (22 in) TL. Maximum Weight: 2.8 kg (6.2 lb).

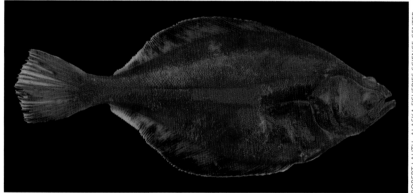

ROBERT LAUTH, ALASKA FISHERIES SCIENCE CENTER

The Ranges: Sea of Okhotsk and northern Kuril Islands to Gulf of Anadyr to Bering Sea (north to at least Saint Lawrence Island) and Monterey. They are common from the Sea of Okhotsk to the Gulf of Alaska and eastern Bering Sea (where they really are abundant), as far north as at least Saint Matthew Island, and then fairly common as far south as Oregon. Intertidal to 1,050 m (3,445 ft), but typically 100–300 m (328–984 ft); one study in the Bering Sea (Hoff and Britt 2005) found pretty good numbers down to 800 m (2,624 ft), so you never know, do you? Eggs: 2.8–3.8 mm. Larvae: hatching length = less than 3.3–6.4 mm. Von Bertalanffy parameters (TL, mm): (females, Gulf of Alaska) L_∞ = 488.6, k = 0.128, t_0 = -0.326; (males, Gulf of Alaska) L_∞ = 419.7, k = 0.161, t_0 = 0.018 (Stark 2004). Stark also supplies von Berts for Bering Sea fish. Length-weight parameters (TL, cm, gr): (sexes combined) W = 0.00326$L^{3.32}$ (Orlov and Binohlan 2009).

SALIENT CHARACTERS: Flatheads are elongate-oval and very flat fish (even for flatfish, which are by definition...flat). The caudal fin is pointy in the center, the pretty-straight lateral line has an accessory branch that runs under the lower eye (it looks like a series of widely spaced pores), the anal spine is relatively large, and the mouth is substantial. Dead ones are reddish-brown to brown, the fins are dark blotched, and the body also can have kind of amorphous darker blotches.

LIFE HISTORY: Flathead soles are relatively cold-water fish found mostly between mid-shelf and shallow slope over soft sediment. Young-of-the-year recruit from the plankton to fine sediments of the shallow shelf (at depths of 40–70 m, 131–230 ft, or so), particularly in bays. Young fish remain relatively shallow, away from adults, for several years before migrating into deeper waters. Young fish can withstand at least slightly estuarine conditions. Flatheads make annual inshore-offshore migrations, as exemplified in Porter (2005): "The continental shelf from the entrance to Prince William Sound to Unimak Island [Gulf of Alaska] contains the highest relative abundance of adult flathead sole off the west coast of North America...During the spring adult flathead sole move from wintering grounds on the upper continental slope onto the continental shelf...the greatest proportion of spawning fish occurs...at depths between 100 and 200 m [328–656 ft]." Spawning fish have been taken in as little as 46 m (151 ft). With the approach of winter, flatheads return to deeper waters. Both juveniles and adults have been taken at night in midwater trawls, leading one to wonder if they might routinely ascend into the water column when it is dark. Flatheads have been found in waters between about -2–12°C (28–54°F), mostly at 7°C (45°F) or less. Flatheads in the southeastern Bering Sea are tending to move further northward as ocean waters warm.

Flatheads live to at least 32 years old. Females grow larger than males and, after 5 years of age, grow faster. Size and age at maturity appears to vary considerably with location. Smith (1936) found that, off Washington, all males were mature by 17.5 cm (7 in) TL and 2 years old. Most females matured by 22.4 cm (9 in) and 3 years old, and all were mature by 26 cm (10 in) (4 years old). A study in the Bering Sea and central Gulf of Alaska (Stark 2004) gave a very different picture. Here, a few females were mature at about 24 cm (9 in) (7 years), 50% at 32 cm (13 in) (about 9 years), and all at about 45 cm (18 in) (about 16 years old). Spawning seasons also seem to be quite variable. Summarizing all studies, flatheads spawn from January–November, probably peaking in the spring. However, even over relatively short distances, peak-spawning times may vary. For instance, Porter (2005) notes that there is a progression of spawning dates as "Most spawning began from early to mid-April near the Kenai Peninsula and then progressed with time southwest into Shelikof Strait and along the Alaska Peninsula." Females produce between 64,000–600,000 eggs per season. Eggs hatch at about 9 days at 9.6°C (49°F) and 21 days at 2.4°C (36°F). Flathead soles feed on a wide range of bottom and near-bottom organisms and their diets vary somewhat with fish size, season, habitat type, and bottom depth. In general, smaller fish eat primarily crustaceans and larger ones feed heavily on brittle stars and fishes. Among the crustaceans, mysid shrimps, pandalid and crangonid shrimps, euphausiids, and gammarid and hyperiid amphipods are often most important. Additional prey include arrow worms, clams, crabs, hermits crabs, polychaetes, sea urchins, sand dollars, medusae, and fish offal. Flatheads appear to feed primarily during daylight hours and one study implied they feed most heavily during the summer. Predators include a host of fishes (e.g., various flatfishes, cod, sablefish, sculpins, and skates), rhinoceros auklets, sea lions and seals.

FISHERY: Early records noted that flatheads were important food fish from Kodiak to Unalaska in the 19th century. Today, they are often taken in subsistence fisheries in places like Adak Island (Aleutian Islands). In the early 20th century, they were readily marketed in Puget Sound. Today, there is a small directed bottom trawl fishery for them in such places as the Gulf of Alaska. Most of the product is head and gutted. As far as sport fishermen are concerned, we have this firsthand account from Jordan (1884a) who recorded that in Puget Sound: "It takes the hook very readily, and affords the boys considerable amusement." Which begs the question about what kind of sense of humor the boys had. Flatheads are still occasionally taken from piers and boats by sport anglers.

ORIGINS AND RELATIONSHIPS: *Hippoglossoides* sp. lived in the Late Oligocene (at least 23 million years ago). A species tentatively called *Hippoglossoides pristinus* was found in a Miocene deposit (at least 5.3 million years old) of Southern California. However, the fossil was not well enough preserved to make detailed comparisons with living species. Based on genetic analyses, flatheads are likely most closely related to Bering flounder.

REMARKS: Work by Burger et al. (2007) on fish from Adak Island implies that levels of arsenic and mercury in at least some individuals may be high enough to give one pause.

Hippoglossus stenolepis
Schmidt, 1904
Pacific Halibut

ETYMOLOGY AND COLLOQUIAL NAMES: *Hippoglossus* comes from two Greek words meaning "horse" and "tongue," referring to the general shape of the fish and *stenolepis* is derived from two Greek words meaning "narrow" and "scales." Whether a

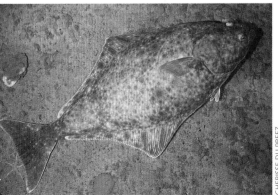

STICKING IT TO THE MAN

In the old days, individual fishermen in dories took most Pacific halibut. These fishermen were transported to the fishing grounds, usually in the Gulf of Alaska or Bering Sea, in schooners. Fishermen were paid a flat amount, in the story below 25 cents per fish, regardless of the halibut's size. Thus a very large halibut, a few of which filled the dory, was only worth as much as a smaller one, and you could put a lot more of the little ones in the boat before having to go back to the mother ship to unload. The following account is from "Two Bits Apiece," an anecdote found in *Fish and Ships*, by Andrews and Larssen (Bonanza Books, 1959). The speaker is an old-time fisherman discussing an incident from his halibut dory fishing days:

"Oh, you could do pretty well on small fish, 'specially on fairly shallow water, but if you got on deep water and caught nothing but soakers [large halibut], then the Lord help you...Yeah, and some of them steamer skippers always had a pet or two on board, relatives and such; then he would see to that their dories were dropped on a shallow chicken-patch ["chickens" were smaller halibut], while the rest of us would be dropped on deep water, where we caught nothing but whales...But then, once in a while we got a chance to fix them bastards, too! Yeah! I remember this here trip, off Cape Ommaney; the son of a bitch of a skipper dropped me right in the gully. Nothing but over-grown soakers there, you know, and hard as hell to haul, wore the skin off my hands the first skate, nothing but red meat all inside my hands. And nothing but goddam soakers, four-five fish, and the dory was loaded. Well, Sir, it so happened that the king salmon was running good, right there in the tide rip. So I ripped loose every damm' thwart and every fish board in the dory—broke a couple of oars, too, and used 'em for floats on my gear! Kept the bight of the gear from sinking too far down—hell, we got a king salmon on every hook that was high enough in the water, and no halibut at all. So we threw them soakers overboard, and loaded the dory up with kings, couple of times. Got four bits a-piece for kings, them days—twice as much as for the halibut!"

Pacific halibut actually resembles a horse's tongue is another matter. In fact, it can be argued that it more closely resembles the tongue of an elephant (*Barrus-glossus*), whale (*Balaenaglossus*), or perhaps comedic actor Zero Mostel (*Zeroglossus*). The Tlingit call them "cháatl" and the Japanese name is "ohyo."

THE BASICS: Maximum Length: 267 cm (9 ft) TL. Maximum Weight: The International Pacific Halibut Commission (IPHC) (1998) reports that the largest documented fish was 227 kg (500 lb), but that they have been reported to 318 kg (700 lb). They also noted that few males reach 36 kg (80 lb) and nearly all halibut over 45 kg (100 lb) are females. The Ranges: Hokkaido and Sea of Okhotsk to northeastern Chukchi Sea (71°12'N, 163°05'W), Bering Sea, and Aleutian Islands to Punta Camalu (Baja California). They are common at least from Sakhalin Island and Sea of Okhotsk to throughout much of the Bering Sea, along the Aleutians, and down to Oregon. 6–1,100 m (20–3,600 ft), perhaps typically from 27–274 m (90–900 ft), although surveys along the Aleutian Islands and in the Bering Sea show that there are fair numbers down to at least 500 m (1,649 ft). Eggs: 2.9–3.8 mm. Larvae: hatching length = 8–9 mm. Length-weight parameters (TL, cm, kg): (sexes combined) W = 0.00869L$^{3.07}$ (Orlov and Binohlan 2009).

SALIENT CHARACTERS: Pacifics are diamond-shaped and kind of thick. Unlike many flatfish species, this one has an almost lunate tail. The lateral line is highly arched, mouth large and chock full of conical teeth (two rows on the upper jaw), and the area between the eyes is slightly concave. On deck, Pacifics are brown, blackish, or green-brown, with lighter markings.

LIFE HISTORY: Pacific halibut are shelf and upper slope fish. Young-of-the-year (at as small as 2.2 cm, 0.9 in, TL) settle out of the plankton in shallow waters (e.g., off Kodiak Island at around 20–30 m, 66–98 ft) of bays and mouths of bays. The smallest fish tend to favor bottoms with the finest particle sizes, while larger juveniles live in sand and mud. Some young ones also live near small bits of structure, including eelgrass. As halibut mature they tend to seek out deeper waters. Adults are found most often over soft seafloors, but they also can inhabit rocky bottoms. While surveying fish off southeastern Alaska, I saw one lying on a sharp-tipped boulder—that had to be really uncomfortable. Pacific halibut have been found in water temperatures between at least -2–13.6°C (28–57°F) and the IPHC believes they prefer temperatures between

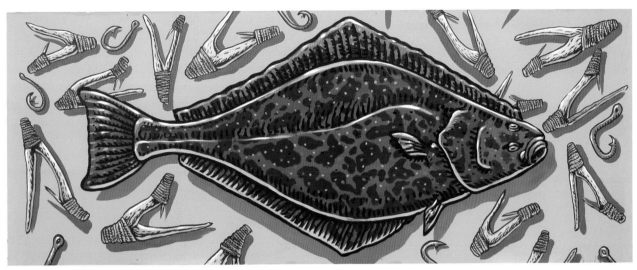

Halibut painting by Ray Troll

3–8°C (37–46°F). However, in a study off eastern Kamchatka, most fish were found in 7–11°C (45–52°F). Perhaps responding to warming ocean temperatures, Pacific halibut in the southeastern Bering Sea appear to be generally moving further northward. Although basically a marine species, halibut are common in some mildly estuarine waters, such as Cook Inlet (Gulf of Alaska). Although halibut undoubtedly spend a great deal of their time lying on the bottom, studies using Pop-up Archival Transmitting (PAT) tags imply that some fish move about in the water column, either feeding or spawning.

In general, Pacific halibut move into relatively shallow waters to feed during warm-water months and retreat to spawn on the deep shelf and shallow slope as waters cool. Whether they stay in relatively circumscribed areas when they do this is perhaps idiosyncratic. Some tagged fish have shown relatively little along-shore movements while others have moved about considerably. For those fish that spawn in southeastern Alaska and British Columbia, the eggs and larvae tend to be carried counterclockwise into the Gulf of Alaska, away from the spawning grounds. The young settle at about 6 months old. Young fish in the Gulf of Alaska tend to migrate eastward (clockwise) toward southeast Alaska and British Columbia. IPHC (1998) states: "Relatively few recoveries of adult halibut released in the Gulf of Alaska have been made in the Bering Sea...the longest recorded migration was from a fish released near Atka island in 1967 and recovered 2,500 miles [4,023 km] south off Coos Bay (Oregon) in 1972. Another halibut tagged off Newport, Oregon in 1989 was recovered just 5 months later near Cape Spencer in southeast Alaska. This fish traveled over 5 nautical miles [8 km] a day...adult halibut tend to return to the same feeding grounds each year." The jury is still out regarding how much population structure exists off North America. Some studies imply that there may be somewhat separate stocks in the eastern and western Pacific and that some population structure may exist in the eastern Pacific. Using parasite assemblages as biological tags, Blaylock et al. (2003) found: "Three groups of adults

were identified: fish from California to the southern Queen Charlotte Islands, those from the northern Queen Charlotte Islands to the central Bering Sea, and those from the central and northern Bering Sea."

As noted in IPHC (1998): "Females usually grow faster and live longer than males. However, the oldest halibut on record is a 55-year-old male. The oldest female is 42 years old." Pacific halibut growth rates vary considerably with geographic location and with time. For instance, beginning in the late 1970s, growth rates of halibut off Alaska declined significantly. This makes generalizations about size at maturity difficult. However, here is a weak-kneed attempt for fish from parts of the Gulf of Alaska, your results may vary. A few females are mature at 8 years old (50 cm, 20 in, FL, or so), 50% at 12 years

MAMA SAID THERE'D BE DAYS LIKE THIS

Collins (1892) wrote that after the first attempt at a Pacific halibut commercial fishery: "At the close of 1889 the outlook for the continuance of the Pacific halibut fishery as an industry of any considerable importance, was decidedly unfavorable; indeed, there was every prospect that it would be abandoned, or at least reduced to a scale only sufficient to supply the limited local demand...there are reasons supposing that it will never rival the halibut fishery of the Atlantic." *Wrong*.

old (mostly between 80–120 cm, 32–47 in), and all are mature by 20 years old (as much as 150 cm, 59 in). Most males are mature by the time they are 8 years old. Spawning occurs along the deeper shelf and upper slope (mostly in 183–457 m, 600–1,500 ft) from November–March. While spawning takes place over a wide area, there do appear to be some discrete hot spots (IPHC 1998 has a map). Females produce between 102,000–4 million or so eggs per season and the eggs and larvae are pelagic. Most of the eggs drift about at depths of 90–183 m (300–600 ft). There is some vague evidence that some mature females may not spawn every year. One study found that eggs hatch after 15–20 days at 5–6°C (41-43°F) and 12–14 days at 7–8°C (45–46°F). Another study noted a hatching time of about 10 days at 9°C (48°F) and 13 days at 6.5°C (44°F). In general, and to make an overly broad generalization, smaller Pacific halibut mostly target crabs, while larger halibut mostly prefer fishes. Other animals often eaten include clams, gammarid amphipods, hermit crabs, shrimps, snails, squids, and octopuses. Predators include fishes (e.g., lampreys, Pacific cod, Pacific halibut, Pacific sleeper sharks, and skates), bald eagles, several tern species, sea lions, seals, orcas, and likely river otters. Sperm whales eat some off of longlines set in the Gulf of Alaska.

FISHERY: Pacific halibut were of great importance to a number

of Northwest Indian and First Nation peoples and are still widely taken in subsistence fisheries. In the case of such tribes as the Makah (Cape Flattery, Washington) and the Haida and Tlingit (further northward), these fish were more important to their diets than were the salmon. The fish were taken by hook and line, often with just gorgeously crafted hooks, and most was dried or smoked for winter use. Preserved halibut were also extensively traded among various peoples. Among some peoples, such as the Haida, halibut were considered "high-class food" along with whales, sea lions, and sockeye salmon. This was because, compared to shellfishes, small birds, and mammals, halibut was relatively uncommon and difficult to procure.

In Alaska, Bean (1887b) recorded that: "The hook consists essentially of 2 pieces of wood fastened together at one end with strips of spruce roots so as to form an acute angle with each other, the longer arm of the angle being armed with a bent, pointed piece of iron; the wood is generally carved so as to represent some animal whose co-operation thus secured will insure successful fishing. The bait (usually herring) is tied on so as to cover not only the hook but also the wooden shaft in which the hook is fastened; halibut will gulp down the bait as long as it lasts, opening their jaws wider and wider; the short arm of the hook, being so fixed as to leave only a narrow space between it and the iron point, will admit of the motion necessary to fasten the fish, but prevents its escape. A halibut thus held with its mouth wide open will soon be drowned, and can easily be taken into a canoe. This Indian style of halibut hook is much more effective than the common halibut hook of civilization. A very common method of fishing for halibut at Sitka is by the use of set-lines, each provided with one hook, a stone sinker, an inflated stomach of seal for a buoy, with a small flag or signal attached to it so as to show when a fish is hooked." Because a large halibut could capsize a canoe, the fishermen used two canoes to capture very large halibut. One fisherman hooked and played the fish, the other clubbed it to death, and then both canoes took it to land.

Swan (1868) hanging with the Native Americans of Cape Flattery (Washington) observed: "When the fish are brought home, they are first landed on the beach, where the women wash and wipe them with a wisp of grass or fern...The heads are taken off first to be dried separately, and the body of the fish is sliced by means of a knife of peculiar construction, somewhat resembling a common chopping knife...The skin is first removed, and the flesh then sliced as thin as possible to facilitate drying; and when perfectly cured, the pieces are wrapped in the skin, carefully packed in baskets, and placed in a dry place. The heads, the back bones, to which some flesh adheres, and the tails, are all dried and packed away separately from the body pieces. When eaten, the skin to which the principal portion of the fat or oil of the fish adheres, is simply warmed, or toasted over the coals, till it acquires crispness...The dried strips from the body are eaten without further cooking, being simply broken into small pieces, dipped in whale oil, and so chewed and swallowed...In former times, dried halibut was to these Indians in lieu of bread; oil in place of butter, and blubber instead of beef or pork."

JANA SUCHY

Jana was aboard the F/V fishing vessel Lualda *off Kodiak when things went wrong. The crew had to throw back about 10,000 pounds of halibut to help save the boat. A navy captain who saw these images said "Only one boat in ten would have come back from that."*

While early white folks also caught lots of halibut, the first large-scale commercial catches were made in 1888, off Washington. The first transcontinental shipment of fresh halibut (from Tacoma to New York packed in ice and salt) was a failure. However, with the successful shipment across the continent in 1893 (Vancouver to Boston) the fishery kicked into high gear, as both Canadian and U.S. ports were quickly handling tonnage of halibut. As usual, fishermen started fishing relatively close to ports, but by as early as 1913, the guys were working in the Gulf of Alaska. The commercial fishery for Pacific halibut began, as did that for Pacific cod, as a dory fishery. However, while cod fishermen used vertical hand lines, the halibut boys used longlines stretched along the bottom (note that, confusingly, these were called "trawls" at the time.) Halibut longlines were grouped in units called "skates" that were perhaps 1,800 feet long. Every 15 feet or so, fishermen would stick on a leader and hook; thus a skate contained about 100 hooks. Skates were tied together in various numbers to form a "string." As with the dory cod fishery, dories would fish in the vicinity of the mother ship, returning to the ship when a full catch was made.

While the commercial halibut fishery has always been based on either fresh or frozen product, in 1931 Booth Fisheries Company starting buying Pacific halibut livers from fishermen in the Northwest. Although Booth was a bit tight-lipped about just what they were doing with the livers, it was rumored they were destined for a Chicago pharmaceutical house for use in the preparation of vitamin A. Booth was very clear that they wanted livers that were "not more than eight days old...Livers should be removed from the fresh fish as soon as possible after catching, and separated from the rest of the viscera, without breaking the gallbladders. Then the gallbladders are removed, the livers put into containers and at once put into the hold of the boat, packed in ice." Then, after a rather long soliloquy on how to store the livers, Booth went on to their final admonition: "All livers when landed must be of a light tan to pinkish tan color; any green livers show that either they have been exposed [to sun and heat] too long, or else the gallbladders have broken." How good was that oil, you ask? This good. Abbott

Laboratories announced that "one pound of halibut liver oil would furnish a daily dose for 45,300,000 rats" or, now that I think about it, for one rat for 124,110 years. The eventual synthesis of vitamin A led to the crash of the halibut liver market and the dreams of glory of liver-lovers everywhere.

Today, U.S. and Canadian vessels still catch Pacific halibut with longlines and the fishery extends from the Bering Sea to off Oregon (a few fish are caught in Northern California waters). The fishery, managed by the joint U.S. and Canadian International Pacific Halibut Commission, is one of the few fisheries that I know of that can claim to be pretty consistently well managed. Good going, people. Pacifics are taken as bycatch in a number of other fisheries.

One of the more entertaining aspects of the commercial halibut industry is the presence of "chalky" halibut. The Canadian Food Inspection Agency defines the chalky condition in halibut as when the muscle is: "Dry and powdery, leaving the sensation of a chalky solution in the mouth (Texture crayeuse)." "Texture crayeuse?" Damn, things always sound yummier when they are in French, don't they? In some places, and during some parts of the year, a substantial number of halibut taken in the commercial longline catch have chalky muscles and are unsaleable. Chalky muscle is related to low (more acidic) pH. Muscle with a pH less than 6 tends to be chalky. Although it still is not completely clear what is going on, it is likely that some combination of halibut physiological state before being caught, the amount of struggle after being caught, and environmental parameters (such as water temperature) all play a role. Additional observations on this condition come from Lowery (2005), who looked at chalky fish and the presence of ambicoloration or "staining." Lowery notes: "Staining is the result of melanophores developing on the blind side of the fish yielding a dull gray or brown appearance. True ambicoloration is the presence of pigment and patterns identical to the eyed side, on the blind side." Stained fish, commonly referred to as "grey halibut" or "greybellies," are sometimes worth less to commercial fishermen. In Pacific halibut, ambicoloration of various sorts is common, as is staining. Lowery found that: "Stained fish had a significantly higher incidence of pH indicative of chalky flesh compared to normal colored fish...In general 90% of stained fish are males and 15% of these fish have the potential to develop chalky flesh."

Sport fishermen also love to catch halibut and it can be argued that the recreational fishery is quite important to the economies of coastal towns. Because sport and commercial extractors often target the same fish, this has led to the usual angst between the two industries, with the usual fear, finger-pointing, and petulance.

ORIGINS AND RELATIONSHIPS: Fossil remains of this species have been taken from 100,000-year-old strata in California. Based on genetic analyses of flatfishes examined from the Pacific (not including Atlantic halibut, mind you), Pacific halibut are most closely related to Greenland halibut or perhaps slender soles. I note that some of our Russian colleagues, at least as recently as 2000, believed the Pacific halibut to be a subspecies of the Atlantic halibut, *Hippoglossus hippoglossus*.

MISCELLANY: 1) While most Pacific halibut have both eyes on the right side of their bodies (they are dextral), occasionally one will have both eyes on the left side. 2) Turek et al. (2009) report that the indigenous peoples of both Nanwalek and Port Graham (Gulf of Alaska) would check their local beaches after storms, looking for halibut tossed up onto the shore by waves. Dang, those must have been substantial combers. 3) Halibut cheeks, the muscles that control jaw movement, are particularly yummy, and in fact, my favorite part of the fish. Gmelch and Gmelch (1985) note that in Sitka (Alaska) the cheeks were often sold separately: "In former times, they were a source of income for Native children, who sold them door-to-door."

IS YOU IS OR IS YOU AIN'T MY BABY?

Want to be able to tell apart male and female Pacific halibut without opening them up? Do what the professionals do, at least do what Gilbert St-Pierre does, and look at the shape of the genital vent. Basically, every halibut has two holes located just behind the pelvic fin. The one closest to the fin is the anus. Don't look at that one it will only confuse you. The other one, the genital vent, varies in shape between the sexes. Female vents are kind of nipple-shaped, while those of males are more like a round and raised volcano crater. Warning, this technique works best on fish 52 cm (21 in) TL and larger; if the fish is smaller than that you are on your own. For lively drawings and more vent talk, see St-Pierre (1992).

Isopsetta isolepis
(Lockington, 1880)
Butter Sole

**ETYMOLOGY AND COLLOQUIAL
NAMES:** *Isopsetta* is Greek for "equal" and
"flounder." So what, you might ask? Well, that
meaning may be lost to the ages. Jordan and
Gilbert (1883) note that Lockington first coined
the name in a manuscript that they had access
to, but son of a gun, either Lockington did not
give a reason for the name or J & G just thought
it was so obvious that they didn't tell us. *Isolepis*
means "equal" and "scale" in Greek. "Scaly-fin
sole" is a fairly recent name and "Bellingham
sole" is an older one. The Japanese word is
"karei-rui."

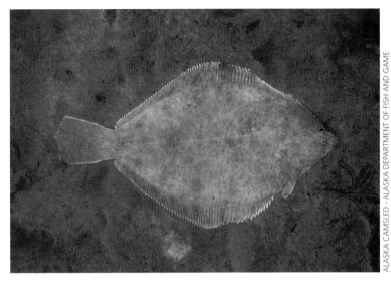

ALASKA CAMSLED - ALASKA DEPARTMENT OF FISH AND GAME

THE BASICS: Maximum Length: 55.2 cm (22 in) TL. Maximum Weight: 1.7 kg (3.7 lb). The Ranges: Southeastern Bering Sea
and Aleutian Islands (west to Amchitka Island) to Ventura (Southern California), typically from Umnak Island (eastern Aleutian
Islands) and eastern Bering Sea to Northern California. 2 m or less to 425 m (7–1,404 ft), but mostly from maybe 18–100 m
(60–328 ft). Eggs: 0.8–1.1. Larvae: hatching length = about 2.7 mm, flexion length = 9–14 mm, transformation length = 1.5 to
greater than 2.1 cm (0.6–0.8 in). Length-weight parameters (TL, mm, kg): (females) W = 0.00000000277L$^{3.2648}$ (RecFin 2009).

SALIENT CHARACTERS: Another of the semi-oval flatfish, butters are small-mouthed and small-eyed, with a pointed
caudal fin, rough scales on the eyed side, and a fairly long lateral line dorsal accessory branch. The eyed sides of dead ones
are various shades of brown, often with yellow, green, and black mottling. The fins are edged in yellow. Live ones are similarly
colored.

LIFE HISTORY: Young-of-the-year (at least as small as 1.8 cm, 0.7 in, SL) recruit from the plankton to coastal waters at
depths of perhaps 2–60 m (7–197 ft) from April–August. At least a few juveniles inhabit eelgrass beds. Although they are usually characterized as an ocean species, butter soles have been taken in at least slightly estuarine conditions in Cook Inlet (Gulf
of Alaska) and in Grays Harbor (Washington). While this species does not make heart-pounding migrations, fish seem to move
somewhat inshore with warm waters and offshore with colder conditions. Off Alaska, they have been taken in waters between
at least 2.5–8.8°C (37–48°F).

Butter soles live to at least 12 years old. Females are larger at any given age than males. Off British Columbia, most males
are mature by about 10 cm (4 in) TL and 2 years old and most females by about 25 cm (10 in) and 3 years old. Spawning occurs
at least from February–April and may extend to a little later in the year. Females produce between 350,000–1,000,000 eggs
per season. Butter soles feed mostly on benthic or epibenthic prey. Polychaetes are often quite important, as are gammarid
amphipods, shrimps, crabs, mysid shrimps, fishes, and clams. Predators include great sculpins, longnose skate, Pacific cod,
Pacific halibut, Pacific and speckled sanddabs, and harbor seals.

FISHERY: Butter soles are small fish. Processing labor costs are high and yield is low so large commercial fisheries for this
species have only occurred on a few occasions. A second strike against them is a discoloration on their blind side (termed "rust
spots") making them unpopular in some locations. In the 19th century, the primitive paranzella trawls off San Francisco caught
large numbers of them, but they did not sell particularly well. In the 1930s, Seattle fish processors would usually not purchase
butters from fishermen unless the fish were first filleted on the boats. Other than such occasional fillet-based fisheries (as one
off British Columbia in the mid-20th century), the only market of any size occurred during the time mink ranching was in style
and people had to feed the little fur-bearers something. Vessel anglers often take them.

ORIGINS AND RELATIONSHIPS: Butter sole remains have been found in approximately 100,000-year-old strata in California. Butter soles are most closely related to English and sand soles and to the two rock soles.

MISCELLANY: 1) Butters occasionally hybridize with English soles in Puget Sound and the Strait of Georgia. 2) One reversed
fish (essentially a mirror image of a normal one) was taken off the Klamath River.

Lepidopsetta

Until 2000, rock sole biologists were happy. They were naïve, but they were happy. And why shouldn't they be happy; there was only one species in the northeastern Pacific, right? Oh, there was a little uncertainty, a smidgeon of doubt, as some thought there might be two subspecies, but who really knew or cared? Then, in the seminal year of 1985, National Marine Fisheries Service (NMFS) biologist Barbara Vinter, in what appears to be an ichthyofaustian bargain, first noticed unidentified flatfish larvae in plankton samples and it all began to unravel. By 1992, NMFS biologists were separating two forms (soon to be two species) of rock soles in the Bering Sea and the damn snake was out of the apple tree and was busily careening around Eden spreading all sorts of sorrow and confusion. And that was because...? Well, because the two species overlap in their distributions over so much seafloor that it meant that all that lovely biological data on "rock sole" taken from the southeastern Bering Sea and Gulf of Alaska to Washington by the Russians, Canadians, and Americans, beginning all the way back in the 1950s, was all kind of whacked, wasn't it? Because, without voucher specimens, how could one know which of the two species one was referring to? So, in the species accounts below, here is what I have done. Because southern rock soles are not taken in the western Pacific (off Kamchatka, for instance), I have assumed that all of the Russian literature on "rock sole" from that area is the northern rock sole. And because southern rock soles are very rare from the Bering Sea, I have assumed that most of the fish studied there are also northern rock soles. Other than that, I have mainly used biological data collected from after about 2000, when Jay Orr and Ann Matarese described the northern rock sole.

Lepidopsetta bilineata
(Ayres, 1855)

Southern Rock Sole

R. HIBPSHMAN

ETYMOLOGY: *Lepidopsetta* is derived from the Greek words for "scaled" and "flounder" and *bilineata* means "2-lined" in Latin, for the branching lateral line. Also known, for a very brutal period, as *Pleuronectes bilineatus*.

THE BASICS: Maximum Length: 59 cm (23 in) TL. Maximum Weight: Perhaps to 3.8 kg (8.4 lb). The Ranges: Atka Island (Aleutian Islands) and southeastern Bering Sea (Slime Bank north of Unimak Island) to Cortes Bank (Southern California). They are most common from the eastern Bering Sea and Alaska Peninsula to maybe off Washington, but you can still find them predictably into Northern California. 11–339 m (36–1,112 ft), mostly in 200 m (656 ft) and less. There are a number of studies that have caught "*Lepidopsetta* sp." in virtually intertidal waters and I assume some of these are southerns. Eggs: 0.8–1 mm. Larvae: hatching length = less than 3.1–4 mm, flexion length = 7.2–greater than 9.7 mm, transformation length = 1–greater than 1.8 cm (0.4–0.7 in). Von Bertalanffy parameters (TL, mm): (females) L_∞ = 520, k = 0.12, t_0 = -0.715; (males) L_∞ = 387, k = 0.182, t_0 = -0.962 (Stark and Somerton 2002). Length-weight parameters (FL, mm, gr): (females) W = $0.00000403L^{3.193}$; (males) W = $0.000004595L^{3.3.164}$ (Szaley et al. 2010).

SALIENT CHARACTERS: Southerns have oval bodies with a strongly arched lateral line above the pectoral fin and a branch of that lateral line running part way along the dorsal fin. Dead ones are various shades of brown, with dark and light blotches and spots. There are dark blotches on the fins. This is from Mecklenburg et al. (2002) on the most important characters separating southerns from northerns: "Blind side bright white, with muscle bands, especially anteriorly, highlighted with glossy white; interorbital space narrow, up to 3 scales at narrowest portion, supraorbital pores almost always more than 4; gill rakers broad and robust, total on 1st arch typically 10 or less, on upper limb 3 or less."

LIFE HISTORY: Ann Matarese et al. (2003) report: "Pelagic larvae begin eye migration as early as 10 mm [0.4 in] SL, but many remaining in the plankton until they are about 30 mm [1 in] SL." Young-of-the-year recruit from the plankton to soft substrate in the nearshore, often in bays. Both young-of-the-year and older juveniles are found in the intertidal, on soft bottoms, but sometimes among kelp, eelgrass, and filamentous algae. A study around Kodiak Island found that one-year-olds were more likely to live on gravelly sand than on other substrata. Adults are also found mainly over sand and gravel. As fish mature, they tend to move into deeper waters. Both juveniles and adults move shallower during spring and summer and deeper in fall and winter. Off Alaska, southerns appear to live in waters between about 2–10°C (36–50°F).

JANNA NICHOLS

Southern rock soles live to at least 28 years old. Females grow to a larger size than males and males grow faster. In the Gulf of Alaska, a few females are mature at about 29 cm (11 in, 6 years) TL, 50% at 34.7 cm (14 in, 9 years), and 100% at about 39 cm (15 in, 13 years). Off California, spawning begins in February and extends at least into spring and perhaps summer. High densities of larvae were taken off Oregon in March. In the Gulf of Alaska, spawning begins in April and probably peaks in June–July, with perhaps a bit continuing into the fall. In a study in the Gulf of Alaska, spawning occurred at bottom depths of 45–127 m (148–417 ft), at an average depth of 78 m (256 ft) and 6°C (43°F). Females produce demersal, adhesive eggs. Southern rock soles feed heavily on polychaetes and brittle stars. Also eaten, often in lesser amounts, are a real witch's brew, composed of such invertebrates as clams, gammarid and hyperiid amphipods, squids, octopuses, isopods, crabs, shrimps, hermit crabs, sipunculid worms, sea stars, sand dollars, sea urchins, sea cucumbers, acorn worms, sea anemones, and fishes. Predators include arrowtooth flounder, Pacific cod, Pacific halibut, and harbor seals, and likely Pacific hakes, great sculpins, flathead and yellowfin soles, and Steller sea lions.

FISHERY: The confusion between southern and northern rock soles has made figuring out their historical importance to fisheries a bit problematic. However, it is likely that both species were taken in some numbers by various indigenous peoples (as is true today) and that commercial fishermen caught both. As far back as the late 19th century, it was noted that 30% of the "flounder" catch in Puget Sound was comprised of rock soles. If we assume that much of the rock sole population off British Columbia and points south is of southern rock soles, then the species is caught in moderate numbers. They are commonly taken by recreational anglers.

RELATIONSIPS: A genetic study of the family Pleuronectidae found that southerns are most closely related to...tah dah... northern rock sole.

Lepidopsetta polyxystra
Orr & Matarese, 2000
Northern Rock Sole

R. HIBPSHMAN

ETYMOLOGY AND COLLOQUIAL NAMES: *Lepidopsetta* is derived from the Greek words for "scaled" and "flounder" and *polyxystra* is derived from the Greek "many" and "raker," referring to the numerous gill rakers. Russian biologists refer to them as "northern two-lined flounder" and "white-bellied flounder." "Shumushu-garei" is a Japanese name. As you aimlessly wander around the web you might encounter a few references to *Lepidopsetta petraborealis* – this was a kind of interim name used for this species before *polyxystra* was coined.

THE BASICS: Maximum Length: 69 cm (27 in) TL. Maximum Weight: 3.4 kg (7.5 lb). The Ranges: Hokkaido, Kuril Islands, and Okhotsk Sea to Gulf of Anadyr and vicinity of Saint Lawrence Island (64°30'N, 170°26'W, Bering Sea) to Puget Sound. Abundant from at least Sakhalin Island and the northern Kuril Islands to the eastern Bering Sea and the Kodiak Island area. 3–5 m (10–16 ft) to 508 m (1,666 ft), mostly in 200 m (328 ft) or less. Several Alaskan studies report catching "*Lepidopsetta* sp."

in more-or-less intertidal waters. "Larvae hatch at >3 mm SL... Different from *L. bilineata*, this species does not begin eye migration until 15 mm SL and most stay in plankton to at least 30 mm SL" (Matarese et al. 2003). Von Bertalanffy parameters (Gulf of Alaska) (TL, mm): (females) L_∞ = 429, k = 0.236, t_0 = 0.387; (males) L_∞ = 382, k = 0.261, t_0 = 0.16 (Stark and Somerton 2002). Von Bertalanffy parameters (Kamchatka and Kurils) (TL, cm): (females) L_∞ = 81.8, k = 0.047, t_0 = -1.189; (males) L_∞ = 40, k = 0.154, t_0 = -0.364 (Kuznetsova and Kunin 2002). Length-weight parameters (TL, cm, gr): (sexes combined) W = 0.00443L$^{3.28}$ (Orlov and Binohlan 2009).

SALIENT CHARACTERS: Northerns are oval, have a highly arched lateral line over the pectoral fin, an extension of that line part way along the dorsal fin, are colored various shades of brown, have the requisite light and dark blotches and spots. Mecklenburg et al. (2002) use the following characters to distinguish this species from southerns: "Blind side uniformly creamy white without glossy white highlights; interorbital space wide, up to 5 scales at narrowest point; supraorbital pores 1–3; gill rakers usually slender and pointed, total on 1st arch typically 10 or more, on upper limb 3 or more."

LIFE HISTORY: Young-of-the-year prefer muddy-sand seafloors that have some structure (like polychaete worm tubes) to break up the monotony. In the Bering Sea and Aleutian Islands, young fish settle out of the plankton in perhaps 7–40 m (23–131 ft) in nearshore bays and estuaries. In aquaria, 1-year-olds were most active at dawn and dusk. As they mature, these fish move into somewhat deeper waters, where they are most commonly found over mud and sand (sometimes with broken shell hash), but they also live around smaller rocks and boulders. Adult males, on average, occupy shallower waters than females, although there is a great deal of overlap. Fish off Alaska are found in waters between -1.1–11.8°C (30–53°F), but mostly in less than 7°C (45°F). Adults move between relatively shallow summer feeding and deeper winter spawning grounds (these are at bottom depths of 100–200 m, 328–656 ft). Russian researchers believe there are two spawning sites off North America, one eastward of the Pribilofs and another north of Unimak Island, at the mouth of Bristol Bay. There is evidence that northerns are tending to move further northward in the eastern Bering Sea, in response to warming sea temperatures.

Northern rock soles live to 27 years old. Males grow faster than females and reach smaller maximum size. A few females are mature at 30 cm (12 in, about 6 years) TL, 50% at 32.7 cm (13 in, 7 years), and 100% at about 36 cm (14 in, 10 years). In the Gulf of Alaska and eastern Bering Sea, spawning peaks in the late spring. In a Gulf of Alaska study, spawning took place on the bottom at depths of 42–61 m (138–200 ft), averaging 45 m (148 ft) and at a temperature averaging 3°C (37°F). Females produce 151,700–404,200 eggs that are adhesive and demersal. Spawning occurs over sand and gravel. Like their close compatriots, the southern rock soles, northerns consume a very wide rang of prey. Polychaetes and gammarid amphipods are often quite important, but various bivalves, sipunculids, isopods, fishes, sea cucumbers, sea stars, crabs, shrimps, sea anemones, squids, snails, mysid shrimps, sand dollars, ascidians, and brittle stars may be in the mix. Most feeding occurs in the late spring and summer. Predators include flathead soles, great and plain sculpins, Pacific cod, Pacific halibut, skates, walleye pollock, and yellowfin soles.

FISHERY: Northern rock soles are taken in subsistence fisheries along the Aleutian Islands. They are captured in moderate numbers by trawlers, often as bycatch in other fisheries. Most of the interest in northern rock soles is for their roe; so non egg-bearing females and, one assumes, the males, are often discarded.

RELATIONSHIPS: Northerns are most closely related to southerns, to no one's intense puzzlement.

Limanda aspera
(Pallas, 1814)

Yellowfin Sole

ETYMOLOGY AND COLLOQUIAL NAMES: *Limanda* is an old name for the European dab, *Limanda limanda*, and that name is derived from a Latin word for "mud," and *aspera* means "rough" in Latin. "Muddab" is another name and the Japanese use "kogane-garei." It was previously known as *Pleuronectes asper*.

THE BASICS: Maximum Length: 49 cm (19 in) TL. Maximum Weight: 1.7 kg (3.7 lb). The Ranges: Korea and Okhotsk Sea to Beaufort Sea off Cooper Island and through Bering Sea and Aleutian Islands to Barkley Sound (British Columbia). Abundant in the Sea of Japan, northern Sea of Okhotsk, much of Bering Sea (particularly in the eastern Bering Sea)

DID YOU KNOW?

Did you know that yellowfin soles living on their winter banks near Unimak and the Pribilof Islands have twice as much fat in their bodies as those found in the spring in Bristol Bay? Well, now you do. (With a tip of the hat to Krivobok and Tarkovskaya 1964).

at least as far north as a few spots in the Chukchi Sea, and to about Cook Inlet. Off North America, they are really abundant in the eastern Bering Sea and are, in fact, the most abundant flatfish there. 5 m or less–600 m (16–1,968 ft); off North America, they are relatively uncommon in more than 250 m (820 ft) and are mostly on the inner continental shelf. Eggs: 0.8–0.9 mm. Larvae: hatching length = 2.3–3.1 mm, transformation length = 1–1.7 cm (0.4–0.7 in). Von Bertalanffy parameters (TL, mm): (females) L_∞ = 376, k = 0.17, t_0 = 2.44; (males) L_∞ = 352, k = 0.16, t_0 = 1.63 (Wilderbuer et al. 1992). Length-weight parameters (TL, mm, gr): (females) W = $0.00000578L^{3.12}$; (males) W = $0.00000896L^{3.043}$ (Wilderbuer et al. 1992).

SALIENT CHARACTERS: Yellowfins are very oval fish, with a highly arched lateral line (over the pectoral fin), no accessory lateral line, and scaled, yellowish or kind of light brown dorsal and anal fins. The eyed sides of dead ones are brown with some darker mottling.

LIFE HISTORY: Yellowfin soles are a dominant species in the eastern Bering Sea, living on the continental shelf and upper parts of the slope. Young-of-the-year recruit from the plankton at lengths as small as 1.2 cm (0.5 in) SL to shallow nearshore waters, including intertidal mudflats. Along with mud and sand bottoms, young ones are also found in nearshore eelgrass. Juveniles live in brackish waters of salinities down to at least as low as 16 ppt. Adults live on soft seafloors. At the extremes, yellowfins have been found in waters between -2.1–13°C (28–55°F). While various studies give slightly different results, yellowfins seem to avoid waters colder than 0°C (32°F) and warmer than maybe 9°C (48°F). Adult yellowfins are quite the migrators; they make extensive inshore-offshore movements. As an example, during the eastern Bering Sea winter, adults live on the deeper shelf and shallow slope (in maybe 100–270 m, 328–886 ft), mostly in three fairly specific wintering grounds. At the same time, a group composed primarily of juveniles lives inshore, sometimes under the ice. Juveniles do not seem to move much until they begin to move offshore at 3–5 years old. In the spring (March–May), adults from these offshore concentrations begin to move inshore (often to 30 m, 98 ft, and less) to spawn (mixing at this time with juveniles); generally fish from different concentrations do not mix. One group goes into Bristol Bay and the other two move into the areas north and south of Nunivak Island. During the summer, adults live in nearshore waters, rarely as deep as 100 m (328 ft), where they associate with the two species of rock soles and Alaska plaice. In the fall, adults move back offshore. While it is clear that most fish make inshore migrations, their average summer depths vary annually. For whatever it is worth, work in the early 1980s found some population differences between fish living in the Bering Sea and those in the Gulf of Alaska.

Yellowfin soles live to 39 years old and it is possible that males and females reach the same maximum age. Growth rates and size at maturity vary greatly between areas and even years and age at maturity vary with depth. In general, females mature at around 10 years old (with a range of 6–18 years) and about 30 cm (12 in) TL (range = 25–36 cm, 10–14 in). Males mature at anywhere between 11–20 cm (4–8 in) and maybe 5–8 years old (fewer studies have been done on males). At least some spawning occurs between April–November, mostly during the summer. Eggs are colorless, gray, or greenish-tinged and females spawn these in 8–11 batches. At least some females then produce another group of eggs and go through the process again. Total fecundity for a series ranges from 295,615–3,635,108 and batch fecundity ranges from 2,400–408,000. Russian scientists report that yellowfins rise up into the water column to spawn. Spawning occurs in shallow waters, mostly down to 30 m (99 ft), but some fish release eggs as deep as 70 m (230 ft) or so. The fertilized eggs are pelagic and they hatch in about 4 days at 13°C (55°F) and will not hatch in waters less than 4°C (39°F). Eggs in the eastern Bering Sea are found at temperatures ranging from 6.4–11.4°C (44–53°F). Yellowfin soles are highly opportunistic predators. While they mostly target benthic or epibenthic prey, in warmer months they have been observed in surface waters feeding on zooplankton. Their diets are highly variable depending upon habitat type and season. Organisms that seem to be most important include polychaetes, echiuran worms, clams, and gammarid amphipods. Other foods are fishes, hyperiid amphipods, crabs, cumaceans, mysid shrimps, ascidians, brittle stars, sand dollars, sea cucumbers, ctenophores, and fish eggs. Young-of-the-year commonly feed on cyclopoid and harpacticoid copepods, and crustacean larvae. Yellowfins are eaten by bigmouth, great, and plain sculpins, Pacific cod, Pacific halibut, various skates, ringed seals, Steller sea lions, and river otters. In one study, pigeon guillemot chicks rejected them, despite all the work their parents went to in providing them.

FISHERY: Wherever they are abundant, yellowfin soles form an important commercial trawl fishery. Early on, way back in the 1950s, vessels from the USSR and Japan made large catches in the eastern Bering Sea. These fish were ground up for fishmeal. Catches peaked in the early 1960s, when the fleet overfished the species. Beginning in the 1960s, someone discovered that yellowfins were fairly tasty and the fishery has aimed at human consumption ever since. Today, the U.S. has its own trawl vessels catching these fish, although the fishery is limited because the fishery catches too many other species as bycatch, including Pacific halibut, Pacific herring, and red king crabs.

ORIGINS AND RELATIONSHIPS: *Pleuronectes asperoides* is a fossil form from the Miocene (at least 5.3 million years ago) thought to be closely related to yellowfin soles. Genetic analyses imply yellowfins are related to Sakhalin soles (*Limanda sakhalinensis*) and perhaps also to American plaice (*Hippoglossoides platessoides*).

MISCELLANY: A left-eyed one was captured in Peter the Great Bay (Russia).

A MEDITATION ON FOOD HABIT STUDIES

This meditation was engendered by a masters thesis by Geoffrey M. Lang (1992), who partly based his research on the results of a survey of the food contents of 11,651 yellowfin sole stomachs. And while he had some assistance examining the contents of these stomachs, he notes that "the majority [were] handled by myself." My lord, he looked at the majority of 11,651 stomachs! Over the years, I have done lots of food habit studies. I looked at white croakers, California scorpionfish, kelp bass, yellowfin croakers, corbinas, olive rockfish, oh, just a whole bunch of species. And initially it's kind of exciting; it's kind of like a treasure hunt. Oh, look, that hunk of mung, why that could be a crab, or maybe a worm, or the keys to Jimmy Hoffa's Cadillac. But each of my studies was only based on a few hundred stomachs. What must it be like to look at "the majority" of 11,651 stomachs? My experience is that after maybe 50 stomachs it becomes boring and by 100 the process is positively stultifying. But if looking at Stomach 100 is stultifying, what must happen at Stomach 5,222? Do you enter some sort of altered state of consciousness? Do you start to levitate? Does your officemate have to secure you to your chair? And then at Stomach 9,805 do great gouts of Greek Fire erupt from your Third Eye, melting your dissecting implements?

Lyopsetta exilis
(Jordan & Gilbert, 1880)
Slender Sole

ETYMOLOGY AND COLLOQUIAL NAMES: *Lyopsetta* means "to loosen" and "flounder" in Greek (likely because of the relatively soft flesh) and *exilis* is Latin for "slender." "Rough sole" and "slim sole" are a couple of older names.

THE BASICS: Maximum Length: 40 cm (16 in) TL. Maximum Weight: At least 228 gr (0.5 lb). The Ranges: Eastern Bering Sea to Boca de Santa Domingo (about 25°30'N) (southern Baja California). Based on larval densities, slenders are relatively abundant from east of Kodiak Island to somewhat south of Punta Eugenia (Baja California). 9–1,145 m (30–3,756 ft), typically from at least 90–350 m (295–1,148 ft). Eggs: 1.4–1.7 mm. Larvae: hatching length = 5.2–5.6 mm, flexion length = 9–13.5 mm, transformation length = 1.6–2.5 cm. Von Bertalanffy parameters (FL, cm): (females) L_∞ = 60.7, k = 0.111, t_0 = -0.18; (males) L_∞ = 44.0, k = 0.2186, t_0 = -0.02 (Demory et al. 1976). Length-weight parameters (TL, cm, gr): W = $0.0034L^{3.235}$ (Love unpubl.).

SALIENT CHARACTERS: These are slender and elongated fish, with a straight lateral line, rounded (or even pointed) dark caudal fin, narrow pectoral fins, high ridge between the eyes, large eyes, and a large mouth. Dead ones are brown with a darker caudal fin. Underwater, their colors and patterns are so very highly variable that you might not want to use these characters. Rather look for the dark caudal fin, large mouth, and reddish head region over the gills ('cause the bones are thin there and the gills show through). Tom Laidig points out that many individuals will have white "tire tracks" (several wide white stripes) running crossways on midbody.

LIFE HISTORY: Slenders are small open-coast flatfish that live on mud and mixed mud-rock bottoms. These are midshelf to upper slope fish; younger ones appear to live in somewhat shallower waters than larger individuals. A study off Oregon and Washington implied that there is some inshore movement during the summer. Fish in Puget Sound may move into shallower

LINDA SNOOK

waters at night. They live in waters at least as cold as 4.1°C (39°F) and as warm as 10.8°C (51°F).

Slenders live to at least 20 years old. Size and age at maturity are poorly known. Smith (1936) looked at Puget Sound fish and estimated age at first maturity, but did not give lengths. Demory et al. (1976) gave growth curves for Oregon fish, but did not look at size at first maturity. So what I did, which is probably really tacky but what the hell, is combine the age-at-maturity data of Smith with the age-length data of Demory and got the following. Most 2-year-old males (about 14 cm, 6 in, TL) are mature, and all 3-year-olds (about 16 cm, 6 in) are mature. A few 3-year-old females (about 16 cm, 6 in) are mature, most 4-year-olds (about 19 cm, 8 in) are mature, and all 5-year-olds (about 20 cm, 8 in) are mature. Slenders spawn mostly from January–June. On the other hand, I have seen ripe females as early as November and others have taken a few fertilized eggs in plankton tows into the summer. Slenders feed both on the bottom and in the water column. Overall, crustaceans (e.g., copepods, euphausiids, gammarid amphipods, and shrimps) and polychaetes tend to be most important. Also consumed are fishes and pelagic tunicates. A fairly wide range of animals prey on slender soles. These include fishes (e.g., arrowtooth flounder, blue sharks, Chinook salmon, great and plain sculpins, lingcod, longnose skate, Pacific cod, Pacific hakes, and rockfishes), common murres, Brandt's cormorants, seals, and sea lions.

FISHERY: Paranzella nets, an early form of bottom trawl, took absolutely huge numbers off Point Reyes (Northern California) in the 19th century. While these fish were occasionally sold in San Francisco fish markets, most were too small and were discarded. They were also taken in some numbers in early Puget Sound fisheries, but again, were rarely marketed. In general, slender soles have been of almost no importance in any commercial fisheries, a cross they bear with conspicuous good grace. Boat and pier anglers only rarely take them.

ORIGINS AND RELATIONSHIPS: Otoliths have been found in Pliocene deposits (at least 1.8 million years old) along the Pacific Coast. Genetic analyses imply the species is closely related to petrale and roughscale soles, and perhaps Pacific halibut.

Microstomus pacificus

(Lockington, 1879)

Dover Sole

Oh, so gooey is the Dover.

ETYMOLOGY AND COLLOQUIAL NAMES: *Microstomus* means "small" and "mouth" in Greek and *pacificus* refers to Point Reyes (Northern California), where the first fish was collected. For what it's worth, Hagerman (1952) writes: "The common name of Dover sole was first suggested by Mr. Stewart, employee of the New England Fish Co., Astoria [Oregon] around 1939 according

CSUMB MARE MBNMS

to the Eureka fishermen." Lovely allusions to mucous are to be had in the older names "slime flounder," "slippery sole," and "smear dab." The Japanese name is "babagarei-rui."

THE BASICS: Maximum Length: 76 cm (30 in) TL. Maximum Weight: 4.6 kg (10.1 lb). The Ranges: Northwestern and southeastern Bering Sea, Aleutian Islands (Stalemate Bank) to just south of Punta San Juanico (25°59'N, 113°17'W) (southern Baja California). They are abundant from somewhere around the western end of the Alaska Peninsula or at least to the first few islands to the west to perhaps off Bahia San Quintin (northern Baja California), and Isla Cedros (central Baja California). 2 m (7 ft) or less to 1,372 m (4,500 ft). Eggs: 2.1–2.7 mm. Larvae: hatching length = about 4.4–6.9 mm, flexion length = 7.8–15 mm, transformation length = 4.3–4.7 cm (2 in), eye migrates to midline at 1.5–2 cm (0.6–0.8 in). Von Bertalanffy parameters (TL, cm) for the area between Washington and Central California: (females) L_∞ = 52.2, k = 0.091, t_0 = -3.2; (males) L_∞ = 48.2,

k = 0.071, t_0 = -6.2 (Brodziak and Mikus 2000). Length-weight parameters (TL, cm, gr) for the area between Washington and Central California: (sexes combined) W = 0.00407L$^{3.248}$ (Brodziak and Mikus 2000).

SALIENT CHARACTERS: They are elongated, small-mouthed, soft, flabby, and very, very slimy. All the rest is commentary. The eyed sides of dead ones are brown, sometimes with darker mottling. Underwater, Dovers can change colors and patterns with some aplomb. We see them from mostly brown with a little dark blotchiness and the occasional white spot, all the way to splotchy white with some brown mixed in. Rick Stanley has observed that, underwater, Dovers have a row of black dots on their dorsal and anal fins and this character seems to hold up fairly well. Hagerman (1952) found: "There is a tendency for sexual dimorphism in the coloration of the fins in the adults; the males usually have black fin rays while the females show a dark brownish coloration."

LIFE HISTORY: This next is kind of cool. After hatching, Dovers can stay in the plankton for 2 years or more (most settle as early as 9 months). When in the water column, these larvae often assume a curled-up, leaf-like position. Young Dovers often settle to the bottom as larger larvae and may complete their metamorphoses 3–6 months after settlement. Settlement to soft sediments tends to occur in the winter and spring, mostly on the mid- and lower continental shelf (but some in 40 m, 131 ft or less, or as deep as 377 m, 1,237 ft), mostly at 3–6.5 cm (1–3 in) SL. Larvae tend to hit bottom in deeper waters and slowly migrate inshore until they find nursery habitat. Doug Markle et al. (1992) suggested that these larvae nocturnally rise into the water column, are transported inshore a bit, then settle back and test their new location until they find something they like.

As Dovers mature, they migrate into deeper and deeper waters with the biggest ones usually in the deepest zones. John Butler et al. (1996) noted: "Off Central California, approximately 85% of the spawning female biomass occurs in the oxygen minimum zone." While adults have been found in depths of 50–1,400 m (164–4,592 ft), they tend to congregate on the continental slope. For instance, Russ Vetter et al. (1994), working off Central California, found the "Maximum spawning biomass in the oxygen minimum zone between 600 and 1,000 m [1,968–3,280 ft]." I wonder if the bulk of the adult population might be somewhat shallower in colder waters, as several studies in the Gulf of Alaska-Aleutian Islands-Bering Sea area report large numbers of adults in the 101–200 m (331–656 ft) range and maximum densities at 301–500 m (987–1,640 ft). In Southern California, Dovers tend to move into deeper waters during warm water

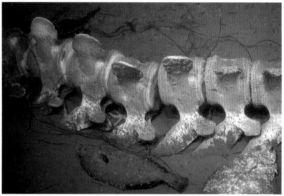

years. Along the Pacific Coast, they live in at least 2.3–11.2°C (36–52°F). While many Dovers live on mud, we see a surprising number of them on mixed mud and hard bottoms and occasionally right on rocks.

Younger Dovers tend to move into somewhat shallower waters during the spring and return to deeper ones in the fall, and larger fish may also move into a bit shallower water as temperatures increase. A few individuals make substantial alongshore movements (as much as 579 km, 360 mi), although most fish do not seem to make large geographic migrations. In Puget Sound, Dovers appear to move inshore at night. Despite their being relatively common in Southern California, Dovers don't seem to reproduce there in any great numbers based on a lack of larvae in the area. Most Southern California fish probably come south as larvae produced by those living above Point Conception. There are no discrete populations between Alaska and California.

Dover soles live to at least 60 years old. Females grow larger and faster than males. Growth rates for both males and females vary among geographic sites. For instance, Brodziak and Mikus (2000) found that fish living off Oregon–southern Washington grew more slowly than did those to the north and south. There are simply oodles of papers dealing with size and age at maturity. I am sitting here in my lab trying to figure them out and, frankly, I just don't care enough to do the heavy lifting. So, why don't you look at the following: Hagerman (1952), Harry (1959), Yoklavich and Pikitch (1989), Hunter et al. (1990, 1992), and Brodziak and Mikus (2000), and see what you think? Okay, now I feel guilty. Here is what Brodziak and Mikus found in their study of Dovers off Washington, Oregon, and Northern California. 1) Males mature at smaller sizes and younger ages than females. 2) Males and females mature at a smaller size and younger age in the more northern part of the study area. As I mentioned, these parameters varied along the coast and for females in each area, size and age at 50% ranged from 28.2–35.3 cm (11–14 in) TL (average 33.4 cm, 13 in) and 6–9 years old (average 8 years old). For males, these values were 22.4–29.5 cm (9–12 in) (average 27.1 cm, 11 in) and 3–7 years (average 5 years). When do Dovers spawn? If you review all of the literature, it looks like there may be at least a little spawning in every month. Having said this, off California and Oregon, spawning typically begins as early as November and runs to May or a little beyond, with a spring peak. Further north, in the Gulf of Alaska, most spawning seems to occur somewhat later. For instance, Hirschberger and Smith (1983) reported spawning in January, and April–August, with a May–June peak. Females are batch spawners (typically with about 9 batches per year) and produce about 1,000–15,000 eggs per batch and anywhere from 20,000–265,000 eggs per year. Smaller females may spawn earlier and perhaps have shorter spawning seasons. Dovers eat both burrowing organisms and those that live on the seafloor surface. In practice, this translates to lots of polychaetes, various amphipods, brittle stars, and bivalves. Also frequently consumed are ostracods, echiuran and sipunculid worms, shrimps, sea cucumbers, sea urchins, snails, scaphopods, hermit crabs, isopods, and, rarely, fishes. Dovers are eaten by Pacific halibut, Pacific sanddabs, Pacific sleeper sharks, petrale soles, sablefish, short-spine thornyheads, spiny dogfish, walleye pollock, Brandt's cormorants, common murres, harbor seals, California and Steller sea lions, Pacific white-sided dolphins, and probably river otters.

FISHERY: Until fairly recently, Dovers had a sort of, well, tepid relationship with the commercial fishing industry. While it is true that back in the 19th century Dovers were sold in the San Francisco fish markets with something approaching aban-don (they comprised maybe 5% of the "flounder" catch), that is the exception that proved the rule. The problem was that the basic limpness, not to say sliminess, of this species made it a hard sell indeed. Smith (1936), surveying the fisheries of Washington, noted that they were of no commercial value: "The slime sole, as the name implies, is very slimy and is repulsive to handle." Interestingly, way back in 1893, Alexander noted that icing these fish makes the flesh firmer. This salient piece of information was apparently lost to the fishing industry for about 60 years, because as Hagerman (1952) noted: "The phenom-enal rise in the importance of this species [in the 1940s] in comparison to other flatfishes is an outcome of the efforts of the fishing industry to supply the unlimited demands of the government and the civilian markets during the period of WWII...It was learned that by the quick-freeze method the soft tissues of the fish would harden and produce a marketable fillet." Today there is a robust trawl fishery for them. I was on federal jury duty in Los Angeles a few years ago and, living more than 100 miles from the courthouse, Uncle Sam put me up in a hotel right next to Chinatown. In between being kicked off three jury panels in three days—likely due to my libertarian views on drug possession—I visited a number of the interesting restaurants in the vicinity. I was impressed by the number of take-out restaurants that served whole, deep-fried Dovers.

Dovers, with their little bitty mouths, are only occasionally taken by sport fishermen.

ORIGINS AND RELATIONSHIPS: A fossil relative, *Microstomus tochigiensis*, is known from a Miocene deposit (at least 5.3 million years ago) in Japan. Dover sole fossils are known from strata at least 100,000 years old. Genetic studies imply that Dovers may be closely related to rex and deepsea soles.

MISCELLANY: And a fine kettle of odds and ends we have for you today. 1) Both ambicolored fish and those with diffuse pigmentation (a dark gray blind side) have been found. 2) Dovers without tails have been caught off Oregon. 3) A golden-col-ored one was taken off Eureka. 4) Hagerman (1952) noted that he had seen "A ventrally directed branch from the lateral line on the eyed side." 5) Two sinistral fish, with eyes on the left side of the body, were taken off Northern California. 6) As Dovers grow larger, the water content of their bodies increases, causing a condition called "jellied." This watery muscle reduces the amount of energy needed to grow large and may be particularly useful in the low oxygen environment many adults find them-selves in.

REMARKS: In Waldo Wakefield's (1990) PhD thesis, our guy writes: "Along the 400-m transect during March, there were three instances where the asteroid [sea star], *Rathbunaster californicus*, had extended one of its arms along the body surface of *M. pacificus*. One can only speculate about the function of this observed behavior and I choose not to." Discretion is the better part of valour, Dr. Wakefield?

You wouldn't think it, but a live Dover in an aquarium is about the most endearing animal on the planet. I once visited a refrigerated tank full of Dovers at the National Marine Fisheries Service lab in La Jolla. Instead of lying inert on the bottom, as we see them underwater, when these fish saw someone coming they swam over, stood up on their tails, and stuck their faces against the glass. They looked for all the world like pop-eyed flying squirrels.

Parophrys vetulus
Girard, 1854
English Sole

ETYMOLOGY AND COLLQUIAL NAMES: *Parophrys* means "near" and "eyebrow" (the narrow interorbital spaces) in Greek and *vetulus* is "old man" in Greek. Often called just "sole" in the 19th century, later on the Canadians tended to use "lemon flounder" or "lemon sole," while U.S. researchers called them "pointed-nosed soles" during the same period. In 1949, the California state government changed the name to "English sole."

THE BASICS: Maximum Length: 61 cm (24 in) TL. Maximum Weight: 2.3 kg (5.1 lb). The Ranges: Nunivak Island (Bering Sea) and Agattu Island (Aleutian Islands) to Bahia San Cristobal (central Baja California). Commonly at least from about Umnak Island (Aleutian Islands) to Bahia de Sebastian Vizcaino (central Baja California). Intertidal zone (juveniles) to about 550 m (1,800 ft), but mostly in less than 200 m (656 ft). Eggs: 0.8–1.1 mm. Larvae: hatching length = 2.3–2.9 mm, flexion length = 7.6–11.5 mm, transformation length = 1.7–1.8 cm (0.7 in). Lots of folks have looked at growth rates, including Smith and Nitsos (1969), Van Cleve and El-Sayed (1969), Ehrhardt (1973), Demory et al. (1976), and Fargo and Kronlund (2000). That's too many estimates to give you, so here is one from Oregon, smack dab in the middle of the species' range. Von Bertalanffy parameters (FL, cm): (females) L_∞ = 46.7, k = 0.143, t_0 = -4.67; (males) L_∞ = 36.3, k = 0.256, t_0 = -1.08 (Demory et al. 1976). Most studies have estimated von Bertalanffy parameters, but those rogues, Fargo and Kronlund, present a number of Schnute growth parameters for British Columbia fish. Who knows, you might like those. Similarly, seemingly anyone with a scale and a pencil has tried their hand at length-weight relationships, but out of shear cussedness, here is one from Holland (1969). Length-weight parameters (TL, mm, gr): $W = 0.00001168L^{3.012}$.

SALIENT CHARACTERS: English have an elongated body, slender head, bluntly pointed snout, squared off caudal fin, and small mouth. Dead ones are brown or yellow-brown on the eyed side (sometimes with dark reddish spots, a reddish-brown tinge, or yellow lines at the bases of the dorsal and anal fins), and white or maybe pale yellow on the blind side. Underwater, they can be splotched, speckled, and spotted with brown, tan, and white.

LIFE HISTORY: Young-of-the-year recruit from the plankton (as small as 1.4 cm, 0.6 in, SL) to estuaries and, less commonly, in very shallow coastal waters (and occasionally to depths of at least 52 m, 171 ft). Young fish that settle along the open coast subsequently tend to migrate into bays. In Southern California, where English are very rare in bays and estuaries, almost all settlement occurs along the coast. Young fish settle out over a wide time period. In a study in Yaquina Bay (Oregon), fish settled from November–July, with peak months varying from November–May depending on year. Other studies have observed settlement into September. Within larger embayments, such as Puget Sound, juvenile recruiting areas may vary between years, making it difficult to point to one particular chunk of mud and declare that the best nursery ground. In bays, English (particularly the youngest ones) are found over mud flats, in channels (when they are slightly larger), and in eelgrass beds. Juveniles can be pretty dense in some estuaries, with estimates of as many about 2,000 fish per hectare. Young fish generally stay in the estuary nursery grounds for less than one year; the vast majority leave by late summer or fall, although a few over-winter and then migrate out. By the time they are maybe 15 cm (6 in) TL, most fish are in coastal waters. As they grow, fish move into progressively deeper waters, where adults live over muddy, sandy, or mixed sediment-rock seafloors. English winter in relatively deep waters (where spawning occurs) and move into more shallow ones as waters warm. At least in Puget Sound, they can rise into the mid-waters or even the surface at night. Another study in Puget Sound found that adults might segregate by sex; males tended to be found in areas with relatively fine sediments. Chris Rooper (2002) commented that adults make "extensive along-shelf migrations during

SOUL SURVIVOR

A sole sole on her soul did dwell,

"If I'm soul-less will I go to Hell?

Thus conversely I wish

To converse with angelfish

I would then be in Heaven, truth to tell."

winter to suitable spawning habitat on mud and sandy bottoms." English are tolerant of a fairly broad range of temperatures (at least 3.9–21°C, 39–70°F) and salinities as low as at least 12 ppt.

English soles live to at least 23 years old. Females grow larger than males and males reach their maximum size faster. Growth rates vary considerably between areas, as does length and age at maturity. Sampson and Al-Jufaily (1999) found that, coastwide, female length and age at 50% maturity were about 23 cm (9 in) FL, and 4–7 years old. In addition, "growth rate and length at 50% maturity have decreased substantially relative to observations from the 1950s, but age at 50% maturity has increased." Males tend to mature at 2–3 years old and when slightly smaller than females. Other papers on the subject that you might enjoy include Harry (1959), Van Cleve and El-Sayed (1969), and Lassuy (1989). English may spawn throughout the year, although looking at studies conducted in various places up and down the coast it appears that it mostly occurs from September to perhaps April, maybe with a January or February peak off the West Coast and a late spring–summer one in Alaskan waters; peaks seem to vary annually. Large females begin to spawn earlier in the season than small ones. Females will spawn in waters at least as cold as about 7.8°C (46°F) and produce 150,000–2,100,000 pelagic and nonadhesive eggs. The fertilized eggs are buoyant and hatch in 3.5–12 days, with the larvae remaining in the plankton for perhaps 6–10 weeks. These are opportunistic

MARIO JOSEPH BELLANTI is being hailed by his co-splitters at the Paladini, Inc., fish cutting tables at San Francisco as the world's champion sole filleter, his record being 90 lbs. of sole per hour. The Paladini fish splitters issue a challenge to all comers, and will back Mario Joseph with marbles, matches or sole.

PACIFIC FISHERMAN 1930, 34(32):13

benthic feeders. Dietwise, that translates to raiding the larder for polychaetes, bivalves (particularly clams and clam siphons), crustaceans (e.g., gammarid and harpacticoid amphipods, mysid shrimps, and shrimps), snails, sand dollars, brachiopods, brittle stars, and fishes. At least in Puget Sound, English appear to feed during both day and night. Predators include arrowtooth flounder, butter and English soles, big and longnose skates, lingcod, Pacific hakes, sablefish, saddleback gunnels, spiny dogfish, staghorn sculpins, common murres, Brandt's, common, and pelagic cormorants, California sea lions, harbor seals, Pacific white-sided dolphins, and probably river otters. In one study, pigeon guillemot chicks rejected English soles.

FISHERY: Because they were easy to catch in the relatively primitive trawls of the time, English were a very important food fish as far back as at least the 1880s around San Francisco and in Puget Sound. For many decades, they remained quite important in trawl fisheries along much of the Pacific Coast, from at least British Columbia to Central California, as both a fresh product and in the mink food industry. In some locations, their sometimes heavy nematode worm infestations made selling English a difficult task. Today, the commercial trawl fishery is relatively small, because of this species' relatively small size and the perception that some individuals have an off-flavor. Research by Geise (2007) found nothing gustatorily off-putting, but did discover that fish from different areas did have somewhat different flavors. Because females grow larger than males, almost the entire fishery is composed of females.

Recreational anglers catch them on occasion.

ORIGINS AND RELATIONSHIPS: In the University of California, Berkeley, Paleontological Museum there are otoliths attributed to this species that were found in Miocene deposits (at least 5.3 million years old) from Santa Cruz County (California). I don't know if these identifications have been verified. Fossil English sole have been recovered from Late Pliocene (at least 1.8 million-year-old) deposits in Southern California. English sole remnants have also been taken from 100,000-year-old strata in California. Genetic studies imply that English are most closely related to sand soles and also to southern rock soles, butter soles, and starry flounder.

MISCELLANY: 1) In some areas, fish fins and fin rays are often infected with the red-colored nematode worm *Philometra americana*. 2) Both partial and completely ambicolored fish have been noted. 3) A study of English soles in Puget Sound has yielded the disquieting information that estrogenic compounds entering the water may have led to an altering of the spawning cycle of female fish, extending the season out by a few months. In additional, this study found several intersex fish (where gonads contain both male and female tissues). 4) Julianne Kalman, who pays attention to these kinds of things, reports that English soles (and to a lesser extent Dover soles) have a "bitter fishy" smell. And on such a tenuous strand doth Science march on.

REMARKS: The hybrid sole, *Inopsetta ischyra*, found from at least the Strait of Georgia to San Francisco Bay, is formed when English soles are naughty with starry flounder. In what now seems like a pathology, English soles also sometimes hybridize with butter soles.

Platichthys stellatus
(Pallas, 1787)
Starry Flounder

BERNARD P. HANBY

ETYMOLOGY AND COLLOQUIAL NAMES: *Platichthys* means "flat" and "fish" in Greek and *stellatus* is "starry" in Greek. In San Francisco of the 19th century, starries were just called "flounder." "Rough jacket" and "grindstone" are several names that refer to this species' rough skin. Turner (1886) noted that the Alaska natives used "Na Tu'g nuk," derived from "Na tuk," meaning "boot." Turner also notes that this fish was called "Slapjack Reba," as were other flatfishes (see Arctic flounder). The Tlingit name is "wankashxéet" and the Japanese one is "numa-garei."

THE BASICS: Maximum Length: 91 cm (36 in) TL. Maximum Weight: 5.1 kg (11.3 lb). Older records that may or may not be accurate suggest starries can grow to 9.1 kg (20 lb). The Ranges: Seas of Japan and Okhotsk, to East Siberian Sea, Chukchi Sea, Beaufort Sea to Bathurst Inlet (Northwest Territories) and Viscount Melville Sound (Nunavut) (and perhaps to Queen Maud Gulf, Arctic Canada), and Bering Sea to Los Angeles Harbor (Southern California). They are common in the seas of Japan and Okhotsk, throughout the Aleutian Islands and Bering Sea (to about Norton Sound) to Central California, and occasional in the Santa Barbara Channel. They are occasional along most of the Chukchi and Beaufort seas, apparently becoming more abundant at about the Tuktoyaktuk Peninsula eastward to at least Kugluktuk [Coppermine] (Amundsen Gulf). Intertidal to about 600 m (1,968 ft), mostly in 100 m (328 ft) or less. Eggs: 0.9–1.3 mm. Larvae: hatching length = 1.9–2.1 mm, transformation length = 8.3–10.5 mm. Age-length relationship figures or tables are found in Orcutt (1950), Lawrence et al. (1984), and Kolpakov (2005). Length-weight parameters (TL, mm, kg): (sexes combined) $W = 0.00000000163L^{3.34}$ (Recfin 2009).

SALIENT CHARACTERS: Dead starries are instantly recognizable by the alternating yellow or orange and dark bars on their dorsal, caudal, and anal fins. Underwater, the lighter bars may also be whitish. If that doesn't give it away, the oval body, mostly squared-off caudal fin, and extremely rough skin on their eyed side (caused by the star-shaped scales) should do it.

LIFE HISTORY: Starries are primarily nearshore flatfish with a distinct penchant for freshwater, at least in their youth. Most, but not all, young-of-the-year settle out (when as small as 0.9 cm, 0.4 in, SL) into fresh or brackish waters, the rest recruit to very shallow soft substrates on the open coast. Young fish will often swim up rivers; they have been taken 32 km (20 mi) up the Fraser River and 120 km (75 mi) up the Columbia River. As they mature, starries tend to inhabit more saline waters, but a few adults either remain in estuaries or reenter freshwater on occasion. For instance, a study in Kamchatka found that adults entered estuaries at high tides to feed. In a summer study along the Tuktoyaktuk Peninsula (Beaufort Sea), many large fish remained in salinities of 4–8 ppt. In estuaries and nearshore waters, starries are found on both mud bottoms and in eelgrass beds, and they have been reported around bottom drift algae and near reefs. Starries will occasionally swim upward into surface waters, during both day and night, and in some locations move a bit inshore in the evening. While apparently only cursorily documented, starries appear to move inshore to spawn. Although there is not much evidence that these fish make long along-coast migrations, for whatever it is worth it should be noted that, of fish tagged in the Columbia River, one traveled 201 km (125 mi) south to Yaquina Bay and another 209 km (130 mi) north to northern Washington. While most starries are found on the shallow- or mid-shelf, some fish live in considerably deeper waters. Orcutt (1950), for instance, notes that about 909 kg (2,000 lb) were taken by a trawler in 274 m (900 ft) or more off Monterey. Starries can tolerate water temperatures down to at least -1.8°C (29°F).

Starries live to at least 42 years old and females grow larger than males. Fish appear to live much longer in the cold waters of the Arctic (42 years) and Sea of Japan (21 years) than off California (a weenie 8 years, although someone should relook at California fish). In a study in Monterey Bay, almost all males were mature at 2 years old (around 26 cm, 10 in) TL and all were mature at 3 years old (37 cm, 15 in). A few females as small as 29 cm (11 in) and 3 years old were mature and all females 4 years old (and perhaps 37 cm, 15 in) were mature. In the Sea of Japan, starries larger than about 24 cm (10 in) (4 years) are mature. Regarding their spawning season, well, in a 10-year survey of San Francisco Bay fishes, starry flounder larvae were taken throughout the year, implying year-round spawning. However, other studies have shown a more restricted, November–July, season. Fish off California tend to spawn in mostly November–February, while for those further north it is later in the year (June and July in the Beaufort Sea). Females produce anywhere from 914,000–2,287,000 eggs per season. The eggs are pelagic and hatch in 68 hours at 12.5°C (55°F) and 110 hours at 10.5°C (51°F). Eye migration begins at around 24 days when a fish is 7 mm SL. While their diets vary with location and year, it is safe to say that starries eat a very wide range of prey. Young-of-the-year tend to eat various small crustaceans (e.g., gammarid and harpacticoid amphipods, copepods, cumaceans, and mysid shrimps), polychaetes, and clam siphons. Larger fish add whole clams (and other bivalves) and fishes, along with brittle stars, sand dollars, crabs, hermit crabs, shrimps, ascidians, and snails. In shallow, muddy areas starries often eat everyone's favorite phallic-shaped mudflat animal, the fat innkeeper. Predators include leopard sharks, spiny dogfish, striped bass, white sturgeons, bald eagles, great blue herons, harbor and ringed seals, Steller sea lions, beluga whales, and river otters.

FISHERY: Starry flounder were a valuable food fish for most native peoples. Turner (1886) noted that some of the native peoples living at Saint Michael on the Bering Sea, were very fond of them. On the other hand, Aleuts living along the Aleutians did not care for the species, and would often throw them back when caught. On the third hand, Swan (1857), writing about the Native Americans living in Willapa Bay (Washington) in the 1850s, commented: "The turbot and flounders are caught while wading in the water by means of the feet. The Indian wades along slowly, and, as soon as he feels a fish with his feet, he steps quickly on it and holds it firmly till he can reach hold of it with his hand, when he gives it a jerk, and away it flies far into the flats. This process is repeated till enough fish are caught, when they are picked up, put in a basket, and carried to the canoe. The turbot [starry flounder] are much like the English turbot, but smaller; the largest I have ever seen weighed twenty pounds. They are easily taken by this method of the Indians, as their rough backs prevent them slipping from under the feet."

In the 19th century, starries were the most important flatfish in the commercial catch, comprising about 50% (by weight) of the entire flatfish catch on the Pacific Coast. One of the reasons for this is that they were abundant in nearshore waters, often in quiet bays and, compared to many other more offshore species, were easily taken. During the 1880s, for instance, Humboldt Bay was a major supplier of starries to San Francisco, so major that the fishermen fished out the bay in almost no time. Good job, guys. During the 20th century, as technology allowed for harvesting of other species, starries became a relatively minor part of the flatfish fishery, mostly from San Francisco northwards. Today, they are commercially harvested in large numbers along the Asian coast and form the basis of small trawl fisheries along the eastern north Pacific. Starries tend to be less valuable (on a per pound basis) than such species as petrale and sand soles.

This is a very important recreational species that is taken by vessel, pier, and shore fishermen, mostly from Morro Bay northward.

ORIGINS AND RELATIONSHIPS: A *Platichthys* sp. has been reported from the Oligocene (at least 23 million years ago) of the Caucasus area of Europe. The extinct species *Platichthys miostellatus* was found in Miocene deposits (at least 5.3 million years ago) from Japan. Starry flounder remains have been reported from strata at least 100,000 years old in California. Genetic analyses imply that starries are most closely related to butter and southern (and we assume northern) rock soles, and also English and sand soles. Another genetic study found longhead dabs and arctic flounder to be close relatives. So confusion still reigns supreme.

MISCELLANY: 1) Here's something kind of interesting: The degree to which starries are either left-eyed (sinistral) or right-eyed (dextral) varies with geographic location. For instance, fish from California and Puget Sound tend to be 50–60% sinistral, in Alaska the percentage jumps to 67%, and in Japan it's 100%. 2) Here's something else that is cool: This species produces a number of proteins that it uses as antifreeze. Fish from California appear to produce less of these molecules than do those individuals living in Alaska waters. 3) Albino and ambicolored ones have been caught.

REMARKS: Starries occasionally hybridize with English soles to form *Inopsetta ischyra*. *Inopsetta* is found from at least the Strait of Georgia (and likely further north) to San Francisco Bay. And in the western Pacific, starries hybridize with the stone flounder, *Kareius bicoloratus*.

THE WAGES OF SIN

Think overfishing is the province of folks with big nets, big ships, and big egos? Lawsy no, think again. Here's what David Starr Jordan wrote in 1887: "Humboldt Bay used to be the spawning grounds for immense numbers of the large flounder [*Platichthys stellatus*]. The fish were so abundant as to completely line the bottoms of the deep channels." Note the past tense? So what happened? A major fishery developed in 1874, shipping starries to the hordes of flounder eaters in San Francisco. There were about 100 people in the fishery and as many as 3 tons of flounder were shipped at a time. And then they caught most of them and the fish never, ever, came back in those big numbers.

Pleuronectes glacialis
Pallas, 1776
Arctic Flounder

ETYMOLOGY AND COLLOQUIAL NAMES: *Pleuronectes* is Greek for "side" and "swimmer" and *glacialis* means "icy" in Latin. "Polar flounder" is another recent name. Turner (1886) notes that small flatfishes were often called "slapjack reba" in Alaska: "At Saint Michael's [Norton Sound] I was once on the wharf where several natives were fishing. One of the natives was a woman who had but a few days before come from Nulato and had never seen a Flounder in her life. She soon caught one of these fish, and when she

NOAA FISHERIES

saw that it was different from any other fish she had ever seen her astonishment knew no bounds. The fish gave a flop and exposed its white lower parts. The woman gave a scream and shouted, 'Slapjack Reba.' The word slapjack is universally known for the pancake or griddle-cake, and reba is the Russian word for fish. At the present time the Flounders are usually called 'Slapjack Reba.'" A number of folks call this one *Liopsetta glacialis*.

THE BASICS: Maximum Length: 44 cm (17 in) TL. Maximum Weight: 3.3 kg (7.3 lb). The Ranges: Arctic Russia to Labrador; Okhotsk Sea; off Alaska, from Beaufort Sea to southeastern Bering Sea and Aleutian Islands. In North America, they are abundant from at least the Bristol Bay area (eastern Bering Sea) to at least Tuktoyaktuk Harbor (Beaufort Sea). Barely subtidal waters to perhaps 91 m (298 ft), but mostly in 10 m (3 ft) and shallower. Larvae: hatching length = average 5.6 mm. Length-weight parameters (FL, mm, gr): (sexes combined) W = 0.0000076L$^{3.12}$ (Palmer and Dugan 1990).

SALIENT CHARACTERS: Arctics are elongated-oval, have a prominent ridge between the eyes, a slightly rounded caudal fin, a little dorsal extension to the lateral line on the head, and a pronounced anal spine. The eyed sides of dead ones are brown with darker markings, dark spots on the dorsal and anal fins, and the blind side is white to lime green.

LIFE HISTORY: Arctic flounder are cold-water fish that prefer shallow, brackish, and mud-bottomed habitats. Small individuals tend to live in backwaters. In the Beaufort and Chukchi seas, fish move slightly offshore in fall and return as waters warm in the spring. They do not seem to make extensive along-shore movements, although one tagged in the Alaska National Wildlife Reserve (Beaufort Sea) moved 62 km (39 mi) before it was recaptured. They are tolerant of a wide range of salinities and will occasionally ascend into freshwater. Similarly, they can tolerate water temperatures between at least -1–13.5°C (30–56°F). Spawning occurs under the ice in nearshore waters. At certain times, they form single-sex aggregations.

This species lives to at least 28 years old. Females grow larger, live longer, and may grow faster than males. Growth rates vary widely with region. In general, most fish mature at between 4–8 years old and 13–20 cm (5–8 in) TL. Males tend to mature at a slightly younger age and smaller size than females. Arctics spawn from at least March–June in the Tuktoyaktuk region. Females produce 50,000–200,000 pelagic eggs. Larvae hatch in 22–42 days at a mean temperature of 1°C (31°F). Benthic and epibenthic invertebrates such as polychaetes, sea squirts, clams, and crustaceans dominate Arctic flounder diets.

FISHERY: Arctic flounder are a minor part of various artisanal fisheries.

MISCELLANY: 1) In an unsavory remark, Turner (1886) noted tumors on the sides, at the bases of the fins, and near the gills, in the summer months. 2) A hermaphroditic one was caught in the Beaufort Sea.

Pleuronectes quadrituberculatus
Pallas, 1814
Alaska Plaice

ETYMOLOGY AND COLLOQUIAL NAMES: *Pleuronectes* is Greek for "side" and "swimmer" and *quadrituberculatus* means "having four tubercles" in Latin. "Lemon sole" was another name and the Japanese word is "tsuno-garei."

THE BASICS: Maximum Length: 62 cm (24 in) TL. Maximum Weight: 3.5 kg (7.7 lb). The Ranges: Sea of Japan to Chukchi Sea (as far northward as 70°16'N, 163°58'W) and Gulf of Alaska to southeastern Alaska, near Ketchikan; one record from Bellingham Bay (Washington). They are abundant from the Sea of Japan and Sakhalin to the Bering Sea (in the eastern Bering Sea to about 62°N) and still relatively common in the Gulf of Alaska as far east as about Kodiak Island-Cook Inlet. 5–500 m

(16–1,640 ft), except reported to 900 m (2,952 ft) in winter in Okhotsk Sea. Off North America, mostly in 40 to about 150 m (131–492 ft); largest fish will live in somewhat deeper waters. On the Asian side, this species appears to inhabit much deeper waters, reportedly wintering in 400–900 m (1,312–2,952 ft). Eggs: average 1.8 mm. Larvae: hatching length = 5.6–5.9 mm, transformation length = 10.7 mm. Von Bertalanffy parameters (probably TL, mm): (females) L_∞ = 501.7, k = 0.156, t_0 = 2.09; (males) L_∞ = 379.2, k = 0.204, t_0 = 1.83 (Zhang et al. 1998). Length-weight parameters (probably TL, mm, gr): (females) W = 0.006148L$^{3.217}$; (males) W = 0.05677L$^{2.576}$ (Zhang et al. 1998).

SALIENT CHARACTERS: Alaska plaice are oval, although their slightly pointy heads are convex on the dorsal side. They have a rounded caudal fin, a lateral line that has a short branch over the top of the head, small mouth, and most of their teeth are on the blind side. Dead ones are the usual olive to dark brown on the eyed side, but surprise, surprise, they are yellow on the blind side.

LIFE HISTORY: Almost all Alaska plaice are found on the continental shelf. Although there is only fragmentary data on this, it appears that juveniles tend to settle out in less than 25 m (82 ft) or perhaps 50 m (164 ft), in the summer and fall, and over sand and mud. Older juveniles are found over soft seafloors and tend to stay in shallower waters than the adults. In the eastern Bering Sea, this translates to usually 50 m (164 ft) and shallower (although there are reports of juvenile plaice in waters as deep as about 100 m, 328 ft). During the summer, adults migrate into the shallower parts of their depth range, when the sexes are at least somewhat segregated. For instance, Zhang et al. (1998) found that in the eastern Bering Sea, females are

most abundant in waters deeper than 60 m (197 ft), while males are found mostly in 45–55 m (148–180 ft). Alaska plaice live at temperatures between -2.1–11.7°C (28–53°F) in the Bering Sea, commonly in perhaps 0–3°C (32–37°F). Kevin Bailey helped me sort out what to me was a confusing movement pattern. He writes that based on his take of the scientific literature: "They are in deep shelf waters in the winter, move inshore to spawn in spring between 50 and 100 m [164-328 ft], and then continue moving inshore in summer and back offshore in winter. However, the extent of their inshore migration is limited by temperature; porridge that is not too cold (the middle shelf cold pool) but not too hot (inner shelf warms up in summer)." It is not known if there is more than one stock off North America.

Alaska plaice live to at least 37 years old. Females grow larger than males. In the eastern Bering Sea, a few females are mature at 27 cm (11 in, 7 years) TL, 50% at 31 cm (12 in, 8 years), and all are mature at 39 cm (15 in, about 11 years). A study off western Kamchatka found the "large-scale maturation" of males was at 26–30 cm (10–12 in, 6–7 years) and females at 32–36 cm (13–14 in, 8–9 years old). Spawning occurs from March to perhaps July, mostly from April–June with peak season varying between years. In the eastern Bering Sea and Gulf of Alaska, based on location of eggs, spawning occurs at bottom depths of 50–100 m (164–328 ft). Females appear to be batch spawners and produce 56,000–521,000 eggs per season. APs feed most heavily on polychaetes, clams, and other bivalves, crustaceans (e.g., gammarid amphipods, shrimps, and hermit crabs), and echiuroids, and occasionally on ascidians, brittle stars, sea urchins, sand dollars, and fishes. Several studies found evidence that Alaska plaice do not feed in the winter and perhaps do not feed at night. Predators include other Alaska plaice, flathead soles, great and plain sculpins, and walleye pollock.

FISHERY: Historically, Alaska plaice have been most important in various subsistence fisheries. Most of the commercial catch occurs as bycatch in various trawl fisheries.

RELATIONSHIPS: One study of flatfish genetics found that Alaska plaice were perhaps most closely related to such species as longhead dabs and starry flounder.

MISCELLANY: The blood of Alaska plaice contains peptide molecules that act as antifreeze.

Pleuronichthys

Members of the genus *Pleuronichthys*, usually called "turbot" off our coast, are of only minute commercial importance. I mainly see them for sale at dockside fishermen's markets. A fossil turbot, *Pleuronichthys veliger*, lived during the Miocene (at least 5.3 million years ago) in Southern California.

Pleuronichthys coenosus

Girard, 1854

C-O Sole

The last thing a worm is likely to see.

ETYMOLOGY AND COLLOQUIAL NAME: *Pleuronichthys* is Greek for "side" and "fish" and *coenosus* means "muddy" in Latin. Often called "C-O turbot" by those in the out-crowd.

THE BASICS: Maximum Length: 36 cm (14 in) TL. Maximum Weight: 431 gram (1 lb). The Ranges: Southeastern Alaska (landed at Sitka but catch locality not known; well documented from sites farther south near Etolin Island and Ketchikan) to Punta Abreojos (southern Baja California). They are common at least as far north-ward as Vancouver Island and relatively high densities of larvae have been found as far south as Punta Eugenia (Baja California). 0–350 m (0–1,146 ft), mostly in perhaps 5–30 m (16–98 ft). Eggs: 1.2–1.6. Larvae: hatching length = about 3.7 mm, flexion length = 6.1–8.5 mm, transformation length = 8.2–11.4 mm. Length-weight parameters (TL, mm, kg): (females) W = $0.000000000573L^{3.576}$ (RecFin 2009).

SALIENT CHARACTERS: This species is oval, with a prominent ridge between the eyes, a very characteristic dark spot in the center of the caudal fin rays, and a crescent mark where the caudal fin rays meet the rest of the body. This makes the "c-o" pattern, although when you think about it, it really is an "o reversed-c" pattern (see picture below), which, I suppose, is too hard to say. There is also a dark spot in midbody. Goodness, but c-o soles can come in a vast array of colors and patterns. Pink, yellow, cream, white, and brown are the most common, although you often see them almost solid white, and an occasional one has a blue ring or two. If you see a turbot that is brightly, one might say garishly, marked, it is likely to be a c-o.

LIFE HISTORY: Young-of-the-year (at least as small as 1.7 cm, 0.7 in, SL) recruit to nearshore waters (at least between 6–21 m, 20–70 ft). They are found in estuaries and other embayments and on the open coast. More perhaps than any other *Pleuronichthys*, this one likes to live near hard stuff. You can find them on soft stuff close to reefs, in eelgrass beds, along breakwaters; well, you get the picture. Chris Grossman reports on what might have been spawning behavior: "I did a night dive at Pyramid Cove,

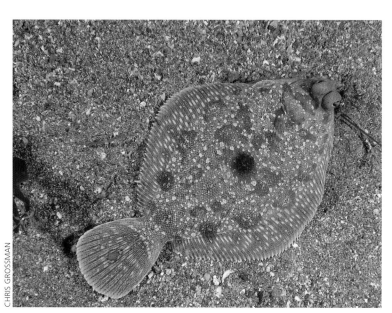

San Clemente Island. I came across a pair of flat fish I believe were ready to mate. I interrupted them and they kept moving away, however I followed. The pursuing fish started off mottled, then turned almost white, then back to a very dark mottled pattern."

No one has done a study on growth rates: a 26.2 cm (10 in) TL fish I aged was maybe 6 years old. C-Os spawn throughout the year, but may have a peak from about March to maybe October. Young fish, to perhaps 10 cm (4 in) SL, feed primarily on gammarid amphipods and other small crustaceans. As they grow, they begin to target polychaetes, along with smaller numbers of crabs, shrimps, brachiopods, clams, brittle stars, and, rarely, fishes. C-Os will swim into the water column and then dive head first into the seafloor while hunting for worms. Thus far, only

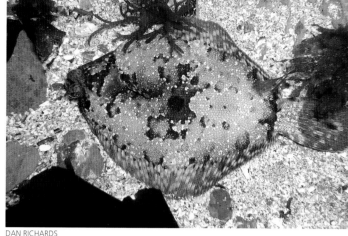
DAN RICHARDS

copper rockfish and bottlenose dolphins have been reported as predators.

FISHERY: Historically, they formed a small part of the commercial "sole" catch. One problem was that, while the fish were large enough for the fillet market, they were too difficult to skin. C-Os are occasionally taken by recreational anglers, particularly those fishing from piers.

MISCELLANY: One fish from Puget Sound was reported to be both partially albino and partially ambicolored.

Pleuronichthys guttulatus

Girard, 1856

Diamond Turbot

PETER BRYANT

ETYMOLOGY: *Pleuronichthys* is Greek for "side" and "fish" and *guttulatus* is Latin for "with small spots." As late as 2010, at least one paper used the old name, *Hypsopsetta guttulata*, a name redolent with alliteration.

THE BASICS: Maximum Length: 45.7 cm (18 in) TL. The Ranges: Cape Mendocino (Northern California) to Cabo San Lucas (southern Baja California), with an isolated population in the Gulf of California. Common from about Tomales Bay (Northern California) to at least (based on larval densities) Bahia Magdalena (southern Baja California). Surf to 46 m (150 ft), mostly in 20 m (66 ft) and less.

Eggs: 0.8–0.9 mm. Larvae: hatching length = about 2.2 mm, flexion length = 4.6–5.2 mm, transformation length = 6.6–8.8 mm. Von Bertalanffy parameters (SL, mm): (sexes combined) L_∞ = 198.3, k = 0.1, t_0 = 0.31 (Lane 1975). Length-weight parameters (SL, mm, gr): (sexes combined) W = $0.00002213L^{3.044}$ (Lane 1975).

SALIENT CHARACTERS: Diamonds are really the only flatfish with a diamond shape. They have a small mouth and a long dorsal accessory lateral line. The eyed side is gray or brownish, often with blue spots. The blind side has a splash of yellow around the mouth.

LIFE HISTORY: Larvae drift about for 5–6 weeks. Young-of-the-year recruit in very shallow waters, at lengths as small as 0.4 cm (0.2 in) SL. Diamonds live in estuaries, lagoons, and shallow coastal waters. In tropical areas, you can find them in mangrove forests. Most live over sand or mud, often in eelgrass beds. They are tolerant of fairly fresh water (in San Francisco Bay down to 8.4 ppt, and one was found 1 km (0.6 mi) up a Baja California stream), as well as highly saline conditions (to about 60 ppt). Temperature tolerance is at least as low as 8°C (46°F). Spawning areas are poorly understood. Some takes place in San Francisco

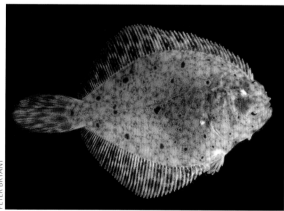
PETER BRYANT

A juvenile.

Bay. While it is unlikely that diamonds move about much, Chris Onuf's (1987) work in Mugu Lagoon implies that these fish may leave the lagoon during spawning season. Diamonds that live in the Gulf of California are pretty isolated from fish on the outer coast as there appears to be significantly reduced gene flow between the two populations.

It is hard to know just how long diamonds live. Lane (1975) found fish as old as 6 years, while Baxter (1966), providing no data on how he arrived at these numbers, says 8–9 years. Baxter also notes that "fish probably reach sexual maturity in their second or third year" which corresponds to maybe 14–18 cm (6–7 in) SL based on Lane's growth curve. And man, if you look at the literature about when ripe females are found and when eggs and larvae are taken, the data is all over the map. Suffice it to say that at least some spawning likely takes place throughout the year. Larvae remain in the plankton for 5–6 weeks. Diamonds tend to target clam siphons, polychaetes, and crustaceans (e.g., shrimps, crabs, gammarid amphipods, and cumaceans). On occasion, they also consume fat innkeepers, snails, and fishes. Predators include staghorn sculpins and eared grebes (although these birds are reported to have a very tough time actually swallowing one).

FISHERY: Diamonds were an occasional catch of Native Americans. In 19th-century San Diego and San Francisco, diamonds were an important part of the local commercial fishery and were a popular food fish. Some time in the 20th century, as such shallow water gear as beach seines were outlawed, diamonds assumed an only negligible part of the commercial flatfish catch. They are quite popular with pier and shore anglers, however.

MISCELLANY: One ambicolored one was taken in Southern California.

Pleuronichthys verticalis
Jordan & Gilbert, 1880
Hornyhead Turbot

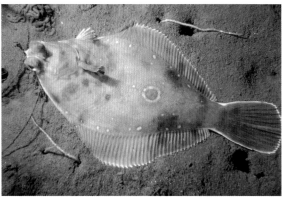

ETYMOLOGY: *Pleuronichthys* is Greek for "side" and "fish" and *verticalis* comes from the Latin and refers to the crown of the head, an allusion to the spiny ridge between the eyes.

THE BASICS: Maximum Length: 36.8 cm (15 in) TL. Maximum Weight: 835 gr (1.8 lb). The Ranges: Oregon to Bahia Magdalena (southern Baja California); isolated population in Gulf of California. Common from at least off San Francisco to Punta Abreojos (southern Baja California). 5–237 m (16–777 ft), typically from about 10–100 m (33–330 ft). Eggs: 1–1.2. Larvae: hatching length = less than 2.4 mm, flexion length = 5–7.2 mm, transformation length = 7.9–11 mm. Length-weight parameters (TL, cm, gr): W = $0.009L^{3.173}$ (Love unpubl.).

SALIENT CHARACTERS: These are oval with one or two sharp spines between the eyes. Dead ones are brown or yellowish-brown with dark, gray, or light mottling or vermiculations, and sometimes white speckling. Live ones can range from tan or brown to light and sand colored. Included can be dark and light blotches, eyespots (often on the caudal fin), and fine white stippling.

LIFE HISTORY: Young-of-the-year settle at about 1.8 cm (0.7 in). In general, hornyheads are most abundant in semi-protected and open coast environments; they are relatively uncommon in estuaries and enclosed bays. They live over soft sediment, sometimes near structure.

Hornyheads are said to live to 25 years (Cooper 1994), which sounds too long to me, but there you are. Females grow larger than males. Cooper (1994) found that females mature at 15–16 cm (6 in) SL (10–15 years) and males at 9–10 cm (4 in) (4 to perhaps 10 years). Although, admittedly, I have no data for this species, for a dwarf flatfish to wait 10 years to mature seems counter-intuitive. This species is a batch spawner and spawns throughout the year, although some egg and larval data imply heaviest spawning may take place in spring–summer, but don't hold me to that. There is some evidence that, at least during some times of the year, the sexes aggregate separately. Hornyheads really dig (pun intended) polychaetes. Other prey

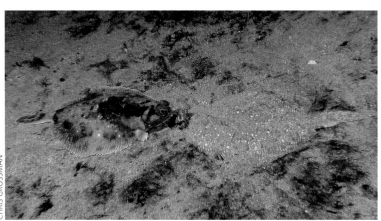

include clam siphons, crabs, various amphipods, sea anemones, brachiopods, snails, nemerteans, and fishes. Predators include California halibut, staghorn sculpins, and harbor seals.

FISHERY: In the late 19th and early 20th centuries, hornyheads were a fairly important part of the "sole" catch off California. Today, they are rarely found in markets. Hornyheads are occasionally taken by boat, pier, and shore anglers.

MISCELLANY: Ambicolored fish, as well as albino ones and those having diffuse pigmentation (a dark gray blind side) have been taken.

Psettichthys melanostictus
Girard, 1854
Sand Sole

ETYMOLOGY AND COLLOQUIAL NAMES: *Psettichthys* means "turbot" and "fish" in Greek and *melanostictus* is also Greek, for "black" and "spotted." "Sand sole" goes back to the 19th century. Other names include "sand brill" and "fringe sole." They are called "karei-rui" in Japanese.

THE BASICS: Maximum Length: 63 cm (25 in) TL. Maximum Weight: 2.2 kg (5.1 lb). The Ranges: Southeastern Bering Sea and Aleutian Islands (from Unalaska Island) and Gulf of Alaska to La Jolla (Southern California). They are mostly found from the western end of the Alaska Peninsula to Monterey Bay, although there appear to be some spots in the eastern Bering Sea that have quite a few. Intertidal to 325 m (1,066 ft), typically in 50 m, 164 ft) and less. Eggs: 0.8–1 mm. Larvae: hatching length = 2.1–2.8 mm, flexion length = 7.5–10.3 mm, transformation length = 1.4–greater than 2.3 cm (0.6–0.9 in). Von Bertalanffy parameters (FL, mm): (females) L_∞ = 376.1, k = 0.79, t_0 = -0.16; (males) L_∞ = 310.5, k = 0.6, t_0 = -0.68 (Pearson and McNally 2005). Additional von Bert parameters are in Demory et al. (1976). Length-weight parameters (FL, mm, gr): (females) W = $0.00674L^{3.1367}$; (males) W = $0.0175L^{2.8294}$ (Pearson and McNally 2005). Additional length-weight relationships are in Demory et al. (1976) and Wildermuth (1983).

SALIENT CHARACTERS: This one is easy. The rays comprising the front part of the dorsal fin are thin, elongate, and are not completely connected by a membrane to one another. See, I told you it was easy. They also have large mouths, an accessory lateral line that branches part way along the dorsal fin, and the eyed side of dead ones are various shades of brown, gray, or kind of green, and covered in dark sprinkles. Live ones are often a mass of light, tan, and dark flecks, dots, and irregular spots.

LIFE HISTORY: Young-of-the-year settle at lengths at least as small as 1.5 cm (0.6 in) TL, to estuaries (where they can tolerate nearly freshwater) and shallow coastal waters. Juveniles are found in very shallow, often intertidal waters, and then tend to migrate into somewhat deeper coastal waters as they mature. However I have, on occasion, found adults in shallow embayments. Both juveniles and adults favor soft seafloors, although juveniles often live in eelgrass beds.

Sand soles live to at least 10 years old. Females may live longer than males and appear to grow larger. Almost all 2-year-old males (about 25 cm, 20 in, FL) and females (about 31 cm, 12 in) are mature. They spawn at least from January–August, with a spring peak. Females produce between 900,000–1,400,000 eggs per season. Sand sole eggs are pelagic and the eggs hatch in about 5 days at 7–9°C (45–49°F). Juveniles feed primarily on crustaceans (e.g., mysid shrimps, gammarid amphipods, cumaceans, and shrimps). Older fish mostly eat fishes, along with the previously mentioned crustaceans, squids, brittle stars, and clams. Predators include arrowtooth flounder, black and yellowtail rockfishes, Chinook and coho salmon, jack mackerel, steelhead, yellowfin soles, and harbor seals.

FISHERY: Sand soles have been a reasonably important commercial species since the 19th century. They were particularly favored in the early trawl fisheries of Puget Sound and San Francisco. Today, they are only occasionally landed by commercial fishermen, but on a per-pound basis, they tend to be worth about twice what many other flatfishes bring in. They are commonly taken by anglers from boats, piers, and sandy shores.

RELATIONSHIPS: Based on genetic analyses, sand soles are perhaps most closely related to English and butter soles and to the two rock sole species.

Reinhardtius hippoglossoides
(Walbaum, 1792)
Greenland Halibut

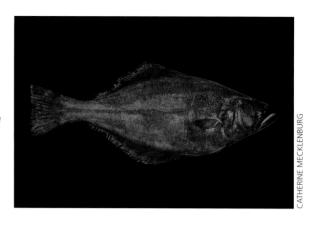

CATHERINE MECKLENBURG

This is just one of the more interesting flatfish we have. Hey, it is dark on both sides and seems to spend at least some of its time up in the water column.

ETYMOLOGY AND COLLOQUIAL NAMES: *Reinhardtius* refers to Johannes Christofer Hagemann Reinhardt (1776–1845), Danish zoologist and professor at the University of Copenhagen. *Hippoglossides* means "halibut" and "resemblance" in Greek. "Greenland turbot" is often used by elements in the federal government. The Russians call them "Greenland turbot," "black halibut," and "Pacific black halibut." I note some Greenland halibut have been marketed as "Pacific seabass." The Japanese call them "karasu-garei."

THE BASICS: Maximum Length: 130 cm (51 in) TL. Maximum Weight: At least 44.5 kg (97.9 lb). The Ranges: North Atlantic, Arctic, and North Pacific; Japan and Okhotsk seas to Bering, Chukchi, and Beaufort seas, and Aleutian Islands and Gulf of Alaska to just south of U.S.-Mexico border. On this side of the planet, they are common from Sakhalin Island, Sea of Okhotsk, and northern Kuril Islands to the Bering Sea and Aleutian Islands. 14–2,000 m (46–6,562 ft). Juveniles are fairly common in waters as shallow as maybe 50 m (164 ft) and adults are often found from perhaps 300–1,000 m (984–3,280 ft). Egg diameter = 4–4.5 mm. Larvae: hatching length = 0.6–1.6 cm (0.2–0.6 in), flexion length = 2.5–2.7 cm (1 in), transformation length = 4.5–6.5 cm (1.8–2.6 in). Von Bertalanffy parameters (TL, cm): (sexes combined) L_∞ = 86.2, k = 0.125, t_0 = -0.233 (Gregg et al. 2006). Length-weight parameters (TL, cm, gr): (females) W = $0.00155L^{3.45}$; (males) W = $0.00288L^{3.28}$ (Orlov and Binohlan 2009).

SALIENT CHARACTERS: Greenland halibut have two features that are just standouts. First, they are colored black, brown, or gray on both eyed and blind sides (the blind side may also be blue). The blind side may be a bit paler than the eyed one. Second, the upper (left) eye is kind of on the midline of the body, so it is visible from the blind side. They are diamond-shaped, have a slightly forked caudal fin, large mouth, and teeth to match.

LIFE HISTORY: After they are spawned, the eggs drift in pretty deep water, at depths of about 600–1,000 m (1,968–3,280 ft). As they develop, the larvae move into progressively shallower waters. In the eastern Bering Sea, young-of-the-year Greenlands settle out of the water column starting at about 6 cm (2 in) FL. However, western Bering Sea fish as small as 2.5 cm (1 in) have been taken on the bottom in shallow waters. The actual depth of settlement is not well understood, although it has been described as the "middle shelf" in the eastern Bering Sea by Sohn et al. (2010), where they settle to the seafloor during late summer. Juveniles tend to be found on the continental shelf (until maybe 4–5 years old) and adults on the continental slope and both live mostly on soft seafloors. Greenlands can tolerate water temperatures between about -2–10°C (20–50°F), but perhaps mostly at a bit below 0–5°C (32–40°F). Young fish are more tolerant of colder waters than are adults. Warming temperatures in the southeastern Bering Sea have led to a tendency for this species to move further northward than before. Spawning takes place over the continental slope (deeper than 200 m, 656 ft, and down to at least 1,100 m, 3,608 ft). Unusual for the flatfishes, Greenlands frequently feed well off the seafloor and have some (for flatfish) unique morphological characters to go with that. As Alton et al. (1998) note: "Unlike that of most flatfish, the migrating eye does not move completely to one side but stops at the top of the head which presumably results in a greater field of vision...plus the equally well-developed musculature of both sides of the body, helps to explain this species' tendency to feed off the sea bottom." Fish of all sizes make excursions into the midwaters, often hundreds of meters above the bottom, and usually at night. Little is known about this species' horizontal migrations. In the eastern Bering Sea, young fish tend to recruit to the seafloor in the northern shelf area and slowly migrate southward as they mature. In the spring, mature fish may move into slightly shallower waters (but still on the continental slope) to spawn. Limited tagging studies in the Bering Sea imply that there is some movement, as tagged fish have motivated as much as 687 km (371 nm) before recapture. On average, adult females may live part of the year in waters deeper than males.

Greenland halibut may live to at least 36 years old and females grow larger than males. However, at this time, no one has yet come up with a good way to age them, so who knows how long they might live. Size and age at maturation is poorly known. Generally, males mature at a slightly younger age than females and fish mature between 4–13 years old (perhaps mostly at 5–10 years) and 48–80 cm (19–32 in) TL. In the Bering Sea, spawning season is poorly known, but has been stated to occur from September or October to March or perhaps May, maybe peaking in January and February. Off Sakhalin, fish spawn as early as August. Females take longer than one year to bring up eggs to maturation. Females may not be batch spawners and, worldwide, they produce between 2,000–262,000 pelagic eggs per year. In the Atlantic, eggs hatch 53 days after fertilization when held at 4°C (39°F). Fishes, many, many species of them, dominate the diets of Greenland halibut. Squids are also locally important, and some polychaetes and octopuses are also consumed. Predators include flathead and yellowfin soles, great sculpins, other Greenland halibut, sablefish, walleye pollock, bald eagles, northern fur, ribbon and ringed seals, Steller sea lions, and narwhals.

FISHERY: Most of the commercial catch of Greenland halibut on our side of the world is made in the Bering Sea. They were taken there in some numbers by Russian and Japanese fishermen starting in the 1950s, although because they were confused with arrowtooth flounder the actual catch levels are not known. Greenlands formed a major fishery in the eastern Bering Sea into the late 1970s, catches have kind of gone into the toilet since then. Originally captured mostly by trawls, longlines now account for much of the catch and they are also taken as a bycatch in other fisheries. The species is often sold headed, gutted, and frozen and finds particular favor in Japan. Greenlands are only rarely taken by recreational anglers.

RELATIONSHIPS: One genetic study implied Greenlands were most closely related to Pacific halibut.

REMARKS: It is said (although who "It" is, I dare not say) that Greenlands will swim with their ventral (as opposed to their blind) side down, like "normal" fish.

OTHER SPECIES

Atheresthes evermanni
Jordan & Starks, 1904
Kamchatka Flounder

Evermanni refers to Barton Warren Evermann (1853–1932). Kamchatkas reach 110 cm (43 in) TL and 8.5 kg (18.7 lb). They range from the seas of Okhotsk and Japan to the Gulf of Anadyr (western Bering Sea) to the eastern Bering Sea and the southwestern Gulf of Alaska. They are abundant from the Sea of Okhotsk and northern Kuril Islands throughout much of the Bering Sea (in the eastern Bering Sea perhaps most abundant north of 54°N) and along the Aleutian Islands to about Kodiak Island. Found from 25–1,200 m (83–3,960 ft),

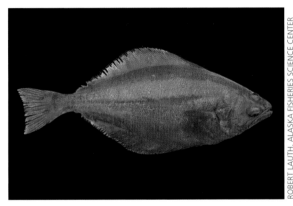

they are perhaps most abundant from 100–600 m (328–1,968 ft), although there seem to be places where there are considerable numbers of fish in waters deeper than that. Young fish tend to be found in shallower waters than adults; larger ones tend to live on the continental slope. While these fish have been found in temperatures ranging from -1.3–10°C (30–50°F), optimal temperatures seem to be around 2–4°C (36–39°F). At least in some areas, some adults move into slightly shallower waters (onto the continental shelf) in the spring. Kamchatka flounder reach a maximum age of at least 33 years old. Females are larger at age than males, but males reach maximum size faster. Females grow larger than males (the guys reach perhaps 67 cm, 27 in, FL). Off the northern Kuril Islands, males mature at between 35–65 cm (14–26 in) TL (50% at 45 cm, 18 in). For females, the lengths are 50–70 cm (20–28 in), and about 60 cm (24 in), respectively. Fish in the Bering Sea may mature at slightly smaller sizes, 50% maturity lengths for males is reportedly 41 cm (16 in) and for females 46 cm (18 in). Spawning occurs from at least December–March (and perhaps from September–April) and females reportedly produce between 220,000–1,386,000 eggs per season. Kamchatkas feed primarily on fishes, crangonid and pandalid shrimps, crabs, squids, and octopuses. Smaller amounts of gelatinous zooplankton, polychaetes, mysid shrimps, euphausiids, and sponges are also eaten. While these flounder do feed in the winter, it is at a lower level than later in season. Predators include Atka mackerel, Pacific cod, Pacific halibut, Pacific lampreys, and Pacific sleeper sharks. The eyes of this species are often infected with the parasitic copepod *Phrixocephalus cincinnatus* (see arrowtooth flounder). Kamchatkas are important commercial fish in the western Pacific (like off the northern Kurils and southeastern Kamchatka) and apparently make up a small amount of the "arrowtooth flounder" fishery in the Northern Pacific. This species is most closely related to the arrowtooth flounder. Von Bertalanffy parameters (FL, cm): (females) L_∞ = 93.9, k = 0.085, t_0 = -1.519; (males) L_∞ = 62.3, k = 0.157, t_0 = -1.411 (Zimmerman and Goddard 1996). Length-weight parameters (TL, cm, gr): (females) W = $0.00343L^{3.29}$; (males) W = $0.0162^{2.88}$ (Orlov and Binohlan 2009). The eggs are bathypelagic and 2–3.5 mm in diameter.

Clidoderma asperrimum
(Temminck & Schlegel, 1846)
Roughscale Sole

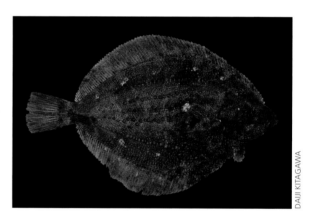

Roughscales grow to 62 cm (24 in) TL and 4.4 kg (9.7 lb). They are found from the Yellow, Japan and Okhotsk seas to the Bering Sea to off Half Moon Bay (Central California), in 15–1,900 m (50–6,233 ft). They are perhaps most abundant from the north-eastern Sea of Japan to off southeastern Kamchatka, typically in 400–900 m (1,312–2,952 ft). Roughscales are found in temperatures between about 0–12.8°C (32–55°F), perhaps mostly at 1–3.5°C (34–38°F). These soles live to at least 20 years old, spawn from February–May in the western Pacific (mostly in 500–1,000 m, 1,640–3,280 ft), and feed primarily on such seafloor organisms as brittle stars and amphipods. In the northern Kuril Islands and off southeastern Kamchatka, they are caught as by-catch in trawl fisheries, and are very popular in Japanese fish markets. Bean (1877b) found that they were widely used as food in Alaska, on the Aleutian Islands, and into the Bering Sea. A fossil of this species was found in Pliocene deposits (at least 1.8 million years old) in Japan. Genetic studies imply roughscales may be most closely related to slender and petrale soles. Length-weight parameters (TL, cm, kg): (sexes combined) W = $0.00001054L^{3.153}$ (Tokranov and Orlov 2003).

Embassichthys bathybius
(Gilbert, 1890)
Deepsea Sole

Deepsea soles grow to 52 cm (21 in) TL and at least 1.0 kg (2.2 lb). They range from Hokkaido to the Bering Sea and to northern Baja California (32°38'N, 119°24'W). This is a deep-water species, inhabiting depths from 91–1,433 m (300–4,700 ft), but mostly between 500–1,400 m (1,640–4,592 ft). The few that have been taken in trawl studies have inhabited waters of 3.1–5.5°C (38–42°F). Deepseas tend to live in the oxygen minimum zone and, like Dover soles, they have watery muscles. Deepseas live on sediment, cobble/sediment, and I have seen them lying amid boulders or even right on rocks. Deepseas spawn during the winter through at least May. They feed mostly on polychaetes, small crustaceans (e.g., mysid shrimps and caprellid and gammarid amphipods), sea anemones, brittle stars, and octopuses. Although there is no directed fishery for them, they are occasionally taken in the Dover sole trawl fishery, where they are ingloriously processed with the Dovers. Once in a while some angler, clearly just donkeying around, catches one. Several genetic analyses reveal that deepseas are closely related to rex and Dover soles. I note that this species was called *Microstomus bathybius* in at least one paper. A wave of the future or something that went very, very wrong? Eggs: 2.7–3.1 mm. Larvae: hatching length = about 9 mm, flexion length = 1.5–1.6 cm (0.6 in), transformation length = greater than 6 cm (2 in).

MBARI_2006

Hippoglossoides robustus
Gill & Townsend, 1897

Bering Flounder

CATHERINE W. MECKLENBURG

Bering flounder grow to 52 cm (21 in) TL. They live in the northern Sea of Japan, Okhotsk Sea, Pacific off Kamchatka, and Commander Islands to Bering Sea, East Siberian and Chukchi seas (as far west as 172°32'E and as far north as at least 72°N), and eastward to about Bathurst Inlet, south of Dease Strait (68°20'N, 107°41'W), Nunavut, Canada, and south to the Alaska Peninsula. Berings appear to be common from the Sea of Okhotsk and northern Kurils to the Chukchi Sea and the eastern Bering Sea. They live from the intertidal zone to about 532 m (1,745 ft). Most surveys imply that this species lives primarily on the continental shelf and mostly in maybe 25–150 m (82–492 ft). This is a really cold-water loving species, often found at temperatures below 0°C (32°F) (although they will occasionally deign to swelter in as much as 7.9°C, 46°F) and down to at least -2.1°C (28°F). It can tolerate at least mildly brackish waters (down to at least 29.4 ppt). Perhaps as a response to ocean warming, fish in the southeastern Bering Sea are tending to shift northward. Spawning occurs in shallow bays. Bering flounder live to at least 29 years old and females grow larger than males. In the western Bering Sea, mature females are as small as 25 cm (10 in) TL. Spawning appears to take place from April–June and eggs and larvae are pelagic. They feed on fishes, along with such benthic and epibenthic crustaceans as amphipods, shrimps, and hermit crabs. Predators include Arctic cod, Pacific halibut, bearded seals, and beluga whales. Genetic studies demonstrate that Berings are most closely related to flathead soles. Eggs: 2.0–2.7 mm. Von Bertalanffy parameters (SL, mm): (females) L_∞ = 206, k = 0.215, t_0 = 0.009; (males) L_∞ = 180, k = 0.23, t_0 = -0.185 (Smith et al. 1997). Length-weight parameters (SL, mm, gr): (sexes combined) W = 0.00000489L$^{3.25}$ (Smith et al. 1997).

Limanda proboscidea
Gilbert, 1896

Longhead Dab

Longheads grow to 41 cm (16 in) TL and are found from Hokkaido and the Okhotsk Sea to the Beaufort Sea and eastward to Bathurst Inlet (68°20'N, 107°41'W), Nunavut, Canada, and to the eastern Bering Sea, north of Unimak Island. They may possibly range as far eastward as Queen Maud Gulf, Canadian Arctic. They live at depths of 5 m or less (16 ft) to 125 m (410 ft), perhaps commonly from 30–100 m (98–328 ft). Longheads are found from -2 to at least 11.8°C (28–53°F) and, perhaps in response to warming temperatures, are

CATHERINE W. MECKLENBURG

tending to move northward in the southeastern Bering Sea. They are common from the Sea of Japan to the northern Bering Sea. Longheads spawn May–August, females produce 78,700–841,000 eggs, and eggs and larvae are pelagic. They eat polychaetes, mysid shrimps, gammarid amphipods, copepods, cumaceans, and clams. Predators include cod, sculpins, skates, and various flatfishes. A genetic study of a range of pleuronectids found that longheads were likely closely related to arctic flounder and starry flounder. Eggs: 0.7–0.9 mm.

Pleuronichthys decurrens
Jordan & Gilbert, 1881
Curlfin Sole

Curlfins reach 44 cm (17 in) TL and perhaps 42 cm (17 in). A 36.3 cm (14 in) fish weighed 774 grams (27 oz). They are found from the Aleutian Islands (off the northwest coast of Unimak Island) and Gulf of Alaska to just south of Punta San Juanico (25°59'N, 112°35'W) (southern Baja California). They are at least fairly common from Puget Sound to at least Bahia San Quintin (northern Baja California), and probably further south, from the surf zone to depths of 349 m (1,146 ft), and typically between about 18–70 m (60–230 ft). Curlfins live both in estuaries and other protected waters and on the open coast, in soft sediments and along rock-sand interfaces. Young-of-the-year settle when at least as small as 3.6 cm (1 in) TL. Curlfins live to about 10 years old. They appear to spawn throughout the year, with perhaps a peak in the spring. In general, polychaetes are the most important part of their diet. Other prey include nudibranchs, brittle stars, gammarid and caprellid amphipods, crabs, snails, squids, and sea anemones. Predators include Pacific hakes, yellowtail rockfish, Brandt's cormorants, and harbor seals. Like other *Pleuronichthys*, this species has historically been of only minor commercial importance. They are occasionally taken by anglers. Based on physical characters, this species appears to be most closely related to the spotted turbot. An ambicolored one has been taken. Eggs: 1.8–2.1 mm. Larvae: hatching length = about 4.9–5.5 mm, flexion length = 7.8–11 mm, transformation length = 1 to more than 2.1 cm (0.4–0.8 in).

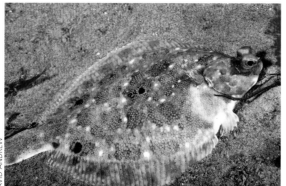

Pleuronichthys ritteri
Starks & Morris, 1907
Spotted Turbot

Spotteds definitely reach a mighty 29 cm (11 in) TL, and are reported to 33 cm (13 in). A 28.5 cm (11 in) TL fish weighed 328 gr (12 oz). They range from Northern California (37°55'N) to southern Baja California (24°12'N, 111°21'W) and in the upper Gulf of California, commonly from Southern California to about Cabo San Lazaro (24°45'N) (southern Baja California). Although they have been taken in 1–197 m (3–646 ft), in Southern California they appear to be relatively uncommon in depths deeper than perhaps 30 m (98 ft). Young-of-the-year settle out in shallow waters at as small as 1.8 cm (0.7 in) SL. In some areas, juveniles remain in the shallows for a considerable period. This is a soft substrata species, found both in protected waters and estuaries (e.g., Alamitos Bay, Southern California, and Estero de Punta Banda and Bahia San Quintin, northern Baja California) and on the open coast. They seem to mostly avoid structure, but the occasional one inhabits eelgrass beds or sits next to a rock. During warm-water periods, they tend to become more abundant in Southern California waters. My data imply that this species matures at 15–18 cm (6–7 in) TL. Like some other *Pleuronichthys*, it looks like spotted turbot spawn throughout the year, albeit perhaps at a lower level during the winter. They really like polychaetes, but also dine on sea anemones, squids, snails, and a wide assortment of small crustaceans. Spotteds were never a particularly important commercial species and they are only rarely taken in the sport catch. Based on physical characters, this species is most closely related to curlfin soles. Fossil remains are known from 100,000-year-old strata in California. Folks occasionally find an ambicolored or albino one. Eggs: 0.9–1.3 mm. Larvae: flexion length = 4.5–5.6 mm, transformation length = 6.4–10 mm. Length-weight parameters (TL, cm, gr): $W = 0.018L^{2.899}$ (Love unpubl.).

WILLIAM E. RITTER

Dr. Ritter was a tireless researcher, administrator, and publicizer of science and, with Edward W. Scripps and his sister, Ellen Browning Scripps supplying the largesse, created that mighty juggernaut of marine science, Scripps Institute of Oceanography. Ritter and Scripps spent a great deal of time together and came up with a really wide range of schemes to better humanity. For instance, in an attempt to help educate the public regarding science, Scripps and Ritter started a science news service. Considering that about half of all Americans still don't believe in evolution, one wonders if that effort was less than a complete success.

My favorite Ritterism was the following, penned by him to the president of the University of California in the early 20th century (and noted in *More Than Gold in California*, see below): "Detailed comprehensive, continuous and long-continued observation and experiment are necessary. These are the two golden keys that will lead us farthest into the mighty arcana of the life of the sea." Yes, "mighty arcana," indeed. The next time my wife, Jane, asks me what I have done at the lab today, I will casually let drop that I was using the two golden keys to burrow into the mighty arcana of the life of the sea.

William Ritter's wife, Dr. Mary Bennett Ritter (1860–1949), is at least as interesting a character as her husband. Dr. Ritter was one of the early female physicians in California, practicing in Berkeley in the late 19th century. A fierce supporter of women's health issues and of equal access to education, her autobiography, *More than Gold in California* (Berkeley, California, 1933) provides a peek into the lives of California women during a time of great change and promise.

FAMILY ACHIRIDAE— American Soles

The Achiridae are marine and freshwater fishes found from North America to South America, mostly in warmer waters. There are about seven genera and perhaps 33 species; one species is found along the Pacific side of Baja California. American soles are oviparous and have planktonic eggs and larvae. Keys and illustrations of the various tropical eastern Pacific species are found in Fischer et al. (1995).

Achirus mazatlanus
(Steindachner, 1869)
Pacific Lined Sole

GERALD ALLEN

ETYMOLOGY AND COLLOQUIAL NAMES: *Achirus* means "without hands" in Greek (referring to the absent or rudimentary pelvic fins) and *mazatlanus* comes from its first capture near the city located on the west coast of Mexico. Other names include "comalito," "lenguado," "tepalcate," and "sol mexicano."

THE BASICS: Maximum Length: 20 cm (8 in) TL. The Ranges: Islas Coronados (northern Baja California) to Puerto Pizarro (Peru), including Gulf of California. In the Pacific, abundant at least as far north as Bahia Magdalena (southern Baja California). 1–55 m (3–180 ft). Eggs: 0.7–0.8 mm. Larvae: hatching length = 1.3–1.7 mm, flexion length = 2.5 mm. Metamorphosis complete at about 2.8–4.7 mm. Von Bertalanffy parameters (TL, cm): (sexes combined) L_∞ = 20.9, k = 0.091 (Warburton 1979). Length-weight parameters (TL, cm, gr): W = $0.013L^{3.078}$ (Warburton 1979).

SALIENT CHARACTERS: Lined soles are gray or brown and have a series of fine lines running dorsal-ventrically across the body. The eyed side has a number of hairlike projections.

LIFE HISTORY: Pacific lined soles live in shallow, coastal, soft-bottom areas. They spend much of their lives in coastal lagoons and frequently enter freshwater. Juveniles, in particular, are found in lagoons and amid mangroves. They likely spawn in spring–summer and eat crustaceans, polychaetes, and detritus.

FISHERY: No one catches them intentionally, 'cause they are just really small; an occasional one is eaten by a local.

FAMILY CYNOGLOSSIDAE—Tonguefishes

Tonguefishes are sinistral marine (occasionally freshwater-entering) flatfishes that are mostly found in tropical and subtropical waters (California tonguefish being a notable exception) throughout the world. There are three genera and about 127 species, of which eight are found within our range, but only two (*Symphurus atricaudus* and *S. oligomerus*) reach into Southern California. Tonguefishes are oviparous and have planktonic eggs and larvae. Fischer et al. (1995) illustrates and has keys to the tonnage of tonguefishes in the tropical eastern Pacific.

So what's the deal? Amazingly few fishes are named after human (or other) body parts. Given our predilection for naming fishes after other animals, such as cats, dogs, and lizards, one looks in vain for heartfish, kidneyfish, or urinary bladder fish.

Symphurus atricaudus
(Jordan & Gilbert, 1880)
California Tonguefish

KEVIN LEE

ETYMOLOGY: *Symphurus* means "together," "to grow," and "tail" in Greek and *atricaudus* is "black" and "tail" in Latin.

THE BASICS: Maximum Length: 21 cm (8 in) TL. The Ranges: Barkley Sound (Vancouver Island) to Gulf of California; also reported off northern Peru. They are at least occasional as far north as Grays Harbor (Washington) and certainly common from Northern California southward. Surf to 455 m (1,492 ft), perhaps typically from about 5–140 m (16–459 ft). Eggs: 0.7–0.8 mm. Larvae: hatching length = about 1.9 mm, flexion length = 8.6–10.8 mm, transformation length = 1.9–2.4 cm (0.7–0.9 in). Length-weight parameters (TL, cm, gr): W = 0.0037L$^{3.306}$ (Love unpubl.).

SALIENT CHARACTERS: Tonguefish are easily recognized by their slim bodies, little bitty eyes and mouth, and the fact that they are so slimy you won't be able to pick them off the deck. Any little slimy flatfish that you eventually stop trying to pick up is likely to be a tonguefish. Really, my son, Elan, described it as trying to pick up a fish with Velcro for a belly. Dead ones are brown or grayish, with a series of dark bars and a blackish tail. Underwater, California tonguefish are brownish-gray with very faint bars. At night, the barring often becomes darker and the tail turns blacker.

LIFE HISTORY: Tonguefish are benthic fish that live in estuaries, bays, and along the open coast, on soft seafloors and around eelgrass. Young-of-the-year (occasionally as small as 1 cm, 0.4 in, SL) recruit from the plankton into shallow waters (to as deep as 9 m, 30 ft). Young fish are most likely to inhabit very shallow waters. Tonguefish can tolerate salinities down to 5.4 ppt, but are far more common in 15 ppt and greater.

Tonguefish mature at about 11 cm (4 in) SL. They spawn at least from April–October (and perhaps in lower numbers throughout the year) and females may produce at least 3 batches of eggs per season. They are nocturnal feeders and focus on soft-bottom small crustaceans. Gammarid amphipods are very important, and they also target crabs, polychaetes, harpacticoid and caprellid amphipods, gnathiid isopods, cumaceans, isopods, snails and brittle stars. Very occasionally they eat small fishes. Predators include California halibut, California lizardfish, copper rockfish, leopard sharks, Brandt's, double-crested, and pelagic cormorants, California sea lions, and harbor seals.

FISHERY: There is no recreational or commercial fishery for this little species, although Villadolid (1927) wrote that it was a "good food fish," but too small to be commercially important.

ORIGINS: A fossil tonguefish, *Symphurus* sp., has been found in Miocene deposits (perhaps as much as 13 million years old) from Southern California. Remains of California tonguefish reportedly occur in 100,000-year-old Southern California strata.

MISCELLANY: 1) Ambicolored ones are fairly common and some individuals may enjoy diffuse pigmentation (a dark gray blind side). 2) A dextral (right-eyed) fish was captured near Long Beach (Southern California).

FAMILY BALISTIDAE—Triggerfishes

The balistids are mostly tropical and subtropical fishes, found in marine systems throughout the world. Most triggerfishes are relatively nearshore reef forms. There are 11 genera and about 40 species. Five species have been found within our range, three of which live as far north as Southern California. Triggerfishes are oviparous, with eggs laid in nests and guarded by a parent, and planktonic larvae. The name "trigger" comes from this fish's ability to lock and unlock the anterior dorsal spines. Balistids lived at least as far back as the Early Oligocene (35 million years ago) of southern Europe. Check out Fischer et al. (1995) for keys and illustrations of the tropical eastern Pacific species.

As noted by the aptly-named Salmon et al. (1968), the triggers "produce sounds by movements of the pectoral fins against the side of the body. The air bladder evaginates to form 2 bilateral lobes covered by thin scales at the area of contact between the fins and body wall."

Balistes polylepis
Steindachner, 1876

Finescale Triggerfish

ETYMOLOGY: *Balistes* comes from the Latin word "ballista," a device that shoots arrows (referring to the trigger-like spine) and *polylepis* means "many scales" in Greek. In Mexico, they are variously called "cochi," "cochito," and "pez puerco."

THE BASICS: Maximum Length: 80 cm (32 in) TL. Maximum Weight: At least 4.5 kg (10 lb) and perhaps to 7.3 kg (16 lb). The Ranges: Metlakatla (southeastern Alaska) to San Antonio (about 33°32'S) (central Chile), including Gulf of California and Hawai'i. Finescales became pretty common off Southern California during the 1982–1983 El Niño, but their numbers have dropped since then. We might expect another pulse to arrive when conditions are favorable. 3–512 m (10–1,680 ft), perhaps typically in 30 m (98 ft) or less. Larvae: hatching length = less than 1.6 mm, flexion length = 3.8–4.5 mm, transformation length = about 1.1 cm (0.4 in). Von Bertalanffy parameters (TL, cm): (sexes combined) L_∞ = 55.8, k = 0.17, t_0 = -1.7 (Barroso-Soto 2007). Length-weight parameters (TL, cm, gr): (sexes combined) W = $0.0547L^{2.66}$ (Barroso-Soto 2007).

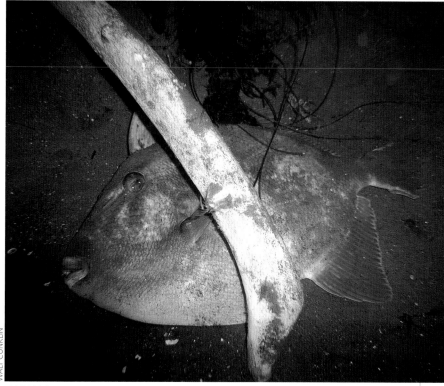

WALT CONKLIN

Shhhhhhh...It's sleeping.

SALIENT CHARACTERS: Finescales are deep-bodied, compressed, and have a singular-looking dorsal fin; it has three spines, a gap, and then the soft rays. The mouth is small and filled with incisor-like teeth, and the gill slit is very small. Finescales are brown and there may be blue spots on the head, blue rims on the median fins, and blue lips.

LIFE HISTORY: Finescales are very distinctive reef and semi-reef fish. Young ones are often found under drifting material. Once they begin to associate with reefs, the small ones have relatively restricted movements. Larger fish spend more of their time on the sand near reefs and have larger home ranges; in a study in the Gulf of California, an individual was seen on a reef for 31 months. This same study demonstrated that an individual may leave an area for weeks at a time before returning.

In the northern Gulf of California, they move into the intertidal at high tide. While they are usually solitary, finescales reportedly form aggregations on the bottom during the reproductive season. Finescales rest at night, usually inside reefs, often lying on their sides.

A 53 cm (21 in) TL fish was 7 years old, but it is likely they live considerably longer than this. Along the Baja California coast and in the Gulf of California, spawning appears to occur from about May–October. Females make their nests on sand near or in reefs and females guard the fertilized eggs. Finescales mostly feed on such benthic invertebrates as snails, bivalves, various crustaceans, echinoderms, sponges, sea urchins, and polychaetes, as well as the occasional fish. These fish are active during the day and on brightly moonlit nights, usually feeding on the sand near their rocky abodes. Burrowing prey are exposed when the fish, hovering vertically over the sediment, sends a jet of water spewing forth. They also follow other fishes, such as diamond stingrays, that dig around in the seafloor. Predators include sailfish, striped marlins, and California sea lions.

FISHERY: Finescales form an important fishery in the Gulf of California and down along the Mexican coast. They are eaten fresh and frozen, both whole and filleted. They are also a common bycatch in the shrimp trawl fisheries of the region. In Southern California, they are occasionally caught from shore, piers, and boats.

ORIGINS: An extinct *Balistes* lived during the Late Miocene (at least 5.3 million years ago) in Southern California.

FAMILY TETRAODONTIDAE—Puffers

And now we come to the puffers. Puffers are mostly marine (although some species do live in estuarine and fresh waters) and mostly tropical and subtropical fishes that are found throughout the world. There are 19 genera and about 130 species, of which six species live within our range, and three have been taken at least as far north as Southern California. By drawing either water or air (when at the surface) into a sac coming off the stomach, puffers do, indeed, inflate. Puffers are oviparous and have pelagic larvae. The family Tetraodontidae evolved at least as far back as the Middle Eocene of southern Europe, about 50 million years ago. The numerous puffer species living in the eastern Pacific are figured and semi-described in Fischer et al. (1995).

Aside from their interesting behaviors, pufferfishes are best known for killing people undiscerning enough to eat them in unsophisticated ways. In Japan, pufferfishes are often called "fugu" and "fugu poisoning" or "pufferfish poisoning" are common terms for what happens to you if you eat a toxin-laced piece of puffer. Fugu poisoning usually starts with a slight numbness of the lips and tongue that begins between 20 minutes and 3 hours after ingestion. This can be followed by headache, nausea, diarrhea, and/or vomiting and then increasing paralysis. Death can occur within 20 minutes or as long as 8 hours or more. Most pufferfish poisoning occurs in Japan, where folks just can't seem to get enough of that finger-licking fugu. And most, but not all, of these poisonings come from home consumption. Restaurant chefs who wish to prepare fugu must be licensed by the Japanese government and that seems to minimize the number of restaurant-related incidents, although they do still occur. Japan-wide, it seems kind of difficult for everyone to agree on the number of cases of fugu poisoning. During the early part of the 20th century more than 100 deaths a year were reported, but Thomas and Scott (*All Stings Considered*, University of Hawai'i Press, 1997) state that that number has recently dropped to perhaps 5 deaths a year. They also note that there have been 3 deaths related to fugu eating in California, all from imported Japanese pufferfishes. About 700 tons are harvested from the Gulf of California and, as of 2002, there had been 18 fatalities in Baja California Sur in 30 years – so, shoot, that's pretty good odds, right?

It is a constant source of amazement that people still eat the bad parts of puffers. And it's not like folks don't know that eating pufferfish can be like gargling razor blades. There is evidence that way back in about 2,500 B.C., the Egyptians understood these fishes were poisonous. One Japanese paper notes that the earliest Asian record of pufferfish poisoning comes from a Han Dynasty (202 B.C.E.–220 A.D.) document detailing the death of a diner after consuming pufferfish liver. And Captain James Cook wrote that he had fallen ill after merely tasting the liver of one animal. And then there are the rather pointed observations from the pen of Engelbert Kaempfer (1651–1716). Kaempfer was a German botanist and physician who, having visited Japan in 1690, played a key role in introducing the soybean to Europe. His book, *Amoenitatum Exoticarum*, contained the first written description by a Westerner of the soybean plant, along with detailed descriptions of how to make both soy sauce and miso. Here is what Kaempfer wrote regarding pufferfish in Japan: "He is rank'd among the poisonous Fish, and if eat whole, is said unavoidably to occasion death. ...the Head, Guts, bones, and all the garbage must be thrown away, and the flesh carefully wash'd and clean'd before it is fit to eat. And yet many People die of it, for want, they say, of thoroughly washing and cleaning it." That seems pretty clear to me. And, in fact, it was more than pretty clear to the Japanese of the time, for Kaempfer goes on to say that: "[Japanese] People that by some long and tedious sickness are grown weary of their lives, or are otherwise under miserable circumstances, frequently choose this poisonous fish, instead of a knife or halter to make away with themselves. A Neighbor of my Servant at Nagasaki being so strongly infected with Pox, that his nose was ready to drop off, resolv'd to make this Meal, in order to get rid at once both of his life and distemper."

Gee, remind me never to get the Pox.

TETRODOTOXIN, YOU ARE A VERY NAUGHTY MOLECULE

The reason pufferfishes and their relatives have such a bad rap is because of a compound called *tetrodotoxin*. This is a remarkably lethal neurotoxin, really one of the big ones. Some people have had a great deal of fun comparing it to other toxins, noting that it is ten times as deadly as the venom of the many-banded krait of Southeast Asia, 10–100 times as lethal as black widow spider venom, and more than 10,000 times deadlier than cyanide. They will comment that a single milligram, an amount that can be placed on the head of a pin, is enough to kill an adult human. These folks should have their meds closely monitored.

In puffers, tetrodotoxin is usually found in various internal organs, skin, and, more rarely, in the muscle. There is wide variability in the amount of toxin in the same organ between individual fishes and the amount of toxin may change with season. Early on, it was assumed that the fishes produced the toxin themselves. However, it turns out that this compound is found in a number of unrelated marine organisms, including some other fish groups, sea stars, crabs, marine snails, flatworms, sea squirts, ribbonworms, and arrow worms. Away from the sea, a few frogs carry it, as do some newts and salamanders. While many of these animals seem to utilize the toxin for defensive purposes, the Australian blue-ringed octopus is able to inject it into prey, thus using tetrodotoxin for offense. The latest theory is that the toxin is actually produced by bacteria, such as *Vibrio alginolyticus*, living in the intestines of a host and the host may utilize the bad stuff for their own purposes.

Sphoeroides annulatus
(Jenyns, 1842)
Bullseye Puffer

ETYMOLOGY AND COLLOQUIAL NAMES: *Sphoeroides* is Greek for "sphere" and "resemblance" [kind of clever, that one] and *annulatus* is Latin for "ringed." "Botete," "pez globo," and "tamborillo" are some of the names used in Mexico.
THE BASICS: Maximum Length: 48 cm (19 in) TL. The Ranges: Redondo Beach (Southern California) to Pisco (Peru), including the Gulf of California. 1–105 m (3–344 ft). In southwestern Mexico, they are most abundant in 20–40 m (66–131 ft). Larvae: hatching length = less than 2.2 mm, flexion length = about 4.3–5.3 mm, transformation length = about 5.3 mm.
SALIENT CHARACTERS: Along with that typical puffer shape (kind of elongated body, small dorsal and anal fins pushed way back on the body, and beaky mouth), bullseyes have a dark back, with dark or brown blotches and spots on back and sides interrupted by lighter channels (forming concentric circles).
LIFE HISTORY: Very young fish may live in the open water among drifting algae; juveniles mostly inhabit lagoons, mangroves, and estuaries. Older fish frequent lagoons, various types of open coast reefs, and adjacent sand patches. These fish burrow in sandy patches at night and forage by day along reefs and in sand.

Bullseyes mature at 28–30 cm (11–12 in) TL. Along the central Pacific Mexican coast and in the Gulf of California, bullseyes reportedly spawn from April–November. The eggs are demersal and adhere to hard surfaces, but not to each other. They hatch in 65–90 hours at 27°C (81°F). Bullseyes feed on bivalves (e.g., oysters and clams), snails, crabs, fishes, and corals. A fish likely to have been this species ate a sea snake.

KEVIN LEE

FISHERY: Bullseye puffers are an important commercial species in Mexico. Martinez-Palacios et al. (2002) note that it is the most common pufferfish along the northwest coast of the Gulf of California and is "Considered a delicacy and commands high prices in local markets because of the tasty, white, firm boneless flesh…Mexico is currently the second largest exporter of puffer in the world." In general, this species appears to have a low tetrodotoxin content, although an occasional Gulf of California fish with relatively high tetrodotoxin has been found and some human deaths in that area have been attributed to consuming puffers. The folks in Mexico are interested in farming them. Juveniles are often taken as bycatch in Gulf of California shrimp fisheries.

ORIGINS: A fossil species, *S. hyperostosus*, lived during the Pliocene (at least 1.8 million years ago) on the east coast of the United States.

EARLY DARWIN AWARD

Among his other works, the Jesuit scholar Father Francisco Javier Clavigero (1731–1787) wrote a history of the founding of the Catholic missions of Baja California. Still a readable work, *The History of [Lower] California* recounts the following cautionary tale. In 1706, the Jesuit Brother Bravo, 10 soldiers, and some locals, were near Loreto (Gulf of California) searching for likely sites for missions. While traveling along the coast: "One of the soldiers found a bonfire in which some Californian [native] fishermen had roasted fish a short time before, and especially some *botetti* [pufferfish, likely *Sphoeroides annulatus*], the liver of which contains a very active and violent poison. The [native] fishermen, because they knew this, had eaten the flesh and left the livers on some shells. A soldier, seeing them, wished to eat them, and he invited 3 of his companions. A Californian who saw them called out at once, saying: 'Do not eat, do not eat, because it will kill you.' The soldier, scorning the advice, began to eat and to share it with the other three. One of them ate a little; another only chewed it, but without swallowing it; and the last one only touched it, keeping it to eat later. The first of the four soldiers died in half an hour, the second shortly afterward; the third remained unconscious until the following day; and this one, as well as the fourth, felt weak and uncomfortable for many days. The two dead men were buried…and the two sick ones were taken to Loreto; and so that expedition came to nothing."

Well, I wouldn't say "nothing." We did learn to listen to the locals when they start screaming "Don't eat that!"

FAMILY DIODONTIDAE—Porcupinefishes

Porcupinefishes are rather distinctive, rotund fishes with the ability to puff up and flaunt a veritable bouquet of spines. Many, or perhaps all, species secrete a toxin in their skins. There are 6 genera and at least 19 species, three of which are found within our range, all as far north as Southern California. Porcupinefishes are oviparous and have planktonic eggs and larvae. The family is known from as far back as the Middle Eocene (about 50 million years ago) of southern Europe and the Caucasus.

Diodon holocanthus
Linnaeus, 1758
Balloonfish

A pokey nearshore species.

ETYMOLOGY AND COLLQUIAL NAMES: *Diodon* is Latin for "porcupine" and *holocanthus* means "wholly" and "spine." Other names include "freckled porcupinefish," "longnose porcupinefish," or "longspined balloonfish." They are called "harisenbon" in Japan and "Pez erizo" and "puerco espin" in Mexico.
THE BASICS: Maximum Length: 60 cm (24 in) TL. The Ranges: Circumglobal; Japan, and from La Jolla (Southern California) to Easter Island, including Gulf of California. 1–100 m (3–328 ft). Eggs: 1.7–1.8 mm. Larvae: hatching length = 1.9–2.1 mm.
SALIENT CHARACTERS: Balloonfish have long spines (particularly on the head) and have no spots on the body.
LIFE HISTORY: Young-of-the-year recruit to the seafloor when at least as small as 6 cm (2 in) SL. However, pelagic juveniles as large as 8.6 cm (3 in) have been taken. Balloonfish live over rocks and occasionally sand, in warm nearshore waters. In the Gulf of California, they spawn at dawn and dusk in pairs. A male approaches a female, keeping competing males away at the same time, and follows her, nudging her abdomen. If receptive, the female begins to rise in the water column with the male pushing her along. Eggs and sperm are released near the surface. In Hawaiian waters, they spawn from February–September, perhaps peaking in May–June. Eggs hatch in 4–5 days at about 25°C (77°F). In aquaria, eggs sink to the bottom 12–24 hours before hatching. Balloonfish are nocturnal predators, target-

OCTAVIO ABURTO-OROPEZA

ing such benthic organisms as crabs, hermit crabs, snails, sea urchins, mantis shrimps, shrimps, and fishes. In some areas, balloonfish follow stingrays, hoping they stir up sediment and thereby expose prey. Predators include dolphinfish.
ORIGINS: Fossils of the extinct *Diodon scillae* have been taken from Miocene deposits (at least 5.3 million years old) of Southern California. There is also a fossil species named *Oligodiodon vetus* from the Miocene of Monterey.
FISHERY: They are of small economic importance, mainly in the drying-and-inflating industry.

OTHER SPECIES

Chilomycterus reticulatus
(Linnaeus, 1758)
Spotfin Burrfish

Burrfish grow to about 75 cm (30 in) TL and 4.1 kg (9 lb). They are found around the world in tropical waters as far north as the southern Kuril Islands and Long Beach Harbor (Southern California) to Chile. They inhabit reefs and occasionally sandy areas at depths of 1–141 m (3–462 ft). Burrfish eat mollusks, bivalves, gastropods, corals, and crabs.

GERALD ALLEN

Diodon hystrix
Linnaeus, 1758
Porcupinefish

Porcupinefish grow to 91 cm (36 in) TL and 2.8 kg (6.2 lb). They are found worldwide in tropical waters and in the eastern Pacific they range from Laguna Beach (Southern California) to Chile, including the Gulf of California, in 1–135 m (3–443 ft). They are rare both in Southern California waters and along most of the Pacific Coast of Baja California. Off southwestern Mexico, porcupinefish are most abundant in 20–40 m (66–131 ft). Juveniles may stay in pelagic waters until they are at least 19.1 cm (8 in) SL. Porcupinefish are found

OCTAVIO ABURTO-OROPEZA

mostly in shallow, warm, coastal waters over both soft sediments and high relief reefs. You can often find them around small boulders, rhodoliths (unattached, hard, red algae that resembles coral), and such structure-forming invertebrates as black corals. They occasionally visit lagoons and estuaries. These are nocturnal predators that feed on a wide variety of bottom-oriented prey, such as crabs, bivalves, snails, shrimps, corals, polychaetes, and fishes. Among their predators are tiger sharks and red-tailed tropicbirds. And then there is this from Klawe (1964): "In 1958, the author, while on an expedition off the Pacific coast of Colombia, observed a sea snake and *Diodon histrix* [sic] floating on the surface next to the drifting vessel. The fish was inflated and facing the snake, which appeared to be trying to bite the fish's head; however, it seemed unable to get hold of the fish. The animals were observed for only a brief period as they drifted by." Porkies may be most closely related to the Indo-Pacific species, *Diodon liturosus*, and to the balloonfish. Young sharksuckers sometimes attach to them. The eggs are 1.9–2.1 mm in diameter. Length-weight parameters (TL, cm, gr): (sexes combined) $W = 0.1934L^{2.472}$ (Kulbicki et al. 2005).

FAMILY MOLIDAE—Molas or Ocean Sunfishes

Basically highly modified pufferfish, molas are marine fishes found throughout the world. They come in three genera and perhaps five species. Two species (*Mola mola* and *Ranzania laevis*) have been taken within our range. All molids are oviparous and have planktonic eggs and larvae. The family Molidae appears to have arisen during the Middle Eocene (likely more than 42 million years ago) in the form of the fossil mola, *Eomola bimaxillaria*, from southwest Russia. *Austromola angerhoferi* was a huge, 3.2 m-long mola from the Early Miocene (about 22 million years ago).

These are striking and rather endearing fishes. Bass et al. (2005) note that they "lack caudal bones, ribs, pelvic fins, spine or girdles and have fewer vertebrae than any other fish...Metamorphosis from larvae to adult is remarkable in that, unlike most fish, they pass through two distinct larva phases – a typical Tetraodon-like larval and another highly transformative stage resulting in the complete absorption of the tail." And, in fact, what looks in molids like a little flappy tail fin (called the clavus) is actually modified elements of the dorsal and anal fins.

Mola mola
(Linnaeus, 1758)
Ocean Sunfish.

A pelagic fish that has lost all semblance of dignity.

ETYMOLOGY AND COLLOQUIAL NAMES: *Mola* means "millstone" in Latin. Goode (1884) noted: "They float lazily, with one of the bright sides of the body just at the surface. As they float, the waves ripple and break over them, and the heavy pectoral fins move slowly to and fro through the air; thus lying, they are very conspicuous objects, and may be seen at long distances. From this habit of sunning themselves they have gained the name of Sun Fishes." On the other hand, "mola" is the name most of us use. "Manbo" is the Japanese name.

THE BASICS: Maximum Length: Confirmed to 2.7 m (8.9 ft) TL; possibly to 4 m (13.1 ft). Maximum Weight: more than 2,250 kg (5,000 lb). The Ranges: Circumglobal in temperate and tropical waters. In our part of the world, from the southern Kuril Islands to the Gulf of Alaska and southward to Las Cruces (33°29'S) (central Chile), including the Gulf of California. In the western Pacific, mola are common to about the south Kuril Islands and in the northeastern Pacific as far north as at least the west coast of Vancouver Island. Sea surface to 644 m (2,113 ft). Length-weight parameters (TL, cm, kg): $0.0454L^{3.0496}$ (Coull et al. 1989).

SALIENT CHARACTERS: A fish that put the "o" in oval (along with the "l" in lugubrious, the "s" in squinch, and the "h" in hapless), mola have a flap where the caudal fin should be, a pitiful little gill slit, long oar-like dorsal and anal fins, and leathery skin. They are grayish on backs and silvery below.

PHIL COLLA

LIFE HISTORY: This is a uniquely shaped pelagic species that, in our waters, is often seen resting at the surface. Although they live off California throughout the year, mola seem to be most abundant in the fall. The smallest fish in the Scripps Institution of Oceanography collection, a pie-sized fish 26.5 cm (10.6 in) TL long, was collected off La Jolla (Southern California) in September. Fish of all sizes often hang out near kelp beds and around drifting kelp mats, where they are frequently cleaned by señoritas, halfmoons, and other pickers. Although they do not seem to form large schools, they will cluster in groups of 10–15. Most folks see mola when they come to the surface and flop on their sides or when they leap out of the water. This basking may be a way to warm up after making deep dives into colder waters. In the tropics, mola do not appear to come to the surface. Although they appear ungainly lying at the surface, mola are graceful and powerful swimmers when underwater. We frequently see them making pretty good time when hundreds of feet below the surface. Mola are tolerant of a wide range of temperatures, at least between 1.8–29.3°C (35–85°F). Based on fish tagged in Southern California (Cartamil and Lowe 2004), mola can make extensive vertical movements, often diving hundreds of meters (encountering temperatures of 6.8–21°C, 44–70°F, on a dive), and then returning to surface or near surface waters. In this study, mola were most active during the late night and, in particular, daylight hours. These fish also traveled considerable horizontal distances, averaging 27 km (17 mi) per day. Although the scale of movements along the eastern Pacific is unclear, mola may not make large-scale migrations. However, a fish tagged off Cape Cod in the Atlantic traveled about 3,000 km (1,864 mi) to the Gulf of Mexico, so who knows? Genetic studies imply that there may be significant differences (and hence reduced interchange) between fish living in the Indo-Pacific and those living in the Atlantic-Mediterranean. Mola do not spawn off the West Coast off the U.S., although spawning does occur in the eastern tropical Pacific and off Japan.

No one knows how long mola live (or if they do they aren't telling) or how fast they grow. However one fish in the Monterey Bay Aquarium (albeit fed on a high-protein diet) gained 113.6 kg (250 lb) in 14 months. Individual mola have been kept in captivity for over eight years and researchers have estimated a maximum life span of at least 20 years. Females grow larger than males. Mola in Japanese waters may mature at about 200 cm (79 in) TL and apparently spawn from August–October. Females are multiple spawners and produce hundreds of millions of eggs. Mola feed on a variety of pelagic organisms, including squishy things like medusae, pelagic tunicates, ctenophores, by-the-wind-sailors (*Velella velella*), as well as fishes. Some benthic prey, including brittle stars, mollusks, and hydroids have also been found in their digestive tracts. Black marlins, blue sharks, California sea lions, and orcas are known to eat them.

FISHERY: Native Americans living on Santa Catalina and San Clemente islands (Southern California) caught mola (some of them apparently quite large) in substantial numbers.

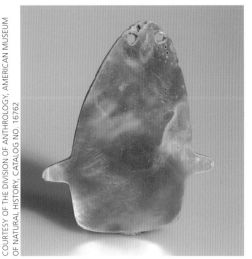

COURTESY OF THE DIVISION OF ANTHROLOGY, AMERICAN MUSEUM OF NATURAL HISTORY, CATALOG NO. 16762

A polished abalone shell necklace piece from a Native American site in Southern Callifornia.

Historically, there was no organized commercial fishery for this species, although Bennett (1840), riding aboard a whaler in the Pacific, noted: "The liver of the Sun Fish [sic] has a bright-yellow colour, and yields a large quantity of oil, which is much valued by sailors as an external application for sprains, bruises, and rheumatic pains." Today, there appears to be no directed commercial fishery for this species, although you can find them in fish markets in Japan and Taiwan. In the northeastern Pacific, mola are commonly taken as bycatch in offshore drift nets set for such species as swordfish. Mola are only occasionally caught by recreational anglers off California.

ORIGINS AND RELATIONSHIPS: The oldest member of the genus *Mola*, *M. pileata*, is traceable back to the Middle Miocene of Europe. A *Mola* sp. has been found from the Middle Miocene (about 16–17 million years ago) of Southern and Central California. *Mola mola* appears to be closely related to *Mola ramsayi*, which Bass et al. (2005) believe is an often-overlooked species that lives in the Southern Hemisphere. Yoshita et al. (2009) report that there may be un undescribed *Mola* living around Japan.

MISCELLANY: 1) The barnacle *Lepas* sp. was found attached in the esophagus of one fish. 2) There appeared to be a die-off of over 100 small fish off Monterey in the summer and fall of 1961. The cause(s) of the deaths were unclear. 3) Fugu poisoning has been noted in this species. 4) When I was but a budding graduate student I saw a mola come to the surface, flop on its side, and get pecked by a gull. The gull then swam away, the mola flipped over, and the gull came back and resumed pecking. "Dang," thought I, "here is an instance of undocumented cleaning behavior. Let me sharpen my quill and submit this to a biology journal." Imagine my chagrin, then, when we find this from Holder (1910a): "Mr. T. McD. Potter told me that near San Clemente Island he once came upon a moonfish of the largest size that was lying flat on the surface, and about it was a school of yellowtail feeding on the goose barnacles and other streaming parasites that infested the monster, as they were darting at it, apparently biting it; but that they were feeding on the parasites was shown by the fact that the fish did not resent the attentions, submitting to them with same indifference as does the ox, rhinoceros, and other animals which allow ox-biters and other birds to run over them in their search for parasites...Gulls doubtless carry on a similar work as I have seen them sitting on this fish out at sea." 5) Here's a really, really weird story related to me by Shane Anderson. On three occasions he has seen octopuses hanging onto mola. How could a bottom-dwelling octopus wind up clinging to a surface-midwater dwelling mola? One possible transfer point is drifting kelp mats. Octopuses are sometimes found among them and mola often swim around and through them. Alternately, mola may spend more time near the bottom than we know. 6) What are those thin strands that stream back from a mola's body? Parasitic copepods of the genus *Pennella*. 7) Gelatinous tissue under the skin helps keep a mola buoyant.

FUN PAGES

Matt Kotch "Spawn of the Dead."

PACIFIC FISHERMAN – Russian Sardine Threat Serious

From a declassified and formerly encrypted message transmitted from the Russian Embassy in London to the Moscow headquarters of the OGPU [the Soviet intelligence service]. The message, dated 4 May 1931, was from Soviet agent Josef Bluyodin (1907–1995)[1] to Major Yvgenie Grunov (1899–1975)[2], Deputy Secretary of the Herring, Sardine, and Shad Desk of OGPU.

"Comrade Grunov, as directed, on 26 February 1931 I embarked on the SS *Golden Poppy* (formerly SS Gregory Zinoviev, formerly SS Alexander Kamanev, formerly SS Leon Trotsky, formerly SS Alexander Kerensky, formerly SS Czar Nicholas II) with nine cases of canned sardines. I report to you herein that I safely transported the sardines through customs. Canned under the "Heroic Red Banner Sardine Cannery #5, Fulfilling the Second Five Year Plan as directed by Comrade Stalin, and at the Same Time Denouncing the Filthy Kulaks, May We Spit in Their Faces" brand, I noted only one small dent and a damaged label. I have taken up residence at the boarding house of a Mrs. Gibbons, in Histon, a small town near Cambridge.

PACIFIC FISHERMAN

THE ORGAN OF THE COMMERCIAL FISHERIES OF THE PACIFIC.

SOUTHERN EDITION

SEATTLE—
71 Columbia St.
MILLER FREEMAN, President

SAN FRANCISCO—
369 Pine St.
L. K. SMITH, Manager

LOS ANGELES—
257 South Spring St.
STEDMAN H. GRAY, Editor

PORTLAND—
446 Morrison St.
C. L. HILLYARD, Advertising Manager

Vol. 29   No. 5

APRIL, 1931

Russian Sardine Threat Serious

Only a High Grade Pack Can Keep California's Output to the Fore in European Markets, Say San Francisco Sardine Men Returning From Abroad

Two San Francisco sardine men returning recently from European visits report Russian sardines are crowding the California pack in English and Continental markets and advise that California can hold its position in these fields only by producing and exporting a high-grade product.

One of the travelers was H. G. Maxson, vice-president and general manager of the F. E. Booth Co., Inc., which operates sardine canneries at Monterey and Pittsburg. The other was E. A. Archibald, head of the Coastwise Mercantile company, San Francisco food brokers.

Mr. Maxson reports he found Russian sardines in central European markets packed in 1-lb. oval cans of exactly the same size and appearance as the California pack. There are two grades of Russian sardines, he says, one, the higher grade, being packed in a labelled can and the second, or the lower grade, coming unlabelled.

California Pack Better

None of the Russian sardine pack is equal in quality to the California output, Mr. Maxson says. The higher grade, he finds, is only passing fair in quality and the second grade is poor. However, he points out, the Russian pack is selling and is bringing repeat orders. The Russian sardines sell for around $2 per case abroad as against between $2.50 and $3 for the California pack.

H. C. MAXSON
Vice-President and General Manager of F. E. Booth Co., Inc., who says California's dominance in sardine markets of Europe is threatened by Russia.

California canner who has a well established brand, who packs for quality and who doesn't try to sell inferior goods has little to fear from this threat."

Mr. Maxson had some of the Russian sardines shipped to San Francisco

"Without a doubt this Russian competition is hurting the California sardine in Europe," Mr. Maxson says, "but the and on their arrival early in April expected to cut them and examine their contents carefully.

He also reported he found competition in Europe from sardines or pilchards packed in Germany, probably at North Sea points. These sardines are smaller than the California fish and would run about twelve to a 1-lb. oval can. The Germans pack their fish in half-pound ovals something along the lines of the quarter oils.

Packed Same As California

Mr. Archibald says Russian competition is a very serious threat to the California sardine in European markets. "Soviet agents are bringing sardines and mackerel into London, Paris and Hamburg and selling below the prices of California-packed fish," he advises. "Russian sardines are not as good as our sardines but are good enough to get by. When I was in Amsterdam the Russians were selling sardines: 48 1-lb. ovals to a case, at $2.20, while California goods at around $3 per case were not sold. I even heard of sardines from Russia being offered, c. i. f., at $1.75 per case in London and $2 in Amsterdam but believe these prices were for only a small lot. I was told the Russians had fifty or sixty thousand cases warehoused in London and Amsterdam.

"The Russian sardines are packed in tomato sauce and are in 1-lb. oval cans, exactly the same as the California fish. They even print labels like ours

As ordered, I have been preparing sardine and cucumber sandwiches (Mrs. Gibbons is nice enough to let me use her kitchen), then standing at the entrance to Trinity College and passing them out to students as they leave for lunch. Thus far, I have had only limited success in turning the conversation to the need for solidarity with Soviet workers as most of the students wish only to complain about the quality of the sardines; apparently the amount of salt added to the pack was too high. To compensate, I have reduced the number of sardines in each sandwich and added a second layer of cucumber. Unfortunately, a blight has affected the local cucumber crop and the price has increased dramatically over the last two weeks, necessitating my having to request additional funds from the Embassy to cover these unforeseen expenses. Despite what I perceive to be the issue with the sardines, I have struck up a friendship with several students, notably Messrs Philby, Maclean, and Burgess, as well as a French teacher who just graduated from Trinity, named Blunt (he is the only one who has not been critical of the sardines). Indeed, I feel confident that despite the obstacles that the Heroic Red Banner Sardine Cannery #5 have thrown in my path, I can convince these young men to assist us in our cause.

Also, as you have requested, I purchased two girdles (Angel Squeeze Brand, "Now with Much More Rubber"), size 18, for Mrs. Grunov. The requested items will be sent by diplomatic pouch on 7 May."[3]

[1] Mr. Bluyodin was later recalled to Moscow in November 1934. Fearing execution in the rampant purges of the time, he did not return to the Soviet Union, but rather dropped out of sight, only to reappear as "James Swansby" in Lerwick, Shetland Islands, some years later. Explaining his thick accent as a birth defect, "Swansby" ran a ladies undergarment shop in Lerwick from 1947 to 1959 and later taught the Shetland Island fiddling technique to several generations of island children.

[2] In 1936, Major Grunov, his wife, and young daughter escaped the Soviet Union and, traveling on forged passports, made their way to the White Russian community in Shanghai. Interned by the Japanese during World War II, Grunov later worked as a fisheries biologist for both the Nationalist and, after 1949, Communist governments (His autobiography *Red Herring*, was published by Red Star Publishers, Beijing, 1971). After his death in 1975, both his wife and daughter emigrated to New Zealand.

[3] Kids, this is just a riff. The newspaper article was real, though.

BRAIN CLOGGERS

I don't like word puzzles. For some reason I find them faintly irritating. Nevertheless, in the interest of providing a full, intellectual experience, here are three that should keep you occupied for a while.

Question 1:

Take the name of a common Southern California fish [of 7 letters] and form the name of a medium-sized Central Asian city [of 8 letters] known for its shashlik and fried fish.

Step 1: Keep the first and last letters of the fish's name, these form the first and last letters of the city's name.

Step 2: For the 2nd letter of the city's name, use the first letter of the name of a fairly common, highly contagious skin infection, usually caused by Group A streptococci bacteria or by *Staphylococcus aureus*.

Step 3: For the 3rd letter, use the first letter of a Northern Renaissance painter whose polyptych set a new standard for reality.

Step 4: For the 4th letter, use the first letter of the surname of the character in *War and Peace* who gets a commission in the guards due to the influence of Prince Vassily.

Step 5: For the 5th letter, use the first letter of the name of the pope who promulgated the First Crusade at the Council of Piacenza.

Step 6: For the 6th letter, use the 8th letter in the title of a 1942 movie starring Greer Garson.

Step 7: For the 7th letter, use the first letter of the Greek goddess of gluttony.

7: Adephagia

Solution letters are in italics. Step 1: Keep *g* and *n*. Step 2: *Impetigo*. Step 3: *Jan van Eyck*. Step 4: *Drubetskoy, Boris*. Step 5: *Urban*. Step 6: Mrs. *Miniver*. Step

Answer 1: Grunion to Gijduvan (a city in Uzbekistan).

Question 2:

Changing one or more words at a time, go from the name of a North Pacific fish (hint: it is composed of 2 words) to a central claim of existentialism. Here's an example of the process: Dover sole—sole food—food for thought—thought provoking.

Answer 2: Pacific cod—codpiece—piece of eight—eightfold path—path of least resistance—resistance is futile—futile existence—existence precedes essence.

Question 3:

Here is a list, in alphabetical order, of some West Coast fishes. Reorder them in the order in which the countries of their describers entered World War II. And to forestall any angry letters, no, I am not implying that any of the ichthyologists listed below were responsible for that conflagration.

Carcharhinus longimanus, Carcharhinus porosus, Galeorhinus galeus, Lumpenus sagitta, Rhamphocottus richardsonii, Sarda chiliensis, Sebastes borealis, Sebastes caurinus, Squatina californica, Tetrapturus angustirostris, and *Tetrapturus audax.*

Trick question: *Galeorhinus galeus* (Linnaeus). Sweden was neutral in World War II.

Chilean (1945).

8) *Tetrapturus audax* (Philippi). This is a tricky one. Rodolfo Amando Philippi was born in Germany, but did much of his work in Chile. So I am calling him

7) Tie: *Squatina californica* (USA) (Ayres) *Carcharhinus longimanus* (Poey) (Cuba) (8 December 1941).

6) *Tetrapturus angustirostris* Tanaka (Japan, 7 December 1941).

5) *Carcharhinus porosus* (Ranzani) (Italy, 10 June 1940).

4) *Sebastes borealis* Barsukov (USSR, 17 September 1939).

3) *Lumpenus sagitta* Wilimovsky (Canada, 10 September 1939).

2) Tie: *Sebastes caurinus* (Richardson) (Great Britain); *Sarda chiliensis* (Cuvier) (France) (3 September 1939).

1) *Rhamphocottus richardsonii* Günther (Germany, 1 September 1939).

Answer 3:

So YOU want to be a Mink Farmer?
Take the Mink Farmers' Test and Find Out!

As so many of us have discovered to our discomfiture, mink farming is not for the faint of heart, for there is many a slip twixt baby mink and coat. And a mink's diet can be one of those slips. Apparently, you just can't feed your hink (a contraction of "herd of mink") a bucket of sardines and let it go at that, as fur quality, growth rate, and pelt length all vary with diet.

Fortunately, much of the leg (or perhaps paw) work has been done by the folks at the Agricultural Experimental Station at Oregon State University. In a series of groundbreaking experiments, they fed minks a range of diets and recorded the results.

So, let's look in on: J. Adair et al. 1966. Mink Nutrition Research 1965 Progress Report. Agricultural Experiment Station, Oregon State University, Special Report 207 and see if you can be a mink farmer. Just match the diets (left) with the results (right).

Mink

Mostly Mink

DIETS

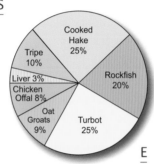

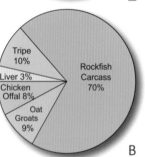

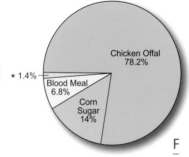

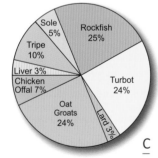

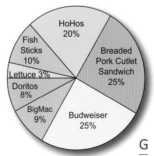

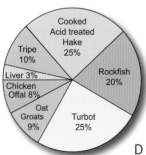

RESULTS

1. A similar hake product, which was cooked only, resulted in animals slightly smaller in size and lower in color.

2. Still believes there are weapons of mass distruction in Iraq.

3. Inclusion of high levels of oat groats in the mink ration produced exceptionally large males with improved fur color but quality slightly below control mink.

4. Conventional, high-fish type ration including oat groats as the "cereal" produced dark mink of large size that were well-furred but of average color. This group is the control against which others are compared.

5. Replacing all the whole fish species with rockfish carcass resulted in shorter pelts equal in color but lower in quality than controls at lower feed costs.

6. Pacific hake, cooked and acidified, substituted for 25% of other fish species produced large, well-colored mink lower in quality than controls.

7. A greatly simplified ration based on turbot gave outstanding production until a feed source change in October interfered with consumption, resulting in severe weight losses and mortality.

SCORING

1-2 right = Hopeless Jerk
3-4 right = Lost in Murk
5-6 right = Other, slightly better, things that rhyme with "urk."
More than 6 right = Minkman (or Minkwoman, or Minkperson, or whatever term gives absolutely no offense to any individual other than, one assumes, the minks).

Answers: 1-E; 2-G; 3-C; 4-A; 5-B; 6-D; 7-F

ANCHOVY GIBBER

Never let it be said that Canadians are not on the cutting edge of technology. I know what you are thinking: "That sure doesn't look like the anchovy gibber that I grew up with." And you are right; this was a workhorse anchovy gibber, not like the effete tabletop model you keep next to the espresso machine.

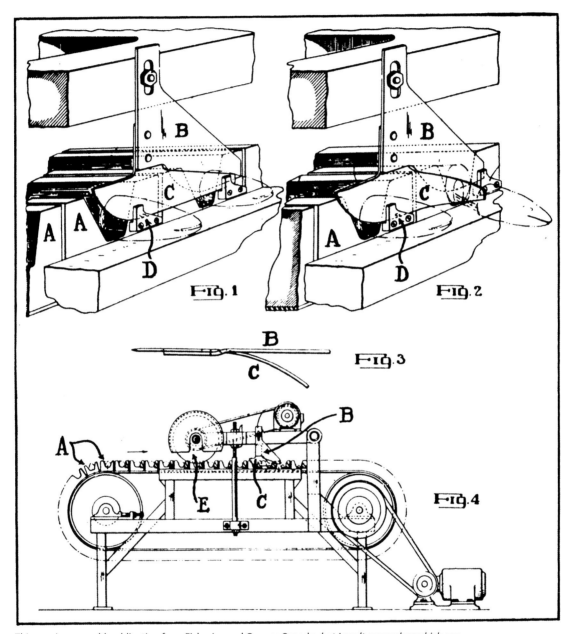

This was in some old publication from Fisheries and Oceans Canada, *but I can't remember which one.*

mmm, Tastes Just Like Chicken

Kind of at a loss for what to do with that great vat o'herring your brother-in-law gave you for helping him put a new head gasket on his 1964 Renault? And, parenthetically, need a sure-fire showstopper for the next Elks beer fest? Well, just like the Mounties saving that English-speaking school marm from the clutches of a Partie Quebecois backbencher, your rescue comes from this charming recipe courtesy of the Fisheries Research Board of Canada:

"Bloater Paste - Herring were scaled, beheaded, gibbed and washed. After brining for 10 minutes in saturated salt brine, they were drained, spread on trays and smoked for 30 minutes at 140° F. After this period of smoking it was generally possible to remove most of the bones by grasping the protruding end of the backbone where the head was cut off and drawing it out. The fish should then be finely macerated in a suitable machine:

To 10 pounds of ground fish the following were added:

     5 oz. of tomato puree

     2 oz. spiced vinegar

     1 lb. of fresh ground pork fat

     2 oz. of corn starch

After thorough mixing, the paste was then ready to dispense into the containers for heat processing. They were packed in the regular 2-oz. paste cans and processed for 30 minutes at 240°F."

And yes, we thought you would never ask. As defined by the Oxford English Dictionary, a *bloater* is a very slightly salted and lightly smoked herring. Its first mention was about 1832, "Herrings, at Yarmouth where the method of curing is unrivalled, called 'Yarmouth bloaters.'"

I think before the Stones made it big they may have been called the Yarmouth Bloaters.

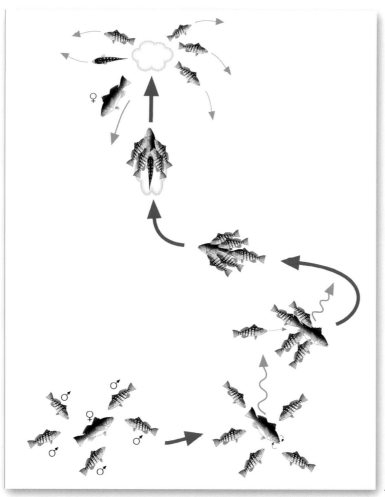

A schematic of kelp bass spawning behavior by Larry Allen. Bertie was supposed to put this on page 359 but she forgot, and when we realized it, it was too late. But then we felt kind of guilty about it, so here it is.

GLOSSARY

(Being a Reasonably Accurate Guide to Some of the More Arcane Terms in CMTYWTKATFOTPC)

AMBICOLORATION: In flatfishes, ambicoloration refers to the occasional occurrence of color on the blind side of those flatfishes whose blind sides are usually white. This color may occur on either part or all of the blind side.

AMPHIPOD: A dreadful little shrimp-like creature distantly related to crabs, shrimps, and barnacles. Most are small and identifying them to species is a chore, let me tell you. On the other hand, many species of fishes simply dote on them, lending support to Nietzsche's belief that "All of life is a dispute over taste and tasting."

ANADROMOUS: The behavior of being born in fresh water, migrating for at least a short time to marine conditions, then returning to fresh water to reproduce.

ANAL FIN: The fin that is just south of a fish's private parts.

BARBEL: A little fleshy organ that often hangs down in the vicinity of a fish's mouth. Not only can fishes touch potential food items with their barbels, they can also taste them with that organ. If we had taste receptors in our fingers, shaking hands would be a whole different trip.

BATHYPELAGIC: Loosely, animals that are bathypelagic live in the water column (not associated with the bottom) in deep waters (maybe deeper than 1,000 m, 3,280 ft). The reality is that at least some fishes that are called bathypelagic also appear to spend some time on or associated with the sea floor.

BENTHIC: Associated with the sea floor.

BIOLUMINESCENCE: Bioluminescence refers to the production of light by organisms. Fishes may produce light all by themselves, using chemicals in their bodies, or they may culture bacteria that produce the light. Either way, in most instances, this light is blue-green.

BRANCHIOSTEGAL RAYS: Bones, usually slender, that support the gill membrane.

BULBUS ARTERIOSUS: This is a flexible chamber that connects the heart to the ventral aorta. In fishes, this structure kind of controls and modulates blood as it flows from the heart toward the gills. I once discovered a new-to-science protozoan parasite that infected the bulbus arteriosus of rockfishes. I was going to name it after my girl friend (a parasite of the heart, *très romantique*) but, to my everlasting regret, I was talked out of it.

CAUDAL FIN: The tail fin.

CLASPER: Claspers are formed from the posterior part of the pelvic fin of male cartilaginous fishes. They serve to channel semen into a female's reproductive organ, because, well, *something* has to.

CONTINENTAL SHELF: This is that part of the sea floor that extends outwards from land to a bottom depth of maybe 140–150 m (460–492 ft). The shelf tends to drop off slowly and where the decline sharpens (the *shelf break*) begins the *continental slope*.

CONTINENTAL SLOPE: Following on the heels of the continental shelf (see above), we have the continental slope, an area of sea floor that tends to rapidly decline in depth. Together, the slope and shelf form the *continental margin*.

COPEPOD: This is another group of the ubiquitous crustaceans, this one often found in huge swarms in the water column.

DEEP SCATTERING LAYER: The DSL (use these initials wisely and a cachet and brio you did not know you owned will be yours) is an assemblage of water column invertebrates and fishes that rises towards the surface in the evening and retreats deeper with the sun. It is said that some early oceanographers, using the primitive sonars of the time, thought this layer was the sea floor. Then they noticed that the "bottom" was rising and falling and that they had made something of asses of themselves. While they have mostly gotten over that embarrassment, it is still kind of a sensitive point, so go easy on them.

DEMERSAL: In this tome meant to describe fishes that live on or near the bottom.

DETERMINATE FECUNDITY: Females with determinate fecundity produce all of the eggs they will spawn in a given season at the beginning of the season. This contrasts to those with indeterminate fecundity, those that keep producing eggs throughout the season.

DORSAL FIN: The fin that sits on the back of fishes. Some species have one dorsal fin, other have two, and a blessed few have three.

DW: This is disk width and refers to skates and rays only and means the greatest distance between the pectoral fins.

EPIBENTHIC: Epibenthic, in the context of this book (and really that is all we are concerned about right now) refers to fishes that pretty much live close to the bottom.

EPIPELAGIC: This describes organisms that live in the open waters near or at the ocean's surface and down to maybe 200 m (656 ft).

EUPHAUSIID: Euphausiids (also called krill) are small crustaceans that are found all over the world and, parenthetically, harbor one of the relatively rare words in the English language with a double i (hyperiid, gnathiid, taxiing, radii, genii, and inferii are some others).

FECUNDITY: Unless otherwise stated, this means the number of eggs or young that a female fish produces in a season. In some cases, I refer to *batch fecundity*, the number of eggs or young produced at one go by a female that may release gametes more than once per season.

FL: This refers to *fork length* and is an important measure because if your fork is too small, you might accidentally bite your finger, and if it is too large you might get a hernia picking it up. It is also the measurement from the tip of the snout to the fork in the caudal (tail) fin.

LATERAL LINE: The lateral line is formed by a series of pores, each containing a hair-like structure that bends as water hits it. The direction these structures bend tells the fish something about water motion around it. Most, but not all fishes, have at least one lateral line on each side of the body.

LEPTOCEPHALUS LARVA: This is a flattened, transparent larva of eels, bonefish, and other kind of primitive fishes of the superorder Elopomorpha. Compared to more traditional fish larvae, leptocephali tend to stay in the water column longer and grow larger before settling out of the plankton.

MESOPELAGIC: In comparison to epipelagic creatures, mesopelagic ones live a bit deeper in the water column, down to some poorly defined depth, but maybe about 1,000 m (3,280 ft).

MIXED LAYER: That part of the upper water column that is mixed (and hence fairly uniform) by such things as waves and currents.

OPERCULUM: In fishes, it's that hard bony flap that covers and protects the gills – kind of like a cheek.

OTOLITH: Otoliths are small structures (formed from calcium carbonate in bony fishes) found in the inner ears of fishes. Among other functions, otoliths help a fish hear and let it know when it is upside down or right side up.

OVIPAROUS: Fishes that are oviparous produce eggs that develop outside the female's body. Fertilization may occur either inside a female or after the eggs are released but the embryos are given no extra nutrients other than the original yolk.

PARTURITION: In fishes, the act of giving birth to larvae or juveniles. So, and not to put too fine a point to it, sea perches, rockfishes, and some sharks, for instance, parturate, while many other fishes, those releasing eggs, spawn.

PECTORAL FIN: This is a paired fin (one on each side of the body) and is located about where your arms are stuck on.

PELAGIC: "Pelagic" comes from the Greek term for "open sea" and that kind of sums it up.

PELVIC FIN: The pelvic fins are paired fins located on the underside of a fish's body. In many fishes, the pelvics are located right about where James Pierce's nipples are situated in the 1927 version of *Tarzan and the Golden Lion*.

PLACOID SCALE: Scales found on sharks, skates, and rays that are, at heart, modified teeth.

POLYCHAETE: The love child Pollyanna had with the Scarecrow during the time she left her novels and visited the Emerald City. Upon returning to her novels, Pollyanna was heard to say that she never regretted the affair and was, in fact, glad to have done it. Oh, and they are also a class of generally marine annelid worms.

PPT: A shorthand way of writing *parts per thousand* one of the ways that salinity is defined. To give you a frame of reference, sea water tends to be a bit more than 34 parts per thousand, so values less than that mean that the water is less saline.

SL: This refers to *standard length* and is the distance from the tip of the snout to the posterior end of the last vertebra. Basically, this measurement excludes the caudal fin and likely was developed by museum workers who often had to contend with preserved fishes that had lost their tails.

THERMOCLINE: That part of the water column (located just below the mixed layer) where temperature drops abruptly with depth.

TL: *Total length* is measured from the tip of the snout to the longest lobe of the caudal (tail) fin. This is my favorite of the three most common measurements (SL, FL, and TL) of bony fishes and I always have a faint sense of disquiet when fishes are measured any other way.

UPWELLING: Upwelling describes the process whereby wind-driven surface waters are driven away from the coast and then replaced by cooler and more nutrient-rich waters. These nutrient-rich waters promote plankton growth and thus serve as feeding grounds for many fish species.

VIVIPAROUS: Viviparity is a mode of reproduction in which the mother provides some form of nutrition, other than just a yolk, to a developing embryo, in utero.

YOUNG-OF-THE-YEAR: A juvenile fish, from the time it settles out of the plankton until it's first birthday.

REFERENCES

Aalbers, S. A. 2008. Seasonal, diel, and lunar spawning periodicities and associated sound production of white seabass (*Atractoscion nobilis*). Fishery Bulletin 106:143–151.

Abookire, A. A. 2006. Reproductive biology, spawning season, and growth of female rex sole (*Glyptocephalus zachirus*) in the Gulf of Alaska. Fishery Bulletin 104:350–359.

Abookire, A. A., J. T. Duffy-Anderson, and C. M. Jump. 2007. Habitat associations and diet of young-of-the-year Pacific cod (*Gadus macrocephalus*) near Kodiak, Alaska. Marine Biology 150:713–726.

Abookire, A. A., J. F. Piatt, and S. G. Speckman. 2002. A nearsurface, daytime occurrence of two mesopelagic fish species (*Stenobrachius leucopsarus* and *Leuroglossus schmidti*) in a glacial fjord. Fishery Bulletin 100:376–380.

Aburto-Oropeza, O. 2009. The role of nursery habitats and climate variability in reef fish fisheries in the Gulf of California. PhD Thesis, University of California, San Diego.

Adreani, M. S. 2003. Reproductive behavior and mating system of the temperate wrasse *Halichoeres semicinctus* (Pisces: Labridae). Masters Thesis, California State University, Northridge.

Adreani, M. S., B. E. Erisman, and R. R. Warner. 2004. Courtship and spawning behavior in the California sheephead, *Semicossyphus pulcher* (Pisces: Labridae). Environmental Biology of Fishes 71:13–19.

Agassiz, L. 1853. Extraordinary fishes from California, constituting a new family. The American Journal of Science and Arts 16:380–390.

Aguirre-Villaseñor, H., E. Morales-Bojorquez, R. E. Moran-Angulo, J. Madrid-Vera, and M. C. Valdez-Pineda. 2006. Biological indicators for the Pacific sierra (*Scomberomorus sierra*) fishery in the southern Gulf of California, Mexico. Ciencias Marinas 32:471–484.

Alcalay, O. M. and P. C. Sikkel. 1994. Diel periodicity of hatching of demersal eggs in the temperate damselfish, *Hypsypops rubicundus*. Bulletin of Marine Science 54:565–569.

Allen, G. H. 2001. The ragfish, *Icosteus aenigmaticus* Lockington, 1880: a synthesis of historical and recent records from the North Pacific Ocean and the Bering Sea. Marine Fisheries Review 63:1–31.

Allen, L. G., A. M. Findlay, and C. M. Phalen. 2002. Structure and standing stock of the fish assemblages of San Diego Bay, California from 1994 to 1999. Bulletin of the Southern California Academy of Sciences 101:49–85.

Allen, L. G., R. E. Jensen, and J. R. Sears. 1990. Open coast settlement and distribution of young-of-the-year California halibut (*Paralichthys californicus*) along the southern California coast between Point Conception and San Mateo Point, June–October, 1988, p. 145–152. *In* C. W. Haugen (ed.). The California halibut, *Paralichthys californicus*, resource and fisheries. California Department of Fish and Game, Fish Bulletin 174.

Allen, L. G., T. E. Hovey, M. S. Love, and J. T. W. Smith. 1995. The life history of the spotted sand bass (*Paralabrax maculatofasciatus*) within the southern California Bight. California Cooperative Oceanic Fisheries Investigations Report 36:193–203.

Alton, M. S., R. G. Bakkala, G. E. Walters, and P. T. Munro. 1988. Greenland turbot *Reinhardtius hippoglossoides* of the eastern Bering Sea and Aleutian Island region. NOAA Technical Report NMFS 71.

Altringham, J. D. and R. E. Shadwick. 2001. Swimming and muscle function, p. 313–344. *In* B. Block and E. D. Stevens (eds.). Tuna: physiology, ecology, and evolution. Academic Press, San Diego.

Alvarado Bremer, J. R., M. G. Hinton, and T. W. Greig. 2006. Evidence of spatial genetic heterogeneity in Pacific swordfish (*Xiphias gladius*) revealed by the analysis of LDH-A sequences. Bulletin of Marine Science 79:493–503.

Alvarado Bremer, J. R., G. M. Leclerc, and B. Ely. 1998. Mitochondrial and nuclear DNA analyses in the study of swordfish, *Xiphias gladius*, population structures, p. 211–217. *In* I. Barrett, O. Sosa-Nishizaki, and N. Bartoo (eds.). Biology and fisheries of swordfish, *Xiphias gladius*. NOAA Technical Report NMFS 142.

Alvarado-Castillo, R. and R. Félix-Araga. 1998. Crecimiento de *Istiophorus platypterus* (Pisces: Istiophoridae) en la boca del Golfo de California. Revista de Biologia Tropical 46(1):115–119.

Ames, K. M. and H. D. G. Maschner. 1999. Peoples of the northwest coast. Thames and Hudson, London.

Anderson, M. E. 1980. Aspects of the natural history of the midwater fish *Lycodapus mandibularis* (Zoarcidae) in Monterey Bay, California. Pacific Science 34:181–194.

Anderson, M. E., D. E. Stevenson, and G. Shinohara. 2009. Systematic review of the genus *Bothrocara* Bean 1890 (Teleostei: Zoarcidae). Ichthyological Research 56:172–194.

Andres, K. S. and T. W. Anderson. 2004. Habitat-dependent recruitment of two temperate reef fishes at multiple spatial scales. Marine Ecology Progress Series 277:231–244.

Andrews, A. H., G. M. Cailliet, and K. H. Coale. 1999. Age and growth of the Pacific grenadier (*Coryphaenoides acrolepis*) with age estimate validation using an improved radiometric ageing technique. Canadian Journal of Fisheries and Aquatic Sciences 56:1339–1350.

Andriyashev, A. P. 1954. Fishes of the northern seas of the USSR. Akademiya Nauk Soyuza Sovetskikh Sotsialisticheskikh Respublik, Translation by Israel Program for Scientific Translation, 1964.

Anislado-Tolentino, V. and C. Robinson-Mendoza. 2001. Age and growth for the scalloped hammerhead shark, *Sphyrna lewini* (Griffith and Smith, 1834) along the central Pacific coast of Mexico. Ciencias Marinas 27:501–520.

Anon. 1931. Shark-liver oil excels. California Fish and Game 17:183.

Anon. 1945. Shark skins. Fisheries Research Board of Canada, Progress Reports of the Pacific Coast Stations Number 63:45.

Anthony, K. M. 2009. Translocation, homing behavior and habitat utilization of oil platform-associated groundfishes in the east Santa Barbara Channel, California. Masters Thesis, California State University, Long Beach.

Arita, G. S. 1969. Sexual dimorphism in the cyclopterid fish *Eumicrotremus orbis*. Journal of the Fisheries Research Board of Canada 26:3262–3265.

Armstrong, R. H. and J. E. Morrow. 1980. The Dolly Varden charr, *Salvelinus malma*, p. 99–140. *In* E. K. Balon (ed.). Charrs. W. Junk, The Hague, The Netherlands.

Arora, H. L. 1951. An investigation of the California sand dab, *Citharichthys sordidus* (Girard). California Fish and Game 37:3–42.

Atkinson, C. E. 1939. Notes on the life history of the tidepool Johnny (*Oligocottus maculosus*). Copeia 1929(1):23–30.

Bailey, K. M. and L. Ciannelli. 2007. Walleye pollock, p. 85–93. *In* R. B. Spies (ed.). Long-term ecological change in the northern Gulf of Alaska. Elsevier, Amsterdam, The Netherlands.

Bailey, K. M., R. C. Francis, and P. R. Stevens. 1982. The life history and fishery of Pacific whiting, *Merluccius productus*. California Cooperative Fisheries Investigations Report 23:81–98.

Bailey, K. M., T. J. Quinn II, P. Bentzen, and W. S. Grant. 1999. Population structure and dynamics of walleye pollock, *Theragra chalcogramma*. Advances in Marine Biology 37:179–255.

Baird, R. C. 1971. The systematics, distribution, and zoogeography of the marine hatchetfishes (family Sternoptychidae). Harvard Museum of Comparative Zoology Bulletin 142:1–128.

Bakkala, R. G. 1970. Synopsis of biological data on the chum salmon, *Oncorhynchus keta* (Walbaum) 1792. United States Department of the Interior, FAO Species Synopsis 41.

Bakkala, R., K. Wakabayashi, and T. M. Sample. 1985. Results of the demersal trawl surveys, p. 39–191. *In* R. G. Bakkala and K. Wakabayashi (eds.). Results of cooperative U.S.-Japan groundfish investigations in the Bering Sea during May– August 1979. International North Pacific Fisheries Commission, Bulletin 44.

Balart, E. F., A. González-Cabello, R. C. Romero-Ponce, A. Zayas-Alvarez, M. Calderón-Parra, L. Campos-Dávila, and L. T. Findley. 2006. Length-weight relationships of cryptic reef fishes from the southwestern Gulf of California, México. Journal of Applied Ichthyology 22:316–318.

Baltz, D. M. and E. E. Knight. 1983. Age, growth, reproductive characteristics, and seasonal depth distribution of the spotfin surfperch, *Hyperprosopon anale*. California Fish and Game 69:97–104.

Barker, M. W. 1979. Population and fishery dynamics of recreationally exploited marine bottomfish of northern Puget Sound. PhD Thesis, University of Washington, Seattle.

Barnhart, P. S. 1932. Notes on the habits, eggs and young of some fishes of southern California. Bulletin of the Scripps Institution of Oceanography Technical Series 3, Number 4:87–99.

Barnhart, P. S. 1936. Marine fishes of southern California. University of California Press, Berkeley, California.

Barnett, L. A. K., R. L. Earley, D. A. Ebert, and G. M. Cailliet. 2009. Maturity, fecundity, and reproductive cycle of the spotted ratfish, *Hydrolagus colliei*. Marine Biology 156:301–316.

Barraclough, W. E. 1948. The hag-fish (*Polistotrema stoutii*) in British Columbia. Fisheries Research Board of Canada Progress Report, Pacific Coast Stations Number 74:57–58.

Barroso-Soto, I., E. Castillo-Gallardo, C. Quiñez-Veláquez, and R. E. Morán-Angulo. 2007. Age and growth of the finescale triggerfish, *Balistes polylepis* (Teleostei: Balistidae), on the coast of Mazatlán, Sinaloa, Mexico. Pacific Science 61:121– 127.

Barss, W. H. 1993. Pacific hagfish, *Eptatretus stouti*, and black hagfish, *E. deani*: the Oregon fishery and port sampling observations, 1988–92. Marine Fisheries Review 55(4):19–30.

Bass, A. H., D. Bodnar, and M. Marchaterre. 1999. Complementary explanations for existing phenotypes in an acoustic communication system, p. 493–514. *In* M. D. Hauser and M. Konish (eds.). The Design of Animal Communication. MIT Press, Cambridge, Massachusetts.

Bass, A. L., H. Dewar, T. Thys, J. T. Streelman, and S. A. Karl. 2005. Evolutionary divergence among lineages of the ocean sunfish family, Molidae (Tetraodontiformes). Marine Biology 148:405–414.

Baumgartner, T. R., A. Soutar, and V. Ferreira-Bartrina. 1992. Reconstruction of the history of Pacific sardine and northern anchovy populations over the past two millennia from sediments of the Santa Barbara Basin, California. California Cooperative Oceanic Fisheries Investigations Reports 33:24–40.

Baxter, J. L. 1960. A study of the yellowtail. California Department of Fish and Game, Fish Bulletin 110.

Baxter, J. L. 1966. Inshore fishes of California. California Fish and Game.

Bayer, R. D. 1980. Size and age of the tube-snout (*Aulorhynchus flavidus*) in the Yaquina Estuary, Oregon. Northwest Science 54:306–310.

Bayliff, W. H. 1980. Synopsis of biological data on the northern bluefin tuna, *Thunnus thynnus* (Linnaeus, 1758), in the Pacific Ocean. Inter-American Tropical Tuna Commission, Special Report 2:261–293.

Beacham, T. D., D. E. Hay, and K. D. Le. 2005. Population structure and stock identification of eulachon (*Thaleichthys pacificus*), an anadromous smelt, in the Pacific Northwest. Marine Biotechnology 7:363–372.

Beamesderfer, R. C. P., M. L. Simpson, and G. J. Kopp. 2007. Use of life history information in a population model for Sacramento green sturgeon. Environmental Biology of Fishes 79:315–337.

Beamish, R. J. 1980. Adult biology of the river lamprey (*Lampetra ayresi*) and the Pacific lamprey (*Lampetra tridentata*) from the Pacific Coast of Canada. Canadian Journal of Fisheries and Aquatic Sciences 37:1906–1923.

Beamish, R. J., G. A. McFarlane, and J. R. King. 2005. Migratory patterns of pelagic fishes and possible linkages between open ocean and coastal ecosystems off the Pacific coast of North America. Deep-Sea Research II 52:739–755.

Bean, T. H. 1887a. The cod fishery of Alaska, p. 198-226. *In* G. B. Goode, The Fisheries and Fishery Industries of the United States. Section 5, Volume 1. United States Commission of Fish and Fisheries.

Bean, T. H. 1887b. The fishery resources and fishing-grounds of Alaska, p. 81–115. *In* G. B. Goode, The Fisheries and Fishery Industries of the United States. Section 3. United States Commission of Fish and Fisheries.

Bean, T. H. and B. A. Bean. 1897. Contributions to the natural history of the Commander Islands. XII. Fishes collected at Bering and Copper Island by Nikolai A. Grebnitski and L. Stejnger. Proceedings of the United States Natural History Museum 19:237–254.

Beckmann, A. T., D. R. Gunderson, B. S. Miller, R. M. Buckley, and B. Goetz. 1998. Reproductive biology, growth, and natural mortality of Puget Sound rockfish, *Sebastes emphaeus* (Starks, 1911). Fishery Bulletin 96:352–356.

Behrents, K. C. 1983. The comparative ecology and interactions between two sympatric gobies, *Lythrypnus dalli* and *Lythrypnus zebra*. PhD Thesis, University of Southern California.

Bell, M. A. 1976. Evolution of phenotypic diversity in *Gasterosteus aculeatus* superspecies on the Pacific Coast of North America. Systematic Zoology 25:211–227.

Benet, D. L., E. J. Dick, and D. E. Pearson. 2010. Life history aspects of greenspotted rockfish (*Sebastes chlorostictus*) from central California. NOAA Technical Memorandum NMFS-SWFSC-446.

Bennet, F. D. 1840. Narrative of a whaling voyage round the globe from the year 1833 to 1836. Volumes 1 and 2. Richard Bentley, London.

Bennett, D. E. and R. S. Wydoski. 1977. Biology of the redtail surfperch (*Amphistichus rhodoterus*) from the central Oregon coast. United States Fish and Wildlife Service, Technical Paper 90.

Benoit, D., Y. Simard, and L. Fortier. 2008. Hydroacoustic detection of large winter aggregations of Arctic cod (*Boreogadus saida*) at depth in ice-covered Franklin Bay (Beaufort Sea). Journal of Geophysical Research 113. C06S90.

Bensussen, M. D. 1976. Chemical, shelf-life, and sensory problems associated with the use of ratfish (*Hydrolagus colliei*) in food formulation. Master Thesis, University of Washington, Seattle.

Bernardi, G. 2005. Phylogeography and demography of sympatric sister surfperch species, *Embiotoca jacksoni* and *E. lateralis* along the California coast: historical versus ecological factors. Evolution 59:386–394.

Bernardi, G. 2009. The name of the father: conflict between Louis and Alexander Agassiz and the *Embiotoca* surfperch radiation. Journal of Fish Biology 74:1049– 1055.

Bernardi, G. and G. Bucciarelli. 1999. Molecular phylogeny and speciation of the surfperches (Embiotocidae, Perciformes). Molecular Phylogenetics and Evolution 13:77–81.

Bernardi, G. and D. Talley. 2000. Genetic evidence for limited dispersal in the coastal California killifish, *Fundulus parvipinnis*. Journal of Experimental Marine Biology and Ecology 255:187–199.

Bernstein, B. 1977. Selective pressures and coevolution in a kelp canopy community in southern California. PhD Thesis, University of California, San Diego.

Best, E. A. 1963. Contribution to the biology of the Pacific hake, *Merluccius productus* (Ayres). California Cooperative Oceanic Fisheries Investigations Reports 9:51– 56.

Bestor, T. C. 2004. Tsukiji. University of California Press, Berkeley.

Bettaso, R. H. and J. N. Young. 1999. Evidence for freshwater spawning by striped mullet and return of the Pacific tenpounder in the lower Colorado River. California Fish and Game 85:75–76.

Birch, A. N. 1976. A letter from New Westminster. The Beaver, Autumn, p. 42–44.

Bizzarro, J. H. 2005. Fishery biology and feeding ecology of rays in Bahia Almejas, Mexico. Masters Thesis, San Francisco State University.

Blackburn, J. E. and P. B. Jackson. 1982. Seasonal composition and abundance of juvenile and adult marine finfish and crab species in the nearshore zone of Kodiak Island's eastside during April 1978 through March 1979. Final Report, Outer Continental Shelf Environmental Assessment Program, Research Unit 552.

Blackett, R. F. 1968. Spawning behavior, fecundity, and early life history of anadromous Dolly Varden, *Salvelinus malma* (Walbaum) in southeastern Alaska. Alaska Department of Fish and Game, Research Report Number 6.

Blake-Knox, H. 1866. Glances into the ichthyology of the County Dublin. The Zoologist, Second Series Number 14.

Blaylock, R. B., L. Margolis, and J. C. Holmes. 2003. The use of parasites in discriminating stocks of Pacific halibut (*Hippoglossus stenolepis*) in the northeast Pacific. Fishery Bulletin 101:1–9.

Block, B. A., J. R. Finnerty, A. F. R. Stewart, and J. Kidd. 1993. Evolution of endothermy in fish: mapping physiological traits on a molecular phylogeny. Science 260:210–214.

Bobko, S. J. and S. A. Berkeley. 2004. Maturity, ovarian cycle, fecundity, and age- specific parturition of black rockfish (*Sebastes melanops*). Fishery Bulletin 102:418–429.

Boehlert, G. W. and M. M. Yoklavich. 1984. Reproduction, embryonic energetics, and the maternal-fetal relationship in the viviparous genus *Sebastes* (Pisces: Scorpaenidae). Biological Bulletin 167:354–370.

Bonar, S. A., G. B. Pauley, and G. L. Thomas. 1989. Species profiles: life histories and environmental requirements of coastal fishes and invertebrates (Pacific Northwest). Pink salmon. United States Fish and Wildlife Service, Biological Report 82(11.88).

Bonfil, R., M. Meyer, M. C. Scholl, R. Johnson, S. O'Brien, H. Oosthuizen, S. Swanson, D. Kotze, and M. Paterson. 2005. Transoceanic migration, spatial dynamics, and population linkages of white sharks. Science 310:100–103.

Bonnaterre, J. P. 1788. Tableau encyclopédique et methodique des trois règnes de la nature...Ichthyologie. Panckoucke, Paris.

Bonnot, P. 1931. A record catch of smelt. California Fish and Game 17:185.

Bottinelli, D. J. and L. G. Allen. 2007. A re-evaluation of age, growth, and batch fecundity in the California barracuda, *Sphyraena argentea*, from southern California based on specimens taken from 2000 to 2002. California Fish and Game 93:167–199.

Boustany, A. M., K. C. M. Weng, S. D. Anderson, P. Pyle, and B. A. Block. 2008. Case study: white shark movements in the North Pacific pelagic ecosystem, p. 82–86. *In* M. D. Camhi, E. K. Pikitch, and E. A. Babcock (eds.). Sharks of the open ocean biology, fisheries, and conservation. Blackwell, Oxford. Bulletin 6:41–48.

Bowers, P. M. and M. L. Moss. 2001. The North Point Wet Site and the subsistence importance of Pacific cod of the northern Northwest Coast, p. 168–177. *In* S. C. Gerlach and M. S. Murray (eds.). People and Wildlife in Northern North America. BAR International Series 944.

Boyd, J., C. Brumwell, and R. A. MacLeod. 1953. Investigation of the source of an offensive odour in a shipment of gray cod. Fisheries Research Board of Canada, Progress Reports of the Pacific Coast Stations Number 96:20–21.

Brantley, R. K. and A. H. Bass. 1994. Alternative male spawning tactics and acoustic signals in the plainfin midshipman fish *Porichthys notatus* Girard (Teleostei; Batrachoididae). Ethology 96:213–232.

Bray, R. N. and M. A. Hixon. 1978. Night-shocker: Predatory behavior of the Pacific electric ray (*Torpedo californica*). Science 200:333–334.

Bray, R. N., A. C. Miller, and G. G. Geesey. 1981. The fish connection: A trophic link between planktonic and rocky reef communities: Science 214:204–205.

Brett, J. R. 1979. Some morphological and behavioural adaptations of pile perch (*Rhacochilus vacca*) feeding on mussels (*Mytilus edulis*). Canadian Journal of Zoology 57:658–664.

Briggs, J. C. 1953. The behavior and reproduction of salmonid fishes in a small coastal stream. California Department of Fish and Game, Fish Bulletin 94.

Brill, R. B. and P. G. Bushnell. 2001. The cardiovascular system of tunas, p. 79–120. *In* B. A. Block and E. D. Stevens (eds.). Tuna: Physiology, Ecology, and Evolution. Academic Press, San Diego.

Brodziak, J. and R. Mikus. 2000. Variation in life history parameters of Dover sole, *Microstomus pacificus*, off the coasts of Washington, Oregon, and northern California. Fishery Bulletin 98:661–673.

Brothers, E. B. 1975. The comparative ecology and behavior of three sympatric California gobies. PhD Thesis, University of California, San Diego.

Brown, E. D. 2002. Life history, distribution, and size structure of Pacific capelin in Prince William Sound and the northern Gulf of Alaska. ICES Journal of Marine Science 59:983–996.

Bruce, B. D. 2008. The biology and ecology of the white shark, *Carcharodon carcharias*, p. 69–81. *In* M. D. Camhi, E. K. Pikitch, and E. A. Babcock (eds.). Sharks of the Open Ocean Biology, Fisheries, and Conservation. Blackwell, Oxford.

Brunnschweiler, J. M. 2006. Sharksucker-shark interaction in two carcharhinid species. Marine Ecology 27:89–94.

Buckley, T. W. 1997. Substrate associated recruitment of juvenile *Sebastes* in artificial reef and natural habitats in Puget Sound and the San Juan Archipelago, Washington. Washington Department of Fish and Wildlife Report RAD97-06.

Bureau of Commercial Fisheries. 1937. The commercial fish catch of California for the year 1935. Division of Fish and Game of California, Fish Bulletin 49.

Bureau of Marine Fisheries. 1949. The commercial fish catch of California for the year 1947 with an historical review 1916–1947. California Department of Fish Game, Fish Bulletin 74.

Burge, R. T. and S. A. Schultz. 1973. The marine environment in the vicinity of Diablo Cove with special reference to abalones and bony fishes. California Department of Fish and Game, Marine Technical Report 19.

Burger, J., M. Gochfeld, C. Jeitner, S. Burke, and T. Stamm. 2007. Metal levels in flathead sole (*Hippoglossoides elassodon*) and great sculpin (*Myoxocephalus polyacanthocephalus*) from Adak Island, Alaska: potential risk to predators and fishermen. Environmental Research 103:62–69.

Burridge, C. P. 2002. Antitropicality of Pacific fishes: molecular insights. Environmental Biology of Fishes 65:151–164.

Busby, M. S. 1998. Guide to the identification of larval and early juvenile poachers (Scorpaeniformes: Agonidae) from the northeastern Pacific Ocean and Bering Sea. NOAA Technical Report NMFS 137.

Busby, M. S., A. C. Matarese, and K. L. Mier. 2000. Annual, seasonal, and diel composition of larval and juvenile fishes collected by dip-net in Clam Bay, Puget Sound, Washington, from 1985 to 1995. NOAA Technical Memorandum NMFS-AFSC-111.

Butler, J. L., K. A. Dahlin, and H. G. Moser. 1996. Growth and duration of the planktonic phase and a stage based population matrix of Dover sole, *Microstomus pacificus*. Bulletin of Marine Science 58:29–43.

Byerly, M. M. 2001. The ecology of age-1 copper rockfish (*Sebastes caurinus*) in vegetated habitats of Sitka Sound, Alaska. Masters Thesis, University of Alaska Fairbanks at Juneau.

Cailliet, G. M. and D. W. Bedford. 1983. The biology of three pelagic sharks from California waters, and their emerging fisheries: a review. California Cooperative Oceanic Fisheries Investigations Reports 24:57–69.

Cailliet, G. M., H. F. Mollet, G. G. Pittenger, D. Bedford, and L. J. Natanson. 1992. Growth and demography of the Pacific angel shark (*Squatina californica*), based upon tag returns off California. Australian Journal of Marine and Freshwater Research 43:1313–1330.

Campbell, G. and R. A. Collins. 1975. The age and growth of the Pacific bonito, *Sarda chiliensis*, in the eastern North Pacific. California Fish and Game 61:181–200.

Cárdenas, L., C. E. Hernández, E. Poulin, A. Magoulas, I. Kornfield, and F. P. Ojeda. 2005. Origin, diversification, and historical biogeography of the genus *Trachurus* (Perciformes:Carangidae). Molecular Phylogenetics and Evolution 35:496–507.

Carey, F. G. and B. H. Robison. 1981. Daily patterns in the activities of swordfish, *Xiphias gladius*, observed by acoustic telemetry. Fishery Bulletin 79:277–292.

Carey, F. G. and J. M. Teal. 1969. Mako and porbeagle: warm-bodied sharks. Comparative Biochemistry and Physiology 28:199–204.

Carey, F. G., J. M. Teal, J.W. Kanwisher, and K. D. Lawson. 1971. Warm bodied fish. American Zoologist 11:135–144.

Carl, G. C. 1964. Some common marine fishes of British Columbia. British Columbia Provincial Museum, Handbook No. 23.

Carlisle, J. G. Jr., J. W. Schott, and N. J. Abramson. 1960. The barred surfperch (*Amphistichus argenteus* Agassiz) in southern California. California Department of Fish and Game, Fish Bulletin 109.

Carlson, H. R. 1995. Consistent yearly appearance of age-0 walleye pollock, *Theragra chalcogramma*, at a coastal site in southeastern Alaska, 1973–1994. Fishery Bulletin 93:386–390.

Cartamil, D. P. and C. G. Lowe. 2004. Diel movement patterns of ocean sunfish *Mola mola* off southern California. Marine Ecology Progress Series 266:245–253.

Carter, W. R. III. 1965. Racial variations of the arrow goby, *Clevelandia ios* (Jordan and Gilbert 1882) in Puget Sound and on the coast of Washington State. Master Thesis, University of Washington, Seattle.

Cass, A. J., R. J. Beamish, and G. A. McFarlane. 1990. Lingcod (*Ophiodon elongatus*). Canadian Special Publication of Fisheries and Aquatic Sciences 109.

Chamberlain, D. W. 1979. Histology of the reproductive systems and comparison of selected morphological characters in four eastern Pacific species of *Citharichthys* (Pisces: Bothidae). PhD Thesis, University of Southern California.

Chapman, F. A., J. P. Van Eenennaam, and S. I. Doroshov. 1996. The reproductive condition of white sturgeon, *Acipenser transmontanus*, in San Francisco Bay, California. Fishery Bulletin 94:628–634.

Chereshnev, I., M. Nazarkin, M. Skopets, D. Pitruk, A. Shestakov, M. Yabe, G. Shinohara, and N. Suzuki. 2001. Annotated list of fish-like vertebrates and fish in Tauisk Bay (northern part of the Sea of Okhotsk), p. 64–86. *In* A. V. Andreev and H. H. Bergmann (eds.). Biodiversity and ecological status along the northern coast of the Sea of Okhotsk. Institute of Biological Problems of the North, Dalnauka, Vladivostok, Russia.

Chiang, W.-C., C.-L. Sun, S.-Z. Yeh, and W.-C. Su. 2004. Age and growth of sailfish (*Istiophorus platypterus*) in waters off eastern Taiwan. Fishery Bulletin 102:251– 263.

Chilton, E. 2010. Maturity and growth of female dusky rockfish (*Sebastes variabilis*) in the central Gulf of Alaska. Fishery Bulletin 108:70–78.

Chow, S. 1998. Genetic comparison of Pacific and Mediterranean swordfish, *Xiphias gladius*, by RFLP analysis of the mitochondrial D-loop region, p. 239–244. *In* I. Barrett, O. Sosa-Nishizaki, and N. Bartoo (eds.). Biology and Fisheries of Swordfish, *Xiphias gladius*. NOAA Technical Report NMFS 142.

Chute, G. R. 1930. Seen kow. California Fish and Game 16:23–35.

Clark, F. N. 1925. The life history of *Leuresthes tenuis*, an atherine fish with tide controlled spawning habits. California Fish and Game Commission, Fish Bulletin 10.

Clarke, T. A. 1970. Territorial behavior and population dynamics of a pomacentrid fish, the garibaldi, *Hypsypops rubicunda*. Ecological Monographs 40:189–212.

Clarke, T. A. 1971. Territory boundaries, courtship, and social behavior in the garibaldi, *Hypsypops rubicunda* (Pomacentridae). Copeia 1971(2):295–299.

Clarke, A. D., A. Lewis, K. H. Telmer, and J. M. Shrimpton. 2007. Life history and age at maturity of an anadromous smelt, the eulachon *Thaleichthys pacificus* (Richardson). Journal of Fish Biology 71:1479–1493.

Clausen, D. M. 2008. The giant grenadier in Alaska. American Fisheries Society Symposium 63:413–450.

Clemens, W. A. and G. V. Wilby. 1949. Fishes of the Pacific Coast of Canada. Fisheries Research Board of Canada. Bulletin 68.

Cobb, J. N. 1918. Increasing our Pacific Coast fishery resources. State Council of Defense, Sacramento, California.

Cobb, J. N. 1919.The canning of fishery products. Miller Freeman, Seattle, Washington.

Cole, K. S. 1983. Protogynous hermaphroditism in a temperate zone territorial marine goby, *Coryphopterus nicholsii*. Copeia 1983(3):809–812.

Cole, K. S. 1984. Social spacing in the temperate marine goby *Coryphopterus nicholsi*. Marine Biology 80:307–314.

Coleman, R. M. 1992. Reproductive biology and female parental care in the cockscomb prickleback, *Anoplarchus purpurescens* (Pisces: Stichaeidae). Environmental Biology of Fishes 35:177–186.

Collette, B. B. and L. N. Chao. 1975. Systematics and morphology of the bonitos (*Sarda*) and their relatives (Scombridae, Sardini). Fishery Bulletin 73:516–625.

Collette, B. B. and G. Klein-MacPhee. 2002. Bigelow and Schroeder's Fishes of the Gulf of Maine. Smithsonian Institution Press, Washington, D. C.

Collette, B. B., J. R. McDowell, and J. E. Graves. 2006. Phylogeny of recent billfishes (Xiphioidei). Bulletin of Marine Science 79:455–468.

Collette, B. B., C. Reeb, and B. A. Block. 2001. Systematics of the tunas and mackerels   (Scombridae), p. 5–30. *In* B. A. Block and E. D. Stevens (eds.). Tuna: Physiology, Ecology, and Evolution. Academic Press, San Diego.

Collins, J. W. 1892. Report on the fisheries of the Pacific Coast of the United States, p. 3–269. United States Commission of Fish and Fisheries. Part XVI. Report of the Commissioner for 1888. Appendix I.

Colton, M. and R. J. Larson. 2007. Aspects of the life history of treefish, *Sebastes serriceps* (Sebastidae). California Cooperative Fisheries Investigations Reports 48:177–190.

Compagno, L. J. V. 1988. Sharks of the order Carcharhiniformes. Princeton University Press, Princeton, New Jersey.

Compagno, L. J. V. 2001. Sharks of the world. Volume 2. Bullhead, mackerel and carpet shark (Heterodontiformes, Lamniformes and Orectolobiformes). FAO Species Catalogue for Fishery Purposes No. 1, Volume 2.

Cooksey, D. J. 1980. Age, growth and maturity of the ocean whitefish, *Caulolatilus princeps*. Masters Thesis, California State University, Long Beach.

Cooper, J. G. 1863. On new genera and species of Californian fishes—Number II. Proceedings of the California Academy of Sciences (Series 1) 3:93–97.

Cooper, L. D. 1994. Aspects of the life history of hornyhead turbot, *Pleuronichthys verticalis*, off southern California. Southern California Coastal Water Research Project Annual Report 1992–93.

Cope, J. M. 2004. Population genetics and phylogeography of the blue rockfish (*Sebastes mystinus*) from Washington and California. Canadian Journal of Fisheries and Aquatic Sciences 61:332–342.

Cope, J. M. and A. D. MacCall. 2005. Status of kelp greenling (*Hexagrammos decagrammus*) in Oregon and California waters as assessed in 2005. Stock Assessment, Pacific Fisheries Management Council.

Cope, J. M. and A. E. Punt. 2005. Status of cabezon (*Scorpaenichthys marmoratus*) in California waters as assessed in 2005. Stock Assessment, Pacific Fisheries Management Council.

Coull, K. A., A. S. Jermyn, A. W. Newton, G. I. Henderson, and W. B. Hall. 1989. Length/weight relationships for 88 species of fish encountered in the northeast Atlantic. Scottish Fisheries Research Report Number 43.

Cowan, R. E. 1933. Alexander S. Taylor, 1817–1876. Quarterly of the California Historical Society 12(1):18–24.

Craig, M. T. and P. A. Hastings. 2007. A molecular phylogeny of the groupers of the subfamily Epinephelinae (Serranidae) with a revised classification of the Epinephelini. Ichthyological Research 54:1–17.

Craik, G. J. S. 1978. A further investigation of the homing behaviour of the intertidal cottid, *Oligocottus maculosus* Girard. PhD Thesis, University of British Columbia, Vancouver.

Crane, P., T. Viavant, and J. Wenburg. 2005. Overwintering patterns of Dolly Varden *Salvelinus malma* in the Sagavanirktok River in the Alaska North Slope inferred using mixed-stock analysis. Alaska Fisheries Technical Report Number 84.

Crawford, S. S. and A. M. Muir. 2008. Global introductions of salmon and trout in the genus *Oncorhynchus*: 1870–2007. Reviews of Fish Biology and Fisheries 18:313–364.

Croker, R. S. 1933. The California mackerel fishery. California Division of Fish and Game, Fish Bulletin 40.

Croker, R. S. 1934. The spawning of *Atherinops insularum insularum*. Copeia 1934(1):43.

Croker, R. S. 1936. Smoked, salted and dried sea foods of California. California Fish and Game 22:1–12.

Cross, J. N. 1981. Structures of a rocky intertidal fish assemblage. PhD Thesis, University of Washington, Seattle.

Cross, J. N. 1988. Aspects of the biology of two scyliorhinid sharks, *Apristurus brunneus* and *Parmaturus xaniurus*, from the upper continental slope off Southern California. Fishery Bulletin 86:691–702.

Crow, K. D., Z. Kanamoto, and G. Bernardi. 2004. Molecular phylogeny of the hexagrammid fishes using a multi-locus approach. Molecular Phylogenetics and Evolution 32:986–997.

Cruz-Martinez, A., X. Chiappa-Carrara, and V. Arenas-Fuentes. 2004. Age and growth of the bull shark, *Carcharhinus leucas*, from southern Gulf of Mexico. Journal of Northwest Atlantic Fishery Science 35:367–374.

Dall, W. H. 1870. Alaska and its Resources. Lee and Shepard, Boston. Reprinted by Arno and the New York Times.

Dark, T. A. 1975. Age and growth of Pacific hake, *Merluccius productus*. Fishery Bulletin 73:336–355.

David, L. R. 1943. Miocene fishes of southern California. Geological Society of America Special Papers Number 43.

David, L. R. 1956. Tertiary anacanthin fishes from California and the Pacific Northwest; their paleoecological significance. Journal of Paleontology 30:568–607.

Davies, S., A. Griffiths, and T. E. Reimchen. 2006. Pacific hagfish, *Eptatretus stoutii*, spotted ratfish, *Hydrolagus colliei*, and scavenger activity on tethered carrion in subtidal benthic communities off western Vancouver Island. Canadian Field- Naturalist 120:363–366.

Davis, C. D., G. M. Cailliet, and D. A. Ebert. 2007. Age and growth of the roughtail skate *Bathyraja trachura* (Gilbert 1892) from the eastern North Pacific. Environmental Biology of Fishes 80:325–336.

Dayneko, J. R. 1975. Life history of the rockpool blenny, *Hypsoblennius gilberti* (Jordan), at Point Fermin, California. Masters Thesis, California State University, Long Beach.

DeCicco, A. L. 1997. Movements of postsmolt anadromous Dolly Varden in northwestern Alaska. American Fisheries Society Symposium 19:175–183.

De Crosta, M. A., L. R. Taylor Jr., and J. D. Parrish. 1984. Age determination, growth, and energetics of three species of carcharhinid sharks in Hawaii, p. 75–95. *In* R. W. Grigg and K. Y. Tanoue (eds.). Proceedings of the Second Symposium on Resource Investigations in the Northwestern Hawaiian Islands. Volume 2. Sea Grant Miscellaneous Report UNIHI-SEAGRANT-MR-84-01.

De La Cruz Agüero, J. and V. M. Cota Gómez. 2006. Length-weight relationships of 10 deep-sea fish species from the Mexican Pacific Ocean. Journal of Applied Ichthyology 22:319–321.

DeMartini, E. E. 1978. Apparent paternal care in *Liparis fucensis* (Pisces: Cyclopteridae). Copeia 1978(3):537–539.

DeMartini, E. E. 1985. Social behavior and coloration changes in painted greenling, *Oxylebius pictus* (Pisces: Hexagrammidae). Copeia 1985(4):966–975.

DeMartini, E. E. 1986. Reproductive colorations, paternal behavior and egg masses of kelp greenling, *Hexagrammos decagrammus*, and whitespotted greenling, *H. stelleri*. Northwest Science 60:32–35.

DeMartini, E. E. 1988. Size-assortative courtship and competition in two embiotocid fishes. Copeia 1988(2):336–344.

DeMartini, E. E. 1991. Annual variations in fecundity, egg size, and the gonadal and somatic conditions of queenfish *Seriphus politus* (Sciaenidae). Fishery Bulletin 89:9–18.

DeMartini, E. E. and M. E. Anderson. 1980. Comparative survivorship and life history of painted greenling (*Oxylebius pictus*) in Puget Sound, Washington and Monterey Bay, California. Environmental Biology of Fishes 5:33–47.

DeMartini, E. E. and B. G. Patten. 1979. Egg guarding and reproductive biology of the red Irish lord, *Hemilepidotus hemilepidotus*. Syesis 12:41–55.

DeMartini, E. E., T. O. Moore, and K. M. Plummer. 1983. Reproductive and growth dynamics of *Hyperprosopon argenteum* (Embiotocidae) near San Diego, California. Environmental Biology of Fishes 8:29–38.

DeMartini, E. E., J. H. Uchiyama, and H. A. Williams. 2000. Sexual maturity, sex ratio, and size composition of swordfish, *Xiphias gladius*, caught by the Hawaii-based pelagic longline fishery. Fishery Bulletin 98:489–506.

DeMartini, E. E., J. H. Uchiyama, R. L. Humphreys Jr., J. D. Sampaga, and H. A. Williams. 2007. Age and growth of swordfish (*Xiphias gladius*) caught by the Hawaii-based pelagic longline fishery. Fishery Bulletin 105:356–367.

Demory, R. L., M. J. Hosie, N. T. Eyck, and B. O. Forstberg. 1976. Marine resource surveys on the continental shelf off Oregon, 1971–74. Commercial Fisheries Research and Development Act, Completion Report, Oregon Department of Fish and Wildlife.

Dempster, R. P. and E. S. Herald. 1961. Notes on the horn shark, *Heterodontus francisci*, with observations on mating activities. Occasional Papers of the California Academy of Sciences 33.

Deriso, R. B., M. N. Maunder, and W. H. Pearson. 2008. Incorporating covariates into fisheries stock assessment models with application to Pacific herring. Ecological Applications 18:1270–1286.

DeWitt, J. W. 1955. A record of an attack by a leopard shark (*Triakis semifasciata* Girard). California Fish and Game 41:348.

Didier, D. A. 2004. Phylogeny and classification of extant Holocephali, p. 115–135. *In* J. C. Carrier, J. A. Musick, and M. R. Heithaus (eds.). Biology of Sharks and Their Relatives. CRC Press, Boca Raton, Florida.

Diener, D. R. 1976. Hermaphroditism in fish: a comparative study of the reproductive biology and endocrinology of the California Labridae. PhD Thesis, University of California, San Diego.

Domeier, M. L. 2006. An analysis of Pacific striped marlin (*Tetrapturus audax*) horizontal movement patterns using pop-up satellite archival tags. Bulletin of Marine Science 79:811–825.

Dorn, M., K. Aydin, S. Barbeaux, M. Guttormsen, B. Megrey, K. Spallinger, and M. Wilkins. 2007. Gulf of Alaska walleye pollock, p. 51–168. *In* Stock Assessment and Fishery Evaluation Report for the Groundfish Resources of the Gulf of Alaska. North Pacific Fishery Management Council, Anchorage, Alaska.

Drazen, J. C. 2002. Energy budgets and feeding rates of *Coryphaenoides acrolepis* and *C. armatus*. Marine Biology 140:677–686.

Drazen, J. C., S. K. Goffredi, B. Schlining, and D. S. Stakes. 2003. Aggregations of egg- brooding deep-sea fish and cephalopods on the Gorda Escarpment: a reproductive hot spot. Biological Bulletin 205:1–7.

Drilling, C. C. and M. S. Grober. 2005. An initial description of alternative male reproductive phenotypes in the bluebanded goby, *Lythrypnus dalli* (Teleostei, Gobiidae). Environmental Biology of Fishes 72:361–372.

Dryfoos, R. L. 1965. The life history and ecology of the longfin smelt in Lake Washington. PhD Thesis, University of Washington, Seattle.

Duffy-Anderson, J. T., K. M. Busby, and L. Ciannelli. 2002. Consequences of a superabundance of larval walleye pollock *Theraga chalcogramma* in the Gulf of Alaska in 1981. Marine Ecology Progress Series 243:179–190.

Duncan, K. M., A. P. Martin, B. W. Bowen, and H. G. deCouet. 2006. Global phylogeography of the scalloped hammerhead shark (*Sphyrna lewini*). Molecular Ecology 15:2239–2251.

Dunn, J. R. 1997. Charles Henry Gilbert (1859–1928): pioneer ichthyologist of the American West, p. 265–290. *In* T. W. Pietsch and W. D. Anderson (eds.). Collection Building in Ichthyology and Herpetology. Allen Press, Lawrence, Kansas.

Ebert, D. A. 1991. Observations on the predatory behaviour of the sevengill shark *Notorynchus cepedianus*. Sound African Journal of Marine Science 11:455–465.

Ebert, D. A. 2003. Sharks, rays, and chimaeras of California. University of California Press, Berkeley.

Ebert, D. A. and L. J. V. Compagno. 2007. Biodiversity and systematics of skates (Chondrichthyes: Rajiformes: Rajoidei). Environmental Biology of Fishes 80:11– 124.

Ebert, D. A. and C. D. Davis. 2007. Descriptions of skate egg cases (Chondrichthyes: Rajiformes: Rajoidei) from the eastern North Pacific. Zootaxa 1393:1–18.

Ebert, E. E. and C. H. Turner. 1962. The nesting behavior, eggs and larvae of the bluespot goby. California Fish and Game 48:249–252.

Ebert, D. A., W. D. Smith, and G. M. Cailliet. 2008. Reproductive biology of two commercially exploited skates, *Raja binoculata* and *R. rhina*, in the western Gulf of Alaska. Fisheries Research 94:48–57.

Ebert, D. A., J. R. Maurer, S. M. Ainsley, L. Barnett, and G. M. Cailliet. 2009. Life history and population dynamics of four endemic Alaskan skates: determining essential biological information for effective management of bycatch and target species. North Pacific Research Board Project Final Report 715.

Ebert, D. A., W. T. White, K. J. Goldman, L. J. V. Compagno, T. S. Daly-Engel, and R. D. Ward. 2010. Resurrection and redescription of *Squalus suckleyi* (Girard, 1854) from the North Pacific, with comments on the *Squalus acanthias* subgroup (Squaliformes: Squalidae). Zootaxa 2612:22–40.

Eckert, S. A. and B. S. Stewart. 2001. Telemetry and satellite tracking of whale sharks, *Rhincodon typus*, in the Sea of Cortez, Mexico, and the north Pacific Ocean. Environmental Biology of Fishes 60:299–308.

Eckmayer, W. J. 1979. Age and growth of four surfperches (Embiotocidae) from the outer harbor of Anaheim Bay, California. California Fish and Game 65:265–272.

Edwards, G. D. 1970. Observation of mating behavior of the striped perch and notes on possible reproductive activity of the rainbow perch. California Fish and Game 56:205–206.

Ehrhardt, N. M. 1973. Population dynamics of English sole (*Parophrys vetulus*) off the coast of Washington. PhD Thesis, University of Washington, Seattle.

Eigenmann, C. H. 1891. The spawning seasons of San Diego fishes. American Naturalist 25:578–579.

Eigenmann, C. H. 1892. The fishes of San Diego, California. Proceedings of the United States National Museum 15:123–178.

Eigenmann, C. H. and R. S. Eigenmann. 1889. Notes from the San Diego Biological Laboratory. The West American Scientist 6:147–150.

Elliott, J. 1992. The role of sea anemones as refuges and feeding habitats for the temperate fish *Oxylebius pictus*. Environmental Biology of Fishes 35:381–400.

Elliott, K. H. and A. J. Gaston. 2008. Mass-length relationships and energy content of fishes and invertebrates delivered to nestling thick-billed murres *Uria lomvia* in the Canadian Arctic, 1981–2007. Marine Ornithology 36:25–34.

Erisman, B. E. and L. G. Allen. 2005. Color patterns and associated behaviors in the kelp bass *Paralabrax clathratus* (Teleostei:Serranidae). Bulletin of the Southern California Academy of Sciences 104:45–62.

Erisman, B. E. and L. G. Allen. 2006. Reproductive behaviour of a temperate serranid fish *Paralabrax clathratus* (Girard), from Santa Catalina Island, California, U.S.A. Journal of Fish Biology 68:157–184.

Eschmeyer, W. N., E. S. Herald, and H. Hammann. 1983. A field guide to Pacific Coast fishes of North America. Houghton Mifflin, Boston.

Espino Barr, E., M. G. Cabello, E. G. Cabral Solis, A. Garcia Boa, and M. Puente Gómez. 2008. Growth of the Pacific jack *Caranx caninus* (Pisces: Carangidae) from the coast of Colima, México. Revista de Biologia Tropical 56:171–179.

Evermann, B. W. and E. L. Goldsborough. 1907. The fishes of Alaska. Bulletin of the United States Bureau of Fisheries 26:219–360.

Fall, J. A., D. Koster, and M. Turek. 2007. Subsistence harvests of Pacific halibut in Alaska, 2006. Alaska Department of Fish and Game, Division of Subsistence, Technical Paper Number 333.

Fargo, J. and A. R. Kronlund. 2000. Variation in growth for Hecate Strait English sole (*Parophrys vetulus*) with implications for stock assessment. Journal of Sea Research 44:3–15.

Feder, H. M., C. H. Turner, and C. Limbaugh. 1974. Observations on fishes associated with kelp beds in southern California. California Fish and Game, Fish Bulletin 160.

Félix-Uraga, R., V. M. Gómez-Muñoz, C. Quiñónez-Velázquez, F. N. Melo-Barrera, K. T. Hill, and W. Garcîa-Franco. 2005. Pacific sardine (*Sardinops sagax*) stock discrimination off the west coast of Baja California and southern California using otolith morphometry. California Cooperative Oceanic Fisheries Investigations Reports 46:113–121.

Fergusson, I. K., L. J. V. Compagno, and M. A. Marks. 2000. Predation by white sharks *Carcharodon carcharias* (Chondrichthyes: Lamnidae) upon chelonians, with new records from the Mediterranean Sea and a first record of the ocean sunfish *Mola mola* (Osteichthyes: Molidae) as stomach contents. Environmental Biology of Fishes 58:447–453.

Field, J. C. and R. C. Francis. 2006. Considering ecosystem-based fisheries management in the California Current. Marine Policy 30:552–569.

Field, J. C., E. J. Dick, and A. D. MacCall. 2007. Stock assessment model for the shortbelly rockfish, *Sebastes jordani*, in the California Current. NOAA Technical Memorandum NMFS-SWFSC-405.

Field, J. C., R. C. Francis, and K. Aydin. 2006. Top-down modeling and bottom-up dynamics: linking a fisheries-based ecosystem model with climate hypotheses in the northern California Current. Progress in Oceanography 68:238–270.

Field, J. C., E. J. Dick, D. Pearson, and A. D. MacCall. 2010. Status of bocaccio, *Sebastes paucispinis*, in the Conception, Monterey and Eureka INPFC areas for 2009. Pacific Fisheries Management Council, Stock Assessment.

Fierstine, H. L. 2006. Fossil history of billfishes (Xiphioidei). Bulletin of Marine Science 79:433–453.

Fischer, W., F. Krupp, W. Schneider, C. Sommer, K. E. Carpenter, and V. H. Niem. 1995. Guia FAO para la identificación de especies para los fines de la pesca. Pacifico centro-oriental. 3 Volumes. FAO, Rome, Italy.

Fisher, J. P. and W. G. Pearcy. 1983. Reproduction, growth and feeding of the mesopelagic fish *Tactostoma macropus* (Melanostomiatidae). Marine Biology 74:257–267.

Fitch, J. E. 1951. The whale shark, *Rhineodon typus*, off northern Baja California. California Fish and Game 37:351.

Fitch, J. E. 1952. Toxicity and taxonomic notes on the squaretail, *Tetragonurus cuvieri*. California Fish and Game 38:251–252.

Fitch, J. E. 1963. A review of the fishes of the genus *Pleuronichthys*. Los Angeles County Museum, Contributions in Science Number 76.

Fitch, J. E. and R. J. Lavenberg. 1971. Marine food and game fishes of California. University of California Press, Berkeley, Los Angeles, California.

Flamming, B. E., D. A. Ebert, and G. M. Cailliet. 2008. Reproductive biology of deep- sea catsharks (Chondrichthyes: Scyliorhinidae) in the eastern North Pacific. Environmental Biology of Fishes 81:35–49.

Follett, W. L. 1936. The unbarred phase of the California surf-fish, *Amphistichus argenteus*. Copeia 1936(2):117–118.

Follett, W. L. 1942. Another aberrant color-phase of *Amphistichus argenteus*. Copia 1942(1):49–50.

Follett, W. I., D. Gotshall, and J. G. Smith. 1960. Northerly occurrences of the scorpid fish *Medialuna californiensis* (Steindachner), with meristic data, life-history notes, and discussion of the fisheries. California Fish and Game 46:165–175.

Forrester, C. R. 1969. Life history information on some groundfish species. Fisheries Research Board of Canada, Technical Report 105.

Freeman, M. C., N. Neally, and G. D. Grossman. 1985. Aspects of the life history of the fluffy sculpin, *Oligocottus snyderi*. Fishery Bulletin 83:645–655.

Fritzsche, R. A. 1980. Revision of the eastern Pacific Syngnathidae (Pisces: Syngnathiformes), including both recent and fossil forms. Proceedings of the California Academy of Sciences 42:181–227.

Froeschke, B., L. G. Allen, and D. J. Pondella II. 2007. Life history and courtship behavior of black perch, *Embiotoca jacksoni* (Teleostomi: Embiotocidae), from southern California. Pacific Science 61:521–531.

Fry, D. H. Jr. 1936. A preliminary summary of the life history of the Pacific mackerel. California Fish and Game, 22(1):30–39.

Funes-Rodriguez, R., J. F. Elorduy-Garay, A. Hinojosa-Medina, and A. Zárate- Villafranco. 2009. Interannual distribution of Pacific hake *Merluccius productus* larvae in the southern part of the California Current. Journal of Fish Biology 75:630–646.

Gadomski, D. M. and S. M. Caddell. 1991. Effects of temperature on early-life-history stages of California halibut *Paralichthys californicus*. Fishery Bulletin 89:567– 576.

Garcia-Contreras, O. E., C. Quinónez-Velázquez, R. E. Morán-Angulo, and M. C. Valez-Pineda. 2009. Age, growth, and age structure of amarillo snapper off the coast of Mazatlán, Sinaloa, Mexico. North American Journal of Fisheries Management 29:223–230.

Gardner, M. M. 1999. Working on white womankind: white working women in the San Francisco anti-Chinese movement, 1877–1890. Journal of Social History 33:73–95.

Garrison, K. J. and B. S. Miller. 1982. Review of the early life history of Puget Sound fishes. Fisheries Research Institute, University of Washington Publication 8216.

Gburski, C. M., S. K. Gaichas, and D. K. Kimura. 2007. Age and growth of big skate (*Raja binoculata*) and longnose skate (*R. rhina*) in the Gulf of Alaska. Environmental Biology of Fishes 80:337–349.

Geise, L. A. 2007. Evaluation of the off-flavor in English sole (*Parophrys vetulus*) using descriptive analysis techniques and consumer testing. Masters Thesis, Oregon State University, Corvallis.

Gende, S. M., T. P. Quinn, and M. F. Willson. 2001a. Consumption choice by bears feeding on salmon. Oecologia 127:372–382.

Gende, S. M., J. N. Womble, M. F. Willson, and B. H. Marston. 2001b. Cooperative foraging by Steller sea lions, *Eumetopias jubatus*. Canadian Field-Naturalist 115:355–356.

Gerke, B. L. 2002. Spawning habitat characteristics of Pacific herring (*Clupea pallasii*) in Prince William Sound, Alaska. Master Thesis, University of Alaska, Fairbanks.

Gillispie, J. G., R. L. Smith, E. Barbour, and W. E. Barber. 1997. Distribution, abundance, and growth of Arctic cod in the Northeastern Chukchi Sea. American Fisheries Society Symposium 19:81–89.

Glubokov, A. I. 2009. New data on the blue-eyed searcher *Bathymaster signatus* (Bathymasteridae, Perciformes) from the northwestern part of the Bering Sea. Journal of Ichthyology 49:154–161.

Gluyas-Millán, M. G. and C. Quiñonez-Veláquez. 1997. Age, growth, and reproduction of Pacific mackerel *Scomber japonicus* in the Gulf of California. Bulletin of Marine Science 61:837–847.

Gmelch, G. and S. B. Gmelch. 1985. Resource use in a small Alaska city-Sitka. Alaska Department of Fish and Game, Division of Subsistence Technical Paper Number 90.

Gobalet, K. W., P. D. Schultz, T. A. Wake, and N. Siefkin. 2004. Archaeological perspectives on Native American fisheries of California, with emphasis on steelhead and salmon. Transactions of the American Fisheries Society 133:801–833.

Goldman, K. J. and J. A. Musick. 2006. Growth and maturity of salmon sharks (*Lamna ditropis*) in the eastern and western North Pacific, and comments on back- calculation methods. Fishery Bulletin 104:278–292.

Gomelyuk, V. E. 2000. Comparative analysis of everyday behavior and mode of the life of three species of *Hexagrammos* (Hexagrammidae, Scorpaeniformes) in summer. Journal of Ichthyology 40:74–85.

Gonzalez-Acosta, A. F., G. de la Cruz-Agüero, and J. de la Cruz-Agüero. 2004. Length- weight relationships of fish species caught in a mangrove swamp in the Gulf of California (Mexico). Journal of Applied Ichthyology 20:154–155.

Goode, G. B. 1884. The fisheries and fishery industries of the United States. U. S. Government Printing Office, Washington, D. C.

Goodman, D. H., S. B. Reid, M. F. Docker, G. R. Haas, and A. P. Kinziger. 2008. Mitochondrial DNA evidence for high levels of gene flow among populations of a widely distributed anadromous lamprey *Entosphenus tridentatus* (Petromyzontidae). Journal of Fish Biology 72:400–417.

Gorbunova, N. N. 1970. Spawning and development of greenlings (family Hexagrammidae), p. 121–185. *In* T. S. Rass (ed.). Greenlings: Taxonomy, Biology and Interoceanic Transplantation. Academy of Sciences of the USSR, Transactions of the Institute of Oceanology, Volume 59. Israel Program for Scientific Translations.

Graham, J. B. and K. A. Dickson. 2001. Anatomical and physiological specializations for endothermy, p. 121–165. *In* B. A. Block and E. D. Stevens (eds.). Tuna: Physiology, Ecology, and Evolution. Academic Press, San Diego.

Graves, J. E. and J. R. McDowell. 1995. Inter-ocean genetic divergence of istiophorid billfishes. Marine Biology 122:193–203.

Green, J. M. and L. R. Mitchell. 1997. Biology of the fish doctor, an eelpout, from Cornwallis Island, Northwest Territories, Canada. American Fisheries Society Symposium 19:140–147.

Gregg, J. L., D. M. Anderi, and D. K. Kimura. 2006. Improving the precision of otolith- based age estimates for Greenland halibut (*Reinhardtius hippoglossoides*) with preparation methods adapted for fragile sagittae. Fishery Bulletin 104:643–648.

Gresh, T., J. Lichatowich, and P. Schoonmaker. 2000. An estimation of historic and current levels of salmon production in the Northeast Pacific ecosystem. Fisheries 25(1):15–21.

Grijalva-Chon, J. M., K. Numachi, O. Sosa-Nishizaki, and J. de la Rosa-Velez. 1994. Mitochondrial DNA analysis of North Pacific swordfish *Xiphias gladius* population structure. Marine Ecology Progress Series 115:15–19.

Groce, J. K. 2002. Influence of life history and lipids on the bioaccumulation of organochlorines in demersal fishes. Master Thesis, San Diego State University.

Groot, C. and L. Margolis. 1991. Pacific salmon life histories. UBC Press, Vancouver.

Gudkov, P. K., M. V. Nazarkin, and Yu. E. Vostretsov. 2005. Reconstruction by fossil otoliths of the structure of population of Pacific navaga *Eleginus gracilis* (Gadidae) that inhabited Amur Bay 2400–2450 years ago. Journal of Ichthyology 45:295–300.

Gustafson, R. G., M. J. Ford, D. Teel, and J. S. Drake. 2010. Status review of eulachon (*Thaleichthys pacificus*) in Washington, Oregon, and California. NOAA Technical Memorandum NMFS-NWFSC-105.

Gustafson, R. G., W. H. Lenarz, B. B. McCain, C. C. Schmitt, W. S. Grant, T. L. Builder, and R. D. Methot. 2000. Status review of Pacific hake, Pacific cod, and walleye pollock from Puget Sound, Washington. NOAA Technical Memorandum NMFS- NWFSC-44.

Haaker, P. L., D. O. Parker, and K. C. Henderson. 1984. Observations of harbor seal, *Phoca vitulina richardsi*, feeding in southern California waters. Bulletin of the Southern California Academy of Sciences 83:152–153.

Hagerman, F. B. 1952. The biology of the Dover sole, *Microstomus pacificus* (Lockington). California Fish and Game, Fish Bulletin Number 85.

Haldorson, L., M. Prichett, D. Sterritt, and J. Watts. 1993. Abundance patterns of marine fish larvae during spring in a southeastern Alaskan bay. Fishery Bulletin 91:36– 44.

Hale, L. F. 2005. Age and growth of the round stingray, *Urobatis halleri*, at Seal Beach, California. Masters Thesis, California State University, Long Beach.

Hall, J. D., P. Bisson, and R. E. Gresswell (eds.). 1997. Sea-run cutthroat trout: biology, management, and future conservation. Oregon Chapter, American Fisheries Society, Corvallis.

Halstead, B. 1995. Dangerous marine animals that bite, sting, or are non-edible. Cornell Maritime Press, Centreville, Maryland.

Halstead, B. and N. C. Bunker. 1952. The venom apparatus of the ratfish, *Hydrolagus colliei*. Copeia 1952(3):128–138.

Hamilton, S. L., J. E. Caselle, J. D. Standish, D. M. Schroeder, M. S. Love, J. A. Rosales- Casian, and O. Sosa-Nishizaki. 2007. Size-selective harvesting alters life histories of a temperate sex-changing fish. Ecological Applications 17:2268–2280.

Hamlett, W. C., G. Kormanik, M. Storrie, B. Stevens, and T. I. Walker. 2005. Chondrichthyan parity, lecithotrophy and matrotrophy, p. 395–434. *In* W. C. Hamlett (ed.). Reproductive Biology and Phylogeny of Chondrichthyes; Sharks, Batoids, and Chimaeras. Vol. 3. Science Publishers, Enfield, New Hampshire.

Harper, R. D. and J. F. Case. 1999. Disruptive counter illumination and its anti-predatory value in the plainfin midshipman *Porichthys notatus*. Marine Biology 134:529– 541.

Harry, G. Y. Jr. 1959. Time of spawning, length at maturity, and fecundity of the English, petrale, and Dover soles (*Parophrys vetulus*, *Eopsetta jordani*, and *Microstomus pacificus*, respectively). Research Briefs, Fish Commission of Oregon 7:5–13.

Hart, J. L. 1967. Fecundity and length-weight relationship in lingcod. Journal of the Fisheries Research Board of Canada 24:2485–2489.

Hart, J. L. 1973. Pacific Fishes of Canada. Fisheries Research Board of Canada. Bulletin 180.

Hart, J. L. and J. L. McHugh. 1944. The smelts (Osmeridae) of British Columbia. Bulletin of the Fisheries Research Board of Canada 64.

Harvey, J. T. 1987. Population dynamics, annual food consumption, movements, and dive behaviors of harbor seals, *Phoca vitulina richardsi*, in Oregon. PhD Thesis, Oregon State University.

Hatler, D. F. 1976. The coastal mink of Vancouver Island, British Columbia. PhD Thesis, University of British Columbia, Vancouver.

Hauser, L. 2009. The molecular ecology of dogfish sharks, p. 229–252. *In* V. F. Gallucci, G. A. McFarlane, and G. G. Bargmann (eds.). Biology and Management of Dogfish Sharks. American Fisheries Society.

Hawgood, B. J. 1994. The lifes and viper of Dr Patrick Russell MD FRS (1727–1805): physician and naturalist. Toxicon 32:1295–1304.

Hay, D. E. and T. D. Beacham. 2005. Stock identification of eulachon (*Thaleichthys pacificus*), an anadromous smelt in the eastern Pacific. www.ices.dk/products/cmdocs/2005/k/k/405

Hay, D. E., M. C. Healey, D. M. Ware, and N. J. Wilimovsky. 1992. Distribution, abundance, and habitat of prey fish on the west coast of Vancouver Island, p. 22– 50. *In* K. Vermeer, R. W. Butler, and K. H. Morgan (eds.). The ecology, Status, and Conservation of Marine and Shoreline Birds on the West Coast of Vancouver Island. Canadian Wildlife Service, Occasional Paper No. 75.

Hay, D. E., K. A. Rose, J. Schweigert, and B. A. Megrey. 2008. Geographic variation in North Pacific herring populations: Pan-Pacific comparisons and implications for climate change impacts. Progress in Oceanography 77:233–240.

Heard, W. R. 1991. Life history of the pink salmon (*Oncorhynchus gorbuscha*), p. 19– 230. *In* C. Groot and L. Margolis (eds.). Pacific Salmon Life Histories. UBC Press, Vancouver.

Heath, K. L. I. 1980. Comparative life histories of two species of anchovies, *Anchoa delicatissima* and *A. compressa* (F. Engraulidae), from Newport Bay, California. Masters Thesis, California State University, Fullerton.

Hedley, J. 1997. Bank' ribbon-fish (*Regalecus glesne* Ascanius, 1772): a review of occurrences in British waters. Transactions of the Natural History Society of Northumbria 57:191–206.

Helm, R. C. 1990. Population dynamics of an intertidal eel blenny, *Cebidichthys violaceus*: diet, growth, homing, and avian predators. PhD Thesis, University of California, Davis.

Herald, E. S. 1939. The opah (*Lampris regius*) and its occurrence off the California coast. California Fish and Game 25:228–232.

Herald, E. S. and W. M. Ripley. 1951. The relative abundance of sharks and bat stingrays in San Francisco Bay. California Fish and Game 37:315–329.

Hershberger, P. K., R. M. Kocan, N. Elder, and J. R. Winton. 2004. Potential impacts of infectious diseases to populations of Pacific herring in Puget Sound. 2003 Georgia Basin/Puget Sound Research Conference Proceedings 2004.

Hicks, A. C., M. A. Haltuch, and C. Wetzel. 2009. Status of greenstriped rockfish (*Sebastes elongatus*) along the outer coast of California, Oregon, and Washington. Pacific Fisheries Management Council, SAFE version, 27 October 2009.

Hight, B. V. and C. G. Lowe. 2007. Elevated body temperatures of adult female leopard sharks, *Triakis semifasciata*, while aggregating in shallow nearshore embayments: evidence for behavioral thermoregulation? Journal of Experimental Marine Biology and Ecology 352:114–128.

Hill, K. T., G. M. Cailliet, and R. L. Radtke. 1989. A comparative analysis of growth zones in four calcified structures of Pacific blue marlin, *Makaira nigricans*. Fishery Bulletin 87:829–843.

Hinton, M. G. 2003. Status of swordfish stocks in the eastern Pacific Ocean estimated using data from Japanese tuna longline fisheries. Marine and Freshwater Research 54:393–399.

Hirschberger, W. A. and G. B. Smith. 1983. Spawning of twelve groundfish species in the Alaska and Pacific Coast regions, 1975–81. NOAA Technical Memorandum NMFS F/NWC-44.

Hobson, E. S. and J. R. Chess. 1986. Relationships among fishes and their prey in a nearshore sand community off southern California. Environmental Biology of Fishes 17:201–226.

Hobson, E. S. and J. R. Chess. 2001. Influence of trophic relations on form and behavior among fishes and benthic invertebrates in some California marine communities. Environmental Biology of Fishes 60:411–457.

Hobson, E. S., W. N. McFarland, and J. R. Chess. 1981. Crepuscular and nocturnal activities of Californian nearshore fishes, with consideration of their scotopic visual pigments and the photic environment. Fishery Bulletin 79:1–30.

Hoff, G. R. and L. L. Britt. 2005. Results of the 2004 Eastern Bering Sea upper continental slope survey of groundfish and invertebrate resources. NOAA Technical Memorandum NMFS-AFSC-15.

Hoff, G. R., T. W. Buckley, J. C. Drazen, and K. M. Duncan. 2000. Biology and ecology of *Nezumia liolepis* and *N. stelgidolepis* from the west coast of North America. Journal of Fish Biology 57:662–680.

Holder, C. F. 1908. Big game at sea. Hodder and Stoughton, London.

Holder, C. F. 1910a. Recreations of a sportsman on the Pacific Coast. G. P. Putnam's and Sons, New York.

Holder, C. F. 1910b. Sport fishing in California and Florida. Bulletin of the Bureau of Fisheries. Volume 28. United States Government Printing Office.

Holder, C. F. 1910c. The Channel Islands of California. Hodder and Stoughton, London.

Holder, C. F. 1913. The game fishes of the world. Hodder and Stoughton, London.

Holland, G. A. 1969. Age, growth, and mortality of races of English sole (*Parophrys vetulus*) in Puget Sound, Washington. Pacific Marine Fisheries Commission Bulletin 7.

Holts, D. B. and D. W. Bedford. 1990. Activity patterns of striped marlin in the southern California Bight, p. 81–93. *In* R. H. Stroud (ed.). Planning the Future of Billfishes. Proceedings of the Second International Billfish Symposium, Kailua-Kona, Hawaii, August 1–5, 1988. Part 2: Contributed Papers.

Hop, H., H. E. Welch, and R. E. Crawford. 1997. Population structure and feeding ecology of Arctic cod schools in the Canadian High Arctic. American Fisheries Society Symposium 19:13–39.

Horn, M. H. 1980. Diel and seasonal variation in abundance and diversity of shallow- water fish populations in Morro Bay, California. Fishery Bulletin 78:759–770.

Hosie, M. J. and H. F. Horton. 1977. Biology of the rex sole, *Glyptocephalus zachirus*, in waters off Oregon. Fishery Bulletin 75:51–60.

Hovey, T. E. and L. G. Allen. 2000. Reproductive patterns of six populations of the spotted sand bass, *Paralabrax maculatofasciatus*, from southern and Baja California. Copeia 2000(2):459–468.

Hovey, C. B., L. G. Allen, and T. E. Hovey. 2002. The reproductive pattern of barred sand bass (*Paralabrax nebulifer*) from southern California. California Cooperative Oceanic Fisheries Investigations Reports 43:174–181.

Hubbock, C. E. 1927. Striped bass as I know them. California Fish and Game 13:25–27.

Hubbs, C. A. 1921. The ecology and life-history of *Amphigonopterus aurora* and of other viviparous perches of California. Biological Bulletin 40:181–209.

Hubbs, C. L. and A. N. Wick. 1951.Toxicity of the roe of the cabezon, *Scorpaenichthys marmoratus*. California Fish and Game 37:195–196.

Hughes, G. W. 1985. The comparative ecology and evidence for resource partitioning in two pholidid fishes (Pisces: Pholididae) from southern British Columbia eelgrass beds. Canadian Journal of Zoology 63:76–85.

Hughes, S. E. 1974. Stock composition, growth, mortality, and availability of Pacific saury, *Cololabis saira*, of the northeastern Pacific Ocean. Fishery Bulletin 72:121–131.

Hulbert, L. B., M. F. Sigler, and C. R. Lunsford. 2006. Depth and movement behaviour of the Pacific sleeper shark in the north-east Pacific Ocean. Journal of Fish Biology 69:406–425.

Humann, P. and N. DeLoach. 2004. Reef fish identification Baja to Panama. New World Publications, Jacksonville, Florida.

Humann, P. and N. DeLoach. 2008. Coastal fish identification California to Alaska. New World Publications, Jacksonville, Florida.

Hunter, J. R., J. L. Butler, C. Kimbrell, and E. A. Lynn. 1990. Bathymetric patterns in size, age, sexual maturity, water content, and caloric density of Dover sole, *Microstomus pacificus*. California Cooperative Oceanic Fisheries Investigations Reports 43:132–144.

Hunter, J. R., B. J. Macewicz, N. C.-H. Lo, and C. A. Kimbrell. 1992. Fecundity, spawning, and maturity of female Dover sole *Microstomus pacificus*, with an evaluation of assumptions and precision. Fishery Bulletin 90:101–128.

Hutchinson, C. E., C. R. Kastelle, D. K. Kimura, and D. R. Gunderson. 2007. Using radiometric ages to develop conventional ageing methods for shortraker rockfish (*Sebastes borealis*), p. 237–249. *In* J. Heifetz, J. Dicosimo, A. J. Gharrett, M. S. Love, V. M. O'Connell, and R. D. Stanley (eds.). Biology, Assessment, and Management of North Pacific Rockfishes. Alaska Sea Grant Program, AK-SG- 07-01.

Hyde, J. R. and R. D. Vetter. 2009. Population genetic structure in the redefined vermilion rockfish (*Sebastes miniatus*) indicates limited larval dispersal and reveals natural management units. Canadian Journal of Fisheries and Aquatic Sciences 66:1569–1581.

Hyde, J. R., C. Kimbrell, L. Robertson, K. Clifford, E. Lynn, and R. Vetter. 2008. Multiple paternity and maintenance of genetic diversity in the live-bearing rockfishes *Sebastes* spp. Marine Ecology Progress Series 357:245–253.

Ibâñez Aguirre, A. L. and M. Gallardo-Cabello. 2004. Reproduction of *Mugil cephalus* and *M. curema* (Pisces: Mugilidae) from a coastal lagoon in the Gulf of Mexico. Bulletin of Marine Science 75:37–49.

Iglauer, E. 1992. Fishing with John. Harbour Publishing, Madeira Park, British Columbia.

IPHC (International Pacific Halibut Commission). 1998. The Pacific halibut: biology, fishery, and management. Technical Report Number 40.

Ishida, M. 1994. Phylogeny of the suborder Scorpaenoidei (Pisces: Scorpaeniformes). Bulletin of the Nansei National Fisheries Research Institute 27.

Itoh, T., S. Tsuji, and A. Nitta. 2003. Migration patterns of young Pacific bluefin tuna (*Thunnus orientalis*) determined with archival tags. Fishery Bulletin 101:514– 534.

Jagielo, T. H. and F. R. Wallace. 2005. Assessment of lingcod (*Ophiodon elongatus*) for the Pacific Fisheries Management Council. Washington Department of Fish and Wildlife, October, 2005.

Jangaard, P. M. 1974. The capelin (*Mallotus villosus*). Canadian Department of the Environment. Fisheries Marine Service Bulletin 186.

Jensen, A. C. 1966. Life history of the spiny dogfish. Fishery Bulletin 65:527–554.

Jensen, A. S. 1948. A contribution to the ichthyofauna of Greenland. Spoila Zoologica Musei 9:1–182.

Jensen, G. C. 2005. A unique feeding method by a teleost fish, the fourhorn poacher *Hypsagonus quadricornis* (Agonidae). Biological Bulletin 209:165–167.

Jewitt, J. R. 1987. The adventures and suffering of John R. Jewitt: captive of Maquinna. University of Washington Press, Seattle.

Johnson, C. R. and J. P. Adams. 1970. Biology of *Zaniolepis latipinnis* (Zaniolepidae) in relation to vertical distribution. Copeia 1970(4):769–771.

Johnson, K. W. 2004. Status report: Census of lingcod nesting activity in the Edmonds Underwater Park. 2003 Georgia Basin/Puget Sound Research Conference Proceedings.

Johnson, S. W., A. D. Neff, and J. F. Thedinga. 2005. An atlas on the distribution and habitat of common fishes in shallow nearshore waters of southeastern Alaska. NOAA Technical Memorandum NMFS-AFSC-157.

Johnson, S. W., J. F. Thedinga, A. D. Neff, P. M. Harris, M. R. Lindeberg, J. M. Maselko, and S. D. Rice. 2010. Fish assemblages in nearshore habitats of Prince William Sound, Alaska. Northwest Science 84:266–280.

Jones, A. C. 1962. The biology of the euryhaline fish *Leptocottus armatus* Girard (Cottidae). University of California Publications in Zoology 67:321–368.

Jones, B. C. and G. H. Geen. 1977. Reproduction and embryonic development of spiny dogfish (*Squalus acanthias*) in the Strait of Georgia, British Columbia. Journal of the Fisheries Research Board of Canada 34:1286–1292.

Jones, E. C. 1971. *Isistius brasiliensis*, a squaloid shark, the probable cause of crater wounds on fishes and cetaceans. Fishery Bulletin 69:791–798.

Jones, K. 2004. Pier fishing in California. 2nd Ed. Publishers Design Group, Roseville, California.

Jordan, D. S. 1884a. The flat fishes and soles of the Pacific Coast, p. 184–189. *In* G. B. Goode (ed.). The Fisheries and Fishery Industries of the United States. Section I. United States Commission of Fish and Fisheries.

Jordan, D. S. 1884b. The herrings of the Pacific Coast, p. 568–569. *In* G. B. Goode (ed.). The Fisheries and Fishery Industries of the United States. Section I. United States Commission of Fish and Fisheries.

Jordan, D. S. 1887. Part XVI. The fisheries of the Pacific Coast, p. 589–630. *In* G. B. Goode (ed.). The Fisheries and Fishery Industries of the United States. Section II. United States Commission of Fish and Fisheries.

Jordan, D. S. 1892. The fisheries of California. Overland Monthly 20(119):469–478.

Jordan, D. S. 1905. California's gift to civilization. *In* L. H. Irvine (ed.). A History of the New California, Its Resources and People. The Lewis Publishing Company, New York.

Jordan, D. S. 1922. The Days of a Man. World Book Publishing, New York, New York.

Jordan, D. S. and B. W. Evermann. 1896. The fishes of North and Middle America: a descriptive catalogue of the species of fish-like vertebrates found in the waters of North America, north of the Isthmus of Panama. Bulletin of the United States National Museum. No. 47.

Jordan, D. S. and C. H. Gilbert. 1880. On the oil-shark of southern California (*Galeorhinus galeus*). Proceedings of the United States National Museum 3:42– 43.

Jordan, D. S. and C. H. Gilbert. 1883. Synopsis of the fishes of North America. Bulletin of the United States National Museum No. 16.

Jorgensen, S. J., D. M. Kaplan, A. P. Klimley, S. G. Morgan, M. R. O'Farrell, and L. W. Botsford. 2006. Limited movement in blue rockfish *Sebastes mystinus*: internal structure of home range. Marine Ecology Progress Series 327:157–170.

Jorgensen, S. J., C. A. Reeb, T. K. Chappel, S. Anderson, C. Perle, S. R. Van Sommeran, C. Fritz-Cope, A. C. Brown, A. P. Klimley, and B. A. Block. 2009. Philopatry and migration of Pacific white sharks. Proceedings of the Royal Society B doi:10.1098/rspb.2009.1155.

Joseph, D. C. 1962. Growth characteristics of two southern California surffishes, the California corbina and spotfin croaker, family Sciaenidae. California Department of Fish and Game, Fish Bulletin 119.

Junquera, S., E. Román, J. Morgan, M. Sainza, and G. Ramilo. 2003. Time scale of ovarian maturation in Greenland halibut (*Reinhardtius hippoglossoides*, Walbaum). ICES Journal of Marine Science 60:767–773.

Kaplan, I. C. and T. E. Helser. 2007. Stock assessment of the arrowtooth flounder (*Atheresthes stomias*) population off the west coast of the United States in 2007. NOAA National Marine Fisheries Service, Northwest Fisheries Science Center, Fishery Resource Analysis and Monitoring, Seattle, Washington.

Kato, S. 1990. Report on the biology of Pacific hagfish, *Eptatretus stouti* and the development of its fishery in California. United States Department of Commerce, National Marine Fisheries Service Tiburon Laboratory, California. Unpublished Manuscript.

Kendall, R. L. 2002. Capital punishment. Fisheries 27(7):33–34.

Kent, D. L. and J. B. Marliave. 1997. Early life history of the arrow goby, *Clevelandia ios* (Jordan & Gilbert), Gobiidae. Micronesica 30:15–23.

Ketchen, K. S. 1972. Size at maturity, fecundity, and embryonic growth of the spiny dogfish (*Squalus acanthias*) in British Columbia waters. Journal of the Fisheries Research Board of Canada 29:1717–1723.

Ketchen, K. S. 1975. Age and growth of dogfish *Squalus acanthias* in British Columbia waters. Journal of the Fisheries Research Board of Canada 32:43–59.

Ketchen, K. S. 1986. The spiny dogfish (*Squalus acanthias*) in the northeast Pacific and a history of its utilization. Canadian Special Publication of Fisheries and Aquatic Sciences 88.

Kilambi, R. V. and A. C. DeLacy. 1967. Heterogeneity of surf smelt, *Hypomesus pretiosus* (Girard), in the State of Washington, as judged by incidence of larval *Anisakis* (Nematoda). Journal of the Fishery Research Board of Canada 24:629– 633.

Kilambi, R. V., F. M. Utter, and A. C. DeLacy. 1965. Differentiation of spawning populations of the surf smelt *Hypomesus pretiosus* (Girard) by serological methods. Journal of the Marine Biological Association of India 7:364–368.

Kimura, D. K., A. M. Shimada, and F. R. Shaw. 1998. Stock structures and movement of tagged sablefish, *Anoplopoma fimbria*, in offshore northeast Pacific waters and the effects of El Niño-Southern Oscillation on migration and growth. Fishery Bulletin 96:462–481.

King, J. R. and G. A. McFarlane. 2006. Shift in size-at-age of the Strait of Georgia population of Pacific hake (*Merluccius productus*). California Cooperative Oceanic Fisheries Investigations Reports 47:111–118.

Kinnetic Laboratories Inc. 1980. Chapter 5. Fish and macroinvertebrate assessment program. Final Report. Predischarge Monitoring Study, Santa Cruz Wastewater Facility. KLI-80-11.

Kiraly, S. J., J. A. Moore, and P. H. Jasinski. 2003. Deepwater and other sharks of the U. S. Atlantic Ocean Exclusive Economic Zone. Marine Fisheries Review 65(4):1– 63.

Kishinouye, K. 1923. Contributions to the comparative study of the so-called scombroid fishes. Journal of the College of Agriculture, Imperial University of Tokyo 8:293–475.

Kizevetter, I. V., E. F. Kleie, A. A. Kirillova, O. M. Mel'nikova, V. M. Myasoedova, and L. Ya. Ertel. 1965. Technological characteristics of Bering Sea fishes, p. 191–258. *In* P. A. Moiseev (ed.). Soviet Fisheries Investigations in the Northeastern Pacific. Part IV. Israel Program for Scientific Translations, 1968.

Klawe, W. L. 1964. Food of the black-and-yellow sea snake, *Pelamis platurus*, from Ecuadorian coastal waters. Copeia 1964(4):712–713.

Klawe, W. L. and T. P. Calkins. 1965. Length-weight relationship of black skipjack tuna, *Euthynnus lineatus*. California Fish and Game 51:214–216.

Klimley, A. P. 1987. The determinants of sexual segregation in the scalloped hammerhead shark, *Sphyrna lewini*. Environmental Biology of Fishes 18:27–40.

Klimley, A. P. 1993. Highly directional swimming by scalloped hammerhead sharks, *Sphyrna lewini*, and subsurface irradiance, temperature, bathymetry, and geomagnetic field. Marine Biology 117:1–22.

Klimley, A. P. and D. G. Ainley (eds.). 1996. Great white sharks: the biology of *Carcharodon carcharias*. Academic Press, San Diego.

Klimley, A. P. and D. R. Nelson. 1981. Schooling of scalloped hammerhead shark, *Sphyrna lewini*, in the Gulf of California. Fishery Bulletin 79:356–360.

Knaggs, E. H. and R. H. Parrish. 1973. Maturation and growth of Pacific mackerel, *Scomber japonicus* Houttuyn. California Fish and Game 59:114–120.

Kneebone, J., L. J. Natanson, A. H. Andrews, and W. H. Howell. 2008. Using bomb radiocarbon analyses to validate age and growth estimates for the tiger shark, *Galeocerdo cuvier*, in the western North Atlantic. Marine Biology 154:423–434.

Kohler, N. E., J. G. Casey, and P. A. Turner. 1995. Length-weight relationships for 13 species of sharks from the western North Atlantic. Fishery Bulletin 93:412–418.

Kohlhorst, D. W., L. W. Miller, and J. J. Orsi. 1980. Age and growth of white sturgeon collected in the Sacramento-San Joaquin estuary, California: 1965–1970 and 1973–1976. California Fish and Game 66:83–95.

Kolpakov, N. V. 2005. On the biology of *Platichthys stellatus* (Pleuronectidae) in coastal waters of northern Primorye. Journal of Ichthyology 45:594–606.

Kolpakov, N. V. and N. T. Dolganova. 2006. On the biology of *Blepsias cirrhosus* (Hemitripteridae) from coastal waters of Northern Primorye. Journal of Ichthyology 46:454–459.

Korsmeyer, K. E. and H. Dewar. 2001. Tuna metabolism and energetics, p. 35–78. *In* B.Block and E. D. Stevens (eds.). Tuna: Physiology, Ecology, and Evolution. Academic Press, San Diego.

Kostow, K. 2002. Oregon lampreys: natural history, status, and analysis of management issues. Oregon Department of Fish and Wildlife.

Kramer, D. and P. E. Smith. 1970. Seasonal and geographic characteristics of fishery resources. California Current Region—II. Pacific saury. Commercial Fisheries Review 32(6):47–51.

Kramer, D. E., W. Barass, B. Paust, and B. Bracken 1995. Guide to northeast Pacific flatfishes. University of Alaska Sea Grant College Program, Marine Advisory Bulletin No. 47.

Krejsa, R. J. 1964. Reproductive behavior and sexual dimorphism in the manacled sculpin, *Synchirus gilli* Bean. Copeia 1964(2):448–450.

Krivobok, M. N. and O. I. Tarkovskaya. 1964. Chemical characteristics of yellowfin sole, cod and Alaska pollock of the southeastern part of the Bering Sea, p. 271– 287. *In* P. A. Moiseev (ed.). Soviet fisheries investigations in the northeastern Pacific. Part 1. Israel Program for Scientific Translations, 1968.

Kronman, M. Unpublished manuscript. From hooks to harpoons--the story of Santa Barbara Channel fisheries.

Kulbicki, M., N. Guillemot, and M. Amand. 2005. A general approach to length-weight relationships for New Caledonian lagoon fishes. Cybium 29:235–252.

Kulikov, M. Yu. 1965. Vertical distribution of sablefish (*Anoplopoma fimbria* Pallas) on the Bering Sea continental slope, p. 157–161. *In* P. A. Moiseev (ed.). Soviet Fisheries Investigations in the Northeastern Pacific. Part IV. Israel Program for Scientific Translations, 1968.

Kuo, C.-M. 1970. Taxonomic, growth, and maturation studies on the bonitos of the temperate eastern Pacific Ocean. PhD Thesis, University of California, San Diego.

Kusher, D. L., S. E. Smith, and G. M. Cailliet. 1992. Validated age and growth of the leopard shark, *Triakis semifasciata*, with comments on reproduction. Environmental Biology of Fishes 35:187–203.

Kuznetsova, E. N. and A. M. Kunin. 2002. New data on the biology of the northern white-bellied flounder *Lepidopsetta polyxystra* in Pacific waters off the northern Kuril and southeast Kamchatka. Journal of Ichthyology 42:289–293.

Lackey, R. T. 2002. Salmon recovery: learning from successes and failures. Northwest Science 76:356–360.

Lafferty, K. D. and A. K. Morris. 1996. Altered behavior of parasitized killifish increases susceptibility to predation by bird final hosts. Ecology 77:1390–1397.

Lai, H.-L., M. A. Haltuch, A. E. Punt, and J. M. Cope. 2005. Stock assessment of petrale sole: 2004. Pacific Fisheries Management Council, Stock Assessment.

Laidig, T. E., D. E. Pearson, and L. L. Sinclair. 2003. Age and growth of blue rockfish *(Sebastes mystinus)* from central and northern California. Fishery Bulletin 101:800–808.

Lamb, A. and P. Edgell. 2010. Coastal fishes of the Pacific Northwest. Harbour Publishing, Madeira Park, British Columbia.

Lane, E. D. 1975. Quantitative aspects of the life history of the diamond turbot, *Hypsopsetta guttulata* (Girard), in Anaheim Bay, p. 153–173. *In* E. D. Lane and W. Hill (eds.). The Marine Resources of Anaheim Bay. California Departmentof Fish and Game, Fish Bulletin 165.

Lang, G. M. 1992. Food habits of three congeneric flatfishes: yellowfin sole, *Pleuronectes asper*, rock sole, *P. bilineatus*, and Alaska plaice, *P. quadrituberculatus*, in the eastern Bering Sea, 1984–1988. Masters Thesis, University of Washington, Seattle.

Lassuy, D. R. 1989. Species profiles: life histories and environmental requirements of coastal fishes and invertebrates (Pacific Northwest). English sole. United States Fish and Wildlife Service, Biological Report 82(11.101), TR EL-82-4.

Last, P. R., W. T. White, and J. J. Pogonowski eds. 2007. Descriptions of new dogfishes of the genus *Squalus* (Squaloidea: Squalidae). CSIRO Marine and Freshwater Research Paper 014.

Laurel, B. J., C. H. Ryer, B. Knoth, and A. W. Stoner. 2009. Temporal and ontogenetic shifts in habitat use of juvenile Pacific cod (*Gadus macrocephalus*). Journal of Experimental Marine Biology and Ecology 377:28–35.

Lauth, R. R., J. L. Guthridge, D. W. Cooper, and S. W. McEntire. 2010. Behaviorial ecology of color patterns in Atka mackerel. Marine and Coastal Fisheries: Dynamics, Management, and Ecosystem Science 2:399–411.

Lauth, R. R., J. Guthridge, D. Nichol, S. W. McEntire, and N. Hillgruber. 2007. Timing and duration of mating and brooding periods of Atka mackerel (*Pleurogrammus monopterygius*) in the North Pacific Ocean. Fishery Bulletin 105:560–570.

Lavenberg, R. J. and J. E. Fitch. 1966. Annotated list of fishes collected by mid-water trawl in the Gulf of California, March–April 1964. California Fish and Game 52:92–110.

Lawrence, M. J., G. Lacho, and S. Davies. 1984. A survey of the coastal fishes of the southeastern Beaufort Sea. Canadian Technical Report, Fisheries and Aquatic Science 1220.

Lea, R.N. 1980. Systematics and zoogeography of cusk-eels of the family Ophidiidae, subfamily Ophidiinae, from the eastern Pacific Ocean. PhD Thesis, University of Miami.

Lea, R. N., R. D. McAllister, and D. A. VenTresca. 1999. Biological aspects of nearshore rockfishes of the genus *Sebastes* from central California. California Department of Fish and Game, Fish Bulletin 177.

Leaman, B. M. 1980. The ecology of fishes in British Columbia kelp beds. I. Barkley Sound *Nereocystis* beds. Marine Resources Branch, Ministry of Environment, Province of British Columbia, Fisheries Development Report 22.

Lecomte, F., W. S. Grant, J. J. Dodson, R. Rodríguez-Sánchez, and B. W. Bowers. 2004. Living with uncertainty: genetic imprints of climate shifts in east Pacific anchovy (*Engraulis mordax*) and sardine (*Sardinops sagax*). Molecular Ecology 13:2169– 2182.

Lefebvre, K. A., S. Bargu, T. Kieckhefer, and M. W. Silver. 2002. From sanddabs to blue whales: the pervasiveness of domoic acid. Toxicon 40:971–977.

Levings, C. D. 1969. The zoarcid *Lycodopsis pacifica* in Outer Burrard Inlet, British Columbia. Journal of the Fisheries Research Board of Canada 26:2403–2412.

Leviton, A. E. and M. L. Aldrich. 1997. Theodore Henry Hittell's, The California Academy of Sciences, A Narrative History: 1853–1906. California Academy of Sciences, San Francisco, California.

Limbaugh, C. 1955. Fish life in the kelp beds and the effects of kelp harvesting. University of California, Institute of Marine Resources, IMR Ref. 55-9.

Limbaugh, C. 1961. Life-history and ecologic notes on the black croaker. California Fish and Game 47:163–174.

Limbaugh, C. 1963. Field notes on sharks, p. 63–94. *In* P. W. Gilbert (ed.). Sharks and Survival. D. C. Heath and Company, Boston.

Lin, B., Z. Zhang, Y. Wang, K. P. Currens, A. Spidle, Y. Yamazaki, and D. A. Close. 2008. Amplified fragment length polymorphism assessment of genetic diversity of Pacific lamprey. North American Journal of Fish Management 28:1182–1193.

Lindley, S. T. and M. S. Mohr. 2003. Modeling the effect of striped bass (*Morone saxatilis*) on the population viability of Sacramento River winter-run Chinook salmon (*Oncorhynchus tshawytscha*). Fishery Bulletin 10:321–331.

Little, A. G., S. C. Lougheed, and C. D. Moyes. 2010. Evolutionary affinity of billfishes (Xiphiidae and Istiophoridae) and flatfishes (Pleuronectiformes): independent and trans-subordinal origins of endothermy in teleost fishes. Molecular Phylogenetics and Evolution 56:897–904.

Litzow, M. A., J. F. Piatt, A. K. Prichard, and D. D. Roby. 2002. Response of pigeon guillemots to variable abundance of high-lipid and low-lipid prey. Oecologia 132:286–295.

Liu, K.-M., P.-J. Chiang, and C.-T. Chen. 1998. Age and growth estimates of the bigeye thresher shark, *Alopias superciliosus*, in northeastern Taiwan waters. Fishery Bulletin 96:482–491.

Liu, K.–M., C.-T. Chen, T.-H. Liao, and S.-J. Joung. 1999. Age, growth, and reproduction of the pelagic thresher shark, *Alopias pelagicus* in the northwestern Pacific. Copeia 1999(1):68–74.

Lockington, W. N. 1877. The long–jawed goby. American Naturalist 11:474–478.

Lockington, W. N. 1879a. Notes on Pacific Coast fishes and fisheries. American Naturalist 13:684–687.

Lockington, W. N. 1879b. Notes on some fishes of the coast of California. No. 1. American Naturalist 13:299–308.

Lockington, W. N. 1879c. Notes on the fishes of the Pacific Coast – No. 2. Mining and Scientific Press 39(7):102.

Lord, J. K. 1866. The naturalist in Vancouver Island and British Columbia. Richard Bentley: London.

Losey, G. S. Jr. 1968. The comparative behavior of some Pacific fishes of the genus *Hypsoblennius* Gill (Blenniidae). PhD Thesis, University of California, San Diego.

Losey, G. S. Jr. 1969. Sexual pheromone in some fishes of the genus *Hypsoblennius* Gill. Science 163:181–183.

Lourie, S. A., A. C. J. Vincent, and H. J. Hall. 1999. Seahorses: an identification guide to the world's species and their conservation. Project Seahorse. London, UK.

Love, M. S. and K. Johnson. 1998. Aspects of the life histories of grass rockfish, *Sebastes rastrelliger*, and brown rockfish, *S. auriculatus*, from southern California. Fishery Bulletin 87:100–109.

Love, M. S. and W. V. Westphal. 1981. Growth, reproduction, and food habits of olive rockfish, *Sebastes serranoides*, off central California. Fishery Bulletin 79:533– 545.

Love, M. S., M. Yoklavich, and L. Thorsteinson. 2002. The rockfishes of the Northeast Pacific. University of California Press, Berkeley.

Love, M. S., P. Morris, M. McCrea, and R. Collins. 1990. Life history aspects of 19 rockfish species (Scorpaenidae: *Sebastes*) from the Southern California Bight. NOAA Technical Report NMFS 87.

Love, M. S., B. Axell, P. Morris, R. Collins, and A. Brooks. 1987. Life history and fishery of the California scorpionfish, *Scorpaena guttata*, within the southern California Bight. Fishery Bulletin 85:99–116.

Love, M. S., A. Brooks, D. Busatto, J. Stephens and P. A. Gregory. 1996. Aspects of the life histories of the kelp bass and barred sand bass (*Paralabrax clathratus* and *P. nebulifer*) from the southern California Bight. Fishery Bulletin 94:472–481.

Love, M. S., G. E. McGowen, W. Westphal, R. J. Lavenberg, and L. Martin. 1984. Aspects of the life history and fishery of the white croaker, *Genyonemus lineatus* (Sciaenidae), off California. Fish. Bull. 82:179–198.

Lowe, C. G., D. T. Topping, D. P. Cartamil, and Y. P. Papastamatiou. 2003. Movement patterns, home range, and habitat utilization of adult kelp bass *Paralabrax clathratus* in a temperate no-take marine reserve. Marine Ecology Progress Series 256:205–216.

Lowe, C. G., B. M. Wetherbee, G. L. Crow, and A. L. Tester. 1996. Ontogenetic dietary shifts and feeding behavior of the tiger shark, *Galeocerdo cuvier*, in Hawaiian waters. Environmental Biology of Fishes 47:203–211.

Lowe, S. A., D. M. Van Doornik, and G. A. Winans. 1998. Geographic variation in genetic and growth patterns of Atka mackerel, *Pleurogrammus monopterygius* (Hexagrammidae), in the Aleutian archipelago. Fishery Bulletin 96:502–515.

Lowery, E. 2005. Ambicoloration and flesh quality in Pacific halibut, *Hippoglossus stenolepis*, p. 233–243. IPHC Report of Assessment and Research Activities 2005.

Macewicz, B. J. and J. R. Hunter. 1994. Fecundity of sablefish, *Anoplopoma fimbria*, from Oregon coastal waters. California Cooperative Oceanic Fisheries Investigations Reports 35:160–174.

MacFarlane, G. A. and M. W. Saunders. 1997. Fecundity of Pacific hake (*Merluccius productus*) for three stocks off the west coast of North America. California Cooperative Oceanic Fisheries Investigations Reports 38:114–119.

MacGinitie, G. E. 1935. Ecological aspects of a California marine estuary. American Midland Naturalist 16:630–765.

MacGinitie, G. E. 1939. The natural history of the blind goby, *Typhlogobius californiensis* Steindachner. American Midland Naturalist 21:489–505.

MacNair, L. S., M. L. Domeier, and C. S. Y. Chun. 2001. Age, growth, and mortality of California halibut, *Paralichthys californicus*, along southern and central California. Fishery Bulletin 99:588–600.

Magnuson, J. J. and J. H. Prescott. 1966. Courtship, locomotion, feeding, and miscellaneous behavior of Pacific bonito (*Sarda chiliensis*). Animal Behavior 14:54–67.

Mahan, W. T. 1988. Reproductive biology of the bay pipefish (*Syngnathus leptorhynchus* Girard) from South Humboldt Bay, California. Master Thesis, Humboldt State University, Arcata.

Malecha, P. W., D. H. Hanselman, and J. Heifetz. 2007. Growth and mortality of rockfishes (Scorpaenidae) from Alaska waters. NOAA Technical Memorandum NMFS-AFSC-172.

Maloney, N. E. 2004. Sablefish, *Anoplopoma fimbria*, populations on Gulf of Alaska seamounts. Marine Fisheries Review 66(3):1–12.

Maloney, N. E. and J. Heifetz. 1997. Movements of tagged sablefish, *Anoplopoma fimbria*, released in the eastern Gulf of Alaska, p. 115–121. NOAA Technical Report NMFS 130.

Manzer, J. I. 1972. Length-weight relationship for pomfret. Journal of the Fisheries Research Board of Canada 29:1079–1081.

Marchetti, M. P. and G. A. Novitt. 2003. Effects of hatchery rearing on brain structure of rainbow trout, *Oncorhynchus mykiss*. Environment Biology of Fishes 66:9–14.

Markevich, A. I. 2004. Parental behavior of the male greenlings *Hexagrammos otakii* and *H. octogrammus* (Hexagrammidae). Journal of Ichthyology 44:521–526.

Markle, D. F., P. M. Harris, and C. L. Toole. 1992. Metamorphosis and an overview of early-life-history stages in Dover sole *Microstomus pacificus*. Fishery Bulletin 90:285–301.

Marko, P. B., L. Rogers-Bennett, and A. B. Dennis. 2007. MtDNA population structure and gene flow in lingcod (*Ophiodon elongatus*): limited connectivity despite long- lived pelagic larvae. Marine Biology 150:1301–1311.

Marliave, J. B. 1975. The behavioral transformation from the planktonic larval stage of some marine fishes reared in the laboratory. PhD Thesis, University of British Columbia, Vancouver.

Marliave, J. B. 1976. A theory of storm-induced drift dispersal of the gasterosteid fish *Aulorhynchus flavidus*. Copeia 1976(4):794–796.

Marliave, J. B. 1981a. High intertidal spawning under rockweed, *Fucus distichus*, by the sharpnose sculpin, *Clinocottus acuticeps*. Canadian Journal of Zoology 59:1122– 1125.

Marliave, J. B. 1981b. Spawn and larvae of the Pacific sandfish, *Trichodon trichodon*. Fishery Bulletin 78:959–964.

Marliave, J. B. 1986. Lack of planktonic dispersal of rocky intertidal fish larvae. Transactions of the American Fisheries Society 115:149–154.

Marliave, J. B. 2003. Scorpaeniformes III. Grzimek's Animal Life Encyclopedia, p. 179– 194. Volume 5. Fishes II.

Marshall, L. J. and W. T. White. 2005. Reproduction in sharks and rays. JMBA Global Marine Environment, Summer, p. 14–15.

Marshall, W. H. and T. Wyllie Echeverria. 1992. Age, length, weight, reproductive cycle and fecundity of the monkeyface prickleback (*Cebidichthys violaceus*). California Fish and Game 78:57–64.

Martinez-Palacios, C. A., M. A. Chávez Sánchez, G. S. Papp, I. A. de la Parra, and L. G. Ross. 2002. Observations on spawning, early development and growth of the puffer fish *Sphoeroides annulatus* (Jenyns, 1843). Journal of Aquaculture in the Tropics 17:59–66.

Martin, L. K. and G. M. Cailliet. 1988. Age and growth determination of the bat ray, *Myliobatis californica* Gill, in central California. Copeia 1988(3):762–773.

Maschner, H. D. G., M. W. Betts, K. L. Reedy-Maschner, and A. W. Trites. 2008. A 4500-year rime series of Pacific cod (*Gadus macrocephalus*) size and abundance: archaeology, oceanic regime shifts, and sustainable fisheries. Fisheries Bulletin 106:386–394.

Mason, J. C. and A. C. Phillips. 1985. Biology of the bathylagid fish, *Leuroglossus schmidti*, in the Strait of Georgia, British Columbia. Canadian Journal of Fisheries and Aquatic Sciences 42:1144–1153.

Matarese, A. C., D. M. Blood, S. J. Picquelle, and J. L. Benson. 2003. Atlas of abundance and distribution patterns of ichthyoplankton from the northeast Pacific Ocean and Bering Sea ecosystems based on research conducted by the Alaska Fisheries Science Center (1972–1996). NOAA Professional Paper NMFS 1.

Matsui, T., S. Kato, and S. E. Smith. 1990. Biology and potential use of Pacific grenadier, *Coryphaenoides acrolepis*, off California. Marine Fisheries Review 52(3):1–17.

Matta, M. E. and D. R. Gunderson. 2007. Age, growth, maturity, and mortality of the Alaska skate, *Bathyraja parmifera*, in the eastern Bering Sea. Environmental Biology of Fishes 80:309–323.

McBride, R. S., A. K. Richardson, and K. L. Maki. 2008. Age, growth, and mortality of wahoo, *Acanthocybium solandri*, from the Atlantic coast of Florida and the Bahamas. Marine and Freshwater Research 59:799–807.

McCart, P., P. Craig, and H. Bain. 1972. Report of fisheries investigations in the Sagavanirtok River and neighboring drainages. Report to Alyeska Pipeline Services Co., Bellvue, Washington.

McCosker, J. E. and R. N. Lea. 2006. White shark attacks upon humans in California and Oregon, 1993–2003. Proceedings of the California Academy of Sciences, Fourth Series, 57:479–501.

McCully, H. 1956. An undescribed type of migration in king salmon, *Oncorhynchus tshawytscha* (Walbaum). California Fish and Game 42:189–198.

McDonald, J. L. 1871. Hidden treasures; or fisheries around the North-West Coast. Procter Brothers, Gloucester, Massachusetts.

McFarlane, G. A. and R. J. Beamish. 1985. Biology and fishery of Pacific whiting, *Merluccius productus*, in the Strait of Georgia. Marine Fisheries Review 47(2):23–34.

McFarlane, G. A. and J. R. King. 2003. Migration patterns of spiny dogfish (Squalus acanthias) in the North Pacific Ocean. Fishery Bulletin 101:358-367.

McFarlane, G. A. and J. R. King. 2006. Age and growth of big skate (*Raja binoculata*) and longnose skate (*Raja rhina*) in British Columbia waters. Fisheries Research 78:169–178.

McFarlane, G. A. and M. W. Saunders. 2006. Dispersion of juvenile sablefish, *Anoplopoma fimbria*, as indicated by tagging in Canadian waters, p. 137–150. NOAA Technical Report NMFS 130.

McGowen, G. E. 1977. Ichthyoplankton populations in south San Diego Bay and related effects of an electricity generating station. Masters Thesis, San Diego State University.

McKenzie, J. 2005. Needlefish injury to a fisherman. JMBA Global Marine Environment (2), p. 17–19.

Mecklenburg, C. W., T. A. Mecklenburg, and L. K. Thorsteinson. 2002. Fishes of Alaska. American Fisheries Society, Bethesda, Maryland.

Mehta, R. S. and P. C. Wainwright. 2007. Raptorial jaws in the throat help moray eels swallow large prey. Nature 449:79–82.

Melo-Barrera, F., R. Félix-Uraga, and C. Quiñez-Velázaquez. 2003. Growth and length- weight relationship of the striped marlin, *Tetrapturus audax* (Pisces: Istiophoridae), in Cabo San Lucas, Baja California Sur, Mexico. Ciencias Marinas 29:305–313.

Menzies, A. 1924. California journal of the Vancouver Expedition, 1790–1794. California Historical Society Quarterly 2:265–340.

Metz, C. W. 1912. The fishes of Laguna Beach, California, I. First Annual Report Laguna Marine Laboratory, p. 19–60.

Mgaya, Y. D. 1995. Age and growth analysis of the mosshead sculpin *Clinocottus globiceps* Girard 1857 (Pisces: Cottidae) from Helby Island, British Columbia. Journal of Applied Ichthyology 11:50–59.

Miller, D. J. and R. N. Lea. 1972. Guide to the coastal marine fishes of California. California Department of Fish and Game, Fish Bulletin 157.

Miller, E. F. and L. G. Allen. 2006a. Captive breeding of spotted sand bass, *Paralabrax maculatofasciatus*, in southern California. California Fish and Game 92:98–105.

Miller, E. F. and L. G. Allen. 2006b. Observations on the mating behavior of captive spotted sand bass (*Paralabrax maculatofasciatus*). Bulletin of the Southern Academy of Sciences 105:17–29.

Miller, E. F., D. S. Beck, and W. Dossett. 2008a. Length-weight relationships of select common nearshore southern California marine fishes. Bulletin of the Southern California Academy of Science 107:183–186.

Miller, E. F., D. J. Pondella II, L. G. Allen, and K. T. Herbinson. 2008b. The life history and ecology of black croaker, *Cheilotrema saturnum*. California Cooperative Oceanic Fisheries Investigations Report 49:191–201.

Miller, E. F., J. P. Williams, D. J. Pondella II, and K. T. Herbinson. 2009. Life history, ecology, and long-term demographics of queenfish. Marine and Coastal Fisheries: dynamics, management, and ecosystem science 1:187–199.

Miller, L. W. and R. J. McKechnie. 1968. Observation of striped bass spawning in the Sacramento River. California Fish and Game 54:306–307.

Misitano, D. A. 1980. A record of internal fertilization in the roughback sculpin *Chitinotus* [sic] *pugetensis* with descriptive notes on their early larvae. Copeia 1980(1):162–164.

Mitani, I., M. Kamei, and T. Shimizu. 1986. Some aspects of biology and fisheries of skilfish (*Erilepis zonifer* (Lockington)) off Japan. Bulletin of the Kanagawa Prefectural Fisheries Experimental Station 7:23–27 [In Japanese].

Møller, P. R. and P. Gravlund. 2003. Phylogeny of the eelpout genus *Lycodes* (Pisces, Zoarcidae) as inferred from mitochondrial cytochrome *b* and 12S rDNA. Molecular Phylogenetics and Evolution 26:369–388.

Mollet, H. F. 2002. Distribution of the pelagic stingray, *Dasyatis violacea* (Bonaparte, 1832), off California, Central America, and worldwide. Marine and Freshwater Research 53:525–530.

Mollet, H. F., G. Cliff, H. L. Pratt Jr., and J. D. Stevens. 2000. Reproductive biology of the female shortfin mako, *Isurus oxyrinchus* Rafinesque, 1810, with comments on the embryonic development of lamnoids. Fishery Bulletin 98:299–318.

Morales-Nin, B. 1994. Growth of demersal fish species of the Mexican Pacific Ocean. Marine Biology 121:211–217.

Morris, R. W. 1956. Clasping mechanism of the cottid fish *Oligocottus snyderi* Greeley. Pacific Science 10:314–317.

Morrison, S. V. 2004. A historical analysis of the Pacific Northwest spiny dogfish (*Squalus acanthias*) fishery, its co-management regimes and lessons for future management. Masters Thesis, University of Washington, Seattle.

Mortimer, C. 1750. The description of a fish name *Opah guiniensium* shewed to the Royal Society by Mr. Ralph Bigland. Royal Society Philosophical Transactions 46:518–520.

Moser, C. 1926. Reminiscences of the west coast of Vancouver Island. Acme Press, Victoria.

Moser, H. G. (ed.). 1996. The early stages of fishes in the California Current region. California Cooperative Oceanic Fisheries Investigations Atlas Number 33.

Moser, H. G., R. L. Charter, P. E. Smith, N. C. H. Lo, D. A. Ambrose, C. A. Meyer, E. M. Sandknop, and W. Watson. 1993. Distributional atlas of fish larvae and eggs in the California Current region: Taxa with 1000 or more total larvae, 1951 through 1984. California Cooperative Oceanic Fisheries Investigations Atlas 31.

Moulton, L. L. 1977. An ecological analysis of fishes inhabiting the rocky nearshore regions of northern Puget Sound, Washington. PhD Thesis, University of Washington, Seattle.

Moulton, P. L., T. I. Walker, and S. R. Saddlier. 1992. Age and growth studies of gummy shark, *Mustelus antarcticus* Günther, and school shark, *Galeorhinus galeus* (Linnaeus), from Southern Australian waters. Australian Journal of Marine and Freshwater Research 43:1241–1267.

Moyle, P. B. 2002. Inland fishes of California. University of California Press, Berkeley.

Munehara, H. 1991. Utilization and ecological benefits of a sponge as a spawning bed by the little dragon sculpin *Blepsias cirrhosus*. Japanese Journal of Ichthyology 38:179–184.

Munehara, H. and K. Shimazaki. 1991. Embryonic development and newly hatched larvae of the little dragon sculpin *Blepsias cirrhosus*. Japanese Journal of Ichthyology 38:31–34.

Musienko, L. N. 1970. Reproduction and development of Bering Sea fishes, p. 161–224. *In* P. A. Moiseev (ed.). Soviet Fisheries Investigations in the Northeastern Pacific. Part V. Israel Program for Scientific Translations, 1972.

Nakabo, T. (ed.). 2002. Fishes of Japan. Tokai University Press, Tokyo.

Nakano, H. and J. D. Stevens. 2008. The biology and ecology of the blue shark, *Prionace glauca*, p. 140–151. *In* M. D. Camhi, E. K. Pikitch, and E. A. Babcock (eds.). Sharks of the Open Ocean Biology, Fisheries, and Conservation. Blackwell, Oxford.

Nakano, H. and M. Tabuchi. 1990. Occurrences of the cookiecutter shark *Isistius brasiliensis* in surface waters of the North Pacific Ocean. Japanese Journal of Ichthyology 37:60–63.

Natanson, L. J. and, get this, 15 co-authors. 2008. Ontogenetic vertebral growth patterns in the basking shark *Cetorhinus maximus*. Marine Ecology Progress Series 361: 267–278.

Navia, A. F., A. Giraldo, and P. A. Mejía-Falla. 2006. Notas sobre la biología y dieta del toyo vieja (*Mustelus lunulatus*) en la zona central de pesca del Pacífico Colombiano. Investigaciones Marinas, Valparaíso 34:217–222.

Neer, J. A. and G. M. Cailliet. 2001. Aspects of the life history of the Pacific electric ray, *Torpedo californica* (Ayres). Copeia 2001(3):842–847.

Nelson, J. L. 1970. Reproductive behavior of two sympatric fish of the genus *Hypsoblennius* (Gill). Masters Thesis, San Diego State College.

Nelson, J. S. 2006. Fishes of the World. John Wiley and Sons, Hoboken, New Jersey.

Nelson, J. S., W. C. Starnes, and M. L. Warren. 2002. A capital case for common names of species of fishes—a white crappie or a White Crappie. Fisheries 27(7):31–33.

Ngoile, M. A. 1978. Biology of the redtail surfperch, *Amphistichus rhodoterus* in Northern California. Humboldt State University, Arcata.

Nielsen, J. L. 1999. The evolutionary history of steelhead (*Oncorhynchus mykiss*) along the US Pacific Coast: developing a conservation strategy using genetic diversity. ICES Journal of Marine Science 56:449–458.

Nordell, S. E. 1994. Observations of the mating behavior and dentition of the round stingray, *Urolophus halleri*. Environmental Biology of Fishes 39:219–229.

Norman, J. R. and F. C. Fraser. 1949. Field book of giant fishes. G. P. Putnam's Sons, New York.

Norris, K. S. and J. H. Prescott. 1961. Observations on Pacific cetaceans of Californian and Mexican waters. University of California Publications in Zoology 63:291–402.

O'Connell, C. P. 1953. The life history of the cabezon *Scorpaenichthys marmoratus* (Ayres). California Department of Fish and Game, Fish Bulletin 93.

O'Connell, V. 1993. Submersible observations on lingcod, *Ophiodon elongatus*, nesting below 30 m off Sitka, Alaska. Marine Fisheries Review 55(1):19–24.

O'Connell, V., C. Brylinsky, and D. Carlile. 2003. Demersal shelf rockfish assessment for 2004, p. 617–657. *In* Stock Assessment and Fishery Evaluation Report for the Groundfish Resources of the Gulf of Alaska. Appendix B. North Pacific Fishery Management Council, Anchorage, Alaska.

Olsen, J. B., S. E. Merkouris, and J. E. Seeb. 2002. An examination of spatial and temporal genetic variation in walleye pollock (*Theragra chalcogramma*) using allozyme, mitochondrial DNA, and microsatellite data. Fishery Bulletin 100:752–764.

Onuf, C. P. 1987. The ecology of Mugu Lagoon, California: an estuarine profile. United States Fish and Wildlife Service, Biological Report 85(7.15).

Orcutt, H. G. 1950. The life history of the starry flounder *Platichthys stellatus* (Pallas). California Department of Fish and Game, Fish Bulletin 78.

Orlov, A. M. 2005. Bottom trawl-caught fishes and some features of their vertical distribution in the Pacific waters off the north Kuril Islands and south-east Kamchatka, 1993–1999. Aqua, Journal of Ichthyology and Aquatic Biology 9:139–160.

Orlov, A. M. and C. Binohlan. 2009. Length-weight relationships of deep-sea fishes from the western Bering Sea. Journal of Applied Ichthyology 25:223–227.

Orlov, A. M. and V. A. Ul'chenko. 2002. A hypothesis to explain onshore records of long-nose lancetfish *Alepisaurus ferox* (Alepisauridae, Teleostei) in the North Pacific Ocean. Marine and Freshwater Research 53:303–306.

Orlov, A. M. and A. M. Tokranov. 2008a. Some ecological and biological features of giant and popeye grenadiers in the Pacific waters off the northern Kuril Islands and southeastern Kamchatka. American Fisheries Society Symposium 63:225–260.

Orlov, A. M. and A. M. Tokranov. 2008b. Specific features of distribution, some features of biology, and the dynamics of catches of smooth lumpsucker *Aptocyclus ventricosus* (Cyclopteridae) in waters of the Pacific Ocean off the Kuril Islands and Kamchatka. Journal of Ichthyology 48:81–95.

Orlov, A. M., V. F. Savinykh, and D. V. Pelenev. 2008. Features of the spatial distribution and size structure of the Pacific lamprey *Lampetra tridentata* in the North Pacific. Journal of Marine Biology 34:276–287.

Ormseth, O. A. and B. L. Norcross. 2009. Causes and consequences of life-history variation in North American stocks of Pacific cod. ICES Journal of Marine Science 66:349–357.

Ortega-Garcia, S., A. Klett-Traulsen, and R. Rodriguez-Sánchez. 2006. Some biological aspects of blue marlin (*Makaira nigricans*) in the recreational fishery at Cabo San Lucas, Baja California Sur, Mexico. Bulletin of Marine Science 79:739–746.

Ortega-Salas, A. A. and H. Reyes-Bustamante. 2006. Fecundity, survival, and growth of the seahorse *Hippocampus ingens* (Pisces: Syngnathidae) under semi-controlled conditions. International Journal of Tropical Biology 54:1099–1102.

Orr, J. W. and A. C. Matarese. 2000. Revision of the genus *Lepidopsetta* Gill, 1862 (Teleostei: Pleuronectidae) based on larval and adult morphology, with a description of a new species from the North Pacific and Bering Sea. Fishery Bulletin 98:539–582.

Östlund-Nilsson, S., I. Mayer, and F. A. Huntingford. 2007. Biology of the three-spined stickleback. CRC Press, Boca Raton, Florida.

Outram, D. 1984. Georges Cuvier. Manchester University Press, Manchester, England.

Pacific Fisherman. 1931. Steelheads-frozen fish de luxe. Pacific Fisherman 29(9):50– 52.

Pacific Fisherman. 1932. Bottom fishing—the mainstay of the San Diego fresh fish trade. Pacific Fisherman 30(12):33.

Palko, B. J., G. L. Beardsley, and W. J. Richards. 1982. Synopsis of the biological data on dolphin-fishes, *Coryphaena hippurus* Linnaeus and *Coryphaena equiselis* Linnaeus. NOAA Technical Report NMFS Circular 443.

Palmer, D. E. and L. J. Dugan. 1990. Fish population characteristics of Arctic National Wildlife Refuge coastal waters, summer 1989. United States Fish and Wildlife Service, Alaska Fisheries Progress Report.

Panchenko, V. V. 2002. Age and growth of sculpins of the genus *Myoxocephalus* (Cottidae) in Peter the Great Bay (the Sea of Japan). Journal of Ichthyology 42:516–522.

Parker, S. J., P. S. Rankin, J. M. Olson, and R. W. Hannah. 2007. Movement patterns of black rockfish (*Sebastes melanops*) in Oregon coastal waters, p. 39–57. *In* J. Heifetz, J. Dicosimo, A. J. Gharrett, M. S. Love, V. M. O'Connell, and R. D. Stanley (eds.). Biology, assessment, and management of North Pacific rockfishes. Alaska Sea Grant Program, AK-SG-07-01.

Parra, T. R., W. A. Palsson, and R. E. Pacunski. 2001. Abundance, mate and den fidelity of wolf-eel (*Anarrhichthys ocellatus*) in Puget Sound, Washington. Puget Sound Research 2001.

Parrish, R. H. and A. D. MacCall. 1978. Climatic variation and exploitation in the Pacific mackerel fishery. California Department of Fish and Game, Fish Bulletin 167.

Patzner, R. A., E. J. Goncalves, P. A. Hastings, and B. G. Kapoor (eds.). 2009. The biology of blennies. Science Publishers, Enfield, New Hampshire.

Paul, J. M., A. J. Paul, T. J. Vogeler, and J. P. Doyle. 1997. Biological investigations on Pacific sandfish (*Trichodon trichodon*) in the northern Gulf of Alaska, p. 87–94. *In* Forage Fishes in Marine Ecosystems. Alaska Sea Grant Program Report 97-01. University of Alaska.

Pearcy, W. G., J. P. Fisher, and M. M. Yoklavich. 1993. Biology of the Pacific pomfret (*Brama japonica*) in the North Pacific Ocean. Canadian Journal of Fisheries and Aquatic Sciences 50:2608–2625.

Pearcy, W. G., J. Fisher, R. Brodeur, and S. Johnson. 1985. Effects of the 1983 El Niño on coastal nekton off Oregon and Washington, p. 188–204. *In* W. S. Wooster and D. L. Fluharty (eds.). El Niño North. Washington Sea Grant Program, University of Washington, Seattle.

Pearson, D. E. and S. V. G. McNally. 2005. Age, growth, life history, and fisheries of the sand sole, *Psettichthys melanostictus*. Marine Fisheries Review 67(4):9–18.

Peden, A. E. and D. E. Wilson. 1976. Distribution of intertidal and subtidal fishes of northern British Columbia and southeastern Alaska. Syesis 9:221–248.

Pedersen, M. 1985. Puget Sound Pacific whiting, *Merluccius productus*, resource and industry: an overview. Marine Fishery Review 47(2):35–38.

Penttila, D. 1978. Studies of the surf smelt (*Hypomesus pretiosus*) in Puget Sound. State of Washington Department of Fisheries, Technical Report 42.

Peppar, J. L. 1965. Some features of the life history of the cockscomb prickleback, *Anoplarchus purpurescens* Gill. Masters Thesis, University of British Columbia, Vancouver.

Perez, C. R. 2005. Age, growth, and reproduction of the sandpaper skate, *Bathyraja kincaidii* (Garman, 1908) in the eastern North Pacific. Masters Thesis, California State University, Monterey Bay.

Pérez-España, H., F. Galván-Magaña, and L. A. Abitia-Cárdenas. 1998. Growth, consumption, and productivity of the California killifish in Ojo de Liebre Lagoon, Mexico. Journal of Fish Biology 52:1068–1077.

Perry, Brian. 2009. Cookie-cutter sharks 'sort of a mosquito of the sea.' Maui News, 21 March.

Petersen, C. W., C. Mazzoldi, K. A. Zarrella, and R. E. Hale. 2005. Fertilization mode, sperm characteristics, mate choice and parental care patterns in *Artedius* spp. (Cottidae). Journal of Fish Biology 67:239–254.

Pfeiler, E. 1996. Allozyme differences in Caribbean and Gulf of California populations of bonefishes (*Albula*). Copeia 1996(1):181–183.

Pfeiler, E. 2008. Resurrection of the name *Albula pacifica* (Beebe, 1942) for the shafted bonefish (Albuliformes: Albulidae) from the eastern Pacific. Revista Biologica Tropical 56:839–844.

Pfeiler, E., D. Padrón, and R. E. Crabtree. 2000. Growth rates, age and size of bonefish from the Gulf of California. Journal of Fish Biology 56:448–453.

Pfeiler, E., J. Colborn, M. R. Douglas, and M. E. Douglas. 2002. Systematic status of bonefishes (*Albula* spp.) from the eastern Pacific Ocean inferred from analyses of allozymes and mitochondrial DNA. Environmental Biology of Fishes 63:151– 159.

Pfeiler, E., B. G. R. Bitler, R. Ulloa, A. M. van der Heiden, and P. A. Hastings. 2008a. Molecular identification of the bonefish *Albula esuncula* (Albuliformes: Albulidae) from the tropical eastern Pacific, with comments on distribution and morphology. Copeia 2008(4):763–770.

Pfeiler, E., T. Watts, J. Pugh, and A. M. van der Heiden. 2008b. Speciation and demographic history of the Cortez bonefish, *Albula* sp. A (Albuliformes: Albulidae), in the Gulf of California inferred from mitochondrial DNA. Journal of Fish Biology 73:382–394.

PFMC (Pacific Fisheries Management Council). 2003. Appendix F. U. S. West Coast highly migratory species: life history accounts and essential fish habitat descriptions. U.S. West Coast Highly Migratory Species Plan Development Team.

Phillips, J. B. 1932a. Circle gill netting for smelt. California Fish and Game 18:149–155.

Phillips, J. B. 1932b. Unusually good fishing in and off Monterey Bay. California Fish and Game 18:21–24.

Phleger, C. F., J. Patton, P. Grimes, and R. F. Lee. 1976. Fish-bone oil: percent total body lipid and carbon-14 uptake following feeding of 1-^{14}C-palmitic acid. Marine Biology 35:85–89.

Pierce, B. E. and K. B. Pierson. 1990. Growth and reproduction of the tidepool sculpin *Oligocottus maculosus*. Japanese Journal of Ichthyology 36:410–417.

Pietsch, T. and J. R. Dunn. 1997. Early collection building in Puget Sound and adjacent waters: the 1880 expedition of David Starr Jordan (1851–1931) and Charles Henry Gilbert (1859–1928), p. 279–290. *In* T.W. Pietsch and W. D. Anderson Jr. (eds.). Collection Building in Ichthyology and Herpetology, American Society of Ichthyologists and Herpetologists, Special Publ. 3.

Pietsch, T. and D. B. Grobecker. 1987. Frogfishes of the world. Stanford University Press, Stanford, California.

Pinkas, L. 1966. A management study of the California barracuda *Sphyraena argentea* Girard. California Department of Fish and Game, Fish Bulletin 134.

Polovina, J. J., D. Hawn, and M. Abecassis. 2008. Vertical movement and habitat of opah (*Lampris guttatus*) in the central North Pacific recorded with pop-up archival tags. Marine Biology 153:257–267.

Polovina, J. J., M. Abecassis, E. A. Howell, and P. Woodworth. 2009. Increases in the relative abundance of mid-trophic level fishes concurrent with declines in apex predators in the subtropical North Pacific, 1996–2006. Fishery Bulletin 107:523– 531.

Pondella, D. J. II and L. G. Allen. 2008. The decline and recovery of four predatory fishes from the Southern California Bight. Marine Biology 154:307–313.

Pondella, D. J. II, L. G. Allen, J. A. Rosales Casian, and T. E. Hovey. 2001. Demographic parameters of golden spotted rock bass *Paralabrax auroguttatus* from the northern Gulf of California. Transactions of the American Fisheries Society 130:686–691.

Pondella, D. J. II, J. T. Froeschke, L. S. Wetmore, E. Miller, C. F. Valle, and L. Medeiros. 2008. Demographic parameters of yellowfin croaker, *Umbrina roncador* (Perciformes: Sciaenidae), from the Southern California Bight. Pacific Science 62:555–568.

Porter, S. M. 2005. Temporal and spatial distribution and abundance of flathead sole (*Hippoglossoides elassodon*) eggs and larvae in the western Gulf of Alaska. Fishery Bulletin 103:648–658.

Prasad, R. R. 1948. The life history of *Clevelandia ios* (Jordan and Gilbert). PhD Thesis, Stanford University.

Pratt, H. L. Jr. and J. C. Carrier. 2005. Elasmobranch courtship and mating behavior, p. 129–169. *In* W. C. Hamlett (ed.). Reproductive Biology and Phylogeny of Chondrichthyes; Sharks, Batoids, and Chimaeras. Vol. 3. Science Publishers, Enfield, New Hampshire.

Preston, D. and M. Preston. 2004. A pirate of exquisite mind. Walker and Company, New York.

Prince, E. S. 1906. British Columbia fish and fisheries. Pacific Fisherman 4(1):31–39.

Pruter, A. T. 1966. Commercial fisheries of the Columbia River and adjacent ocean waters. Fishery Industrial Research 3:17–68.

Purcell, C. M. 2009. Genetic analysis of population structure in striped marlin, *Tetrapturus audax*, in the Pacific Ocean. PhD Thesis, University of Southern California.

Pyle, P., M. J. Schramm, C. Keiper, and S. D. Anderson. 1999. Predation on a white shark (*Carcharodon carcharias*) by a killer whale (*Orcinus orca*) and a possible case of competitive displacement. Marine Mammal Science 15:563–568.

Quast, J. C. 1968. Estimates of the populations and the standing crop of fishes, p. 57–79. *In* W. J. North and C. L. Hubbs (eds.). Utilization of Kelp-bed Resources in Southern California. California Department of Fish and Game, Fish Bulletin 139.

Quinn, T. P. 2005. The behavior and ecology of Pacific salmon and trout. AmericanFisheries Society and University of Washington Press. Bethesda, Maryland and Seattle, Washington.

Ragland, H. C. and E. A. Fischer. 1987. Internal fertilization and male parental care in the scalyhead sculpin, *Artedius harringtoni*. Copeia 1987(4):1059–1062.

Randall, J. E. 1992. Review of the biology of the tiger shark (*Galeocerdo cuvier*). Australian Journal of Marine and Freshwater Research 43:21–31.

Rathbun, R. 1884. Notes on the decrease of lobsters. Bulletin of the United States Fish Commission 4:421–423.

Rathbun, R. 1893. Report upon the inquiry respecting food fishes and the fishing grounds, p. 97–171. United States Commission of Fish and Fisheries, Part XVII. Report of the Commissioner for 1889–1891.

RecFin. 2009. Pacific States Marine Recreational Fisheries Monitoring. http://www.recfin.org.

Rechnitzer, A. B. and C. Limbaugh. 1952. Breeding habits of *Hyperprosopon argenteum*, a viviparous fish of California. Copeia 1952(1):41–42.

Reeb, C. A., L. Arcangeli, and B. A. Block. 2000. Structure and migration corridors in Pacific populations of the swordfish *Xiphius gladius*, as inferred through analyses of mitochondrial DNA. Marine Biology 136:1123–1131.

Regan, C. T. 1908. Report on the marine fishes collected by Mr. J. Stanley Gardiner in the Indian Ocean. The Transactions of the Linnean Society of London. Second Series. Zoology 12:217–255.

Reid, R. 1990. Research on the fishery and biology of the hagfish. California Environmental Affairs Agency, Contract Number A800–185.

Ribot-Carballal, M. C., F. Galván-Magaña, and C. Quiñóz-Velázquez. 2005. Age and growth of the shortfin mako shark, *Isurus oxyrinchus*, from the western coast of Baja California Sur, Mexico. Fisheries Research 76:14–21.

Rickey, M. H. 1995. Maturity, spawning, and seasonal movement of arrowtooth flounder, *Atheresthes stomias*, off Washington. Fishery Bulletin 93:127–138.

Ries, E. 2007. Tales of the golden years of California ocean fishing 1900–1950. Monterey Publications, Laguna Hills, California.

Ripley, W. E. 1946. The soupfin shark and the fishery, p. 7–38. *In* The Biology of the Soupfin *Galeorhinus zyopterus* and Biochemical Studies of the Liver. California Division of Fish and Game, Fish Bulletin 64.

Roach, S. W. and J. S. M. Harrison. 1948. Canning of anchovies. Fisheries Research Board of Canada, Progress Reports of the Pacific Coast Stations Number 77:106– 111.

Robards, M. D. and J. F. Piatt. 1999. Biology of the genus *Ammodytes*, the sand lances, p. 1–16. *In* M. D. Robards, M. F. Wilson, R. H. Armstrong, and J. F. Piatt. Sand lance: A Review of Biology and Predator Relations and Annotated Bibliography. United States Forest Service, Pacific Northwest Research Station, Research Paper PNW-RP-521.

Robards, M. D., J. F. Piatt, and G. A. Rose. 1999. Maturation, fecundity, and intertidal spawning of Pacific sand lance in the northern Gulf of Alaska. Journal of Fish Biology 54:1050–1068.

Robards, M. D., G. A. Rose, and J. F. Piatt. 2002. Growth and abundance of Pacific sand lance, *Ammodytes hexapterus*, under differing oceanographic regimes. Environmental Biology of Fishes 64:429–441.

Robinson, J. B. 1960. The age and growth of striped bass (*Roccus saxatilis*) in California. California Fish and Game 46:279–290.

Rocha-Olivares, A. 1998. Age, growth, mortality, and population characteristics of the Pacific red snapper, *Lutjanus peru*, off the southeast coast of Baja California, Mexico. Fishery Bulletin 96:562–574.

Rocha-Olivares, A., M. Bobadella-Jiménez, S. Ortega-Garcia, N. Saavedra-Sotelo, and J. R. Sandoval-Castillo. 2006. Mitochondrial variability of dolphinfish *Coryphaena hippurus* population in the Pacific Ocean. Ciencias Marinas 32:569–578.

Rogers, B. J., M. E. Wangerin, and D. E. Rogers. 1983. Seasonal composition and food web relationships of marine organisms in the nearshore zone of Kodiak Island – including ichthyoplankton, zooplankton, and fish. A report of the fish component of the study, p. 541–658. Environmental Assessment of the Alaskan Continental Shelf. Final Reports of the Principal Investigators. Volume 17. Biological Studies. United States Department of Commerce and United States Department of the Interior.

Rodgers, E. W., R. L. Earley, and M. S. Grober. 2007. Social status determines sexual phenotype in the bi-directional sex changing bluebanded goby *Lythrypnus dalli*. Journal of Fish Biology 70:1660–1668.

Rodriguez-Romero, J., D. S. Palacios-Salgado, J. López-Martinez, S. Hernández Vázquez, and J. Velázquez-Abunader. 2009. The length-weight relationship parameters of demersal fish species off the western coast of Baja California Sur, Mexico. Journal of Applied Ichthyology 25:114–116.

Rojo-Vázquez, J. A., G. Lucano-Ramirez, and S. Ruiz-Ramirez. 2009. Length-weight relationships for coastal fish species from the gillnet artisanal fishery in the central Mexican Pacific. Journal of Applied Ichthyology 25:497–498.

Rooper, C. N. 2002. English sole transport during pelagic stages on the Pacific Northwest coast, and habitat use by juvenile flatfish in Oregon and Washington estuaries. PhD Thesis, University of Washington, Seattle.

Roppel, P. 1982. Alaska's salmon hatcheries, 1891–1959. National Marine Fisheries Service, Portland, Oregon.

Rosenthal, R. J. 1980. Shallow water fish assemblages in the northeastern Gulf of Alaska: habitat evaluation, species composition, abundance, spatial distribution and trophic interaction. U. S. Department of Commerce, NOAA, Environmental Assessment of the Alaskan Coast 17:451–540.

Rosenthal, R. J., L. Haldorson, L. J. Field, V. Moran-O'Connell, M. G. LaRiviere, J. Underwood, and M. C. Murphy. 1982. Inshore and shallow offshore bottomfish resources in the southeastern Gulf of Alaska (1981–82). Alaska Coastal Research and University of Alaska, Juneau.

Ruiz-Campos, G., A. F. González Acosta, and J. De Cruz Agüero. 2006. Length-weight and length-length relationships for some continental fishes of northwestern Baja California, México. Journal of Applied Ichthyology 22:3314–315.

Ruiz-Campos, G., S. Contreras-Balderas, M. de Lourdes Lozano-Vilano, S. González- Guzmán, and J. Alaníz-García. 2000. Ecological and distributional status of the continental fishes of northwestern Baja California, Mexico. Bulletin of the Southern California Academy of Sciences 99:59–90.

Russell, F. E. 1965. Marine toxins and venomous and poisonous marine animals. Advances in Marine Biology 3:255–384.

Russell, V. G. 1927. Pearl essence in San Pedro. California Fish and Game 13:216–217.

Rutecki, T. L. and E. R. Varosi. 1997. Distribution, age, and growth of juvenile sablefish, *Anoplopoma fimbria*, in southeast Alaska, p. 45–54. NOAA Technical Report NMFS 130.

Rutenberg, E. P. 1970. Survey of the fishes of family Hexagrammidae, p. 1–103. *In* T. S. Rass (ed.). Greenlings, taxonomy, biology, interoceanic transplantation. Academy of Sciences of the USSR, Transactions of the Institute of Oceanology, Volume 59. Israel Program for Scientific Translations.

Sadovy, Y. and M. L. Domeier. 2005. Perplexing problems of sexual patterns in the fish genus *Paralabrax* (Serranidae, Serraninae). Journal of Zoology, London 267:121– 133.

Sak, B. P. 1990. Age, growth and reproductive characteristics of the plainfin midshipman (*Porichthys notatus*) in Monterey Bay, with notes on seasonal movements. Masters Thesis, San Francisco State University.

Sakanari, J. A. and M. Moser. 1986. Lesion induction by the plerocercoid *Lacistorhynchus tenuis* (Cestoda) and wound healing in the striped bass, *Morone saxatilis* (Walbaum). Journal of Fish Biology 28:289–296.

Sala, E., O. Aburto-Oropeza, G. Paredes, and G. Thompson. 2003. Spawning aggregations and reproductive behavior of reef fishes in the Gulf of California. Bulletin of Marine Science 72:103–121.

Salmon, M., H. E. Winn, and N. Sorgente. 1968. Sound production and associated behavior in triggerfishes. Pacific Science 22:11–20.

Sampson, D. B. and S. M. Al-Jufaily. 1999. Geographic variation in the maturity and growth schedules of English sole along the U.S. west coast. Journal of Fish Biology 54:1–17.

Saunders, M. W. and G. A. McFarlane. 1993. Age and length of maturity of the female spiny dogfish, *Squalus acanthias*, in the Strait of Georgia, British Columbia, Canada. Environmental Biology of Fishes 38:49–57.

Saunders, M. W., B. M. Leaman, and G. A. McFarlane. 1997. Influence of ontogeny and fishing mortality on the interpretation of sablefish, *Anoplopoma fimbria*, life history. NOAA Technical Report NMFS 130.

Scammon, C. M. 1870. The Pacific Coast cod-fishery. Overland Monthly 4(5):436–440. Schaefer, K. M. 1999. Comparative study of some morphological features of yellowfin (*Thunnus albacares*) and bigeye (*Thunnus obesus*) tunas. Inter-American Tropical Tuna Commission Bulletin 21(7):489–526.

Schaefer, K. M. 2001. Reproductive biology of tunas, p. 225–270. *In* B. A. Block and E. D. S. Stevens (eds.). Tuna: Physiology, Ecology, and Evolution. Academic Press, San Diego.

Schaefer, K. M. and D. W. Fuller. 2002. Movements, behavior, and habitat selection of bigeye tuna (*Thunnus obesus*) in the eastern equatorial Pacific, ascertained through archival tags. Fishery Bulletin 100:765–788.

Schaefer, K. M. and D. W. Fuller. 2007. Vertical movement patterns of skipjack tuna (*Katsuwonus pelamis*) in the eastern equatorial Pacific Ocean, as revealed with archival tags. Fishery Bulletin 105:379–389.

Schaefer, K. M., D. W. Fuller, and B. A. Block. 2007. Movements, behavior, and habitat utilization of yellowfin tuna (*Thunnus albacares*) in the northeastern Pacific Ocean, ascertained through archival tag data. Marine Biology 152:503–525.

Schaefer, M. B. 1936. Contribution to the life history of the surf smelt (*Hypomesus pretiosus*) in Puget Sound. Washington Department of Fisheries Biological Report 35B:1–45.

Schaffner, F. C. Jr. 1982. Aspects of the reproductive ecology of the elegant tern (*Sterna elegans*) at San Diego Bay. Masters Thesis, San Diego State University.

Schmitter-Soto, J. J. and J. L. Castro-Aguirre. 1991. Edad y crecimiento de *Prionotus stephanophrys* (Osteichthyes: Triglidae) en la costa occidental de Baja California Sur, México. Revista de Biologia Tropical 39:23–29.

Schultz, E. T. 2008. A sex difference in seasonal timing of birth in a livebearing fish. Copeia 2008(3):673–679.

Sciarrotta, T. C. and D. R. Nelson. 1977. Diel behavior of the blue shark, *Prionace glauca*, near Santa Catalina Island, California. Fishery Bulletin 75:519–528.

Scofield, N. B. 1914. The tuna canning industry of southern California. California Fish and Game Commission, 23rd Biennial Report:111–122.

Seaman, G. A., L. F. Lowry, and K. J. Frost. 1982. Food of beluga whales (*Delphinapterus leucas*) in western Alaska. Cetology 44:1–19.

Semakula, S. N. and P. A. Larkin. 1968. Age, growth, food, and yield of the white sturgeon (*Acipenser transmontanus*) of the Fraser River, British Columbia. Journal of the Fisheries Research Board of Canada 25:2589–2602.

Señán, J. 1962. The letters of José Señán, O. F. M. Ventura County Historical Society.

Sepulveda, C. A., S. Kohin, C. Chan, R. Vetter, and J. B. Graham. 2004. Movement patterns, depth preferences, and stomach temperatures of free-swimming juvenile mako sharks, *Isurus oxyrinchus*, in the Southern California Bight. Marine Biology 145:191–199.

Shaw, F. R. and D. R. Gunderson. 2006. Life history traits of the greenstriped rockfish, *Sebastes elongatus*. California Fish and Game 92:1–23.

Shelekhov, V. A. and D. V. Baginskii. 2000. Finding of toothless specimens of daggertooth *Anotopterus nikparini* (Anotopteridae) during winter off the southern Kuril Islands. Journal of Ichthyology 40:485.

Shenker, J.M. 1983. Distribution, size relationships, and food habits of juvenile king-of- the-salmon, *Trachipterus altivelis*, caught off the Oregon coast. Fishery Bulletin 81:161–164.\

Sherwood, N. M., A. L. Kyle, H. Kreiberg, C. M. Warby, T. H. Magnus, J. Carolsfeld, and W. S. Price. 1991. Partial characterization of a spawning pheromone in the herring *Clupea harengus pallasi*. Canadian Journal of Zoology 69:91–103.

Shestakov, A. V. and M. V. Nazarkin. 2006. On the biology of the white-spotted greenling *Hexagrammos stelleri* and the masked greenling *H. octogrammus* (Hexagrammidae) from Taui Bay of the Sea of Okhotsk. Journal of Ichthyology 46:677–680.

Shimada, A. M. and D. K. Kimura. 1994. Seasonal movements of Pacific cod, *Gadus macrocephalus*, in the eastern Bering Sea and adjacent waters based on tag- recapture data. Fishery Bulletin 92:800–816.

Sigler, M. F., S. A. Lowe, and C. R. Kastelle. 1997. Area and depth differences in the age-length relationship of sablefish, *Anoplopoma fimbria*, in the Gulf of Alaska, p. 55–63. NOAA Technical Report NMFS 130.

Sikkel, P. C. 1994a. Filial cannibalism in a paternal-caring marine fish: the influence of egg developmental stage and position in the nest. Animal Behavior 47:1149– 1158.

Sikkel, P. C. 1994b. Why female garibaldi prefer males with young eggs: a test of the parental investment hypothesis. Ethology Ecology and Evolution 6:191–211.

Sikkel, P. C. 1995. Diel periodicity of spawning activity in a permanently territorial damselfish: a test of adult feeding hypotheses. Environmental Biology of Fishes 42:241–251.

Sikkel, P. C. 1998. Competitor intrusions and mate-search tactics in a territorial marine fish. Behavioral Ecology 9:439–444.

Silberberg, K. R., T. E. Laidig, and P. B. Adams. 2001. Analysis of maturity in lingcod, *Ophiodon elongatus*. California Fish and Game 87:139–152.

Simenstad, C. A. 1971. The feeding ecology of rock greenling, *Hexagrammos lagocephalus*, in the inshore waters of Amchitka Island, Alaska. Masters Thesis, University of Washington, Seattle.

Simenstad, C. A., J. S. Isakson, and R. E. Nakatani. 1977. Marine fish communities, p. 451–492. *In* M. L. Merritt and R. G. Fuller (eds.). The Environment of Amchitka Island, Alaska. Technical Information Center, Energy Research and Development Administration TID-26712.

Sims, D. W. and V. A. Quayle. 1998. Selective foraging behaviour of basking sharks on zooplankton in a small-scale front. Nature 393:460–464.

Sims, D. W., E. J. Southall, V. A. Quayle, and A. M. Fox. 2000. Annual social behaviour of basking sharks associated with coastal front areas. Proceedings of the Royal Society of London B 267:1897–1904.

Sims, D. W., E. J. Southall, A. J. Richardson, P. C. Reid, and J. D. Metcalfe. 2003. Seasonal movements and behaviour of basking sharks from archival tagging: no evidence of winter hibernation. Marine Ecology Progress Series 248:187–196.

Skillman, R. A. and M. Y. Y. Yong. 1976. Von Bertalanffy growth curves for striped marlin, *Tetrapturus audax*, and blue marlin, *Makaira nigricans*, in the central North Pacific Ocean. Fishery Bulletin 74:553–566.

Skogsberg, T. 1939. The fishes of the family Sciaenidae (croakers) of California. Division of Fish and Game of California, Fish Bulletin 54.

Smith, B. D., G. A. McFarlane, and A. J. Cass. 1990. Movements and mortality of tagged male and female lingcod in the Strait of Georgia, British Columbia. Transactions of the American Fisheries Society 119:813–824.

Smith, G. B. 1981. The biology of walleye pollock, p. 527–551. *In* D. W. Hood and J. A. Calder (eds.). The Eastern Bering Sea Shelf: Oceanography and Resources. Volume 1. United States Department of Commerce, Office of Marine Pollution Assessment.

Smith, J. G. and R. J. Nitsos. 1969. Age and growth studies of English sole, *Parophrys vetulus*, in Monterey Bay, California, p. 73–79. Pacific Marine Fisheries Commission Bulletin 7.

Smith, J. L. B. 1956. Pugnacity of marlins and swordfish. Nature 178:1065.

Smith, K. L. Jr. and N. O. Brown. 1983. Oxygen consumption of pelagic juveniles and demersal adults of the deep-sea fish *Sebastolobus altivelis*, measured at depth. Marine Biology 76:325–332.

Smith, K. R., D. A. Somerton, M.-S. Yang, and D. G. Nichol. 2004. Distribution and biology of prowfish (*Zaprora silenus*) in the northeast Pacific. Fishery Bulletin 102:168–178.

Smith, R. L. and J. G. Gillespie. 1988. Notes on the biology of the Bering poacher, *Occella dodecaedron* (Tilesius), and the sturgeon poacher, *Agonus acipenserinus* Tilesius in the southeast Bering Sea. Copeia 1988(2):454–460.

Smith, R. L., M. Vallarino, E. Barbour, E. Fitzpatrick, and W. E. Barber. 1997. Population biology of the Bering flounder in the Northeastern Chukchi Sea. American Fisheries Society Symposium 19:127–132.

Smith, R. T. 1936. Report on the Puget Sound otter trawl investigations. Washington Department of Fisheries, Biological Report No. 36B.

Smith, S. E. 2005. Leopard shark mating observed off La Jolla, California. California Fish and Game 91:128–135.

Smith, S. E., D. W. Au, and C. Show. 1998. Intrinsic rebound potentials of 26 species of Pacific sharks. Marine and Freshwater Research 49:663–678.

Smith, S. E., R. C. Rasmussen, D. A. Ramon, and G. M. Cailliet. 2008. The biology and ecology of thresher sharks (Alopiidae), p. 60–68. *In* M. D. Camhi, E. K. Pikitch, and E. A. Babcock (eds.). Sharks of the open ocean biology, Fisheries, and Conservation. Blackwell, Oxford.

Smith, W. D. 2005. Life history aspects and population dynamics of a commercially exploited stingray, *Dasyatis dipterura*. Masters Thesis, San Francisco State University.

Smith, W. L. and M. T. Craig. 2007. Casting the percomorph net widely: the importance of broad taxonomic sampling in the search for the placement of serranid and percid fishes. Copeia 2007(1):35–55.

Smith, W. L. and W. C. Wheeler. 2004. Polyphyly of the mail-cheeked fishes (Teleostei: Scorpaeniformes):evidence from mitochondrial and nuclear sequence data. Molecular Phylogenetics and Evolution 32:627–646.

Smyder, E. A. and K. L. M. Martin. 2002. Temperature effects on egg survival and hatching during the extended incubation period of California grunion, *Leuresthes tenuis*. Copeia 2002(2):313–320.

Sohn, D., L. Ciannelli, and J. T. Duffy-Anderson. 2010. Distribution and drift pathways of Greenland halibut (*Reinhardtius hippoglossoides*) during early life stages in the eastern Bering Sea and Aleutian Islands. Fisheries Oceanography 19:339–353.

Speare, P. 2003. Age and growth of black marlin, *Makaira indica*, in east coast Australian waters. Marine and Freshwater Research 54:307–314.

Spratt, J. E. 1975. Growth rate of the northern anchovy, *Engraulis mordax*, in southern California waters, calculated from otoliths. California Fish and Game 61:116–126.

Squire, J. L. Jr. 1990. Distribution and apparent abundance of the basking shark, *Cetorhinus maximus*, off the central and southern California coast, 1962–85. Marine Fisheries Review 52(2):8–11.

Sribhibhadh, A. 1959. Racial variations in the populations of the crested blenny, *Anoplarchus purpurescens purpurescens* Gill, in the Puget Sound area. Masters Thesis, University of Washington, Seattle.

Stadler, J. M. 1988. Feeding biology of the northern clingfish *Gobiesox maeandricus*: diet, morphology, and behavior. Masters Thesis, University of Washington, Seattle.

Stahl, J. P. and G. H. Kruse. 2008. Spatial and temporal variability in size at maturity of walleye pollock in the eastern Bering Sea. Transactions of the American Fisheries Society 137:1543–1557.

Stanley, R. D., M. McAllister, P. Starr, and N. Olsen. 2009. Stock assessment for bocaccio (*Sebastes paucispinis*) in British Columbia waters. Canadian Advisory Secretariat Research Document 2009/055.

Stanley, R. D., P. Starr, and N. Olsen. 2009. Stock assessment for canary rockfish (*Sebastes pinniger*) in British Columbia waters. Canadian Advisory Secretariat Research Document 2009/013.

Stark, J. W. 2004. A comparison of the maturation and growth of female flathead sole in the central Gulf of Alaska and south-eastern Bering Sea. Journal of Fish Biology 64:876–889.

Stark, J. W. 2008. Age- and length-at-maturity of female arrowtooth flounder (*Atheresthes stomias*) in the Gulf of Alaska. Fishery Bulletin 106:328–333.

Stark, J. W. and D. A. Somerton. 2002. Maturation, spawning and growth of rock soles off Kodiak Island in the Gulf of Alaska. Journal of Fish Biology 61:417–431.

Starr, R. M., V. O'Connell, S. Ralston, and L. Breaker. 2005. Use of acoustic tags to estimate natural mortality, spillover, and movements of lingcod (*Ophiodon elongatus*) in a marine reserve. Journal of Marine Technology Society 39:19–30.

Stauffer, G. D. 1985. Biology and life history of the coastal stock of Pacific whiting, *Merluccius productus*. Marine Fisheries Review 47(2):2–7.

Stearley, R. F. and G. R. Smith. 1993. Phylogeny of the Pacific trouts and salmons (*Oncorhynchus*) and genera of the family Salmonidae. Transactions of the American Fisheries Society 122:122–133.

Stearns, R. E. C. 1888. Reminiscences of a naturalist, biographical, etc. II. The Western American Scientist 4:1–3.

Stein, D. L., J. C. Drazen, K. L. Schlining, J. P. Barry, and L. Kuhnz. 2006. Snailfishes of the central California coast: video, photographic and morphological observations. Journal of Fish Biology 69:970–986.

Stephens, J. S. Jr. 1983. The fishes of King Harbor: a nine year study of fishes occupying the receiving waters of a coastal steam electric generating station. Occidental College Research and Development Series 83-RD-1.

Stephens, J. S. Jr., R. K. Johnson, G. S. Key, and J. E. McCosker. 1970. The comparative ecology of three sympatric species of California blennies of the genus *Hypsoblennius* Gill (Teleostomi, Blenniidae). Ecological Monographs 40:213– 233.

Stepien, C. A. 1986. Life history and larval development of the giant kelpfish, *Heterostichus rostratus* Girard, 1854. Fishery Bulletin 84:809–826.

Stepien, C. A. 1987. Color pattern and habitat differences between male, female and juvenile giant kelpfish (Blennioidei: Clinidae). Bulletin of Marine Science 41:45– 58.

Stepien, C. A., M. Glattke, and K. M. Fink. 1988. Regulation and significance of color patterns of the spotted kelpfish, *Gibbonsia elegans* Cooper, 1864 (Blennioidei: Clinidae). Copeia 1988(1):7–15.

Stevenson, D. E. and A. C. Matarese. 2005. A revision of the North Pacific fish family Bathymasteridae (Perciformes: Zoarcoidei). Proceedings of the Biological Society of Washington 118:367–406.

Stevenson, D. E., J. W. Orr, G. R. Hoff, and J. D. McEachran. 2007. Field guide to sharks, skates, and ratfish of Alaska. Alaska Sea Grant.

Stewart, H. 1977. Indian fishing, early methods on the northwest coast. Douglas & McIntyre, Vancouver and University of Washington Press, Seattle.

Stick, K. C., and L. Hreha. 1989. Summary of the 1988 Washington/Oregon experimental thresher shark gill net fishery. State of Washington Department of Fisheries Progress Report 275.

St. Mary, C. M. 1996. Sex allocation in a simultaneous hermaphrodite, the zebra goby *Lythrypnus zebra*: insights gained through a comparison with its sympatric congener, *Lythrypnus dalli*. Environmental Biology of Fishes 45:177–190.

Stone, L. 1876. Report of operations in California in 1873, p. 377–427. United States Commission of Fish and Fisheries. Part III. Report of the Commissioner for 1873–4 and 1874–5.

Stout, H. A., R. G. Gastafson, W. H. Lenarz, B. B. McCain, D. M. VanDoornik, T. L. Builder, and R. D. Methot. 2001. Status review of Pacific herring (*Clupea pallasi*) in Puget Sound, Washington. NOAA Technical Memorandum NMFS-NWFSC- 45.

St-Pierre, G. 1992. Visual determination of sex in live Pacific halibut. ICES Journal of Marine Science 49:373–376.

Suckley, G. 1874. On the North American species of salmon and trout, p. 91–160. United 1872–1873, Appendix 3.

Sun, C.-L., C.-L. Huang, and S.-Z. Yeh. 2001. Age and growth of the bigeye tuna, *Thunnus obesus*, in the western Pacific. Fishery Bulletin 99:502–509.

Swan, J. G. 1857. The northwest coast or, three years' residence in Washington Territory.First published by Harper and Brothers. University of Washington Press paperback edition, 1972.

Swan, J. B. 1868. The Indians of Cape Flattery. Smithsonian Contribution to Knowledge.

Swan, J. B. 1880. The surf-smelt of the northwest coast, and the method of taking them by the Quillehute Indians, west coast of Washington Territory. Proceedings of the United States National Museum 3:43–46.

Swan, J. B. 1885. Report on black cod of the North Pacific Ocean. Bulletin of the United States Fish Commission 5:225–234.

Swift, C. C., J. L. Nelson, C. Maslow, and T. Stein. 1989. Biology and distribution of the tidewater goby, *Eucyclogobius newberryi* (Pisces: Gobiidae) of California. Natural History Museum of Los Angeles County, Contributions in Science Number 404.

Swift, C. C., T. R. Haglund, M. Ruiz, and R. N. Fisher. 1993. The status and distribution of the freshwater fishes of Southern California. 92:101–167.

Szalay, P. G., N. W. Raring, F. R. Shaw, M. E. Wilkins, and M. H. Martin. 2010. Data report: 2009 Gulf of Alaska bottom trawl survey. NOAA Technical Memorandum NMFS-AFSC-208.

Tack, S. L. 1970. The summer distribution and standing stock of the fishes of Izembek Lagoon, Alaska. Masters Thesis, University of Alaska, Fairbanks.

Tally, D. M. 2000. The role of resident fishes in linking habitats of a southern California salt marsh. PhD Thesis, University of California, San Diego.

Tamburri, M. N., E. T. Peltzer, G. E. Friederich, I. Aya, K. Yamane, and P. G. Brewer. 2000. A field study of the effects of CO_2 ocean disposal on mobile deep-sea animals. Marine Chemistry 72:95–101.

Tarp, F. H. 1952. A revision of the family Embiotocidae (the surfperches). California Fish and Game, Fish Bulletin 88.

Taylor, I. G. and V. F. Gallucci. 2009. Unconfounding the effects of climate and density dependence using 60 years of data on spiny dogfish (*Squalus acanthias*). Canadian Journal of Fisheries and Aquatic Sciences 66:351–366.

Taylor, P. B. 1963. The venom and ecology of the California scorpionfish *Scorpaena guttata* Girard. PhD Thesis, University of California, San Diego.

Terry, A., G. Bucciarelli, and G. Bernardi. 2000. Restricted gene flow and incipient speciation in disjunct Pacific Ocean and Sea of Cortez populations of a reef fish species, *Girella nigricans*. Evolution 54:652–659.

Thomas, J. C. 1968. Management of the white seabass (*Cynoscion nobilis*) in California waters. California Department of Fish and Game, Fish Bulletin 142.

Thomerson, J. E., T. B. Thorson, and R. L. Hempel. 1977. The bull shark, *Carcharhinus leucas*, from the upper Mississippi River near Alton, Illinois. Copeia 1977(1):166–168.

Thompson, J. E. and R. W. Hannah. 2010. Using cross-dating techniques to validate ages of aurora rockfish (*Sebastes aurora*): estimates of age, growth and female maturity. Environmental Biology of Fishes 88:377–388.

Timmons, M. and R. N. Bray. 1997. Age, growth, and sexual maturity of shovelnose guitarfish, *Rhinobatos productus* (Ayres). Fishery Bulletin 95:349–359.

Tokranov, A. M. 1988. Reproduction of sculpins of the genus *Gymnocanthus* (Cottidae) in the coastal waters of Kamchatka. Journal of Ichthyology 28:124–128.

Tokranov, A. M. 1993. Sexual dimorphism in sea poachers (Agonidae) off Kamchatka. Journal of Ichthyology 33:113–122.

Tokranov, A. M. and A. M. Orlov. 2003. On the distribution and biology of roughscale sole *Clidoderma asperrimum* (Temminck et Schlegel, 1846) in the Pacific waters off the northern Kuril Islands and southeastern Kamchatka. Bulletin of the Sea Fisheries Institute Issue 2, No. 159, p. 67–80.

Treble, M. A., S. E. Campana, R. J. Wastle, C. M. Jones, and Jesper Boje. 2008. Growth analysis and age validation of a deepwater arctic fish, the Greenland halibut (*Reinhardtius hippoglossoides*). Canadian Journal of Fisheries and Aquatic Sciences 65:1047–1059.

Tribuzio, C. A., G. H. Kruse, and J. T. Fujioka. 2010. Age and growth of spiny dogfish (*Squalus acanthias*) in the Gulf of Alaska: analysis of alternative growth models. Fishery Bulletin 108:119–135.

Tricas, T. C. 1982. Bioelectric-mediated predation by swell sharks, *Cephaloscyllium ventriosum*. Copeia 1982(4):948–952.

Turek, M., N. Ratner, W. E. Simeone, and D. L. Holen. 2009. Subsistence harvests and local knowledge of rockfish *Sebastes* in four Alaskan communities. Alaska Department of Fish and Game Technical Paper Number 337.

Turner, C. H. and E. E. Ebert. 1962. The nesting of *Chromis punctipinnis* (Cooper) and a description of their eggs and larvae. California Fish and Game 48:243–248.

Turner, C. H., E. E. Ebert, and R. R. Given. 1969. Man-made reef ecology. California Department of Fish and Game, Fish Bulletin 146.

Turner, L. M. 1886. Contributions to the natural history of Alaska. Signal Service, U. S. Army Arctic Series No. 11. U. S. Government Printing Office, Washington D. C.

Uchida, R. N. 1981. Synopsis of biological data on frigate tuna, *Auxis thazard*, and bullet tuna, *A. rochei*. NOAA Technical Report NMFS Circular 426.

Uchiyama, J. H. and C. H. Boggs. 2006. Length-weight relationships of dolphinfish, *Coryphaena hippurus*, and wahoo, *Acanthocybium solandri*: seasonal effects of spawning and possible migration in the central North Pacific.

VanBlaricom, G. R. 1978. Disturbance, predation, and resource allocation in a high- energy sublittoral sand-bottom ecosystem: experimental analyses of critical structuring processes for the infaunal community. PhD Thesis, University of California, San Diego.

Van Cleve, R. and S. Z. El-Sayed. 1969. Age, growth, and productivity of an English sole (*Parophrys vetulus*) population in Puget Sound, Washington, p. 52–71. Pacific Marine Fisheries Commission Bulletin 7.

Van Dykhuizen, G. and H. F. Mollet. 1997. Growth, age estimation and feeding of captive sevengill sharks, *Notorynchus cepedianus*, at the Monterey Bay Aquarium. Australian Journal of Marine and Freshwater Research 43:298–318.

Van Hasselt, J. C. 1823. Uittreksel uit een' brief van Dr. J. C. van Hasselt, aan den Heer C. J. Temminck. Algemein Konst- en Letter-bode I Deel (no. 21):329–331.

Vega, N. M., V. F. Gallucci, L. Hauser, and J. Franks. 2009. Differences in growth in the spiny dogfish over a latitudinal gradient in the northeast Pacific, p. 169–179. *In* V. F. Gallucci, G. A. McFarlane, and G. G. Bargmann (eds.). Biology and Management of Dogfish Sharks. American Fisheries Society.

Verissimo, A., J. R. McDowell, and J. E. Graves. 2010. Global population structure of the spiny dogfish *Squalus acanthias*, a temperate shark with an antitropical distribution., Molecular Ecology 19:1651–1662.

Vetter, R. D., E. A. Lynn, M. Garza, and A. S. Costa. 1994. Depth zonation and metabolic adaptation in Dover sole, *Microstomus pacificus*, and other deep-living flatfishes: factors that affect the sole. Marine Biology 120:145–159.

Villablanca, F. and R. Nakamura. 2008. Population genetics of the commercially important cabezon. University of California San Diego, Sea Grant Program. Final Report.

Villadolid, D. V. 1927. The flatfishes (Heterostomata) of the Pacific Coast of the United States. PhD Thesis, Stanford University.

Wakefield, W. W. II. 1984. Feeding relationships within assemblages of nearshore and mid-continental shelf benthic fishes off Oregon. Masters Thesis, Oregon State University.

Wakefield, W. W. II. 1990. Patterns in the distribution of demersal fishes on the upper continental shelf off central California with studies on the role of ontogenetic vertical migration in particle flux. PhD Thesis, University of California, San Diego.

Warburton, K. 1979. Growth and production of some important species of fish in a Mexican coastal lagoon system. Journal of Fish Biology 14:449–464.

Wares, P. G. 1971. Biology of the pile perch, *Rhacochilus vacca* in Yaquina Bay, Oregon. United States Fish and Wildlife Service, Technical Paper No. 57.

Warner, R. R. 1975. The reproductive biology of the protogynous hermaphrodite *Pimelometopon pulchrum* (Pisces: Labridae). Fishery Bulletin 73:262–283.

Warner, R. R. and R. K. Harlan. 1982. Sperm competition and sperm storage as determinants of sexual dimorphism in the dwarf surfperch, *Micrometrus minimus*. Evolution 36:44–55.

Watters, D. L., D. E. Kline, D. H. Coale, and G. M. Cailliet. 2006. Radiometric age confirmation and growth of a deep-water marine fish species: the bank rockfish, *Sebastes rufus*. Fisheries Research 81:251–257.

Weaver, P. Jr. 1892. Salt water fisheries of the Pacific Coast. Overland Monthly 20(116):149–163.

Webb, P. W. and J. R. Brett. 1972a. Oxygen consumption of embryos and parents, and oxygen transfer characteristics within the ovary of two species of viviparous seaperch, *Rhacochilus vacca* and *Embiotoca lateralis*. Journal of the Fisheries Research Board of Canada 29:1543–1553.

Webb, P. W. and J. R. Brett. 1972b. Respiratory adaptations of prenatal young in the ovary of two species of viviparous seaperch, *Rhacochilus vacca* and *Embiotoca lateralis*. Journal of the Fisheries Research Board of Canada 29:1525–1542.

Weiss, E. F. Jr. 1969. The age and growth of the marine cottid *Leptocottus armatus*. Proceedings of the Montana Academy of Sciences 29:63–71.

Welch, D. W. and R. P. Foucher. 1988. A maximum likelihood for estimating length-at- maturity with application to Pacific cod (*Gadus macrocephalus*) population dynamics. Canadian Journal of Fisheries and Aquatic Sciences 45:333–343.

Welch, D. W. and P. M. Pankhurst. 2001. Visual morphology and feeding behaviour of the daggertooth. Journal of Fish Biology 58:1427–1437.

Wells, A. W. 1986. Aspects of ecology and life history of the wooly sculpin, *Clinocottus analis*, from southern California. California Fish and Game 72:213–226.

Wespestad, V. G., L. W. Fritz, W. J. Ingraham, and B. A. Megrey. 2000. On relationships between cannibalism, climate variability, physical transport, and recruitment success of Bering Sea walleye pollock (*Theragra chalcogramma*). ICES Journal of Marine Science 57:272–278.

Wiebe, J. P. 1968a. The effects of temperature and day length on the reproductive physiology of the viviparous seaperch, *Cymatogaster aggregata* Gibbons. Journal of the Fisheries Research Board of Canada 46:1207–1220.

Wiebe, J. P. 1968b. The reproductive cycle of the viviparous seaperch, *Cymatogaster aggregata* Gibbons. Journal of the Fisheries Research Board of Canada 46:1221–1234.

Wild, A. 1986. Growth of yellowfin tuna, *Thunnus albacares*, in the eastern Pacific Ocean based on otolith increments. Bulletin of the Inter-American Tropical Tuna Commission 18(6):423–482.

Wilderbuer, T. K., G. E. Walters, and R. G. Bakkala. 1992. Yellowfin sole, *Pleuronectes asper*, of the eastern Bering Sea: biological characteristics, history of exploitation, and management. Marine Fisheries Review 54(4):1–18.

Wildermuth, D. A. 1983. Length-weight regression analysis for thirty-eight species of sport caught marine fishes. State of Washington Department of Fisheries Progress Report Number 189.

Wiley, J. W. 1973. The life history of the bluespot goby (*Coryphopterus nicholsii*). Masters Thesis, California State University, Fullerton.

Williams, G. C. 1954. Differential vertical distribution of the sexes in *Gibbonsia elegans* with remarks on two nominal subspecies of this fish. Copeia 1954(4):267–273.

Williams, G. C. 1957. Homing behavior of California rocky shore fishes. University of California Publications in Zoology 59:249–284.

Williams, G. C. and D. C. Williams. 1955. Observations on the feeding habits of the opaleye, *Girella nigricans*. California Fish and Game 41:203–208.

Willson, M. F. and R. H. Armstrong. 1998. Intertidal foraging for Pacific sand-lance, *Ammodytes hexapterus*, by birds. Canadian Field-Naturalist 1112:715–716.

Willson, M. F., R. H. Armstrong, M. C. Hermans, and K. Kaski. 2006. Eulachon: a review of biology and an annotated bibliography. National Marine Fisheries Service AFSC Processed Report 2006-12.

Willson, M. F., R. H. Armstrong, M. D. Robards, and J. F. Piatt. 1999. Sand lance as cornerstone prey for predator populations, p. 17–44. *In* M. D. Robards, M. F. Wilson, R. H. Armstrong, and J. F. Piatt. 1999. Sand Lance: A Review of Biology and Predator Relations and Annotated Bibliography. United States Forest Service, Pacific Northwest Research Station, Research Paper PNW-RP-521.

Wine, V. L. and E. H. Knaggs. 1975. Maturation and growth of jack mackerel, *Trachurus symmetricus*. California Department of Fish and Game, Marine Resources Technical Report 32.

Wingert, R. C. 1975. Comparative reproductive cycles and growth histories of two species of *Xiphister* (Pisces: Stichaeidae), from San Simeon, California. Masters Thesis, California State University, Fullerton.

Witteveen, B. H., R. J. Foy, and K. M. Wynne. 2006. The effect of predation (current and historical) by humpback whales (*Megaptera novaeangliae*) on fish abundance near Kodiak Island, Alaska. Fishery Bulletin 104:10–20.

Witzell, W. N. 1987. Selective predation on large cheloniid sea turtles by tiger sharks (*Galeocerdo cuvier*). Japanese Journal of Herpetology 12:22–29.

Wolfe, R. J. 1979. Food production in a western Eskimo population. PhD Thesis, University of California, Los Angeles.

Wooton, R. J. 1976. The biology of the sticklebacks. Academic Press, London.

Wright, W. G. and J. A. Raymond. 1978. Air-breathing in a California sculpin. Journal of Experimental Zoology 203:171–176.

Wydoski, R. S. and D. E. Bennett. 1973. Contributions to the life history of the silver surfperch (*Hyperprosopon ellipticum*) from the Oregon coast. California Fish and Game 59:178–190.

Yoklavich, M. M. and E. K. Pikitch. 1989. Reproductive status of Dover sole *Microstomus pacificus*, off northern Oregon. Fishery Bulletin 87:988–994.

Yano, K., J. D. Stevens, and L. J. V. Compagno. 2007. Distribution, reproduction and feeding of the Greenland shark *Somniosus* (*Somniosus*) *microcephalus*, with notes on two other sleeper sharks, *Somniosus* (*Somniosus*) *pacificus* and *Somniosus* (*Somniosus*) *antarcticus*. Journal of Fish Biology 70:374–390.

Yoklavich, M. M. and E. K. Pikitch. 1989. Reproductive status of Dover sole *Microstomus pacificus*, off northern Oregon. Fishery Bulletin 87:988–994.

Yoshita, Y., Y. Yamanoue, K. Sagara, M. Nishibari, H. Kuniyoshi, T. Umino, Y. Sakai, H. Hashimoto, and K. Gishima. 2009. Phylogenetic relationship of two *Mola* sunfishes (Tetraodontiformes: Molidae) occurring around the coast of Japan, with notes on their geographical distribution and morphological characters. Ichthyological Research 56:232–244.

Young, P. H. 1969. The California partyboat fishery, 1947–1967. California Department of Fish and Game, Fish Bulletin 147.

Yudin, K. G. and G. M. Cailliet. 1990. Age and growth of the gray smoothhound, *Mustelus californicus*, and the brown smoothhound, *M. henlei*, sharks from central California. Copeia 1990(1):191–204.

Yuen, H. S. H. 1970. Behavior of skipjack tuna, *Katsuwonus pelamis*, as determined by tracking with ultrasonic devices. Journal of the Fisheries Research Board of Canada 27:2071–2079.

Zbinden, M., D. Mazzi, R. Künzler, C. R. Largiader, and T. C. M. Bakker. 2003. Courting virtual rivals increase ejaculate size in sticklebacks (*Gasterosteus aculeatus*). Behavioral Ecology Sociobiology 54:205–209.

Zeiner, S. J. and P. Wolf. 1993. Growth characteristics and estimates of age at maturity of two species of skates (*Raja binoculata* and *Raja rhina*) from Monterey Bay, California, p. 87–99. *In* S. Branstetter (ed.). Conservation Biology of Elasmobranchs. NOAA Technical Report NMFS 115.

Zenger, H. H. Jr. 2004. Data report: 2002 Aleutian Islands bottom trawl survey. NOAA Technical Memorandum NMFS-AFSC-143.

Zhang, C. I., T. K. Wilderbuer, and G. E. Walters. 1998. Biological characteristics and fishery assessment of Alaska plaice, *Pleuronectes quadrituberculatus*, in the eastern Bering Sea. Marine Fisheries Review 60(4):16–27.

Zhu, G., Y. Zhou, L. Xu, and X. Dai. 2009. Growth and mortality of bigeye tuna *Thunnus obesus* (Scombridae) in the eastern and central tropical Pacific Ocean. Environmental Biology of Fishes 85:127–137.

Zimmerman, M. 1997. Maturity and fecundity of arrowtooth flounder, *Atheresthes stomias*, from the Gulf of Alaska. Fishery Bulletin 95:598–611.

Zimmerman, M. and P. Goddard. 1996. Biology and distribution of arrowtooth, *Atheresthes stomias*, and Kamchatka, *A. evermanni*, flounders in Alaskan waters. Fishery Bulletin 94:358–370.

Zolotov, O. G. and A. M. Tokranov. 1991. Feeding characteristics of greenlings and Irish lords during spawning in the upper sublittoral of Eastern Kamchatka. Journal of Ichthyology 31(3):146–155.

DIANE O'LEARY

INDEX

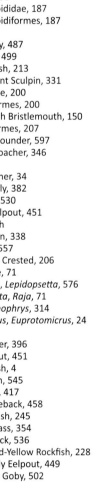

FOUR COMPLETELY UNEXPECTED BONUS PAGES

Are you shocked because you expected the book to be 668 pages long and here you are on the 669th page? Well, not as surprised as were we.

Yesterday, DNP, our printer, reminded us that unless the number of pages in the book was divisible equally by 16 (books come in 16-page signatures), the book would cost more to print and bind. As most of you know, 668 is not divisible equally by 16; however, 672 is. This book is costing a bloody fortune to produce as it is, so we elected to add four more pages.

Now, we could have just put in four more pages and called them "Notes." We have seen that done in field guides and have always wondered who actually wrote in the back of books and what kind of "notes" did they write. "Saw same damn Speckledwinged Fungus Sucker today, how I wish it would either fly north for the summer or die." "Call of Gargling Tanager irritating beyond words." "Feeling upon seeing the Rainbow Breasted Chickadee so ineffable I cannot write it here, so will only write that it is really, really, seriously ineffable."

No, clearly we were not going to do that.

Fortunately, we had a few nice images and snappy little tidbits digitally lying around and no place to put them.

Until now.

KAWIKA CHETRON

TODD WINNER

WHAT IS A FISH?

Pierre Teilhard de Chardin, the visionary French Jesuit-scientist, perhaps said it best when he wrote that fishes are an "Assemblage of monstrous complexity". And, even given Father de Chardin's penchant for such mystical constructs as the "noosphere" and "Omega point," it is clear that the term "fishes" really is hard to define.

KEVIN LEE

From the Land of Wretched Excess –

USE OF DYNAMITE TO RECOVER TAGGED SALMON

Tyler, R.W. 1960. United States Fish and Wildlife Service,
Special Scientific Report – Fisheries No. 353.

DID YOU KNOW?

That you can get anywhere between 23 and 47 gallons of oil from a ton of sardines? Well, you can.

(Bureau of Commercial Fisheries 1937).

MILTON LOVE

PACIFIC FISHERMAN

JANUARY 1906　　ANNUAL　　PRICE 50 Cts

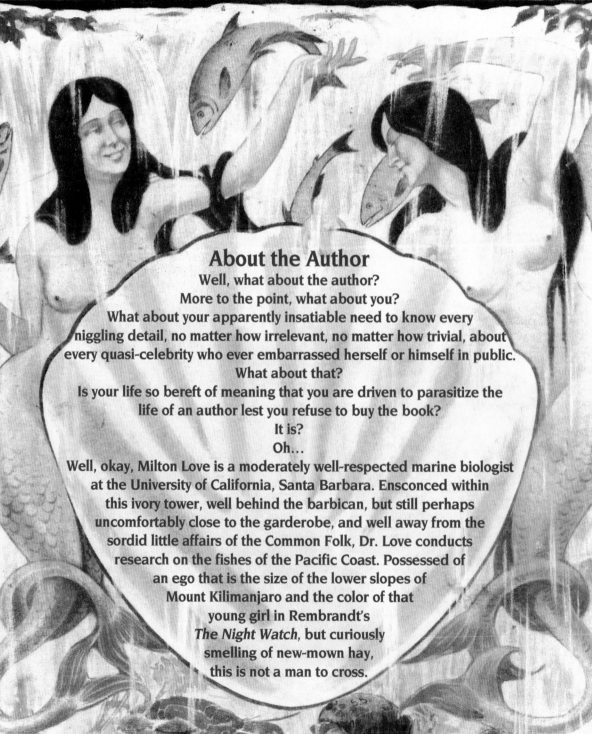

About the Author

Well, what about the author?
More to the point, what about you?
What about your apparently insatiable need to know every
niggling detail, no matter how irrelevant, no matter how trivial, about
every quasi-celebrity who ever embarrassed herself or himself in public.
What about that?
Is your life so bereft of meaning that you are driven to parasitize the
life of an author lest you refuse to buy the book?
It is?
Oh…
Well, okay, Milton Love is a moderately well-respected marine biologist
at the University of California, Santa Barbara. Ensconced within
this ivory tower, well behind the barbican, but still perhaps
uncomfortably close to the garderobe, and well away from the
sordid little affairs of the Common Folk, Dr. Love conducts
research on the fishes of the Pacific Coast. Possessed of
an ego that is the size of the lower slopes of
Mount Kilimanjaro and the color of that
young girl in Rembrandt's
The Night Watch, but curiously
smelling of new-mown hay,
this is not a man to cross.